H.

1363 So. Columbine

$\begin{cases} 252 \\ 265 \end{cases}$

$\begin{cases} 497 \\ 503 \end{cases}$

$\begin{cases} 437 \\ 440 \end{cases}$

$\begin{cases} 260 \\ 220 \end{cases}$ may 17

KROEBER

ANTHROPOLOGY

RACE · LANGUAGE · CULTURE
PSYCHOLOGY · PREHISTORY

HARCOURT, BRACE AND COMPANY

New York

I.2.57

A. L. KROEBER: ANTHROPOLOGY

New Edition, Revised 1948

Contents

CHAPTER FOUR: LIVING RACES

CHAPTER FIVE: PROBLEMS OF RACE DIFFERENCE

CHAPTER SIX: LANGUAGE

CHAPTER SEVEN: THE NATURE OF CULTURE

CHAPTER EIGHT: PATTERNS

CHAPTER NINE: CULTURE PROCESSES

CHAPTER SEVENTEEN: LATER PREHISTORY AND ETHNOLOGY IN THE OLD WORLD

CHAPTER EIGHTEEN: AMERICAN PREHISTORY AND ETHNOLOGY

List of Figures

CHAPTER ONE

What Anthropology Is About

I. ANTHROPOLOGY, BIOLOGY, HISTORY

ANTHROPOLOGY is the science of man. Of course, this literal, etymological meaning is too broad and general. More precise would be: "the science of man and his works and behavior." But even this needs an addition to make it sufficiently specific, since no one means to claim sciences like physiology and psychology as parts of anthropology. Now physiology and psychology focus their attention on particular men, whom they examine as individuals. This gives a clue to the additional limitation we are seeking. Anthropology obviously is concerned not with particular men as such, but with men in groups, with races and peoples and their happenings and doings. So let us take as our provisional basic definition the following: "Anthropology is the science of groups of men and their behavior and productions." This will include any findings on the total human species, since this constitutes an aggregate of races or peoples, a sort of supergroup or total society.

However, man is an animal or organism and he is also a civilized being having a history and social qualities. Thus he is investigated—different aspects of him are investigated—both by the organic or biological or life sciences and by what are sometimes called the historical and more generally the social sciences. True, this latter term, "the social sciences," though commonly used, is not easy to define satisfactorily. But we can leave this difficulty for the philosopher of science. In practice, anthropology is mostly classified as being both a biological science and a social science. Some universities recognize this fact by having certain courses of anthropological study count as the one and certain as the other, or perhaps even the same course counting either way. Such a situation of double participation is unusual among the sciences. If anthropology is not concerned so predominantly with man as an animal, or with man as a social human having a history, that it can be set outright in either the life or the social-historical science category, both aspects are evidently represented significantly in its subject matter. Could it be that the specific subject of anthropology is the interrelation of what is biological in man and what is social and historical in him? The answer is Yes. Or, more broadly, anthropology does at least concern itself with both organic and social factors in man, whereas nearly all other sciences and studies deal with one or the other. Anthropology concerns itself with both sets of factors because these come associated in human beings in nature. Often they are even intertwined in one and the same phenomenon, as when a person is born with hereditary musical capacity and develops this further by study and training. They are not always easy to disentangle; but they must be separated if the processes at work are to be understood. That job is peculiarly the anthropologist's.

2. ORGANIC AND SOCIOCULTURAL ELEMENTS

To the question why a Louisiana Negro is black and longheaded, the answer is ready. He was born so. As cows produce calves, and lions, cubs, so Negro springs from Negro and Caucasian from Caucasian. We call the force at work heredity. Our same Negro is reputed amiable and easy-going. Is this too an innate quality? Offhand most of us might reply Yes. He sings at his corn-hoeing more frequently than the white man across the fence. Is this also because of his heredity? "Of course—he is made so," might be a common answer, "Probably—why not?" a more cautious one. But now our Negro is singing the "Memphis Blues," which his great-grandfather in Africa assuredly did not sing. As for the specific song, heredity can obviously no longer be the cause. Our Negro may have learned it from an uncle, or perhaps from his schoolmates; quite likely he acquired it from human beings who were not his ancestors, or over the radio, acquired it as part of his customs, like being a member of the Baptist Church and wearing overalls, and the thousand other things that come to him from without instead of from within. At these points heredity is displaced by tradition, nature by nurture, to use a familiar jingle. The efficient forces now are quite different from those which made his skin black and his head long. They are causes of another order.

The particular song of the Negro and his complexion represent the clear-cut extremes of the matter. Between them lie the good nature and the inclination to melody. Obviously these traits may also be the result of human example, of "social environment," of contemporary tradition. There are those who so believe, as well as those who see in them chiefly the effects of inborn biological impulse. Perhaps these intermediate dubious traits are the results of a blending of nature and nurture, the strength of each varying according to the trait or the individual examined. Clearly, at any rate, there is room here for investigation and weighing of evidence. A genuine problem exists. This problem cannot be solved by the historical or social sciences alone, because they do not concern themselves with heredity. Nor can it be solved by biology, which deals with heredity and allied factors but does not go on to operate with the nonbiological principle of tradition or with what is acquired by men when they live in societies.

Here, then, is one distinctive task for anthropology: the interpretation of those phenomena into which both innate organic factors and "social" or acquired factors enter or may enter.

The word "social" is the customary untechnical one for the nonorganic or more-than-organic phenomena referred to. It is, however, an ambiguous word and therefore sometimes a confusing one. As will shortly be pointed out, "social" refers to both social and cultural phenomena. Until the distinction between them has been made, we shall either put "social" into quotation marks or use "sociocultural" instead.

3. ORGANIC OR "PHYSICAL" ANTHROPOLOGY

The organic sciences underlie the sociocultural ones. They are more immediately "natural," less "humanized" in their concern. Anthropology therefore accepts and uses the general principles of biology: the laws of heredity and the doctrines of cell development and evolution, for instance, and all the findings of anatomy, physiology, embryology, zoology, palaeontology, and the rest. Its business has been to ascertain how far these principles apply to man, what forms they take in his particular case. This has meant a concentration of attention, the devising of special methods of inquiry. Many biological problems, including most physiological and hereditary ones, can be most profitably attacked in the laboratory, or at least under experimental conditions. The experimental method, however, is but rarely available for human beings living in groups. Sociocultural phenomena have to be taken as they come and laboriously sifted and resifted afterward, instead of being artificially simplified in advance, as is done in laboratory experimentation.

Then, too, since anthropology is operating biologically within the narrow limits of one species, it has sometimes been driven to concern itself with minute traits, such as the zoologist is rarely troubled with: the proportions of the length and the breadth of the skull—the famous cephalic index—for instance; the number of degrees the arm bones are twisted, and the like. Also, as these data had to be used in the gross, unmodifiable by artificially varied conditions, it has been necessary to secure them from all possible varieties of men, different races, sexes, ages, and their nearest brute analogues. The result is that biological or physical anthropology—"somatology" it is sometimes called in Anglo-Saxon countries, and sometimes simply "anthropology" in continental Europe—has in part constituted a sort of specialization or sharpening of certain aspects of general biology. It has become absorbed to a considerable degree in certain particular phenomena, such as human species or subraces and methods of studying them, about which general biologists, physiologists, and students of medicine are usually but vaguely informed.

4. SOCIOCULTURAL ANTHROPOLOGY

The sociocultural sciences, usually, but somewhat loosely, called the social sciences, overlie the organic sciences. Men's bodies and inborn equipment are back of their deeds and accomplishments as shaped by tradition, and are primary to their culture or civilization as well as to their aggregations in societies. The relation of anthropology to sociocultural science has therefore been in a sense the opposite of its relation to biological science. Instead of specializing, anthropology has been occupied with trying to generalize the findings of history. Historians can never experiment; sociologists, economists, and other social scientists only rarely. Historians deal with the unique; for to a degree every historical or social or cultural event has something unparalleled about it. They do not lay down laws, nor do they verify them by the artificial trials of experiment. But anthropology looks for such general and recurrent processes as may occur in the multifarious events of history and in the diverse societies, institutions, customs, and beliefs of mankind. So far as such processes can be extricated or formulated, they are generalizations.

It has sometimes been said that social and cultural anthropology—that part of the subject which is concerned with the more-than-merely-organic aspects of human behavior—seems preoccupied with ancient and savage and exotic and extinct peoples. The cause is a desire to understand better all civilizations, irrespective of time and place, in the abstract, or as generalized principles if possible. It is not that cave men are more illuminating than Romans, or flint knives more interesting than fine porcelains or the art of printing, which has led anthropology to bear heavily on the former, but the fact that it wanted to know about cave men and flint knives, which no one else was studying, as well as about the Romans and printing presses that history tells us about so fully. It would be arbitrary to prefer the exotic and remote to the familiar, and in principle anthropology has never accepted the adjudication sometimes tacitly rendered that its proper field should be restricted to the primitive as such. As well might zoology confine its interest to eggs or to protozoans. It is probably true that some researches into early and savage history, especially in the initial stages of anthropology, have sprung from an emotional predilection for the forgotten or the neglected, the obscure and the strange, the unwonted and the mysterious. But such occasional personal aesthetic trends cannot delimit the range of a science or determine its aims and methods. Innumerable historians have been inveterate gossips, but one does not therefore insist that the only proper subject of history is backstairs intimacies.

This, then, is the reason for the special development of those subdivisions of anthropology known as *archaeology,* "the science of what is old" in the career of humanity, especially as revealed by excavations of the sites of prehistoric occupation, and *ethnology,* "the science of peoples" and their cultures and life histories as groups, irrespective of their degree of advancement.[1]

5. EVOLUTIONARY PROCESSES AND EVOLUTIONISTIC FANCIES

In their more elementary aspects the two strands of the organic or hereditary and the sociocultural or "environmental" run through all human life. They are distinct as mechanisms, and their products are distinct. Thus a comparison of the acquisition of the power of flight respectively by birds in their organic development out of the ancestral reptile stem millions of years ago, and by men as a result of cultural progress in the field of invention during the past generation, reveals at once the profound differences of *process* that inhere in the ambiguous concept of "evolution." The bird gave up a pair of walking limbs to acquire wings. It added a new faculty by transforming part of an old one. The sum total of its parts or organs was not greater than before. The change was transmitted only to the blood descendants of the altered individuals. The reptile line went on as it had been before, or if it altered, did so for causes unconnected with the evolution of the birds. The airplane, on the contrary, gave men a new faculty without diminishing or even impairing any of those they had previously possessed. It led to no visible bodily changes, no alterations of mental capacity. The invention has been transmitted to individuals and groups not derived by descent from the inventors; in fact, it has already influenced the fortunes of all of us. Theoretically, the invention is transmissible to ancestors if they happen to be still living. In sum, it represents an accretion to the stock of existing civilization rather than a transformation.

Once the broad implications of the distinction which this example illustrates have been grasped, many common errors are guarded against. The program of eugenics, for instance, loses much of its force. There is certainly much to be said in favor of intelligence and discrimination in mating, as in everything else. There is need for the acquisition of more exact knowledge on human heredity. But, in the main, the claims sometimes made that eugenics is necessary to preserve civilization from dissolution, or to maintain the flourishing of this or that nationality, rest on the fallacy of recognizing only organic causes as operative, when sociocultural as well as organic ones are active—when indeed the superhereditary factors may be much the more powerful ones. So, in what are miscalled race problems, the average thought of the day still reasons confusedly between sociocultural and organic causes and effects.[2] Anthropology is not yet

[1] Ethnography is sometimes separated, as more descriptive, from ethnology, as more theoretically or more historically inclined.

[2] An example is the still lingering fallacy that individual development of organs by use somehow gets incorporated into the heredity of descendants. This fallacy rests on the misapplication to organic situations of a valid sociocultural mechanism. An example in reverse

in a position always to state just where the boundary lies between the contributing organic causes and the superorganic or "sociocultural" causes of such phenomena. But it does hold to their fundamental distinctness and to the importance of their distinction, if true understanding is the aim. Without sure grasp of this principle, many of the arguments and conclusions in the present volume will lose their significance.

Accordingly, a designation of anthropology as "the child of Darwin" is misleading. Darwin's essential achievement was that he imagined, and substantiated by much indirect evidence, a mechanism through which organic evolution appeared to be taking place. The whole history of man, however, being much more than an organic matter, a merely or strictly Darwinian anthropology would be largely misapplied biology. One might almost as justly speak of a Copernican or a Newtonian anthropology.

What has greatly influenced some of the earlier anthropology, mainly to its damage, has been not Darwinism, but the vague idea of progress, to the organic aspect of which Darwin happened incidentally to give such support and apparent substance that the whole group of evolutionistic ideas, sound and unsound, has luxuriated rankly ever since. It became common practice in the older anthropology to "explain" any part of human civilization by arranging its several forms in an evolutionary sequence from lowest to highest and allowing each successive stage to flow spontaneously, without specific cause, from the preceding one. At bottom this logical procedure was astonishingly naïve. In these schemes we of our land and day stood at the summit of the ascent. Whatever seemed most different from our customs was therefore reckoned as earliest, and other phenomena were disposed wherever they would best contribute to the straight evenness of the climb upward. The relative occurrence of phenomena in time and space was disregarded in favor of their logical fitting into a plan. It was argued that since we hold to definitely monogamous marriage, the beginnings of human sexual union probably lay in the opposite condition of indiscriminate promiscuity. Since we accord precedence to descent from the father, and generally know him, early society must have reckoned descent from the mother and no one knew his own father. We abhor incest; therefore the most primitive men normally married their sisters. These are fair samples of the conclusions or assumptions of the classic evolutionistic school of anthropology of, say, 1860 to 1890, which still believed that primal origins or ultimate causes could be determined, and that they could be discovered by speculative reasoning. The roster of this evolutionistic-speculative school was graced by some illustrious names. Needless to say, these men tempered the basic crudity of their opinions by wide knowledge, acuity or charm of presentation, and frequent insight and sound sense in concrete particulars. In their day, two generations or three ago, under the spell of the concept of evolution in its first flush, and of the postulate of

is the ascription of environmentally or historically produced cultural backwardness to organic and hereditary inferiority.

progress at its strongest, such methods of reasoning were almost inevitable. Today they are long since threadbare; they have descended to the level of newspaper science or have become matter for idle amateur guessing. They are evidence of a tendency toward the easy smugness of feeling oneself superior to all the past. These ways of thought are mentioned here only as an example of the beclouding that results from bad transference of biologically legitimate concepts into the realm of the history of human society and culture, or viewing these as unfolding according to a simple scheme of progress.

6. SOCIETY AND CULTURE

The relation between what is biological and what is sociocultural has just been said to be a sort of central pivot of anthropology, from which the range of the subject then extends outward on both sides, into the organic and into the more-than-organic. It is now necessary to consider the more precise relation of society and culture within the "organic-plus." In man, social and cultural phenomena normally occur associated much as the joint sociocultural phenomena co-occur with the organic ones. Nevertheless, the social and the cultural aspects within the larger sociocultural field can nearly always be distinguished.

The Latin word *socius* denotes a companion or ally, and in their specific sense the words "society" and "social" refer to associations of individuals, to group relations. When we speak of social structure, or the organization of society, it is clear what is meant: the way a mass of people is constituted into families, clans, tribes, states, classes, sets, clubs, communities, and the like. A society is a group of interrelated individuals.

But in a much wider sense the word "social" is also used, loosely, for whatever transcends the biological individual: for what we have so far designated as more-than-organic or sociocultural. Thus popular usage and university curricula recognize the physical, the biological, and the social sciences. The last-named usually comprise history, government, economics, sociology, anthropology, human geography.[3] All these branches of study deal not only with man but with men. In fact they deal primarily with the interrelations of men, or groups of men.

It so happens that man is an essentially unique animal in that he possesses speech faculty and the faculty of symbolizing, abstracting, or generalizing. Through these two associated faculties he is able to communicate his acquired learning, his knowledge and accomplishments, to his fellows and his descendants —in fact, even to his ancestors, if they happen to be still alive and are willing to listen to him. So he transmits much of his ideas, habits, and achievements to succeeding generations of men. This is something that no other animal can do, at least not to any significant degree. This special faculty is what was meant

[3] Psychology is sometimes also partly included, sometimes reckoned rather with the biological sciences.

when someone called man the "time-binding" animal. He "binds" time by transcending it, through influencing other generations by his actions.

Now the mass of learned and transmitted motor reactions, habits, techniques, ideas, and values—and the behavior they induce—is what constitutes *culture*. Culture is the special and exclusive product of men, and is their distinctive quality in the cosmos.

Not only is culture a unique phenomenon, but it can be said to have a large degree of influence. Of course culture can appear and go on only in and through men, men in some kind of societies; without these it could not come into being nor maintain itself. But, given a culture, the human beings that come under its influence behave and operate quite differently from the way they would behave under another culture, and still more differently from the way they would act under no culture. In the latter case they would be merely animals in their behavior. They are human beings precisely because they are animals plus a culture. Somehow human beings began long ago to produce culture and have continued ever since to produce it. In that sense culture derives wholly from men. But the other side of the picture is that every human being is influenced by other men who in turn have been influenced by still others in the direction of maintaining and developing certain ideas, institutions, and standards. And a shorthand way of expressing this is to say that they are all influenced by the culture they grow up in; in fact, in a broad way, they are dependent on it for most of the specific things they do in their lives. Culture is therefore a powerful force in human behavior—in both individual and social behavior. Any given form of culture, whether of the Eskimo or of our contemporary Western civilization, has behind it a long history of other forms of culture by which it was conditioned and from which it derives. And in turn each culture is changing and shaping the forms of culture that will succeed it and which therefore more or less depend on it. Culture thus is a factor that produces enormous effects, and as such we study it.

To be concrete, the reason our Louisiana Negro of a few pages back sings the blues, goes to a Baptist church, and cultivates corn is that these things are parts of American culture. If he had been reared in the Africa of some of his forefathers, his dress, labor, food, religion, government, and amusements would have been quite different, as well as his language. Such is what culture does to men. And, as has been pointed out, the process of transmission, a process of acquisition by learning by which culture is perpetuated and operates on new generations, is quite different from the process by which heredity—another indubitable force—operates on them. Equally distinct are the results. No religion, no tool, no idea was ever produced by heredity.

Culture, then, is all those things about man that are more than just biological or organic, and are also more than merely psychological. It presupposes bodies and personalities, as it presupposes men associated in groups, and it rests upon them; but culture is something more than a sum of psychosomatic qualities and actions. It is more than these in that its phenomena cannot be wholly understood in terms of biology and psychology. Neither of these sciences claims to be able to explain why there are axes and property laws and etiquettes and prayers in the world, why they function and perpetuate as they do, and least of all why these cultural things take the particular and highly variable forms or expressions under which they appear. Culture thus is at one and the same time the totality of products of social men, and a tremendous force affecting all human beings, socially and individually. And in this special but broad sense, culture is universal for man.[4]

This brings us back to the relation of society and culture. Logically, the two are separate, though they also coexist. Many animals are social. Ants and bees and termites are very highly socialized, so much so that they can survive only in societies. But they have no culture. There is no culture on the subhuman level. Ants get along without culture because they are born with many highly specific instincts; but men have only few and general instincts. Society without culture exists on the subhuman level. But culture, which exists only through man, who is also a social animal, presupposes society. The speech faculty makes possible the transmission and perpetuation of culture; and speech could evidently arise only in a somewhat socially inclined species, though the most socialized animals, the social insects, are held together by instinctive drives and do not need speech. In man, however, language helps bind his societies successfully together. And then culture, with its institutions and morals and values, binds each of them together more and helps them to achieve more successful functioning.

Human society and culture are thus perhaps best viewed as two intimately intertwined aspects of a complex of phenomena that regularly occur only in association; whereas on the subhuman level, societies occur but there is no significant culture.

The occurrence of cultureless true societies among the insects makes it clear that, much as living bodies and "minds" underlie societies and cultures, and precede them in evolution, so also, in turn, society precedes and underlies culture, though in man the two always happen to come associated. At any rate, society is a simpler and more obvious concept to grasp than is culture. That is apparently why sociocultural phenomena—the phenomena of man's total history in the broadest sense, which necessarily contain both social facts and cultural facts—usually have their social aspects recognized first. The result has been that

---

[4] Culture as dealt with by the anthropologist is obviously different from what is signi-fied by speaking of "a man of culture," or "a cultured person," in the popular sense, when high culture, or special refinement of it, is meant. Similarly with the word "civilization." When we ordinarily, as laymen, speak of "civilized" and "uncivilized" peoples, we mean, more precisely, peoples of advanced and backward culture, respectively. By many anthro-pologists, ever since Tylor, the words "civilization" and "culture" are often used to denote the same thing; and always they denote only degrees of the same thing.

the social-plus-cultural combination came at first to be called merely "social," and in popular and general use still carries that ambiguous name.

For those who like their thinking concrete, it may help if they conceive the sociocultural total in man as similar to a sheet of carbon paper, of which the fabric side represents society and the coated side culture. It is obvious that to use carbon paper effectively, we must distinguish the sides. And yet the sheet is also a unit. Moreover, in certain respects, as when we are not concerned with manifolding but only with some operation like sorting, counting, or packing, a sheet of carbon paper is comparable to and is handled like a sheet of uncoated paper—which in turn would correspond to the cultureless animal societies. But if what we are interested in is the use of carbon paper, the impressions made by it, or if we wish to understand how it makes them, then it is the specific carbon coating that we must examine, even though this comes only as a sort of dry-ink film carried by paper of more or less ordinary cellulose fabric and texture. Like all similes, this one has its limitations. But it may be of help in extricating oneself from the confusing difficulty that the word "social" has acquired a precise and limited meaning—society as distinguishable from culture—in anthropology and sociology, while still having a shifting double meaning—society including or excluding culture—in popular usage and in many general contexts.

There is a real difficulty in the confusion that results from the varying usage of the word "society." The difficulty is unfortunate; but it can be met by keeping it constantly in mind. In the present book, the effort is made to be consistent in saying "culture" or "cultural" whenever anything cultural is referred to. "Social" or "society" are used only with specific reference to the organization of individuals into a group and their resulting relations. Culture, on the contrary, whatever else it may also be—such as a tremendous influence on human behavior—is always first of all the *product* of men in groups: a set of ideas, attitudes, and habits—"rules" if one will—evolved by men to help them in their conduct of life.[5]

[5] A further complication arises from the fact that human societies are more than merely innate or instinctual associations like beehives or anthills, but are also culturally shaped and modeled. That is, the forms which human association takes—into nations, tribes, sects, cult groups, classes, castes, clans, and the like—all these forms of social structure are as much the result of varying cultural influences as are the particular forms of economies, technologies, ideologies, arts, manners, and morals at different times and places. In short, specific human societies are more determined by culture than the reverse, even though some kind of social life is a precondition of culture. And therewith social forms become part of culture! This seemingly contradictory situation is intellectually difficult. It touches the heart of the most fundamental social theorizing. A good many anthropologists and sociologists still shrink from facing the problem or admitting the situation to be significant. The beginner is therefore advised not to try to master the difficulty at this stage, but to wait till he has finished the book. He will then presumably understand what the problem is and be in a position either to accept the solution suggested here, or to give his own answer. And if not, he will still be in the company of a lot of professional social scientists of good standing.

7. ANTHROPOLOGY AND THE SOCIAL SCIENCES

All the so-called social sciences deal with cultural as well as social data. Caesar's reform of the calendar was a cultural innovation. His defeat of the senatorial party was a social event, but it led to institutional and therefore cultural changes, just as it affected thousands of individual lives for better or worse. When a historian analyzes Caesar's character and motivation, he has in fact gone beyond both society and culture and is operating in the field of informal, biographical, individual psychology. In economics, a banking system, the gold standard, commerce by credit or barter, are institutions, and hence cultural phenomena.

Of all the social sciences, anthropology is perhaps the most distinctively culture-conscious. It aims to investigate human culture as such: at all times, everywhere, in all its parts and aspects and workings. It looks for generalized findings as to how culture operates—literally, how human beings behave under given cultural conditions—and for the major developments of the history of culture.

To this breadth of aim, one thing contributed. This was the early anthropo· logical preoccupation with the very ancient and primitive and remote, which we have already mentioned as a possible foible or drawback. Unlettered peoples leave no biographies of their great men to distract one with personalities, no written histories of rulers and battles. The one thing we know about them is their customs; and customs are culture. The earliest men in fact have left us evidence of just two things: parts of their organic bodies, as represented by their bones; and, more abundantly, their culture, as represented by those of their tools and implements which happened to be of stone and imperishable, plus such of their customs as may be inferable from these tools.

Now while some of the interest of anthropology in its earlier stages was in the exotic and the out-of-the-way, yet even this antiquarian motivation ultimately contributed to a broader result. Anthropologists became aware of the diversity of culture. They began to see the tremendous range of its variations. From that, they commenced to envisage it as a totality, as no historian of one period or of a single people was ever likely to do, nor any analyst of his own type of civilization alone. They became aware of culture as a "universe," or vast field, in which we of today and our own civilization occupy only one place of many. The result was a widening of a fundamental point of view, a departure from unconscious ethnocentricity toward relativity. This shift from naïve self-centeredness in one's own time and spot to a broader view based on objective comparison is somewhat like the change from the original geocentric assumption of astronomy to the Copernican interpretation of the solar system and the subsequent still greater widening to a universe of galaxies.

A considerable differentiation of anthropology occurred on this point. The other social sciences recognized culture in its specific manifestations as they became aware of this or that fragment or aspect of it—economic or juridical or political or social. Anthropologists became aware of culture as such. From that they went on to try to understand its generic features and processes and their results.

This is one of the few points that sets off from anthropology a science which in the main is almost a twin sister: sociology. Sociologists began mainly with the analysis of our own civilization; they kept the exotic in its place. Therefore as regards culture they tended to remain autocentric somewhat longer. Also, in dealing with ourselves, they dealt mainly with the present, and from that they went on to deal with the future, immediate and ultimate. This inevitably gave to much of early sociology some reformist or ameliorative coloring, and often a program for action. On the contrary, the reproach used to be directed at anthropology that it did not concern itself with practical solutions, or aim at betterment. So far as this was true, it had at least the virtue of helping anthropology to remain a general or fundamental science, undistracted by questions of application from its search for basic findings and meanings. One other distinction is that sociology has been more concerned with strictly social problems: the relations of classes, the organization of family and society, the competitions of individuals within a group. The names are indeed significant here: sociology tends to be concerned with society, anthropology with *anthropos,* man, and his specifically human product, culture.

All in all, however, these are only differences of emphasis. In principle, sociology and anthropology are hard to keep apart. Anthropologists rate Sumner as one of the great names in the history of the study of man; and they feel they stand on common ground with American sociologists like Thomas, Ogburn, Chapin, Sorokin, Wirth, MacIver, Parsons, and Lynd, to name only a few, and with Britons and Frenchmen like Hobhouse, Ginsberg, Durkheim, and Mauss. Sociologists on their side have been if anything even more hospitable. Almost to a man they are culture-conscious, know anthropological literature well, and use it constantly.

The relations of anthropology to psychology are obviously important. The nature of human personality—or let us say simply human nature—must enter vitally into all of man's social and cultural activity. However, the relations of anthropology and psychology are not easy to deal with. Psychologists began by taking their own culture for granted, as if it were uniform and universal, and then studying psychic behavior within it. Reciprocally, anthropologists tend to take human nature for granted, as if it were uniform, and to study the diverse cultures which rest upon it. In technical language, we have two variables, "mind" and culture, and each science assumes that it can go ahead by treating the other variable as if it were constant. All psychologists and anthropologists now know that such constancy is not actual. But to deal with two variables, each highly complex, is difficult; and as for specific findings, only beginnings have as yet been made. This whole set of problems of cultural psychology is taken up in one of the later chapters of this book.

The foregoing will make clear why anthropology is sometimes still regarded as one of the newer subjects of study. As a distinct science, with a program of its own, it is relatively recent, because it could hardly become well organized until the biological and the social sciences had both attained enough development to specialize and become aware of the gap between themselves, and until culture was recognized as a specific and distinctive field of inquiry.

But as an unmethodical body of knowledge, as an interest, anthropology is plainly one of the oldest of the sisterhood of sciences. It could not well be otherwise than that men were at least as much interested in each other as in stars and mountains and plants and animals. Every savage is a bit of an ethnologist about neighboring tribes and knows a legend of the origin of mankind. Herodotus, the "father of history," devoted half of his nine books to pure ethnology. Lucretius, a few centuries later, tried to solve by philosophical deduction and poetical imagination many of the same problems that modern anthropology is more cautiously attacking with concrete methods. Until nearly two thousand years after these ancients, in neither chemistry nor geology nor biology was so serious an interest developed as in anthropology.

CHAPTER TWO

Man's Place in Nature

8. ANTECEDENTS TO MAN'S DEVELOPMENT

A NUMBER of major achievements had to be made in the development of life before there could be man. There are more than a dozen such basic innovations, to pause only at the most fundamental ones. These underlie the possibility of human existence and have actually preceded it in evolution.

This is not an insinuation that there was any predetermination of such a sequence of developmental steps leading to ourselves. That the steps happened is all that we can say. But they had to happen, if there was to be man. Conceivably, a quite different series of evolutionary advances might have made possible the coming on the stage of a type as skilled, intelligent, and successful as man, or even superior to him, but different from him. Conceivably, that very thing may have happened on some other planet or in some other galaxy. But on this our own earth, we can read its history in only one way: as it actually happened. What follows, then, is a tally of some of the more dramatic turns of the road which our preancestors traversed through nature before becoming man.

This will not be the usual story of new and higher kinds of animals coming on the scene in successive periods of geology—the age of mailed fishes, the age of reptiles, the age of mammals. We can assume that history as more or less familiar in outline. What concerns us more, with our focus on man as an eventual product, is the specific features of body build and body use that had to be developed before there could even be a prospect of man's developing. It is his *significant antecedents* that count. These are features which we are likely to take for granted: things like heads, legs, senses, nervous system, body heat; like the capacities for play, for sleeping, for living long enough to learn, and for dwelling together in societies. But Nature, if we may momentarily personify her, could not take these features for granted. They were not there when life began on earth. Most of them did not get achieved till long after. They were developed haltingly, partially, one-sidedly, by something like rare and slow steps of trial and error, through aeons and aeons of painfully hesitating evolution.

It is the more outstanding of these structures and faculties that are specially significant for understanding man's place in the totality of nature: for realizing what his humble and unconscious ancestors had to acquire and achieve before he could become man—before he could be even a mammal and a primate, let alone an animal able to develop speech and culture.

This analysis we can make without having to recite the full roster of the conventional periods of geology. But we do have to refer to some of the major groups of animals, the subkingdoms or phyla [1] into which the animal kingdom is classified. Those which follow are the ones we shall have occasion to mention.

Protozoa,[2] the single-celled animals, like the amoeba or the paramecium. The Protozoa underlie all the various kinds of many-celled animals—underlie them in being more basic in structure as well as presumably preceding them in time of origin. But the Protozoa are too tiny in size, too brief in duration of life, too simple in basic plan, to have ever become capable of any commanding place in nature. Their significance is as a start that that had to be made if there was to be anything further in evolution, not as an accomplishment in themselves. So we can pass them over with this mention.

The *Sponges*—perhaps the simplest of the many-celled phyla of animals.

The *Coelenterates:* corals, sea anemones, jellyfish. The name refers to their having a "hollow inside."

Echinoderms, "spiny-skins," include starfish, sea urchins, sea cucumbers, and other such sluggish forms.

Mollusks have fleshy parts—a "foot," a mantle, a siphon—and they often secrete a shell outside their body. They range from immobile forms like oysters through slow-moving snails to swift cephalopods—squids and octopuses.

Of *Worms,* formerly sometimes put all together into the one phylum *Vermes,* two or three phyla are now generally recognized. Of these the segmented annelids, typified by the familiar earthworm, are the only ones we shall need to linger on a bit, on account of their seeming to represent a simpler attempt at the plan of organization of the arthropods.

The *Arthropods*—"jointed-footers," also formerly called *Articulata* because of the elaborate way in which their segments are put together or articulated—include

---

[1] Singular, phylum.   [2] Singular, protozoon.

crustaceans, arachnids, insects. Crustaceans comprise crabs, lobsters, shrimps, and many minute forms—all water dwellers, or at least gill-breathing. Arachnids include spiders, ticks, mites, scorpions, and other types regularly unpleasant to ourselves. The arthropods, and among them especially the insects, have been and still are one of the most successful manifestations of life. They show the greatest number of species of any phylum, and probably the greatest diversity of forms.

The *Vertebrates*—fishes, amphibians, reptiles, birds, and mammals—have a vertebral column as the main axis of their internal skeleton, which contrasts so sharply with the arthropod exoskeleton. Technically, the subkingdom is named the *Chordates* after the spinal cord, but the genuine vertebrates constitute 99 per cent of the chordates. The remainder are retrogressive sessile forms, such as tunicates, skull-less forms like amphioxus, or jawless lampreys.

9. MANY-CELLED PROBLEMS: MOUTHS, VENTS, HEADS, TAILS

One of the problems confronting many-celled animals from the beginning was that of their shape, the structure of this shape, and the functional diversification of cells to correspond with the structure. A mere multiplication of like cells into an indefinitely large but uniform aggregate would have only little advantage over the same number of cells each constituting a self-sufficient organism. Some sort of pattern or plan of differentiating direction had to develop before there could be further evolution. The sponges represent such a plan—one of the oldest, and therefore evidently a successful one: it still functions, though humbly. There are four or five kinds of cells in a sponge: those that secrete the horny or silicious skeleton with which we wash; those which contract the openings into it; ciliated ones that whip the water for food and digest it; and so on. But, except for being more or less cavernous, a sponge has little describable shape. One species differs from the next in the pattern according to which it grows rather than by a specific form which it attains. The sponge is at the minimum of individuation. There are no differentiated organs, no nerves, and therefore no sense organs. A generalized continuity still pervades the whole cell aggregate. We can just barely call a particular sponge a particular organism.

The simplest readily definable form of many-celled animal is that of the coelenterates—corals, sea anemones, and jellyfish. They possess a coelum or hollow, a definite body-cavity, in which food is enclosed and absorbed. The opening of this cavity may be construed as a mouth, which a sponge or a protozoan cannot be said yet to possess. Note however that there is no vent: undigestible parts of food, and excretions, are ejected via the mouth; oral-anal differentiation has not yet occurred. More yet than a mouth, the coelenterates have a nervous system. This is a diffuse network of nerves, without any massing of nerve tissue in centers, ganglia, or brains. In fact, there is not enough organ specialization in these animals to make even an incipient brain of any use. No specifically differentiated sense organs, such as eyes or ears, have been discovered, other than tentacles sensitive to touch, to chemicals, and to heat. Movements consist of slow wavings and curlings and closures of the tentacles; of a sudden defensive contraction of the entire organism upon hurtful contact; and in some free-floating forms, of similar contractions expelling the water from the body cavity and thus pushing themselves upward. Many coelenterates are sessile: they spend their lives sitting in one place. And all are radial in plan: they are live cups with fringes and the power of closing.

With a body cavity, a mouth is implicit, but not yet a head. Heads are an achievement that life succeeded in making only after it had run a considerable course. With a forward end to an organism, setting the direction in which it travels, we are given also a hind end and a lengthwise axis of the body. With such an axis, we also get—not perhaps by mere logic of space, but certainly de facto in almost all headed animals—an upper and an under side: one habitually hugging the ground or the sea bottom, the other more exposed. With fore and aft and top and bottom established, right and left follow automatically. For things that travel, it is ordinarily advantageous to have their right and left sides equal and alike, as in a ship or a motorcar or a tractor: "bilaterally symmetric" is the technical term. The advantage is mechanically founded. It is obvious what would happen to the motion of a ship whose starboard was bulkier than its port side. On the contrary, however, both vehicles and animals ordinarily travel better if their top and bottom are rather thoroughly different in form and function. Internal lack of right-left symmetry is no disadvantage provided the weight of the two halves is kept equal; and this is as true of our viscera, with the heart on one side and the liver on the other, as of many machines.

Secondarily, cephalization and bilateral symmetry have resulted in other gains, such as the possibility of the organism's centralizing or grouping its organs—plumping them, as it were. The first great advantage of a head and symmetry, however, was undoubtedly in regard to motion. Not all symmetrical animals with a head are swift; but all swift ones have heads and symmetry. Twice at least in the history of life do good-sized groups of animals seem to have given up their bilateral symmetry: most of the echinoderms and most of the mollusks. Perhaps this was because in both cases they developed limy skeletons or shells, and armor protection cuts down mobility, in living things as in fighting ships. Some of the echinoderms, like the starfish, which returned to the radiate plan of the coelenterates, move, but at an incredibly slow crawl. Others, like the crinoids, are sessile, on stalks. Among mollusks, the snails are proverbial for their slow reactions and nearly unique in being twisted screw-fashion in one direction. This twist is a device for coiling most of the animal up compactly, instead of having it drag or bob around awkwardly behind its single, sliding belly-foot, as would happen if the body remained symmetrical. Snails accordingly atrophy their right and have their left side grow into their top, rear, and insides. Other mollusks, comprising most of the bivalves, have given up even slow travel; and an oyster, for instance, is asymmetrical in any dimension. On the contrary, the most mobile and intelligent of the mollusks the squids and the octopuses, have regained or retained their original bilateral symmetry and are very definitely cephalized.

With a head end evolved, it would normally be advantageous to have the mouth within this, and especially so to have set within the head the eyes or other sense organs that help direct motion, also jaws or other parts that take or hold or chew food. Such a gathering of active or sensitive parts needs a corresponding gathering of nerve tissue; and it is in the symmetrical animals that we find knots or ganglia of nerve, and finally brains. At first these are by no means limited to the head; but at any rate they tend to be most strongly developed there. This is already evident in the flatworm *Planaria,* whose head has a pair of eyes of sorts, though its mouth is just a tube out of its belly. It is more evident in the annelid segmented earthworm, which though blind has its mouth near the front tip of the body. Here there is a definite concentration of nerve matter in a ring around the oesophagus, culminating in an almost-brain above the oesophagus. There is a similar ganglion, or a pair of them, in each segment. In some of the free-swimming marine annelid worms, which have sensory antennae and gills at the end of the head, the brain concentration is greater than in the earthworm. Also, worms show synapses or connective intertwinings of the ends of separate nerve cells, something to which coelenterates have not yet attained.

The basic earthworm type of nervous system is retained all through the articulate or arthropod subkingdom—in crustaceans, spiders, insects. The pair of parallel nerve chains runs from segment to segment close to the underside. In the lower forms, each segment contains a pair of ganglia, or a fused ganglion; in the higher, there is always a brain in the head, whereas the centers in thorax and abdomen are variously consolidated, and in some species are united into one great thoracic ganglion. This is of course a plan quite different from that of the vertebrates, which are not repetitively segmented, therefore lack segmental ganglia, and have the main nerve chain in the back instead of the belly, protected by the vertebral column or notochord. Also, the vertebrates from the beginning concentrated nearly all sense organs as well as jaws and teeth in the head, and protected this with a skull, so that a nerve concentration within the head was basic to their structure. The successive developments and encroachings of later parts of the brain, with corresponding growths of "intelligence," are outlined in § 12. The last chapter in this process is constituted by the cerebral cortex, which first appears in reptiles and has its fullest development in the primates.

A vent for excreting seems to be a less significant counterpart of the head, and more or less of the same age developmentally. It is found for instance in the echinoderms, some of which, originally symmetrical, have returned externally to the radiate plan of structure characteristic of the headless and ventless coelenterates. There is often a strange economy in life forms that makes a single part serve more than one function. Bowel and kidney waste, for instance, may be ejected by the same or separate orifices—or even the genital products, which are so different in kind. In crustaceans and insects these last leave the body by their own opening, whereas in the vertebrates, up to the mammals, the vent for the three functions mostly is common; and even in the mammals there is a joint "genito-urinary" tract.

Tails—though we men have long since lost our ancient ones, at least externally—were important in their day. The prime function of course is locomotory. Genuinely effective tails come in with the vertebrates, among the fishes. Lower forms, especially in their larval phases, have all kinds of side and hind-end appendages, to flail or flip or jerk with. Lobsters shoot themselves backward by suddenly squeezing their tail against their body, a bit reminiscent of the way an octopus also progresses backward by squeezing water out through its siphon tube—a sort of jet propulsion. The fish is the first organism to have its hind appendage an integral part of its body, streamlined into it, and yet specifically shaped for side-to-side sculling and practically continuous progress. On land, this form of locomotion is not feasible; and though most amphibians and reptiles have kept their tail, many mammals have again lost it, or when they retain it, it serves new functions, of balance, prehensility, or fly-chasing; [3] and in the air, birds have long since replaced structural tails by superstructural ones of feathers.

10. SIZE, BONE, LIMBS

Size has been an important quality to acquire. Not that the bigger the better, but lack of size below a certain threshold is a definite handicap. This is largely because body surface tends to increase as the square of length, but weight as the cube. The very small animal therefore is swayed by every current or wave of water or air. Its medium tends to move it, where the large animal moves through the medium; the tiny one's best control is by clinging or crawling—methods that abrogate or reduce locomotion. All the really gigantic animals, past or present—sharks, whales, dinosaurs, elephants—have been members of the highest subkingdom, the vertebrates. The largest nonvertebrate, the giant squid, belongs to the most active, sensorily keenest, and perhaps most plastically intelligent order in all the invertebrate subkingdoms. Analogously, it is almost surely no accident that man is the second largest living primate, and that in general intelligence the gorilla, the largest, about ties for second place with the chimpanzee, the fourth largest.

Bone is a definite achievement. Or rather, an articulated endoskeleton is such; and bone made the best skeletal substance—strong, light, and discontinuous—once the vertebrates came onto land and had to carry their weight instead of floating it. Limy deposits outside, as in the starfish, the oyster, and the snail, slow up mobility and may abolish it. The active squid secretes itself only a spot

[3] When the ancestral whales returned to the sea, they re-evolved a fishlike tail, but in a horizontal instead of a vertical plane. This position is perhaps connected with the need for constant coming up to the surface to breathe.

of shell and then grows its soft tissues around it, with the result that it has, strictly and structurally, no skeleton at all, but a pretty good functional ersatz backbone. Insects have an exoskeleton of chitin that works excellently, but only at their size. A man-size insect would probably be a complete failure, finding it difficult to move, almost impossible to grow by molting, equally so to be warm-blooded; not to mention that minute breathing tubes could not begin to supply so large a bulk with oxygen. It is true that there were caddis-fly and grass-hopper-like insects with 30-inch wing spread in the Carboniferous period, at the very beginning of the known fossil-insect record. We do not know precisely what made them die out; but nature did not repeat the endeavor—they were evidently not a success. The largest living insects are all slow and clumsy; and even crabs have to add so much lime to their chitin that their largest species are sluggish.

True legs—that is, jointed limbs containing an inner or an outer skeleton and primarily serving locomotion, secondarily other functions—have been evolved only twice: by arthropods and vertebrates. Many small organisms move through water by cilia, hairlike fringes that wave or beat,[4] or by flail-like appendages for jerking or kicking. Others just wriggle, like worms; or slowly protrude pseudo-pods, like the starfish; or crawl by contractile waves in their belly muscle, as do snails and slugs. The squids and octopuses have skeletonless tentacles primarily for grasping and holding; their swimming locomotion is by squirting or by waving membrane fins. As to true legs, those of anthropods number many in the lower orders—ten in crabs, eight in spiders, six in insects—as against the basic vertebrate pattern of four. Among water dwellers, legs seem to be a handi-cap rather than aid to speed—compare crabs with fishes and squids. But on land, legs are correlated with speed among runners, and equally so among flyers after conversion of legs into wings in birds and bats.

Adaptation of running legs into holding forelimbs has taken place in several mammalian orders, on a lower partial level perhaps most markedly among beavers, squirrels, and other rodents; then, more thoroughly, in the primates, in connection with arboreal habitat. It was however the grasping of tree branches by primates in escape and travel that led to the handling of food, and was to lead ultimately to the handling and then the making of tools. Our arboreal ancestry thus is an antecedent that proved to be of great importance. A modicum of size also entered this situation: definitely small animals like shrews, mice, lizards, and frogs can climb and live in trees without grasping hands; toenails or pads on the feet mostly suffice to hold them; or if not, their slight weight prevents falls from being fatal, even from great heights. On the other hand, ordinary-sized monkeys, being functionally four-handed and therefore essen-tially without feet properly fitted for ground travel, were pretty well confined

---

[4] Cilia occur as low in the scale of evolution as one-celled animals, and as high as on the mucous membrane of our human nostrils.

to their tree habitat, which obviously is a quite limited and somewhat narrowing environment. It is difficult to imagine much primitive technology being invented among a race whose extremities were undifferentiated as between climbing and manipulative uses, and which would dare to descend to the ground only fitfully. With increasing size and weight there was a return to the ground among some of the primates. With the baboons this involved also a return to full four-footed locomotion on the level. With the gorilla and the chimpanzee, the return was barely a half-and-half affair: they remain awkward and feeble erect walkers, mostly travel on all fours on the ground, and often swing from arm to arm along tree limbs. This means that their arms and hands still serve locomotion—in fact, locomotion of two quite different kinds. We men have feet serviceable for ground travel and for little else; and we have long straight legs, and therewith have widened the limited arboreal environment of the primates to one that extends as far as land goes. At the same time we fortunately kept, from the former life in the trees, our grasping, manipulating forelimb hands. In other words, men alone among the primates are two-footers and two-handers. As regards structure, this is not strictly so, the anatomists tell us; but as regards use, it is essentially true. We are the only mammal whose two pairs of limbs serve two wholly different sets of functions and do so effectively; and both functions, locomotion and manipulation, are of broad, generalized, fundamental importance. We have in this differentiated combination, accordingly, one of the bases that not only made culture possible but made an effective culture possible. Incidentally, our development of real hands capable of using tools contributed to freeing the human mouth from holding, fighting, catching, and the like, which functions it has among most mammals. With the load of these activities removed, it may well be that the mouth was readier than ever before to serve as a speech organ in addition to an eating organ, as soon as the brain cortex was ready to do its part.

A contributing element to this result again was—size. If ancestral men when they left the trees had been fifteen inches tall and had weighed five pounds, the descent to the ground might easily have been fatal to them before they could evolve much culture. And if they had succeeded, their weapons, no matter how skilled, would at first have had to be thoroughly puny. It was a sound instinct that leds Wells in his *Time Machine* to make his Morlocks not a monkeylike ancestral form, but decadent men, shrunken to diminutiveness, expert mechanics but hiding in deep shafts instead of freely roaming the earth.

11. BODY TEMPERATURE AND VISION

Warm-bloodedness is the faculty of the organism to maintain its own proper constant body temperature, independent of its surroundings. The temperature of most animals is that of their environment, on which they are therefore dependent. Warm-blooders might be said to carry around with them a spot of environment made by themselves, so far as heat is concerned. This autonomous control is of course a tremendous advantage. It is analogous to the advantage that primitive man later had over even the warm-blooded subhumans, once he had learned to carry fire around or to make it. Only the two highest classes of vertebrates are warm-blooded: the birds and the mammals. They are reckoned highest partly because of possessing this attribute.

Acute vision, the ability to see sharp instead of blurred, is uncommon rather than common in the animal kingdom, perhaps because it requires not only a highly developed eye but considerable concentration of organized nerve matter. Even most mammals see motion or gross outline rather than exact details of shape, and many are color-blind. Sharp vision depends upon the presence of a fovea (macula lutea), a little pit of special sensitivity in the retina. Birds have this, and primates have it; and we have it as part of our primate inheritance. Birds need acute vision so as not to smash themselves up when landing from flight, much as a plane wants an illuminated airport, or a fog dispeller, during night landings. Monkeys need clear vision when landing from leaps in the trees. Here again we have a piece of our characteristic human luck: both that our ancestors turned arboreal, and when later they descended again, that they managed to keep their sharp eyesight. Our fine hands would certainly be much less useful if we could see only hazily, as does a dog or a horse. On account of its relation to space control, sight is the most important of the senses for high-powered muscular co-ordination; [5] and it is even more important as a basis for everything mechanical, for all the technological part of culture. Smell and hearing differ from sight in being more diffuse. They can warn of what is around the corner, and therefore help organisms to evade their hunters, or to find their prey or water. They serve the primal business of surviving. As soon as the level of more than survival is entered, sight takes precedence. It is hard to imagine blind animals at play, for instance.

We have left to the last what is possibly the most important consideration of all: organization of nerve matter into a brain of higher faculties.

12. NERVES AND BRAIN

Plants contain no nerve matter and therefore lack nervous irritability. All animals have at least areas of special excitability, though they do not all have nerves, let alone a nervous system. Some of the Protozoa show definite neuro-motor masses or strands for perception and feeding. These are grouped in and near hairlike cilia for feeling at the "head" end of the animal, and especially around the inside of what might be called its mouth opening. There are also motor strands for contracting the whole organism. This is really a precocious

[5] Among very small animals, such as insects, sight is not so important for co-ordination, nor for control of alighting from flight or leaps, because these animals are generally too light to break themselves by impact.

organization for a unicellular animal. It is actually more advanced than that found in the most backward many-celled animals, the sponges.

Sponges have the beginnings of muscle tissue, with some power of contraction for a short distance beyond the point of stimulus, if the latter is strong. These cells are undifferentiated receptor-effectors: sensitive muscle tissues, in simple language. There is no nerve tissue for perception as such nor conduction as such, in sponges. They are accordingly less organized, nervously, than the most advanced Protozoa. Presumably this is so because the integration of a number of cells into a diversely functioning unit is a more difficult achievement than the internal differentiation of a single cell.

With the coelenterates, we have seen (§ 9) that there is the beginning of a nervous system. Polyps and sea anemones have certain cells on the surface that are specially sensitive and are directly connected with contractile cells below them. We can accordingly speak of differentiated receptors and effectors, or sets of sense-organ and muscle cells. Sometimes a third set of cells is interposed. In that case we really have conductive nerve tissue also.

In the jellyfishes, there is enough of this sort of nervous matter to form a nerve net extending through the organism. An excitation at a single spot may therefore be diffused and result in the contraction of the whole body. However, the network is pretty uniform and there is no mechanism for central control. In the umbrella-shaped medusa jellyfish, long, movable, sensitive tentacles hang down from the rim of the umbrella. Just inside the rim, these are all interconnected by means of a nerve ring, which represents a definite condensation of conductive tissue as compared with the nerve net. Yet there still is nothing like ganglia or concentrations of nerve matter in masses. In fact, the nerve substance in the ring is continuous, not broken into neurons or cells, and therefore without nerve-cell joints, as synapses might be called. Transmission is more than two hundred times slower than in the fastest human nerves; and it works indifferently either way, according as it gets started. In a famous experiment, a nerve ring was dissected out. On stimulation, the impulse went around and around the ring, contracting the immediately adhering muscle, but unable to discharge itself into the organism. Trapped in the nerve ring, the impulse circulated at a speed of about a foot and a half a second, until in eleven days it had traveled 457 miles! It was tiring then, but less so than the muscles; and it finally stopped because there was enough regenerated tissue to absorb the nervous impulse. It is hard to imagine an apter illustration of the thoroughly mechanical character of neuropsychic activity at this undifferentiated level of evolution.

Above the coelenterates, nerve matter consists mainly of neurons, discontinuous elongated or branching cells connected by synapses. This plan allows both more differentiation and more centralization than the continuous nets or rings of nerve tissue. In the flatworms and segmented worms, the crustaceans and insects, there is an organized "ladder type" of nervous system of two main strands running the full length of the body near its underside, with branches for each segment or limb. The concentration of this nerve tissue into ganglia or miniature brains at the forward end, with a grouping around the swallowing part of the throat in the earthworm, has already been mentioned in § 9 in connection with the evolution of heads. A description of our own brain as an enormous supra-oesophagal ganglion mass would be not too incorrect.

In worms and insects, the head ganglia somewhat dominate the behavior of the animal as a whole, but not altogether so. Earthworms gradually conditioned to take a right-hand turn because a left-hand exit led only to sandpaper and electric shocks, hesitated but took the right turn after their brain end was amputated. This indicates that the acquired habit of making the proper turn was channeled in the whole body, or at any rate in the total nervous system, and not in the brain alone.

The vertebrate nervous system differs from that of the arthropods and worms in being developed from a single main, dorsally situated spinal cord instead of a double-strand ventral nerve "ladder." In the ancestral lowly amphioxus, there is only this cord, without thickening or massing into brain; but it also has no skull. In the fishes, there is a brain, but the cord still outweighs it. The brain lies in line with the cord, with its several bulbous parts, such as cerebellum, midbrain, and endbrain, one behind the other. These parts are well differentiated in function in fishes: the midbrain largely serves sight, the endbrain smell.

In the amphibians, the brain begins to equal the spinal cord in weight; in the reptiles and birds, it is heavier; in mammals, progressively so. Thus a cat's brain outweighs its cord four times, a macaque monkey's eight times, a man's fifty times.

The greatest evolutionary development occurs in the forebrain or in the endbrain or telencephalon. The base or floor of the endbrain is a gray and white striped mass, whence its name corpus striatum; the sides and roof constitute the pallium or "cloak." On the pallium as a foundation the cerebral cortex is gradually built up as higher forms develop. In fishes the main work of co-ordination and integration for the total organism seems to be done in the corpus striatum; almost the whole of the covering pallium serves smelling. Higher up in the scale, the original pallium is distinguished as the archipallium from the later-developed neopallium that overlies it on the sides and behind, and which is in turn overlaid by the cerebral cortex, the "brain rind" or "bark." In mammals the archipallium is largest in keen-smelling forms or in primitive ones like the marsupials; it is altogether lost in the dolphins, who roam the seas without smelling.

The cortex appears first in the higher amphibians, such as the frog. It is larger in reptiles, still larger in mammals. Here it is mostly emancipated from direct relation to any single sensory system, such as the pallium and the archipallium had to the sense of smell. The cortex is rather an intermediary between sensory systems. Its most distinctive function is mnemonic, on which in turn associations and rapid learning can be based. The cortex is like an indexed filing system, from which even single remote experiences can be brought out to be correlated with new ones.

The mammalian cortex is part gray, part white. The white parts, as elsewhere in the brain, consist chiefly of nerve fibers. The gray matter of the cortex consists largely of the cell bodies with their shorter dendrites or ramifications and synapses. The oxygenation, metabolism, and blood supply of the gray matter are higher, compared with the white. The gray, largely outer part of the human cortex has been estimated to aggregate less than a cubic inch in volume, to weigh around 13 grams, but to contain 92 billion separate cells. The total cortex is much larger, enveloping the hindmost cerebellum as well as the cerebrum portion of the endbrain to which it properly belongs. Most of the thickness of the cortex in fact is composed of an endless network of white fibers, the interconnections of which make possible an infinity of combinations and conditionings. It is the number of these that may be assumed as an index of intelligence, much more so than the convolutions or corrugations of the cortex surface.

The foregoing are some of the more significant steps of organic evolution preceding man, as regards structure. It remains to review the more important functional developments that life achieved, or had begun to achieve, before man came on the scene, and of which he was the inheritor from the time of his beginning.

13. SEX

Sex is a device for reshuffling the elements of heredity by first splitting them up, and in the end producing new individuals of greater variety. Sex extends well down into the plant kingdom, though in most species plants are bisexual, bearing flowers that have both stamens and pistils; or if the flowers are separate in sex, as in the tassel and the ear of maize, they nevertheless occur on the same plant. For whole individuals to have flowers of only one sex is much less common in plants, though it occurs, as in willows and yews; but it is evidently a secondarily recurrent character of no great evolutionary depth or significance. Thus the goatsbeard genus, in which some plants carry only male flowers and others only female, crops up secondarily in the rose family, the vast majority of whose genera and species have male and female elements side by side in the same flower. Sex in plants thus tends strongly to be hermaphrodite.

In animals, hermaphroditism also occurs, but is less characteristic, especially of the higher forms. Thus many lower mollusks are bisexual or hermaphroditic, but the free-swimming, active, and intelligent cephalopods are unequivocally unisexual. Vertebrates are bisexual. Arthropods also are basically unisexual; but parthenogenesis—"virgin birth" or sexless propagation from unfertilized eggs—occurs here and there among the insects, including some of their highest forms, such as the bees. Apparently this represents a reversion for coping with special situations.

Since reproductive fertility is cut in half in unisexual species by the inability of males to give birth, sex must have some definite compensation of survival value, else sex-differentiated forms would gradually have been wiped out. The compensation is in the cumulatively double heredity of each individual—already sixteenfold for great-great-grandchildren—which ensures a much greater mixture of genes, and therefore a greater variability of hereditary constitution. And this again makes for greater selective plasticity of the line of descent, and therewith for increased adaptability. With rigorous repetitiveness of the generations, a species theoretically succumbs as soon as it no longer fits its environment. If it constantly varies, some of its members may survive, or even flourish, in a changed environment that eliminates the majority. Sex is thus a form of insurance, of paying a premium to scatter risk and now and then to win a bonus. With its relation to specific adaptability, sex seems almost inescapable for all the highest forms of life.

14. WATER, LAND, AIR

The medium in which nearly all organisms function is either water or the combination of being on land and in the air. The geological record, as well as comparative structure and function, indicates strongly that life in water came first. Thus even in land animals and plants the reproductive cells require liquid surroundings. This priority may be due to the fact that chemical reactions and osmosis are "easier" or more active in liquids. Also, the density of protoplasm being close to that of water, the effect of gravity is very slight in water, and certain mechanical problems of support and motion are much more easily met there than on land.[6] There is very little to hold up: the water itself does nearly all of that. Hence a minimum of stiff framework is needed in marine life. If there are hard parts, they mostly serve as protective armor, as in crabs or clams or corals. The drawback is that the density of the liquid medium offers resistance to rapid motion. Among land animals the medium by which the body is surrounded normally is air, which is over a thousand times "thinner" or less resistive than water; and in all except quite small animals, most of the difficulty of rapid motion on land lies in overcoming the chaining pull of gravity. All terrestrial forms are therefore in a sense crawlers on the bottom of their medium, whereas in water there are in addition to crawlers also free-swimming forms and still more floating ones. The main lines of evolutionary development which have attained to swift, sustained, and controlled power of swimming are surprisingly few: the fishes and the cephalopod mollusks, the two most advanced marine groups. This small number of groups is surpassed by that of the branches of

---

6 This is not incompatible with the possibility that the density of protoplasm is itself the result of its having originated in a water medium.

insects, reptiles, birds, and mammals which have separately reverted to life and motion in water, although remaining air-breathing. A number of marine phyla or classes include adult or larval forms that essentially float, though they may also kick or flail or jerk or squirt or wriggle or whip themselves occasionally for short distances and without much precision of direction. Mostly they drift passively with whatever currents they find themselves in. There is hardly a counterpart to this in terrestrial life. Sessile forms are wholly confined to water: there are no land equivalents to sponges, corals, crinoids, mussels, barnacles, and tunicates—representing as many different subkingdoms.[7]

All in all, water seems to have been favorable to the origin of life, to the development of mechanisms of protection, to limited or spasmodic mobility, and therewith to restricted intelligence and restricted power of adaptation to situations. All the lowest subkingdoms of animals are exclusively water-inhabiting; so are all forms without power of locomotion. Swimming, the best type of progress in water, has been reattained by terrestrial forms; but flying, its counterpart in air, has not been achieved by any water animals. Within the phyla that on the whole are undoubtedly the highest of all—or let us say the most active and most variedly capable; namely, the arthropods and vertebrates—within these the most advanced classes are mainly terrestrial in habitat and wholly air-breathing: the insects on the one hand, the birds and the mammals on the other.[8]

15. SLEEP AND PLAY

Sleep appears to be a function of higher nervous organization. We men divide our days between periods of conscious activity and periods of withdrawal into unconsciousness. Lower animals give little evidence of letting themselves sink into phases of diminished activity and awareness, other than conditions like the torpor that often is a direct result of cold, or in the sudden but temporary inactivity in the face of danger popularly called "playing possum." Mainly, the withdrawing from external stimuli which we call sleep seems to be recuperation from the responsiveness and activity of the higher vertebrates, and perhaps a function of their warm-bloodedness or autonomous temperature. There is also a subdifference between birds and mammals. With the great majority of birds, waking and sleep are automatic responses to presence or absence of light. Mammals both respond to a greater variety of stimuli, such as temperature or danger, and show more voluntary control of sleeping and waking according as the situation involves boredom, risk, breeding excitement, and the like.

[7] And the tunicates or ascidians are chordates—that is, members, and probably degenerated ones, of the subkingdom of which the vertebrates constitute the main mass.

[8] The one contrary instance of marine forms more advanced than their terrestrial relatives is the rather narrow one of the molluskan cephalopods, which surpass the land snails and slugs.

The two lowest groups of primates, tarsiers and lemurs, are nocturnal, but all other primates are diurnal and seem genuinely to sleep at night.

Play may be defined as wasteful but pleasurable bodily activity performed for its own sake; that is, in response primarily to internal stimuli. On the whole, the lower animals are not sufficiently organized nervously to play, in this meaning of the word. Many are not sufficiently motile. It is doubtful whether play exists even among so highly organized a group as the insects. True, we see the dragonfly darting about, the butterfly fluttering, the midges dancing in the sun; and they are no doubt experiencing a sort of euphoria. But the first two are in the way of finding their food, or their mate; the last is warming up for his courtship; there is always a business involved. And such quasi-play in insects always characterizes only their final, adult, and often brief stage, in contrast with vertebrates, whose playfulness occurs in youth. A butterfly, for instance, spends its youth in the sullenly voracious business of feeding and growing, with its senses, limbs, and mobility much limited. Its adolescence is the stuporlike pupa period of seclusion and immobility. It is only the adult imago ready for mating and death that can properly be said even to act as if it played.

The heavily socialized ants and bees, who are in some ways the most highly developed of insects, lack play altogether. They labor for their fellows, for the hive, its young and its future. Activity is serious, often grim, almost ceaseless. Everything is subordinate to communal welfare; play would distract from this. When an ant relaxes, it is to be fed or cleaned by a self-sacrificing fellow.

Among the arthropods lower than insects, the individualistic spiders, scorpions, crustaceans, life is even grimmer. The male fiddler crab executes a sort of posturing dance, but it is to court females.

Even the vertebrates, when they are cold-blooded, show only traces of playfulness, mostly in connection with mating, and such activities are probably more tense than relaxed. It is only among the warm-blooded vertebrates that well-developed play appears. In the birds, this is still preponderantly attached to mating. It is then that the peacock struts, the pigeon pouts, sparrows chatter and quarrel, songbirds sing; if there is a special plumage, it is assumed now. It is only occasional species such as crows and magpies, to a certain somewhat dour extent also parrots, which are playful apart from courtship, which become mischievous or aggressively tricky, and can serve as human playmates. It is also among these birds that thievishness appears—the picking up and hiding of bright but useless objects. Nesting penguins similarly steal stones from one another. But young birds consistently show no impulse to play. They clamor to be fed, or go about feeding themselves, with a deadly seriousness.

It is among mammals that playfulness is most fully developed, and in youth rather than in connection with reproduction. In fact, mammalian mating tends to be hard, competitive, often vicious. Nor does the mother ordinarily play much with her young; mostly she seems patiently indulgent of their pranks.

In general the carnivorous animals play most and often continue into maturity. All the canines and felines, the bears and raccoons, and the skunk are familiar examples; the seals are among the most addicted. Their protein food is concentrated, so that a meal satisfies for hours, and thus gives them well-fed leisure. Then, food does not occur spread out for them in indefinite amounts like pasture, but has to be found and run down and caught, by means of high sensory activity and motor co-ordination, which are then available for energy play in the periods of leisure. But there are also some carbohydrate-eating animals that are definitely playful, besides lambs and calves with their awkward gambols: the elephant, for instance, and the goat.

Monkeys of course play, but on the whole they are perhaps to be characterized rather as emotional than as playful. They cuddle and hug, embrace and quarrel. They are strongly concerned with their personality interrelations, and establish intricate chains of relationship of dominance. Some of their pursuings may be the stronger chasing the weak in anger rather than sport. Probably a good part of their play is autistic, like gymnastic exercise, instead of mutual. Most monkeys want companionship and affection, but they are full of greed and envy and prone to tyrannize. The baboons, who are large and powerful, seem to play little. They are sturdily selfish and oppressive toward one another, although against the outsider they may resist as a group. Another quality that contributes to keeping some species of monkeys from playfulness is their diffused, nearly continuous sexuality, which is expressed directly, without courtship play. All in all, it is perhaps not unfair to say that emotionality keeps most monkeys from playing as much as their muscles and senses would allow.

But with the anthropoids, the manlike apes, we begin to approach human behavior. They are inquisitive, they get along better with one another than the monkeys, their sexuality is less obtrusive and less diffuse. The playfulness of the young chimpanzee is proverbial and probably equal to that of an energetic child. Even the more melancholy orang and the sluggish gorilla are not far behind. Adults lose playfulness, partly on account of increasing body weight, but no doubt largely because the disposition changes with the maturing of the sexual glands, as in most mammals.

Play impulses in the wide sense are exceedingly significant in man, because in rechanneled form they motivate great areas of human behavior and important achievements of culture. This refers not only to games and sports, but to the influence of curiosity, of desire for variety, of mental restlessness, in the arts and sciences and fashions. If our ancestors had been wholly lacking in playfulness, we should probably have had many fewer aesthetic and intellectual developments in human culture (§ 148). Not that songs or poems or philosophies are mere play or made in play. But they are superutilitarian: pleasurable outlets for excess energy rather than responses to actual needs, and they are thus based on impulses akin to those of play, sublimated as well as matured.

16. AGE AND YOUTH

Two related qualities that are rooted in man's biological heredity, but which have contributed to the success of his unique sociocultural experiment, are a long life span and within this a proportionally long youth. According as we count youth as terminating at sexual maturation or at full growth, youth covers respectively a fifth or a fourth of a long, above-normal life. As it works out, this gives us plenty of time to learn and master our "social heritage." And the fifty or so additional years that in favorable cases are left us beyond youth suffice us to do something satisfactory and full with this heritage once it is learned. This is presumably just a piece of our good fortune. We certainly have no reason to believe that nature anticipatorily evolved a long life for us in order to make us fit vessels for culture when it was only later on that we were to develop the faculty for receiving culture. But if under evolution our youth had happened to eventuate differently, and to be markedly briefer than it actually is, the total culture developed by the human species would probably have been considerably simpler and considerably less. With the one or two years of immaturity of a dog or a cow—to select two familiar animals, one several times smaller and the other larger in mass than we—and a total span of twelve or fifteen years allotted to ourselves, it is obvious how much more meager would be our control of speech, skills, institutions, and ideas. Unquestionably, a short life, and probably still more a short youth, would have put a low ceiling over human possibilities of cultural attainment. There is no direct evidence that as man began to develop culture his longevity increased under the competition of natural selection, those strains which matured more slowly now first having a definite edge of survival advantage in that their members could acquire better skills, speech, and organization. But it is theoretically conceivable that this happened; and in any event, once man had culture, his possession of this culture would prevent his hereditary longevity from shortening in evolution, at least as long as natural selection was operative.

On subhuman precultural levels, longevity is connected with a number of factors, such as size, activity, and fertility. Other things being equal, larger animals live a longer span. A rat outlasts a mouse, a cat a rat, a lion a cat, an elephant the lion. But this holds with reservations, especially when the species are far apart: a bull outweighs five men, but a man may outlive four or five bulls. Also, once a certain life span has become a trait of a species, it is not altered much by giantism or dwarfism, except to a minor extent negatively at both extremes. Big dogs have ten to twenty times the bulk of little ones, but about the same duration of life; that, apparently, became fixed in the genes, the germ plasm, when dogs crystallized into a species; great whales become sexually mature in two years, and seem rarely to live more than two decades. It is inactivity, sluggishness, keeping the candle burning dim, which is evidently connected with the relative longevity of seventeen-year locust larvae, tortoises, and perhaps parrots.

Fertility can be seen as one special negative aspect of activity. In addition, fertility tends to correlate—also antithetically—with longevity. A rabbit, producing large litters in rapid succession, does not have to live long to multiply fiftyfold. After that, the welfare of the species is probably better served by one of her fresh daughters than by having the original mother survive. If rabbits bore only one young at a time at intervals of several years, they would probably die out even if they lived a century, being weak and defenseless. But the elephant, being immune as prey, except to man, and therefore with a low mortality wastage on the way, can get by with his very slow fertility because of his longevity. Yet if he lived no longer than a cow, his species would presumably soon die out, unless it could alter to speed up conceptions and pregnancies.

The foregoing considerations apply chiefly to mammals and birds. It is worth while to glance at conditions among the insects, the class of animals often rated as next to the vertebrates in degree of advancement, and surpassing them in variety and number of species. The most striking difference is that on the whole the immature, prereproductive stages of insects, corresponding to youth in vertebrates, take up most of their life span. It is in the highly specialized insects that the succession of distinct stages—egg, larva, chrysalis, imago—is most accentuated. The first three of these stages are given over to growth and development; the last, essentially to reproduction, and it is often quite brief. In many species a sort of disintegration death follows quickly upon deposition of the eggs. From the vertebrate point of view this is a pretty sorry way of doing, leaving the individual no room for any dignity of personality: not even such as a lion or a bull or a raven or an eagle has. Larval life does not add up much of a stock of experiences and skills for the adult insect to operate with. Nine-tenths of life is used in being a mere eating and growing and passively transforming machine in order to enable the final tenth to function as an egg-fertilizing or egg-laying machine. In the higher vertebrates, growing-up occupies a minority fraction of the whole life span, and its seriousness is relieved by the play impulses we have discussed. And within the longer reproductive phase of vertebrates, sex and reproduction as such actually comprise only a small part of the total activities. To us culture-bearing men, the gearing of the insect organism must inevitably seem particularly inhuman because of its thoroughgoing exclusion of all functions that might contribute even potentially to the development of something like culture.[9]

[9] This highly predetermined disposition is most characteristic of those insect orders, such as butterflies, beetles, and flies, in which the metamorphic stages are highly differentiated. Insects in which the stages are less marked, such as crickets, grasshoppers, and roaches, may be equally or more repugnant to our immediate feelings, but consideration of their life-cycle career arouses less ideological antipathy in us because its general profile is more like that of vertebrates. In line with this is the fact that their behavior is somewhat

It is interesting that the highly socialized ants, bees, and termites have their span of youth and adulthood proportioned inversely from most insects: a short youth, a long age. The ratio may even approximate that of weeks to years. This reversal is undoubtedly a correlate of socialization, and especially of one particular aspect of socialization: the fact that the majority of members in the community are functionally sexless and contribute to its welfare by their labors as "workers." Obviously, the longer they operate, the more benefit does the community get out of them; and mostly they live until they have literally worn themselves out. Ant workers may live up to three or fours years, queens perhaps double to quadruple that; those are remarkable ages for animals at once so small and so active. The brevity of their youth also fits into the total picture of high socialization. Infancy traversed in a matter of weeks instead of months means less absorption of the colony's labor of tending and feeding, and a correspondingly larger building-up of the community's reserves, or its utilization in nourishing additional broods and therewith increasing the populational strength of the society. Also, youth is not a period of learning with the social insects—first because they possess no transmitted culture, and second because their larvae are helpless and undeveloped. It is obvious that in species whose faculties are essentially "instinctive," and relatively little developed by learning and practice, a protracted youth would do next to nothing to make individuals more capable and useful members of society, whereas a brief youth makes them less of a drain and burden.

In short, the lack of capacity for culture and speech (§ 18, 20) among the social insects, as compared with men, is correlated with their relatively much shorter period of immaturity. A culture-bearing and culture-dependent animal like man would no doubt long since have succumbed if human youth had been as brief and as vegetative as that of the ants. But the ants in turn might have lost out in the struggle for survival if they had had to support their young for as long a span, relatively, as human children. On the other hand, apart from culture, it is clear that among the insects socialization is mostly associated with a brief youth, nonsocialization generally with a brief maturity. Man, as the only animal that is both social and cultural, seems consequently to have been pulled both ways. But on the whole, the factors correlated with successful development of culture which make for prolonged youth have been stronger in our species than the factors correlated with successful social development which make for a brief youth.

Among our nearest relatives, the anthropoid apes, the corresponding proportion is not known. Youth is traversed with definitely greater rapidity by the chimpanzee, the orang, and the gorilla. Corresponding stages of development, as marked by dentition, full brain size, sexual maturation, are reached in from half to three-fourths the number of years required by man; perhaps three-fifths

more like that of vertebrates in that it seems to contain less instinctual predetermination and more adaptive responsiveness than the behavior of most metamorphosing insects.

to two-thirds would be not far from a fair average (§ 24-26). Unfortunately, there is no direct evidence on anthropoid longevity. Estimates based on signs of senility suggest a duration of possibly two-thirds of human life. Thus the indications are that anthropoids, while somewhat shorter-lived than we are, distribute their life span in much the same proportion between growing up and being adult. This is only one of a number of close similarities between man and the anthropoids which allow the inference that the development of the faculty for speech and culture was in the nature of a lucky accident of mutation in our heredity. It seems to have been superimposed on a series of basic constitutional traits that the anthropoid ancestors shared with our ancestors, rather than that the decisive mutation was preceded by a long sequence of human specialization away from the anthropoids.

As between the two classes of warm-blooded vertebrates, most birds brood their eggs and literally feed their young as an equivalent to the mammals' suckling theirs; but the period of immaturity and helplessness is relatively shorter in birds. Even large species attain their full growth and faculties in a remarkably short time. This difference is surely correlated with the fact that birds in general possess more instinctive faculties, have to learn less, and apparently do learn less in living, than mammals.

17. SOCIALIZATION

Many lower animals tend to aggregate without being truly social; that is, they cluster, but they do not aid, support, or protect one another. Their eggs or young, for instance, are shed forth and left to take care of themselves. Animals begin to be genuinely social whenever a mother suckles or feeds her young, or when a pair guards them. This makes nearly all birds and mammals social; but the socialization is of a familial or parent-offspring type. From this there must be distinguished the sociability of gregarious animals like sheep. These feel more comfortable in one another's company; but they do not feed or aid each other. Also, the membership of a herd, not being based on kinship, is likely to be transiently shifting; it is reckoned an aggregation, not a true society.

Highly organized animal societies are those which may become large but have a specific structure; which depend on defined interindividual relations; and in which a degree of devotion to the welfare of the community as a whole is evident. Such highly organized societies have developed twice, on a significant scale, in the evolution of life: in man and among the social insects. These two groups are both advanced, but they are also very different. Their societies present striking similarities; yet some of these similarities are analogous rather than homologous. The most fundamental difference is that human societies, beyond the immediate family group, operate with and through culture, but that ants, bees, and termites manage, as was said in § 6, to possess highly developed societies—without which most of them could not survive—without having culture ɔr anything corresponding to it, so far as we can see. In man, society and culture come so intertwined that one never occurs without the other. The presence of cultureless societies among the insects accordingly is an aid in distinguishing the two concepts in the abstract (§ 6). Moreover, man's place in nature, what is common in his status and what is unique, becomes better defined from the comparison, which is also a contrast.

We shall consider first those features which all the social insects have in common as compared with man. After that, the distinction will be given more depth by a comparison of the two chief types of social insects.

18. THE SOCIAL INSECTS

All the many species of ants, honeybees, and termites are thoroughly social. Indeed, it could well be argued that they are more socialized than we. On the whole, the individual in an insect society subordinates his own welfare to that of the group more than most human beings do. Many species live in large communities of thousands to hundreds of thousands or millions of individuals—as populous as human towns or even great cities. Each such community has always a fixed abode, with limits as definite as a city, from which individuals forage but to which they always return, and where the young are reared. But all members of such a hive, hill, or city are normally the descendants of one mother or "queen." [10] A city community among these insects is therefore also a family, in the strict biological sense. The life of the community revolves about the care and feeding of the queen mother, since on her all population increase and replenishment depend, and about the feeding, nursing, and rearing of the young. These young are quite helpless, like small human babies; but unlike babies they remain so until they are fully adult. They cannot feed themselves, or move themselves, or clear themselves of their excrement; in many cases they cannot even come unaided out of their pupa case or cocoon when ready to emerge as adults. All this feeding and rearing, the nest-building and accumulation of surplus food, fall to the lot of the mass of the population, the sterile workers. Between them and the queen mother there is a marked difference of function, and consequently of bodily structure as well as of impulses or drives. This distinction between reproductive queen and sterile worker is fundamental to the plan of ant, bee, and termite society. Human societies may or may not have castes; the perpetuation and existence of the higher insect societies rests upon castes. Conversely, the integration of castes is complete in these insect societies: there is no exploitation. A queenless community and a communityless queen (after the first start of a colony) are alike doomed to extinction. With this interdependence of castes so basic, it is no wonder that some species of ants and most termites have gone further and have added castes or subdivided them—especially a soldier caste for

---

[10] If she dies, one of her fertile daughters replaces her. Such a new queen is therefore really the sister of the hive members.

offense or defense or both. This professional army again may be differentiated into an aggressive corps with powerful jaws; a sort of flame-throwing or gas-throwing service that squirts a dangerous liquid; a defensive or shield-bearing division that blocks the gate with an enormous impermeable forehead. Workers, in turn, may come in two or even three sizes for indoor and outdoor labor; or they may serve as repositories for honey regurgitated for other members of the hive until they become distended into veritable honeypots or storage bins— a striking example of how the lower cultureless animals may accomplish with their bodies a purpose that man would achieve with a tool or an artifact.[11] Nor are the castes always inflexible. Certain ants use their large-jawed soldiers to crush for them hard-shelled seeds that the workers can bring in but cannot crack. When autumn comes on and the harvest of these seeds is over, when the community goes into winter retreat and ordinarily need fear no further insect enemies, these warrior-millers have become useless and would be a drain on the hoard of the hive. Like the drones among the honeybees, they are therefore killed by the workers—a striking exemplification of the superhuman strength of the overintegrative or totalitarian impulses: not only individuals but even classes are sacrificed for the good of the society.

One other feature of parallelism must be mentioned. Contrary to bees and wasps, all working ants and termites are wingless: they perform their particular labors on or under the ground and therefore travel on their legs. The fertile males and females, however, fly. This is an ancestral inheritance from their common true-insect or hexapod stock and has evidently been retained as an advantage to the perpetuation of the species, which thereby can start new communities over a wide area, instead of each new colony's adjoining the old and perishing with it in any local drought, flood, or other adversity. It is the workers and soldiers, the mass of the community, who among both ants and termites have become specialized away from the original insect condition into wingless-ness and infertility. The fertile females mate with the males after a dispersion flight, of which the nuptial flight or aerial mating of the honeybee is an extreme form. No doubt because of this method of mating abroad, the fertile males and females have also retained the ancestral insect eye—they need to find each other; the workers are poor-sighted or blind.

Immediately after mating, the female shakes off her now useless wings, finds a crevice or makes a burrow, and proceeds to rear a family. Among the ants she does this alone; among the termites, with her partner—a difference the full significance of which we shall see in a moment (§ 19). She begins to lay eggs, to feed the larvae when they hatch, either with what she can forage or with her own saliva, into ingredients of which the henceforth useless parts of her body—wing muscles, optic lobes, and such—are converted. This is a process

[11] Strictly, the honeypots occur among ants, the squirters (nasuti) and shield-bearers among termites; it is the principle of bodily caste-differentiation according to function or service that remains alike.

analogous to that of mammalian milk feeding; not in its physiology or chemistry, which no doubt is quite different in detail, but in its functional mechanism and in the psychic affects and satisfactions by which it must be accompanied. During the whole period of her solitary rearing of this first brood, the prospective queen, although temporarily functioning as a worker, takes no nourishment herself, often for months. Though the initial litter, when hatched into adulthood, is usually undersized or otherwise not quite complete, it immediately begins to operate. It forages, extends the nest, and the like; and above all, begins to feed the queen, who responds by laying more eggs. These, now provisioned by their elder sisters, grow into complete and full-sized worker adults. Only when the community is strong—numerous and well provisioned—do fertile males and females begin to be born, and the cycle of swarming out into new independent colonies can be repeated. This however takes time; and for a community to reach the point where it can bud off communities, to spread and carry on the species, several years are ordinarily required. This means that the queen, on whom everything pivots, must have a long life, and that workers who can survive to help rear innumerable younger sisters and brothers immensely strengthen the hive, especially during its period of upswing. Indeed, queen ants have been known to live fifteen years and workers from three to four—long durations for animals so small; and the indications for termite longevity are similar. It has already been mentioned that the combination of a brief larval and pupal stage and a long working adulthood makes the favorable pattern for prosperity of a highly communized, instinctually endowed type of society, which does not depend on transmission of learned experience; and this pattern has become the universal rule among ants and termites.

There remain some other notable habits of ants and termites: the "agriculture," keeping of "cattle," total wars, and slave-raiding of some species. These habits of course are of special interest because of their resemblance to human institutions. But human agriculture, stock-raising, slavery, and totalitarian war of exploitation are universally accepted as having been invented, and as transmitted by teaching or learning; that is, as being cultural products. It is difficult to accept the corresponding social-insect activities as cultural in nature, because ants and termites neither use nor make tools, nor, as will shortly be shown (§ 19), do they seem to possess that apparently indispensable part and condition of culture which we call language. With these basic elements of culture lacking, it is hard to believe that the social insects really have developed institutional portions of culture. It is more likely that the similarities to man are merely analogous—resemblances of result rather than of mechanism. The actual mechanism of ant slavery and domestication thus would presumably be a directly organic, congenital, instinctual one, in distinction from the suprahereditary, devised, and learning-transmitted human institutions.

When we cast about for such an organic mechanism, it appears that practically everything in the practices in question can be subsumed under the impulses and practices of symbiosis, and that symbiosis is widespread also in the nonsocial realms of the animal kingdom. There is, for instance, the familiar example of the hermit crab who likes a sea anemone on the snail shell he inhabits; and how, if his shell lacks an anemone, he will set one there. This habit may well in the long run have survival value for the hermit-crab species, as is generally supposed. And it evidently satisfies something in the crab's congenital nature—makes him feel more at ease, "relieves a tension." But no one would think of assuming that the crab was taught the practice by his mother, or that he had learned it from his fellows. The symbiosis of ants with their ant slaves, beetle livestock, or fungi is obviously more complex than the crab-anemone relation, but there seems no reason to believe that it is basically different in kind.

Moreover, close analysis shows how really different the workings of social insect and social human practices are: for instance, on "agriculture." Before going out on her marriage flight, a nubile *Atta* queen ant "takes a good meal of fungus." Mated and secure in her little dugout, which is the first cell of her kingdom, she regurgitates this fungus mass, which begins to grow. She manures it and lays her first eggs on it; on hatching, the larvae eat the fungus; when they emerge adult, the queen's realm contains both a society of workers and a bearing vegetable garden; whereupon she retires in state to laying eggs for the further enlargement of the colony. The whole of this "farming" is evidently in its origin a by-product of feeding and reproduction; this by-product, having survival value, came to be part of the congenital behavior mechanism of the species. It is a fairly complex and special symbiosis; it has in it nothing of an invented and learned custom.

So some of the slaveholding ants are shown by the gradation of the habits of different species to have begun with eating the pupae of other nests, then to have progressed to carrying them home to store and devour at leisure, and finally to have arrived at the stage of saving the pupae so long that some of them managed to hatch before they could be eaten, whereupon the irrepressible drive of ants to labor on behalf of their community makes these "slaves" seem to "work for" their "masters." Another line of development is parasitic: the fertilized queen, in certain species, is unable to found her own nest. She therefore invades the colony of another species, kills its queen, or somehow attracts and seduces the workers until they kill her, and then takes her place—with the result that the workers rear her changeling brood instead of their own blood sisters. Where the parasitism is extreme, as when the invading species is so built that it can perhaps fight but not work, the interlopers are dependent for sustenance on their hosts. But as these consist only of nonreproducing workers, they finally die off, whereupon the "masters" also perish.

Perhaps the most significant inference to be derived by the anthropologist from the study of social insects is the light they throw on the nature of society and culture. Human beings all live in societies and they all have culture. This co-occurrence of society and culture is so constant in man that the two appear like two aspects of one set of phenomena. If we had no other knowledge, we might easily assume that societies and cultures could only coexist. The social insects show that society and culture are distinct, not only conceptually but in the phenomena of nature. The communities of ants, bees, and termites allow no escape from this conclusion. Though wholly cultureless, according to all indications, they are as tightly knit, as socially centered, as any human society—if anything more so. The origin of societies now reinforced with culture, somewhere in man's early development, accordingly was a novel and unique event in the history of life on this earth.

19. TWO CONVERGENT SOCIALIZATIONS: ANTS AND TERMITES

So far, the social insects have been viewed as a unit in comparison with man, with whom they certainly contrast as vividly as they agree. However, these insects comprise several thousand species, hundreds of genera, more than a dozen families, and two main stems or orders. Naturally, there is far more variability among these forms than would appear from the foregoing account, where emphasis has been laid on the common or uniform characters. Especially there are significant differences between the most highly socialized groups in one main "order," the ants and the honeybees, and the equally socialized termites of the other order. The insect contrast with human societies thus is double, really; and it acquires depth from consideration of the duality.

Ants are hymenoptera, and relatives of bees, wasps, gallflies, and sawflies, of which some are social, some subsocial, others wholly individualistic. The termites are isoptera, related to the *Blattoidea* or cockroaches, and descended jointly with them from the protoblattoids, who were already distinct from the protohymenoptera in the Palaeozoic Permian period. The two lines of socializing development accordingly have been quite distinct for 200-odd million years, as the geological ages are customarily computed. Evolution, starting from two separate points, has repeated itself to a quite astonishing degree; just as, starting from still another point, it has partially repeated itself again, though less closely, in producing the social animal man.

The difference in structure of ants and termites in parts and organs is a matter of technical features involving more entomology than can be gone into here. But there are also physiological, functional, and life-cycle differences. These can be grouped around diet and reproduction; let us say, to be concrete, around wood and spermatheca.

Ants eat insect and other flesh, seeds, honey, sugary excretions or secretions of aphids and other insects—all concentrated, high-grade foods, most of which must be got in the open world. Most termites eat wood—an exceedingly abundant but low-grade food; they have chosen a quantitative instead of a qualitative course. To nourish themselves on this, they must not only eat a great deal, but must be infested with an intestinal biota of Protozoa that helps them assimilate it. This fauna they pass on to one another by regurgitating much of their food, also by eating one another's partly-digested excrement. As they eat, they also burrow, and thus excavate their nest. Where they raise hills, these consist largely of their excreta, which harden in air. City-building and feeding are therefore all intertwined by the termites; the ants differentiate the two functions sharply.

Then, like most wood-eaters, the termites literally bore from within, probably in the main for safety. This means that they are adapted to live in the dark, in warmth, and with a minimum of oxygen. So they avoid light, have whitish, soft bodies, no great energies; they depend on numbers, or on defensive fighting. Ants on the contrary are strong, hard, tense, high-strung: many of them prey on termites—as a group they are probably the termites' most destructive enemies. In ant evolution, the workers are evidently the first caste developed; in some species there are potentially or partly fertile workers; the soldiers are a later specialization. On the contrary, some termite species show potentially fertile soldiers, which suggests that among them these preceded the workers.

The female ant, along with the wasp and the bee, possesses a spermatheca, a receptacle in which the male sperm is stored and kept alive for a lifetime, being withdrawn in infinitesimal quantity as needed. One mating therefore suffices. Thereafter the queen has both sexual substances at her disposal and the male can be dispensed with. He is dispensed with. He dies after mating: at any rate he goes off; it is the female who alone starts the burrow and brings up her first young. From then on, until it is time for new colonies to form, males are useless: so the whole society is a female one—workers and soldiers as well as queen.

The termite, remaining structurally more generalized, has no spermatheca. Hence the male is indispensable if a large, long-term, increasing brood is to be raised continuously. The result is that the start of a new termite society is made by male and female conjointly, as already mentioned, as against the solitary ant female. In fact, the first burrow is excavated by the co-operating pair; and fertilization, at least in some species, begins only after they have established this home. Moreover, fertilization goes on for life. The female's belly grows until it may be as large as a finger and she is practically incapable of locomotion; but the male remains with her in the royal chamber, constantly solicitous. There is something appealingly human in this permanent conjugal affection, compared with the utter unconcern of the queen ant for her partner and her divorce from him after she has received from him what she needs for her business in life. But, contrariwise, the diet of the ant is not so different from our own, after allowance is made for size and opportunity, especially in contrast to the disgusting food habits of the termite.

The permanent conjugation of the termite sexes only founds the behavior pattern, as it were. It is continued in the fact that the working and fighting offspring, the great mass of the society, are also of both sexes, instead of female only as with the ant. There are male and female major workers, male and female minor workers, male and female soldiers, and so on. Whatever caste there may be among termites is always bisexual, even though both sexes are in most castes sterile. And the two sexes of one caste are more alike than one caste is to another. In short, the termites follow out the principle of sexual equivalence throughout, in structure as well as function. Their whole social organization is based on this principle, in distinction from the ants who, with their hymenopterous relatives, the wasps and bees, leave the male only one spot in their scheme of things, the momentary and individualistic act of transference of his sperm to the storage sack of the female. The ants and the bees build their whole social life on the one sex, the male reappearing only when new societies are to be formed.

It is clear that we have here closely parallel societies operating on principles distinct at two fundamental points, both in turn resting on anatomical and physiological structure. The distinctions cut deep: ants and termites, springing from different stems of insects, have had a separate history for tens of millions of years, only later approximating each other in their social habits, though to an increasing and striking degree. After the first divergence from the remote common insect ancestry, there was a convergence toward full socialization with all its implications. In the end, the two behaviors have run parallel, with considerable accompanying superficial modification of structure, but without suppression of fundamental pattern of structure.

20. ANIMAL COMMUNICATION

We have seen how a nubile ant flies forth, usually in simultaneous seasonal swarms from all mature colonies in an area, mates, leaves her partner, breaks off her wings, goes underground, and prepares a chamber that is the start of a new colony. There she lays her first eggs, tends and feeds this brood, who become her first workers; after which she confines herself to laying more eggs destined to become additional workers, and then, after a while, eggs that become fertile females and males for founding new colonies. This means that in the continuity between community and community, each of which may run to hundreds of thousands of members, everything funnels down to the life of a single individual—the fertilized queen—and from there builds up again. What the younger community reproduces from its parent community in the way of castes and their varied activities all passes through the one minute physique of the queen's body. It is obvious that this passing-along must be a very different process from the "tradition" or "handing-through" which transmits culture from one generation of a society to another. Human generations overlap: members of a society are of all ages; strictly, one cannot say where within a society one generation ends and the next begins. But among ants absolutely all members of a society except one are literal sisters (and later on a few brothers) because they are all the children of that one pivotal member. Even if a human society counted not eighty thousand but eight hundred, or only eighty, it would be manifestly impossible to pack all the knowledges, skills, and faculties of so many individuals into one body, brain, and memory, for unimpaired transmission to the next generation. The impairment would be heavy, and distortion equally so. Yet the habits and the techniques of an anthill will be unimpairedly identical with those of its parent anthill in the same environment. Evidently cultural transmission is not operative as between anthills, or down the generations of social insects; but congenital, instinctual heredity is operative. Only through this mechanism of heredity could so faithful a copy be reproduced and rereproduced, and transmission by learning be dispensed with.

With this point clear, another follows. The social insects cannot have language—not in the human sense—because language is learned.

Communications of a sort they undoubtedly have; but these, like the noises of all animals other than man, are not language, except metaphorically—something like the language of flowers, or the language of machine guns, which can also be "understood." As here used, the term "language" properly denotes a system of audible symbols able to communicate objective facts. A bird's chirp, a lion's roar, a horse's scream, a man's moan express subjective conditions; they do not convey objective information. By objective information we mean what is communicated in such statements as: "There are trees over the hill," "There is a single tree," "There are only bushes," "There were trees but are no longer," "If there are trees he may be hiding in them," "Trees can be burned," and millions of others. All postinfantile, nondefective human beings can make and constantly do make such statements, though they may make them with quite different sounds according to what speech custom they happen to follow. But no subhuman animal makes *any* such statements. All the indications are that no subhuman animal even has any impulse to utter or convey such information. It is doubtful whether it possesses any concept as generalizing or abstract as "tree," "bush," "burn." This seems to hold as essentially for dogs and apes—or for that matter for parrots—as for insects.

Parrots can reproduce series of speech sounds fairly adequately, but they cannot, except by lucky coincidence, convey intelligible objective information. Dogs can learn to respond to dozens of words and phrases; this might be called passive participation in speech. Chimpanzees, with larynxes, tongues, and lips similar to ours, do not even try to learn to reproduce human words to which they respond in their behavior. There is an old epigram that the reason animals do not speak is that they have nothing to say. Its psychology is somewhat crude, but fundamentally correct. At least, they appear to lack the impulse to say anything, in the sense that "to say" means objective communication.

In some respects the belief that perhaps dies hardest is that the social insects must have something like a language even though we have not yet succeeded in hearing or seeing it. They have societies as we have; they have elaborate and highly adaptive habits which look like institutions until we examine closely their methods of acquisition and functioning; why should they not have communications comparable to our speech? It will be worth analyzing a case that at its anthropocentric face value strongly suggests ability to convey objective fact.

It is known that when a honeybee has first found a new source of honey, an unexploited patch of flowers, other bees from the same hive soon appear there. How is this brought about?

Bees have excellent memories for place. They first orient themselves by recall, then fly to their objective in a "beeline." New masses of flowers attract them from a distance by color. Their color vision is similar to ours, except for probable inability to see the full red end of our spectrum and ability to see some distance beyond the violet. Once among flowers, their preference is to visit only one species at a time. In this they may be guided by smell as well as sight. At any rate, when they return with a load of honey, they reek of the perfume of that species. If the patch is previously unvisited, the haul rich, the nectar unusually sweet and strong, the bee is stimulated by the booty in her crop into a reaction of euphoria or triumph. This is expressed in a peculiar whirling "dance" performed on her return to the hive.[12] The bees there watch her, crowd around, stretch out their antennae at her, smell her. She then returns to her discovery for more; before long her fellows appear there too, in increasing numbers. They have not followed her trail by sight or smell, as we might expect them to do. In actuality, they leave the hive and circle wider and wider around, evidently searching for the impact of a volume of the same smell that the discoverer exuded during her dance. One by one, more and more of them find her patch of flowers, or perhaps other patches equally fresh and strong. Returning, each one now performs the same dance and incites others, until most of the active workers may be visiting the one species of flower. But as they drain off the untapped superabundant supply, or its sugar strength grows dilute, the dances grow laxer with weaker stimulus, and finally cease.

The dance is a reflex to an above-average, highly satisfactory stimulus. It acts as a new stimulus of excitement to other individuals. The cue indicating the particular flower species is merely the reek of the scent of the particular species, physically brought into the hive by the discoverer. The finding of sources of supply is by search and trial and error. Thus there is no purposive communication of factual information anywhere in the chain of events. It looks as if we could rule the bees out from having a communicating language.

---

[12] This is about as close to "play" as the serious-minded social insects come (§ 15).

21. THE PRIMATE ORDER IN WHICH MAN IS RANGED

Man, apes, monkeys, lemurs, and the tarsier were long since grouped together by Linnaeus, at the foundation of modern biology, as constituting the order of *Primates,* one of the dozen or so first subdivisions of the *Mammals* as a class. Their being mammals means that in addition to having a bony skeleton, a spinal cord with vertebral column, skull and jaw, four limbs with a maximum of five digits, and lungs—all of which they share with reptiles and birds—they are also warm-blooded, viviparous, suckling, and furry, and possess diversified teeth. The basic pattern of these mammalian teeth is three incisors, one canine, four premolars, and three molars on each side of each jaw, 3-1-4-3, or 44 in all. This formula may be reduced, and the teeth may vary greatly in shape according to species, but the formula itself is not otherwise altered or expanded.

Both the most backward primates and the geologically oldest ones show definite resemblances to another order of mammals, the generalized one called insect-eaters or insectivores. This order includes moles, shrews, and tree shrews. All the insectivores are small. Their size prevents them from preying on anything larger than insects. Consequently they did not evolve specialized tusks, claws, strength, or habitat adaptations. Instead they remained generic in structure and widely open to evolutionary change. As protein-eaters having to catch live food, they needed a degree of co-ordination, quickness, and intelligence in their make-up. Such is the ancestral background of our larger "family," in nontechnical parlance the background of our order, the primates in biological nomenclature. Generalization, littleness, and quickness were the qualities of this root stock that were most important for the future.

One special feature has to be added. The particular subdivision of the insectivores from which the primates are generally believed to derive are the ancestral tree shrews. This fact set our whole primate group off on the tack of arboreal life from the start. Most of them have remained on the trees ever since; and while the baboons, the gorilla, and we have long since come down off them again (the gorilla really not so long ago), the return to the ground, at any rate in the case of man, was with some important acquisitions: especially the fundamental one of complete, clean differentiation of arms and legs, structurally and functionally.

The actual fossil record of primates takes us back to the Eocene, at the beginning of the Tertiary, several tens of millions of years ago—perhaps twenty or fifty times as far back as the appearance of anyone who can be properly called a man. Here, at the beginning of the Tertiary, are found an American lemuroid family called *Notharctidae,* and the Old World one of the *Adapidae,* both with 40 of the original 44 teeth, formula 2-1-4-3. There are also a number of fossil genera of tarsioids, again both in the New and the Old World. The modern representatives of these two suborders, lemuroids and tarsioids, are much fewer and more restricted. Both have evidently fought a losing competition.

In fact the tarsioids have shrunk to one species, the spectral tarsier, surviving in spots in the East Indian islands. This is a quarter-pound, rat-tailed, enormous-eyed, nocturnal animal. It frequents the bush, clasps limbs with pads on its fingers, leaps or hops, lives on insects, sees badly in the light, and sleeps during the day. The tarsier's smell sense is poor, its acuity of vision in the dark is high. Correlated with this specialized sense development is a large visual center in the cerebral cortex. The development of the brain and other features put the tarsier nearer to the higher primates than are the lemurs; or to be more exact, ancestral near-tarsiers are thought to have been the direct ancestors of the higher primates.

The side branch of the lemurs has done best in remote and protected Madagascar, where three-fourths of its species survive. The lemurs are nocturnal, furry, snouted; they have their eyes on the sides of the head, with nonstereoscopic vision; and the olfactory lobes in their brains are large. Their faces often look like those of raccoons, civet cats, or foxes. Most of them eat both insects and fruits.

22. MONKEYS

Allied to tarsier and lemurs in having 36 teeth (2-1-3-3), as against the 32 (2-1-2-3) of the higher primates, are the South American or platyrrhine monkeys, also called *Cebidae*. Geologically, they have been found to extend as far back as the Miocene. Living forms include capuchins (*Cebus*), howlers (*Alouatta*), spider monkeys (*Ateles*), and marmosets (*Hapale*). They are short in the face or snout, domed in the skull; the nostrils are on the side of the nose. They are always long-tailed; only these among the primates have prehensile tails that can be used to hang from. They are smallish in size, the maximum weight attained by any species being perhaps 20 pounds, which is far below not only anthropoid apes but baboons. In social behavior all New World monkeys differ markedly from Old World ones. While promiscuous, they are less sexualized and less jealous, and are nearly free from the overmastering impulse of the Old World monkeys to exert dominance and oppress their fellows. They have sometimes been considered less intelligent than other monkeys and apes in tests; but *Cebus* individuals differ markedly one from the other. Klüver's famous female *Cebus* "genius" was rated by him as superior to the manlike apes in solving mechanical problems.

The *Cercopithecidae* or catarrhine monkeys of the Old World agree with the anthropoids and man in having 32 teeth (2-1-2-3). The oldest fossil is Parapithecus, from the Oligocene. This is one period farther back in the Tertiary than the platyrrhine fossils in America. But where so few bones are involved, and those mostly mandibles, mere luck of discovery may play a large part. Specialties of the catarrhines are cheek pouches for stuffing food; sitting pads or ischial callosities, and the sexual swelling and coloring of these. Best known are the macaques (*Macaca*) distributed from India to Borneo and Japan, and including the rhesus; and the baboons and their allies, limited to Africa and Arabia. The baboons have redescended to the ground. They are large and powerful, and walk and run four-legged and plantigrade on their soles and palms. They have also redeveloped a long snout, and great canine teeth; the epithet "dog-faced" (*Cynocephalus*) is appropriate. Best known through the studies of Carpenter, Zuckerman, Maslow, and others, the interpersonal behavior of both macaques and baboons, in the free state as well as in captivity, is aggressive, greedy, jealous, cruel, selfish, shot through with constant sexuality and impulse to dominate.

23. APES

The *Simiidae,* or apes proper in the modern usage of that word, are the anthropoid or manlike apes. They approximate us in structure: they are tailless, for instance. They are also nearer to us in size than other primates; for if the gibbon is much smaller, the gorilla is much heavier than we. The fossil history of the anthropoids has been traced back to the Oligocene Propliopithecus. Later, in Miocene-Pliocene times, there were Pliopithecus and a group of genera associated with Dryopithecus. Once more it is probably only the imperfection of the palaeontological record that makes these anthropoids seem to have evolved earlier than the less-advanced South American platyrrhines. The anthropoid fossils consist mostly of jaws with teeth; they have been found in Egypt, Europe, and India. None has ever been discovered in America.

The anthropoids number four, or technically five. Gibbon (*Hylobates*) and siamang (*Symphalangus*) together constitute the *Hylobatidae.* Then there are the orang-utan (*Simia*), chimpanzee (*Pan*), and gorilla (*Gorilla*). The first three are Asiatic-East Indian; the two latter, African; all are tropical.

The gibbon ranges from Assam in India through Farther India into the larger Dutch East Indies; the allied siamang is restricted to Sumatra. They are both long-limbed but light: 12 to 15 pounds for the gibbon, nearly double for the siamang. Gibbons are wholly arboreal, and progress largely by brachiating or pendulum-swinging from one handhold to the next, interspersed with leaps from the arm. In length of leg compared to trunk the gibbon exceeds all the other anthropoids and stands next to man. But this proportionate leg length is surpassed by an even greater arm length, which is really enormous. And this in turn is part of his arboreal adaptation—hanging and swinging far more than standing or walking. It also keeps him from being a very close relative of man.

24. THE ORANG-UTAN

The orang-utan—"forest person" in the original Malay—is the other Far Eastern anthropoid ape, surviving only in Borneo and part of Sumatra. He is about of a size with man and the chimpanzee. But he definitely diverges more from ourselves than does the chimpanzee, in structure as well as behavior. This differentiation expresses the degree to which the orang is specialized for life in the trees and is tied to such life.

The adult male orang-utan averages at least a foot less in height than a man because of his short legs. But he surpasses him by a couple of feet in reach or span because of his long arms. The trunk is thicker-set than ours and brings his average weight to perhaps a bit above the human male average: 165 pounds or 75 kilograms. Females are markedly smaller: only about half as heavy. The skin is brown, the hair definitely reddish and quite long. The forehead is relatively high, the face and nose unusually flat even for an ape. Very conspicuous in adult males are a pair of hairless cheek pads of tough fibrous tissue framing the face; also, enormous air pouches extending from the throat well down the breast and over the shoulders into the neck. Such air sacs occur also in females, and in other apes, but never of the same size as in the male orang. Their function is not known, nor is that of the cheek pads; but the two together give the male orang a monstrous moon face surmounting a gigantic double chin or crop; such neck as he has is concealed. In this face are set: eyes close together; a pair of nostrils just below them; an incredibly long upper lip; and a mouth that looks like a long, tight, down-curved slit when at rest, because the lip edges have no eversion whatever.

The orang's gnomelike appearance is accentuated by the extreme shortness of his legs compared with the length of his arms, hands, and feet. His arm-leg proportion is 170; man's is only 88; the other large anthropoids are intermediary. Our middle-finger tip, and the gorilla's, reach two-thirds of the way down the thighbone; the chimpanzee's almost to the knee; the orang's just halfway from the knee to the ground. The orang's hand and foot both have the greatest absolute length of any primate. Fingers and toes are tremendously elongated; thumb and big toe, though not malformed, are so short as to look like ridiculous stubs projecting from the wrist and heel. "Big toe" of course fits only man; in all the apes it is not the longest; but in the orang the whole of it, even its tip, lies in the hind half of the foot. The chimpanzee looks like an unflattering but still humorous caricature of ourselves, the gorilla like a somewhat brutal exaggeration, but the orang like a deformity. These are "hominicentric" subjective reactions, of course, but, though affective, they do express the respective degree and kind of differentiations of the big apes from man.

Among the trees the orang is altogether too heavy to leap, and he can brachiate only as far as branches are stout enough to sustain his swinging weight. Beyond that he has to find limbs that cross over from the next tree and are sufficiently big to trust his weight to; if there is doubt, he feels them out first. Anything like tearing through the woods overhead is as out of the question for the orang as it would be for a middle-aged man. That he nevertheless progresses rapidly in spite of his caution is due to his frequenting dense tropical rain forest, climbing skillfully, and no doubt being experienced in perceiving the best way ahead in the tangle. On the ground he is proportionately clumsy. He can stand erect, but does not voluntarily walk upright. Mostly he goes on all fours, with the tips of fingers and toes bent under; or he plants his arms ahead like crutches and swings his trunk and legs forward between. Neither can be a rapid or an effective gait. Compare the simple plantigrade hands and feet of the baboons, who are really readapted for ground-running. The orang is in the dilemma of trying to remain wholly up in the trees while having become too heavy for acrobatics.

This same incongruity, or attempting the nearly impossible, may account for some of the salient habits and attitudes of the orang. He is definitely more solitary than the other apes, being encountered either actually alone or in what seem to be mere biological families. It looks as if he were too heavy to huddle in groups in treetops. Then as to disposition: this is described as melancholy, apathetic, unaggressive—introvert in comparison with the chimpanzee. The orang is equally affectionate, but he is certainly less outgoing about it. While he has been much less intensively studied than the chimpanzee, the indications are that he is little if any behind him in general intelligence. He will learn to ride bicycles, smoke cigars, eat at table, and do other circus tricks about as well as the chimpanzee. Yet in that case, why the unresponsiveness? Again one thinks of the influence of his habitat adaptation that is pushed so near its physical limit and which must constantly enforce safety-first deliberateness and a careful avoidance of impulsiveness.

25. THE CHIMPANZEE

The chimpanzee is probably, all in all, the living ape nearest to man. He is practically never at the opposite end of the scale in his proportions when man and the apes are seriated, and he is often next to man. This last is often true of the gorilla also. But the gorilla's mere bulk must differentiate him widely in his functioning even where his proportions are similar to ours. On the other side, the gibbon is too small and light, and the orang, though his size is about that of a man, is too set-up for a highly specialized life in the trees. In the wild, chimpanzees sleep in trees, but spend about two-thirds of the day on the ground. They also do more of their traveling along the ground than above it between trees. At the same time they climb and brachiate easily. All this suggests a degree of generalization nearer to that of man than that found among other apes.

The chimpanzee weighs less than a man. The average is around 50 kilograms or 110 pounds. Females run about a fifth less, or about the same as the proportional human difference. The chimpanzee is considerably shorter than we, averaging under five feet for males. Most of the difference is in the leg, ours being absolutely about half as long again. The rest is in the neck: the chimpanzee's chin, or bottom of the lower jaw, being about as far below his shoulder level—almost down to his collarbone and sternum—as ours is clear above that level. His trunk, on the contrary, is as long or longer than ours, and considerably broader and thicker in shoulders and chest. The arm is not very different from a human one in absolute length, but more evenly massive; owing to the long body and short leg, the finger tips come lower down the leg. The thigh and calf are about the same in diameter as a man's, but their excessive shortness makes them look actually bigger around; relatively, of course, they are much more thickset. All in all, the chimpanzee's gross bodily proportions are much the nearest to ours of all the apes. He might fairly be described as a considerably undersized human being with powerful neck, chest, and arms, whose underpinning is not weak like the orang's, but sturdy and short; in all, a sort of rugged, well-proportioned dwarf.

With this size and weight, it is hard to understand how Bauman's chimpanzees could have pulled ropes from three to five times as hard as heavier young men pulled them: up to 1260 pounds for a two-hand yank by a female! Later tests do not confirm this really extraordinary strength; but on the other hand, the later tests were unnatural for the animals, in having them pull upward while standing erect.

The chimpanzee's skin is black to brown; his short hair is mostly black but grays with age. The skull is low, with a thick torus or bar of bone shadowing the recessed eyes. The ears are large and round, and stand out from the head like a bat's. Photographs seem to show no white in the chimpanzee's eye, though white does appear in the gorilla's; and there is a less beady effect than in the orang. The chimpanzee's external nose is perhaps the least protuberant of any anthropoid's. But the nostrils are less accentuatedly broad and framed than in the gorilla. As in all apes, the membranous edge of the lips—the part naturally red in man—is narrow and tucked in. The lips in the larger sense— that is, the total fleshy flaps bordering the mouth—are long and very mobile. The lower one is often protruded like a gutter, especially when full of food, and is then inspected. The wide slit of the mouth tends to turn up at the corners, especially in the young, giving them a pleased or humorous expression, in contrast with the orang's glum droop.

While chimpanzees spend much more time on the ground than orangs, they seem to be as good as orangs in climbing, swinging, and brachiating in the trees or along their cages, perhaps because of their one-third less weight.

On the ground they are better than orangs, as might be expected from their relatively longer and sturdier legs. Like all the anthropoids, they walk normally on all fours. In this, the legs are straight, in contrast to a bend at the knee in erect stance. The feet are held about as flat as ours, except that the toes may be kept slightly arched. The first toe—our big toe—spreads out from the others at an angle as if the animal were trying to use it like an opposable thumb to *grasp* the ground or a limb, which in fact is just what it is built for. In the quadrupedal gait the shoulders are higher than the hips, because of the greater length of arm, and this even though some height is lost by the walk's being on the knuckles of the bent-under fingers. Erect progression is rare, and apparently slower and more fatiguing: both back and knees are somewhat bent. The crutchlike gait of swinging the legs between the arms is used chiefly on slopes.

It is not known how long a chimpanzee can live, but there are data on most other aspects of his tempo of living. It is clear that his rates of growth and maturation are definitely faster than ours: perhaps one-half to two-thirds as long, on the average. Here are some comparisons, the chimpanzee always stated first, man second.

Intrauterine life, 8 months; man, 9. Appearance of first milk teeth: month 3; [13] 4-8. Last milk tooth: month 15-16; 20-36. First permanent teeth: year 3; 4-7. Last teeth: year 11; 20±. Cranial capacity at birth, proportion of final: 46%; 26%. Age of attainment of full cranial capacity: year 6; 18. Fusion of epiphyses, first: year 7; 15; last: year 11-15; 25. Menarche: year 8-11; 16. Termination of body growth, males: year 12; 20-21. Appearance of controls, in weeks after birth: [14] On back, raising head, 5; 15; rolling over, 8-10; 29; sitting unsupported, 13; 31; pulling self erect, 15; 47; standing free: 20; 62; walking unassisted, 25-29 (on all fours); 64 (on feet only).

Temperamentally, chimpanzees are outstanding in their responsiveness. Especially in youth they like people and their own kind. Their feelings are lively; the expression of them is often vehement. They grimace, cuddle, beat with their arms, or throw tantrums on slight provocation. They are generally cheerful, and, like sea lions, they are natural show-offs. Nor are they as greedy, selfish, and sexualized as many of the smaller monkeys; and as they much more nearly approximate us in size and general functioning, it is no wonder that they are favorites equally with showmen, the public, and psychologists.

There is one matter of ability in which chimpanzees partly resemble and partly differ from us in a manner of which the significance is not altogether clear. This concerns memory and the related function of what the psychologists call the "delayed-response faculty." As regards recognition memory, chimpanzees show about the degree of this we might expect from what we know of

---

[13] Figures following year, month, or week are *ordinals*. Thus "month 3" means "in the third month."

[14] One chimpanzee ("Alpha") as against average of 25 babies.

children, dogs, and other mammals. They recognize companions and human friends after months or years, and react with pleasure. They also recognize situations to which they have learned the answer and established a successful habit response: they fall back almost without hesitation into the familiar groove of action. This sort of reaction can be directly observed. On the other hand, delayed-response behavior is studied in formal tests. A stimulus is given, such as letting a chimpanzee see some food. Then the food is buried, or set in a receptacle of particular color or shape, which is promptly taken away. After a stated time has elapsed, the chimpanzee is let into the yard where the burial was made, or in front of several different receptacles, to see whether he can still pick out the right spot or the right box. The results are extremely interesting: Chimpanzees react far better and longer to positional stimuli than to those of form, color, or quality. For instance, chimpanzees even after two days of delay will go directly to where they have seen food buried and will dig it up. What is in a way even more convincing is that after four days they have forgotten the precise spot but search the correct vicinity. But if it is a matter of "holding" the proper color or shape of a box in which they have seen a banana or an orange put, they can do this for only about half an hour. Human beings react about equally well to the two kinds of tests after the same interval.

It has consequently been inferred that the chimpanzee is able to form some sort of representation or internal image response to a positional situation, and can carry this over the interval during which he is prevented from acting; but that his ability to form an idea or a symbol of a shape or a color is much more weakly developed. Since we human beings can do this last equally well, and since we have language, it has been thought that we employ covert or suppressed language movements—"thoughts" or ideas—in such cases. Put simply, we remember that something has been put in a red box by saying or "thinking" the *word* "red."

This is important if true. But then, how is it that chimpanzees recognize their friends, and even fall back into the channel of operating with familiar objects, after much longer periods than they can recall where food was buried? First, *recognizing* a situation is evidently a simpler and easier process than *remembering* it enough to re-create it. Next, the artificiality of the delayed-response experiment perhaps cuts in to produce an artificial result. In nature, responses tend to be immediate. If they are blocked, new stimuli ordinarily impinge, and the delayed responses just do not get acted out. The whole type of experiment which first stimulates, then blocks or frustrates, and then releases has something unnatural about it. Men, living in a sense "unnaturally" under culture, as they do whenever they accept duties and responsibilities, get trained in modifying or postponing many of their responses. Cultureless subhumans generally either act the response out or inhibit it completely. It is therefore questionable what the difference in blocked reaction to positional and non-positional stimuli really means. But it is clear why the two Yerkes operating with such tests find so great a difference, and Koehler, observing unblocked recognition, is unaware of a difference between the two kinds of stimuli. Koehler's chimpanzees were in the position we are in when we meet a long-separated brother, or when we resume swimming, paddling, skating, or driving after ten years away from water, ice, or cars. There may be a moment's hesitation, or conscious fear, but then we slide back into the slot of preserved memory or habit functioning.

In short, what is not wholly clear is whether it is primarily the chimpanzee's memory-functioning or his response to artificial testing that is different from ours.

26. THE GORILLA

The gorilla comes in two geographically separated races, sometimes counted as distinct species. There is a lowland form in the heavy forest of French Equatorial Africa, which covers a fraction of the territorial range of the chimpanzee. Hundreds of miles to the east, along the edge of the Belgian Congo, the mountain gorilla inhabits a bamboo forest whose altitude is from seven thousand feet up.

The gorilla is much the largest and heaviest surviving primate, and he must certainly rank among the very largest primates ever evolved. He is not a giant in height, but he is almost incredibly massive. With body length in human range—from over 5 to about 6 feet—his weight is at least three times ours. Males ten to fifteen years old, corresponding in adulthood to humans of eighteen to twenty-five, weigh at the lowest in the three hundreds, more often in the four, five, or six hundreds of pounds; females weigh from 300 to 400 pounds. This means that trunk, neck, and limbs, as well as the bones in them, are enormously thick and powerful. Everything seems exaggerated: the beetling brow ridges of the skull, its high ridges or crests for attachment of muscles the powerful, jutting jaw. The neck buries the occiput of the skull; above, the rear of the cranium rises to an extraordinary peak, not of brain but of bony ridge, neck muscle, and callosity. Chest girths measured range from 50 to 69 inches; there is no waist constriction, the paunch is large, and the trunk tapers somewhat only as it approaches the hips. What with wide shoulders, long arms, and large hands, the span is enormous: from one and a quarter to one and a half times the body height.

Both skin and hair are black or nearly so; the hair grays with age.

The nose is like a diagonal beveling-off of the great upper jaw, chiefly revealing two wide nostril cavities. The eyes are sunk deep below the brow shelf, from which a long scooplike concavity rises in profile to the occipital peak. It is a face that easily expresses ferocity, because its obvious power only too readily suggests to us weaker human beings what the animal might do if angered. However, observation, or even prolonged study of photographs, tones down the impression of savage brutality. One comes to feel that the gorilla's features—and this is corroborated by his postures and movements—express above all self-sufficiency, dignity, reserve, consciousness of strength, and relative indifference to surroundings. The effect tends to become one of aloofness and of a heavy, slow thoughtfulness; almost of a certain nobility. Such an impression is fairly in accord with what observers report on gorilla behavior and temperament. If as quiet and faithful an animal as a St. Bernard dog were magnified to weigh from 500 to 600 pounds, most of us would stand in a degree of awe of him and would presumably be ready to construe signs of his irritation as symptoms of incipient ferocity.

The gorilla sits or occasionally squats much like a heavy-set man. He is much inclined to lean against something while seated; in captivity a corner is preferred to a straight wall. A doorway is favored because it provides both back rest and foot brace. A favorite stance is on one foot, the other leg bent up with the foot against a tree or a wall on which the back also leans, and one hand taking hold above and behind the head. All this leaning has a very human effect; most animals do not practice it at all: it is a sort of tool-using. A gorilla stands free, with spread and bent legs, to do particular things, such as reaching, beating his chest or slapping his belly, fighting or getting ready to fight, or play wrestling. In this last, a pair clinch, jaws over shoulders, and each tries to bite the back of the other's neck. All this is about what a bear stands up for.

Ordinary locomotion of the gorilla is as definitely quadrupedal as a bear's, though a man can presumably outrun a gorilla about as much as a bear can outrun a man. The gorilla's feet, which are the most human of anthropoid feet, are flat-soled on the ground, with the first toe well spread away from the others. It is not the longest but it is considerably the biggest toe. In quadrupedal stance, the hind legs tend to be spread apart, but not flexed. The front legs, as we might appropriately call the arms in this position, are longer, often bowed forward, and rest on the knuckles; that is, the middle finger-joints. These knuckles showing at the edge of a roundish fist at the end of a massive arm made bigger and more shapeless by longish hair give a suggestion of an elephant leg planted on the ground. In walking, the "hind" feet are not in line with the front. One foot is set squarely between the two hands, the other definitely outside. The gait therefore sidles markedly—that is, the axis of the trunk is carried not in the line of motion, but diagonal to it.

On account of the length of the arms, in all-fours position the gorilla's shoulders are considerably higher than his rump, with a bit of swayback between, due no doubt to the animal's great weight. Between the shoulders, the great head hangs out, the profile of the back line rising to its highest point with the peak over the rear of the head. Apparently in this position the eyes look down somewhat. To look out level from under the brows, the head has to be thrown back, still farther elevating its peak. The whole quadrupedal stance of the gorilla has something almost sad about it, as if it were ill-adapted and not coming off very well.

Young gorillas climb, but cautiously; and they brachiate, but not often. As they get their full weight, serious tree-climbing and branch-swinging are obviously over. Even sleeping nests for adults are presumably most often on the ground or on bedded masses of vegetation. It would take a pretty sizable tree crotch to support a quarter-ton body.

His giantism colors everything about the gorilla, from his motions to his disposition. Five times as heavy as a chimpanzee, he could not maintain the latter's volatility and restless responsiveness without being a complete physiological misfit. Although the gorilla has been much less studied, available observations suggest a degree of intelligence very similar to the chimpanzee's but expressed through a quite different temperament and rapport, with most of the difference between them being apparently a function of size.

The following are epithets applied to gorillas by psychologists and other observers: cautious; conservative; not skillful mechanically or manually; watchful; incurious; unimitative and countersuggestible; introverted and aloof; demure or dignified; stoical; constructive rather than destructive; not quarrelsome, but good-natured, at least while young; fearless, deliberate, and determined. There are no doubt more personality traits in this list than can be explained as due merely to size. But as compared with a chimpanzee, it is evident that the gorilla's qualities are something like those of a Newfoundland dog compared to a fox terrier. In tests of memory, box-stacking, and the like, and in observations of smear-painting, nest-building, responding to a mirror, and play, gorilla and chimpanzee come out much alike when allowance is made for the gorilla difference of slower physique and disposition.

While authentic data are pretty scrappy, growth and development seem to be somewhat slower than in the chimpanzee, but definitely more rapid than in us. The first milk teeth erupt perhaps within two months, sitting up comes at five, walking at eight months. Born smaller and lighter than a human baby, a female gorilla is likely to approach 100 pounds by the age of five, a male to surpass it. Three females living just off Fifth Avenue in New York, and estimated to be seven, eight, and ten years old in late 1946, were believed to weigh 180, 200, and 210 pounds respectively. The authenticated weighings in the 400-, 500-, and 600-pound range have all been of animals estimated to be not over fifteen years old. The daily intake of food supporting this rapid growth is about 6 per cent of the body weight, or, with water, close to 10 per cent. Nearly all the food is carbohydrate. The bulk that has to be consumed is bound to affect disposition and behavior.

27. MAN AMONG THE ANTHROPOIDEA

Man and his ancestors are usually made into a separate family in the order of the primates: the *Hominidae*. So are what we have been calling the anthropoid or manlike apes or simply apes, technically named the family *Simiidae*.

Do these names reflect a positive opinion that gorilla, chimpanzee, orang, sia-mang, and gibbon form one group of common origin that can be contrasted with all men as another though related group? Or are the names perhaps merely hangovers from a pre-evolutionary descriptive classification that set man apart because he had speech and "reason," and put the great apes together because they were similar in constituting a sort of hairy mockery of ourselves? There remains a certain hesitation in the technical answers to this question. There are no easy answers, as is shown by the term *"Anthropoidea"* being used some-times for the *Simiidae* or great apes proper; sometimes for them plus man—that is, for all man-size and untailed primates; sometimes more broadly still to in-clude the monkeys, or all primates except lemurs and the tarsier.

Let us first look at some family trees (Fig. 1). The meaning of these lies in which limbs split into what branches, and where on the ladder of time. A split near the trunk, or far down the ladder, denotes ancientness of connection and therefore remoteness of relationship. It is like going down five generations to a great-great-grandmother and climbing back up five to reach a third cousin: he is indubitably somewhat related, but he is not a near relation.

Every authority seems agreed that the gibbon is such a third cousin. He branched off in the early Oligocene, 25 to 30 million years ago according to one of the radiation-based estimates of the age of the earth's strata.[15] The gibbon branches off somewhere in the vicinity of the fossil Propliopithecus and shortly after the Eocene fossil Parapithecus. The gorilla and the chimpanzee, as well as we, and even the orang, have to go back as far as that remote crotch to trace blood connection with the gibbon. Obviously he was the first to leave the com-pany and go off on his own development.

From the Miocene, 10 to 15 million years ago, we have two fossils, Dryo-pithecus and Sivapithecus, which may have lasted into the Pliocene. Somewhere about the time that those two forms appeared, there was another branching. Possibly this split was single, and consisted of the remaining apes (orang, chim-panzee, gorilla) going one way and man the other. Such is the view of Keith and Broom and the present view of Hooton. Or perhaps the split was double, first the orang branching off from the chimpanzee-gorilla-man group and then this latter group promptly subdividing. That is how Gregory sees it and Hooton formerly considered it. All these authorities are high-grade: it just is well to realize that in matters like this the best experts will differ, because evidence on ancient days is always incomplete and gaps in knowledge have to be bridged over by opinion. Actually in this case the differences are largely formal and

[15] Computed from degree of loss of radioactive constituents in rocks of different rela-tive ages. This is only one of several ways of computing the lapse of geological time. These methods lead to different results; none of them are certain; but the radiation method has been in most favor in the last decade or so. Even the radiation-based figures vary, according to the authority, as to the beginning of the Oligocene and the Miocene respectively; 40 and 25 million years are also estimated, besides the 25 to 30 and 10 to 15 cited in the text.

really quite slight, because in two of the four genealogies the two branchings come one right after the other,[16] really differing only as to whether it was the orang who first separated off (Gregory) or man (Broom). Actually the dissenters are Keith and Hooton, who have the orang stay with the gorilla and the chimpanzee until the early Pliocene.

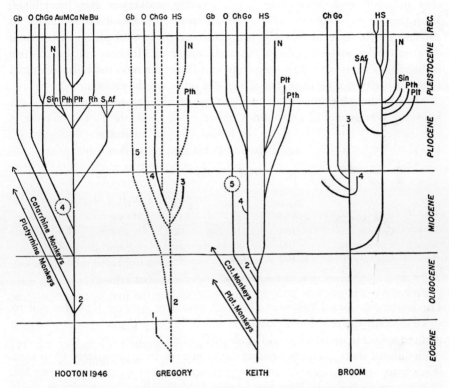

FIG. I.   MEN AND APES: FOUR FAMILY TREES

Relationships of fossil and living forms, according to four authorities: redrawn to facilitate comparison. HS, *Homo sapiens,* living man: Au, Ng, Ca, Mo, Bu, Australian, Negro, Caucasian, Mongoloid, Bushmen races. Living apes: Gb, O, Ch, Go: gibbon, orang, chimpanzee, gorilla. Extinct men (Chapter Three): N, Neandertal; Sin, Sinanthropus; Pth, Pithecanthropus; Plt, Piltdown; Rh, Rhodesian. Extinct apes: 1, Parapithecus; 2, Propliopithecus; 3, Sivapithecus; 4, Dryopithecus; 5, Pliopithecus.—S Af, South African forms Australopithecus, Paranthropus, Plesianthropus (§ 42).

This leaves only the gorilla-chimpanzee differentiation to be placed in time. Broom sets this in the very end of the Miocene, Gregory on the Miocene-Pliocene boundary, Hooton formerly put it early in the Pliocene. Obviously the authorities are once more close together. Hooton in 1946 and Keith postpone this

[16] Which may be a polite technical way of saying that they are unsure whether man or orang was the first to branch off from the rest, but that the two events were not far apart.

gorilla-chimpanzee split until the Pliocene-Pleistocene transition; that is, 1 to 2 million years ago, more or less, as against 5 to 10 million years of the other opinions.

Taking these genealogies at face value, we should have to conclude that man belonged *among* the *Simiidae* or apes, since in his genetic ancestry he is as close to gorilla and chimpanzee as is the orang, and closer than the gibbon. With this view the current static classification of the *Hominidae* as *outside of* and co-ordinate with the *Simiidae* is in flat contradiction. Of course such a clash does not make us lose faith in the authenticity of "science," as soon as we realize that in this case both genealogy and taxonomy rest partly on admitted facts but partly also on construal of fact—in other words, on opinion.

Huxley long ago compared man and the manlike apes. He determined the following percentages of measured lengths:

MAN AND MANLIKE APES

(Percentages) *

	Spinal Column	Arm	Leg	Hand	Foot
European man	100	*80*	**117**	*26*	35
Gorilla	100	115	96 †	36 †	41
Chimpanzee	100	96 †	90	43	39 †
Orang	100	**122**	*88*	**48**	**52**

* Heavy type, **maximum**; italics, *minimum*. † Nearest to man.

Huxley wrote when Darwinian evolution was new doctrine that was still resisted in many quarters as shocking. He was trying to prove relationship of man and the apes. He therefore used the above figures chiefly to argue that the apes often differed more from one another than some one of them differed from man. Thus man and chimpanzee differ 16 per cent in arm length, but orang and chimpanzee 26 per cent. If such a relation held for all or most traits, it would tend to suggest that man should be classified in the group of the apes rather than alongside it, much as the reconstructed family trees have already suggested.

However, what Huxley in the ardor of his argument did not note is that, in the proportions cited, man is regularly at one end of the ape scale, at either the maximum or the minimum of the joint range. This gives us pause, because it seems to suggest that man does after all stand off on one side by himself. At any rate such would be the compelling inference if it held true for enough other traits beyond the four just cited from Huxley. One thinks at once of the obvious human specializations for which it does hold: erect posture, big brain, little jaw, no projecting canines, hairless body, long head hair, and so on. But these features obtrude just because they differentiate us; and a fair judgment ought to be based on all traits, or at least on a reasonably random sample of all. Such a comparison has never been made systematically, and would prove to be pretty elaborate. An incomplete survey quickly shows that there are some traits in which man does stand within the ape range. Accordingly he is not always on this or that side of it. But it shows also that such traits are not particularly numerous, that some have little visible significance, and that in others man's middle position is due to some secondary or special factor which causes this or that ape now and then to deviate beyond man without basic relationships seeming to be involved.

Huxley himself cited one such instance. For the gibbon, he found the arm, leg, hand, and foot lengths to be respectively 173, 133, 50, and 46 per cent of the spinal column. That gives a relative arm and hand length greater even than in the long-armed orang, and farther away from man. But the gibbon leg proportion of 133 surpasses the human one of 117 almost as much as that surpasses the gorilla's of 96. In other words, here is a case where man seems to be caught squarely intermediate between two apes! But it is a spurious instance, as a little analysis quickly reveals. The gibbon is ultra-arboreal, slim, and light. He has a tiny body but spidery limbs. His legs are long not in themselves but only when they are measured against his reduced, miniature torso. The significant point at issue is whether the leg is long because the animal is built for ground walking, or whether the arm is long because it is built for limb-swinging. A direct interlimb comparison is therefore really the most pertinent. In the case of the bigger apes, who are more or less our size, it does not seriously matter if the trunk or the spine length is used as a scale of reference. But with the feathery, light gibbon, trunk length is misleading on this interlimb proportion. With the comparison made directly between the limbs, Huxley's figures for arm/leg length reconvert to: man, 68 per cent; chimpanzee, 107; gorilla, 120; gibbon, 130; orang, 139.[17] This is certainly convincing. The gibbon is back among the apes, and not only does man now stand again at one end of the series, all by himself; but his limb proportions are decisively reversed from those of all the apes—well under 100 as against above 100.

Most traits or proportions that have definite meaning for the characteristic functioning and behavior of the several species come out this way, with man off to one side of all the apes. Where such is not the case, and man finds himself caught in the middle of the group of his anthropoid cousins, it seems to be usually because the feature in question has been chosen not for its significance in life, but for convenience of measurement. Such proportion traits are the cephalic index or ratio of head breadth to head length; proportion of chest breadth to chest depth; proportion of foot length to trunk length. Not one of these has any known meaning that can be told in words; they seem quite indifferent from the angle of abilities or that of behavior.

[17] Hooton, using Schultz's measures of the body in place of the mounted skeletons of Huxley, gets results that are consistently 20 per cent to 30 per cent higher but follow the same *order*: man, 88; chimpanzee and gorilla, 136-140; gibbon, 162; orang, 170; siamang, 170.

All this leaves us then with man pretty closely related to the anthropoid apes. In fact, possibly man is a nearer cousin to the chimpanzee and the gorilla than either of these is to the orang—certainly nearer than to the gibbon. Nevertheless, at every significant point man long since began to edge off to one side of this group of his closest kin and has consistently kept edging away from them. Meanwhile, to be sure, the apes have also differentiated from one another: the chimpanzee from the orang, the gorilla even more markedly from the gibbon. But however far the anthropoid species have spread apart from what they were originally, it is clear that man has spread away even farther. There is then a basis of justification for the descriptive classification of him as a hominid, of them as simiids. While maintaining our kinship with the apes, we have also pretty regularly managed to transcend it.

28. ANTICIPATIONS OF CULTURE AMONG APES: INVENTION

It is evident that the great apes are close to ourselves anatomically. It is also clear that they are close to us physiologically and psychologically, in their mental make-up and most of their faculties. At the same time, their total behavior, and the capacities inferable from their behavior, differ conspicuously from our total behavior and capacities. It is also pretty plain that, basically and in the large, most of the behavior practiced by men but not by apes is the result of man's possessing genuine language and genuine culture. There is no doubt that the acquisition by ancestral man of these two related activities—"gifts" they would have been called formerly—was an event of unusual novelty on this planet, if an evolutionary development may be verbally telescoped into an event. Now it is just possible that this development came as a sudden leap; that it came as a sort of supermutation—in the genes—of inherited faculty which suddenly added to the existing process of hereditary transmission the beginning of a powerful new process of nonhereditary transmission. But the run of scientific experience is that vehement changes and sudden decisive overturns are rare in nature. Just on probability, the betting would be strong that the faculty for culture did not spring fully formed out of the blue, but developed through transitions. Or at least, if the final act of achievement was a relatively swift and drastic one, it was preceded by minor anticipations, by significant premonitory symptoms. That is why an inquiry into how near the apes have come to manifesting culture and speech is important. It might even be said in a sense that the less actual culture we find them to have, the more precious will be the slight evidences of their rudiments or foreshadowings of it.

The case for a sort of protoculture among apes is probably strongest as regards tools. The anthropoids now and then use ready-made tools, and occasionally they will make them. Captive chimpanzees take up sticks to draw to themselves food that is outside the bars beyond reach of their arms. They beat with sticks for the same purpose, or cast ropes or ropelike objects. If the desired food is out of reach overhead, if jumping to reach it has led to failure, and if there is no other chimpanzee about that can be climbed onto and used as a take-off for a higher leap, many of them finally have recourse to moving a box or other convenient object under the prize. If, after they have learned to use a box, the food is hung still higher, chimpanzees may learn to pile a second box on the first; and the more versatile ones will pile three or four. Gorillas and monkeys will also do this. It has justly been pointed out that the piling of the second box on the first is psychologically a quite different thing from moving the first box; there is in it the element of combination, or construction. In a small way, the difference is somewhat like that between rolling a stone and building with stones.

When the convenient reaching tool happened to be a bundle of straws, one chimpanzee, finding the straw too soft to engage and move a banana, without hesitation stiffened the bundle by doubling it. Even then the tool was ineffective, so she redoubled it. That it was now too short to reach the banana rendered the result ineffectual, but this does not detract from her credit as an inventor: she grasped the problem and knew in principle what to do about it. Incidentally, the proclivity of chimpanzees to try to use pliable, ropelike objects for tools is an unexplained foible of the species.

Especially interesting is the rather rare but repeated observation of two canes being joined one into the other to draw in food that lies beyond the reach of a single cane. This is indubitable tool-making; especially so when the end of a stick is chewed down to fit into the hollow of a cane.

How far apes under proper stimuli might progress in devising tools for themselves is difficult to say; just as the observations leave it somewhat obscure how far slower-witted individuals tend to profit by imitating or making the discoveries of a more inventive one. There are however some interesting observations as to the circumstances of the process of invention.

First, the chimpanzee strongly dislikes the strain of situations that call upon his rudimentary inventive faculties. The process of invention is visibly and disagreeably arduous for him. His first impulse is to give up, or to become angry, if he cannot arrive at a solution by purely physiological means such as leaping or biting. Characteristic is the fact that if an implement for reaching is in line of vision with the desired object, it is usually promptly utilized. If on the other hand a previously handled and well-known stick lies behind the ape's back as he faces the food, it may not be "thought of" or noticed and taken up for a long time. This is true especially if the experiment is a novelty to the animal: with repetition, he finds the stick more quickly; but the first time he usually does not remember or observe it at all until after repeated renunciations and recurrences of desire. Emotions clearly are important, constituting a strong resistive factor. The individuals who meet difficult problems most readily, and carry their little inventions farthest, are evidently those best able to control or inhibit the desire or other emotion which the prospective goal arouses in them.

But emotions of another kind can be an impelling influence toward invention. These are the social emotions. His desire for affection, and for approbation from human beings, certainly helps a chimpanzee to invent tools. In a state of nature it is probable that competitive emotion—jealousy—is even more stimulating. Significant is Koehler's observation of the behavior of an adult female chimpanzee when a loaded box or heavy obstacle was placed to interfere with her reaching food beyond the bars. She was perfectly capable of moving the obstacle; but the problem weighed on her for two hours. When however a young unconfined chimpanzee began to stray in the general direction of the food, she suddenly seized the heavy box, shoved it out of the way without hesitation, and grasped the prize out of reach of the competitor. Next day she found the same solution in one minute without first letting herself go into a fit of depression.

The same chimpanzee objected to using sticks for reaching unless they were, so to speak, thrust into her hands by their placement. For half an hour she neglected a stick that was close behind her and which, as a retinal image, she saw whenever in aimless irritation she turned around; but she would not see it with her mind. After a while she stood on the stick. She must have felt it with her soles; but again, as a personality, she refused to receive the sense impression. After half an hour a free chimpanzee came near the food. The jealousy which his approach excited was now utilized to repress the sulking emotion hitherto displayed; suddenly the ignored stick was perceived, seized, and used to draw in the food.

These observations may not throw much light on the question of how far apes possess culture. They do however suggest something as to the psychology that underlies human culture, and which is a factor in what we are accustomed to term its progress. They indicate that the total elimination of competitive factors among men would lessen effort in individuals and might deprive civilization of one of its principal prerequisite impulses. The data suggest further why the institutions, codes, and ethics of all peoples have so strongly emphasized inhibition; why, for instance, courage—the repression of fear—has always been esteemed a high if not the highest virtue; and why, similarly, all social groups condemn incest. Not that the anthropoid apes set up moral standards. But all human groups do; they have evidently learned, on the basis of individual life experiences, the social importance of restraints. The historical inference is that from soon after the time when men began to possess institutions at all, and were able to formulate these in speech, they have never seriously swerved from an insistence on some sort of a social limitation on the natural sex impulse.

Play is evidently an important element in chimpanzee invention. Situations are often first met, or devices prepared, not from a desire to achieve a useful end, but as a matter of sport or amusement, as a means of satisfying pure manipulative interest; utilization comes later. There are plenty of cultural parallels: the use of gunpowder first for fireworks, of the pneumatic tire for sport bicycling, of animal domestication probably for the satisfaction of having pets (§ 148, 165). There is in many men an element that makes them strive for mastery or excellence or perfection of achievement for its own sake, apart from the satisfaction of any definable utilitarian need. It is the driving of such impulses to the point of physiological discomfort, even of bodily strain or damage, that can give organized sport and science and art a certain quality of "unnaturalness." At their fullest, they are exaggerations if not perversions of the play impulse.

No chimpanzee seems capable of being so extreme; he is too unintelligent, from our point of view, but also too sensible, too direct, too concordant physiologically. For better or for worse, however, we men are prone to this exaggeration of the play impulse; and, again for better or for worse, the exaggeration has perceptibly aided the gradual accretion of the stock of culture, as well as the betterment of athletic records; as is discussed in more detail in § 127-128.

The chimpanzee in his youth is as playful, restless, curious, and explorative as any human being. He does not go very far in tool invention, because his central nervous system seems to become quickly and healthily fatigued by situations that put on the nervous system any strain that cannot be promptly discharged into striped-muscle activity. He is physiologically a clear extravert. The gorilla is generally described as imbued with more sense of personal dignity, reticence, and caution even to the point of countersuggestibility. Evidence as to whether in the field of pure intellect the gorilla is the equal of the chimpanzee will have to wait until we have learned to establish satisfactory relations with him in terms of his withdrawing temperament.

The demonstrated ape trait is lack of patience in the solution of a problem, of irritation, sulking, or ignoring as soon as difficulties are encountered which cannot be solved by direct use of hands, feet, or mouth.

This is of interest because it finds a parallel in the history of culture. There was required actually less skill to fashion many of the ground or polished stone implements of the New Stone Age than some of the specialized chipped ones of the Old Stone Age, tens of thousands of years earlier (§ 259). The reason seems to be that while chipping requires definite manual control, it is a rapid process. A dozen failures occupy little time; each may suggest the possibility of an improvement; and the thirteenth attempt may be reasonably satisfactory. Grinding, however, although one of the simplest of operations, is of necessity slow. Very early man was apparently better able to mobilize a fair degree of manipulative skill than a great amount of patience. This resemblance to the ape—and to children—may be only a coincidence, but looks as if it were more than that.

That the chimpanzee possesses the beginning of an ability to reverse his primary impulses is shown by a series of experiments. After a group of the animals had learned to use a stick to gather in food from beyond their reach, the fruit was placed behind a barrier, in a low, open, three-sided box with the farther side broken out. To get his banana, the ape had therefore either to lift it with his stick out over the front or side edge of the box, which was almost impossibly difficult for him; or he had to reverse his first impulse of scraping the fruit toward himself, and instead push it farther away, until it was clear of the box; after which of course the familiar raking-in process could success-fully commence. Without exception the apes found this problem difficult. Some never solved it except when the box was partly turned to help them; others only by the aid of accident, such as the banana's rolling favorably; and even those who had learned the necessary reversal tended occasionally to relapse into their earlier, direct, impossible efforts. Still, some of them did learn, and with practice came to perform quickly and efficiently.

This experiment developed a type of success that has its parallel in culture: invention partly by accident (§ 147). The banana, prodded by the stick, rolls or bounces near an open corner of the box, or entirely clear of it, and the animal immediately sees a solution that has been beyond his grasp while the problem remained unmitigated. After this partial aid by chance, the whole problem may soon be mastered.

The chimpanzee depends much more than we do on muscular strength and gymnastic skill. Even the most intelligent anthropoids manifest little sense of statics. They pile three or four boxes randomly and precariously and then climb on top and balance their own bodies to counteract the imbalance of the me-chanical pile. Boxes are set on a narrow end or an edge and the animal tries to mount them—in some cases even succeeds because of his natural acrobatic capacity. Gorillas proceed more like human beings in adjusting and trying out the boxes; but they are much heavier animals, and with much less climbing and jumping impulse. Of course a solution that depends for its effectiveness primarily on muscular skill is in that degree farther from an invention in the cultural sense. An imperfect tool suffices; the congenital body makes up the deficiency. If men had the strength of arm and jaw of the great apes and their enormous canine teeth, they would no doubt have continued for a long time to meet many situations with muscle rather than with tools.

The impulse to perform with his body is strong in the cleverest chimpanzee; by comparison, performance with a tool is usually clumsy and always an arduous act at first. Given a suspended banana and an available pole, his first impulse is to climb the pole before it can fall and make a quick grab at the fruit—a sort of pole-vault reaching. Sticks are brandished threateningly in play combat. But let a chimpanzee lose his temper, and he drops his stick and plunges into attack with hands and teeth.

Nevertheless some use of tools is spontaneous. Stones are hurled. Sticks are used to dig in play or for roots; to tease fowls or other animals behind wire netting; to touch fire, lizards, live wires, or other things that provoke both curi-osity and fear. In removing filth from his body, the chimpanzee prefers a stick, a chip, a leaf, or a rag to his fingers. He will lick up ants, or hold out a straw

for the ants to crawl on and then lick them off. He has not been observed, outside of posed problems, to manufacture tools or to lay them aside for the future;
he does certainly, without human stimulation, use simple tools that come to
hand, and use them in a way that in a human being we should call intelligent.

Sometimes an ape sits down in front of a problem that has baffled him,
detaches himself from his previous efforts, and looks the situation over, seemingly thinking. How far he may actually "study" the situation is difficult to say;
but he certainly appears reflective. Suddenly then, sometimes, the solution comes
and is applied without hesitation or awkwardness. Again, it may come overnight and with seeming irrelevance. When a human being acts in this manner
we say that he has thought the problem out. At any rate the ape's solution may
come as a whole, as an abrupt synthesis; it looks suspiciously like what in ourselves we would call an insight.

Left to themselves, chimpanzees are destructive. They love to demolish.
Like small children who have grown up uncontrolled, they derive immediate
satisfaction from prying, ripping, biting, and deliberately smashing. Once they
begin, they rarely desist until an object has been reduced to its components.
They learn with difficulty to lace shoes; they find spontaneous pleasure in un-
lacing them. They love to pick knots, as a special form of taking things apart;
they have no inclination to tie or fasten things. The impulse to construct is
infinitely weaker than that to destroy; it is called into activity only by special
problems, and the solution of these is trying.

One of the few exceptions is nest-building. This the chimpanzee does from
an early age, and apparently without being taught. So do gorillas and orangs.
Here we seem to have a genuine case of what in the older terminology was called
"specific instinct." Nest-building is psychologically interesting because it is directed toward an inanimate objective outside the body. But, according to both
Koehler and Yerkes, as well as Nissen, the building is partly a drawing and
tucking of branches under the body. Some of the twigs snap off and help to
hold in place the branches that remain half-attached to the tree. In this way a
tolerable mat or platform is built up. This however remains, during the act
of building, in contact with the ape's body; it is built against his skin, he feels
it during the process of construction, and the autistic sensations aroused may be
an important element in the carrying out of the process. The orang even seems
to cover himself with nest. Some captive chimpanzees, if trees are not available
or loose material does not suffice, lay down a ring of hay or the like which outlines their body and merely suggests the nest—a nest gesture, as it were. This is
an indubitable though simple construction.

The powerful impulses of chimpanzees toward destructiveness may help to
explain further one phenomenon in the history of early human culture already
touched upon: the long precedence in time of the chipping over the grinding
technique in stone. After all, the earlier and grosser process of production by
fracture is one of breaking apart. Grinding, being so slow as to be almost

imperceptible in its results, must be quite inadequate as a means of satisfying the demolition impulse. As an object is slowly rubbed into form, there is probably rather a sense of shaping and constructing. Of course, the Abbevillean and Acheulian hand axes (§ 263, 273) are not by-products of a mere interest in cracking boulders; they are too definitely adaptive, too patternized, too utilizable as tools. But preceding them are ruder flake tools and putative tools (§ 260). In the light of ape behavior we may venture the tentative inference that our ancestors were like chimpanzees and children—and many modern human adults—in taking pleasure in demolition.[18] Learning among other things to smash boulders, and especially nodules of flint, which would be resistive but then shatter cleanly, they may have found themselves provided with attractively sharp and shining flakes, affording a novel toy. Manipulation of these may have led to the discovery that the flakes furnished the possibility of a new satisfaction in hacking or scraping other objects. From such play in turn might have grown increasing habits of tool use, leading, when the mechanism of culture fixation and transmission became sufficiently developed, to the manufacture of tools as tools.

29. OTHER POSSIBLE FORESHADOWINGS OF CULTURE

The occasional use of tools in place of limbs, or as extensions of organs, is the most fully authenticated case of precultural or protocultural manifestations by the apes. This is not too surprising, since a few species much lower than primates are authentically reported to make regular use of inanimate objects in certain particular situations. Thus the solitary wasp *Sphex urnarius* carefully selects a pebble that fits her jaws and then uses it to tamp down the dirt filling that closes the burrow in which she has deposited an egg and a paralyzed caterpillar. This is particularly interesting because it is tool use not through intelligence but as part of a specific instinct, that is, through heredity. In the Galápagos Islands there is a tree finch, *Camarhyncus* or *Cactospiza pallida,* which feeds by using a spine or a thorn or a small stick to impale or rout out insects that are too far down in crevices of bark for it to reach with its bill. More relevant to the problem of the origin of culture is noninstinctual toolmaking or invention, as just discussed; this seems to be confined to the primates and has been most often reported of chimpanzees. Possible anticipations of culture other than technological or inventive activities are hazier than the foregoing, but the following are some suggestive situations.

Chimpanzees are indifferent about being clothed; perhaps it might be said that they tend to dislike, but accept, clothes, although they appreciate a blanket in which to wrap themselves at night. On the contrary, they voluntarily drape themselves with strings and rags, wearing these for hours or days. The satisfac-

[18] The gorilla, and the small *Cebus* monkey, are described as exploratory rather than destructive.

tion is clearly in the wearing as distinct from the act of putting on. The heightening of kinaesthetic bodily consciousness appears to be what gives the pleasure. Chains or strings or pendants that swish and sway with the motion of the body are favored. These observations confirm what has long since been concluded from observation of men; namely, that human dress for protection and for human adornment spring from separate sources or motives.

A group of Koehler's chimpanzees, in digging, discovered some white earth. Tasting it and finding it inedible, they spat it out. Wiping their lips on the wall, they saw it whitened. This soon became a game. First with their lips and then with their hands—this order is perhaps significant—they painted with white earth whatever walls and surfaces were available, but rarely their own bodies. There was no attempt at design or figure. The stuff was smeared on, and the more the appearance of a surface changed, the greater the satisfaction. The pleasure apparently lay in using the muscles to produce a visible external effect. Similar painting or drawing has been reported for gorillas and *Cebus* monkeys.

These observations accord with the behavior of very small children, whose first spontaneous attempts at what we are wont to call drawing or painting normally result in nothing more than smearing or drawing arcs. It is evident that the small child, left to himself, does not attempt to draw a house or a dog or a man. He converts a white paper into a red or black one, a monotonous into a variegated surface. Like the chimpanzee, he gets a kinaesthetic pleasure from his motor discharge, accompanied by the pleasure he gets from seeing the defacement or alteration achieved. This is not yet art; it is subaesthetic motor functioning out of which art accomplishments can develop.

A pair of young chimpanzees in playing began to stamp and circle about a post. Others then ranged themselves alongside until they formed a ring, presenting much the appearance of a savage tribe in a dance. But while the stamping of each ape was definitely heavier with one foot, there was no unison—only a tendency to keep time together. And there was nothing to show that the dancing followed any pattern—that there was imitation in the cultural sense, with social acceptance of a form. The dancing of one individual stimulated other individuals into analogous behavior; but the performance of each apparently remained an unconditioned physiological response. When the gamboling of one lamb sets others to gamboling, or when one startled sheep runs and the flock follows, the lambs or the sheep do not possess culture because they follow one another's example. If one ape had devised or learned a new dance step or a particular posture or an attitude toward the post about which the dance revolved; and if these new acts were taken up by other chimpanzees and became more or less standardized; especially if these survived beyond the influence of the inventor, were taken up by other communities, or passed on to generations after him—in such a case we could legitimately feel that we were on solid ground of an ape culture. But of this there is no indication.

It is the same with chimpanzee fads in smearing chalk, or the game of teasing chickens by unexpectedly jabbing them with a stick through the wire mesh. These actions are comparable to the vogue that a game has among ourselves, to the fact that the first boy who brings out his kite or his marbles in spring is likely to set other boys of his school to bringing out their kite and marbles. What is cultural in such phenomena is not the fact that one individual leads and others follow, but the game or fashion as such. The kite, the manner of manipulating the marbles, the cut of a garment, the tipping of one's hat— these remain as cultural facts after every physiological and psychological consideration of the individuals involved has been exhausted. Of any such institutional residuum of unmitigatedly cultural material there is as yet no clear demonstration among the apes.

Religion is difficult to conceive without formulated ideas, and thus without speech. Even its rudiments could therefore hardly be looked for among the apes. Yet there may be some subcultural anticipations. Koehler made a rude rag animal with shoe-button eyes which vaguely suggested a miniature donkey. It was altogether too crude to be mistaken for a live animal, yet had sufficient resemblance to one to set it off from ordinary inanimate natural objects, or from artifacts such as boxes and chairs. The apes responded instantly with manifestations of fear. It was not terror as great as an ox or a camel inspired; it can perhaps best be characterized as similar in its expression to what human beings would call awe. There was not a trace of either the frank curiosity or the later unresponsiveness that a new lifeless object provoked; interest there was, but also respectful staying at a distance for a long time. Even food placed in proximity to the image was shunned, and was snatched only at last and cautiously, with a precipitate retreat. A dog manifested a similar interest in the figure, except that, being carnivorous and therefore a basically aggressive organism, his interest took the form of hostility. He convinced himself, however, as soon as he dared, of the inanimateness of the image, and from then on was completely indifferent to it. The chimpanzee, like ourselves, is less "practical," perhaps as the result of possessing more imagination.

The relation to religion of this reaction of the chimpanzees lies in their manifesting something like the awe that is regarded as an important or essential ingredient of what we call the religious feeling: the religious thrill. It is generally recognized that religion could not well originate without the presence of emotions of which awe may be taken as the prototype, and that these emotions tend to persist or to be reawakened in religion, no matter how crystallized this becomes with time. Also, the kind of object that arouses the awelike feeling in chimpanzees has a certain quality of resemblance to the basic concepts of religion. Souls, ghosts, spirits, deities, like stuffed rag donkeys, do not occur in ordinary experience; like them, also, they are thought to be at once similar to living bodies and different from them. A dummy donkey with button eyes evidently is literally supernatural to a chimpanzee, or at any rate is close to being supernatural. We can say pretty positively that the ape does not have a religion; we can also say pretty positively that he acts at times somewhat as if he were religious. Another way of putting it is that there are certain situations in which apes manifest reactions which strongly suggest feelings similar to those experienced by human beings in religious connections, but that there is no indication whatever that apes have any religion itself or that they are capable of the systematic conceptualization that a religion involves.

On the side of speech it is remarkable that the apes are completely deficient in imitativeness of human beings. Observations, experiments, and training attempts like those of Furness and Boutan are uniformly negative. At this point the successful manual adaptations are significant that are shown by circus-trained chimpanzees and orangs and by those brought up in close human associations. Such apes do learn easily to ride bicycles, to smoke cigars, to brush their teeth, to eat with a spoon, to go to bed, and to do a hundred other things the family is doing. They cannot be taught to speak at all. They do not seem even to have the least impulse to imitate the speech of their human associates, or, if willing to try, they are wholly at a loss how to do so. This is the more striking because of the general similarity of their mouth parts to our own—a similarity that is certainly far greater than that of a parrot's or a magpie's mouth.

All in all, it is clear that we have in the anthropoid apes beings remarkably close to ourselves. They are animals behaving in many respects like men and differently from other animals. Impulses that we are accustomed to regard as specifically human, such as "painting" and hanging things on our bodies, prove to be present in them in rudimentary form. What they do lack totally, so far as we can judge, is speech and culture. In this regard they are as subhuman as the other mammals and the birds. This is really remarkable in view of their possessing one of the ingredients going into the make-up of culture: inventiveness. That the tools an ape now and then devises are simple and crude is to be expected; that he can and does originate them makes us wonder why he did not pass on to develop an elementary culture. The absence of speech undoubtedly is an important factor in this deficiency.

With the ape inventive but cultureless, the question arises whether we have not perhaps hitherto exaggerated the importance of invention in human culture. We are wont to think of it as the creative or productive element in civilization. The idea of progress, which has so powerful a hold on the unconscious as well as the conscious thought of our day, may have led us to overemphasize the role of invention. Perhaps the thing that essentially makes culture is precisely the transmissive and preservative elements, the relational or binding factors. It may be that invention, for all its dynamic potential for change, will prove to be what in the long pull is incidental in culture, despite the fact that it has become the tendency of the day to look upon it as primary. What may ultimately be recognized as counting for more is the way the patternings of culture shape themselves to permit or prevent or induce invention, or, for that matter, other changes of civilization. This shaping of patterns is a matter of interrelations of culture content; and what appears to be indispensable for the existence of such interrelations is a certain social relation, an organization, or form, almost a standardization. The fundamental thing about culture then would be the way in which men relate themselves to one another by relating themselves to their culture material. If however the relational forces in culture phenomena are the intrinsic ones, then the indispensability of speech to the very existence of culture becomes understandable. It is the fact of communicating, perhaps, more than the thing communicated, that counts. At any rate the fact that speech, to the best of our knowledge, is as thoroughly wanting among the anthropoids as is culture tends to confirm this conception.

These problems will be gone into at greater length in the chapters on culture, especially Chapters Seven to Eleven.

30. HUMAN SPECIALIZATIONS AND THEIR INTERRELATIONS

Many of the described anatomical human specializations away from the general primate stock, and then from the narrower protoanthropoid stock, are interrelated, structurally and functionally. Particularly interrelated are brain, jaw, posture, hands, feet, and vision. A failure of any one of these to develop as it actually did would have interfered with the evolutionary development of the others—in some cases considerably, in others vitally. Most fundamental, of course, was the brain development, and specifically that of the brain cortex, where the culture-and-speech faculty must be thought to be localized, so far as it is localized. A chimpanzee brain in an otherwise human body would certainly not have led to those accomplishments of man which it is the business of history and anthropology to tell about. But contrariwise a human brain originating in chimpanzee bodies might conceivably have led to a world not so very different from our human one, though a more unlovely one. The critical phases of the species would in that case presumably have come early in its history, in connection with difficulties of travel and spread, of self-defense in the open, of dietary limitations, and possibly some technological restrictions due to lack of a fully opposable thumb. But once our hypothetical ape with culture-geared human brain had survived these initial handicaps and had piled up a measurable stock of cultural contrivances, his culture would presumably have been as successfully adapted to his physique, and to survival, as ours is to our physique. Tool grips would in that case have been shaped for nearly thumbless hands instead of thumbed ones. Travel on foot would presumably have had added to it at an earlier time transport by riding or on wheels or on stilts or the like. And with such minor modifications there might have been a general mode and subvarieties of cultural living fairly parallel to our own.

Of least specific importance in the matter of human specialization is vision, because our eye faculties seem to differ little from those of the apes and monkeys.

It need only be reaffirmed that without the kinds of eyes we have our hands would be much limited in their manipulations, and with these restricted a fine brain would often be ineffectual in coping with tangible situations. But the qualities we chiefly needed in our eyes to make the rest of our bodies fully effective—namely, their being set to look forward together instead of apart at the sides, their muscular co-ordination and stereoscopic faculty, and their sharpness of vision in the fovea—were acquired early in primate evolution.

Color vision, by the way, seems to have been of consequence chiefly for the aesthetic potentialities it added. Its survival value was and is relatively low; many large groups of animals never see colors. Nor are the 5 per cent or so of color-blind male human beings (§ 72) seriously handicapped in living in the culture evolved by the 95 per cent of color-seeing men and nearly 100 per cent of women. Only a few professions using color signals are closed to them, even in our mechanized contemporary civilization. And until rather recently, nearly all the color-blind got through life without their or their associates' suspecting the condition. The first reference in history seems to have been less than three hundred years ago, in 1684, and the first scientific description was that of the chemist Dalton in 1794. Of course color-blindness, being hereditary, was presumably just as frequent before these dates as afterward. The point is that if it could go unnoticed in history until then, it cannot be a very material defect.

31. THE UNKNOWN ORGANIC BASIS OF THE FACULTY FOR CULTURE

The foregoing discussions have established culture and speech as essential possessions limited strictly to human beings. Some faint approaches toward culture are discernible here and there in the animal kingdom, especially among the great apes, as just discussed in § 28-29. Also, it seems to be established that certain birds possess a mimetic faculty and inclination which bring it about that some of them can modify their specific hereditary and instinctual song. They modify it in conformity toward phonographed bird song to which they are exposed for a sufficiently long period in youth, whether such song be merely that of a slightly different strain or race, or of a different species. Further, once trained in such a modification of their congenital song, the older birds will similarly influence the younger birds reared within earshot of their voices, so that a sort of tradition is carried on. This is externally very like human tradition. But it differs fundamentally from the transmission of culture and speech in that it is wholly lacking in the conveyance of any facts or any ideas; it does not contain an element of abstraction. It is obviously allied to the mechanically reproductive faculty of parrots, magpies, and mynahs, which learn to repeat fragments of speech but do not learn to convey objective meanings.

These slight and ineffectual approaches to language or culture possess a very real interest in that they show that the human faculty for these behaviors is not something entirely outside of nature, is not a sort of foreign body or miracle mysteriously injected into the otherwise continuous course of natural events. There are just enough subhuman anticipations of speech and culture, just enough stirrings and foreshadowings toward them, to make clear that their development has its roots in animal structure and evolution as completely as has the development of our bodies and physiology. But the fact of such rooting should not cause us to overlook the other fact that the great vine of culture and speech which has grown in man out of this rooting is a thousandfold as large and strong as the poor, rare, struggling, seedling counterpart among nonhuman animals. Destroy our culture and speech capacity, and it is clear that well over 99 per cent of what fills our human lives specifically, of our total actions and behavior, would be obliterated.

Now the remarkable thing is that while the results or outgrowths of the faculty for culture are so great—and for the rest of this argument let us consider speech included in culture—by contrast man's visible equipment, his whole structure as it is analyzed, is so closely similar to that of the apes. That we are nearly hairless, that our teeth are smaller and our thumbs more opposable, that we are better built for prolonged standing and walking—these are anatomical and physiological differences of detail and degree, and mostly of no very great degree. But the difference as regards culture is one of so enormous a degree, when we consider its effects—complete absence of religion, law, art, and science among even the most manlike apes or the most socialized insects—as to become virtually equivalent to a difference in kind.

It seems that this situation drives us to one conclusion: From the angle of what is organic and hereditary in nature, the evolutionary acquisition of capacity for culture was an organically small thing, a by-product, which at first was so insignificant that a nonterrestrial observer would perhaps have overlooked it. Even now the most advanced biological science cannot level a finger and say: This is when and how culture faculty developed, out of such and such an antecedent, and here is where it still resides and basically operates. The "here," the anatomical seat of the faculty, is presumably in the cortex of the brain. But this cortex differs from that of the cultureless apes only in being somewhat larger, somewhat thicker, presumably somewhat more complex with a somewhat greater number of nerve cells and interconnections of them. There is no new organ, no new layer, no new chemical substance that we know of, peculiar to the human cortex. The "somewhat" heightening, the elaborating of degree, of the structure of the apelike cortex, seems to have sufficed to turn the trick. It seems to have started our ancestors on the path of a culture which then grew cumulatively. That is, the culture accumulated, or could accumulate, independently of further evolution of anatomical structure or heredity, so far as we know.[19]

[19] This is an anticipation of what will be more fully set forth below, but the point must be made here if man's peculiar place in nature is to be defined thoroughly. See particularly § 49, 99, 112-115.

This situation, in turn, suggests that from the angle of organic evolution, which means change in heredity, the increment or mutation that first introduced the capacity for culture was a very small increment. It may have been no more than a change in one chromosome, perhaps no more than in a few genes. The individual organism in which this new constitutional factor [20] first cropped out may well have been still overwhelmingly like its parents and ancestors in total appearance and behavior, in bodily shape, motivations, and abilities. But on top of this likeness, the innovating or mutant individual manifested a new inclination to communicate, to learn and to teach, to generalize from the endless chain of his discrete feelings, actions, and experiences. And therewith he began to be able to act as a receiver and a transmitter, and to begin the accumulation that is culture. We cannot in the least prove by evidence that this is what happened; but it is very difficult, in the light of what we know of heredity and of culture, to conceive that it did not happen.

With the appearance, in the stream of anthropoid-hominid heredity, of the first gene bearing the faculty of cultural acquisition, a critical point may be said to have been reached in evolution. There had been critical points passed before: the first head, the first eye, the first brain, the first warm blood. But this one was different in that the genetic change set something going outside of heredity also: a process that could be operative only through organisms and by their agency, but which would have a growth and development of a separate kind, apart from germ-plasm development: cumulatively instead of recapitulatively, and with each idea or invention making others possible.

Critical points—tipover limits, we might call them—occur scattered all through nature. Thus, when a book on a table is shoved an eighth of an inch farther until its center of gravity is just over the table edge, it topples. Or water is chilled degree after degree without notable change of its properties until it reaches 0° C and turns to solid ice. Or two gases will explode only when their mixture reaches a certain proportion and the necessary flash point is reached. These are recurrent critical points. The critical point in evolution that resulted in the birth of the faculty for culture is infinitely more dramatic because quite probably it was reached only once in the earth's history. And it was dramatic too in that at the time of the event its effects probably were only infinitesimally perceptible, whereas the ultimate effects were to become indefinitely great for the species concerned, and were often to react back on the physical and organic streams of nature, as when men change the face of the earth by their labors, or exterminate or propagate animals and plants.

[20] Or possibly the first one of a series of related factors successively reinforcing one another.

32. SPECIALIZATIONS ASSOCIATED WITH POSTURE

If now, leaving these somewhat wide-range reflections, we return to concrete specializations and review the human particularities, those peculiarities which characterize man as against his nearest ape relatives, it appears that much the greatest number of such differentiating features fall into three groups, each consisting of a set of traits correlated with one another around a nucleus. These nuclei may for convenience be designated as posture, brain size, and domestication.

Hands, feet, and posture are intimately interconnected. We are built to walk and stand erect indefinitely long, with a "double" curvature of our backbone—really a triple one: convex at rump and at shoulders and neck, concave at small of the back. The apes have a single convex curve forward. They do not stand well, nor walk erect freely. Usually they progress on the ground on all fours, planting their weight on their soles and knuckles. If not too heavy, they perhaps most often climb or swing, and progress by brachiating—"arming" it from an overhead support instead of "legging" it over the ground underfoot. This, as we have seen (§ 21-26), is connected with the arboreal habitat of the primates generally, which the anthropoids retain, with only incipient abandonment by the chimpanzee and somewhat more by the ponderous gorilla. The result is that both apes and monkeys are functionally quadrumanous, four-handed, as compared with ourselves—as already told in § 10. The clean differentiation into feet for walking on the ground and hands for taking and holding is unique to man. So is full opposability of the thumb, which is obviously useful in tool-handling but may be as much of a detriment as an advantage in swinging from and to branches. Yet if our ancestors had not once lived for a long time in the trees, along with the rest of the primates, we should probably never have had any kind of hand. The clever or lucky thing we "did" was to come down out of the trees after we had hands, and early enough to re-evolve a pretty fair true foot—that is, a limb extremity built for general terrestrial locomotion.

Erect posture in one sense is essentially an expression of this full differentiation in the function of our two pairs of limbs. If the hands were really to be emancipated to serve as manipulators, they had better come wholly off the ground; and the mechanical end, and in a sense the perfection, of this new type of design was complete erectness, with whatever correlated changes in backbone, pelvis, leg, and foot were involved, if they could be attained. And they were reasonably attainable, as the evolutionary outcome showed.

Man is the only vertebrate, perhaps the only animal, that stands and moves fully erect: with his head directly over his feet, his legs vertical, his trunk and neck on a vertical axis, even his arms essentially vertical when at rest. Our forefathers of some centuries ago saw in this posture a symbol of his aspiring toward

God, or of an inherent "upwardness," "rectitude," or worthiness. We of today rule such subjective and moral judgments out of our biology; but the thorough uniqueness undoubtedly has certain significances that are also objective, and not moral: significances of cause and effect, or let us say of history and correlation. There are evidently certain mechanical and organic problems to be solved, or requirements that have to be met, before erect posture becomes feasible; and these problems are presumably by no means simple, else erect forms would have been evolved repeatedly in nature. There are only incomplete approximations. Birds are bipedal but not erect; their trunk is at most slanting, often nearly horizontal, when they are on the ground; in flight it is fully horizontal. The kangaroo's legs are flexed, the thighs being horizontal at rest; and they are both braced and balanced at the hip by a long, massive tail. The plane of the kangaroo's pelvis is vertical, not horizontal, and the trunk slopes definitely forward. And so in every subhuman case; the erectness is only partial, or false, or can be maintained only momentarily. Evidently a series of conditions had to be fulfilled before the cluster of traits co-ordinated with fully erect posture could be successfully achieved and preserved in evolution. Presumably adaptation to arboreal life was one such antecedent. Subsequent full return to the ground almost certainly was another. A minimum of size may also have been necessary for the innovation to be successful.

33. BRAIN SIZE

The size of the human brain is another uniqueness. This holds especially for absolute size. It holds less for relative size, since in animals of the same structure and development, the smaller will always have the proportionally larger brain. The reason for this is that a house cat, weighing perhaps one-fiftieth of a tiger or a lion, will nevertheless have just about as many sensations to receive and as many and complex motions to execute, and apparently cannot do this work with a brain fully shrunk to one-fiftieth of the lion's. So its brain actually weighs one-tenth that of a lion, or relatively five times as much. In the same way, a mouse's brain is of course smaller than a rat's, but a greater fraction of a mouse than of a rat consists of brain: 2 per cent as against .05 per cent. Similarly, as between a hummingbird and an eagle, a sparrow (one-twentieth of its body) and an ostrich (one three-thousandth), a 2-ounce lizard (one four-hundredth of its body) and a 400-pound alligator (one fifteen-thousandth). A similar difference holds as between infant and adult in the same species. Thus a male white baby's brain makes up a full tenth of his body weight at birth (320-340 grams of 3000-3500), as against only about 2 per cent when it has become adult.[21] In a rough sort of way, brain size perhaps tends to be larger by about

<hr>

[21] This is on the basis of brain weight in grams holding constant at seven-eighths the cranial capacity (§ 57, 60) in cubic centimeters in man. A child is born with a fourth of its ultimate brain volume or slightly better, has doubled this probably by its ninth month, and

the square while body size is larger by the cube; or inversely as regards shrink-age—square root versus cube root.

Man's brain weight is about one-fiftieth his body weight; around 3 pounds out of 150. The absolute mass of this fiftieth is surpassed by only a very few giants among living animals. These are the whales, the bodies of whose larger species range up to 100 tons; elephants that weigh 5 tons; possibly but probably not the rhinoceros and the hippopotamus, though there appear to be few authentic figures available as to these. This means that among land animals we must proceed to bodies at least twenty times heavier than man's before the human brain is surpassed in mass. Cattle and horses, the bulk of which will balance five to ten men on the scales, have brains much smaller than each of the ten.

The table shows the elephant as the only land animal with a brain larger than a man's. The great whales, with a total weight up to a thousand times that of a man, manage to get on with only four or five times our brain mass: they are a sort of warm-blooded mushrooms. The small whales on the contrary make a surprisingly good showing: a 300-pound porpoise not only has a bigger brain than we but approaches us in its ratio of brain to body. That this is no error of observation is shown by the stupid-looking walrus, which is half again as heavy as a cow but has a brain three times as heavy; and by the seals, whose brains equal those of land carnivores five to ten times as heavy. The cause, or need, of this sea-mammal brain size is not clear; but it may explain the popularity of the seal in circuses. Tame animals generally have smaller brains, or at least larger bodies without increased brains, than their wild ancestors. Compare the Cape buffalo with cattle, the quagga with our horses.

The lightness of the gibbon's brain shown by the table is surprising; it is barely bigger than the brains of subanthropoid monkeys weighing only half as much. And the supposedly primitive platyrrhine American monkeys like the *Cebus,* spiders, and howlers match evolutionistically higher Old World catarrhines like the rhesus rather closely in mass and in ratio. This accords with the judgment of some observers as to their intelligence (§ 22).

Even as compared with our closest relatives, chimpanzee and gorilla, the human disproportion is glaring. The full-grown chimpanzee weighs about seven-tenths as much as a man, his brain around three-tenths as much. An adult male gorilla weighs a good 200 per cent *more* than a man, his brain at its maximum record is well over 50 per cent *less,* to judge by volume of the skull case (§ 26). Then too, we have already seen (§ 31) that the human brain differs from the ape brain rather little in its structure—at any rate in its gross structure, which is basically quite homologous. But as soon as we turn to mass, the difference of three to one is more than perceptible: it is striking.

has attained three-fourths of the total around the age of two and a half or three years. Thus the development of most of the brain mass, and its most rapid rate of growth, occur in the period of least intellectual functioning.

BRAIN AND BODY WEIGHTS OF MAMMALS

	Brain (Kilograms)	Body (Kilograms)	Body-brain Ratio, approx
Mammals			
Blue whale	6.8	58,000.	8,500
Humpback whale	5.78	35,000.	6,000
Finback whale	5.36	38,000.	7,000
Elephant, African	5.7	6,650.	1,170
Elephant	4.7	3,000.	640
Elephant	4.	2,000. *	500 *
White whale (6, ♂, ♀)	2.35	400.	170
Porpoise	1.73	140.	80
Man—see also below	1.32	62.	47
Walrus	1.13	670.	600
Dromedary, domestic	.76	400. *	530 *
Hippopotamus	.72	1,350.	1,900
Hippopotamus	.58	1,750.	3,000
Giraffe	.70	1,220.	1,750
Giraffe	.68	530. *	750.*
Horse, maximum (5♂)	.71	480.	700·
Cape buffalo (2♂)	.67	650.	1,000
Quagga zebra (3♂)	.58	275.	480
Horse, domestic	.53	370.	700
Polar bear (2)	.50	260.	520
Cattle (200 Holstein cows)	.42	570.	1,400
Cattle (213 Jersey bulls)	.41	410.	1,000
Grizzly bear	.39	150.	375
Harbor seal	.27	12.6 *	50 *
Ringed seal	.25	40.	160
Tiger (2)	.26	185.	700
Lion (2)	.26	190.	700
Wild pig	.18	55.	300
Uintatherium (extinct, Eocene), estim.	.15	2,000.	13,000
Coyote	.085	8.5	100
Dog, domestic (9)	.08	13.5	170
Cat, domestic (10)	.025	3.3	130
Opossum (4, ♂, ♀; marsupial)	.0048	1.15	240
Norway rat	.0024	.45	200
Mole (insectivore)	.0012	.04	35
Mouse	.0004	.02	50
Shrew (68, ♂, ♀; insectivore)	.00035	.017	50
Primates			
Man (41, ♂, ♀)	1.32	62.	47
Chimpanzee (♂)	.44	57.	130
Chimpanzee (♀)	.33	44.	135
Orang (10♂)	.37	73.	200
Orang (11♀)	.30	36.	120
Black spider monkey (17♂, ♀; platyrrhine)	.115	9.1	80
Red spider monkey (63♂, ♀; platyrrhine)	.11	7.6	70
Gibbon (9♂; anthropoid)	.09	6.	70
Rhesus macaque (11♂, ♀; catarrhine)	.09	3.5	40
Cebus capuchin (14♂, ♀; platyrrhine)	.07	3.1	45
Black howler (28♂, ♀; platyrrhine)	.05	6.2	125
Brown howler (6♂, ♀; platyrrhine)	.04	3.2	75
Marmoset (16♂, ♀; platyrrhine)	.022	.85	40

* Probably not fully grown. This would presumably not affect very much the absolute brain weight, but it would certainly lower the body-brain weight ratio.

What we have, then, by and large, that is outstandingly unique about the ..uman brain is two things. One is its exceptional weight—exceptional among both our near kin and our more remote size mates. The other is its functional ability to symbolize and abstract and transmit. It would be hard to believe that these two unique features are not somehow related. Not that one can infer in the absolute from quantity to quality: the case of the cat and the tiger show that. Nor is it at all sure that the human bearer of a brain of 1700 cc is necessarily more intelligent than one with 1300 cc. Yet the brain mass of man compared with that of our nearest and same-sized relatives, and the symbolizing or thinking faculty of man, are both so extraordinarily singular that their co-ocurrence must indicate some sort of connection, however indirect and unexplained as to mechanism. What may chiefly be involved is an increase in the number of possible interconnections of neuron cells, greater even than the increase in number of cells which follows the increase in mass. This would be on the principle of a bigger switchboard meaning a more complex one also; or of a series of numbers going up, but the frequency of their possible combinations going up faster still. This comparison must not be taken as a proven explanation, but it suggests in contour what may have happened in early human evolution. Whatever the detail of brain structure that underlies the kind of psychosomatic functioning that makes human culture possible, it is almost certain to be associated with that unique multiplication of brain mass which characterizes *Homo sapiens*. Even in our remote fossil precursors Sinanthropus and Pithecanthropus (§ 37-38), who were only rudimentarily culturalized, the brain bulk is already fully double that of the ape average.

34. SPECIALIZATIONS ASSOCIATED WITH SELF-DOMESTICATION

Man has been said to be a domesticated animal, which is of course in one sense an absurdity, because there is no domesticator. But man may without objection be called self-domesticated in that, while he is not kept or bred or used by another species, he does live under conditions of shelter, of normally stable food supply, and of absence of rigorous natural selection, much like the domesticated animals. The mechanism is different, but some of the results are the same. This point is discussed further in a subsequent chapter (§ 73); but it will be of interest to list here those anatomical peculiarities associated with our "self-domestication." They comprise: probably, the long hair on our heads, which has no exact parallel among mammals; the near-hairlessness of most of our bodies, which is atypical except for very thick-hided, or armored, or wholly aquatic mammals such as elephants, armadillos, and whales; curly and woolly hair; the partial albinism that in man we call fair skin, blond hair, and blue eyes; and perhaps jaw reduction, brachycephalization (§ 60), steatopygia (§ 64), and lip eversion.

It is evident that most of these specializations associated with self-domestication are related to appearance rather than to the viability or the success of the species. They have no positive survival value in themselves. In fact they seem to be either indifferent or sometimes even on the negative side as regards survival. But they might be described as having aesthetic significance, so far as such a term is applicable in biology—as in connection perhaps with the effects of sexual selection, or with the "elegance" of form mentioned by palaeontologists as sometimes attained by mature lines of evolution.

35. GENERALIZED HUMAN TRAITS

In summary, then, apart from the rather superficial features connected with self-domestication, the specializations of man are essentially those connected with his brain and his erectness. He lacks all the various specializations that come to mind when we think of elephant, seal, whale, bat, anteater, sloth, armadillo, cat, beaver, porcupine, deer, giraffe, or kangaroo. He has kept all four of his original limbs, and each of them retains its full five digits, just as these are tipped with nails and neither hoofs nor claws. He has kept the basic mammalian dentition well preserved in differentiation of kind and only slightly reduced in number. He is quite extraordinarily able to thrive on any one of a variety of different diets. In fact he may well be classed with the bears and the pigs as omnivorous. He is only moderately swift in any one mode of locomotion, but can make tolerable shift at a greater number of modes than most mammals or submammalian forms: running, jumping, climbing, burrowing, swimming. And his distribution is one of the widest of all mammals, partly, it is true, because he can to some extent control his environment through fire and housing, but evidently in some measure preculturally also, especially as compared with the other primates.

In short, where man is significantly specialized, he tends also to be uniquely specialized. The rest of him appears to be rather unusually well generalized, in function as well as in structure. And generalization is normally a precondition for further development in organic evolution.

CHAPTER THREE

Fossil Man

36. NATURE OF THE FOSSIL STORY

WE HAVE reviewed man's place in nature—his position in the animal kingdom and in evolution, and his relations with subhuman brutes as well as his specializations away from them. In the pages that follow there will be given an outline of the discoveries made of specimens of incipient and former man—of the fossils that are the step-by-step evidence of the development of our bodies to their present form.

The word "outline" is used advisedly, for the story is still a spotty one, no doubt containing more gaps than positive knowledge. But it is a story that is filling in fast. All of the evidences have been gathered in the past hundred years, probably half of them since 1910. These evidences are of two kinds. First, they consist of actual bones of ancient men, more or less fossilized or mineralized. Second, the evidence comprises facts associated with the bones and suggesting or sometimes proving their age. Such facts again are of three kinds: geological, palaeontological, and archaeological.

Geological data refer to the earth's crust of rocks: the successive layers of these, erosion, terracing, and the effects of glaciation.

Palaeontological data—which are sometimes also included among geological ones because geologists find them so useful—are the fossil remains or impressions of former animals or plants. Since these animals or plants largely developed in certain evolutionary sequences, many of which by now are well known, the presence of bones of this or that particular extinct species of horse or elephant or camel in the same deposit with the skeleton of an ancestral man may definitely fix the age of that human type. It will not indicate it within a hundred or even a thousand years, but in certain cases it may fairly well pin it down within ten thousand. It will certainly tell whether we are facing an age nearer five thousand or fifty thousand or five hundred thousand years.

Finally, archaeological evidences are cultural and man-made ones. They are tools, artifacts, or constructions by human hands as they come associated with human bones. Fortunately, this kind of man-made evidence becomes proportionately more abundant as the human skeletons are later and therefore the time intervals are shorter. It is in regard to the short periods that the geologist and the palaeontologist are at a disadvantage. Their data range over hundreds of millions of years, so that from their angle a million more or less is often quite insignificant. It is only now and then that their tools will cut fine—where there are glacial or other special evidences available. But the whole human story falls essentially within the last million years. The archaeologist or prehistorian therefore deals with a much shorter total span and is trained to try to make finer time discriminations. The estimates of the geologist and the palaeontologist are accordingly the fundamental ones for the age of human fossils, but likely to be somewhat roughhewn, whereas the archaeologist's estimates are secondary, but may be more refined.

Geologically, the time in question for man is the Pleistocene period—roughly, the last million years or so of the earth's history. Some reckon it as only half a million years long, some as six hundred thousand. The word "Pleistocene" means "most recent" in the geological past. The period is also called the Glacial epoch. It is followed by the very brief Holocene or "wholly recent." Being only about ten thousand years long, the Holocene is really the geologist's today, his present tense. Occasionally someone has claimed a pre-Pleistocene age for this or that human fossil. There is as yet no single find of anything in man's direct line of ancestry that prevailing opinion dates as far back as that. But some of our nearer subhuman collateral relatives undoubtedly do go back into the pre-Pleistocene—see the family trees in Figure 1. The Pleistocene or age of man's emergence was at one time designated the fourth, or Quaternary, main era of geological time. The Cenozoic, or preceding age of mammals, was—and still is—the Tertiary, just as the still earlier age of reptiles or Mesozoic was sometimes called the Secondary. However, of the several subdivisions of the Tertiary, it is only the last, the Pliocene, which so far has come into even dubious consideration for man. True, we must of course have had direct ancestors during the Pliocene. But there are no fossils we can safely identify as such; nor can we accurately reconstruct by imagination what our Pliocene ancestors presumably were like—whether they were already essentially human or still subhuman.

The area in question is the Eastern Hemisphere, or at least such parts of it as were at one time or another accessible without navigation, and had not so rigorous a climate as to be unlivable for hairless mammals without clothing and houses and originally without fire. As a matter of fact, more separate finds of fossil man have been made to date in Europe than in Africa, Asia, and Australasia together. But this is merely the result of search having been begun in Europe because scientific curiosity and method were more advanced there. There is nothing to suggest that fossil man favored that miniature continent over others. In fact, the very first discoveries were all made by western Europeans in western Europe, in France and adjacent Spain, England, Belgium, and western Germany. The first discovery by a non-European and non-Caucasian was made in 1929, by the Chinese palaeontologist Pei. As recently as 1914, only one find from outside Europe—Java man—had been announced and authenticated; in 1948 there were between fifteen and twenty. It can be anticipated that by 1978 there will be considerably more evidence from the other continents than from Europe.

The Americas may have to be excepted. All claims yet made for really high antiquity of man in the Western Hemisphere have blown up under critical checking. This fits in with the total absence from the Western Hemisphere of true apes and even higher monkeys, both extinct and surviving. Man must have immigrated into America, if we are to judge from where his nearest relatives live. Evidently he immigrated late—very late, geologically. His stone handiwork has now been found repeatedly in association with late Pleistocene extinct bisons, elephants, horses, and sloths (§ 278-280). The time involved may be as much as twenty thousand or twenty-five thousand years, but again it may be no more than ten thousand. In any event it is only a small fraction of the period during which man surely has existed in the Old World.

There are now so many discoveries that the story of fossil man has become complicated in details. This story is more readily comprehended if it is first organized around the major and uncontroverted types, with the deviant and doubtful cases relegated to subsequent and briefer treatment. Even the surer types are sufficiently numerous to warrant their classification according to stage of development or nearness to ourselves. Three such stages or levels are being more and more generally recognized: Protoanthropic, Palaeoanthropic, and Neanthropic—"first," "old," and "newer" human. These do not follow each other as clean-cut as stair steps or as separate as ladder rungs; they do overlap somewhat in time. But there is no question as to their general and total order of succession. Among proven forms, the Protoanthropic ones begin and end earliest, the Palaeonanthropic ones come next, and the Neanthropic ones are latest—in fact, all living races are Neanthropic in type.

Grouped in the larger way, then, there are first of all, well back in the Pleistocene, Java and Peking man, both now abundantly authenticated and similarly primitive. Certain more dubious early forms can be construed in tentative relation to them. As a group, these constitute the Protoanthropic basic type.

Next among the positives, and on the whole considerably later, the most famous form is Neandertal man, who lived in Europe during the last glaciation and is closely associated with the archaeological implement stage known as the Mousterian period of the Old Stone Age. A whole array of forms in Africa, Asia, Oceania, as well as Europe—Rhodesian, Palestine, Solo, Heidelberg man —can be related to Neandertal either in time or in type. At any rate they are all Palaeoanthropic.

With the last glaciation passing away and the Pleistocene entering its terminal stage, and with human culture in the final phase of the Old Stone Age— in the Upper Palaeolithic, in technical terms—man was Neanthropic, "new human." He belonged to our living species, and differed from us only as a subspecies or race. The most familiar name in this period is Cro-Magnon. This fossil type, it is generally agreed, did not die out, but developed or blended or outright carried on into the historical populations of Europe. All other known Neanthropic types, whatever their area of occurrence, can be related, by degree of similarity or difference, either to the Cro-Magnon or to some living race.

Beyond all this, when we come to the geological Recent and the archaeological Mesolithic and Neolithic periods, we are almost at the threshold of documentary history and wholly in the realm of still living races.

With this general framework in mind, let us now review the better-substantiated types.

37. PITHECANTHROPUS

Pithecanthropus erectus, the "erect ape man," was determined from the top part of a skull, a thighbone, and two molar teeth found in 1891 under fifty feet of deposits by Dubois, a Dutch surgeon, near Trinil in central Java. The skull and the thigh lay some distance apart but at the same level. The straightness and length of the thigh indicated an upright posture and a tall stature—around 5 feet 7 inches was estimated—and gave rise to the specific name *erectus.* That the thigh and the skull belonged to the same species, or even individual, seemed probable then, but is now seriously doubted; the thighbone is probably from a later man, and got secondarily introduced into the deposit. The teeth were questioned even earlier, and are now generally considered to be from orangs. The skullcap, however, is unassailable, and has since been completely corroborated by additional finds. Historically, it is probably the most important skull ever discovered: its influence on scientific and popular thinking has been extraordinary. It was in 1891 by far the most primitive human or prehuman fossil yet found—in fact it remains among the most primitive today. And it was the first recovered anywhere outside Europe.

The period of the Pithecanthropus stratum was at first thought to be terminal Pliocene or earliest Pleistocene. Most, but not all, of the animals in the beds are extinct. Java, along with Borneo and Sumatra, was then, or had recently been, a peninsula of the mainland of Asia. Since Dubois's excavations, the stratigraphy has been refined, and three main Pleistocene horizons have been defined on the basis of fauna: Djetis, Trinil, and Ngandong. These are respectively early, middle, and late Pleistocene, and perhaps correspond more or less to the three Pleistocene interglacial periods of Europe and North America. The Pithecanthropus remains are from the Trinil or middle horizon, and therefore definitely less ancient than formerly believed, though old enough—a quarter-million to a half-million years.

A second expedition to Java in 1909 failed to find any additional remains, except for one tooth, probably of recent man; but, beginning in 1936, a third, by von Koenigswald, made a series of discoveries that completely confirm and elaborate Dubois's original cranium and extend our knowledge. Pithecanthropus 2 is smaller than the original No. 1, but more of it is preserved, and it is probably female. Pithecanthropus 3 is more fragmentary; 4, almost certainly male, is also broken and incomplete, but most fortunately includes part of the upper jaws with teeth as far forward as the canine. There is also a fragment of a lower jaw with the four right back teeth; this is designated as mandible B. These later finds of 1936 to 1939 are from Sangiran, near Trinil, and from the Trinil horizon of fossils. From Modjokerto, out of the earlier Djetis horizon of lower Pleistocene age, there is the skull of a child which happened to get differently named, but is almost certainly related to Pithecanthropus if not the same. Finally, in 1941 von Koenigswald found at Sangiran a second lower jaw which is larger and more massive than anything else human or protohuman, and may prove to be that of a new species.

We thus know Pithecanthropus pretty well above the neck. The skull case is more or less the length and breadth of that of modern man, but definitely lower by at least a quarter. Hence the forehead slopes back very flat. The brain content or capacity of the skull is nearly double that of a male gorilla and fully double that of a chimpanzee, but only two-thirds that of modern man. This small capacity coexists with total horizontal length and breadth which are close to our own, for at least three reasons: the lesser height already mentioned; just about double thickness of skull wall in Pithecanthropus, which of course reduces the content; and finally the enormous supraorbital torus or eyebrow ridge jutting forward over the eyes like a shelf and giving the skull an extra external length without any internal correspondence. Weidenreich estimates 900, 775, 900 cc capacity for skulls 1, 2, 4. This compares with 655 cc for the largest male gorilla examined, running down to around 400 in smaller males and females and in chimpanzees. The corresponding capacities in other fossil races are given below in the respective sections devoted to them. The comparative figures in the table in § 55 show Pithecanthropus generally at the farthest end of the scale from modern man in the various proportions and angles of the brain case.

As to the face, we have nearly all the upper jaw and palate of skull 4, along with 11 teeth, and the fragmentary lower jaw mandible B with four back teeth. These two jaws are from different individuals, but fit each other approximately.

The one preserved canine is small compared with that of apes; but it does protrude a little beyond the other teeth. Pithecanthropus is the only fossil on the human side of the line that shows this ape trait, except the controversial Piltdown form. There is even a small diastema or adjacent space to receive the canine of the opposite jaw.

The specific name *erectus* was based on the original thighbone. The modern specialists most familiar with the Pithecanthropus remains and horizon no longer believe that this thigh belongs to the skulls. It is too long and slender, and is thought to have come from a more recent source. Four fragments that Dubois, many years later in Holland, found among miscellaneous bones he had brought from Trinil, and which he construed as parts of Pithecanthropus femora, are also generally counted out. But under the rules of priority of biological nomenclature, the name *"erectus"* will stick, whether appropriate or not. Very likely Pithecanthropus did walk fully upright; it is just that now we are no longer sure of having the evidence. Also, the tall stature of around 5 feet 7 inches that used to be computed from the thighbone goes into discard: not disproved, but unproved.

Skull 4 is more massive and rugged than 1, 2, 3. Weidenreich, who described it, thinks this quality is greater than can be accounted for by sex difference alone, and separates 4 from 1, 2, 3 as a distinct species, which he calls *Pithecanthropus robustus* instead of *erectus*. It remains to be seen whether this segregation becomes generally accepted. The *robustus* specimen has a bit of a fore-and-aft crest or keel along the top of the skull, a very heavy occipital torus or cross ridge, and is excessively broad at the base, from which it slopes up almost like a gabled roof (Fig. 2). The back half and base of the vault of this skull are preserved, along with the maxilla, the enormous palate, and 11 teeth. The front of the vault can be approximately restored from individuals 1 and 2, and much of the lower jaw from mandible B. The result is the assemblage shown in Figure 3, which can be taken as roughly reliable.

All in all, Pithecanthropus—whether he was all *erectus* or also of *robustus* species—was hominid and not an ape; but he was the least-developed of all ancestral humans yet known. He was evidently terrestrial, not arboreal; and it is generally believed that he possessed speech and made and used some tools.

A child's skull found at Modjokerto in Java in 1936 is from the Djetis horizon or lower Pleistocene and is therefore older than Pithecanthropus. It lacks face, jaws, and teeth. The age at death cannot be determined. The fontanelles are closed, which happens in modern man at about two years; but the skull is smaller than that of a modern one-year-old—about a third less, or around 650 cc. The length is 138 mm; the breadth, 110 mm; the calotte height (HX in Fig. 5, § 55) is 62 mm or the same as that of the original Pithecanthropus 1. Of course, babies cannot be directly compared with adults; no infant could have a thick skull, or supraorbital ridges. Nevertheless, there is enough that seems primitive in this child skull to suggest that it ties up with Pithecanthropus. It may or may not be an infant member of the same species: palaeontologically it is older. Provisionally it is perhaps better referred to as the "Modjokerto child" than set up as a separate species, which might have to be abandoned again, or merged, as more discoveries are made. The proposed name *Homo modjokertensis* is unfortunate because its *Homo* would imply that this baby is definitely more similar to us than is Pithecanthropus; which it seems to be no one's intent to affirm.

Found in 1941, again at Sangiran, but perhaps very much older than Pithecanthropus, is a fair-sized chunk of a lower jaw containing the two right premolars and the first molar. Mandible and teeth are positively on the human side as against the ape; but they are conspicuously bigger than in Pithecanthropus mandible B or in any other fossil or protohuman form. In fact they can only be characterized as gigantic. Hence von Koenigswald, the discoverer, named the form to which they belong *Meganthropus palaeojavanicus,* the "ancient Javanese big human." The massiveness of this specimen is remarkable. It is nearly half again as thick as the Heidelberg jaw (§ 39) and more than half again as thick as Sinanthropus (§ 38). Withal, the proportion and the characteristics of the jawbone as well as the teeth are thoroughly human. There is a sort of confirmation, or exaggeration, of Meganthropus in some even more

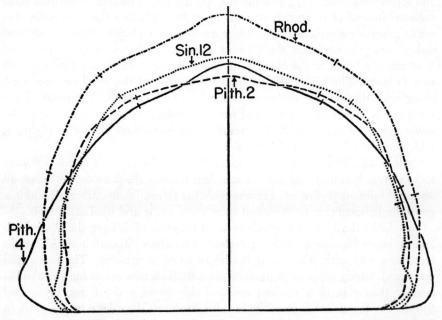

FIG. 2.   CROSS SECTION OF SKULLS: PITHECANTHROPUS AND OTHERS

Skull vault of *Pithecanthropus robustus* No. 4 (§ 37), showing his greater basal breadth and sagittal crest compared with *Pithecanthropus erectus* No. 2 (§ 37) and with *Sinanthropus pekinensis* No. 12 (§ 38), and Rhodesian man (§ 47), who surpasses them all in height. (After Weidenreich)

enormous fossil hominid teeth that have turned up in South China; they will be described in the next section in connection with Sinanthropus of that country.

With all the extraordinary knowledge we now have of Pithecanthropus, considering his remote age, some large problems have also become apparent. First of all, if Weidenreich is right, there were two Pithecanthropus species, *erectus* and *robustus,* roaming Java at about the same time; in fact three human forms, if we count the large Meganthropus. Possibly these were not all exactly contemporary, but succeeded one another; yet to date there is no stratigraphic evidence that they did so. Then there is the Modjokerto child, whose faunal associations appear to make it precede Pithecanthropus by a whole segment of the Pleistocene—two or three hundred thousand years or so. We know no Pithecanthropus children, and no Modjokerto adults; so the two types are only

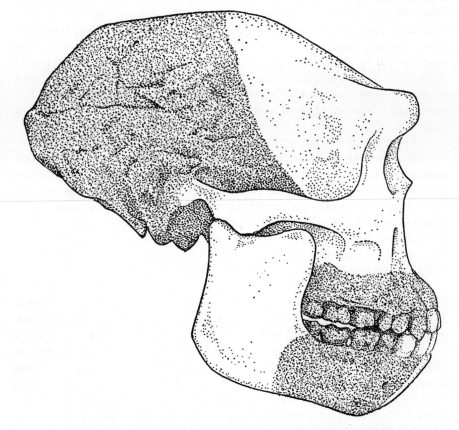

FIG. 3. RECONSTRUCTION OF PITHECANTHROPUS

Profile of the partial skull vault and face of Pithecanthropus 4 (*robustus*) with lower jaw of Pithecanthropus B joined. Reconstructed parts are left unshaded: the forehead and brow are based on skulls 1 and 2 (*erectus*). (After Weidenreich)

loosely relatable. Finally, Java has also given us Solo man (§ 48), whose fossil bed is late Pleistocene, and who should therefore be Palaeoanthropic in form, and in many respects is such, but in other ways, such as brain size, still comes fairly close to Pithecanthropus, and who may therefore be more Protoanthropic than Palaeoanthropic.

38. SINANTHROPUS

A Protoanthropic fossil form rivaling Pithecanthropus in importance and age is that of Sinanthropus in China. At Choukoutien, in the first hills about forty miles southwest of Peking, exploration was begun in 1921 in a broken-down cave rich in Pleistocene fossils. In 1926, two hominid teeth were recognized among the bones excavated four years before. In 1927, another tooth, a lower molar, was found, and upon its characters Davidson Black daringly established the new genus and species *Sinanthropus pekinensis,* "the Chinese man of Peking." The next year, parts of two lower jaws and some skull fragments were recovered. Late in 1929, a complete skull vault, that of an adolescent, was found in situ by the Chinese palaeontologist Pei; and in 1930 a second partial skull, adult, was put together in the laboratory from pieces excavated. On Black's death, Weidenreich took charge, and in 1936, after a find of additional jaw pieces and a number of teeth, three more skulls were discovered, as well as fragments of facial bones. The entire research was most authentically conducted by a group of Chinese, European, and American collaborators.

Altogether, 14 skulls or parts of skulls have been recovered, plus several mandibles. Five of these skulls are complete enough to yield most of the customary measurements and have been included in the tables in § 55 and 56. As many as 147 Sinanthropus teeth from 32 individuals have been found; 83 of these are embedded in jaws or in close association with them, the rest loose. Body bones are much scarcer than skull, jaw, and tooth remains. It is estimated that the bones found come from nearly 40 different individuals. These are about half male and half female; and again, half of them are adult.

By general agreement, the age of the deposits is somewhere near middle Pleistocene. In detail, opinions differ somewhat. The palaeontologist Teilhard de Chardin puts Sinanthropus near the bottom of the middle Pleistocene. This would presumably correspond with the early portion of the Second Interglacial period in Europe. Pei puts it early in the Pleistocene, conjecturally equatable with the First Interglaciation. Such a degree of difference in interpretation is proportional to the newness of a field of knowledge: divergence of opinion would normally be greater about China or Java than in long-studied Europe. There is also sometimes a tendency to see your own area as having the greater antiquity. Teilhard, for instance, whose work has been associated with Sinanthropus, puts both the Djetis and the Trinil horizons of Modjekerto and Pithecanthropus definitely into middle Pleistocene; Von Koenigswald, working in Java, makes Djetis "typical lower Pleistocene," and De Terra agrees with him. The general opinion now is that Pithecanthropus and Sinanthropus are of about the same age, middle or early middle Pleistocene, and that they are also close together in form as variants of one basic type.

Thus, the Sinanthropus cranial vaults show a form much nearer to Pithecanthropus than to Neandertal or any other fossil human type or living or fossil ape. But the skull is a little higher, has a fuller or less sloping forehead, and somewhat greater capacity than Pithecanthropus. The capacity estimates for the five most nearly complete skulls average nearly 1050 cc—say some 15 or 20 per cent larger than Pithecanthropus. It might be said that where Pithecanthropus is archaic and somewhat specialized, Sinanthropus is also archaic but a bit more generalized in his features. That is, he was more open to development toward modern man than was the Java form. He, or a form like him, would serve rather well as a starting point from which Neandertal, Rhodesian, and modern man could have evolved.

A special point is that the available Sinanthropus skulls have little or none of the intrabone air chamber known as the frontal sinus, whereas this is well developed in Pithecanthropus, Solo, Neandertal, and most living races of man, as it is in the gorilla and most races of chimpanzee. On the contrary, the orang teams up with Sinanthropus in lacking the sinus.

The mandibles are fairly primitive. The teeth however are human. There is no large, protruding canine tooth. The last molar is humanly specialized in its reduced size. The incisors are shovel-shaped as in modern Mongoloids. All in all, the teeth are farther advanced toward recent human type than is the jaw— a condition which is true also of Heidelberg man (§ 39).

The best-preserved thighbone suggests a stature of 156 cm. This is about the same as that of Japanese, Eskimo, and several other living races, or not quite 5 feet 2 inches. The ratio or index of humerus to femur (upper-arm to upper-leg bone) appears to be somewhat greater—that is, in favor of the arm—than in later man: Sinanthropus, .79; Neandertal proper, .72; recent and living races, .70-.75. Compared with the anthropoids—chimpanzee, 1.01; gorilla, 1.17; orang, 1.36—Sinanthropus is thus just a shade more apelike in this feature, if our scant data are authentically representative.

Many more skull bones and jawbones than body bones of Sinanthropus have been found. In fact, the numerical disproportion is striking. Also, most of the few limb bones have been cracked or crushed, as if for marrow. All of the skulls lack at least part of the base, as if this had been broken away so the brains could be got at. All this suggests that Sinanthropus sometimes ate his own species. We shall encounter such primitive cannibalism again (§ 48).

Almost as important as the fossils themselves is the evidence at Choukoutien that Sinanthropus used fire and stone and bone implements. These are discussed in § 273 and 277.

Sinanthropus and Pithecanthropus not only belong to the same stage or degree of human evolution but are actually rather surprisingly similar, all in all. Their differences are like those between species, not between genera. As compared with the apes on the one hand, and even with later fossil human forms like Neandertal on the other, to say nothing of modern man, the Java and Peking forms constitute a clear unit, probably a single genus. Theoretically, *Pithecanthropus pekinensis* would seem to be a more fitting name for our form than Sinanthropus. A change of nomenclature is not advocated because hasty alterations of name lead to confusions, and in a few years new discoveries might change the picture still further, or back toward the original interpretation. However, the underlying similarity of the two forms is one of the most significant facts about them.

Gigantopithecus. In another part of China, the south, there lived at one time a form known to date only from three apparently human but gigantic molar teeth, bought in a pharmacy, where fossils and "dragon teeth" enjoy high repute with old-fashioned Chinese as medicine of virtue. On the basis of these teeth von Koenigswald constituted a new genus and species of fossil ape, *Gigantopithecus blacki;* and in 1945 Weidenreich gave a full description and comparison of these teeth—but claimed them as definitely human! It is the size of these teeth that is astounding. For instance, two of them, lower-jaw wisdom teeth, measure 22 and 22.3 mm in length, or almost exactly seven-eighths of an inch. The average for modern man is barely 11 mm. The biggest Sinanthropus hind molar is 12.4 mm, in Pithecanthropus mandible B, 12.5. The apes too are surpassed: the chimpanzee average is 11; the orang, 13; the gorilla, 18 or 19. The South African Australopithecoids (§ 42) fare no better: they run to 16 and 17. The largest ancestral ape fossil, *Dryopithecus giganticus,* has a lower third molar only 19.2 mm long. If Weidenreich is correct in interpreting Gigantopithecus as hominid—the possibility of which is increased by the human quality of the supersize Javanese Meganthropus mandible and teeth—then a gigantic-jawed and perhaps gigantic-bodied Palaeoanthropic form living in East Asia at some time well back in the Pleistocene is indicated. More than that can hardly be said until, first, Weidenreich's diagnosis of the teeth as ancestrally human and not from an anthropoid ape is generally accepted; second, until other parts of the skeleton appear; and finally, until the faunal bed and Pleistocene age of the remains are determined. As of 1947, Hooton and others frankly doubted whether anyone was able to class the Gigantopithecus molars as decisively human or decisively anthropoid.

39. HEIDELBERG MAN

Knowledge of Heidelberg man rests on a single piece of bone—a lower jaw found in 1907 by Schoetensack at a depth of nearly eighty feet in the Mauer sands not far from Heidelberg, Germany. Like the Pithecanthropus remains, the Heidelberg specimen lay in association with fossils of extinct mammals, a fact which makes possible its dating. It was originally assigned to the Second Interglacial period, but of late has more often been attributed to the First Interglacial, in line with the recent tendency to push man's existence back through more and more of the Pleistocene.

The jaw is larger and heavier than any modern human jaw. The ramus, or upright part toward the socket, is enormously broad, as in the anthropoid apes. A true chin is completely lacking; but the chin area does not recede so much as in the apes. Apart from its massiveness, the jaw is much more human than apelike. The contour of the jaw as seen from above is human (oval), not simian (narrow and oblong).

The teeth are very definitely human. They are not even abnormally large— smaller in fact than those of the Neandertal youth from Le Moustier (§ 44). They are set close together, with their tops flush, as in man; the canines lack the tusklike character they retain in the apes.

Since the skull and the limb bones of this form are wholly unknown, it is somewhat difficult to picture the type as it appeared in life. Every indication is that it was closer to ourselves than were Pithecanthropus and Sinanthropus. This relationship is expressed by the name *Homo heidelbergensis,* which recognizes the type as belonging to the genus man. The tendency of late is to regard Heidelberg as quite likely nothing more than an early form of Neandertal man (§ 44), or a rugged individual specimen of him.

40. THE PILTDOWN FORM

This form is reconstructed from several fragments of a female brain case, some small portions of the face, nearly half the lower jaw, and a number of teeth, including a large canine or eyetooth, found in 1911-12 by Dawson and Smith-Woodward in a gravel layer at Piltdown in Sussex, England. Later, small fragments of a second skull, very similar though slightly less thick, and a tooth were found two miles from the original site. The name assigned, *Eoanthropus dawsoni,* or "Dawson's dawn man," was meant to take this fossil out of the human genus and into a genus of its own like Pithecanthropus and Sinanthropus. Of course, this merely reflects the opinion of the namer.

Great importance has been ascribed to this discovery, but too many of its features remain uncertain to build large conclusions upon it safely. The age cannot be positively fixed with assurance. The deposit is only a few feet below the surface, and in the open; the associated fossils have been washed or rolled into the layer; some of them are certainly much older than the skull, belonging to animals characteristic of the Pliocene; that is, the Tertiary, preceding the Pleistocene in which belong all the other fossils discussed here.

The skull capacity has been estimated by Woodward at 1070 cc, later at about 1300; by Keith successively at nearly 1500, 1400, and 1360. This last is probably as reliable a figure as can be inferred from the fragmentary remains. The skull proper is not particularly primitive. In fact, except for unusual thickness of the bones, the skull might pass as modern. The jaw and the teeth, on the other hand, while distinguishable from those of a chimpanzee, resemble them markedly. They are certainly less human than the Pithecanthropus, Sinanthropus, and Heidelberg jaw and teeth, which are presumably earlier. Particular difficulty is made by the canines, which project beyond the other teeth, as in apes, monkeys, and carnivores. No other manlike form yet discovered shows such projection, except Pithecanthropus to a slight degree. This human skull and simian jaw of Piltdown are an almost incompatible combination. More than one expert has got over the difficulty by assuming that the skull of a human being and the jaw of an ancient ape happened to get associated in the same gravel. But the principal objections to this way out of the impasse are that no Pleistocene anthropoid-ape fossils have yet been found in England or western Europe, and that the accidental association of parts of a man and an ape would be extremely unlikely to occur twice, as in the main and the supplementary find at Piltdown.

In view of these difficulties, the claim that the Piltdown skull belongs to a distinct genus *Eoanthropus* is to be viewed with reserve. That the jaw and teeth pertain to an early human form seems equally doubtful. Miller in 1915, Saller and Hrdlička independently in 1930, Friederichs in 1932, have all denied that the skull and the jaw can have come out of the same body. Weidenreich, as late as 1943, calls the Piltdown association a "chimaera" that should be "erased from the list of human fossils." It is true that the doubts have come from Continental and American sources: nearly all British experts have pronounced in favor of the authenticity, age, and importance of Eoanthropus, and some non-Britons, like Hooton, agree with them. But in addition to the anatomical difficulties, the associated faunal remains are of different periods; so are the few associated artifacts—both eoliths and palaeoliths (§ 260, 263); and geologically the bone contents of the deposit are really not accurately datable at all. Therefore it seems fair to hold that Piltdown should be accorded definitely less weight than other well-known fossils in the reconstruction of the developmental history of man. Its title may yet prove perfectly good, but it certainly is clouded now. If we could omit the apelike jaw, the Piltdown brain case would fit fairly well into the group of British Pleistocene skulls of *Homo sapiens* type discussed below in § 54.

41. AFRICANTHROPUS

Africanthropus njarasensis is a discovery, made by Kohl-Larsen in 1935, whose definitive description is one of many delayed by World War II. The site is in northern Tanganyika, near Lake Njarasa, appearing more often as Lake Eyassi on modern maps. The age of the deposit has not been clarified: associated fossils range from Pliocene to living animals. The human remains, heavily mineralized, lay embedded in sandstone, from which they were being loosened by wind erosion. They consist of about 200 fragments, nearly all of them as small as coins. These appear to build up into most of one skull and parts of at least one other. Some preliminary data given by Weinert include:

Teeth, primitive but human, not large, much worn
Canine teeth not projecting
Frontal bone thick (9 mm) with large air sinus
Supraorbital ridges heavy
Dimensions, estimated: length 191 mm, internal length 150, breadth 143, calvarial height 75, height above ear aperture 98
Capacity 1100-1160 cc
Indices (see § 55-56): length-breadth 75, calvarial height 39, bregma position 39, internal-external length 79

If these figures and proportions are sustained by the final reconstitution and measurements, they suggest a Protoanthropic type similar to Pithecanthropus and Sinanthropus, according to Weinert. However, authentic reconstruction from so many small fragments is very difficult, and experience has shown that first reports on new discoveries run some risk of an enthusiasm exaggerating primitiveness or age. No judgment as to a fossil human form is wholly reliable until it reflects the consensus of several experts. That we do not have for Africanthropus. Weidenreich regards the form as being not more than Palaeoanthropic in degree of primitiveness. Hooton considers the reconstruction speculative and Weinert's interpretation as unsound as Weidenreich considers the claims of Piltdown to be. It is evidently safest to build nothing at all on this fossil form at present.

42. THE AUSTRALOPITHECUS GROUP

Australopithecus africanus, the "African southern ape," was found at Taungs in Bechuanaland in 1924, and recovered and described by Dart. Contrary to most fossil skulls, it consists mainly of face, teeth, and partial mandible; the brain case is represented by a "natural cast" of limestone deposited inside. The full milk teeth are present and the first permanent molars were coming into use. In a human child this dentition would correspond to an age of about six years.

Australopithecus transvaalensis, an adult form, later renamed *Plesianthropus transvaalensis,* was discovered by Broom in 1936 at Sterkfontein in the Transvaal. There is again a natural endocranial cast, also various fragments of skull, including upper jaw and canine and molar teeth.

Paranthropus robustus was found soon after at Kromdraai, Transvaal, also by Broom. Strictly speaking, a boy discovered it, somewhat as Australopithecus and Plesianthropus came to light in quarrying operations. But Dart and Broom were the men to see the significance of the fragments and to salvage and describe them. Again, there are fragments of skull and upper jaw, and, this time, most of one side of a lower jaw with the four back teeth still in place.

The jaws of these Australopithecoids are said to protrude definitely less than in the apes. But the brain size remains at about the upper limit of that of the apes: around 450, 440, 600-650 cc skull capacity for the three forms in the order of their discovery (the second is probably female, the third male). These capacities compare with ape maxima: chimpanzee female 440 cc, male 470, gorilla female 555, male 655; but in Pithecanthropus-Sinanthropus the range is from about 775 to 1225.

The Australopithecoids are asserted to have walked erect. This inference is on the somewhat slender basis of the slope of the condyles or bearings where the skull articulates on the top vertebra, and of pieces of knee and elbow joint. It does seem highly probable that these South African types were ground-living, not arboreal.

The teeth, which have been described in most detail, are positively on the human side. The canines project beyond the other teeth, but not very much, and there is no diastema or space for them in the opposing jaw. The dental arch is rounded in front with the sides nearly parallel farther back. This is nearer the human shape—rounded in front, diverging behind—than to the ape shape—square in front, with long parallel sides behind, the whole rectangular with the great eyeteeth at the corners. All three of the South African fossils have back teeth bigger than anything human, whether Pithecanthropus, Sinanthropus, Heidelberg, or later forms. The last molar is the largest, as in Pithecanthropus. This is a peculiarity. In human beings, from Sinanthropus on, the back molar is the most reduced; in the chimpanzee and the gorilla it about matches either the first or the second.

All in all, the Australopithecoids seem pretty surely to represent neither a human ancestor nor a mere deviant ape group, but a third line of evolutionary development, independent of the two others and intermediate to them because derived from the same ancestry farther back.

The three Australopithecoid forms definitely agree in certain unique features, and in spite of minor divergences corroborate one another. In fact, it is certain that there once was a South African Australopithecus group or family, the *Australopithecinae,* whose basic unity is rather disguised by their having been split up into three genera each with its own coined name. What is still weakest in our understanding of this group is its time period. The general belief is that this was Pliocene. But the faunas at Taungs and Sterkfontein are dissimilar, that of Taungs seeming the earlier. As late as 1940, Broom still considered it probably Pliocene, while he provisionally made the Sterkfontein fauna upper Pleistocene. This would leave an interval of around half a million or more years between the two fossils. The prevailing opinion appears to be that the child skull is most likely lower Pleistocene, the two others middle Pleistocene.

This dating eliminates the Australopithecus group as possible ancestors of man. They are too late for that: Pithecanthropus and Sinanthropus were about contemporary with them and are already far more human. The Australopithecoids must, therefore, be construed as a separate evolutionary shoot interestingly parallel to both men and the apes.

43. SUMMARY OF PROTOANTHROPIC FORMS

If now we review the fossil forms so far considered, we have Pithecanthropus and Sinanthropus as definitely hominid but Protoanthropic forms, each abundantly authenticated by a number of individuals, and dating from around mid-Pleistocene—an age from a quarter-million to a half-million years in popular terms. Both of these forms were men who walked, worked, and probably talked. Eoanthropus is still in controversy. Even if all its claims are completely vindicated, it will not fall into the same classificatory slot or evolutionary groove as Pithecanthropus and Sinanthropus: its skull is more evolved, its teeth and jaw less evolved. The Australopithecoids are important, but not men. They seem to represent a third evolutionary line parallel with man and with gorilla-chimpanzee—a sort of endeavor of a near-missing-link to perpetuate itself by evolving somewhat on its own. Heidelberg, on the other hand, so far as we can judge from the single jaw available, is as likely to be an early manifestation of the next human stage, the Palaeoanthropic phase, as of the Protoanthropic one.

44. PALAEOANTHROPIC FORMS: NEANDERTAL MAN, CLASSIC PHASE

In the consideration of Palaeoanthropic men, Neandertal occupies a natural first place.

Neandertal man was the first fossil human form to be determined as such and remains probably the most accurately known as well as the best publicized. In contrast with all the preceding forms, he is a full and indubitable man—not quite a member of our own species *sapiens,* but an undisputed charter member of our genus *Homo,* in distinction from the Something-or-other-anthropuses we have so far dealt with. He is, also, definitely more recent than they.

Neandertal remains have been found at about twenty different sites in and near Europe, and range from practically complete skeletons through skulls to jaw fragments and teeth, mostly conforming closely to one recognizable type. All the earlier discoveries were made in western Europe and date from the time of the last or Würm Glaciation, whose peak may be set at about 40,000 years ago, or say 50,000 to 25,000.[1] This geological period corresponds in time to the period of cultural prehistory known as the Mousterian (§ 264). Some of the more recent discoveries are reckoned as pre-Würm, from the Riss-Würm Interglacial period—the third and last interval between the big glaciations—corresponding to a pre-Mousterian or Acheulian cultural period. These two groups of finds will be considered separately, in this and the next section. The number of finds, the near-completeness of some of them, and their assured concentration in time give the total Neandertal material a striking evidential massiveness, mainly beyond controversy or doubt.

The first recognized discovery was made in a cave of the little Neander gorge in the valley of the Düssel near Düsseldorf in northwestern Germany in 1856. "Valley" is *Thal* or *Tal* in German, according as the older or the more modern spelling is followed; the pronunciation is the same—*t*, not *th*. The modernized form, Neandertal, is used here; for the formal biological Latin name there are technical rules of priority, and *Homo neanderthalensis* is customary. *Homo primigenius* and *Homo mousteriensis* have also been used as synonyms.

Actually, the first recorded discovery of Neandertal remains was made in 1848 at Gibraltar, but the import of this skull was not recognized until many years later. In fact, the geological age and the ancestral position of the original Neandertal man from Düsseldorf were long contested by an authority as world-famous as the German pathologist Virchow. Not until a find at Spy virtually duplicated the Düsseldorf fossil did it become certain that an early human type was involved and not merely a later pathological or aberrant individual.

MOST IMPORTANT NEANDERTAL FINDS OF THE FOURTH GLACIATION

1848	Gibraltar 1	Spain	Skull, woman's
1856	Neandertal	Düsseldorf, Germany	Skull, parts of skeleton
1887	Spy 1, 2	Namur, Belgium	Skulls, parts of skeleton
1908	La Chapelle-aux-Saints	Corrèze, France	Skeleton with skull
1908	Le Moustier	Dordogne, France	Youth's skeleton with skull
1909+	La Ferrassie 1, 2	Dordogne, France	Partial skeletons, ♂, ♀
1910	Jersey	English Channel	Teeth
1911	La Quina H5	Charente, France	Skull, woman's
1916	La Quina H18	Charente, France	8-year-old child
1926	Gibraltar 2	Spain	5-year-old's skull
1929+	Saccopastore	Rome, Italy	Three skulls, undescribed
1935	Monte Circeo	Rome, Italy	Skull, male, undescribed

Neandertal man was below the average stature for modern man: he averaged 160-165 cm for males; that is, about 5 feet 3 inches to 5 feet 5 inches. A definite curvature of his thighbone indicates a knee habitually somewhat bent,

---

[1] Other figures are also given, according to which method of estimating is used.

and probably a slightly stooping or slouching attitude. All his bones are thick-set: his musculature must have been powerful. The chest was large, the neck bull-like, the head hung forward upon it. This head was massive: its capacity averaged 1500 cc or more for males, which is above that for modern European whites. But, though even larger externally than internally, the head was rather low, and the forehead sloped back. The supraorbital ridge was heavy and continuous across the base of the forehead; the eyes peered out from under beetling brows. The face was large and long, the eye orbits large, the nose very large—both wide and projecting. The jaws were prognathous, though not more so than in many Australians and Negroes; there was a chin, but it receded.

SOME MEASUREMENTS OF NEANDERTALS

Fossil	Skull Capacity	Stature
Neandertal	1400 cc	5′ 4 (or 1)″
Spy 1	(1500 cc)	5′ 4″
Le Moustier	1560 cc	
La Chapelle-aux-Saints	1610 cc	5′ 3 (or 2)″
La Ferrassie 1		5′ 5″
Average of modern European males	1450 cc	5′ 6 to 7″
Gibraltar	1215 or 1270 or 1300 cc	
La Quina	1350 cc	
La Ferrassie 2		4′ 10″
Average of modern European females	1300 cc	

Some of the special measures and proportions, such as the calvarial height index, in which Neandertal man is transitional between earlier and later forms, are discussed in § 55. However, he has his own specializations also. One of these is the size of the brain. Whereas Pithecanthropus and Sinanthropus still had a skull capacity between those of apes and modern men, Neandertal actually surpassed us. To put it another way, ape, Pithecanthropus, and Sinanthropus skull vaults are low-domed *because* their brains are small; but Neandertal is relatively low-domed *despite* a very large brain; whereas modern skulls are high without the brain's being supersize. (See Fig. 4.)

Another specialization is the curvature of the thighbone, which is definitely greater in Neandertal than in apes or Protoanthropic or Neanthropic men. The percentage ratio of distance between chord and arc of this bone, to its length, has been calculated as: Neandertal proper, 4.9; Spy, 4.6; as against chimpanzee, 2.9; gorilla, 2.7; Sinanthropus, 2.2; Mt. Carmel (§ 46), 1.9-2.7; and various recent and living races, 1.5-3.5.

The artifacts found in Mousterian deposits show that Neandertal man chipped flint tools in several ways, knew fire, and buried his dead (§ 264). It may be assumed as certain that he spoke some sort of language. This assumption is made for two reasons. First, because his brain was nearly modern in

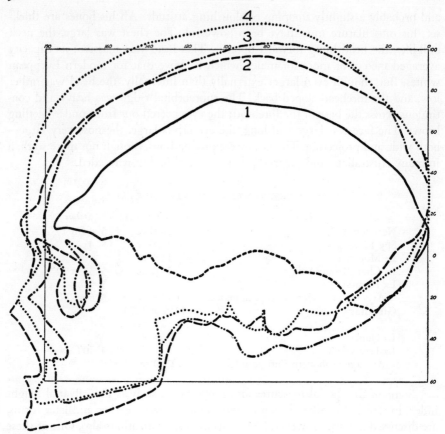

FIG. 4. SKULL VAULT PROFILES: PROTOANTHROPIC, PALAEOAN-
THROPIC, AND NEANTHROPIC

Skulls of: 1, Pithecanthropus 1; 2, Neandertal of La Chapelle-aux-Saints; 3, Sixth
Dynasty Egyptian; 4, Old man of Cro-Magnon; combined after Keith. The close approxi-
mation of Neandertal to recent man is evident, and so is the full frontal development of
Cro-Magnon.

type, as well as large. Second, because it is hard to conceive how his culture
could have been passed on from generation to generation over thousands of
years except through the medium of speech.

45. NEANDERTAL MAN: INTERGLACIAL OR EASTERN PHASE

It so happens that all the earlier discoveries of Neandertal so far discussed
were made in western Europe and had overwhelming associations both with
the last great ice age, or Würm Glaciation, and with the Mousterian phase of

Old Stone Age culture. Thus there grew up, a generation ago, the equation:

$$\text{Neandertal} = \text{Mousterian} = \text{Würm}$$

as one of the fixed pivots in the intricate story of developing man. Discoveries in central Europe—Germany, Italy, Yugoslavia, perhaps southern Russia—began to be made later and continued later. They showed indubitable Neandertals, but Neandertals which pretty consistently had earlier associations than those in western Europe. The geological and faunal associations pointed to the Riss-Würm Interglacial period; the cultural ones to the Acheulian or Pre-Mousterian.

While these more easterly discoveries somewhat diffuse the previously sharp picture of the place in time of Neandertal man, they do have the virtue of giving us a racial type to go with the Acheulian and Pre-Mousterian cultures, which have long been known from thousands of flint implements. It had been suspected that the bearers of these pre-Würm cultures might also be Neandertalers, or something fairly closely related; it is gratifying now to know it. The Neandertal range is thus enlarged eastward in geography and backward in time.

Some of the principal finds of Riss-Würm Interglacial Neandertal bones are:

NEANDERTALOID REMAINS ATTRIBUTED TO THIRD INTERGLACIAL PERIOD

1892	Taubach	Weimar, Germany	Tooth
1899+	Krapina	Croatia	20 individuals, badly broken
1914+	Ehringsdorf	Weimar, Germany	Senile and child's lower jaws
1925	Ehringsdorf	Weimar, Germany	Skull vault, female
1933	Steinheim	Near Stuttgart	Female skull

So far as there are differences in physique, the central-European finds appear to be less aggressively Neandertal in type. The Steinheim skull, in particular, is more delicate than anything ancient from western Europe. The Krapina remains, too, are morphologically more advanced toward modern man. The same "progressiveness" seems to hold for Ehringsdorf. This tendency is interesting, because it is the opposite of what one might infer from the indicated greater age. It may be that Neandertal man after reaching western Europe during the last ice age "retrogressed" in the direction of developing a local subrace of increased massiveness and ruggedness. Such a view of diverging trends would also fit in with the picture of Palestinian man (§ 46), who was evidently modifying in the opposite direction—away from Neandertalism toward Neanthropic man.

The Krapina bones show considerable variability, as might be expected among so many individuals. They are too shattered to yield any reliable figures of skull capacity. Ehringsdorf has been estimated, rather doubtfully, at 1450 cc, but Steinheim as low as 1070.[2]

[2] Other techniques of "measurement" gave from 992 to 1239 cc.

46. PALESTINIAN MAN

Palestine contains remains of a type that is Neandertaloid rather than full Neandertal. This type was first discovered in 1925 by Turville-Petre near Capernaum in Galilee. He found the frontal part of a skull in a Mousterian cave deposit. In 1931, McCown discovered the skeleton of a child, followed in 1932 by 11 other individuals in a Levalloiso-Mousterian culture deposit in two caves, et-Tabun and es-Skhul ("The Oven" and "The Kids"), in Wady el-Mughara ("Cave Canyon") near Mt. Carmel. Two of the twelve, a woman's skeleton, 1, and a man's lower jaw, 2, are from Tabun. The other bones are from Skhul: of these, 4, 5, 9, all male, are the most nearly complete skeletons. The faunal as well as the cultural remains of the layers in which the human bones were embedded in hard breccia show that the Tabun and Skhul skeletons are contemporaneous in age: they are all not only Levalloiso-Mousterian, but from the Last Interglacial period. This makes them coeval with the Neandertaloids of central Europe and earlier than the "classic" or glacial Neandertals of western Europe.

The full description by McCown and Keith emphasizes the high variability of the Mt. Carmel people, a variability greater than in modern local communities. Thus the Tabun-1 woman links with Neandertal, the Skhul-4 man at the other extreme with the Neanthropic Cro-Magnon type. There is almost as much difference between the robust mandible of Tabun 2 and that of Skhul 5 as between those of Heidelberg and La Chapelle Neandertal. This variability might be due to Palaeoanthropic and Neanthropic strains having happened to meet and hybridize in Palestine; but the authors hold to the alternative hypothesis that the Mt. Carmel race was unstable and plastic because it was in the throes of differentiating evolution. However, they make this race or species not ancestral to later Cro-Magnon, but a Neandertoloid collateral or cousin of the Cro-Magnon ancestor. Therefore they name their type *Palaeoanthropus palestinensis,* to be affiliated with *Palaeoanthropus krapinensis, ehringsdorfiensis, neanderthalensis,* and *heidelbergensis* in that order of relationship. We need not go so far as to accept this change in technical nomenclature; yet the renaming unquestionably does reflect the basic facts and the degree of affinity of these several types.

The figures that follow suggest the range of variation of Mt. Carmel man. The Tabun cave woman agrees closely with the Neandertal Gibraltar skull in measurements, proportions, and capacity, and with other female Neandertals in stature. The best-preserved adult males have skull capacities between 1500 and 1600 cc, or within the Neandertal male range and above that of modern man. Their stature, however, runs from 5 feet 5 inches up to 5 feet 10, instead of the 5 feet 5 maximum for Neandertal. The limb bones also show a lither and lighter body.

PALESTINIAN MAN

	Skull Capacity	Skull Circumf.	Int/Ext L. Ind.	Calvarial Ht. Ind.	Stature Cm	Feet
Skhul 4 ♂	1550	580	86	49	174	5′ 8.5″
Skhul 5 ♂	1520	523		53	179	5′ 10″
Skhul 9 ♂	1590	560		41	166	5′ 5″
Skhul 6 ♂					171	5′ 7″
Skhul 2 ♀	(1300)				163	5′ 4″
Skhul 7 ♀					158	5′ 2″
Tabun 1 ♀	1270	500	88	47	154	5′ 0.5″
Skhul 1 ch	* 1140					

* 1140 cc in a 3.5 year child equals about 1450 cc adult.

In 111 characters examined, Mt. Carmel man was reckoned like Neandertal man in 16, like Cro-Magnon or modern man in 32, intermediate in 46, indeterminate in 13, peculiar in 4. This seems to indicate fairly his position in the human family tree.

47. RHODESIAN MAN

The Rhodesian type is known from one skull found by miners in 1921, ninety feet deep among innumerable mineralized animal bones, in the zinc mine of Broken Hill Cave in northern Rhodesia. There were also a fragment of a second upper jaw and some other bones, including a tibia. This last is Negroid and is no longer believed to have belonged to the skull. The greatest weakness of the discovery is that there was no scientist on the spot until long afterward, and that the age is indeterminate. The associated fauna is composed wholly of still living forms except for two species. This does not mean so much in the way of recency as it would in most other continents, because the modern South African fauna as a whole is a Pleistocene relict. Still, it suggests that the period was late Pleistocene, more or less within the range of Neandertal man.

This fits with the diagnosis now generally made of Rhodesian man: that he is a collateral equivalent or regional variant of Neandertal. He is more primitive than Neandertal in some respects, more advanced in others. A bestialized Neandertal, he might be called, especially as regards his face. The skull capacity is rather low, about 1280 (or 1325?) cc. The eyebrow ridges are simply enormous. The face is long, large, and gorillalike in its massive coarseness, with prominent nose, marked prognathism, and a long stretch of bone covered by the upper lip. The palate and the dental arch are literally huge, but human in shape. The same holds for the teeth—the canines are flush instead of projecting. The teeth are full of decay cavities—the only sure instance of this modern weakness in any fossil man. The foramen magnum—the aperture by which the spinal cord enters the brain—is well forward, and suggests a level carriage of the head and therefore erect posture.

In summary, the Rhodesian form is advanced far beyond not only the Aus-tralopithecoids (§ 42) but probably also Africanthropus (§ 41), and is well on the Homo level; yet he is marked off from Neandertal and the Neandertaloids—marked off possibly as a separate species—particularly by a characteristic heavi-ness or brutalization of the bones of the face. How far this quality may be racial, or on the contrary individually exaggerated in the single specimen recovered, is hard to say. If we had a second skull, or a skeleton, or geological evidence as to age, or associated stone implements, we could almost certainly place Rhodesian man better. At present he does not fit in closely with anything African, anything Negro, or even anything fossil.

A statistical comparison of 23 characters by Morant leads him to the con-clusion that Rhodesian man and Neandertal man are about equally related, or unrelated, to modern man.

The fossil form nearest to Rhodesian man, of those found already in Africa, is the Florisbad skull (§ 51).

48. SOLO MAN

Solo man was first found in 1931 at Ngandong on the Solo River, only six miles from Trinil, Java, by Oppenoorth, a geologist. Within five years, 11 skulls had been accumulated, all closely similar in type and all lacking parts of the base, as if this had been broken out when the head was taken for a trophy, or perhaps opened to get at the brains to eat. There are no faces, teeth, jaws, or other bones except two broken shinbones. The type was first named *Javanthropus soloensis,* but it seems definitely evolved beyond the Pithecanthropus and Sinanthropus stage, and if a Latin name has to be used it ought perhaps be *Homo soloensis,* it is now agreed. The anatomical determination of advancement beyond Pithecan-thropus fits with the geology: the associated fauna is of Ngandong age, the third Pleistocene horizon in Java, or, in generic terms, late Pleistocene, as compared with mid-Pleistocene for Pithecanthropus.

The half-dozen most nearly complete brain cases are estimated to range from 1035 to 1255 cc in capacity, with a mean of about 1100, if the mended recon-struction of the crushed skulls was sound. This is but little more than the Sinan-thropus average capacity of 1050, and far below the Palaeoanthropic Mousterian mean of more than 1500. His small brain is only one of a number of retarded features of Solo man, and his inclusion in the Palaeoanthropic class is con-testable; though he is advanced beyond the Pithecanthropus, he is more primi-tive than Neandertal. There is some opinion that the Solo type is closer to Rhodesian man than to the European and Palestinian Neandertals. The massive skulls are low but fairly vaulted. The eyebrow ridge or torus, as well as an occipital torus, is heavily developed, indicating powerful jaw and neck muscles.

On the other hand, the mastoid processes, at the base of the skull behind the ear, which are small in the apes, mid-Pleistocene Pithecanthropus, Sinanthropus types, and even in the classic Neandertal, but large in modern man, are fairly well developed in Solo, as well as in Rhodesian and sometimes in Palestinian man.

All in all, Solo looks like what we might conjecture Pithecanthropus to have evolved to on surviving in Java from middle to late Pleistocene.

49. NEANTHROPIC RACES: CRO-MAGNON

The Protoanthropic types with the names ending in *-anthropus* are middle Pleistocene, or possibly in some cases early Pleistocene. The forms like Neandertal, which are near enough us to be called *Homo,* but not yet *Homo sapiens,* fall into the upper or late Pleistocene. We come now to the terminal Pleistocene, the period when in Europe and North America the ice of the last glaciation was still there, but had passed its peak and was fading away. In years, this might be defined, or guessed, as about 25,000 to 8000 B.C. We have more human remains preserved from this period than from earlier ages, naturally enough. And they have finally become *Homo sapiens,* of our own human species. Cro-Magnon man of Europe is the best-known example, but there are others. Culturally, the time is the Upper Palaeolithic, the second, and much briefer, main division of the Old Stone Age. The Lower Palaeolithic, with its Mousterian and pre-Mousterian phases, belongs to Palaeoanthropic man. The Neanthropic Upper Palaeolithic has its successive Aurignacian, Solutrean, Magdalenian phases in Europe (§ 265-270), its Capsian in North Africa, and so on elsewhere—all with a richer inventory of tools, practices, and beliefs than had been developed in the Lower Palaeolithic. Some of the more comprehensive or best-known Cro-Magnon discoveries are listed in the table on the following page.

If Cro-Magnon and other Neanthropic men were of our species, how did they differ from us, or from one another? Evidently as varieties or local subspecies; in ordinary parlance, as races. This would mean that their degree of differentiation was about equal to that which separates, say, any European from a Mongolian. And that is just what it is believed to have been. In fact, some of the late fossil Neanthropic races differed less from modern races of the same continental area than modern races living in different continents differ from each other. The fossil Cro-Magnon is universally accepted as having been already a Caucasian or white man, more similar to living Europeans than these Europeans are to living Mongolians or Negroes. While he was not identical with Europeans, he was definitely of their type or kind. In fact, living Europeans are not all identical with one another, but are subdivided into Mediterraneans, Nordics, Dinarics, Alpines, and so on. Cro-Magnon blood is supposed to have

SOME PRINCIPAL NEANTHROPIC FINDS OF CRO-MAGNON TYPE

Northwest Italy (Riviera)

Grimaldi 1, Enfants	1900-01	Aur.	Cro-Magnon ♂, ♀
Grimaldi 1, Enfants	1900-01	Aur.	"Negroid" ♂, ♀
Grimaldi 4, Cavillon	1872	Aur.	♂
Grimaldi 5, Barma Grande	1884	Aur.?	♂
Grimaldi 5, Barma Grande	1892	Aur.?	Triple burial
Grimaldi 5, Barma Grande	1894	Aur.?	⚹2♂

France

Cro-Magnon, Les Eyzies	1868	Aur.	⚹1 ("old man") ⚹3♂, ⚹2♀, 4, 5 fragm.
La Madelaine, Les Eyzies	1864	Magd.	pr. ♂
Laugerie Basse, Les Eyzies	1872	Magd.	⚹4♂ (⚹1, 3 uncertain age)
Chancelade, nr. Périgueux	by 1889	Magd.	♂
Combe Capelle, Périgord	1909	Aur.	♂
Vallé du Roc, Charente	1923	Sol.? Magd.?	⚹1♀, ⚹2♂
Le Placard, Charente	1881	Magd.?	♀
Le Placard, Charente	1882-83	Magd.?	⚹F♂, ⚹B, C?
Le Placard, Charente	1882-83	Sol.?	⚹I♂
Eguisheim, Colmar, Alsace	1865	?	♂
Solutré, Saône-et-Loire	1923-24	Aur.	⚹2, 3, 4♂, ⚹1, 5♀

England

Cheddar, Somerset	1903	Magd.?	♂
Halling, Kent	1912	Aur.?	♂
Galley Hill, Kent	1888	disputed	

Germany

Oberkassel, near Bonn	1914	Magd.	♂, ♀

Czechoslovakia

Brünn (Brno)	1891	Aur.? Sol.?	⚹1♂
Předmost	1894-95	Sol.?	⚹3, 9♂, ⚹4, 10♀ (of 26 plus individuals)
Lautsch	1881-82	Aur.?	⚹1♂, ⚹2♀?, ⚹3 child
Lautsch	1904-05	Aur.?	⚹5, 6♂
Vestoniče	1925	Aur.	♂

Poland

Ojcow	1902	Aur.	♂

flowed into these several European subraces, and to have been modified in the process, in varying degree. Recognition of this connection is basic in most recent examinations of living European races. The same sort of relation holds in South Africa, East Africa, and Oceania, where the terminal-Pleistocene fossil types appear as ancestral Bushmen, Nilotics, and Australoids. That in West Africa, East Asia, and America no such anticipations of the native races are known probably means only that they have not yet been discovered, or perhaps were

still in a formative stage, or living elsewhere. It does not mean that such anticipations were nonexistent.

Whether any Palaeoanthropic blood also flows in living races is much less
certain. Neandertal and his coevals may represent divergent side lines that died
out, or they may be direct ancestors that later modified to Neanthropic forms,
as has been suggested by the discoverers of the Mt. Carmel people. There have
been yes opinions and no opinions, but they remain opinions. There really is
no telling, as yet, because direct evidence is lacking, and the difference between
Palaeoanthropic man and ourselves is after all greater than that between Neanthropic man and us.

Some available measures, compiled herewith, confirm these general statements as to Cro-Magnon's place in human development. The calculated body-
height mean for males, 1770 mm, very nearly 5 feet 10 inches, is as great as that
of any living race, except for a few of the spindly-gigantic, "ultraleptosome"
(§ 79) castes of East Africa. The Cro-Magnons, however, had robust bones, not
slenderly drawn-out ones; and this proves powerful muscles. The mean skull
length of 197 mm for males, 185 for 10 females, is again big. Still more striking
is the male skull capacity mean of 1660 cc, especially when set against the 1500-
1550 of Neandertal and Mt. Carmel man, the under-1500 of modern Englishmen, the perhaps 1400 grand average of living males of all races.[3]

SOME MALE CRO-MAGNON MEASURES

	Stature in mm	Skull Length in mm	Skull Capacity in cc
Cro-Magnon 1	c.1775	202	1590
Cro-Magnon 3		203	
Grimaldi-Enfants "Negroid"	adol.	192	1580
Grimaldi-Enfants "Non-Negroid"	1890	198	1715
Grimaldi-Barma Grande 2	1770	206	1880
Chancelade	1600	193	1730
Combe Capelle	1660	198	
Solutré "5"		188	1500
Solutré 4		194	
Oberkassel		195	
Lautsch 1		199	1620
Předmost 3	c.1850	201	
Předmost 9	c.1850	196	
Vestoniče		198	
Average, males only	1770	197	1660

[3] Skeletons and complete skulls of Cro-Magnon females are few—smaller bones have
smaller prospects of preservation over long periods. Oberkassel female and Grimaldi
"Negress" capacities of 1370 and 1375 cc and statures of 147 and 159 mm seem unduly
small—nearly 300 cc and 250 mm below the male figures. Evidently these two females are
somewhat off the racial average. The 185-mm head length cited above seems about right;
it is the mean of 10 individuals.

There have been a number of attempts to separate the Upper Palaeolithic skeletal material into subclasses; but no permanent agreement has been attained on these subdivisions or varieties. The principal ones are:

"Brünn" race: Brünn, Brüx, Předmost, perhaps Galley Hill, Combe Capelle
"Grimaldi Negroid" race: two skeletons from "Children's Cave," at Grimaldi
Eskimo resemblances: Chancelade

The concept of a Brünn race has sometimes centered about finds in Czechoslovakia attributed to the Solutrean period, and sometimes on skulls considered more primitive in type than Cro-Magnon, but yet not quite Neandertaloid: they had a supraorbital ridge, for instance, but it was divided above the nose instead of forming a continuous torus all the way across; or they had a skull vault higher than Neandertal but lower than Cro-Magnon. Re-examination shows pretty conclusively that the Brünn race is an abstraction formed by selecting out the more rugged or primitive males, with or without areal bias, and leaving the rest as "true" Cro-Magnons.

The Grimaldi race is based on the skeleton of a woman and a youth, possibly mother and son, buried at one level in the Children's or No. 1 grotto at Grimaldi, the other burials in which, as in the remaining Grimaldi caves, were pure Cro-Magnon. That some traits of these two skeletons were somewhat Negrolike is indubitable. What is questionable is whether there are enough such traits, and whether they are pronouncedly enough Negroid to allow interpreting the two skeletons as of Negro race. Here experts' opinions differ. The case for separateness has become weaker since the finding of a fossil Caucasian type in Algiers—Afalou man, as described in § 50. This discovery makes North Africa to have been Caucasian in Upper Palaeolithic times as it is now, and scarcely leaves much room for a truly Negro race to maneuver into Europe along the Mediterranean, and then disappear again without a trace.

The Chancelade skeleton has certain indubitable Eskimo similarities—broad face, short stature, and so on—but it stands too isolated for more than a remote possibility of representing a distinct race. Rather small peculiarities suffice to set apart a type if they appear consistently in, say, a hundred individuals; but a lone individual must be differentiated very profoundly before it is safe to elevate him into a race. And again, Afalou man, as discussed in the next section, weakens still further the case for separateness.

In fact, Morant has made the experiment of applying statistical treatment to all available European Upper Palaeolithic skulls as if they were from a single, unitary race. If they really were such, the variability of their measured traits and indices should be low. If they included several racial types, the variability would be high. Actually, the variability did come out low—more or less like that of a homogeneous population today. Thus, the aggregate of Upper Palaeolithic skulls showed a low coefficient of variability, one from the other, more often—that is, in more features—than did a series of English skulls from one cemetery; about as often as the skulls from a Carinthian cemetery in Austria; somewhat less often than those of ancient Egyptians from a single cemetery, or than Greenland Eskimo skulls. In short, the Cro-Magnon variability seems to have run about the same as that of sample modern racial populations. This does not positively prove that they were a unitary population of homogeneous origin, but it indicates that such was probable. This is rather remarkable, seeing that the preserved Cro-Magnon skulls range from several European countries and over a period of several thousand years.

Morant has also used another statistical measure, the "reduced coefficient of racial likeness," to compare Cro-Magnon man with a dozen later racial samples or populations. It is interesting that the greatest similarities (lowest co-efficient values) of Cro-Magnon are with the British Neolithic people, coefficient 30; Anglo-Saxons, 34; and prehistoric German Reihengräber, 37. These are all premodern western Europeans, and all longheaded. Fuegians and Eskimo, who happen to resemble Cro-Magnon in being narrow-skulled, broad-faced, brow-ridged, but whose habitat is far away, are less similar, and show coefficients of 49 and 72. Between and around them fall some modern European populations, such as Englishmen, 52, and Basque, 69. Highest in coefficient, and thus most different of all those concerned, are Czechs, 127, and West African Negroes, 153—the latter undoubtedly because they are a highly characterized race long specialized away from anything Caucasian,[4] the Czechs because, though Caucasians, they are specialized roundheads leaning toward "infantilism" and deli-cacy (§ 77), as the Cro-Magnons were rugged and "senescent" in type. In short, what this statistical inquiry reveals is who Cro-Magnon's closest recent and liv-ing relatives are. They are the recent longish-headed populations of western and northwestern Europe. These are the people of today who are least modified from the Cro-Magnon blood.

All of which seems to make out Cro-Magnon as a pretty good proto-Caucasian.

It was the Cro-Magnon race that painted the caves of southern France and northern Spain, and etched and carved bone and ivory with the surprisingly faithful and lively representations of mammoth, bison, boar, reindeer, wild horse, rhinoceros, and the like—the first great art known in human history (§ 270). It is evident that they were a psychologically high-level race as well as a rather magnificent anatomical one.

50. NEANTHROPIC MAN IN NORTH AFRICA: AFALOU

The North African counterpart of Cro-Magnon man is best known from the Algerian site of Afalou bou Rummel, where 50 burials were encountered. The culture was Capsian (§ 275), the North African equivalent in time of the

---

[4] Herewith goes another prop from under the Grimaldi Negroid theory.

Aurignacian-Solutrean-Magdalenian or Upper Palaeolithic of western Europe.[5] North Africa is Caucasian today; and it evidently was so then, for the Afalou type is strikingly like the Cro-Magnon. The two races are distinguishable, but only just so. The Afalou skull vault averages a bit shorter and higher; hence its height-length proportion, or index, is greater; the eye orbits are less markedly low and broad than in Cro-Magnon, and the nose is wider.

SIMILARITY OF CRO-MAGNON AND AFALOU MAN

Means	Cro-Magnon of Europe	Afalou of North Africa
Stature, mm	1770	1710-50
Skull capacity, cc	1660 ♂	1662
Cranial measures		
Length, mm	198	c.193
Breadth, mm	142	c.145
Height (basion-bregma), mm	136	c.141
Minimum width of frontal, mm	99	100
Maximum width face (bizygomatic), mm	143	142
Horizontal circumf. skull, mm	549	547
Indices		
B/L index	73	75
H/L index	69	75
H/B index	96	97
Orbital index	69	73
Nasal index	50	53

Stature, cranial capacity, eyebrow ridges, type of limb bones—all agree remarkably. The two races were tall, strong, broad-shouldered, big-headed, and rugged-skulled. Coon has compared their skulls with the averages for about 50 series of Mesolithic, Neolithic, Bronze, Iron, and early European historical periods, from say 4000 B.C. to A.D. 1000. Cro-Magnon and Afalou agree in standing outside the range of all these others in at least four traits:

Skull capacity, C-M 1660(♂), Af. 1662, 18 other types from 1606 down to 1381
Skull circumference, C-M 549, Af. 547, 33 others from 545 down to 511 (only 3 above 535)
Bizygomatic width, C-M 143, Af. 142, 45 others from 140 down to 125
Orbital index, C-M 69, Af. 73, 43 others from 72 up to 88. (Low index means low, wide eye sockets; high index, high or round sockets.)

This extremeness—being at the end of the range—is precisely what makes Cro-Magnon and Afalou Neanthropic as compared with Recent man. They are both fossil types. They are Pleistocene—terminal Pleistocene, but still within it. Their period ends about ten thousand years ago. So while Cro-Magnon and

---

[5] Technically, the culture is Oranian, but this is merely the Algerian local phase of the Capsian of Tunis, which in a wider sense is also used as a designation for all North African Upper Palaeolithic.

Afalou are already *Homo sapiens,* in fact are Caucasian *sapiens,* they represent him in an earlier form, and thus they ought to be distinguishable—as they are—from later Caucasian forms.

A special interest attaches to the face width of these Neanthropic Caucasians. The fullest measure of this is the bizygomatic diameter just cited—the diameter of the face in front of the ears. It has long been recognized that Cro-Magnon man was "dysharmonic" in combining a broad face with a narrow skull. The figures given in fact show his face to have averaged actually a bit wider (about 1 mm) than his skull. This is a rare trait in the living, characteristic chiefly of Mongoloids, such as the Eskimo and some American Indian tribes. It is largely on such an excess that the theory has been based which tried to connect the Cro-Magnon Chancelade skull with the Eskimo (they both were reindeer hunters, also, and worked bone, and lit lamps). However, Afalou's face is practically as broad as Cro-Magnon's, and while it does not quite come up to the skull breadth, it is within 3 mm of it. But when we make comparison with the 45 more recent series, these average all of 9 mm narrower in the face.[6] This seems to make it pretty clear that it is unsound to select the particular Chancelade skull, or any other single one, or two, or three, for affiliation with a modern race. The more significant fact is that North African as well as European Neanthropic man still was rugged-faced, and heavy-chewing, in comparison with his Caucasian descendants. The Eskimo resemblance is true enough; but it probably means nothing more than that the narrow-skulled Mongoloid Eskimo happened also to develop—as Cro-Magnon perhaps retained—an unusually broad face, presumably because powerful chewing capacity has a survival value in the Arctic.

A mineralized skeleton from Asselar, 250 miles out in the Sahara from Timbuktu, was found in an ancient river bed in a late or terminal Pleistocene faunal association but a doubtful archaeological one. The type is not very primitive, but is of interest because it shows Negroid resemblances; though to which kind of Negroid, authorities are still trying to agree upon.

51. NEANTHROPIC RACES IN SOUTH AND EAST AFRICA

Africa has yielded other Neanthropic and near-Neanthropic discoveries, especially in the south and east.

The fragmentary Florisbad skull discovered in 1933 near Bloemfontein is perhaps the oldest. At any rate it is probably the nearest to being Palaeoanthropic in type among the more recent South African skeletons; wherefore its previous mention in connection with Rhodesian man (§ 47). The associated arti-

---

[6] The range in the 45 populations is from 0 to 18 mm greater skull width. In 41 of the 45 series, the skull excess is greater than in Afalou. The single population whose excess is 0 (strictly, −0.4 mm) is a Norwegian Iron Age type with definitely narrow skull (B/L index 71) and apparent ruggedness of face musculature and bone.

facts are attributed to the South African Middle Palaeolithic, which would presumably date them as equivalent to the Fourth Glaciation in Europe. The associated fossils are assigned to middle Pleistocene, which would correspond to Second-to-Third Glaciation. There is evidently no real assurance as to age, as yet. The type shows both Neandertal and modern features. Thus there is a large and long supraorbital ridge or torus, as in Neandertal, but it is interrupted, as are the smaller ridges of some Cro-Magnon and modern races. Strong prognathism of the jaws looks Negroid, deep depression of the root of the nose, Australoid. There is flat disagreement as to whether this Florisbad skull is more nearly Palaeoanthropic or Neanthropic; and as its period is also undetermined, its status is best left as in doubt.

Of other South African finds, the Cape Flats skull of 1929 probably stands nearest to Florisbad in supraorbitals, teeth, and mastoids.

Undoubtedly Neanthropic is the Boskop type, named for the first skeleton found at Boskop, the Transvaal, in 1913, and including remains from Tzitzikama, Fish Hoek, and Matjes River; possibly also from Springbok Flats. Most of these are archaeologically somewhat dubiously associated with the Middle Palaeolithic, which would be late Pleistocene in geology. The Boskop type skulls are massive and large. Keith calculated 1630 cc for the Boskop specimen, and the others run from 1400 to 1700. The forehead tends to be vertical, the mastoids are small. The face is short, small, and vertical; the teeth are small. Two estimated body heights are 5 feet 2 and 5 feet 6 inches. The type with its bulbous brain and underdeveloped face, jaw, and teeth is an infantile one. Moreover, it strongly recalls the Bushman-Hottentot type of South Africa (§ 64)—which also leans toward infantilism. However, the modern Bushmen are shorter and much smaller-brained; their development out of the Boskop type has been one of shrinkage—unless our ancient skulls represent the preservation chiefly of the more rugged individuals. Some students try also to connect the South African large Negroes with Boskop. Some further connect the Boskop type back to Florisbad, but others see this latter as more "Australoid," which may mean "generically primitive" rather than actual direct relationship with Australia.

From East Africa comes a skeleton found at Oldoway in Tanganyika and five found by Leakey at Gamble's Cave, Elmenteita, in Kenya. These have moderate-sized, narrow skulls—smooth, feeble-browed, narrow-faced. The body height was very great—1770 to 1800 mm—the shoulders narrow, limb bones slender, feet and hands slim. The general type is more Caucasoid than Negroid, perhaps, but not quite either. All this suggests a strain in the living population of East Africa—Somali, Galla, Bahima, in part Nuer and Dinka, between the East Horn and upper Nile—which is also difficult to assign as between Negro and Caucasian,[7] and is most characterized by great attenuation: enormous

[7] Wherefore the name "Hamitic." See § 68.

stature, spindly legs, leptosome proportions and delicate lines throughout, smooth muscles and no ruggedness of bone—a sort of human greyhound. Evidently the type is fairly old, and these Upper Palaeolithic or terminal-Pleistocene skeletons represent its local ancestors.

52. NEANTHROPIC RACES IN ASIA AND OCEANIA

An "upper cave" at Choukoutien is quite distinct in age and contents from the lower one in which the Sinanthropus remains rested. It contains a few extinct species, such as cave bears and cave hyenas, but on the whole the fauna is definitely terminal Pleistocene, probably corresponding to postglacial in Europe. The associated industry shows rather poor chipping of stone, but a degree of advancement in other respects, such as use of bone, of ornaments, and of perforations, which might roughly equate it to the European Upper Paleolithic. Parts of several bodies have been found in this upper cave, including three well-preserved *Homo sapiens* skulls, a male and two females. There is agreement that one female skull is very Melanesian-like, the other Eskimo-like. The elderly male, who was tall and large-brained (1500 cc), is diagnosed as primitive Mongoloid by Weidenreich, as primitive Caucasian and quite Ainu-like by Hooton. These authorities disagree also in their interpretation of the differences between the three individuals. Weidenreich thinks that pure racial types as we know them crystallized out late, and that this group from the upper Choukoutien cave was still undifferentiated. Hooton believes it represents race mixture. A third possibility is "accident"—individual variability every so often slopping over into a fortuitous partial resemblance to some distant racial type. After all, no recent and living races are separated by great gaps.

From Wadjak in Java there are two fossilized skulls, first announced thirty years after their discovery by Dubois, the discoverer of Pithecanthropus. The age, not precisely determined, is either very late Pleistocene or Recent. The skulls are large, with capacities estimated by Dubois at 1550 and 1650 cc. One has a calvarial height index (§ 55) of 52, or within the range of Cro-Magnon man. The other has a palate as huge as the Rhodesian one. The Wadjak type in general is nearer the surviving native Australian than to Neandertal. It is perhaps best described as proto-Australoid—a large-brained form from which the recent Australian might be descended with *recession* of head size and perhaps of body also.

Somewhat similar is the long-known Talgai skull from Queensland, Australia—a fossilized, broken specimen from a fifteen-year-old, assumed to be Pleistocene, but not demonstrably so. It is modern native Australian in general character and smallness of brain case, but is even more prognathous. The palate is nearly as large as in Wadjak 2. Some hold that it is within the range of living Australoid natives.

Very similar in turn to Talgai is a skull from Cohuna, Victoria, in south-eastern Australia, found at little depth in 1925, and without evidence of geological antiquity. The age is quite uncertain. The type, according to Keith, is essentially that of Talgai.

From Australia, also, there is the Keilor skull, found eleven miles from Melbourne in 1940, described in 1943, attributed in time to the equivalent of the Last European Interglacial, and said to have Tasmanian as well as Australian resemblances. The geological age appears to represent opinion rather than demonstration; and there were no associated fossils. To judge by the published measurements, the Keilor skull falls within the range of recent Australoid skulls, except for being much above average size in almost all dimensions and features. Thus, the capacity is about 1590 cc, as against an Australoid average of only 1290! This is more than 100 cc greater than the mean for modern European males. Supraorbital development is negligible. Weidenreich considers Keilor identical in type with Wadjak.

This array gives us fossil man of Neanthropic type, and of late or terminal Pleistocene age, from all continents except the Americas. Presumably the discovery is still to be made in America; perhaps it has actually been made but its age not recognized or admitted. Hooton, in 1946, accepts the Minnesota man, or rather girl, found in 1931 at Pelican Rapids and sponsored by Jenks, as from a glacial lake of an age estimated at 20,000 years, which would be terminal Pleistocene. The skull is not primitive in type, except for unusually large teeth. It will be seen in Chapter Sixteen (§ 278-280) that artifacts indicate man's presence in America in late Pleistocene times beyond any doubt, so that the ultimate discovery of his skeletal remains is to be expected. However there is as yet no indication whatever of man in America prior to the last glaciation.

In the continents of the Eastern Hemisphere, Neanthropic man several times, though not always, approximates or anticipates the local race living in the same area in historical times: Boskop, Elmenteita, Talgai-Cohuna-Keilor, Cro-Magnon, perhaps upper Choukoutien.

53. SUMMARY OF HUMAN FOSSIL DEVELOPMENT

In review and in the aggregate, skeletal material on human bodily development since the middle Pleistocene is fairly abundant and significantly conclusive. There are gaps, but there is also a degree of consecutiveness in the record; and most of the continents are represented. The data group themselves into three stages: (1) formative man, well beyond any ape, already essentially human, but not completely so; (2) old-style man, definitely human but with certain remaining primitive features as well as occasional specializations; (3) the final stage of geological man, already differentiating into anticipations of the living races: a member of the same species as ourselves, though retaining some minor traits of primitiveness. In more technical and compact terms, these three stages

THE STAGES OF EARLY MAN

AREA	SUBHOMINID	PROTOANTHROPIC Middle* Pleistocene	PALAEOANTHROPIC Upper Pleistocene	NEANTHROPIC Terminal Pleistocene	LIVING RACE RELATED TO NEANTHROPIC
Europe	Dryopithecus	(Piltdown?) Heidelberg (?)	Neandertal	Cro-Magnon	Caucasian
North Africa				Afalou	Caucasian
South Africa	Australopithecinae		Rhodesian	Boskop	Bushman
East Africa	Chimpanzee, gorilla	(Africanthropus?)		Elmenteita	East African
West Asia			Mt. Carmel		
East Asia	Orang, extinct	Sinanthropus	(←?) Solo	Upper Choukoutien	(Mongolian)
Indonesia	Orang	Pithecanthropus		Wadjak, etc.†	Australoid
America				‡	American Ind.

* Middle Pleistocene is Second Interglacial, but both Piltdown and Heidelberg are generally attributed to the First Interglacial.
† And Talgai, Cohuna, Keilor in Australia.
‡ There are terminal-Pleistocene implements, but no generally accepted finds of human bones of Pleistocene age.

are Protoanthropic, Palaeoanthropic, and Neanthropic man. The accompanying table summarizes the stages, ages, and continental distribution of the principal forms.

Such are the salient outlines of human physical development since man definitely became man. Those who want only the fundamentals of the story can stop here. The first of the three sections that follow presents some unresolved difficulties of discovery and interpretation which complicate or blur the smooth sequence of development. The other two sections largely corroborate the story as it has been outlined, through the objective but necessarily somewhat technical mechanism of measurements.

54. SOME DOUBTFULS

What will be mentioned in this section contributes nothing to clarity of the basic conception of human bodily development in the Pleistocene—rather the reverse; but it seems only fair to mention some irreconcilable evidences and conflicting opinions.

Four finds, three of them from the lower Thames Valley, and all, like Piltdown, from southeastern England, have made a lot of difficulty. These are Galley Hill, 1888; Bury St. Edmunds, 1882; Lloyds of London, 1925; and Swanscombe, 1935. What they have in common is a combination of attributed great age and relatively modern type. Specifically, they are alleged to be mid-Pleistocene, but to be of *Homo sapiens* type: older than Neandertal in time, but more modern in form; in fact, probably as old as Pithecanthropus and Sinanthropus, but very similar to ourselves. Like Piltdown, they tend to disfigure or complicate an otherwise fairly consistent picture of human development. Of course that is no reason for casting them out of court. But, like every witness that conflicts with the majority, their testimony deserves the closest scrutiny.

Galley Hill man had a stature of around 1600 mm, a narrow and very long head (204 or 205 mm), an eyebrow ridge that was continuous across the frontal bone, other traits that are primitive, such as thick skull bones and small mastoids, and still others that are not primitive, such as a light skeleton, a broad forehead, and no prognathism. He lay in the "hundred-foot terrace" of the lower Thames, which is reckoned as Second Interglacial; but as he was not exhumed by scientists, some have doubted whether he was coeval with it. He is on the whole more modern in type than Neandertal. Coon calls him "without reasonable doubt an extremely generalized form of ancestral white man." Some scholars on the Continent simply forget about his supposed geological antiquity and reckon his type in with Upper Palaeolithic man—viz., Cro-Magnon; but he doesn't quite fit in with this either.

The Bury St. Edmunds skull fragment was associated with Acheulian implements, but in a pit where they might have washed in together. The

Lloyds-of-London skull lay forty-two feet deep, and may have belonged to the fifty-foot terrace, which would make it Third Interglacial instead of Second. Both of these are female skulls with foreheads of modern slope and estimated capacities of modern range, 1300-1350 cc. Neither furnishes as good evidence of age as do Galley Hill and Swanscombe.

The Swanscombe skull consists of one top and the rear bone of the skull vault—parietal and occipital—found on the same level in the hundred-foot terrace about twenty-five feet—and ten months—apart. There is no doubt about their properly belonging in this terrace gravel and about this containing middle-Acheulian implements. There is, however, a view which puts the Acheulian into the Third Interglacial, not the Second (see Fig. 36, § 272). The Swanscombe bones are again a woman's, again suggest a capacity of 1300-1350 cc; and again, except for their thickness, suggest a *sapiens*-like form. All this, incidentally, is pretty close to what holds of the Piltdown skull if we divorce it from the Piltdown jaw and teeth. The chief importance of Swanscombe, which after all is pretty fragmentary, seems to be in confirming the age attributed to the more nearly complete Galley Hill specimen.

The pre-Würm, pre-Mousterian Neandertaloid female skull from Steinheim has also been brought into relation with these aberrant English skulls. In fact, one view frankly unites them all, along with the African Kanam and Kanjera remains, which will be discussed in a moment, into a *Homo sapiens* type, and a Caucasoid one at that, supposed to have been developed by the middle Pleistocene, long before Neandertal and contemporary with Sinanthropus!

All this of course is possible, and would have to be accepted if the evidence for it were quite tight and mandatory. Actually, the evidence for such a view is pretty much pieced together, and a good deal of it none too sure in itself. The one certain age in the series is that of Swanscombe, which is certain in terms of the hundred-foot terrace and of the geologists' verdict that this was laid down in the Second Interglacial. The age of Piltdown is really indeterminable. Formerly, we were asked to believe that Piltdown was important just because the clash between the modernlike skull and the apelike jaw and teeth showed that we were dealing with something that must be very remote and primitive. Now the jaw and teeth are to be discarded as not human, and the skull becomes significant because it shows that men shaped much like ourselves lived as far back as Pithecanthropus and Sinanthropus and earlier than Neandertal!

What we are really confronted with, in this issue, is the respective evidential weight of the Piltdown-Galley Hill-Swanscombe series as against the combined weight of the accumulated evidence for Pithecanthropus, for Sinanthropus, for classical Neandertal of western Europe, for pre-Mousterian Neandertal of central Europe, for the Palestinian Neandertaloids, and for Solo man. For each of these six types there is now a mass of anatomical remains greater than for the supposed early *Homo sapiens* assemblage, and their geological, faunal, and cultural dating is also firmer. The six types relate to each other developmentally so as to make consistent sense as part of a consecutive story. But this consistency disintegrates in proportion as the more questionable claims for an early *sapiens* are admitted. It looks as if the mere mass of coherent evidence were so much greater on one side than on the other as to leave little doubt as to what the verdict must be.

There is almost certainly this much in the early-*sapiens* theory. Not all fossil men or premen were as rugged and brutal as the first-discovered classic Neandertals still were during the last glaciation. The coeval or earlier but more modernized forms in Palestine and central Europe suggest that western-European Neandertal represented either a pocketed survival of the rugged people, or a local regression, while somewhat more advanced types were developing elsewhere. The early-*sapiens* view seems to be an extreme exaggeration of this recognition, propped by selected evidence. It will be noted that all the European skulls adduced as *sapiens*-like are female, except Galley Hill. And it is accepted that modern men—many civilized Caucasians as well as civilized Mongolians and most Negroes—tend toward the feminine and the infantile in general skeletal quality or habitus; but races like Pithecanthropus, Neandertal, and even Cro-Magnon are more masculine and senescent in appearance. An uncorrected selection of women would, therefore, modernize the appearance of any fossil race.

The Kanam and Kanjera material just alluded to was found by Leakey in Kenya. Kanam is a mandible, Kanjera about four fragmentary skulls; all are unquestionably *Homo sapiens*. Yet early Pleistocene and middle Pleistocene are the respective ages claimed. The geology, palaeontology, and prehistory of the region are still in their beginnings, and the important thing scientifically in such case is to refuse to be stampeded into sensational interpretations.

The same holds for the idea of Reck, discoverer of the Oldoway skeleton, that this was lower Pleistocene.

Somewhat different is Keith's diagnosis of the 1929 Springbok Flats find in the Transvaal, which he classes with the East African human fossils of Oldoway and Elmenteita type—though geographically it is much nearer to the Boskop-Fish Hoek sites. Keith may well be right.

Keith also denies the Negroid character of the pair of skeletons from Grimaldi and merges them in Cro-Magnon. On the other hand, Weinert accepts them as Negroid, but reckons Oldoway, Springbok, and Boskop as Cro-Magnon!

From Soviet territory there is a skull from Podkumok in the Caucasus, a burial from Simferopol in the Crimea, and a skull from a cave at Baisun in Uzbekistan. They are tentatively classified thus: the first as Solutrean Neanthropic, the two latter as Mousterian Neandertal.

These doubts and conflicts are cited because it is important to carry always in mind that the story of man's physical development is no cut-and-dried demonstration to which a Q.E.D. can be appended, but something diligently and co-operatively built up from exceedingly scarce and usually fragmentary evidence which has to be searchingly analyzed both anatomically and for its geological, faunal, and cultural associations. Many scholars have worked at this task. No two have agreed at all points in their conclusions. The overwhelming majority have agreed as to certain fundamental findings, and these we can build on as reliable, at any rate until the discovery of new material may alter them. Beyond these general acceptances, there are opinions, biases, enthusiasms, and conservatisms, all of which the nonspecialist should be very chary of, no matter how great the personal authority from which they emanate. In general, it is sound to suspend judgment on any interpretation, no matter how intriguing or clarifying it seems, which has not yet won several expert adherents. It is also important to try to distinguish between factual evidence that is indisputably sure and that which is only probable or possible. And finally, a set of interpretations that give a total fit, a coherent larger picture, naturally carries more weight than discordant ones.

55. THE METRIC EXPRESSION OF HUMAN DEVELOPMENT

The most accurate and objective expression of the relations of the several types of fossil man is, of course, by measurable dimensions, proportions or "indices," and angles. Theoretically, such measures ought to settle all problems without residue of doubt or opinion. Actually, things are not so simple. Many fossil remains are imperfect. Face bones are delicate as against skull vaults and therefore get preserved much less often. What is preserved may be broken into pieces, the reassemblage and fitting together of which call for personal judgment before measurements can even be attempted. Then, many of the anthropometric criteria used in the study of modern races are not successfully applicable to fossils. These include characters observable only in the living, such as complexion, hair texture, measures involving soft tissues like lips and nose, and beyond these, measurable traits that are useful in differentiating recent races but happen to be much less significant in distinguishing one fossil type from another. Such are the cephalic index and the nasal index (§ 60), without which the student of contemporary races would be hamstrung, but in which most fossil races differ so little, and so randomly, that these proportions have almost no value for differential diagnosis. For instance, almost all Pleistocene and Palaeolithic skulls are long and narrow, with their breadth/length proportion on the low side of 77 per cent (= 79 in the living); whereas living races distribute about equally on both sides of that figure as a mid-point.

In compensation, certain other measures do show significant variations between fossil and modern man, or between fossil men of different periods or areas. Four of these have to do with the height of the skull vault, or calvarium. They are the calvarial or calotte height index; the bregma-position index; and the bregma and frontal angles.

Three anatomical points on the surface of the skull are the pivots on which these indices and angles rest. One is the *glabella* (G in Fig. 5), a slight swelling in the bone between the eyebrows and above the root of the nose. The second is the *inion* (I), or the *opisthocranion* (O), at the rear of the skull. The inion and the opisthocranion are fairly close together, but not the same, and preference for one over the other has resulted in some difference of measures among specialists. More about this in a moment. The third pivotal point is the *bregma* (B), where the frontal or forehead bone joins the two parietal or side top bones of the skull; or more technically, where the transverse coronal suture or interbone seam meets the lengthwise sagittal or interparietal suture. Near the bregma, usually somewhat to the rear of it, is the vertex or highest point (H) of the skull.

The inion is the meeting point of two little roughish crests or ridges caused by neck-muscle attachments. The opisthocranion is simply that spot at the back of the head, varying from skull to skull, which, by caliper measurement, is farthest from the glabella. Normally, it lies somewhat above the inion. The glabella-opisthocranion distance is also the diameter used in expressing skull length; but in contrast with the inion, the opisthocranion is not a fixed anatomical point.

Now if we cut or saw a skull lengthwise, or, much more simply, and as is the universal actual practice, project measurements of a median section of it on paper, we should naturally begin with the glabella-opisthocranion or glabella-inion line as a base: GO (or GI). Now to get the height of the skull vault, which is one of the features in which early fossil men differ most consistently from modern men, we erect a perpendicular from this base line to the highest point (H) of the vault, giving us a perpendicular HX (or H_1X_1). The height of this perpendicular, expressed as a percentage ratio of the base line (100 HX : GO or 100 H_1X_1 : GI) is the "calvarial-height index," also called the "calotte-height index."

We can also drop a perpendicular from the bregma B to the base line at Y (or Y_1), and similarly compute the ratio of the preperpendicular part of the base to the total base (100 GY : GO or 100 GY_1 : GI), thus getting the "bregma-position index." This is a numerical indication of how far forward on the skull the bregma lies. A sloping or retreating forehead naturally tends to throw its rear point, the bregma, rearward, as well as low. On the contrary, as the forehead is more high and domed, the bregma lies both more forward and higher, and the GY (GY_1) line shortens. A high-foreheaded skull thus has a numerically low bregma-position index. It is the only measure of the four here considered whose values vary in reverse: as the skull is high, the index is low.

A line BG from bregma to glabella gives an angle with the base line, BGO

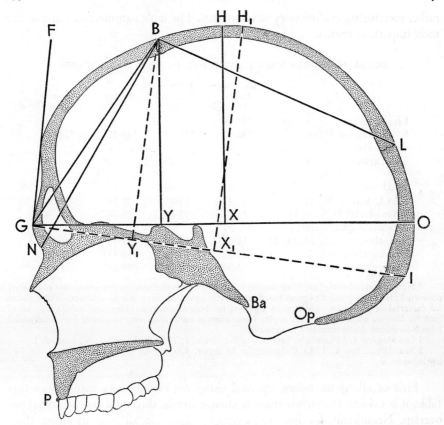

FIG. 5.   METRICAL POINTS AND PROPORTIONS OF THE HUMAN SKULL

Lengthwise section of skull, after Martin, showing points, dimensions, and angles discussed in § 55, 56. In circuit: G, glabella; B, bregma; H, highest point; L, lambda; O, opisthocranion; I, inion; Op, opisthion; Ba, basion; P, prosthion, alveolar point; N, nasion. GO, maximum length; NB, frontal chord; BL, parietal chord. HX:GO, calvarial height index; GY:GO, bregma position index; BGO, bregma angle; FGO, frontal angle. (For inion, the equivalents are: H_1X_1:GI; GY_1:GI; BGI; FGI.)

(or BGI), called the bregma angle, which is greater as the forehead is elevated. The projected line BG, of course, is the chord of the arc BG formed by the outer surface of the frontal bone.

If now we also draw from G a tangent GF to the curvature of this arc, the resulting angle FGO (or FGI) is the "frontal angle," expressing an outside measure of slope, as the bregma angle expresses an inside one.

These four metrical expressions were devised specially for the comparison of fossil skulls, or at any rate are used chiefly in connection with them. They can be derived from incomplete skulls lacking face and base; they relate to the development of the anterior lobes of the brain; and they seem to define a rather convincing evolutionary development. The table summarizes some of the most important results.

SKULL MEASURES SIGNIFICANT FOR HUMAN FOSSIL TYPES

	Calvarial Height Index	Bregma Position Index	Bregma Angle	Frontal Angle
Living races	*51-59			
8 Cro-Magnon †	*46-55	*28-37	*46-57°	*74-90°
Galley Hill	*43		*46°	*76°
Mt. Carmel: Skhul 5	52	33	51°	68°
Tabun 1	38	38	44°	?68°
Rhodesia	41	40	45°	60°
Solo 1, 5, 6, 9, 10, 11	37-43	35-43	41-54°	54-66°
9 Neandertal ‡	33-43	33-40	38-49°	50?-74°
Africanthropus, estim.	39			
Sinanthropus 2, 3, 10, 11, 12	35-41	37-42	38-45°	56-63°
Pithecanthropus 1, 2	33-37	36-43	38-43°	48-55°
Chimpanzee	*22-39	*44-51	*24-28°	

* Figures marked with * are from measurements based on glabella-inion line somewhat summarily converted into corresponding figures based on glabella-opisthocranion line by subtraction of 5 points for calvarial-height index, addition of 2 points for bregma-position index, and subtraction of 6° each for bregma angle and frontal angle. These average conversion intervals have been determined from Neandertal skulls measured both ways.

† Cro-Magnon 1, Chancelade, Combe Capelle, Brünn 1, 3 ♀, Oberkassel ♂, ♀, Lautsch 1.

‡ Neandertal, Spy 1, 2, La Chapelle, Le Moustier, Krapina C, Gibraltar ♀, La Quina 5 ♀, Ehringsdorf ♀.

First of all, as we follow upward along the evolutionary columns in this table, it is evident that while there is change in one direction, consecutive types overlap. Neandertal, for instance, averages higher in all four measures than Pithecanthropus; yet the top Pithecanthropus value falls within the Neandertal range. But the chimpanzee is wholly outside the human and the protohuman range in two of the measures; and in the third, while his individual maximum is within the lower human range, his individual minimum is far below any human minimum.

Sinanthropus seems consistently to show as a shade more advanced than Pithecanthropus.

Neandertal similarly has an edge, but only an edge, on Sinanthropus. In other words, progress between these two is only moderate as regards the *form* of the skull vault; it is in the *size* of his brain that Neandertal has advanced.

The straddling position of Palestinian man is also made clear by the table. The measures for the Tabun-1 woman fall around the middle of the Neandertal figures; for Skhul 5, correspondingly within the Cro-Magnon range.

Galley Hill is so consistently at the very bottom of the Cro-Magnon limit as to militate very strongly against his suggested inclusion in that Upper Palaeolithic group.

The Cro-Magnon range can be considered essentially that of living man.

56. MORE MEASURE COMPARISONS

There are some other specially devised proportions that give quantitative expression to human evolution.

One is the index parietal chord: parietal arc. The parietals are the top center pair of skull bones, between the forehead bone and the back-of-the-head bone. The sagittal suture is where they join in a fore-and-aft curved line along the top of the skull: from bregma to lambda—BL in Figure 5. Along the exterior, this line forms an arc; inside, the chord or straight-line distance bregma to lambda can be measured. The lower the proportion chord:arc, the greater is the curvature or bulge of the top of the skull; the higher the percentage index, the closer together are the diameter and the curve, and the flatter the skull top. Some results are:

PARIETAL CHORD AND ARC RATIO

26 modern populations, males, means	88-91
European Upper Palaeolithic (Cro-Magnon) males, mean	91
Females, 9	92
Mt. Carmel, mean of 4	92
(Tabun 1, 90, Skhul 4, 91, Skhul 5, 92, Skhul 9, 93)	
Neandertals, mean of 7	94
(Spy 1, 91, Krapina, Ehringsdorf, 93, Neandertal, La	
Chapelle, 94, Spy 2, 95, La Quina, 96)	
Rhodesian	96
Sinanthropus, mean of 5	94
(2, 3, 10, 11, 12 : 93, 94, 94, 94, 96)	
Pithecanthropus 1, 2 : 96, 96	96

Somewhat similar is the percentage proportion of diameter length of head (GO in Fig. 5) to the total curve from the root of the nose over top and back of the head to the rear edge of the spinal-cord aperture (foramen magnum) at the base of the skull—technically, the arc nasion to opisthion (in Fig. 5 the arc N-G-B-L-O-I-Op). For this ratio Morant gives:

RATIO OF LENGTH TO OUTER CURVE OF HEAD

Modern populations, males, means	48-51
Cro-Magnon males, mean	50
Mt. Carmel, 51-56, mean	53
Rhodesian	56?
Solo, mean	57
Neandertal: Gibraltar 56, Neandertal	58
Sinanthropus, mean	58
Pithecanthropus 2	58

By this index, Rhodesian man seems slightly nearer to ourselves than is Neandertal; by the preceding, Neandertal is nearer. By both, Cro-Magnon is within the modern range.

Relation of size of face and jaws to size of brain case, which varies so significantly from mammals in general to primates, and from anthropoids to man, is of presumptive significance also in intrahuman evolution. But metrical expression of the relation presents a good many practical and technical difficulties; and too few ancient skulls have their mandible preserved. However, if the nasion, basion, and prosthion or alveolar point (N, Ba, P in Fig. 5) are intact, we can get the distances between them with calipers: and these three distances or lines give us what may fairly be called the "fundamental triangle" of the upper face. The area (A) of this triangle in mm² is calculable. Then there is the length of the total cranial arc (S) from nasion over bregma and lambda to opisthion, N-G-B-L-Op in Figure 5, as already used in the index described in the preceding paragraph. A ratio of these two, A and S, gives us a somewhat arbitrary index of a volume relation; but it is better than nothing. Morant has computed the following:

	$A(mm^2)$	$S(mm)$	$100\ A/S^2$
Modern racial means	2788-3729	360-387	2.11-2.68
6 Cro-Magnon males	3450	398	2.18
Rhodesian	4898	355	3.53
Neandertal: La Chapelle	5095	373	4.04

Cro-Magnon ranks high within the modern variability—that is, low in face-jaw proportion—because of his high figure for brain-vault arc. But Neandertal and Rhodesian man are low, in spite of brain-case sizes which fall within the modern range, because their faces are so much larger than anything modern.

Women regularly have less jaw and face than men. Thus Cro-Magnon women have an index of 2.05 as against male 2.18; the Gibraltar Neandertal shows 3.32 as against La Chapelle's 4.04—her facial triangle of 3905 mm² almost reaches top modern means. Children are even less comparable, because their face and jaws are conspicuously undeveloped. It is maturity that makes us brutelike.

It is also possible to compare the internal-length diameter of the skull with the external one. The difference consists of thickness of skull wall plus thickness of supraorbital ridge or torus. Both are greater in apes and primitive men than in living human races; so the denominator of the fraction, or the percentage ratio, is low in the apes, rises toward modern man.

RATIO OF INNER TO OUTER SKULL LENGTH

Homo sapiens	92
4 Mt. Carmel 85-88, aver.	87
Steinheim 85, Gibraltar 85, Neandertal	86
4 Sinanthropus 83-87, aver.	86
Pithecanthropus 1, 2, each	84
Chimpanzee	81
Gorilla	75

Somewhat related is the attempt to approximate the supraorbital thickness by subtracting the ophryon-occiput length from the usual glabella-occiput length; the ophryon being the lowest point in the middle of the frontal bone, above the eyebrow ridges. The difference in millimeters is assumed as a measure of the thickness.

SUPRAORBITAL THICKNESS

Maximum in any modern individual	11.5
Cro-Magnon males, mean	3
Cro-Magnon maximum, Předmost 3	10
Mt. Carmel (males 13, 13, 13, female 10), mean	12
Neandertal adolescent, Le Moustier	8
Neandertal, 6 adults (Neand., 13, Gibr., ♀13, Spy 1, 14, La Chapelle 15, Spy 2, 15, La Quina, ♀18), mean	15
Rhodesian man	c.21
Sinanthropus (9, 11, 12, 13), mean	11
Pithecanthropus (13, 15), mean	14

Here Pithecanthropus and Sinanthropus are about equaled by Neandertal and Mt. Carmel, and surpassed by Rhodesian man. To put it differently, Palaeoanthropic man went out for brows of thick bone as much as did Proto-anthropic man, and it is only with Neanthropic man that this feature begins to moderate.

The size of the hollow of the limb bones seems definitely to have changed from Protoanthropic and Palaeoanthropic to Neanthropic man. The medullary canal has become larger, its bony wall thinner. Whether this is connected primarily with more storage of marrow, or with generic decrease of skeletal and muscular robustness, has not been worked out. Available figures for percentage of transverse diameter of canal to transverse diameter of thighbone are:

RATIO OF MARROW CANAL TO THIGHBONE

5 Sinanthropus	24, 31, 32, 37, 40	
Average		33
Krapina 2	25	
Krapina 1	29	
La Quina 5	37	
Spy 2	44	
Average, Neandertals		34
Europeans	39-60	
Average		48

In short, only about a third of the thighbone is marrow-hollow in Sinanthropus and Neandertal, but about a half in contemporary Europeans. Nevertheless, individuals of both the ancient types overlap modern individuals.

If there is any one outstanding broader generalization flowing from metric data such as these, it is how much alike fossil men are after all: to one another,

SKULL CAPACITY: APPROXIMATE MEANS

(Measured in cc with seeds or computed from dimensions)

	Males	Females	♂ + ♀ or ?
Anthropoid Apes			
Orang-utan (maximum, 480)	395	360	
Chimpanzee (maximum, 470)	400	390	
Gorilla (maximum, 585 or 655)	510	440	
African Australopithecoids			
Plesianthropus		440	
Paranthropus	600-650		
Protoanthropic Man			
Pithecanthropus 1, 2, 4 (775-935)			870
Sinanthropus 2, 3, 10, 11, 12 (915-1225)			1050
? Africanthropus			1100-1160
? Piltdown		1360	
Palaeoanthropic Man			
Würm Neandertal (Neand., Spy 1, Le Moustier, La Chapelle, ♂; Gibraltar, La Quina, ♀)	1530	1325	
Neandertal (Ehringsdorf, ♂; Steinheim, Rome 1, ♀)	1450	1130	
Palestinian (Skhul 4, 5, 9, ♂; Skhul 2, Tabun 1, ♀)	1550	1285	
Rhodesian	(1325) 1280		
Solo 1, 5, 6, 9, 10, 11 (1035-1255)			1100
? Bury St. Edmunds, Lloyds, Swanscombe		1325	
Neanthropic Man: Homo Sapiens			
Cro-Magnon, 7 ♂ (1500-1880)	1660		
North Africa: Afalou			1660
South Africa: Fish Hoek, Boskop	1600+		
Java: Wadjak 1, 2 (1550, 1650)	1600		
Australia: ?Keilor	1590		
Living Races of Homo Sapiens			
Europeans, generally (1400-1530)	1450	1300	
Chinese, Polynesians	1450		
Australian aborigenes	1270-1330		1290
Andaman Negrito, Vedda, Bushmen (all small-bodied)	1250-1350	1130-1220	

and to us. There are differences, but they are certainly less conspicuous than the similarities; and one form overlaps the next. Pithecanthropus may be only Proto-anthropic, but he is absolutely in the line of human development. In layman's language, he is already a man, though not a quite fully evolved one. And the same holds more so, of course, for his successors.

57. BRAIN SIZE

Finally, it seems worth while to assemble in review the various skull capacities that have already been cited here and there (see the facing page). Here the story is somewhat different. There is a very marked jump from the great apes and the South African fossil Australopithecoids to the earliest men, the Proto-anthropics. Even the lowly Pithecanthropus is already definitely on the human side. The next jump, from Protoanthropic to Palaeoanthropic man, carries us well into the range of brain case of living man, or even above our average; and this size is even increased a little with Neanthropic fossil man. In short, already with Neandertal the human brain had reached its full size. Only the Javanese Solo man is so small-brained as to suggest that he may be not really Palaeoan-thropic at all, but still Protoanthropic.

On the whole, later fossil man preponderates over living man so consistently in skull size, according to this table, as to give the impression that it is our brains which have shrunk in the past few ten thousands of years. This is pos-sible. But so is another interpretation: that it is the large, thick, rugged heads from stout-bodied individuals which have undoubtedly, on the average, the best chance of preservation from decay through the millennia; the small, the delicate, the feminine skulls have more often crumbled away. That would be a reason why Mousterian Neandertal and still more Cro-Magnon man seem to surpass modern Europeans; Mt. Carmel man, modern western Asiatics; Afalou, North Africans; Wadjak and Keilor, recent Australian blackfellows; Fish Hoek and Boskop, South African Bushmen. In other words, most of the Palaeoanthropic and Neanthropic skulls that we know probably represent some degree of selection for overaverage size.

CHAPTER FOUR

Living Races

A RACE is a valid biological concept. It is a group united by heredity: a breed or genetic strain or subspecies. It is not a valid sociocultural concept; the term "race" is usually ambiguous and is best not used in sociocultural situations, as we shall see more fully in § 80. But physical anthropology (§ 3), being concerned with man's organic features, is properly and necessarily concerned with the human races.

58. RACE ORIGINS

Almost everyone sooner or later becomes interested in the problem of the origin of the human races and the history of their development. We see mankind divided into a number of varieties that differ strikingly in appearance. If these varieties are modifications of a single ancestral form, what caused them to alter, and what has been the history of the change?

In the present state of science, we cannot wholly answer these important questions. We know very little about the causes that change human types, and we possess only incomplete information as to the history of races. Stray bits of evidence here and there are too scattered to afford many helpful clues. The very earliest men, as we know them from fossils, are too far removed from any of the living varieties, are too primitive, to link very definitely with the existing races, which can all be regarded as intergrading varieties of a single species,

Homo sapiens. In the latter part of the Old Stone Age, in the Aurignacian period, at a time perhaps twenty-five to eighteen thousand years ago, we commence to encounter remains of Cro-Magnon man (§ 49) which foreshadow the modern races and are believed to have entered into the composition of several European populations of today.[1] We can conclude that the races of man as they are spread over the earth today must have been at least some tens of thousands of years in forming. What caused them to differentiate, on which part of the earth's surface each took on its peculiarities, how they further subdivided, what were the connecting links between them, how the differentiating races may have reblended—on all these points the answer is as yet incomplete.

It is no different in other fields of biology. As long as the zoologist or the botanist reviews his grand classifications or the wide sweep of organic evolution for 50 million or 500 million years back, he seems to obtain striking and simple results. When he turns his attention to a small group, attempting to trace in detail its subvarieties, and the precise relations and history of these, the task is seen to be intricate and the accumulated knowledge is usually insufficient to solve more than a fraction of the problems that arise.

There is, then, nothing unusual in the situation of partial bafflement in which anthropology still finds itself about the human races.

59. RACE CLASSIFICATION

What remains is the possibility of making an accurate survey of the living races in the hope that the relationships a classification brings out may indicate something as to the former development of the races. If for instance it could be established that the Ainu or aborigines of Japan are closely similar in their bodies to the peoples of Europe, we would then infer that they are a branch of the Caucasian stock, that their origin presumably took place to the west of their present habitat, and that they have no connection with the Mongolian Japanese among whom they now live. This is working by indirect evidence, it is true; but sooner or later that is the method to which science always finds itself reduced.

---

[1] Decades ago it began to be asserted that the Cro-Magnon strain still persisted in south-central France, as by Ripley, following French authorities; then also for the modern population of Dalarne in Sweden, for Westphalia in Germany, and so on. Among the European racial types, Coon in 1939 recognized four as partially Palaeolithic in origin: (1), the Brünn type, or Tronder, "in solution" among Scandinavian and British populations; (2), Borreby, "the unreduced brachycephalic strain in Cro-Magnon," a major population element in northern and central Germany; (3), Alpine, a "reduced foetalized" and brachycephalized survivor of the Upper Palaeolithic population of France; (4), Ladogan, containing an east-European Upper Palaeolithic element. These particular derivations, and even some of the types themselves, rest on somewhat speculative opinion; but they illustrate how freely, and without challenge in principle, anthropologists have come to connect modern with late-Palaeolithic Europeans, and thus by implication to admit these as already Caucasian.

The desirability of a trustworthy classification of the human races will therefore be generally accepted without further argument. But the making of such a classification proves to be more difficult than might be imagined. To begin with, a race is only a sort of average of a large number of individuals; and averages differ from one another much less than individuals. Popular impression exaggerates the differences, accurate measurements reduce them. It is true that a Negro and a northern European cannot possibly be confused: they happen to represent extreme types. Yet as soon as we operate with less divergent races we find that variations between individuals of the same race are often greater than differences between the races. The tallest individuals of a short race are taller than the shortest individuals of a tall race. This is called *overlapping;* and it occurs to such an extent as to make it frequently difficult for the physical anthropologist to establish clear-cut types.

In addition, the lines of demarcation between races have time and again been obliterated by interbreeding. Adjacent peoples, even hostile ones, intermarry. The number of such marriages in one generation may be small; but the cumulative effect of a thousand years is often quite disconcerting. Also, the half-breeds or hybrids are as fertile as each of the original types. There is no question but that some populations are nothing but the product of such race crossing. Thus there is a belt extending across most of Africa, and quite wide in East Africa, of which it is difficult to say whether the inhabitants belong more to the Negro or to the Caucasian type. If we construct a racial map and represent the demarcation between Negro and Caucasian by a line, we are really misrepresenting the situation. The truth could be expressed only by inserting a transition zone of mixed color. Yet as soon as we allow such transitions, the definiteness of our classification begins to crumble.

In spite of these difficulties, some general truths can be discovered from a careful race classification and certain constant principles of importance emerge from all the diversity.

60. TRAITS ON WHICH CLASSIFICATION RESTS

Since every human being obviously possesses a large number of physical features or traits, the first thing that the prospective classifier of race must do is to determine how much weight he will attach to each of these features.

The most striking of all traits probably is *stature* or bodily height. Yet this is a trait which experience has shown to be of relatively limited value for classificatory purposes. The imagination is easily impressed by a few inches when they show at the top of a man and make him half a head taller or shorter than oneself. Except for a few groups which numerically are insignificant, there is no human race that averages less than 4 feet 11 inches (150 cm) in height for men. There is none that averages taller than 5 feet 10 inches (178 cm). This means that practically the whole range of human variability in height, from the race standpoint, falls within less than a foot. The majority of averages of populations do not differ more than 2 inches (5 cm) from the general human average of 5 feet 5 inches (165 cm).

Then too, stature has been proved to be rather readily influenced by environment. Each of us is a fraction of an inch taller when he gets up in the morning than when he goes to bed at night. Two races might differ by as much as a couple of inches in their heredity, and yet if all the individuals of the shorter race had been well nourished in a favorable environment, and all those of the taller group were underfed and overworked, the naturally shorter race might well be actually the taller one. All European and American populations for which there are measurements going back from one to three generations, and the Japanese also, have gained from about 2 to 5 cm (1 to 2 inches) or more in height. This is undoubtedly due to the acceleratory rise in the standard of living in Western civilization during the past century. For the same reason the economically better-off classes at any one moment regularly average taller than the poorer classes. Of course there is no reason to believe that this gain will continue indefinitely.

The *cephalic index* expresses in percentage form the ratio of the length and the breadth of the head—both measured with hinged calipers, basically as the diameters of logs are measured. This is perhaps the most commonly used anthropological measure.[2] It has certain definite practical advantages. The head measurements are easily made with accuracy. The index is nearly the same on the living head and on the dead skull, or one is easily converted into the other. This makes it possible to compare present and past generations. The index is also nearly the same for men and for women, for children and for adults. Finally, it seems to be little affected by environment—at least, not in one consistent direction.[3] The consequence is that head form has been widely investigated. There are few groups of people of consequence whose average cephalic index we do not know fairly accurately. The difficulty about the cephalic index

[2] The usual nomenclature for cephalic index is on the basis of rounded numbers: broadheaded or roundheaded, or brachycephalic, above 80; medium-headed, or mesocephalic, between 75 and 80; narrow-headed or longheaded, or dolichocephalic, below 75. Yet, as the average for mankind is in the neighborhood of 79, this terminology makes far more brachycephalic than dolichocephalic peoples. Groups frequently spoken of as longheaded are often really mesocephalic by the accepted definition: a large proportion of Europeans, for instance. It would result in both more accuracy and a better balancing of the limits if the three types of head form were set, as has been suggested, at 81 and 77 in place of 80 and 75. The index of the skull (strictly, the *cranial index*) is two units less than that taken on the living head. In this book, terms like "dolichocephalic" are used *relatively* throughout; that is, as meaning long as compared with others or with the average; not as indicating a specific and technical percentage range.

[3] See § 75. However, the head is easily deformed in infancy by bandages, pads, and cradle pressures, and some peoples have practiced such deformation deliberately. The change of shape does not reduce the size of the brain or harm the child or seem to diminish intelligence, but it may distort the hereditary head form completely.

from the point of view of race classification is that it does not yield broad enough results. It is often useful in distinguishing subtypes, nation from nation, or tribe from tribe; but it is not uniform for the primary races. There is, for instance, no typical head form for the Caucasian race. There are narrow-headed, medium-headed, and broad-headed Caucasians. The same is true of the American Indians, who are on the whole a rather uniform major race, yet vary much in head form.

A tendency toward progressive brachycephalization has often been observed, both in geologic and in historical time, but is unexplained. Virtually all Pleistocene skulls, except at the very end of the period, are narrow. In America, wherever there is an older and a more recent aboriginal type in the same area, the older is regularly the narrower. For Europe the fact has been established repeatedly. Thus, the percentage of the population that is brachycranial—index of 80 and up in the skull, 82 and up in the living—is:

MODERN INCREASE OF FREQUENCY OF ROUNDHEADS

Sweden: modern, 13%; Iron and Middle ages, 3% to 7%

Denmark: modern, 33%; Iron Age, 2%

Bavaria: modern, 83%; Late Mediaeval, 50%; Early Mediaeval, 32%; period of Migrations, 14%

Slavs: modern, 85%; 6th to 12th century, 9%

Greeks: modern, 54%; Classic, 10%

Crete: modern, 38%; Minoan, 9%

The *nasal index,* which expresses the percentage relation of breadth and length of nose, runs much more constant in the great races. Practically all Negroids are broad-nosed, practically all Caucasians narrow-nosed, and the majority of peoples of Mongolian affinities medium-nosed. But the nasal index varies according to the age of the person; it is utterly different in a living individual and a skull; [4] it seems to reflect heredity with more variability than the cephalic index; and finally it tells us nothing about the elevation or profile or general formation of the nose, which is generally observed descriptively.

Prognathism, or the degree of the protrusion of the jaws, is a conspicuous feature of the profile, and would seem to be of some historical importance as a sign of primitiveness, because all other mammals are more prognathous than man. The trait also has a general correlation with the fundamental racial types. Negroes are almost all prognathous, people of Mongolian type moderately so, most Caucasians very slightly. Prognathism is however difficult to measure or to denote in figures. Various apparatuses have been devised without wholly satisfactory results.

---

[4] On the living, broad or platyrrhine noses have an index of breadth compared with length above 85; medium or mesorrhine, between 70 and 85; narrow or leptorrhine, below 70. Skeletally, the same three terms denote proportions above 53, between 48 and 53, and below 48.

The *capacity of the skull* was measured formerly by filling it with shot; now generally with millet or mustard seed, or with water in a highly elastic rubber bag. Shot measurements run about 80 cc the higher. By seed measure, the average for European males is about 1450 cc; for females about 10 per cent lower, or 1300. East Asiatic Mongoloids are about the same, as are the large-bodied Polynesians. Negroes seem to have somewhat less capacity, though the few series available run somewhat variably. Australoids are definitely small, around 1300. Bushmen, Negritos, Veddas, all small-bodied, are also small-brained. It appears that cranial capacity is considerably dependent on bodily size. Slender as well as short races run to small capacities. The heavy Bantu surpass the slighter-framed Sudanese, and Hindus stand well below European Caucasians, just as the shorter Japanese seem to average less than the Chinese. Broad-headed populations show greater cranial capacity than narrow-headed ones: Alpine Europeans (§ 62) generally surpass Nordics in spite of their shorter stature.[5] Individual variability is also unusually great in this measurement. The largest-skulled and the smallest-skulled healthy individuals of the same sex in one population differ sometimes by 500, 600, or 700 cc, or more than one-third of the racial average. Overlapping between races is accordingly particularly marked in cranial capacity. Furthermore, the measurement obviously cannot be taken on the living, except by computation estimates based on diameters, such as have been used also for fragmentary fossil skulls. In spite of its interest as an evolutionary development in the past, especially the more remote ancestry of man (§ 57), cranial capacity is thus of restricted value in distinguishing races.

The *texture of the hair* is now universally regarded as one of the most valuable criteria for classifying races, possibly the most significant of all. Hair is distinguished as woolly in the Negro, straight in the Mongolian, and wavy or intermediate in the Caucasian. This texture depends principally on the diameters of each individual hair as they are revealed in cross section under the microscope; in part also on the degree of straightness or curvature of the root sacs of the hair in the skin. Hair texture seems to run rather rigidly along hereditary racial lines, and to be uninfluenced by factors of age, sex, climate, or nourishment.

Hairiness of the body as a whole is another trait to which more and more attention is coming to be paid. The fullness or scantiness of the beard, and the degree of development of the down which covers the body, are its most conspicuous manifestations. Caucasians are definitely a hairy race, Mongoloids and most Negroids glabrous or smooth-skinned. It is largely on the basis of their hairiness and hair texture that races like the Australoids have been separated from the Negroids, and the Ainus from the Japanese. Strangely enough, baldness occurs most frequently in association with heavy beards and body hair—in line with which fact women are rarely bald.

[5] There is a physicomathematical reason: With a given surface, the contained volume is greater for a sphere than for an elongated shape.

Except possibly for stature, *color* is probably the most conspicuous trait of any race. Under color must be included the complexion of the skin, the color of the hair, and the color of the eyes. All of these are due to varying amounts of the same pigment: melanin.[6] All of them present difficulties to the anthropometrist. There is a complete series of transition shades, and it is difficult to express these differences of shade quantitatively. They readily impress the eye, but it is far from easy to denote them accurately in numbers. Environment also affects skin color markedly. A day's exposure to the sun may darken an individual's complexion by several shades. In spite of these drawbacks, however, complexion remains sufficiently important to warrant consideration in every classification.

Hair color and eye color are practically immune against direct change by environment. They unquestionably are excellent hereditary criteria, although they offer much the same resistance to measurement as does complexion. The utility of these two traits is moreover limited by another factor: their narrow distribution. Blue eyes and blond hair are racially characteristic of only a single major subrace, that of northern Europe. In central Europe they are already much toned down: the prevailing type here is brunet. In southern Europe, blue eyes and blondness rarely occur except where admixture with northern peoples can be traced. Outside of the Caucasian stock, virtually black hair and black eyes are the universal rule for the human family.

Special race traits occur, besides blue eyes and blondness. The Mongolian "slant," "slit," or "oblique" eye is due to an overdeveloped *epicanthic fold* of the eyelid, especially at the inner corner of the eye, partially covering the lash-bearing edge of the lid. It is associated with prominent cheekbones, a flat nose, a smooth forehead. It is found occasionally outside of East Asia, but becomes sporadic as soon as Oceania and America are entered, whereas it is fairly marked among the Bushmen of South Africa. The *Mongolian spot* of bluish pigment in the skin of the lumbar region, gradually fading after birth, was first observed in East Asia, and is probably most frequent there, but occurs also in other races. *Steatopygia,* a heavy deposit of fat in the buttocks, is characteristic of Bushmen and Hottentot women. It serves to accentuate the hollow back and projecting rump which characterize their men as well as themselves. *Supraorbital ridges,* a development of the lower part of the frontal bone of the skull, are marked in all Protoanthropic and almost all Palaeoanthropic fossil types, and are therefore usually regarded as a primitive trait. Among living races, supraorbital ridges are probably most marked among Australoids. They occur also among Veddoids, northern Europeans, and most North American Indians. They are little developed in most African Negroes, and perhaps least of all in East Asiatic Mongoloids. These ridges are perhaps even more a masculine than a "primitive"

---

[6] Except for red-hairedness, which seems due to a separate hereditary factor and pigment. Red hair is most conspicuous with marked blondness, and perhaps is often present otherwise but "smothered" by abundance of melanin.

characteristic; in races in which they occur, their ruggedness and that of the mastoids are used to determine the sex of unidentified skulls. *Baldness,* and its association with hairiness of face and body, have already been mentioned. How far its highest frequency among Caucasians is wholly a congenital race trait or may be added to by environmental factors in their mode of life is not clear. *Shovel-shaped incisor teeth,* concave on the side facing the tongue, are characteristic of Mongoloids, both American and Asiatic.

61. THE GRAND DIVISIONS OR PRIMARY STOCKS

Obviously it would be easiest to arrive at a clear-cut classification by grouping all the peoples of the earth according to a single trait, such as the shape of the nose, or color. But any such classification must be artificial and largely unsound, just because it disregards the majority of traits. The only classification that can claim to rest upon a true or natural basis is one that takes into consideration as many traits as possible, and which weights the important more heavily than the unimportant features. If the outcome of such a grouping leaves some peoples intermediate or of doubtful place in the classification, this result is unfortunate but must be accepted. If we follow this plan and review the peoples of the earth, each with reference to all its traits, we obtain an arrangement something like that given in the table on the following page, and whose geography is roughly mapped in Figures 6 and 7.

This classification is summary in that it operates with the smallest number of classes possible, while attempting at the same time to account for every human group and leave no blanks on the map of the globe. Technically, it is impossible to do this and still remain wholly authentic and accurate; the classification is admittedly simpler than the complex and sometimes conflicting facts warrant. But it is in the interest of clarity to begin with this slightly over-simplified scheme, which is believed to be pretty close to the consensus of almost all anthropological opinion, and to follow this, in § 67-71, with qualifications, refinements, and contrary views.

On the basic view, there are three grand divisions, of which the European, the Negro, and the Chinese type may be taken as representative. These three primary classes are generally called Caucasian, Caucasoid, or Europoid; Negroid; and Mongoloid.[7] The color terms "White," "Black," and "Yellow" are also often used, but it is necessary to remember that they are employed merely as brief convenient labels, and that they have no real descriptive value. There are millions of essential Caucasians—Hindus—who are darker in complexion than millions of Mongoloids—Chinese.

These three main groups account for more than nine-tenths of all the nations and tribes of the world. As to the number of individuals, they comprise

[7] The suffix *-oid* or *-id* means "like."

OUTLINE RACIAL CLASSIFICATION OF MANKIND

Primary Stocks and Races	Texture of Hair of Head	Hair of Body and Face	Head	Nose	Prognathism	Skin Color	Stature	Remarks
CAUCASIAN OR "WHITE"								
Nordic	Wavy	Abundant	Narrow	Narrow	Slight	Very fair	Tall	Often blond, eyes light
Alpine	"	"	Broad	Broad	"	Fair	Above aver.	Hair brown, eyes brown
Mediterranean	"	"	Narrow	Medium	"	Dark white	Medium	"Regular features," graceful
Hindu	"	"	"	Variable	Moderate	Brown	Above aver.	Dark admixture espec. in S.
MONGOLOID OR "YELLOW"								
Mongolian	Straight	Slight	Broad	Medium	Medium	Light brown	Below aver.	Broad face, Mongolian eye
Malaysian	"	"	"	"	"	Brown	Tall to medium	Broad face
American Indian	"	"	Variable	"	"	"	"	
NEGROID OR "BLACK"								
Negro	Woolly	Slight	Narrow	Broad	Strong	Dark brown	Tall	Everted lips
Melanesian	"	"	"	"	"	"	Medium	Some aquiline noses
Pygmy Black	"	"	Broadish	"	"	"	Very short	
Bushman	Peppercorn	"	Narrow	"	Slight	Yellowish	"	Wrinkles, steatopygy, thin lips, Mongolian eye
OF DOUBTFUL CLASSIFICATION								
Australoid	Wavy	Abundant	Narrow	Broad	Strong	Dark brown	Medium	Negroid traits preponderate, some Caucasian resembl.
Veddoid (Indo-Austral.)	"	Moderate	"	Medium	Medium	Brown	Short	Generalized proto-Caucasian, some Australoid resembl.
Polynesian	"	"	Variable	Medium	"	"	Tall	Mongoloid and Caucas. traits, with local Negroid admixture
Ainu	"	Abundant	Narrow	"	"	Light brown	Medium	Prob. generalized Caucasian

Hair and eyes are "black" unless otherwise stated.

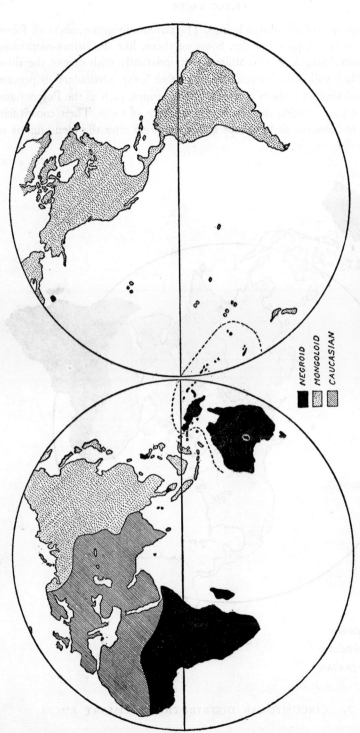

NEGROID
MONGOLOID
CAUCASIAN

FIG. 6. PRIMARY RACIAL STOCKS OF MAN

Outline distribution of the primary racial stocks of mankind according to the threefold classification. Australians, Ainu, Veddoids, Polynesians, etc., are included in the stock with which they appear to affiliate most closely. A larger map with more shadings would be required to do even approximate justice to the intricacies of a complete race classification.

probably 99 per cent of all human beings. The remaining minor, aberrant forms are best kept separate, provisionally. Some of them, like the before-mentioned Ainu and Australoids, appear to affiliate preponderantly with one of the three great classes, but still differ sufficiently in one or more particulars to prevent their being included with them outright. Other groups, such as the Polynesians, seem to be, at least in part, the result of a mixture of races. Their constituent elements are so blended, and perhaps so far modified after the blending, as to be difficult to disentangle.

FIG. 7.   CIRCUMPOLAR DISTRIBUTION: PRIMARY RACES

Each of the three great primary stocks falls into several natural subdivisions. The distribution of these will now be described as it existed before the era of exploration and colonization that began toward the end of the fifteenth century. Although for practical purposes they have been submerged by Caucasians in large parts of the Americas, Australia, and South Africa, it is the native races whose distribution is referred to here.

62. CAUCASIAN RACES

Three of the four major Caucasian races originally lived, in whole or in part, in Europe; the fourth consists of the Hindus. The three European races are the Nordic, the Alpine, and the Mediterranean. More can be recognized, and most authorities insist on a greater number, some of which will be discussed in § 68 to 71, but all admit at least these three. They occupy horizontal belts on the map. Beginning with the Nordic and ending with the Mediterranean, they may be described as successively darker-skinned, darker-eyed, darker-haired, and shorter in stature. The Alpine race, which lies between the two others, is however more than a mere transition; for it is broad-headed, whereas the Nordic and Mediterranean are both relatively narrow-headed.[8] The Nordic type is essentially distributed around the Baltic and North seas. The Mediterranean race occupies the shores of the Mediterranean Sea, in Asia and Africa as well as in Europe. In ancient times it seems to have prevailed everywhere along these coasts. At present the Balkan Peninsula and Asia Minor are mostly occupied by broad-headed peoples of more or less close affinity to the Alpines. This Alpine race is perhaps less homogeneous than the two others. A central Frenchman, a Serb, a southern Russian, and an Armenian are clearly far from identical. In some respects, however, they have enough in common to warrant their being put into the one larger group.

It must be clearly understood that these races have nothing to do with the modern political nationalities of Europe. Northern Germany is prevailingly Nordic, southern Germany, Alpine. Northern Italy is Alpine, the rest of the peninsula Mediterranean. All three races are definitely represented in France. The average northern Frenchman stands racially nearer to the northern German than to his countryman from central France, whereas the latter links up in physical type with the southern German. Nationality is determined by speech, customs, religion, and political affiliations. Its boundary lines and those of race cut right across one another.

The British Isles did not escape the process of race-blending that has gone on in Europe for thousands of years. The bulk of the blood of their inhabitants

---

[8] The narrowness or length of head of the Nordics has been greatly exaggerated in popular repute. They are not nearly as dolichocephalic as Melanesians, most Hindus, many African Negroes, the Eskimo, and so on. In fact, the average of no Nordic European nationality succeeds in falling within the technical limits of dolichocephaly—below 75.

during the past thousand years or longer has been Nordic, but there is a definite
"Iberian"—that is, Mediterranean—strain. The first settlers in America carried
this mixture across the Atlantic, and through the years immigration has increased its compositeness. Scandinavians and northern Germans have added to
the Nordic component in the population of the United States; southern Germans, former Austro-Hungarians, and Russians have added to the Alpine component; and the Italians have injected a definite Mediterranean element. The
Negro alone has not been fully admitted into the make-up of our white society;
but the reverse holds: a considerable percentage of the "colored" people in the
United States are from one-sixteenth to fifteen-sixteenths Caucasian.

The foregoing tripartite classification was chiefly codified in Ripley's famous
Races of Europe in 1899, a work that has been superseded by elaboration rather
than rejection, as is set forth in § 68.

The Hindu is in the main a narrow-headed, dark-skinned Caucasian, not
very different from the Mediterranean. He constitutes the easternmost block of
Caucasians and may therefore be presumed at one time to have entered India
from the northwest. There he seems to have encountered an aboriginal population that may have been Negroid but is more often thought to have been
Australoid or perhaps to have constituted a dark proto-Caucasian or "Indo-
Australoid" race. A fairly thorough intermixture has taken place in India during the last several thousand years, with the result that the original Caucasian
type of the Hindu has been somewhat modified, while most of the less numerous
or less vigorous aboriginal population has been submerged or assimilated. On
the whole, the definite Caucasian type, with somewhat narrower noses and
lighter complexions, is best preserved in the northwest; traces of the dark-
skinned aboriginal race are strongest in southern and eastern India.

Attempts have been made, by citing measurements, to prove the Brahmans
and other high castes of India as being Caucasian in their physical type, and the
low castes as dark-skinned and aboriginal in race. There is some indubitable
correlation to this effect. But it is even more remarkable how small the correlation is; with a limited amount of biased selection or weighting of data, one could
make it disappear. The theory is therefore at least partly of the wish-fulfillment
order. Hindu castes have not kept themselves as pure as they like to believe;
and the racial differentiation within India seems on the whole to be geographical, national, or tribal rather than along the lines of social status.

63. MONGOLOID RACES

The Mongoloid stock divides into the Mongolian proper of East Asia, the
Malaysian of the East Indies, and the American Indian. The differences among
these three types are not very great. The Mongolian proper is the most extreme
or pronounced form. It was probably the latest to develop its present characteristics. For instance, the oblique or "Mongolian" eye is a peculiarity restricted

chiefly to the people of East Asia. The original Mongoloid stock must be looked upon as having been more like present-day Malaysians or American Indians, or intermediate between them. From this generalized type peoples like the Chinese gradually diverged, adding the epicanthic fold of the oblique eye and a certain generic refinement of physique, while the less civilized peoples of America and Oceania kept more nearly to the ancient type.

Within the East Indies, and especially in the Philippines, a less specifically Mongoloid and a more specifically Mongoloid strain can at times be distinguished, which have been called Proto-Malaysian and Deutero-Malaysian. In certain respects, such as relatively short stature and broad nose, the former somewhat approaches the Indo-Australoid type described below. Among the American Mongoloids, the Eskimo appear to be the most particularized subvariety, according to almost all anthropometrists.

64. NEGROID RACES

The Negroid stock falls into two large divisions, the African Negro proper and the Oceanic Papuo-Melanesian. There is in addition a third division, the Dwarf Blacks or Negritos, who are very few in numbers but possess a wide and irregular distribution. The Negroes and the Melanesians, in spite of their being separated by the breadth of the Indian Ocean, are clearly close relatives. A trained observer can distinguish them at sight, but a novice would take a Papuan from New Guinea or a Melanesian from the Solomon or Bismarck islands to be an African. Perhaps the most conspicuous difference is that the broad nose of the African Negro is flat, the broad nose of the Melanesian often aquiline. The latter also has thinner lips, on the whole, and is shorter. The Melanesians probably contain some absorption of alien blood. Their Malayo-Polynesian speech also points to this. How these two Negroid branches came to be located on the opposite sides of a great ocean is a fact that remains unexplained.

The Negrito or Pygmy Negroid race has highly localized representatives in the Philippines, the Malay Peninsula, the Andaman Islands, probably in New Guinea, and in equatorial Africa. These peoples are the true pygmies of the human species. Wherever they are racially pure the adult males are less than 5 feet in stature; in fact, 150 cm, or 4 feet 11 inches, for adult males is usually set as the upper average limit of true Negrito populations; some say 148 cm. Negritos also differ from other Negroids in being relatively broad-headed. Their skin color, hair texture, nose form, and most other traits are, however, the same as those of the other Negroids. They are in no sense malformed, but a well-proportioned small people. Their scattered distribution on two sides of the Indian Ocean is difficult to account for. It is possible that they are an ancient and primitive type which once inhabited much wider stretches of territory in Africa, Asia, and Oceania than it inhabits now. On account of their unaggres-

siveness and backwardness, the Negritos, according to this theory, were gradually crowded to the wall by the larger, more energetic populations with which
they came in contact, until only a few scattered fragments of them now remain.

Another view is that they represent a stunting of stature, or series of genetic
aberrations of unknown cause, from full-size Negroids. They are all forest-
dwelling hunters without settled habitations. Whether this environment and
mode of life might repeatedly produce a selection toward shortness is somewhat
speculative. Their broadish short heads might well be a function of their short
stature—head length decreasing as part of body length.

The Bushmen and in some degree the Hottentots of South Africa may also
be provisionally included with the Negritos, or related to them, although distinctive in a number of respects. They are yellowish-brown in complexion,
wrinkled, longheaded, short and flat eared, very broad and flat nosed, short
armed and legged, hollow-backed, and steatopygous. On the whole, Negroid
characteristics prevail among them. They are, for instance, frizzy, with the head
hair coiling in tight "peppercorn" tufts. In spite of this, some observers have
recognized Caucasoid or Mongoloid features in them. Thus they are non-
prognathous and thin-lipped, and a fair proportion of them show some degree
of epicanthic eye fold. They are a very specialized race, but the extremely short
stature of the Bushmen may justify their tentative grouping with the Negritos.

65. POPULATIONS OF DOUBTFUL POSITION

One thing is common to the peoples who are here reckoned as of doubtful
position in the classification: They all present certain Caucasian affinities without being similar enough to the recognized Caucasians to be included with
them. This is true of the black, wavy-haired, prognathous, beetle-browed Australians, whose first appearance suggests that they are Negroids, as it is of the
brown Polynesians, who appear to have primary Mongoloid connections through
the Malaysians.

The native *Australians* are black-skinned, very broad-nosed, long-legged,
narrow-headed, prognathous, but their hirsuteness, full beards, and wavy head
hair take them out of the pure Negroid sphere. Their heavy eyebrow ridges—in
the bone—are only one of a series of features that lead most observers to reckon
them as, on the whole, the most primitive living race. This was a numerically
limited race. In spite of having a continent to themselves until recently, they
seem never to have comprised more than a couple of hundred thousand souls,
and are now diminished far below that.

In India, Farther India, and the East Indies live a scattered series of uncivilized *Veddoid* peoples more or less alike in being dark, short, slender, wavy-
haired, longish-headed, broad-nosed. The brows are knit, the eyes deep-set, the
mouth large, the jaws peaked, the beard development medium. Resemblances are
on the one hand toward the Caucasian type, on the other toward the Australian,

just as the geographical position is intermediate. The alternative name "Indo-Australoid" is thus appropriate for this group; although "Veddoid" has come into most general use. Typical representatives are the Vedda of interior Ceylon, whence the usual name of the race; some of the backward Dravidian and Munda tribes of India; the Nicobar Islanders; certain of the Moi of Indo-China; the Senoi or Sakai of the Malay Peninsula; the Toala of Celebes. Some also find a Veddoid strain prominent in southeastern Arabia. The Veddoids are almost invariably culturally retarded hill or jungle people who evidently represent an old stratum of population pushed back by Caucasians or Mongoloids, or almost absorbed by them. The dark strain in India seems more probably due to these people than to a true Negroid infusion. Possibly the Indo-Australoids branched off from the Caucasian stem at a very early time before the Caucasian stock was as "white" as it is now. In the lapse of ages the greater number of the Caucasians in and near Europe took on more and more their present characteristics, whereas this backward branch in the region of the Indian Ocean kept its primitive and undifferentiated traits. This is a tempting theory to pursue, but it extends so far into the realm of the hypothetical that its just appraisal must be left to the specialist.

The *Ainu* survive in northern Japan in much the same relation to the Japanese as the Indians occupy to the whites in the United States, except that the contact has been longer and the Ainu are fewer. They are not slant-eyed, their hair is wavy, and they favor bushy beards which give them a superficial resemblance to Russian muzhiks of the old school. Many anthropologists have accordingly reckoned them as an early Caucasoid offshoot or outpost. However, to the north of them, in easternmost Siberia, there lives a series of uncivilized peoples, sometimes grouped together as Palae-Asiatics—"Ancient Asiatics"— who, though generically Mongoloid in type, are less markedly so than the Mongols, Chinese, Japanese, and so on. For instance, their eye fold is less pronounced, and they incline to longish instead of round heads. Take this Mongoloid subtype and let it genetically develop hirsuteness and hair waviness through a mutation in the former relative isolation of the northern Japanese islands, and we have the Ainu pretty well accounted for, without bringing in the Caucasian relationship, which raises other geographic and historical problems. However, neither of the alternative views can as yet be claimed as fully demonstrable.

The *Polynesians,* living within the great island triangle Hawaii-New Zealand-Easter Island, are one of the tall, large-boned, and large-featured races of mankind. There has been much diversity of opinion as to their origin and relationship. There is almost certainly a definite Caucasoid strain in them. The Mongoloid element appears perhaps to be larger, but it is not very specialized Mongoloid. Locally, there may be minor Negroid absorptions—to reach the central Pacific the ancestral Polynesians had to pass by or through archipelagoes which now are Papuo-Melanesian Negroid. The Polynesian race problem is made more difficult by the fact that any population derived from a small number of ancestors, such as a few canoeloads of migrants, is quite likely to manifest now special features that originally were individual peculiarities. In a population sprung from many ancestors, such personal traits may also persist, but ordinarily will reappear only in a few individuals in each generation, and will not come to characterize the average or racial type. Thus the accidents of isolation selection, as well as previous mixture, have contributed to make the classification of Polynesian racial type difficult, though culturally and in speech the Polynesians are not only a well-defined but a closely knit group. Most of the more recent world-wide race classifications tend to emphasize the Caucasoid resemblances of the Polynesians.

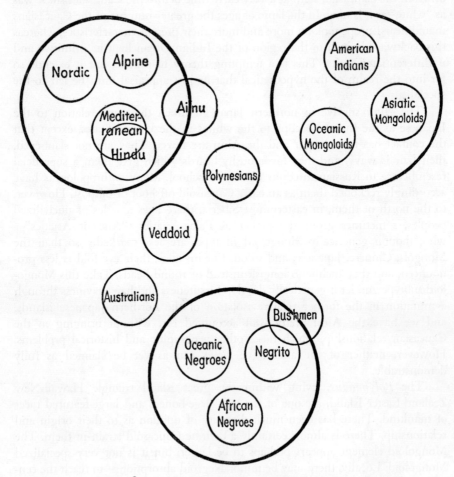

FIG. 8.   RELATIONSHIP OF HUMAN RACES

Distances between the centers of circles are representative of the degree of relationship.

Figure 8 attempts to represent graphically the degree of resemblance and of difference between the principal physical types as they have been summarized in the table and in preceding discussion.

66. CONTINENTS AND OCEANS

One fact about the classification stands out clearly; namely, that the three grand races are not limited to particular continents. It is true that the center of gravity of the Caucasians is in or near Europe, that the biggest block of Negroids is situated in Africa, and that the largest mass of Mongoloids is in Asia. It is even possible that these three types evolved on these three continents. But each of them is *intercontinental* in its recent distribution. Western Asia and northern Africa as well as Europe are Caucasian. There are Negroids in Oceania as well as in Africa, and the Mongoloids are found in Oceania, Asia, and both Americas.

In fact the distribution of the three primary races can better be described as oceanically marginal than as continental. The Caucasian parts of Europe, Asia, and Africa surround the Mediterranean Sea. The African and the Oceanic branches of the Negroid race are situated on the left and right sides of the Indian Ocean. The Mongoloid habitat in Oceania, in East Asia, and in North and South America almost encloses the Pacific Ocean (Figs. 6 and 7).

67. HISTORY OF THE CONTINENTAL AND THE THREEFOLD CLASSIFICATIONS

Most of the early classifications of mankind tried to identify races and continents too closely. The first attempt was that of Linnaeus in the middle of the eighteenth century. He distinguished and described four varieties of mankind, which he called *Europaeus albus, Asiaticus luridus, Americanus rufus,* and *Afer niger;* that is, European White, Asiatic Yellow, American Red, and African Black.

The next classification, that of Blumenbach in 1775, is essentially the same except for adding a fifth or Oceanic variety. Blumenbach's five continental races—Caucasian, Mongolian, Ethiopian, American, and Malayan—long survived in many elementary geographies, usually under the designations of White, Yellow, Black, Red, and Brown.

As time went on, the continental principle of race classification came to be recognized as inadequate, and there was a tendency among anthropologists to accept the distinctness of certain specialized groups, such as Australians, Bushmen, Eskimo, and Ainu, which were often elevated into races substantially equal in rank with the great races like the Mongoloid. Thus the early American writers Nott and Gliddon recognized seven races: European, Asiatic, Negro, American, Malay, Australian, and Arctic. This is the fivefold scheme of Blumenbach with the Australoid and the Eskimo added.

On the other hand, the feeling gained ground, especially among the French physical anthropologists of the mid-nineteenth century, that mankind could be satisfactorily, or at least essentially, accounted for by a division into Caucasian, Negroid, and Mongoloid. Those who adopted this principle tried to fit divergent types like the Australians and the Polynesians into one or the other of these three great groups. Some little doctoring had to be done in this process, and some salient facts estimated rather lightly. It is for this reason that it has seemed best here not to make our tripartite classification too exhaustive. This threefold classification clearly absorbs the great mass of mankind without straining, but it is soundest to recognize that this same basic classification requires a certain margin of extensions along the lines indicated in our table.

68. FINER SUBDIVISIONS OF THE WHITE RACE

While the basic grouping of white Europeans into Mediterraneans, Alpines, and Nordics as first fully developed by Ripley [9] is still accepted, there is also general agreement that more refined distinctions are necessary: that there are several subvarieties of Alpines, of Mediterraneans, and of Nordics. Moreover, there is reasonably close agreement as to most of these subvarieties or local races, as to what distinguishes them, and in what regions they are best characterized. Unfortunately there is much less agreement when it comes to names; here each author is likely to play his preference, as is also true in the field of accounting for origins, where subjective opinions as to mixtures, mutations, Palaeolithic survivals, genetic behavior, environmental influence, and the like have had free run. Fortunately, this last diversity is not a very serious matter, because as yet almost nothing can be proved on *how* any race *came to be* as it is, and any opinion remains just an opinion. On the other hand, *what* races there *are* is much more a matter of fact, once enough measurements and observations are available, and on this the authorities agree much better.

For instance, within the generic Alpine or broad-headed Caucasian subrace, a Dinaric and an Armenoid type are quite generally set off, and a Lapp type is added by some.

The Dinaric type is tall, with a long and large nose, often convex; the face is long, though the head is broad. This type is most prominent northeast of the Adriatic Sea.

By contrast, the specific Alpine type is medium-statured, thick-necked, of pyknic bodily habitus (§ 79), with high forehead, and a nose tending to a concave or snub profile. It can be described as a somewhat infantilized or foetalized type, whereas the rugged-featured Dinaric inclines to the senescent. Alpine distribution proper is more westerly than Dinaric. The center of characterization would perhaps be central France or the Alps, as against Yugoslavia.

[9] Ripley himself still used the language term "Teutonic," but Deniker's "Nordic" quickly replaced it in general usage.

The Armenoid type is brunet, short-headed, and especially high-headed; the nose is both long and prominently convex. The area of characterization is eastern Turkey and adjacent districts.

The Lapps of northerly Scandinavia were formerly classed outright as Mongoloids, but they show perhaps as many Alpine as East Asiatic traits. They are a very short people—under 160 cm—light-framed and small-bodied, with delicate hands and feet. They are brachycephalic, extraordinarily small-jawed, and snub-nosed; and the majority are brunet, though there are some blonds. The Mongoloid eye fold and stiff, jet-black hair are rare. They have without question absorbed some Nordic or East Baltic blood; but their total features do not at all fit the expectable picture of a Nordic-Mongoloid cross. The Lapps live in a hard environment and have never been numerous. They may therefore well represent either a sub-Alpine or a sub-Mongoloid type that has become not only mixed but stunted, infantilized, and otherwise specialized.

The most pronounced or extreme Nordics are those of northwestern Europe, plus of course their descendants by immigration in other continents. A sub-Nordic type is generally accepted as prevalent in northeastern Europe. This East Baltic type is somewhat less tall than the Nordic, heavier-set, broader-headed, and thicker-nosed; the hair tends to be ash-blond instead of golden, the eyes gray or greenish rather than blue. Field Marshal Hindenburg is cited as a classic example. The East Baltic distribution is in northeastern Germany, the former Baltic states, and Finland, Poland, and Russia, especially in the north.[10] Various names have been used for the type: Sub-Nordic, East Baltic, East European, Neo-Danubian; some of these suggest further subdivision or grouping. The term "East Baltic" has the advantage of being geographically descriptive without too many other implications.

The basic Mediterranean race also shows subtypes. If we weight stature, North Africa and the Mediterranoid element in Britain are set off by relative tallness. This strain has been called Atlanto-Mediterranean. As regards features as a whole, the aquiline-nosed, slender Arabians and Egyptians are in some ways Mediterraneans par excellence. Some have made them into an "Oriental" subrace. Persians and Afghans resemble them rather closely, but also approximate the Hindu type. All in all, Mediterraneans tend to considerable uniformity.

In East Africa, in Ethiopia, Somaliland, Kenya, and parts of the Anglo-Egyptian Sudan, whites and blacks abut, and there has been hybridization. The white element is clearly Mediterranoid, and appears stronger than the Negroid, in the areas mentioned. Complexion often gets pretty dark, and the hair crisp, but the nose remains salient, the jaws are straight instead of protruding, the lips do not evert. Most of the peoples are tall and slender, some to an extraordi-

---

[10] Whereas the full-Nordic habitat covers north-central and northwestern Germany, Denmark, Sweden and Norway, Holland, northern France, the British Isles, and Iceland.

nary degree. This hybrid or transitional Mediterranean type has generally been called Hamitic, but as that is the name of a family of languages, it is inadmissible for a biological race, and we shall substitute East African. Some influence of the type extends westward in Africa on the Caucasian-Negro border, and the Nilotic Negro tribes—Dinka, Nuer, Shilluk, and so on—may have derived the ultraelongation of their physique from an absorption of blood of the type under discussion. But the most marked characterization of the type is in the east, in and toward the "Horn" of Africa.

Summarizing, we have:

RACES IN AND AROUND EUROPE

Nordic:	Nordic proper
	East Baltic or Sub-Nordic
Alpine:	Alpine proper
	Dinaric
	Armenoid
	(Lapp—part Mongoloid?)
Mediterranean:	Mediterranean proper *
	Atlanto-Mediterranean *
	Oriental and Irano-Afghan *
	East African (Negroid admixture)

* Not very sharply differentiated.

The Jews everywhere considerably approximate the local Gentile type. In Algiers they tend to resemble Mediterraneans, in Turkey Armenoids, in northern Germany Nordics. There has evidently been more mixture across the religious caste line through the generations than either side likes to admit. To put it differently, normally a part of any Jewish population is physically indistinguishable, by measures or by observation, from the Christians or the Mohammedans of the same area. The part that is differentiable appears to be so through hereditary persistence of either Armenoid or Oriental-Mediterranean traits. In large measure, popular recognition of Jews as such is based on nonracial externals such as name and association, or on expressions in manners, gestures, bodily habits, dress, and the like which conceivably might be racially hereditary but much more probably are socially conditioned and can therefore be learned and unlearned. There is certainly no single crude physical trait that is a safe index of Jewishness. Convex noses are not only Armenoid and Oriental but Mediterranean, Dinaric, East African, Hindu, Papuo-Melanesian, and Plains Indian! What is most characteristic of the so-called Jewish nose is not its total profile—which can be abundantly matched in many Gentile populations—but its "nostrility," a little accentuation of the curl of the nostril where it joins the face. This is a trait that was first noted by a Jewish observer, and which is on the border line between an organic "feature" and a functional "expression."

69. TRAIT DISTRIBUTIONS

Trait maps, such as Figures 9, 10, and 11, are both more accurate and more reliably representative than race maps. If the stature of adult males in a given district averages 168 cm, that is a perfectly definite fact, whose utility is not done away with by the circumstance that any average is an abstraction or generalization, and that the separate individuals of the group may range all the way from

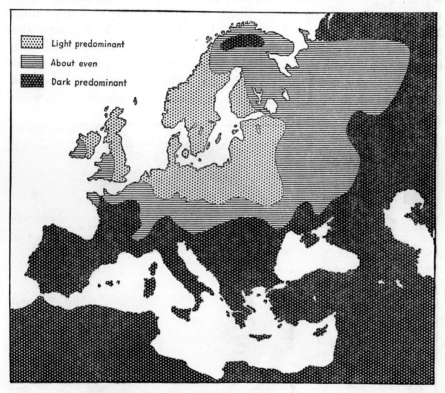

FIG. 9.   HAIR AND EYE COLOR: EUROPE

The regular, graded distribution, here centering around the Baltic, often characterizes single traits. (Modified from Coon and Struck)

145 to 200 cm. But most physical traits pass along through heredity independently of one another.[11] The result is that where there has been shuffling or mixing of populations of different type, an individual can have, say, typical

[11] There are linked traits, such as hair, eye, and skin pigmentation, which all depend on abundance of melanin. But even here the linkage is only partial, else we should not have so many blue-eyed dark heads in Ireland and Wales, and so many brown-eyed blonds in Russia.

Nordic body height, Alpine head form, and Mediterranean color, or any other combination of these or other traits. Now most of Europe has been well shuffled populationally in its long racial history. And from this it develops that individuals conforming in every trait to one racial type, and to that only, are fairly rare. One person is a good Nordic except that his hair is too dark, the next has too broad a face. By the time we have run through a fair sample of a population we may have found 10 per cent of definite Nordics, 5 per cent of indubitable Alpines, 40 per cent who are prevalently Nordic, 30 per cent prevalently Alpine, 10 per cent about evenly Nordic-Alpine, and perhaps 5 per cent more nearly Mediterranean, Dinaric, and scattering. In unit mapping, such a population might have to be entered as Nordic, but it is evident with how much qualification. Actually such a group would differ more from the purest Nordic groups than from some near-by group in which the Alpine element just nosed out the Nordic, and which would accordingly be represented as Alpine on a map whose

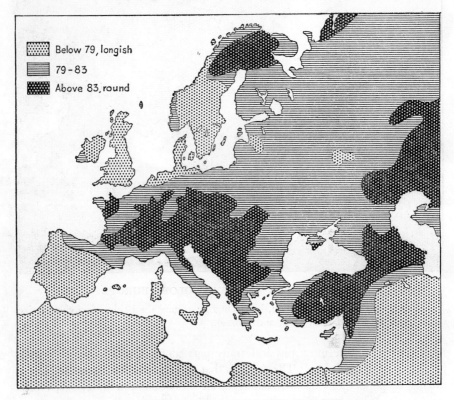

FIG. 10.   CEPHALIC INDEX: EUROPE

An Alpine-Dinaric-Armenoid-Mongoloid wedge of broadheads separates two medium-headed groups: the Nordics and East Baltics on the north, from the several Mediterranean subgroups on the south. (Simplified from Coon and Struck)

units were determined by pluralities. An accurate racial map is therefore normally complicated by having to show "degrees of Nordicness" and the like by means of variations of color and shading; or by interdigitating bars of "Nordic" and "Alpine" color, or colors representative of three or four races, and by varying the width of the bars proportionally to the strength of the several racial elements; all of which makes for loss of that incisive comprehension which is the purpose of a map or diagram.

A partial solution is to color or shade only the areas of most decisive characterization, as in Figure 12 (page 152), leaving the transitional ones blank. If this plan could be extended to contours of intensification for each racial type, it would be almost ideal; but in practice this is scarcely feasible except for traits or features considered one at a time. Trait maps can be made objective, and a series of them builds up into a substitute for a race map. Thus Figures 9, 10,

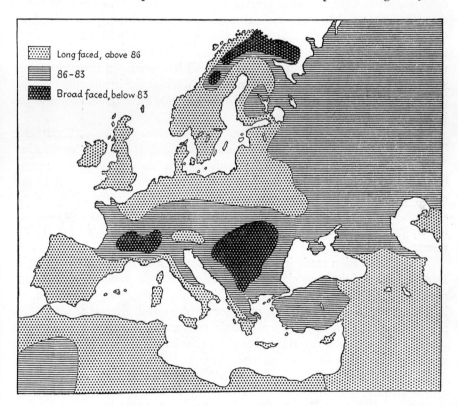

Long faced, above 86

86–83

Broad faced, below 83

FIG. 11.   FACIAL INDEX: EUROPE

Again a wedge, now of broad-faced peoples, separates narrow-faced blonds from narrow-faced Mediterraneans. Within the wedge, the Alpine, Dinaric, and Lapp centers of characterization are evident as areas of specially broad or short faces. Only the short-headed Armenoids are long-faced. (Reduced from Struck)

and 11, used cumulatively, outline not only the basic Nordic-Alpine-Mediter-
ranean classification, but the subdivision of the "Alpine" into Alpines proper,
Dinarics, Armenoids, Lapps, and Mongolians, the separation of blonds into
longish-headed Nordics and roundheaded East Balts, and so on.

70. THE DENIKER, HUXLEY, AND BOAS SCHEMES

It cannot be too much emphasized that all race classifications yet made
rest somewhat on subjective judgments, no matter how much these judgments
may be validated by objective measures and statistics. Similar subjective factors
are present in most of that part of science which cannot be dragged into a laboratory or tested by experiment: evolutionary biology, for instance, or the question
of the age of geological periods in millions of years. This is nothing to be disconcerted over. Opinions may remain personal, but they vary from sensible
through flighty and fantastic to insane ones; and they may be supported by
overwhelming masses of coherent evidence, or again merely by highly selected
and fragmentary data. In short, there are such things as sound judgment and
unsound judgment—or let us say, sounder and less sound—in those realms of
science in which absolute proof is impossible. Much of the intellectual training
of anthropology is precisely in learning to discriminate between better and worse
judgments and better and worse evidence.

For this reason, some additional race classifications will be outlined here.
This will at least protect the reader against the impulse to simplify the situation
for himself by accepting the Kroeber classification as "the true" one. As a matter
of fact, such truth value as it has is bound to be largely proportionate to the
degree in which it reflects a consensus of unprejudiced opinion in previous
schemes. In the end, what is common to nearly all classifications can be accepted
as very probably valid; but their idiosyncrasies must be examined with critical
reserve.

The classification made in 1889 by the Russian-born French anthropologist
Deniker is one of the most elaborate yet devised, and has stood the test of time
remarkably, to judge by the degree to which other anthropologists build upon
it. It recognizes 6 grand divisions, 17 minor divisions, and 29 separate races. The
primary criterion of classification is hair texture. In the following list, the
parenthetical forms at the right give the equivalent terms used in this book,
whenever the difference is mainly one of name.

Perhaps this scheme subdivides the Mediterraneans and the native Americans overfinely, and the East Asiatics unduly little; but these are points of
weighting rather than principle. The one point at which all subsequent opinion
differs from Deniker's is in regard to race 8, his "Assyroid," obviously corresponding to our Armenoid, which he puts not into grand division C, Dark
Caucasoids, but into B, along with Australoids, Veddoids, and East African
dark-skins. This B group might be translated as "neither quite Caucasian nor

DENIKER'S CLASSIFICATION

A. Hair woolly, with broad nose   (NEGROID)
  I. 1. Bushman
  II. Negroid
    2. Negrito
    3. Negro
    4. Melanesian (including Papuan)
B. Hair curly to wavy   (NEGROID TO CAUCASOID)
  III. 5. Ethiopian (Sudan, etc.)   *(East African)*
  IV. 6. Australian
   V. 7. Dravidian (southern India)   *(Veddoid)*
  VI. 8. Assyroid (Kurds, Armenians, Jews) *(Armenoid!)*
C. Hair wavy   (DARK CAUCASOID)
  VII. 9. Indo-Afghan   *(Hindu)*
  VIII. North African
    10. Arab or Semite *(East Mediterranean)*
    11. Berber (North Africa) *(Mediterranean)*
  IX. Melanochroid
    12. Littoral (Atlanto-Medit.) *(Mediterranean)*
    13. Ibero-insular (Spain, Southern Italy) *(Mediterranean)*
    14. Western European   *(Alpine)*
    15. Adriatic (Northern Italy, Balkans) *(Dinaric)*
D. Hair wavy to straight, with light eyes (FAIR CAUCASOID)
  X. Xanthochroid
    16. North European   *(Nordic)*
    17. East European   **(East Baltic)*
E. Hair wavy to straight, with dark eyes (CAUCASOID TO MONGOLOID)
  XI. 18. Ainu
  XII. Oceanian
    19. Polynesian
    20. Indonesian (East Indies)
F. Hair straight   (MONGOLOID)
  XIII. American
    21. South American
    22. North American
    23. Central American
    24. Patagonian
  XIV. 25. Eskimo
  XV. 26. Lapp
  XVI. Eurasian
    27. Ugrian (eastern Russia)
    28. Turco-Tartar (southwestern Siberia)
  XVII. 29. Mongol (East Asia)

* "East Baltic" in the wider sense used in this book. Deniker called the peoples actually living on the East Baltic Sea "Sub-Nordics," and those farther inland, East Europeans or the "Eastern" ᵃace, with a "Vistulan" subrace.

Negroid," just as Deniker's E group consists of races not too certain as between Caucasian and Mongoloid affiliation. This leaves grand division A as Negroid, C and D Caucasoid, F Mongoloid. In other words, under Deniker's apparent complexity, there is the usual threefold primary classification, but with enough recognition of transitions to avoid any oversimplified rigidity.

Huxley's scheme recognizes four main races, or five including a transitional one. These are (1) "Australoids," including Dravidians and Egyptians (*sic*); (2) Negroids, and (3) Mongoloids, both as customarily accepted; (4) Xanthochroi, about equivalent to Nordics and Alpines; (5) Melanochroi, nearly the same as the Mediterraneans, but supposed by Huxley to be hybrid or intermediate between the Xanthochroi and the "Australoids." This classification in effect emphasizes the connection between Australoids and Caucasians, with the Negroids as a distinctive group on one side and the Mongoloids on the other.

Haeckel's classification is basically similar to Huxley's, in that besides the usual three primary stocks—which he elevates into species—he recognizes a separate group comprising Australians, Dravidians, and Vedda-like Indo-Australians.

Boas inclines to contrast Negroids, as one fundamental line of human development, with Caucasoids and Mongoloids joined in another line. In favor of this view is the fact that the Negro is an extreme type of *Homo sapiens* in hair form, pigmentation, nose breadth, prognathism, and lip eversion. Granting this distinctiveness, the East Asiatic Mongolian would have to be selected within the contrasting Caucaso-Mongoloid stock as its most specialized branch—and as on the whole most antithetical to the Negro—with his stiff, long hair, flat face, and epicanthic fold, extreme brachycephalization, and short limbs. In line with this finding is the fact that there are Negro-Caucasoid transitions just as there are Caucasoid-Mongoloid ones, but there are no races that seem clearly intermediate between Negroids and Mongoloids. However, it is evident that such a view as this must not be pressed too far, since the Caucasian also specializes in extreme features: light pigmentation, prominence of nose, orthognathism, and hairiness.

71. THE POLISH, VON EICKSTEDT, AND HOOTON CLASSIFICATIONS

A Polish school of physical anthropologists, under the leadership of Czekanowski, has developed a statistical technique of objectively sorting or factoring a given population into what it believes are its natural racial elements, components, or types: factoring it both qualitatively and quantitatively. The results are interesting to compare with those obtained through the more usual subjective inspectional approach secondarily validated by statistics. What follows is a condensation of Klimek's summary of the findings of the Polish school.

These are the racial types recognized, with the names, as far as possible, converted into those used in this book:

THE CZEKANOWSKI-KLIMEK SCHEME

Black Race

Pygmy
Bushman ("Negroidal")
Congo Negro ("Austro-African")
Sudan Negro ("Nigritian"): The most highly characterized Negro type
Australoid: Wavy-haired, with many primitive traits

White Race, Transitional to Black

Indic ("Mediterranoid"): Related to Mediterranean
East African ("Meridional"): Related to Oriental; perhaps a mixture of it
  with Sudan Negro

White Race

Oriental: East and south of the Mediterranean Sea
Mediterranean: North and west of the Mediterranean Sea
Armenoid
Nordic
(For additional European types resulting from crossing of the elemental
  types, see below.)

Yellow Race, Transitional to White

North Asiatic ("Palaeo-Asiatic"): Siberian sub-Mongoloids, including
  Ainu

Yellow Race

Lapponoid: Enters into several European crossed races; close to the next.
Central Asiatic: Difficult to distinguish from the last, when a component;
  Mongols, etc.; definitely brachycephalic
East Asiatic ("Pacific"): Taller than the last, less brachycephalic; Chinese,
  etc.
Eskimoid ("Arctic")
"Palaeo-American": A longheaded component, chiefly in South America,
  allied to the prehistoric Lagoa Santa skeletal type

In Europe, where analysis of data has been carried farthest, six additional
mixed or hybrid types are recognized by the Poles as due to crossing of four
basic types:
  Sub-Nordic, from Nordic and Lapponoid crossing (= East Baltic in the nar-
rower geographic sense)
  Northwestern, from Nordic and Mediterranean (= Irish, etc.)
  Dinaric, from Nordic and Armenoid [12]
  Littoral, from Mediterranean and Armenoid (a large Mediterranean type, Deni-
ker's Atlanto-Mediterranean subtype)
  Alpine, from Lapponoid and Armenoid [12]
  "Pre-Slavic," from Mediterranean and Lapponoid (Russia, etc. Similar to North
Asiatic)

[12] Thus after Klimek, 1932. Coon, *The Races of Europe,* basing on Czekanowski, 1928,
interchanges the parentage of Dinaric and Alpine from that given above.

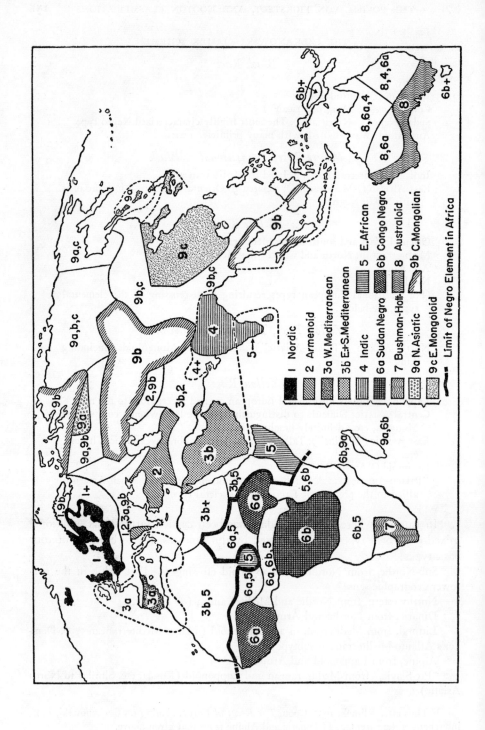

1 Nordic
2 Armenoid
3a W.Mediterranean
3b E+S.Mediterranean
4 Indic
6a Sudan Negro
7 Bushman-Hott.
9a N.Asiatic
9c E.Mongoloid

5 E.African
6b Congo Negro
8 Australoid
9b C.Mongolian

— Limit of Negro Element in Africa

This last, European part of the classification is too schematic and diagrammatic to inspire much confidence that the six types actually did originate in the way stated as hybrids between four original ones. But the European classification is of interest because in the main much the same types are recognized under it as we have encountered before. Through the supposed Lapponoid ingredient in Pre-Slavic, Sub-Nordic, and Alpine, a Sub-Mongoloid element is recognized by the Polish school as stretching through Europe from Russia to France.

Not only Europe but the other continents are for the most part construed by this school as inhabited by populations that represent mixtures of from two to several of these seventeen primary racial components. The prevalence of such hybridization is almost certain, even if it should prove that the precise proportions of the constituent racial elements are not always as determined by the Polish school. Most of the world accordingly is mapped by them as an interdigitation of many colors. This complexity has been reduced in our map of their findings (Fig. 12), by plotting the shadings only on the areas of most definite dominance of the racial types—the areas of their purest characterization—in the Eastern Hemisphere.

The following may be added to supplement this map. An Indic element is recognized as present everywhere in Oceania except in southern Australia. It is strongest in Polynesia, where it seems equivalent to what is called Hindu in this book; elsewhere in Oceania, it is probably equivalent to Veddoid. The Mongoloid constituents in the Pacific are the "Central Asiatic," strongest in Sumatra, Java, and Borneo, and fading out southeastward; and the "East Asiatic," which appears in the Philippines and Celebes, and increasingly supplants the Central Asiatic toward Polynesia. New Guinea and Melanesia are attributed to the two African Negroid races, with varying admixtures of East African and Indic. The extinct Tasmanians are related to the Negroes more nearly than to the Australoids. The Madagascans are Congo Negroes with an infusion of western Indonesians, that is, "Central Asiatic" Mongoloids.

The aborigines of the New World are blends of four Mongoloid races. Of these, the "Palaeo-American" or Lagoa Santa has only slight local representation in North America, and none in the Eastern Hemisphere. The Eskimo survive dominant along the Arctic shores, but the presence of their type is affirmed to be traceable in South America, especially in Patagonia. The East and Central Asiatic types between them are found to have contributed most of the ancestry of the American Indians. The former is represented most strongly in the tall tribes east of the Mississippi, the latter, among rather short-statured, culturally advanced populations like the Maya, the Chibcha, and the Inca.

◀ FIG. 12.   CONCENTRATION AND DILUTION OF RACIAL TYPES

Areas of greatest concentration or purity of racial types (shaded) and of dilution or mixture (lettered only), according to the Polish school. (After Klimek)

So much for the views of the Polish school. The findings are not as clearly demonstrated as the members of the school believe; but most of them make considerable sense, especially if the basic racial "elements" or components are not adhered to too literally. And it is a virtue of the statistical method employed by the school that it emphasizes the mixtures and transitions which undoubtedly characterize much of humanity.

An elaborate classification, fuller even than that of Deniker, is the 1937 scheme of von Eickstedt, who recognizes three subspecies of man: the Albi or Europids, the Leiotrichi or Mongolids and Americanids, and the Afri or Negrids. These subdivide into 13 "series," 38 "varieties" or races, and about 40 additional subvarieties. Thus the Alpines belong, with Dinarids, Armenids, and Turanids, to the "Brachimorph series" of Europids, and subdivide into West Alpines and Lappids. The Melanochroic series of Europids comprises not only Mediterraneans, Orientalids, and Indids, but Polynesids. The "Protomorph" or primitive series of von Eickstedt's Europids contains Veddids and Ainuids. Under his Mongolids, von Eickstedt includes a "series" of "Subnigri" consisting of the "Khoisanid" variety, or the Bushmen and Hottentots. This placing at least emphasizes how aberrant and recalcitrant the Bushmen are. The Australids are degraded into mere East Negrids along with Neo- and Palae-Melanesids. A contact zone of transitional Europo-Afri is recognized; these consist of Aethiopids in East Africa and Indo-Melanids in India. This scheme gives the Hindus a triple racial origin: straight white allied to Mediterranean (Indid); primitive white (Veddid); and transitional black (Indo-Melanid).

The von Eickstedt classification presents several definite specialties or novelties, such as the placing of Polynesians, Bushmen, and Australians. But on the whole it obviously conforms to previous ones, the differences being mostly in degree of elaboration or weighting, and in the coinage of new and somewhat pedantic names.[13]

So as not to give the impression that all the more elaborate race classifications are by Europeans, an American one will also be summarized: Hooton's of 1946.

Hooton recognizes three "primary races" corresponding to the usual primary stocks. Under these he has 23 primary subraces, of which 8 are composite but predominantly White, Negroid, or Mongoloid. Certain of these subraces are again subdivided, sometimes into morphological types, sometimes into secondary subraces.

[13] Since about 1940, the von Eickstedt classification of North American Indians into Pacifids, Centralids, Silvids, and Margids has gained wide currency among archaeologists dealing with the eastern United States and Canada; and this without the von Eickstedt scheme as a whole appearing to be much known to them. Evidently physical anthropologists have so far failed to provide a classification of native types that meets the needs of the archaeologists in this area.

THE HOOTON CLASSIFICATION

I. *White or Caucasoid Primary Race*

1. Mediterranean
   a. Upper Palaeolithic survivals, chiefly in the British Isles
   b. Iranian Plateau
   c. Classic Mediterranean, in a hook-nosed and a straight-nosed subtype
2. Ainu
3. Keltic (light-eyed, dark or red haired, longheaded, mainly in the British Isles)
4. Nordic
5. Alpine
6. East Baltic (blond roundheads)
7. Armenoid (stabilized blend of Classic Mediterranean, Iranian Plateau, and Alpine)
8. Dinaric (stabilized blend of Upper Palaeolithic, Alpine, Armenoid, and Nordic)
9. Nordic-Alpine (individuals intermediate to 4 and 5; 23% of the U.S.)
10. Nordic-Mediterranean (intermediate to 1 and 4; 25% of the U.S.)

COMPOSITE, PREDOMINANTLY WHITE

11. Australian (Archaic White, Tasmanian, plus minor Melanesian)
    a. Murrian, most nearly White; specially in the southeast
    b. Carpentarian, Melanesian increment; in the north
    c. Tasmanoid; refuge areas in Queensland
12. Indo-Dravidian (Classic Mediterranean, Australoid, Negrito, plus varying minor fractions)
    a. Classic Indo-Dravidian: most of northern India; approaching Classic Mediterranean
    b. Armenoid-Iranian Plateau: western and northeastern India
    c. Indo-Nordic: northwestern Himalayas
    d. Australoid or Veddoid: central and southern India
    e. Negritoid: spots in southern India
13. Polynesian (mostly brunet White, plus Mongoloid, plus Melanesian)

II. *Negroid Primary Race*

14. African Negro or Negritian or Forest Negro
15. Nilotic Negro, probably with infusion of "Hamitic" Mediterranean
16. Negrito
    a. Infantile type: in all Negrito populations
    b. Adultiform: among all Negritos, except in the Andamans and the Philippines

COMPOSITE, PREDOMINANTLY NEGROID

17. Tasmanian: Negrito plus Australian
18. Melanesian-Papuan: Negrito, Australoid, hook-nosed Classic Mediterranean, plus fractions
    a. Papuan
    b. Melanesian
19. Bushman-Hottentot: Negrito plus Boskop (§ 51).
    a. Bushman
    b. Hottentot: Bushman plus Negro and Hamitic Mediterranean

III. *Mongoloid Primary Race*

20. Classic Mongoloid
21. Arctic Mongoloid or Eskimoid (including eastern Palaeo-Asiatic tribes)

COMPOSITE, PREDOMINANTLY MONGOLOID

22. Indonesian-Mongoloid or Indonesian-Malay (Mongoloid plus Mediterranean plus Ainu plus Negrito)
    a. Malay-Mongoloid (Indonesia and Farther India, including most Japanese)
    b. Indonesian (Pre-Mongoloid groups in South China, Farther India, and island interiors)
23. American Indian (Mongoloid plus Iranian Mediterranean plus Australoid plus a little Negritoid)
    a. Brachycephals, index 80 and up. Hawk-nosed and snub-nosed subtypes
    b. Dolichocephals, index under 80. Hawk-nosed and snub-nosed subtypes

A marked feature of this classification is the degree to which it admits mixture and makes use of it. The Polish school also holds most populations to be more or less mixed, but depends on statistical segregation of the ingredients. Hooton employs recognition, subsequently supported by sorting according to diagnostic criteria if individual measurements are available. In a simple situation, first judgment by visual observation is perhaps as effective and reliable a procedure as more elaborate and mechanical means; and it is certainly less pedantic. But when from three to six racial ingredients are recognized in a population, and these in different strengths and order of appearance, the majority of individuals are certain to show traits contributed by several of the racial components. One man's hair may derive from race A, his nose from B, his height from C. The next man examined may have the same features respectively from race components D, A, C. If features blend in heredity, as most of them do, many individuals will not even have clear A, B, C, or D hair, noses, or heights. In this event, most members of the population are likely to be indeterminate in most of their features as regards evidence of origin from A or B or C or D. In fact, such indeterminate features might logically be attributed to an infusion of race G, or H, if one had chosen to start with A, B, C, G, or A, B, H, D, instead of A, B, C, D. Everything accordingly depends on which racial ingredients one elects to start his hypothesis with, after inspection; and then, on how one defines the criteria or critical values for sorting out that ingredient. In short, the unscrambling of a composite race into its original pure-race constituents is a process that is far from simple and far from sure. No matter how quantitatively the constituents are defined, and how statistically validated the final analysis is, a subjective factor enters into the process. Consequently the findings are speculative in proportion as the population analyzed is complex in its origins.

So it comes about that some of the Hooton hypotheses are pretty finely spun. Some even seem circular. Thus he makes the Australians Archaic White plus a

Tasmanian and locally a minor Melanesian ingredient. The Tasmanians in turn he sees as predominantly Negrito, plus an Australian element—into which they have presumably already entered! Similarly with the Australoid or Veddoid type (12d) in India, which he evidently relates to the Australian types (11a, b, c) but in a manner of interdependence that is not clear.

Some of the admixtures are also pretty far-flung and ancient for their confident recognition today, especially when only small dosages of an ingredient are claimed. Thus the specific Iranian Plateau element in the American Indians! This appears to be invoked to account for the hawk noses in America. But how and when did Iranian-nosed ancestors travel from Afghanistan to America? And leave no traces along their route? It may be that hawk-nosedness has little probability of originating repeatedly in separate races through independent mutation, and that we must accordingly explain all its recurrences by connection through migration and mixture. But this is not proved; it is only an opinion.

The Negritos in particular are thought by Hooton to have left dashes of their type more or less all over the world. This might well be; but it involves a considerable hypothesis as to their origin and dispersal—considerable in the face of the very little we actually know about their past.

It is also necessary to realize that Hooton's subraces sometimes seem to be intended to account for all the people in an area, but in other areas they represent only a more or less pure morphological type, most of the population being mixed and not specially accounted for. Thus the type of the Classic Mongoloid subrace (20) is described as concentrated in eastern Siberia among tribes like the Tungus Gold and the Mongol Buriat, and also as occurring "frequently" among the northern Chinese. But what the other northern Chinese are, and their southern and central conationals, is not stated. Yet for India, where Guha's views are followed, the classification seems to be exhaustive.

There is also a seeming inconsistency, or at least ambiguity, between subraces such as 7, Armenoid, and 8, Dinaric, which are described as "stabilized blends due to interbreeding," and 9, Nordic-Alpine, and 10, Nordic-Mediterranean, which are "residual mixed types (interbreeds)" or "sortings-out" of individuals intermediate in characters. At any rate, the 23 Hooton subraces evidently are not all of them groups co-ordinate in kind or classificatory rank.

It will be noted that there are a number of traits which are shared by adjoining races: as blondness by East Baltic, Nordic, and partly by Keltic. Similarly with hawk or hook noses. These occur among one subtype of Classic Mediterraneans, among Iranian Plateau Mediterraneans, among Armenoids and Dinarics, and among Hamitic East African Negroes—all in a large continuous area where Europe, Africa, and Asia adjoin. Such continuity of occurrence within a single and freely interbreeding species would almost certainly mean a single origin for the trait, and its spread by mixture of populations. Hooton finds the origin of all hook noses among the Mediterraneans, and has the Armenoids and the Dinarics derive theirs from the more primary Mediterraneans. The view that one particular type of several was the one to have the hook nose first and then give it to the others—this is a finding that goes beyond description and has begun to enter the realm of hypothesis, or frank opinion. For instance, one might alternatively argue with equal logic that it was the Armenoids who first developed this feature and then transmitted it by admixture to the neighboring Iranian and eastern Classic Mediterraneans; for the western Mediterraneans are typically straight-nosed. When it comes to the remote Melanesian-Papuans and American Indians, the case for admixture of a Mediterranean element is obviously still weaker, in proportion to the distances and the long times involved in the view.

The Hooton scheme moves some of its ingredients and composite derivations about with a rather ingratiating insouciance. But once the degree of its speculativeness is recognized, the classification is unusually observant, original, vigorous, and stimulating.

72. BLOOD GROUPS AND GENES

Exceedingly interesting are the data accumulated in recent decades on the racial distribution of blood groups, a set of physiological phenomena of great medical importance in connection with blood transfusions. All human beings belong to one of four classes or "groups," AB, A, B, O, according as their blood serum and blood cells contain specific substances which cause clumping or agglutination of the cells when serum from individuals of certain classes is injected into the blood of other individuals. People of type AB possess two such substances, A and B; those of types A and B, one only; those of O, neither. Any one class is as healthy and viable as another. The difference between them seems not to be reflected in any other bodily trait, in fact can be ascertained only by a physiological test. Further, the factors determining the four classes are inherited by simple Mendelian rules of heredity, in distinction from most human traits, which are multifactor or hybridizing. However, the blood-group factors are triply allelomorphic—A and B both being dominant to O—instead of doubly allelomorphic or alternative—present or absent—as is usual.[14]

A special popular interest has attached to the blood groups because of their legal bearing in cases of disputed paternity. The most important fact in this connection is that individual paternity can never be positively proved by a blood test as such. A particular paternity may be disproved; as when the child is type B, the mother O, and the putative father A. Since A + O cannot yield B, this

[14] In fact, these blood "groups" or types are the first case of threefold allelomorphism established for man. The usual designation for the genes or heredity units in the chromosomes underlying the types of blood are: p for type A; q for B; both p and q for AB; and r for absence of both p and q, resulting in blood type O. The percentage frequency of these genes, which are the hereditary causal factors, is obtained from the frequency of blood types in any given population, by calculation. The formulas are: $r = \sqrt{O}$; $p = \sqrt{(O + A)} - \sqrt{O}$; $q = \sqrt{(O + B)} - \sqrt{O}$.

suspect is not the father of this B. Or again, if it is sure from other circumstances of the case that paternity must rest on one of two men only, one of these may be proved impossible by his blood type, and the other therefore be legally construable as the father. An indeterminate finding is much more frequent than a positive determination.

Finally, and most important for anthropology, many populations, both races and subraces, differ notably in the frequency proportion of individuals belonging to each of the four classes or types. Thus the percentages which the four types constitute of some sample populations is as follows:

BLOOD GROUP PERCENTAGES

Peoples	Type O	Type A	Type B	Type AB
A > 2B				
Swedes	34	51	10	5
English	46	43	7	2
Americans, white	46	41	8	4
Portuguese	38	52	6	3
Italians	36	51	9	4
Austrians	42	40	10	8
Greeks	38	42	16	4
Armenians	22	52	13	13
Philippine Negritos	48	33	14	4
A > B, < 2B				
Russians	41	31	22	6
Poles	32	38	21	9
Uzbek Turks	29	34	27	10
Japanese	31	38	22	8
South Chinese	32	39	19	10
A < B, O < B				
North Chinese	31	25	34	10
Manchus	27	27	38	8
Hindus	30	24	37	8
Gypsies	34	21	39	6
Philippine Moros	25	18	45	12
A± = B±, O > B				
Sumatrans	44	23	29	4
Annamese	42	22	28	7
Congo Negroes	46	22	24	8
Senegal Negroes	43	23	29	5
Madagascans	45	26	24	4
O > A + B + AB				
American Indians, full blood	91	8	1	0
Filipinos	65	15	20	1
Melanesians	54	27	16	3
Australians (natives)	57	38	3	1
Bechuana Negroes	53	19	24	4

The results in hand, which relate to several hundred thousand or millions of tested individuals from hundreds of racial, ethnic, or local populations, sometimes agree and sometimes disagree surprisingly with the usually accepted race classifications. Some East Asiatic Mongolians are thrown into a group with Hindus, others with Poles. The Mongoloid natives of America differ markedly from the Mongoloids of East Asia. The high-A peoples of Europe include Nordics, Mediterraneans, Armenoids, Alpines. The most extreme in low B are not Nordics but Iberian Mediterraneans. The most extreme high B's among whites are found in the Hindus—close racial relatives of the Mediterraneans. Senegal Negroes agree closely with brown Malaysians, but differ from the Negroid Melanesians.

It is clear that we have in these blood-group distributions an intriguing set of data, which crosscut ordinary race relationships. A reason for this irrelevance to race—perhaps the main one—is that we are dealing with a single trait, whereas a race is an expression of the total or average coherence of many traits. Head form, viewed by itself, is similarly irrelevant. Peoples as different as Negroes, Australoids, Hindus, Eskimo, and Spaniards all have long heads. The tallest of all populations are certain East Africans, northern Europeans, Polynesians, and Indians of the central United States—who are completely diverse racially. While some traits, like hair texture and nasal index, do occur in broad, approximate conformity with race, it is evident that many do not; and blood type happens to be one of these.

There is in fact a great deal more local variability among most populations than the few selected figures above show. However, they outline some interesting situations that on the whole are confirmed by fuller data. Thus the region of high frequency of type A is mainly that of southern and western Europe. Class A still exceeds B, but by a smaller ratio, among most of the peoples between western Russia and China and Japan. Type B is definitely in excess in India and again in the area about North China and Manchuria. Among most Negroes, Malaysians, and Farther Indians, A and B percentages are more evenly balanced, neither running very high, and both less than O. Peoples with high O frequency are often those of remote continents or islands or living in isolated groups.

All sorts of theories have been proposed to explain the populational distribution of the four blood types, ranging from hypotheses of very ancient inheritance[15] to development of certain factors in historic times. Thus it has been suggested that type O was the original one for mankind, and that then types A and B originated as separate mutations, A in Europe, B in India, and were subsequently spread by race mixture, persons of class AB having both A and B in their ancestry. However, it is hard to see how North China and Man-

---

[15] All four of the anthropoid apes show A; only the chimpanzee shows O; the other three, B. This does not get us very far in our human problem.

churia could derive much of their blood from India, and how if they did, South China and Japan could retain an excess of A in proportions almost identical with Russia and Poland. On the other hand, the Hungarian Gypsies, historically known as an emigrated group from India, do retain typical Hindu proportions.[16]

No general theory concerning blood-type distribution that will hold water has yet been found. Distributions are not even geographically clear-cut and consistent, but vary and wobble provincially very much as visible race features vary in subraces and local types. Thus, native America, when pureblood, mostly is very high in frequency of O, quite modest in A, extremely low or absent in B. Yet two Blackfoot tribes show 77 per cent A, the near-by Flatheads 42, the Dakota 29, British Columbia Indians 13. Evidently we have here a local center of A strength—but no explanation of the cause, whether by survival, selection, mutation, or mixture. The Eskimo of Greenland and Baffinland also run a rather heavy A, 13 to 56 per cent,[17] or more or less in the range of their O. To be sure, we could say about the Eskimo that they are otherwise marked off as a distinct American subrace. Also they may be relatively recent comers from Asia; with which there would be in accord the further fact of their containing a sprinkling of B—a characteristic Asiatic but un-American component.

In special cases the groupings do have bearing on racial purity or impurity of blood, as for the Gypsies in Hungary, and possibly a somewhat higher B for Jews in A-prevalent areas.[18] But such instances do not help at all to clear up the general problem of the origin and total history of the factors.

As a result of these blood-type findings, it has sometimes been suggested that the whole study of race by the usual methods was on a sterile track and out of date, because the bodies, skins, bones, and hair observed and measured by physical anthropologists were only compositely variable phenotypes—products of hereditary factors; and that what should be studied is these same causal factors of heredity as they appear in the genes in the chromosomes. At present, this is a pure wish-fulfillment proposal. We know hundreds of actual bodily traits or phenotype "appearances" for every known genetic unit character of heredity. In fact, the "laws" of heredity are every year themselves proving to be more ramified, even when we operate on problems simplified by breeding fruit flies in the laboratory. For man, on whom we cannot experiment, whom we have to take as he comes, the genetic situation is now almost as complex as the bodily zygotic one, but its data are far fewer. What evidence we have on human

[16] Thus, different lots of them run 26, 35, 37, 39% B, whereas six Hindu samples range between 32 and 41, but eight Hungarian groups only from 13 to 19.

[17] The center of third highest rank of A among Indians is Navaho 29-31; New Mexico Pueblo 12, 13; Papago 6. Elsewhere, A-frequencies of 5, 10, or 20% occur only where mixture with whites is known to have occurred among the Indians. A few South American cases of high B are probably due to the factor of chance in very small series, or to faulty technique; as Yahgan, 30 B out of 33 cases (!) and Caraja, 31 B out of 61.

[18] Thus, percentages of B respectively among Jews and Gentiles in: Rumania, 18, 14; Netherlands, 13, 10; U.S., 17, 9-14.

heredity to date that can be reduced to formulas, besides the A-B-AB-O blood types, is a few other blood groupings and a limited series of abnormalities. These, for what they are worth, will be further discussed in a moment. But for attacking the total problem of races and their origins and histories, these few present scraps of definite knowledge of human heredity are pitifully inadequate.

The blood types discovered subsequently to the original A-B-AB-O ones are subtypes of A; M-N; the Rh group; secreting factors—and there may be others.

Group A has recently been found really to consist of subgroups A_1 and A_2—which, incidentally, illustrates what was meant a moment back by the assertion that the genetics of unit characters has become ramifying: even the supposed irreducible factors decompose. Pertinent to race are the following observations, which will undoubtedly be added to from year to year. Among whites in Egypt, Russia, Finland, Sweden, Denmark, Germany, England, and the United States, the old A is found to break up into A_1 and A_2 in the ratio of from $3:1$ to $5:1$.[19] Among New York Negroes, the proportion was once $3:1$ and once $3:2$—that is, A_2 is fairly frequent—but the samples were small. Hawaiian Polynesians and the few American Indians tested show practically no A_2.

The M-N factors coexist alongside the A-B-AB-O factors, in the same blood but without relation to them. They do not affect transfusions, and have therefore been less studied. M and N are not in a dominant-recessive relation. Hence there are MN individuals; in fact, they are the most numerous. The most common percentage distribution, the world over to date, is around M 30, N 20, MN 50, corresponding to a gene frequency of m 55-60, n 40-45. This range of ratios holds for all European nationalities tested, for U.S. white Americans, Egyptians, Chinese, Japanese, Koreans, and for the one sample of Negroes tested in New York.[20] This suggests that the great majority of mankind adheres approximately to this pattern. Excess of N has been found only among the Ainu ($n = 57$) and Australian indigenes ($n = 82$). Unusual excess of M has to date appeared among Eskimo ($m = 91, 82$), U.S. Indians ($m = 78, 76, 75$), Hindus ($m = 76$), Arab Beduin ($m = 75, 62$). There is no explanation of why there are these uniformities and divergences. Data on more populations will illuminate the world status of this factor, but no doubt will also show up new problems.

The Rh factor was discovered in 1940, and is a gene unit causing presence or absence of an agglutinogen. Its practical importance lies in the fact that in a certain, but fortunately low, percentage of cases when an Rh-lacking woman carries a child by an Rh-positive man, the Rh element in the blood of the foetus sets up antibodies in the blood of the mother which in turn react destructively

[19] Except that among 400 Irish and 200 Welsh the ratio was about $2:1$.

[20] For 278 "Negroes" the M, N, MN percentages are 28, 22, 50; for 6129 U.S. whites 29, 21, 50!

on the blood of the foetus and may also prevent future live births. The Rh-male-present and female-absent mating thus has a slight negatively selective survival or perpetuation value. Soon however it was found that the Rh genetics were exceedingly ramifying, and by 1946 at least eight types of Rh blood and six or more allelic genes had been recognized. These complexities cannot be gone into here, except for the interesting fact of decisive racial variation. The salient features of the differentiation appear in this tabulation:

RH BLOOD TYPES

(Percentages)

	Rh_-	Rh_1	Rh_2	Rh_1Rh_2	Rh_0	Others
New York, Negroes	8	20	22	5	41	3
New York, whites	15	53	16	13	2	2
India	7	71	5	13	2	3
China	2	61	3	34	1	0
Japan	1	52	8	39	0	0
Mexico, Indians	0	48	9	42	1	0

The most aberrant from all, in this case, appear to be the Negroes, even though random samples of New York "Negroes" are bound to contain considerable white blood. The most alike are Chinese and Japanese; the Mexican Indians stand nearest them. Each racial group specializes in high and low frequency of one or more Rh types of blood.

Many individuals have their blood-type substances present also in other body juices, especially the saliva. Such "secretors" are genetically dominant, non-secretors recessive. The few data in hand indicate some difference in dominant-recessive frequency between Negroes and whites; and there may prove to be many other racial variations.

With all these genetically definite blood-serum types turning up, the prospect improves that we may ultimately be able to distinguish races at least partly by their genetic constitution as well as by the hitherto customary description of their phenotypes. With only the A-B-O genetics known, paternity could be determined, or rather eliminated, in only a minority of cases. But with the A_1-A_2, the M-N, the eight Rh types, and the secretion genetics also available, the determination is now possible, at least theoretically, in perhaps most cases. Turned around, the same applies to race distinctions. In their A-B-O blood grouping, Hindus and North Chinese, who are obviously very different racially, came out practically identical—through accident. So do Sumatrans and West African Negroes. It is however extremely unlikely that accident will make these pairs of peoples alike also in the wholly independent sub-A, M-N, Rh, and other frequencies. Conversely, the Gypsy-Hindu similarity in A-B-O frequency, though it looks good, might still be due to accident. If it is not accidental but based on connection by actual genetic descent, then it should show also in the M-N, Rh, and other frequencies. Or, if it should mainly hold, but with some deviations, then comparison, after data on enough populations are in hand, might indicate with what other racial ingredient the Gypsies had diluted their Hindu blood, or from which Hindu subrace or district they were chiefly sprung. All this future refinement of knowledge is conjectural, but it seems expectable.

These serological traits have been gone into here not because they are the most important in human genetics, but because they are the best known. They operate by the open-or-shut, present-or-absent, Mendelian method. Most human traits do not, or are not known to, operate so simply; or they have a genetic mechanism so complex that it has not been extricated. Skin color, eye color, hair color, hair form, and other visible traits show some approximation to genetic rules in their hereditary transmission, but the approximation is very loose. There may be many factors involved, some perhaps linked instead of independent. The hopes of three or four decades ago that all traits would soon be brought under simple allelomorphic rules have not been realized. Outside of blood characteristics, the human traits positively known to "Mendelize" are rather few, and they consist preponderantly of abnormalities and pathologies—fortunately for the most part infrequent ones. Some such are, or have been claimed to be:

MENDELIAN HUMAN TRAITS

Dominant	Dominant, Sex-linked or Probably So
Brachydactyly (short-fingeredness)	Mandibular prognathism (Hapsburg)
Local albinism	Basedow's disease
Absence of upper lateral incisors	Baldness (?)
Hypospadias	
Huntington's chorea	
Diabetes insipidus	

Recessive	Recessive, Sex-linked or Probably So
Total color-blindness	Red-green color-blindness
Nontasting of PTC *	Nonclotting of blood (haemophilia)
	Atrophy of the optic nerve
	Total albinism
	Addison's disease

* Paraethoxyphenyl thiocarbamide. It is very bitter to most people, but the nontasters do not get even a shred of taste from it. The frequency varies by race. Nontasting occurs in 37 per cent of Arabs, 30 per cent of United States whites, 6 per cent of Chinese, and 6 per cent of American Indians. Here, then, is another simple genetic trait to supplement blood types and subtypes in ultimately aiding us to verify racial connections or mixtures or their absence.

Most of these traits are altogether too rare to be of consequence as regards race. An exception is red-green color-blindness, which can appear in females only as the result of exceptional matings. Some frequencies for it are:

Eskimo, 1 per cent of male population; New Guinea Melanesians, 1 per cent; American Indians, 2; Chinese, 3; Japanese, 3; Chukchi of eastern Siberia, 3; Negroes, American, 4 (possibly raised by white-blood infusion); Egyptian, 5; Lapp, 6; white

American, 8. A high figure of 13 per cent of males for the Toda is almost certainly due to the inbreeding of this small caste-tribe of South India (§ 201). Analogously, there appears to be an unusually high frequency of total albinism, perhaps around .2 per cent, among the inbred and small Zuni and Hopi tribes, and again among the San Blas Indians of Panamá.

73. EFFECTS OF SELF-DOMESTICATION

Among the causal factors shaping races there is to be reckoned man's "domestication," already mentioned in § 34. Man is in certain senses a domesticated animal. Such a statement may at first sound like rank nonsense. We keep domestic animals for use or pleasure: who keeps us? As regards purposiveness, exploitation, and control, it is obvious that we are not tamed animals. It is only that as regards shelter, care, and regularly dependable food supply, men in general live more like their kept animals than like wild ones. We and our cattle both benefit from culture in our mode of living: wild beasts do not. It is a matter of a common protective "artificial" environment, as against a rigorous, competitive, and often harshly selective natural one. Such a change of environment from the feral state might, and actually does, induce changes of form and may induce changes of heredity. As regards the results of his mode of living, accordingly, man can legitimately be considered as the equivalent of a domesticated animal. Let us call him "self-domesticated," and avoid further quarreling about the implications of words.

Below are listed some of the traits that tend to develop in long-domesticated mammals; or, it might be said, have been preserved among them, whereas if they occurred in the wild state as occasional mutations, they would tend to be swamped out by crossbreeding, or to be lost by survival selection if disadvantageous.

1. Hairlessness, as in Chihuahua dogs.

2. Hair curliness or wool, as in sheep, poodles, and even some fowl. There seems to be no parallel in wild nature.

3. Depigmentation, either total as albinization or partial as blondism. Except in the snowy Arctic, there seem to be no albino species of wild mammals, but there are albino races of almost all domestic ones. There are "blond" or yellowish wild species, such as the weasel and the opossum, though there are not very many; but there are no wild blond cattle, horses, cats, or wolves, corresponding to the Jerseys, sorrels, buckskins, yellow dogs, and so on developed in breeding.

4. Overpigmentation or melanism occurs in nature as an alternative color phase in a few species, such as bears and panthers. There are black breeds of nearly all long-domesticated mammals and of some fowls.

5. Excessive fat deposits on rump or tail, as in some Asiatic breeds of sheep. The human equivalent is steatopygia.

6. Reduction of jaw length, as in most dogs compared with wolves and jackals. A further step is reduction of the nose and brachycephalization of the brain case, as in bulldogs, pugs, Pekinese, and some spaniels.

7. Droop ears. These do not occur in nature as a variant of erect ears.

8. A less compact cellular structure of bone has been alleged for some tame animals.

Of these traits, relative hairlessness is common to all living men, but Mongoloids and Negroids have evolved farther than Caucasians, Ainu, and Australoids. Woolly hair of course characterizes the Negroid. Probably the Bushmen are most extreme. They also show steatopygia, trait 5 in the list above. Depigmentation of skin, hair, and eyes is of course Caucasian, with the extreme in Nordics. Mongoloid head hair and eyes are melanized; the Negro adds considerable melanization of skin. Caucasian orthognathism is obviously a form of jaw reduction.

This seems a fair showing. We are unable to derive particular traits from particular conditions of "domesticated" living; but the total series is rather close to being parallel in man and in the animals he keeps. That there are more aberrant and fantastic forms among tame animals, such as tumbling pigeons, deformed and lap dogs, ponies and Percherons, is due to our controlling the heredity of some animals by selection and inbreeding in accord with our fancies or needs. By contrast, human breeding of human beings has often been wholly uncontrolled and apparently has never been really constructively controlled.

74. SELECTIVE FACTORS

It is remarkable how little is really known as to the causes of change of human type and race differentiation. Random genetic mutations, survival selection, adaptation to environment, domestication, may all have been at work; it is very difficult to say in what degree and at what points.

It is obvious that the native habitat of the darkest races, Negroids and Australoids, is in or near the tropics, and it has been thought that their extra melanin provided protection against solar actinic invasion. However, much of the tropics is occupied by brown races—the East Indies and native South America, for instance—and those races seem about as well adapted as the blacks in their tropical areas. The paler of the blond Caucasians perhaps survive less well in the tropics, as a race. Most of them certainly believe so; but then most of them certainly also prefer living in "God's country." It is clear that the prevalently blond populations originated in the cloudy and foggy parts of northern Europe (Figs. 9, 12; pages 145, 152). Possibly demelaninized mutations also occurred elsewhere, but had few or no survival chances except in this actinically protected area. However, even if this were so, it would not prove either that melanin was a handicap in a cool, foggy climate or that an ultraheavy dose of it was positively advantageous—either in low latitudes or in high altitudes.

A causal correlation has also been suggested between the prevalently broad noses of the tropics and the narrow ones of the Arctic—Negroes versus Eskimo and Nordics, for instance. Constricted inner nasal passages might conserve bodily heat in extremely low temperatures. But there is nothing as yet to show that a flat broad nose has any actual advantage in the tropics. Again, therefore, if there is a relation—and this is uncertain—it is only a one-way correlation.

All in all, man is such an unusually tough animal with such wide toleration of environment that it is difficult to pin special adaptive modifications on him. He is one of the very few successful omnivorous mammals—the bear and the pig being his most conspicuous compeers. He ranges from sea level to three-mile elevation of habitat, and from wholly arid to the most humid climates, which is true of almost no other mammal. In resistance to extremes of temperature, he makes up for lack of congenital fur by the cultural aids of clothing, housing, and fire; but at that his precultural range is likely to have been at least as wide as that of any primate. A total generalized habitus (§ 35) is so characteristic of the human species as to make rather improbable the explanation of many of the minor racial peculiarities by environmental adaptations of survival value. These peculiarities may often be due to gene mutations whose value for survival was indifferent. Especially would this be true after culture began to interfere with the rigor of purely organic selection.

75. PLASTICITY

Another human trait, which is perhaps a corollary of being generalized, is plasticity: the ability to change bodily form with environmental change, at least within limits. This was first demonstrated on a major scale by Boas in 1912 in regard to European immigrants in the United States, and has been spottily confirmed elsewhere. What Boas found was that the children of long-headed South Italians born in America were progressively broader-headed than their parents, and that the children of broad-headed Czechs and Jews from Central Europe were progressively longer-headed. Moreover, in all cases there was an increase of stature and a narrowing of face. Roughly, all these alterations were an approach toward the type of Anglo-Saxon descent most prevalent in the United States. A sample of the data follows:

CHANGE OF AMERICAN-BORN MALE DESCENDANTS OF EUROPEAN IMMIGRANTS INTO THE UNITED STATES FROM THE TYPE OF THE IMMIGRANTS (BOAS)

	Broad-headed Types		Narrow-headed Types	
	Bohemians	Jews	Sicilians	Neapolitans
Change in mm in				
Stature	29.0	17.0	1.0	6.0
Width of face	−2.1	−1.1	−1.2	−1.2
Length of head	−0.7	2.2	−2.4	−0.9
Breadth of head	−2.3	−1.8	1.3	0.9
Change in cephalic index	−1.0	−2.0	1.3	0.9
Number of cases	170	654	188	248

The changes in females were parallel. Moreover, American-born descendants differed from European-born descendants of immigrants in much the same way. And the results hold not only as between immigrants in the mass and immigrants' descendants as a mass or statistical average, but for specific immigrants and their own specific children. There can thus be no real question as to the validity of the findings. Above all, the changes of children from parents were greater in proportion as their parents had been longer in the United States. Moreover, analogous results have been obtained elsewhere, as by Shapiro and Hulse on Japanese settling in Hawaii. Roughly, the Hawaiian-born children of immigrants differed from the immigrants much as the immigrants differed—by selection—from the stay-at-home Japanese. Hrdlička found fourth-generation Americans narrower-faced than Europeans. It may therefore be concluded not only that there are certain unknown factors at work on race in the American environment, but, as a general principle, that heredity may be less fixed, less impermeable by outside influences, than had been supposed. As a result, the Boas findings produced considerable stir and some unnecessary controversy. There is nothing in the facts to show that the environment would continue indefinitely to alter the heredity. It might well dent it so far, but no farther. In other words, heredity must be construed as not absolutely rigid, but as plastic within certain presumably narrow limits. This seems reasonable enough.

Moreover, the immigrants to New York moved not only from one continent and climate to another, but from a social environment of country or small town to one of metropolitan congestion and industrial pressure, which would inevitably enforce an altered mode of living, a new set of physiological responses. That a move from rural to urban life brings with it slight modification of anatomical form had been previously found by observers in Germany and Italy (Ammon and Livi). To be exact, they showed that adjacent town and country populations differed; which means either that the very decision to move to cities constitutes a selection, or that those who move are subject to influences which modify their type—or rather, since adults are scarcely any longer modifiable, which modify the type of their children. Specific urban selection seems precluded in the case of American immigration, so that the environmental influence must be admitted. However, it is well to recognize that we do not yet know at all what the environmental factors at work are, nor how they themselves may vary.

In short, what these measurements and their statistical interpretation seem to establish is that hereditary racial types may possess a certain limited degree of plasticity, within the measure of which they can respond to alterations of environment. There is no indication that environment as such will alter a race progressively or cumulatively. If progressive adaptative alterations do occur, it is presumably through natural selection; that is, survival value of certain traits.

76. THE HOLOGENETIC THEORY

The problems of the origin and the development of human races have attracted their full share of theories, ranging from more or less useful working hypotheses to fantasies. A few of these will be reviewed.

The principle of *hologenesis,* developed by Rosa in palaeontology, has been applied to man by Montandon. The theory holds that as evolutionary development begins in a certain direction, part of the organisms involved change rather rapidly; another part, more slowly. The former attain a *precocious* specialization but then stand still; the latter, at first *retarded* in their change, finally achieve a more balanced, successful, varied, and progressive development.

This is how the theory is applied to human racial history by Montandon. The first split of early recent man, he holds, was into a precocious Pygmoid and a more generalized branch. The Bushmen-Hottentots and the Pygmies remain as outdistanced, primitive survivors of their early specialization. The rest of mankind next divided into a precocious southern or Negroid branch and a generalized northern one. Within the southern branch, the Tasmanians split off from the other Negroids as the more precocious; that is, the more primitive. The northern or non-Negroid line of descent similarly divided into Veddoid-Australoids and less differentiated "Amer-Eur-Asiatics"; among these in turn the American Indians were set off as the more "precocious" against Eur-Asiatics. These last again divided into Asiatics, who branched into Eskimo and Mongoloids, and Europeans, who branched into Lapponoids and Europoids; the latter, in turn, apparently consisting of relatively precocious Ainu on the one hand and the Blonds, the Alpine-Armenoids, and the Browns (Mediterraneans) on the other. Including subdivisions not mentioned here, altogether 20 races are recognized.

This hologenetic theory thus boils down to a not very aberrant race classification, from the point of view of results; but it arrives at this goal by a method of its own. This method has something in its favor, but is also open to grave criticism. What it has in its favor is that the "precocious" Bushmen, Pygmies, Tasmanians, Veddoids, and Australoids are generally accepted as carrying primitive traits. The objections are, first, that it is far from sure that these races branched off early in the history of man—in other words, that they are really precocious. Some of them may represent late modifications of type in numerically small populations living in isolation. Second, there are places in the hologenetic system where it is the supposedly generalized "retarded" branch that in the end becomes specialized, as the bulk of the Negroids. Far from being primitive as against the more northerly remainder of humanity, they are now specialized also. In the same way, contrary to Montandon's supposition, the East Asiatic Mongoloids are certainly more differentiated or refined racially than the American Indians, who remain pretty generalized and free from primitive specialties such as Bushmen, Pygmies, Australians, and other supposedly pre-cocious groups show. The same thing can be said of Europoids: The phylogenetically "retarded" Nordics are surely as highly characterized or specialized as the allegedly more precocious Lapps and Ainu. Finally, it is extremely unlikely that the actual evolution of races would rigidly proceed on a basis of merely a two-way split with that split always hinging on the same point of precocity. Nature is too full of conflicting and independent factors to work as simply as a piece of diagrammatic logic.

What the hologenetic scheme does do is to call attention to a series of small populations, usually surviving in the comparative protection of remoteness, isolation, or undesirable habitat, who show certain marked anatomical peculiarities. This holds for Eskimo, Ainu, and Lapps, as well as for the Bushman-Australoid series previously listed. Some of these aberrant types may really be survivals of very ancient and precocious modifications—"mistaken experiments" of evolution. But there is nothing to show that all these types are of this order: others quite possibly are relatively recent developments, connected with their special and isolating environments. In any event, the hologenetic theory makes a blanket assumption in advance instead of trying genuinely to investigate each case and then seeing whether there is a common principle in them all. Accepted not as an explanation, but as a point of view that raises some interesting unsolved problems, it has a certain value.

77. ENDOCRINE THEORIES OF RACE

Sir Arthur Keith has proposed that the origins of racial differences may be found in different functioning of the endocrine or ductless glands. For instance, thyroidal deficiency often makes for a flat face and nose but a bulging forehead; adrenal deficiency, for darkening of the skin; pituitary deficiency, for infantilism; while pituitary hyperfunction may cause acromegaly or enlargement of face and nose. These effects have been clinically determined in individuals. Keith's suggestion is that they were operative also in the formation of the races. Unfortunately, knowledge of racial endocrine differences, structural or functional, is still very fragmentary. Also, the exemplifications cited boil down to glandular deficiencies among Mongoloids and Negroids and to high activity in Caucasians. It seems theoretically improbable that the situation would be as simple as this: Caucasianism consistently due to a plus, other racial types to a minus. Thus Keith relates prominence of nose, chin, and brow ridges in Caucasians to pituitary vigor akin to acromegaly; their higher sexual differentiation, or greater male robustness, to interstitial activity; their fairness, to a "virtue" or plus-functioning of the adrenals. Contrariwise, Mongolian shortness of limbs compared to trunk, and retraction of the nasal part of the face, are held to suggest a mild degree of achondroplasia or short-limbed dwarfism, of bulldog build or pug-facedness, such as is brought on in individuals by defects in the growth-regulating mechanism of the thyroid. Yet it would certainly be peculiar if the differentialism of Caucasians on one side from Mongoloids and Negroids on the other were regularly and one-sidedly due to the former having, in gland after gland, more endocrine activity, and the latter less—which is what the Keith explanation comes to.

Then, even were such racial deficiencies of function substantiated as facts, the first question would be whether they were not attributable to deficiencies in the standard or manner of living—in other words, to factors in the environment. For instance, goiter prevails in some areas adjacent to Switzerland, and in the north-central and western United States, because the soil and the drinking water contain insufficient iodine for the thyroid gland to build up its specific hormone. The lack of material forces many naturally normal thyroid glands to function subpar in these districts. Environmental factors like these would have to be eliminated before genuine hereditary differences characteristic of races were reached.

Finally, while we may grant the probability of some involvement of the endocrines in race differentiation, it appears arbitrary to single them out as a principal causative factor.

What does seem reasonable and sound in the endocrine approach is its *descriptive* application to racial types—a recognition in races of certain general conditions or features known clinically to have endocrine relations; but without an endeavor to pin the major *causation* of race on the glands. Thus there is undoubtedly a habitus or condition which can be called infantile-feminine, or even foetalized; and contrariwise, a masculine-senile habitus. The latter tends toward rugged features, prominent nose, chin, and brows, large hands and feet, long limbs, heavier pigmentation, hairiness, but also baldness. This complex of conditions is due, rather variably, to endocrine-caused acromegaly, to mere maleness, to age, or to combinations of all three factors. The infantile-feminine traits are a smooth face with low nose, high forehead and undeveloped chin, small hands and feet, tendency toward general fattiness, lighter pigmentation, and less hair except on the skull. This habitus, again, is variably due to youth, to femininity, and to thyroidal and pituitary deficiency.

It is evident that a number of races trend toward one or the other type. If the racial inclination is toward the infantile, men and women differ relatively little in appearance; if toward the senile, they differ considerably. In Europe, the Alpine type is infantile, on the whole; the Dinaric and the Nordic, especially of the so-called Palaeolithic Borreby-survival subtype, are senile. The East Asiatics, as exemplified by the Chinese and the Farther Indians, and again by most Malaysians, would be infantile-feminine. In Oceania, Micronesians are more feminine, Polynesians more masculine. Among American Mongoloids, the craggy, big-boned, large-handed, hawk-nosed Plains Indians are obviously senile, and contrast especially with the long-trunked, short-limbed tribes of the South American tropical forest, whose men and women are so strikingly alike in their figures and faces. There is also little doubt which way the balance leans as between Australoids and Negroids: the Australoids have heavy supraorbital ridges, gnarled and tense features, bushy beards; the Negro face by contrast has a smooth forehead, relaxed features, loose lips, little beard.

These observations must not be stretched too far. Their value is essentially descriptive, not explanatory. Both habituses are only polar extremes in a general human range, most of which would be median or little differentiated.

Also, neither habitus should be assumed to be intrinsically correlated with primitiveness. Rather it would appear that both senile-masculine and infantile-feminine traits can occur in retardedly primitive and in secondarily specialized races.

78. THE FINE-COARSE-TYPE THEORY

Less can be said for a bipolar differentiation into fine and coarse types, which has sometimes been used to separate a given population into its supposed racial constituents or origins, as by Baelz for the Japanese. There is no doubt that there are in every population individuals with relatively narrow, high-bridged noses, longer faces, slenderer bodies, tapering fingers; and others who are comparatively short, broad, thickset, heavy, or muscular in the same features. The first will resemble aristocrats in their build; the second, peasants. Moreover, if there are actual aristocrats and peasants in the population, we can expect the aristocrats to lean on the whole more toward the first type, on account of the ways each individual has preponderantly used his body since childhood, and the peasants to the second type. Deft and graceful motions would be socially called for from members of one group; calluses, bulging muscles, and heavy bones would be developed mostly by the other. All this can be anticipated as the double result of individuals' differing from one another and of these particular differences also representing external modifications of heredity by somatic habit functioning as directed by social-class environment. The case is no different in principle from the facts that every population contains both larger and smaller individuals by heredity, and that in addition the best-nourished will average bigger than the underprivileged. It would be an obvious and gratuitous error to try regularly to establish separate racial origins for the large and the small individuals in each population. Now and then a population may be found to segregate into two indubitably separate types, as in East Africa, where the very attenuated, tall, pastoral Bahima aristocracy rules over stockier farmers. But here the differentiation is only incidentally into fine and coarse, primarily into ultratall and leptosome as against a normal majority.

In the case of the Japanese, the fine or Choshiu and coarse or Satsuma types, after having been tied up with the legendary history of Japan, are simply derived, by the Baelz theory, from supposed original types on the East Asiatic mainland. On this mainland the two types can undoubtedly be distinguished in some individuals, as they can be in Japan; but they have there not been segregated populationally, that is, areally or racially. The supposed foundation for the fine-coarse-race hypothesis in Japan therefore boils down to an equally hypothetical assumption made for China.

For China, however, Legendre, while following the essential Baelz logic, has preferred to make a guess of different content. He recognizes a larger, finer, more Europoid constituent, "Assyroid or Aryan" in type and derived—hypothetically—from the West; and a darker, smaller, prognathous, flat-nosed, lower, and coarser Negritoid type, related to "Melanesians and Polynesians"! The great mass of the Chinese people are alleged to be hybrids of these two original elements. This last is of course pure preferential dogmatism. Granting that the total population could be ranged between the two extremes—and there is no effort made to show that quite differently chosen extremes would not fit the Chinese picture equally well—it remains to be proved that the extremes were really original. They might obviously just as well be rare specializations secondarily evolved out of a less-differentiated racial mass. It may be added that Legendre published his view under the sensational title *There Is No Yellow Race*. How hasty his basic race concepts are is evident from his allying his Negritos to Polynesians. Incidentally, Negritos considered as the original population of South China keep cropping up in print, because of references in ancient Chinese literature to aborigines of South China as small and dark— plus no doubt also because the far-fetched and unlikely has a dramatic appeal. With Negritos still in Malaya, Luzon, and the Andamans, it is wholly conceivable that there may also once have been tribes of them in China. But there does not seem to be any discovered evidence to that effect; and it is certainly at the very bounds of probability that a fertile tract like South China, now harboring many tens of millions of straight Mongoloids, should as recently as in the protohistoric period, only two or three thousand years ago, have been the haunt chiefly of scattered bands of Negroid Pygmies.

Views like these have a way of falling to pieces when they are really analyzed. Often, however, they live for two or three generations, either because no one troubles to make the analysis, or because of their appeal to our purely imaginative faculties. These particular theories have been dissected here chiefly as examples of uncritical thinking, of reasoning from arbitrary preferences. Thus the fine-coarse type of race explanation has by no means been limited to China and Japan, but has been applied again and again to racial origins elsewhere.

79. CONSTITUTIONAL TYPES

Constitutional types crosscut races in that they set up a classification of human physique in general, often with special reference to associated temperament, mental activity, and disease incidence. The majority of such typings are bipolar, and they amount in the last analysis to saying that there are broader-bodied and narrower-bodied individuals in every group. To put this simple and in itself harmless finding learnedly, we substitute the terms "eurysome" and "leptosome." Of course the middle majority of any population are not strictly either broad or narrow in physique, any more than they are definitely tall or short, phlegmatic or excitable, extravert or introvert, but are near-average or in-determinate. Interest picks up when associations are allied with a type of mind or liability to certain disease. Thus Kretschmer called the thickset, pyknics; the medium, athletics; and the ultraslender, asthenics; and found that when they go insane, pyknics are more likely to be manic-depressives and asthenics to be schizophrenics. This may well be: the ancients already recognized an apoplectic and a phthisic type whose somatic build is essentially identical with Kretschmer's extreme types. But probably a full half of any population cannot be assigned to either end-type without artificial forcing; nor is the average man in the middle markedly "athletic." On the other hand, concepts like leptosome and eurysome, or lineal and lateral, or for that matter pyknic and asthenic, do often have utility in descriptions of individual physiques or in other specific situations, when they are used without attempt at system-mongering.

Somewhat more varied than the bipolar theories is a fourfold scheme of constitutional types advocated by Sigaud and his followers: cerebral, muscular, respiratory, and digestive. The functional or physiological implications of these body forms are obvious. We can all think of individuals in our acquaintance who neatly fit into one or the other of these classes—also of a great number who fit badly or not at all.

The most recent classification of types, still partially in the mode as of 1948, is Sheldon's. He has somewhat reworked the older pyknic-digestive, muscular-respiratory-athletic, and cerebro-asthenic types, and has trapped them out in an impressive dress of endomorphs, mesomorphs, and ectomorphs on the basis of supposed dominance of the endo-, meso-, and ectoderm in their embryological development. He has also given them temperamental correspondences accord-ing as their tonus is dominantly visceral, muscular ("soma"), or neural. The definitions of the temperaments are incisive and characteristic. Thus, pyknic viscerotonics are described as relaxed, slow, complacent, even-tempered, tolerant, flabby, and without spark, but amiable and quietly sociable and dependent on people; they are fond of comfort, food, digestion, sleep, company, politeness, and affection. Somatotonics, with muscular physiques, are assertive, active, energetic, courageous, dominating, ruthless, callous, indifferent to pain, noisy, claustro-phobic, and extravert; they seek adventure, risk, exercise, competition, and directness. Cerebrotonics, or ectomorphs, with neural loading, are restrained in posture and often in movement, but overresponsive and too fast in reactions. They are socially inhibited, apprehensive, hypersensitive, resistive to routine, unpredictable, secretive, solitary, agoraphobic and introvert, self-conscious. Also, they are poor sleepers, restless in their face and hands, oriented toward age but youthful in appearance. This last type pretty much adds up to a schizophreni-cally inclined temperament, as Kretschmer assigned it to his asthenics; just as

the two other personality types of Sheldon approximate respectively the quiet
and excited phases of cyclothymia. Nevertheless, the type characterizations are
apt: we can all readily recognize individuals of our acquaintance. Sheldon is
evidently a felicitous type-builder. The limitations of the scheme are first, that
in spite of all elaboration of method, the type determinations themselves, plus
the correspondence of anatomy with psychology, retain a subjective constituent.
Secondly, all previous experience with types is to the effect that the majority
of individuals are transitional or indefinite instead of clear-cut in type. The
Sheldon scheme may be an exception, but it will have to prove itself.

In general, it must be remembered that successful instances of any type can
always be found, but that the validity of a general explanation or system is proportionate to its success in accommodating the totality, or at least a near-totality,
of cases without forcing or straining. To date, correlations between all constitutional somatic types and psychological or clinical types remain rather weak. This
is not because psychosomatic correspondences are lacking, but because all types
appear in series of living individuals with much less sharpness than they possess
in the formulator's conception.

80. RACE, NATIONALITY, AND LANGUAGE

The term "race" has here been used in its biological sense, for a group united
in blood or heredity. A race is a subdivision of a species and corresponds to a
breed in domestic animals. Popularly, the word is used in a different sense;
namely, that of a population having any traits in common, be they hereditary
or nonhereditary, biological or sociocultural, organic or superorganic (§ 6). It
is customary, but mainly inaccurate, to speak of the French race, the Anglo-
Saxon race, the Gypsy race, the Jewish race. The French are a nation and a
nationality, with a substantially common speech; biologically, they are three
races considerably mixed, but still imperfectly blended (§ 62). "Anglo-Saxon"
refers primarily to speech, incidentally to a set of customs, traditions, and points
of view that are more or less associated with the language. The Gypsies are a
self-constituted caste, with folkways, occupations, and at least Romany speech
remnants of their own. They have mostly preserved their dark Mediterranoid
type, as well as their high-B blood group, which they brought with them from
India. The Jews, who were once a nationality, for a time even a state, at present
of course form a religious body, which somewhat variably, in part from inner
cohesion and in part from outer pressure, tends also to constitute a social caste
within Western society. The degree to which they have and have not preserved
a distinctive hereditary racial type has already been touched upon (§ 68, 72).
At any rate, attitudes toward Jews obviously depend immeasurably more on
emotional reaction to the social functioning of Jews than on their biology.

It may seem of little moment whether the word "race" is restricted to its
strict biological sense or used more loosely. In fact, however, untold loose

reasoning has resulted from the loose terminology. When one has spoken a dozen times of "the French race," one tends inevitably to think of the inhabitants of France as a biological unit, which they are not. The basis of the error is confusion of organic traits and processes with superorganic or cultural ones, of heredity with tradition or imitation. That civilizations, languages, and nationalities go on for generations is obviously a different thing from their being caused by generation. Slovenly thought, tending to deal with results rather than causes or processes, does not trouble to make this discrimination; and everyday speech, dating from a prescientific period, is ambiguous about it. We say not only "generation" when there is no intent to imply the reproductive process, but "good breeding" (literally, good brooding or hatching or birth) when we mean good home training or education; just as we "inherit" a fortune or a name—sociocultural things—as well as ineradicable traits such as brown eyecolor. Biology has secured for its processes the exclusive use of the term "heredity," and biologists employ the term "race" only with reference to a hereditary subdivision of a species. It is equally important that the word be used with the same exact denotation in anthropology, else all discussion of race degenerates irretrievably into illogical sliding in and out between organic and superorganic factors. The inherently great difficulties which beset the understanding and solution of what are generally called race problems, as discussed in the next chapter, are considerably increased by a confusion between what is and what is not racial, organic, and hereditary.

CHAPTER FIVE

Problems of Race Difference

THIS CHAPTER deals with some aspects of the intricate question of just what are the differences between the functioning of the biological races of man and what they are due to. It tries to establish, not too successfully because of scarcity of conclusive evidence, how much of such differences is racially genetic—that is, organically hereditary—and how much due to historical, sociocultural conditioning; that is, environmental, superorganic causes. The argument therefore deals with one of the basic problems of fundamental science, as it has already been sketched in Chapter One. The present chapter does not deal with what are popularly called "race problems"—which in most cases are not racial but ethnic—namely, the troubles of minority groups and the troubles they give to majorities. The concern is rather with some of the underlying facts and principles in those cases where biological race is really involved.

81. QUESTIONS OF ENDOWMENT AND THEIR VALIDITY

Are the human races alike or dissimilar in mentality and character? Are some lower than others, or are they all on a plane as regards potentiality? The answers to these questions are of theoretical import, and naturally also bear on the solution of the practical and often crucial race problems with which some nations are confronted. The word "race" is here used in its strict or biological sense, as denoting a subspecies or other group set off by heredity (§ 80), not in the loose popular sense of a group set off by speech, religion, or social consciousness.

As long as an inquiry remains sufficiently abstract or remote, the desirability of such inquiry is likely to go unquestioned. As soon, however, as investigation touches conduct—for instance actual relations with other races—sentiment has a way of rising to the effect that perhaps after all the problem does not so much call for understanding as for decision. Thus, in regard to the Negro problem in the United States, it is likely to be said that the immediate issue is what may be the best attitude toward Jim Crow cars and other forms of segregation. Are these desirable or undesirable, fair or unfair? Here are specific problems to which actual conditions press for an answer. Under the circumstances, it will be said, is not an inquiry into the innate capacity of the Negro rather remote, especially when everyone can see by a thousand examples that the Negro is obviously inferior to the Caucasian? He is poorer, more shiftless, less successful. He has made no inventions, produced no great geniuses. He clearly feels himself inferior and comports himself accordingly. Why then raise the issue of capacity at all, unless from a desire to befog the question, to subvert the conclusions of common sense and everyday experience by special pleading that substitutes adroitness for sincerity? In some such form as this, objections may rise in the minds of some.

The answer to such criticism is first of all that racial inferiority and superiority are by no means self-evident truths. Secondly, the belief in race inequalities is founded in emotion and action and then justified by reasoning. That is, the belief is rationalized after it is held, not primarily inferred by pure reason. It may be true, but it is not proved true.

As to what is self-evident, there is nothing so misleading as direct observation. We see the sun move and the earth stand still. It is "self-evident" that the sun revolves around the earth. Yet after thousands of years the civilized portion of mankind finally came to believe that it is the earth that spins. Science had no perverse interest, no insidious motive, in advocating the Copernican instead of the Ptolemaic system; in fact, it was driven to its new belief gradually and reluctantly. It was prescientific humanity, with its direct, homespun, everyday observation, which had really prejudged the matter, and which, because it had always assumed that the earth was stationary, and because every idiot could see that it was so, long combated the idea that it could be otherwise.

As for beliefs founded in emotion and subsequently rationalized, it may suffice to quote from a once famous book by Trotter on mass opinion:

When, therefore, we find ourselves entertaining an opinion about the basis of which there is a quality of feeling which tells us that to inquire into it would be absurd, obviously unnecessary, unprofitable, undesirable, bad form or wicked, we may know that that opinion is a non-rational one, and probably, therefore, founded upon inadequate evidence. Opinions, on the other hand, which are acquired as the result of experience alone do not possess this quality of primary certitude. They are true in the sense of being verifiable, but they are unaccompanied by that profound feeling of truth which belief possesses, and, therefore, we have no sense of reluctance in admitting inquiry into them.

Take the attitude of many a Californian or Australian about the Mongolian; of the average Texan about the Mexican; of the run-of-the-mill Southerner about he Negro; of the Westerner about the local tribes of Indians; of the English-man about the Hindu; of the German even about the Poles and Russians who racially are only barely distinguishable from himself—is not their feeling pretty fairly described by the statement that inquiry into the possibility of racial equal-ity would be "unnecessary," "absurd," or evilly motivated, and that their belief in race superiority rests on an "a-priori synthesis of the most perfect sort," and possesses "the quality of primary certitude"?

In short, the apparently theoretical beliefs held as to race capacity by people who are confronted by an actual race conflict or problem are by no means the outcome of impartial examination and verification, but are the result of the decisions taken and the emotions experienced in the course of acts performed toward the other race. The beliefs rest ultimately on impulse and feeling; their reasoned support is a subsequent bolstering-up. Of course, the fact that a belief springs from emotion does not render that belief untrue; but it does leave the belief scientifically unproved, and calling for investigation.

These conclusions may vindicate inquiry into the relative capacity of races from the charge of being finespun, insidious, impractical, or loaded with bias.

In an approach to the problem, one consideration stands out. If the human races are identical in capacity, or if, though not absolutely alike, they average substantially the same in the sum total of their capacities, then such differences as they have shown in their history or show in their present condition must evidently be the result mainly of circumstances external to heredity. In that case, knowledge of the historical or environmental circumstances, and analysis of the latter, become all-important to understanding. On the other hand, if hereditary racial inequalities exist, one can expect that the historical or cultural influences, however great they may be, will nevertheless tend to have their origin in the hereditary factors and to reinforce them. In that case, differences between two groups would be due partly to underlying heredity and partly to overlying cultural forces tending on the whole in the same direction. Yet even in that case, before one could begin to estimate the strength of the true racial factors, the historical ones would have to be subtracted. Thus, in either event, the first crux of the problem lies in the recognition and stripping-off of cultural, social, or environmental factors, so far as possible, from the complex mass of phenomena which living human groups present. In proportion as these social or acquired traits can be determined and discounted, the innate and truly racial ones will be isolated, and can then be examined, weighed, and compared. Such, at any rate, is a reasonable plan of procedure. We are looking for the inherent, ineradicable elements in a social animal that has everywhere built up around himself an environment—namely, his culture—in which he mentally lives and breathes. It is precisely because in the present inquiry we wish to get below the effects of culture that we must be ready to concern ourselves considerably with these effects, actual or possible.

82. ANATOMICAL EVIDENCE ON EVOLUTIONARY RANK

But first of all it may be well to consider the relatively simple evidence that has to do with the physical form and structure of race types. If one human race should prove definitely nearer to the apes in its anatomy than the other races, there would be reason to believe that it had lagged in evolution. Also there would be some presumption that its arrears were mental as well as physical.

But the facts do not run consistently. One thinks of the Negro as simian. His jaws are prognathous; his forehead recedes; his nose is both broad and low. Further, it is among Caucasians that the antithetical traits occur. In straightness of jaws and forehead, prominence and narrowness of nose, Caucasians in general exceed the Mongoloids. Thus the order as regards these particular traits is: ape, Negroid, Mongoloid, Caucasian. With ourselves at one end and the monkey at the other, the scale somehow seems right. It appeals, and seems significant. Facts of this sort are therefore readily observed, come to be remembered, and rise spontaneously to mind in an argument.

However, there are numerous items that conflict with this sequence. For instance, one of the most conspicuous differences of man from the apes is his relative hairlessness. Of the three main stocks, however, it is the Caucasian that is the most hairy on both face and body.

In texture of hair, as well as sparseness on the body, the Negroid is the most "domesticated" (§ 73) and the most characteristically human.

Ape lips are grayish, thin, but mobile and extrudable almost to being prehensile. Among men, Mongolian lips are perhaps thinnest and Negro ones the most specializedly full and everted.

It is unnecessary to multiply examples. If one human racial stock falls below others in certain traits, it rises above them in other features, insofar as "below" and "above" may be measurable in terms of degree of resemblance to the apes.

It is also clear that some traits may have been acquired independently, may have been secondarily evolved over again. Thus the supraorbital ridges. When one observes the consistency with which these are heavy in most Pleistocene specimens—Pithecanthropus, Sinanthropus, Neandertal, and Rhodesian man—and how the male gorilla shows them enormously developed; and that among living races they are perhaps strongest in the lowly cultured Australian, it is tempting to look upon this bony development as a sign of primitiveness. Yet there is an array of contradicting facts. The youthful gorilla and the adult orang are without supraorbital development. The male gorilla has his powerful brows for the same reason that he has the crests along the top of his skull: they are needed as attachments for his powerful musculature. They are evidently a secondary sex character developed within the species. So among fossil men there were two strains: the second one, represented by the Piltdown, Steinheim,

Swanscombe, and other finds (§ 45, 54), being smooth of forehead. Among living races the Asiatic Mongoloids lack marked supraorbital development; the closely related American Indians possess it rather strongly; some Caucasians and many Negroes show little of the feature; Australians have it most of all. Evidently it would be unsafe to build many conclusions on either the presence or the absence of supraorbital ridges.

Perhaps these instances will suffice to show that even the mere anatomical rating of human races is far from a simple or an easy task. It is doubtful whether as yet it is valid to speak of one race as physically higher or more advanced, or more human and less brutish, than another. This is not an outright denial of the possibility of such differential ratings: it is a denial only of the belief that such differentials have been established.

83. PHYSIOLOGICAL DIFFERENCES

In gross physiology, all human races are much alike. The simpler measures like pulse and respiration rates and body temperatures come out remarkably uniform in group averages, considering how much these features vary between individuals, and in individuals according to momentary activity and health. There appear to be almost no significant racial differences. On temperature, the figures given by Hooton and von Eickstedt differ only slightly, but are in contradiction. If whites have a higher normal temperature than Negroes and American Indians, the difference does not exceed .01 or .02 of a degree Centigrade. Among some 700 Indians of the southwestern United States and northwestern Mexico, Hrdlička found the pulse to average about 60 per minute, in place of the usual 70 or 72. These are mostly high-plateau dwellers; but a small sample of lowland Maya also showed a rate 10 lower than the compared whites. Pulses around 60 have been recorded also for Japanese and for Mongols. This may accordingly prove to be a Mongoloid propensity.

There are a few records on blood pressure. These suggest the seriation: Europeans, Negroes, Chinese, Cuna Indians of Panama, Hindus, Japanese—which does not make too much racial sense. The Japanese are cited at 90-105, Cuna at 105, the Chinese 101-115, as against a white "norm" of 128 for systolic pressure. On the contrary, Adams found an average of only 121 over 81 for American whites, but 128 over 85 for American Negroes in several thousand cases, with the Negro excess increasing with age. There is undoubtedly more hypertension—excessive blood pressure—in American Negroes than in whites, but this falls in the realm of pathology (§ 85) and its cause is in dispute.

Basal metabolism was first worked out on whites, and is rated by formulas that usually include body weight and skin surface as estimated from height. The height-surface ratio may vary racially, and the readings for metabolism of nonwhites may accordingly be somewhat inaccurate. White or nonwhite or both in Cuba, Brazil, Syria, Java, Singapore, and Queensland run below the American-European standard. Some of this deficiency is attributed to climate; quantity and kind of food may also be factors. The principal observations that as of 1946 looked as if they might have racial significance are the following:

Eskimo (4 series), plus 15-26 per cent
Maya and Quiché Indians (4 series), plus 5-8
Araucanian Indians of Chile, plus 10-15
India (7 series), minus 11-18
Chinese outside of China (3 series), minus 12-15
Miao of Kweichou, China, plus 16
Australian aborigines (2 series), minus 11-13
Pureblood Negroes, no satisfactory figures available

The thyroid gland is most directly involved in basal metabolism. This gland is larger in Europeans than in Chinese; larger also in white than in Negro Americans, relatively to the total body. In Europeans the thyroid weighs a bit more than one-two-thousandth of the body, in Javanese less than one-three-thousandth.

Of internal organs, the spleen seems definitely smaller in American Negroes than in whites, also the liver; and the intestines are shorter, but heart and kidneys are about the same. The physiological significance of these differences is not clear.

84. INCIDENCE OF DISEASES

Pathology might seem to promise more than normal physiology. So far as mortality goes, there are enormous differences between races. And the mortality may be largely the result of particular diseases. Measles, for instance, has often been a deadly epidemic to uncivilized peoples, and smallpox has in some regions at times taken toll of a quarter of the population in a year or two. Yet it is shortsighted to infer from such cases any permanent racial predisposition or lack of resistance. The peoples in question have been free for generations from these diseases, and have therefore not maintained or acquired immunity. Their difference from us is thus essentially in environmental experience, not hereditary or racial. This is confirmed by the fact that after a generation or two the same epidemics that at first were so deadly to Polynesians or American Indians sink to almost the same level of mild virulence that they show among ourselves. Up to about 1900-10, most tribes in the United States decreased progressively in numbers. Since that decade, nearly all have first held their own and then increased. They had then been exposed for several generations to our diseases, or to our special strains of them, and had built up partial immunities and resistances more or less like our own.

Then too, immediate environment plays a part. The nonliterate often has no idea of contagion, and still less of guarding against it; he thinks in terms of magic instead of physiology. His remedial treatment is likely to be by a mixture of guesswork, empiricism, magic, and spiritualism. He knows nothing of sepsis, vaccinations, or preventive medicine.

It may be worth while to consider briefly the facts as to mortality from cancer. This dread disease appears to be not contagious, so that the factor of acquired immunity is eliminated. It is regarded as incurable, except by operation or radium or X ray, so that differences in treatment become relatively unimportant. If therefore significant differences in racial liability to cancer exist, they should emerge clearly. There do seem to be such differences. But they are overlaid by other factors external to the organism as it is inherited.

The raw statistics uniformly make cancer seem an overwhelmingly Caucasian disease. Thus, some comparative samples of cancer deaths per 100,000 population in various places within the period 1905-15 run as follows:

DEATHS FROM CANCER, 1905-1915

Johannesburg: whites, 52; Negroes, 14
Natal: whites, 56; Hindus, 11
Hong Kong: Europeans, 53; Chinese, 5
Manila: whites, 51; Filipinos, 27; Chinese, 19
East Indies: Dutch, 81; Singapore and Straits Settlements: natives, 13, 10;
    Ceylon, Calcutta: natives, 5, 11
United States: whites, 77; Indians, 4

However, for some unknown reason climate, as expressed grossly by latitude, is also a factor. Thus for large cities, in the same period:

CANCER IN LATITUDES
(Large cities)

60°-50° N.	106	30° N.-30° S.	38-42
50°-40° N.	92	30°-40° S.	90
40°-30° N.	78		

In some cases occupation is a direct or indirect cause. It was long ago noted that chimney sweeps were particularly liable to cancer. Thus as far back as 1890 they suffered in England, among males of 45-54, 532 cancer deaths a year per 100,000 population, as against an average for all occupations of 118. It is now known that the coal tars in soot are irritants that may stimulate cancerous growths. There are other vocation-frequency differences that remain wholly unexplained—perhaps being due to an indirect functional relation—but which recur decade after decade, so that the fact must be accepted. Thus British gardeners have twice as good a chance of not dying of cancer as brewers, and clergymen as lawyers. And this in spite of gardening and the clerical profession being long-lived occupations with high survival into the old age when cancer is most frequent.

This suggests a third factor besides latitude-climate and occupation; namely, a low general death rate and a consequent large proportion of aged people in the population. In a backward population in the modern world—they need not be primitive, only a couple of generations hygienically behind the times—so many children and young people die of preventable or curable disease that there are relatively few survivors to die of cancer, nephritis, or heart ailments as they become aged. All these latter diseases have in fact shot upward in the last century, and especially in the past fifty years, wherever sanitation and hygiene have been most advanced. This has been in proportion to the marked reduction of deaths from infantile dysentery, diphtheria, smallpox, typhoid, tuberculosis, and pneumonia. Most medical authorities believe that there is an intrinsic increase of both cancer and heart disease among ourselves in contemporary decades. But the eminent medical statistician Dublin believes that for cancer the increase is probably not real. It is obvious that there is a statistical increase due to the change in age distribution; and until this can be reliably computed, the size of the genuine increase will remain in doubt. The influence of the age factor holds for all populations, but it will be particularly strong, as regards an age-weighted disease like cancer, among the economically and medically backward, where most nonwhite peoples find themselves at present.

A fourth factor is the degree of medical observation and treatment. Where there are no X-ray laboratories or examinations, where hospitals or operations are not available or where patients fear or avoid them, and autopsies are not made, cancer deaths may be high, but diagnoses and death certifications will be low. Thus in Hungary, from 1901 to 1904, the reported cancer deaths were 239 per 100,000 among the owners of large farms, 41 among the owners of small farms; 108 among employing blacksmiths, 25 among their employees; 114 among employing tailors, 32 among employed tailors. Obviously, these pairs of groups differed in their economic status and therewith in the degree of their exposure to medical diagnosis.

Here too may be the explanation of why the South African Negro showed a rate of only 14 per 100,000 in the period that the United States Negro showed 56; also why the Chinese rate was as low as 5 in Hong Kong, rose to 19 in Manila and to 26 in Hawaii, while the average for the racially similar Japanese was 62 for the whole of Japan—as compared with 50 for Spain, which is pure Caucasian, but has been economically and medically one of the more backward countries of Europe. In Tokyo and Kyoto the rate soared to 73 and 90 respectively, just as in the United States it is considerably higher for the urban than for the rural population.

Within the United States, also, the rate rises and falls almost parallel for whites and Negroes according to locality; as,

CANCER DEATHS 1906-1910
(per 100,000)

Place	White	Negro
Memphis	59	34
Charleston	73	37
Nashville	74	55
New Orleans	86	73

If allowance is made for the facts that the Negro population of the United States is poorer and less educated than the white; that diagnosis or authentic medical certification of cause of death for the Negro population is more likely to be haphazard; that most Negroes live mainly in low-latitude southern states, the majority of whites in northern states; and that Negroes tend to be rural rather than urban—we derive from this that a considerable differential cancer death rate, such as a third more for the white than the colored, might be reasonably accounted for without bringing race into consideration. More on this in the next section.

In short, what superficially seems to be a notable race difference in cancer liability and mortality turns out to be at least in part due to natural and socio-cultural environment. This is not an assertion that race has nothing to do with the disease—only that the degree of influence of race has not yet been reliably defined and is difficult to define. The variable x of race and the variable y of environment both remain undetermined; but until we can strip off a fairly determinate result of y influence, we are not even coming to grips with the x factor.

Cancer has here served as an illustration only because there are analyzable data available and because the environmental factor of communicability seems to be ruled out, strengthening the first-blush case for its apparent dependence on race. Each separate disease has of course to be examined independently both as to its racial frequency and as to all the factors possibly involved.

Malaria, for instance, has been depicted as a scourge of the light-skinned races, against which Negroids have a large degree of racial—that is, genetic—resistance. Historical theories have been built upon this assumption. For example, there is an attractive hypothesis as to why Madagascar, especially in its coastal lowlands, is prevalently Negro in race but Indonesian in culture. The light-skinned invading people and their descendants were said to die off from fevers, but to leave their culture to the Negroids. Yet where malaria is endemic in Africa, and whites tend to die off from it while black natives flourish, it is reasonably clear that this is because childhood infections have built up the individual Negro's resistance—that is, the resistance of those who survive this rough process of exposure and immunization. In the United States the position of the Negro is superficially the opposite from that in Africa. The Negro death rate from malaria the United States over is eight times higher than that of whites! The reason is, first, that most of the United States no longer has very many deaths from malaria. There being much less malaria around, Negroes on the average acquire less immunity than in Africa. But, second, a much larger proportion of the total Negro population than of the total white population lives in the malarious districts of our South, in rural districts containing undrained areas, in poverty, without screens and sometimes without enough quinine. Hence there is enough infection in and around the lower Mississippi Valley to bring malaria mortality up to an appreciable figure in the Negro total, but only to an inconsiderable proportion of the ten times larger and more widespread white total. In being transported to the United States, the Negro has lost the protection of the childhood immunization of each new generation, but has not gained the white American's protection derived from mostly living in healthy districts and from maximum medical prevention and care. In a sense he has got caught in the middle.

The diagram in Figure 13, illustrating the variations in the history of malaria in the Romagna, proves that factors other than race must often be at work. With the incidence and the severity of the disease changing markedly through the centuries among the members of the same population in the same district of Italy, it is clear that either the malaria amoeba has varied in virulence; or that *Anopheles* mosquitoes have varied in numbers; or that economic or other cultural circumstances have had an effect; or possibly that immunity gets lost and has to be reacquired within the same racial strain. In short, the malaria-to-race relation ends up by once more presenting us with a single equation containing several unknowns.

The eminent bacteriologist and immunologist Zinsser sums up the situation as to racial immunity in the statement that it is most often attributable to individually acquired resistance: genetic factors may occasionally be involved. Even with experimentation on animals, he says, it is hard to determine which kind of immunity—racial or environmental, hereditary or acquired—one is dealing with. Pinner, speaking of tuberculosis, says that a true inheritance of acquired immunity has never been demonstrated. Well, what is difficult for a laboratory

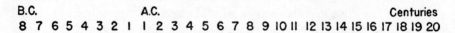

B.C.   A.C.   Centuries
8 7 6 5 4 3 2 1   1 2 3 4 5 6 7 8 9 10 11 12 13 14 15 16 17 18 19 20

FIG. 13.   MALARIA FREQUENCY

Curve of malaria incidence and virulence through twenty-seven hundred years in the Italian Romagna. (From Ackerknecht after Hackett after Celli)

worker, who can set his conditions and controls for animals, is obviously going to be more difficult for the anthropologist, who has to take his facts on man raw as nature and history feed them to him.

85. SPECIALTIES OF NEGRO PATHOLOGY

For some diseases the United States Negro offers a better field for inter-racial comparison than the African, because in spite of social disadvantages, he lives at least roughly in the same environment as the whites he is compared with, or we know enough about his circumstances to make some estimate of his environmental difference. It is true that the statistics would be worth considerably more if the mostly-Negro and the mostly-white in blood had been distinguished instead of being lumped as "colored"; but the future may bring that improvement. The data that follow—and that are tabulated overleaf—are based mainly on what Lewis has brought together.

So as not to pluck perpetually at the one string of difficulty of obtaining positive findings, let us begin with those diseases in which it is most likely, perhaps as good as certain, that Negroes and whites do show genuinely racial—that is, genetic—differences; go on from these to those which can be debated; and end with commentary.

Sickle-cell anemia is virtually confined to Negroes, perhaps wholly so. Some think there is no clear occurrence of it in any individual demonstrably free of suspicion of Negro blood. The anemia occurs as a relapsing disease in a very small proportion of a group of colored people whose blood normally and in health contains "sickle"-shaped cells. This condition is called sicklemia and is shown by about one American Negro in fifteen. It appears not yet to have been proved Mendelian, but is generally considered to be a unit factor of heredity. It may therefore be a race-limited mutation.

Negro resistance to trachoma is high in Africa as well as America, and contrasts with the prevalence of this eye infection in India and the susceptibility of the American Indian.

Hookworm resistance also is marked in Africa. Hospital records and autopsies in Africa confirm also the American experience of relative scarcity of peptic ulcer and urinary stones in Negroes. Gallstone infrequency is likewise established for Trinidad and Jamaican Negroes as well as those in the United States. The high Negro incidence of nephritis is allied to that of hypertension.

Negro resistance to measles and infantile paralysis has a slight statistical doubt cast on it by the fact that both are less common in southern than in northern states.

As to cancer, early records show a greater difference between the two populations than recent ones. The creeping-up presumably means that the Negro now has more diagnosis and treatment than he used to get. The total present rate

COMPARATIVE PATHOLOGY OF NEGROES AND WHITES IN THE UNITED STATES

DIFFERENCE DEFINITE AND MARKED, ALMOST CERTAINLY RACIAL

Lower Incidence for Negroes	Higher Incidence for Negroes
Diphtheria	Sickle-cell anemia
Yellow fever	Whooping cough (frequency × 3)
Haemophilia (nonclotting)	Fibroids in womb (× 5±)
Peptic ulcer	Keloid tumors (× 15±)
Psoriasis	Nephritis
Lupus	
Trachoma	
Surgical suppuration	

DIFFERENCE PERCEPTIBLE, SOME PROBABILITY OF BEING RACIAL

Lower Incidence for Negroes	Higher Incidence for Negroes
Scarlet fever	Lobar pneumonia
Measles	Hypertension
Infantile paralysis	Cerebral hemorrhage
Angina pectoris	Syphilitic heart disease
Arteriosclerosis	Cancer of female genitalia
Coronary occlusion	
Peptic ulcer	
Gallstones	
Urinary stones	
Most cancers	

FACT OR CAUSE OF DIFFERENCE IN DISPUTE

Lower Incidence for Negroes	Higher Incidence for Negroes
Pernicious anemia	Tuberculosis
Diabetes	Syphilis
	Typhoid fever
	Malaria

FACT OF DIFFERENCE WHOLLY UNCERTAIN

Smallpox	Rickets	Mongolian idiocy
Influenza	Epilepsy	Appendicitis
Pellagra		Hypertrophy of prostate

is around two-thirds that of the white; but for women of childbearing age there are more deaths from cancer among Negroes. The differences are perhaps greater qualitatively than in frequency: sarcoma, epithelioma, melanoma are particularly uncommon in Negroes. For the Negro in Africa the situation is pictured somewhat differently. Though the total incidence there is also less, primary carcinoma of the liver, skin cancer, and melanoma are relatively conspicuous, carcinoma of the stomach rare. But, as in America, a larger proportion of all Negro cancers come in middle life. This may mean a racial difference or only that fewer Negroes survive other diseases to die of cancer when they are old.

The records reveal fewer Negro than white diabetes admissions and deaths. But that this is a disease largely of diet and habits is shown by the fact that Frankfort Jews compared with Gentiles—from whom they certainly were not markedly different racially—had a diabetes incidence more than six times as high.

As for tuberculosis, some authorities believe and some disbelieve that there is a racial basis for the admitted difference in virulence. Tuberculosis ranks second in mortality for American Negroes, sixth for whites; fifty years ago it stood highest for both. The clinical descriptions for Negroes still frequently read like those for nineteenth-century whites, among whom a milder fibroid form has now come to be usual. Up to the age of twenty, the colored death rate runs at least three or four times higher. At ten to fourteen years, it is nearly eight times higher. After twenty-five, Negro and white rates more and more approximate. Tuberculosis is obviously a disease in which early diagnosis and persistent, prolonged treatment are of utmost importance, and these in turn are bound to be functions of educational and economic level. In parts of tropical Africa, French reports indicate a "virgin-soil" type of tuberculosis similar to that of previously unexposed American Indians or Polynesians. A fair summing-up for the United States situation seems to be Pinner's, that most of the tuberculosis frequency and mortality of the Negro is probably due to social conditions, but that the form of the disease, and the Negro's lower resistance to it, especially in youth, are probably at least partly founded on a genetic racial difference.

Syphilis is of course par excellence a social disease, and therefore one of the most difficult really to prove a racial basis for. Between 1915 and 1935, the reported death rate for whites increased 44 per cent; for Negroes it increased 38 per cent. Several plausible cultural explanations suggest themselves for this change, or apparent change. But it seems inconceivable that the germ plasm or the hereditary constitution, the genetic basis of the races, could have altered so much in 20 years. There is an old medical problem about yaws, which whites rarely get but many colored peoples in the tropics have frequently. It and syphilis may be two diseases or two "forms" of one disease. There may also be cross-immunity between them.

Smallpox, like typhoid fever, seems to be endemically old and mild in Africa. Pellagra in the United States has a curious distribution. Its reported occurrence is given as from two to five times less common among Negroes, its mortality as two to five times as great. This might mean that, being poor, the Southern Negro actually gets pellagra, which is a diet disease, oftener than do whites, but neither he nor anyone else is likely to pay attention to it till he is on the point of death. For appendicitis, Negro deaths run higher; but here the cure is by surgery, for which Negroes presumably possess both less willingness and less opportunity.

These brief analyses will serve to show that while it is as good as certain that races differ genetically in their pathology, as in other traits, the problem is beset by so many contingencies and pitfalls that exact proof can be brought only rarely, and in general we are lucky if reasonable probabilities can be determined.

86. ACHIEVEMENT AND SOCIAL ENVIRONMENT

One point will have become clear in the course of the foregoing discussion; namely, that the difficulty of coming to positive conclusions is due to two sets of interacting causal factors, the given hereditary ones and the environmental ones that play upon heredity. The environmental factors are themselves a composite of geographical influences and of the economic, emotional, and other social influences that human beings exert upon each other.

If this intermingling of distinct kinds of causes is true of races when considered from the side of physiology and medicine, it is evident that the intermingling will be even more intricate in the mental sphere. After all, bodily functioning varies only within fairly definite limits: when external influences press too strongly upon the innate nature of the organism, the latter ceases to function and dies. The personality, on the other hand, however much its organic structure is given by heredity, depends for its content wholly on experience; and this experience can be thoroughly varied. Individuals of the same organic endowment may conceivably be born either in the uppermost stratum of a highly refined civilization or among backward peasants and remote tribes. Whether this actually happens, and to what degree, is of course precisely the problem we are trying to solve. But that it is theoretically and logically possible cannot be denied. And here a vicious circle of reasoning begins. One argument says: There have been no recognized geniuses among peoples like the Hottentots, and the sum total of their group achievement is ridiculously small; therefore it is clear that the Hottentot mind must be inferior. The opposite argument runs: Hottentot cultural environment is so poor and limited that the finest mind in the world reared under its influence would grow up relatively sterile and atrophied; therefore even if the mind of the Hottentot is intrinsically identical with our own, or at least of equivalent capacity, and Hottentot geniuses have actually been born, they have nevertheless been unable to flourish as geniuses.

Evidently the same facts are before those who advocate these opposite views, but these facts are viewed from diametrically opposite sides. If one starts to travel around the logical circle in one direction, one can keep revolving indefinitely and find ever fresh supporting evidence. If, however, one begins to revolve around the same circle of opinion in the opposite direction, it is just as easy and just as compelling to continue to think in this fashion and to find all testimony corroborative.

In such a situation it is possible to realize that from the point of view of proof, or objective truth, one view is worth as much as the other—which is nothing. It is an emotional bias that inclines one man toward the conviction of race superiority and another toward that of race equality. The proofs in either case are for the most part a mere assembling of ex-parte testimony. It is easy enough to advocate impartiality. The difficulty is in being impartial; because both the hereditary and the environmental factors are in reality unknown quantities. What we have objectively before us is such and such a race or group of people, with such and such present traits and historical record. These phenomena being the product of the interaction of the two sets of causes, we could of course, if we knew the strength of one, compute the strength of the other. But as we have isolated neither, we are dealing with two indeterminate variables. Evidently the only way out of the dilemma, at any rate the only scientific way, is to find situations in which one of the factors is, for the time being, fixed. In that case the strength of the other factor will of course be proportionate to the attainments of the groups.

Actually, such instances are excessively difficult to find. There are occasional individuals with identical heredity; namely, identical twins, produced from the division of a single ovum. In such twins, the strength of environmental influences can theoretically be gauged by the difference in their careers and achievements. Yet such twins are only individuals, and it is risky to make inferences from them to racial groups. It is conceivable that heredity might on the whole be a more powerful cause than environment, but that racial groups would still average substantially alike in their heredity. Because a natively gifted and a natively stunted individual within the group vary conspicuously in achievement, even under similar environment, it does not follow compellingly that races differ in germ plasm because they differ in achievements.

If, on the other hand, one sets out to discover cases of identical environment for distinct racial strains, it becomes apparent that this task is impossible. Analysis quickly shows that the environment is identical only up to a certain point, and that beyond this point important social and cultural divergences begin. Thus, so far as geographical environment goes, the Negro and the white in the southern United States are under the same conditions. There is also uniformity of some of the gross externals of cultural environment. Both Negroes and whites speak English; are Christians; wear store clothes; go to the movies; and so on. But, just as obviously, there are aspects in which their social environment differs profoundly. Educational opportunities are widely different. The opportunity of attaining leadership or otherwise satisfying ambition is wide-open to the white, and practically closed to the Negro. The "color line" inevitably cuts across the social environment and makes of it two different environments.

It might be said that the southern United States furnishes an extreme case of a sharply drawn color line. That is true. But on the other hand there is perhaps no place on earth where something corresponding to a color line is not drawn, some distinction or preference is not made, between two distinguishably different populations occupying the same territory. It sometimes happens that distinctions are diminished and only faintly or subtly enforced, as in modern Hawaii or Brazil, where to outward appearances many racially different populations dwell together without discrimination. Yet examination reveals that the absence of discrimination is rather nominal. As regards the relations and associations of human beings, the welcome they extend or the aloofness that they show to one another, there are always lines drawn. This means not only difference in opportunity, but difference in experience, habit formation, practices, and interests.

87. TESTS ON THE SENSE FACULTIES

This factor of experience enters even into what appear to be the simplest mental operations, the sensory ones. The scant data available from experimental tests indicate that a variety of dark-skinned or uncivilized peoples, including Oceanic and African Negroids, Negritos, Ainus, and American Indians, on the whole slightly surpass civilized whites in keenness of vision and fineness of touch discrimination, whereas the whites are somewhat superior in acuity of hearing and sensitiveness to pain. Yet what do these results of measurements mean?

Vision is tested for its distance ability. The farther off one can distinguish objects or marks, the higher one's rating. Civilized man reads—normally—at fourteen inches. He works with sharp knives, with machines that are exact; he is surrounded by things made with such exact machines; he handles thin paper and filmy fabrics. His women sew and embroider with the sharpest of needles, the finest of thread. Everything about us tends toward close accuracy and away from the haziness of distant observation. The savage, on the other hand, the half-civilized person even, inspects the horizon, watches for game or its dim tracks, tries to peer to the bottom of streams for fish. He does not read, his needles are blunt, his thread is cord, his carving is without precision even though decorative, the lines he makes are freehand and far apart. He has been trained all his life, as it were, for the usual vision tests. If the psychologist reversed his experiment and sought the degree of power to see fine differences at close range, it is possible that the savage might prove inferior.

The whole act of vision in fact involves more than we ordinarily think. After all, seeing is done with the mind as well as with the eye. There is the retinal image, but there is also the interpretation of this image. A sailor descries the distant shore, whereas the landsman sees only a haze on the horizon. To the city dweller a horse and a cow a mile off are indistinguishable. Not so to the rancher. There is something almost imperceptible about the profile of the feeding end of the animal, about its movement, that promptly and surely classes it. He sees the total configuration of the object—dimly perhaps, but he knows what it means. At still longer ranges, where the individual animals have wholly faded from sight, a herd of cattle may perhaps be told from one of horses, by the plainsman, through the different clouds of dust they kick up, or the rate of motion of the cloud. An hour later when the herd is reached and proves to be as said, the astonished traveler from the metropolis is likely to credit his guide's eyes with an intrinsic power greater than that of his own field glasses—forgetting the influence of experience and training.

In keenness of hearing, on the contrary, one would expect the civilized white to come out ahead, as in fact he does; not because he is Caucasian, but because he is civilized, and because the instruments of experimentation, be they tuning forks or ticking watches or balls dropped on metal plates, are implements of civilization. Make the test the howl of a distant wolf, or the snapping of a twig as the boughs bend in the wind, and the college student's hearing might prove duller than that of the Indian or the Ainu. There is a story of a woodsman on a busy thoroughfare, amid the roar of traffic and multifarious noise of a great city, hearing a cricket chirp. When the cricket was actually discovered in a near-by cellar opening and the man in the fur cap was extolled for his miraculous keenness of audition, he dropped a dime on the pavement: at the clink, all the city passers-by stopped and looked around.

As to the pain sense, an introspective, interpretative element necessarily enters into experiments. What constitutes pain? When the trial becomes disagreeable? When it hurts? When it is excruciating? The savage may physiologically feel with his nerve ends precisely as we do. But being reared to a life of chronic slight discomforts, he is likely to think nothing of the sensation until it hurts sharply; whereas we signal as soon as we are sure that the experience is becoming perceptibly unpleasant.

In short, until there shall have been more numerous, balanced, and searching tests made, it must be considered that nothing positive has been established as to the respective sensory faculties of the several human races. The experiments performed are tests not so much of race as of the average experience and habits of groups of different culture.

88. INTELLIGENCE TESTS

If inconclusiveness holds as regards the sense faculties, it might be expected to hold to a greater degree of those higher faculties which we call intelligence; and such is the case. For some decades, intelligence tests have been gradually evolved and improved and standardized, and they are now routine in much personnel selection. During World War I, psychological examinations were introduced in the United States Army on a scale unheard of before. More testing, and more effective testing, was done in World War II; but it was directed rather at sifting out aptitudes or special kinds of ability, and the results have not been classified and published. The same is true of the personnel testing that has become so highly developed in civilian education and industry. The modern techniques are far more refined. But the old World War I draft results still focus better on the comparative race problem because of their very breadth and the sweep of their unselected range.

The purpose of these examinations was to assign men to the tasks best commensurate with their true abilities; especially to prevent the unfit from being entrusted with responsibility under which they would break down and bring failure on larger undertakings. Men subject to dizziness were to be kept from flying; those unable to understand orders, out of active line service. The tests throughout were practical. They were meant to determine whether a given man was fit or unfit. They did not pretend to go into the causes of his fitness or unfitness. This is an important point. Whatever illumination the army intelligence tests shed on the problem of race intelligence is therefore indirect. Different racial or national groups represented in the examinations attain different capacity ratings, but there is nothing in the results themselves to show whether they are due to racial or to environmental factors. Evidence on this point, if it can be derived at all from the tests, has to be analyzed out.

In general, examinees in the United States were rated by being assigned, on the basis of their scores, to grades lettered from A to E, with plus and minus subgrades. The most comprehensive presentation of results is to express the percentage of individuals in each group that made the middle grade C, better than C, and worse than C. On this basis we find:

RESULTS OF ARMY INTELLIGENCE TESTS

Group and Number of Individuals	Below C	C	Above C
Englishmen, 411	9	71	20
White draft generally, 93,973	24	64	12
Italians, 4,007	63	36	1
Poles, 382	70	30	(.5)
Negroes generally, 18,891	79	20	1

These figures at face value seem to show deep group differences in intelligence; and these face values were at first accepted in some quarters. The reason is that they flatter national and race egotism. To be sure, the Englishmen in the American draft make a better showing than the drafted men at large; but this would be complacently explained by saying that the English represent in comparative purity the Anglo-Saxon or Nordic stock which is also the dominant strain among Americans, but which has been somewhat contaminated in their case by the immigration of Latins and Slavs, who rate much lower, as is shown by the Italians and Poles tested. Lowest of all, as might be expected, is the Negro. So runs the superficial but satisfying interpretation of the figures—satisfying if one happens to be of northern-European ancestry.

But there is one feature that raises suspicion. The Italians and the Poles are too close to the Negroes. They stand much nearer to them in intelligence, according to these figures, than they do to the white Americans. Can this be so— at least, can it have racial significance? Are these Mediterranean-Alpines, descendants of the Romans, and these East Baltic-Alpines, so large a strain of whose blood flows in the veins of many white Americans, only a shade superior to the Negro? It sounds like a Nazi opinion. Something must be "wrong" with the figures; that is, they must contain another factor besides race.

A little further dissection of the lump results reveals this factor. The northern Negro far surpasses the southern in his showing. He gets ten times as high a proportion of individuals into the above-average grades, only half as many into the below-average. Evidently the difference is due to increased schooling, improved earning capacity, larger opportunity and incentive: sociocultural environment, in short. So strong is the influence of the environment that the northern Negro—born English-speaking, of course—easily surpassed the foreign-languaged, immigrant-descended Italian in the United States.

FURTHER RESULTS OF ARMY TESTS

Negroes, 5 northern states, 4705	46	51	3
Italians in the U.S. 4007	63	36	1
Negroes, 4 southern states, 6846	86	14	(.3)

Evidently the psychological tests are more a gauge of educational and social opportunity than of race, since the Italian, although brunet, is of course a pure Caucasian.

This conclusion is reinforced by another consideration. The type of test first used in the army had been built up for reasonably literate people speaking English. Among such people it discriminated successfully between the more and the less fit. But the illiterate and the foreigner knowing no English failed completely—not because their intelligence was zero, but because the test involved the use of noncongenital abilities which they had not acquired. A second set of tests, known as Beta, was evolved for those who were obviously ineligible, or proved themselves so, for the old style of test, which was designated as Alpha. The illiteracy of the subjects given the Beta test was in most cases not an absolute one. Men who could not write an intelligible letter or read the newspaper or who had had only half or less of the ordinary grammar-school education, together with aliens whose comprehension of English remained imperfect, were put in the group of "illiterates" or badly educated. Separating now the literates from the illiterates among a number of racial, national, or sectional groups, we find:

ALPHA TEST: LITERATES

Englishmen, 374	5	74	21
White draft generally, 72,618	16	69	15
Alabama whites, 697	19	72	9
New York Negroes, 1021	21	72	7
Italians, 575	33	64	3
Negroes generally, 5681	54	44	2
Alabama Negroes, 262	56	44	(.4)

BETA TEST: "ILLITERATES"

White draft generally, 26,012	58	41	1
Italians, 2888	64	35	1
New York Negroes, 440	72	28	0
Poles, 263	76	24	(.4)
Alabama whites, 384	80	20	0
Negroes generally, 11,633	91	9	(.2)
Alabama Negroes, 1043	97	3	(.1)

It must be borne in mind that the two groups were not set apart as the result of tests, but that the two tests were devised to meet the problem of treating the two groups with reasonable uniformity. The point was to find the excellent man, and the unfit man, with the same degree of accuracy whether he was literate or illiterate. When found, he was assigned to the same grade, such as A, or D minus, whether his examination had been Alpha or Beta.

Now let us observe some of the figures. In 1917, the New York Negro was nearly on a par with the Alabama white among literates, and a bit ahead of him among illiterates. Approximately the two groups came out the same; which means that growing up in a certain part of the country has as much to do with intelligence, even in the rough, as has Caucasian or colored parentage.

The literate Negroes of the draft, irrespective of section, slightly surpassed the illiterate whites.

In every case the literate members of a race or a nationality made a far better showing than the illiterate.

It is now clear also that the important factor of education enters so heavily into the first figures cited that they can mean little if anything as to inherent capacity. Of the Englishmen tested, nine-tenths fell in the literate group; of the Poles, a fifth; of the Italians, a seventh. In the draft generally, nearly three-fourths of the whites were literate; of the Negroes, less than a third.

In short, in spite of the fact that the Beta test was intended to equalize conditions for the illiterate and the semi-illiterate, the outstanding conclusion of the army examinations seems to be that education—cultural advantage—enormously develops faculty. Which is no wonder.

Is there anything left that can positively be assigned to race causation? It may be alleged that within the same section the white recruits regularly surpass the colored. Alabama whites may rate disappointingly, but they do better than Alabama Negroes; New York Negroes show surprisingly well, but they are inferior to New York whites; illiterate whites from the whole country definitely surpass illiterate Negroes; and among literates the difference is still more pronounced. But is this residuum of difference surely racial? As long as the color line remains drawn, a differential factor of cultural advantage is included; and how strong this is there is no present means of knowing. It is possible that some of the difference between sectionally and educationally equalized groups of whites and Negroes is really innate and racial. But it is also possible that most or all of it is environmental. Neither possibility can be demonstrated from the unrefined data available.

Of definite bearing on the cause of part of the differential are some tests cited by Klineberg. These were given in New York to twelve-year-old Negro children, most of whom were born in the South. They were grouped according to how long they had lived in Harlem.

DEVELOPMENT OF NEW YORK CITY NEGRO CHILDREN

Years in New York City	Average I.Q.
1 or 2	72
3 or 4	76
5 or 6	84
7, 8, or 9	92
Born in the North	92

How far the higher I.Q. was due to living in the somewhat less harshly discriminating North, and how far to the stimulating effect of big-city environment, is not known. But, caught at the most susceptible age, these children in a few years made up more than two-thirds of the lag behind whites with which they came North.

That city life with its pace, abundance of contacts, and competitive aspects sharpens native wits—at any rate for good scores in tests—has been known to psychologists. It is presumably one factor in the better rating of northern Negroes, who are largely urban, over southern and mainly rural Negroes. Klineberg ingeniously combined measure of rural-urban difference and racial difference in a series of tests he gave to schoolchildren in Europe. In Hamburg, Paris, and Rome he took average samples, which of course were far from racially pure, but which at least represented respective Nordic, Alpine, and Mediterranean predominance. The tests were the same, except for being administered in German, French, and Italian. The results came out essentially identical: between 212 and 219 by the particular score used. Klineberg also gave the same test to seven lots of rural children in the three countries. In each place, he made sure that not only each child but both its parents were born in the province. Also he accepted for testing only children who visibly conformed in their physique to one of the three basic European racial types. These are the results, by the same scale:

SCORES OF COUNTRY CHILDREN OF THREE RACIAL TYPES

Nordic	Germany	Hanover	198
Mediterranean	France	Pyrenees	197
Alpine	Germany	Baden	194
Alpine	Italy	Piedmont	189
Alpine	France	Auvergne	180
Nordic	France	Flanders	174
Mediterranean	Italy	Sicily	173

First and outstanding, all the yokel groups are behind all the city slickers. It is clear that the urban-rural mode of life has far more influence than intra-white racial membership on the sort of intelligence that is tested by tests. As between the three races, Nordics and Mediterraneans come out a bit on top in the countryside, but also at the bottom; the Alpines hold all the middle places. That Sicily trails the others is very likely due to the fact that Sicilians are the poorest and historically most retarded of the seven groups. Their fellow Mediterraneans in France are relatively high up among the rurals. This set of tests certainly emphasizes the influence of group exposure to conditioning over that of genetic constitution of racial groups.

The influence of the linguistic factor, well recognized by psychologists since the Beta tests, has also been neatly brought out by Klineberg with reference to so-called race. The figures speak for themselves.

VERBAL AND PERFORMANCE SCORES

	Verbal Test Score	Performance Test Score	Superiority in Performance Score
Italians	85	93	8
Chinese, Japanese	89	102	13
U.S. Indians	75	92	17
Mexicans	82	92	10
New York City Jews	96	82	−14

The taciturn, inarticulate Indian made the greatest improvement as soon as he was put to using his brain, eye, and hands instead of brain, ear, and tongue. The Jews were East Side New York City, and therefore mainly children of immigrants from towns; and they were themselves raised not only in the metropolis but in the environment of a group that practices and esteems verbalism. So they came out easy tops in that and a bad last where eyes and hands were involved.

89. STATUS OF HYBRIDS

In nearly all tests of the American Negro, full-bloods and mixed bloods have not been discriminated. It is usually difficult to do so. Yet if races have distinctive endowments, the nature of these is not cleared up so long as individuals who biologically are seven-eighths Caucasian are included with pure Negroes merely because in this country we have the social habitude of reckoning them all as "colored."

In the World War I army examinations an attempt was made to separate one group of colored recruits into darker-skinned and lighter-skinned subgroups, the latter containing those estimated to be mulattoes or less than half Negro. The light group made the better scores: in the Alpha test for literates, 50, the dark Negroes only 30; in the Beta tests for illiterates, the respective figures were 36 and 29.

But is the mulatto subject to any more advantageous environment than the full-blooded Negro? So far as voting and officeholding in the Deep South, riding in Pullman cars, and occupying orchestra seats in theaters are concerned, there is no difference: both are colored and therefore beyond the Jim Crow barrier. But the mulattoes of slavery days were likely to be house servants, brought up with the master's family, absorbing manners, information, perhaps education; their black half-brothers and half-sisters stayed out in the plantation shacks. Several generations have elapsed since those days, but it is probable that the descendants of mulattoes have kept a step or two ahead of the descendants of the pure blacks in literacy, range of experience, and the like. It is well known that modern American Negroes tend to accord higher status among themselves to the lighter-skinned and Caucasian-featured individuals. Successful Negroes tend to marry light-colored spouses. A light skin and a convex nose count for almost as much as a good education or successful parents—both among Negroes themselves in their internal social cleavages, and in getting jobs or other opportunities from whites. To be sure, which is cause and which effect here? Quite likely, our x is both cause and effect, and our y likewise. But all that is being contended for is that any judgment is more or less dogmatic when the causality in the phenomena is surely complex and probably circular.

It is impossible to predict what the social effect of miscegenation will be. The effect undoubtedly varies and must be examined in each case. Thus, Indian half-breeds in one tribe may usually be the result of wholly transient or mercenary unions between inferior whites and the more promiscuous native women and may therefore grow up in an atmosphere of demoralization to which the full-blooded Indian is less exposed. This demoralization would, to be sure, affect character and not intelligence as such; but it might stand in the way of schooling, stability, or sense of security. In another tribe, to the contrary, the half-breed might normally grow up in the house of a permanently settled white father, a squaw man, and in that event would learn English better, go to school earlier and longer, and in the case of a test therefore achieve a higher rating than the full-blood. Where the infusion of white blood, with accompanying economic, literate, and technological benefits, happened a couple of centuries ago, as among the Iroquois, it might have possessed an advantage for a while and then gradually have lost it again.

For Indians, Garth has made a serious endeavor to correlate intelligence rating with proportion of blood. Among 1400 Indian schoolchildren he got results as follows:

TESTS ON INDIANS BY PROPORTION OF BLOOD

	Average I.Q.
4/4 Indian	72
3/4 Indian	74
1/2 Indian	75
1/4 Indian	78

This looks like something. But if we project the series of figures one step farther on, to no-Indian blood, it should come out around 80 for all-white; whereas of course the mean for whites is 100, the scale being based on that as standard. One might predict then that full-whites brought up wholly under the social conditions of American reservation Indians would score 80. Or, to put it differently, two-thirds of the test inferiority of Indians is presumably due to their conditioning environment. The other third may be racial, or it may not, subject to the cautions in the last paragraph.

Perhaps the most elaborate investigation of the relative capacity of hybrids was made by Davenport and Steggerda on race crosses in Jamaica, where Negroes and part-Negroes ("browns") outnumber whites, and where social discrimination is unusually mild for an English-speaking community. The findings were far from clear-cut, though the number of individuals measured seemed reasonably adequate—up to 400 adults and 300 subadults. As almost always, the variability within any one race group was consistently found to be greater than the difference between its average and that of the two other groups.

Thus in musical capacity, six different traits were tested in three age groups—children, adolescents, and adults—and hence there is a total of 54 comparisons among blacks, hybrids, and whites. Only six of these 54 were statistically significant by the formula in customary use among psychologists. Four of these were the average differences by which black children surpassed white children in pitch, time, and rhythm perception, and adult blacks surpassed adult whites in rhythm. But the two other instances of "sureness"—really it is only a very high probability—showed the superiority of white adolescents over both black and brown in perception of intensity of tone, even though among both children and adults the blacks came out first in this trait. In time sense, the surely superior black children lost their supremacy to whites among adolescents, and in both time and pitch they lost it to brown adults. The results point in too many different directions to make much sense. It does look as if in Jamaica at least full-Negroes were perhaps superior in most musical faculties in childhood, but that the mulattoes and the whites drew abreast of them after about age thirteen.

The appended tabular summary of scored "firsts" or superiorities shows clearly this apparent and unexplained age shift in musical ability. But it also shows that when all tests and all ages are taken together, while the whites score tops oftener than do the blacks, the hybrid browns are *not* intermediate but beat them both out—29 as against 24 and 17! However, even a mere dip below the surface of the grand total reveals the cause of this strange result: the investigators happened to get hold of an unusually bright sample of brown fourteen-to-sixteen-year-olds. Thus they carried off 11 firsts in all nonmusical tests as against only 5 by blacks and whites combined. Brown children also led: 9 nonmusical firsts against 7. But brown adults did badly: 3 firsts against 5 by blacks and 8 by whites; or counting in a few additional tests not given to children, the

NUMBER OF "FIRSTS" OR HIGHEST TEST SCORES IN JAMAICA

	Blacks	Browns	Whites
Children			
A. Musical capacity	5	0	1
B. Miscellaneous performance	3	4	1
C. Army Alpha intelligence	0	5	3
TOTAL	8	9	5
Adolescents			
A. Musical capacity	1	2	3
B. Miscellaneous performance	1	5	2
C. Army Alpha intelligence	0	6	2
TOTAL	2	13	7
Adults			
A. Musical capacity	2	3	1
B. Miscellaneous performance	1	3	4
C. Army Alpha intelligence	4	0	4
TOTAL	7	6	9
All Age Total			
A. Musical capacity	8	5	5
B. Miscellaneous performance	5	12	7
C. Army Alpha intelligence	4	11	9
TOTAL	17	28	21
Additional miscellaneous, adults only	0	1	3
TOTAL	17	29	24

score was blacks 5, browns 4, whites 11, in nonmusical superiorities. It is conceivable that one race might show precocious ability compared with another and then lose its edge again. But it is hardly conceivable that a hybrid stock should first surpass both the races of which it was a blend, and then fall behind both of them! We can only conclude that the age and race samples tested were insufficient in size or unevenly selected.

The reliable results of this intriguing investigation accordingly are, first, a fair probability that blacks show a slight early musical superiority over whites and possibly maintain it. Second, in general intelligence the browns are by no means a mere intermediate between Negroes and whites, but show a surprisingly independent and variable superiority and inferiority to both. This last condition can easily be accounted for by irregularities of sampling, or of social condition, but scarcely by genetic hybridity. In short, our principal results are again negative.

90. EVIDENCE FROM THE CULTURAL RECORD OF RACES

An entirely different method of approach to the problem of race capacity is that of examining the cultural record, the achievements in civilization, of groups. While this approach is theoretically possible, and while it is often attempted, it is subject to little control and therefore unlikely to yield dependable conclusions.

First of all, the cultural history of a people must be known for considerable periods before one can validly think of inferring therefrom anything as to the faculties of that people. The reason is that active civilization, as a productive process, is slow to grow up, slow to be acquired. Mere momentum would normally keep the more advanced of two peoples ahead of the other for a long time. In proportion as not nations but groups of nations were involved, the momentum would continue for still longer periods. Civilization flourished for some thousands of years in the Near East, and then about the Mediterranean, before it became established with equal vigor and success in northern Europe. Had Julius Caesar or one of his contemporaries been asked whether by any sane stretch of fantasy he could imagine the Britons and the Germans as inherently the equals of Romans and Greeks, he would probably have replied that if these Northerners possessed the ability of the Mediterraneans they would long since have given vent to it, instead of continuing to live in disorganization, poverty, ignorance, rudeness, and without great men or products of the spirit. And, within limits, Caesar would have been right, since more than a thousand years passed before northern Europe began to draw abreast of Italy in degree and productivity of civilization. Two thousand years before Christ, a well-informed Egyptian might reasonably have disposed in the same sweeping way of the possibility of Greeks and Italians being the equals of his own people in capacity. What had these barbarians ever done to lead one to think that they might yet do great things? Today we brush Negroes and American Indians out of the reckoning with the same offhandedness. And enough of us let slip the same sentiments about Asiatics to antagonize whole great nations like the Chinese and the East Indians, and therewith help to conjure up or to perpetuate difficult international problems.

In general, arguing from performance to potentiality, from accomplishment to achievement, is valid under conditions of set experiment—such as are impossible for races—or in proportion as the number and the variety of observations is large. A single matched competition may decide pretty reliably as between the respective speed capacities of two runners for a given distance. But it would be hazardous to form an opinion from a casual glimpse of them in action while one might happen to be hastening and the other dallying. Least of all would it be sound to infer that essential superiority rested with the one in advance at the moment of observation, without knowledge of their starting points, the difficulty of their routes, the motive or goal of their courses. It is only as the number of circumstances grows from which observations are available that judgment begins to have any weight. The runner who has led for a long time and is increasing his lead, or who has repeatedly passed others, or who carries a load and yet gains ground, may lay some claim to superiority. In the same way, as between human races, a long and intimate historical record, objectively analyzed, gives some legitimate basis for tentative conclusions as to their natural endowment. But how long the record must be is suggested by the example already cited of Mediterranean versus Nordic cultural pre-eminence.

The fallacy that is most commonly committed is to argue from what in the history of great groups is only an instant—the instant at which one's own race or nationality is dominant. The Anglo-Saxon's moment is the present; the Italian's, the Renaissance; the Greek's, the age of Pericles. Usually, too, the dominance holds only for certain aspects: military or economic or aesthetic superiority, as the case may be; inferiorities on other sides are merely overlooked. The Greek knew his own venality and mendacity, but looked down on the barbarian nevertheless. Anglo-Saxon comparative backwardness in the plastic and musical arts is notorious, but does not deter most Anglo-Saxons from believing that they are the elect in quality, and from buttressing this conviction with the evidences of present industrial, economic, and political achievements—and perhaps past literary ones.

91. EMOTIONAL BIAS AGAIN

Inference from record to potentiality where the record of one's own group is favorable, and failure to draw such inference where the achievement of other groups is superior, is a combination of mental operations that is widespread because it arises spontaneously in minds not critically trained. Here is an instance:

One of the great achievements of science in the nineteenth century was Galton's demonstration, in a series of works beginning with *Hereditary Genius*, that the laws of heredity apply to the mind in the same manner and to the same degree as to the body. On the whole this proof has failed to be recognized at its true importance, perhaps because it inclines adversely to popular presuppositions of the independence of the soul and mind from the body, propositions to which many men still adhere emotionally or unconsciously.

From this perfectly valid demonstration, which has been confirmed by other methods, Galton went on to rate the hereditary worth of various races according to the number of their men of genius. Here a fallacy enters: the assumption that all geniuses born are recognized as such. A great work naturally requires a great man, but it presupposes also a great culture. It may be that, historically speaking, a great genius cannot arise in a primitive degree of civilization. That is, the kind of concentrated accomplishment which alone we recognize as a work of genius is culturally impossible below a certain level. Biologically the individual of genius may be there; civilizationally he is not called forth, and so does not get into the record. Consequently it is unsound to argue from the historical record to biological worth. However, this Galton did; and his method led him to the conclusion that the Negro rates two grades lower than the Englishman, on a total scale of fourteen grades, and the Englishman two lower than the fifth-century Athenian.

This conclusion has never been popular. Most people, on becoming familiar with Galton's argument, resist it. Its fallacy is not easy to perceive—if it were, Galton would not have committed it—and the average person is habitually so vague-minded upon what is organic and what is sociocultural or historical that the determination of the fallacy would be well beyond him. His opposition to Galton's conclusion is therefore emotionally and not rationally founded, and his arguments against the conclusion are presumably also called forth by emotional stimulus.

On the other hand, some individuals of this day and land do habitually infer, like Galton, from cultural status to biological worth, so far as the Negro is concerned. The same persons who might eagerly accept the demonstration of a flaw in Galton's argument in favor of Athenian superiority would often become skeptical and resistive to the exposition of the same flaw in the current belief as to Negro inferiority. It is remarkable how frequently and how soon, in making this exposition, one becomes aware of some hearers' feeling that one's attitude is sophistical, unreal, insincere, or motivated by something concealed.

The drift of this discussion may seem to be an unavowed argument in favor of race equality. It is not that. As a matter of fact, the anatomical differences between races would appear to render it likely that at least some corresponding congenital differences of psychological quality exist. These differences might not be profound, compared with the sum total of common human faculties, much as the physical variations of mankind fall within the limits of a single species. Yet they would preclude identity. As for the vexed question of superiority, lack of identity would involve at least some degree of greater power in certain respects in some races. These pre-eminences might be rather evenly distributed, so that no one race would notably excel the others in the sum total or average of its capacities; or they might show some minor tendency to cluster on one rather than on another race. In either event, however, race difference, moderate or minimal, qualitative if not quantitative, would remain as something that could perhaps be ultimately determined.

But it is one thing to admit this theoretical probability and then stop through ignorance of what the differences are, and another to construe the admission as justification of mental attitudes that may be well grounded in historical conditioning but are in considerable measure unfounded objectively.

In short, it is a difficult task to establish any race as either superior or inferior to another, but relatively easy to prove that we entertain a strong prejudice in favor of our own racial superiority.

92. SUMMARY

It would seem that the subject of basic race problems—that is, of the natural endowment of true human races—can be summarized as follows:

The essential difficulty of these problems lies in the fact that the performance of groups is the product of two sets of factors, biological and cultural, both of which are variable and usually not readily separable.

Progress in solution of the problems will be made gradually, and will be hastened by recognition of how few positive determinations have yet been made.

Most of the alleged existing evidence on race endowment is probably worthless.

The remainder probably has some value, but to what degree, and what it demonstrates, cannot yet be asserted.

The most definite determinations promise to eventuate from experiment. If fully controlled experiments in breeding and rearing human beings could be carried out, the problems would soon begin to be solved. Experiments on animals would prove practically nothing, because animals are cultureless—uninfluenced by environment of their own making.

Progress will be aided by increasing shift of attention from the crude consideration of comparative lump rating of the races—that is, as to their gross superiority or inferiority—to a consideration of such specific qualitative differences as they may prove to show. The question of finding the race in which the greatest number of qualitative excellences may be concentrated is subsequent and of much less scientific importance.

Scientific inquiries into race are for the present best kept apart from so-called actual race problems. These problems inevitably involve feeling, usually of considerable strength, which tends to vitiate objective approach. On the other hand, practical problems will no doubt continue to be met practically; that is, morally and emotionally. Whether the Japanese should be forbidden to hold land in California and the Negro be de-facto disfranchised in the Deep South are problems of economics and of group ethics, which unfortunately will probably for some time to come be disposed of emotionally, as at present, irrespective of the possible findings of science upon the innate endowment of the Caucasoid, Mongoloid, and Negroid strains and substrains.

All that has been said here of course applies with even more force to what is miscalled the problem of "racial minorities" when these minorities, such as Poles or Italians or French Canadians or Irish in the United States, or Germans in Alsace or Czechoslovakia, are not racial groups at all but are set apart ethnically or socially or culturally, as by their speech, religion, customs, traditions, or cohesive group loyalties.

CHAPTER SIX

Language

93. LINGUISTIC RELATIONSHIP: THE SPEECH FAMILY

THE QUESTION that the historian and the anthropologist most frequently ask of the philologist is whether this and that language are or are not related. Relationship in such connection means descent from a common source, as two brothers are descended from the same father, or two cousins from a common grandfather. If languages can be demonstrated to possess such common source, it is clear that the peoples who spoke them must at one time have been in close contact, or perhaps have constituted a single people. If, on the other hand, the languages of two peoples prove wholly dissimilar, though their racial types and cultures be virtually identical, as indeed is sometimes found to be the case—witness the Hungarians and their neighbors—it is evident that an element of discontinuous development must somewhere be reckoned with. Perhaps one part of an originally single racial group gradually modified its speech beyond recognition; or under the shock of conquest, migration, or other historical accident it may have entirely discarded its language in favor of a new and foreign tongue. Or the opposite may be true: The two groups were originally wholly separate and distinct in many respects, but, being brought into contact, their cultures interpenetrated, intermarriage followed, and the two physical types became assimilated into one while the languages remained dissimilar. In short, if one wishes full understanding of a people, one must take its language into consideration. This means that the language must be classified. If a classification is to be more than merely logical or theoretical, if it is to be pragmatic and historically significant, it must have reference to relationship, development, origin. In a word, it must be a genetic classification.

The term used to indicate that two or more languages have a common source but are unrelated to certain others, or seem so in the present state of knowledge, is "linguistic family." "Linguistic stock" is frequently used as a synonym. This is the fundamental concept in the historical classification of languages. Without a clear idea of its meaning one involves oneself in confusion on attempting to use philology as an aid to other branches of human history.

There is no abstract reason against referrring to a group of unrelated languages as a "family" because they are all spoken in one area, nor against denominating as "families," as has sometimes been done, the major subdivisions of a group of languages admittedly of common origin. Again, languages that show certain similarities of type or structure, such as inflection, might conceivably be put into one "family." But there is this objection to all such usages: They do not commit themselves on the point of genetic relationship, or they contradict it, or only partially exhaust it. Yet commonness of origin is so important in many connections that it is indispensable to have one term that denotes its ascertainable presence. And for this quality there happens to be no generally understood designation other than "linguistic family," or its synonym, "linguistic stock." This phrase will therefore be used here strictly in the sense of the whole of a group of languages sprung from a single source, and only in that sense. Other groupings will be indicated by phrases like "languages of such and such an area," "subfamily," "division of a family," or "unrelated languages of similar type."

94. CRITERIA OF RELATIONSHIP

The question that first arises in regard to linguistic families is how the relationship of their constituent idioms is determined. In brief, the method is one of comparison. If a considerable proportion of the words and the grammatical forms of two languages are reasonably similar, similar enough to indicate that the resemblances cannot be due to mere accident, these similar words and forms must go back to a common source; and if this source is not borrowing by one language from another, the two tongues are related by descent from a common ancestor. If comparison fails to bring out any such degree of resemblance, the languages are classed in distinct families.

Of course it is possible that the reason two languages seem unrelated is not that they are really so, but that they have in the lapse of ages become so much differentiated that one cannot any longer find resemblance between their forms. In that event true relationship would be obscured by remoteness. Theoretically, there is high probability that many families of languages customarily regarded as totally distinct do go back in the far past to a common origin, and that our ignorance of their history, or inability to analyze them deeply, prevents recognition of their relationship. From time to time it happens that groups of languages which at first seemed unrelated are shown by more intensive study to possess elements enough in common to compel the recognition of their original unity. In that case what were supposed to be several "families" become merged in one. The scope of a particular family may be thus enlarged; but the scope of the generic concept of "family" is not altered.

Whether there is any hope that comparative philology may ultimately be prosecuted with sufficient success to lead all the varied forms of human speech back to a single origin is an interesting speculation. A fair statement is that such a possibility, like any future event, cannot be absolutely denied, but that science is still extremely far from such a realization. Of more immediate concern is an ordering and summarizing of the knowledge in hand with a view to such positive inferences as can be drawn.

In an estimate of the similarity of languages, items that count as evidence must meet two requirements: they must be alike, or traceably similar, or regularly correspondent in sound; and they must be alike or similar or related in meaning. This double requirement holds equally whether full words or separable parts of words, roots, or grammatical forms are compared. The English word *eel* and the French *île,* meaning *island,* are pronounced almost exactly alike, yet their meaning is so different that no sane person would regard them as sprung from the same origin. As a matter of fact *île* is derived from Latin *insula,* and is the source of the English *isle,* whereas *eel* has a cognate in German *aal.* These prototypes *insula* and *aal* being as different in sound as they are in meaning, any possibility that *eel* and *île* might be related is easily disposed of. Yet if the Latin and German cognates were lost, if nothing were known of the history of the English and French languages, and if *île* meant not *island* but, say, *fish* or *water snake,* then it might be reasonable to think of a connection.

Such doubtful cases, of which a certain proportion are likely to be adjudged wrongly, are bound to come up in regard to the less well investigated languages, particularly those of nations without writing, the earlier stages of whose speech have perished without trace. In proportion as more is known of the history of a language, or as careful analysis can reconstruct more of its past stages, the number of such border-line cases obviously becomes fewer.

Before genetic connection between two languages can be thought of, the number of their elements similar in sound and sense must be reasonably large. An isolated handful of resemblances obviously are either importations—loan words—or the result of coincidence. Thus in the native Californian language known as Yuki, *ko* means *go,* and *kom* means *come.* Yet examination of Yuki reveals no further similarities. It would therefore be absurd to dream of a connection: one swallow does not make a summer. This lone pair of resemblances means nothing except that the mathematical law of probability has operated. Among the thousands of words in one language, a number are likely to be similar in sound to words of another language; and of this number again a small fraction, perhaps one or two or five in all, will happen to bear some resemblance in meaning also. In short, the similarities upon which a verdict of genetic relationship is based must be sufficiently numerous to fall well beyond the possibility of mere coincidence; and it must also be possible to prove with reasonable certainty that they are not the result of one language's borrowing words from another, as, for instance, English has borrowed from French and Latin.

At the same time it is not necessary that the similarities extend to the point of identity. In fact, too close a resemblance between part of the stock of two languages immediately raises a presumption of borrowing. For every language is continually changing, and once a mother tongue has split into several daughters, each of these goes on modifying its sounds, and gradually shifting the meaning of its words, generation after generation. In short, where connection is real, it must be veiled by a certain degree of change or distortion.

Take the English word *foot* and the Latin word of the same meaning, *pes*. To offhand inspection the sounds or forms of the two words do not seem similar. The resemblance becomes more definite in other forms of *pes*, for instance the genitive case *ped-is* or the accusative *ped-em*. Obviously the stem or elementary portion of the Latin word is not *pes* but *ped-;* and the *d* is closer to the English *t* of *foot* than is the *s* of *pes*. The probability of relationship is increased by the Greek word for foot, *pous,* whose stem proves to be *pod-*, with vowel closer to that of English. Meanwhile, it would be recognized that there are English words beginning with *ped-,* such as *pedal, pedestrian, pedestal,* all of which have a clear association with the idea of foot. All these words however possess almost exact equivalents in Latin. One would therefore be justified in concluding from these facts what indeed the history of the languages proves: namely, that *pedal, pedestrian,* and *pedestal* are Latin words taken over into English; whereas *foot* and *pes* and *pous,* and for that matter German *fuss,* are derivatives from a common form that once existed in the now extinct mother tongue from which Greek and Latin and English and German are derived.

95. SOUND EQUIVALENCES AND PHONETIC LAWS

The question next arises whether it is possible to account for the distortions that have modified the original word into *foot, ped-,* and so on. What has caused the initial sound of this ancient word to become *p* in Latin and *f* in English, and its last consonant to be *d* in Latin and Greek, *t* in English, and *ss* in German? To answer this seemingly innocent question with accuracy for this one word alone would involve a treatise on the whole group of languages in question; and even then the causes, as causes, could hardly be set down with certainty. But it has proved possible to assemble a large number of instances of parallel "distortion" in which Latin *p* corresponds to English *f*, or *d* to *t*. Evidently philology has got hold of a generalized phenomenon here. Since *father* corresponds to *pater*, *full* to *pl-enus*, *for* to *pro*, *fish* to *piscis*, and so on in case after case, we are evidently face to face with a happening that has occurred with regularity and to which the name "law" is therefore applicable.

The *f* of *foot* and the *p* of *pes* are both lip sounds. They differ pre-eminently in that *f* can be prolonged indefinitely, whereas *p* is produced by a momentary closure of the lips with stoppage of the breath. It is customary to speak of sounds produced by a process like that for *p* as "stops." *F*, on the other hand, is a "continuant," and more specifically a "fricative" or rubbing sound.

The English word *three* begins with a sound which, although conventionally represented by the two letters *th*, is a simple sound and in a class with *f* in being fricative. *Th* is formed by putting the tongue lightly across the teeth, just as *f* is made by placing the lower lip against the edge of the upper teeth. In both cases the breath is expelled with friction through a narrow passage. Now if the fricative *f* is represented in Latin by the stop *p*, then, if regularity holds good, the English fricative *th* ought to be represented in Latin by the stop sound in the corresponding dental position; namely, *t*. The Latin word for *three* is in fact *tres;* for *thin, ten-uis;* for *mother, mater;* for *thou, tu,* and so on. The regularity therefore extends beyond the limits of the single labial class of sounds, and applies with equal force to the dentals; and, it may be added, to the palatals and gutturals as well.

As one passes from English and Latin to German, one finds the initial sound of the word meaning *three, drei,* to be somewhat different from *th* and *t* but still clearly allied, since it also is made by the tongue against the teeth. *D* is a stop like *t,* but the vocal cords vibrate while it is being pronounced, whereas in *t* the vocal cords are silent. *D* is "voiced" or "sonant," *t* "unvoiced" or "surd." Hence the formulation: Latin, surd stop; German, sonant stop; English, fricative. This triple equivalence can be substantiated in other words. For instance, *ten-uis, dünn, thin; tu, du, thou.*

If it is the English word that contains a surd stop, what will be the equivalent in Latin and German? Compare *ten,* Latin *decem,* German *zehn,* pronounced *tsehn.* Again the three classes of sounds run parallel; but the place of their appearance in the three languages has shifted.

The third possible placing of the three sounds in the three languages is when English has the sonant stop *d.* By exclusion it might be predicted that Latin should then show the fricative *th* and the German the surd stop *t.* The word *daughter* confirms this. The German is *tochter.* Latin in this case fails us, the original corresponding stem having gone out of use and been replaced by the word *filia*. But Greek, whose sounds tend to align with those of Latin as opposed to English and German, provides the *th* as expected: *thygater*.

Let us bring together these results so that the eye may grasp them:

SOUND EQUIVALENCES

Latin, Greek	surd stop	sonant stop	fricative
German	sonant stop	fricative	surd stop
English	fricative	surd stop	sonant stop

Latin, Greek	tres	duo	thygater
German	drei	zwei	tochter
English	three	two	daughter

These relations apply not only to the dentals *d, t, th* (*s, z*), which have been chosen for illustration, but also to the labials *p, b, f,* and to the palatals *k, g, h* (*gh, ch*).

It is evident that most of the sounds occur in all three groups of languages, but not in the same words. The sound *t* is common to English, Latin, and German, but when it appears in a particular word in one of these languages it is replaced by *d* and *th* in the two other languages. This replacing is known as a "sound shift." The sound shifts just enumerated constitute the famous Grimm's Law. This was the first important phonetic law or system of sound substitutions discovered in any family. Yet it is only one of a number of shifts that have been worked out for the Indo-European family of languages to which English, German, and Latin belong. So far, only stopped and fricative consonants have been reviewed here, and no vowels have been considered. Other languages, in the Indo-European family and in other families, also show shifts, but often different ones, as between *l* and *n,* or *s* and *k,* or *p* and *k.*

The significance of a shift lies in the fact that its regularity cannot easily be explained on any other ground than that the words in which the law is operative must originally have been the same. That is, Latin *duo*, German *zwei*, English *two* are all only variants of a word that meant "two" in the mother tongue from which these three languages are descended. This example alone is of course insufficient evidence for the existence of such a common mother tongue. But that each of the shifts discussed is substantiated by hundreds or thousands of words in which it holds true—this fact puts the shift beyond possibility of mere accident: the explanation of coincidence is ruled out. The resemblances therefore are both genuine and genetic. The conclusion becomes inevitable that the languages thus linked are later modifications of a former single speech.

It is in this way that linguistic relationship is determined. Where an ancient sound shift, a law of phonetic change, can be established by a sufficient number of cases, argument ceases. It is true that when most of a language has perished, or when an unwritten language has been but fragmentarily recorded or its analysis not carried far, a strong presumption of genetic unity may crowd in on the investigator who is not yet in a position to present the evidence of laws. The indications may be strong enough to warrant a tentative assumption of relationship. But the final test is always the establishment of laws of sound equivalence that hold good with regularity—part-for-part correspondence, the biologist would say.

96. THE PRINCIPAL SPEECH FAMILIES

The number of linguistic families or stocks [1] is not a matter of much theoretical import. From what has already been said it appears that the number can perhaps never be determined with absolute accuracy. As knowledge accumulates and dissection is carried to greater refinements, new similarities will be uncovered and will serve to unite what now seem to be separate stocks. Yet for the practical purpose of classifying and relating peoples the linguistic family will remain an indispensable historical tool. A rapid survey of the principal families will therefore be given.

In Asia and Europe, which must be considered a unit in this connection, the number of linguistic stocks, according to conservative reckoning, does not exceed twenty-five, and may be fewer. The most important of these, in point of number of speakers, is the Indo-European or Indo-Germanic or Aryan family, whose territory for several thousand years has comprised southwestern Asia and the greater part, but by no means all, of Europe. The most populous branches of the Indo-European family are the Indic, Slavic, Germanic, and Romance or Latin. Others are Persian or Iranic, Armenian, Greek, Albanian, Baltic or Lithuanian, and Keltic. From Europe various Indo-European languages, such as English, Spanish, French, Russian, have in recent centuries been carried to other continents, until in some, such as the Americas and Australia, much the greater area is now inhabited by peoples speaking Indo-European. (As the accompanying maps are intended to depict the historical or native distribution of languages, they omit this recent diffusion, important as it is.) It will be noted that the home distribution of Indo-European has the form of a long belt stretching from western Europe to northeastern India, with an interruption only in Asia Minor (Fig. 14). Turkish peoples displaced Indo-Europeans there about a thousand years ago, thus breaking the territorial continuity. It is probable that another link between the western and eastern Indo-Europeans once stretched around the north and east of the Caspian Sea. Here also there are Turks now.

Almost equaling Indo-European in the number of its speakers is the Sinitic family, which is generally held to include Chinese proper with its dialects; the Tibeto-Burman branch; the T'ai or Shan-Siamese branch; and probably some minor divisions.

---

[1] "Linguistic family" and "linguistic stock" are used as synonyms in this book. The criterion of both is not the degree of similarity of the included languages, but the fact (or presumptive fact) of relationship through common descent.

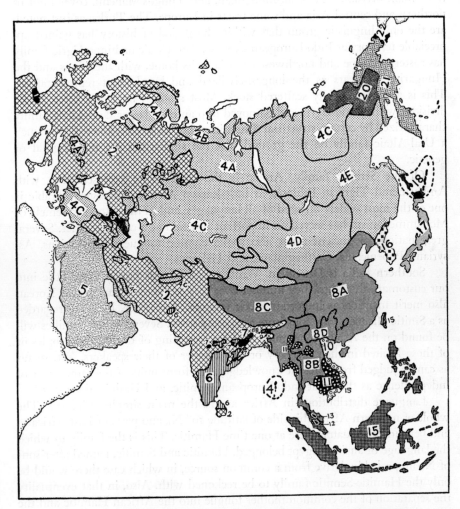

FIG. 14. LINGUISTIC FAMILIES OF ASIA AND EUROPE

1, Basque. 2, Indo-European. 3, Caucasian (perhaps two families). 4, Ural-Altaic (A, Finno-Ugric; B, Samoyed; C, Turkish; D, Mongol; E, Tungus-Manchu). 5, Semitic. 6, Dravidian. 7, Kolarian. 8, Sinitic (A, Chinese; B, Shan-Siamese; C, Tibeto-Burman; D, Miao, Lolo, Moso, etc.). (9, Khasi, belongs to 11.) 10, Annamese. 11, Mon-Khmer. 12, Sakai. 13, Semang. 14, Andaman. 15, Malayo-Polynesian or Austronesian. 16, Korean. 17, Japanese. 18, Ainu. 19, Ket or Yeniseian. 20, Yukaghir. 21, Chukchi-Koryak-Kam-chadal. 22, Eskimo.

In extent of territory occupied the Altaic stock rivals the Indo-European. Its three main divisions, Turkish, Mongolian, and Tungus-Manchu, cover most of northern and central Asia and some tracts in Europe. The Turks, as just noted, are the only linguistic group that within the period of history has gained appreciable territory at Indo-European expense. The Uralic or Finno-Ugric family has eastern Europe and northwestern Asia as its home, with the Finns and the Hungarian Magyars as the longest-civilized and best-known representatives. This is a geographically scattered stock. Most scholars unite the three Altaic divisions with Finno-Ugric and Samoyed into an even larger Ural-Altaic family characterized by certain structural similarities; but some deny the reality of such a Ural-Altaic family on the ground that the similarities are not original or genetic.

Of the Semitic family, Arabic is the chief living representative, with Amharic and Tigré in Ethiopia as little-known African half-sisters. Arabic is one of the most widely diffused of all languages, and as the orthodox vehicle of Mohammedanism has served an important function as a culture-carrier. Several great nations of ancient times also spoke Semitic tongues: Babylonians, Assyrians, Phoenicians, Carthaginians, and Hebrews.

Southern India is Dravidian. While people of this family enter little into our customary thoughts, they number over fifty millions. Japanese and Korean also merit mention as important stock tongues. Annamese, by some regarded as a Sinitic offshoot, may constitute a separate stock. Several minor families will be found on the Asiatic map, most of them consisting of uncivilized peoples or of those limited in their territory or the number of their speakers. Yet, so far as can be judged from present knowledge, they form units of the same order of independence as the great Indo-European, Semitic, and Ural-Altaic stocks.

Language distributions in Africa are in the main simple (Fig. 15). The whole of northern Africa this side of latitude 10° N., and parts of East Africa to and beyond the equator, were at one time Hamitic. This is the family to which the language of ancient Egypt belonged. Hamitic and Semitic, named after sons of Noah, probably derive from a common source, in which case there would be only the Hamitic-Semitic family to be reckoned with. Also, in that eventuality the separation of the common mother tongue into the African Hamitic and the Asiatic Semitic divisions must have occurred in very ancient times. In the past thousand years Hamitic has yielded ground before Semitic, owing to the spread of Arabic in Mohammedan Africa.

Africa south of the equator is the home of the great Bantu family, except in the extreme southwest of the continent. There a tract of considerable area, though of small populational density, was in the possession of the backward Bushmen and Hottentots, distinctive in their physical types as well as their languages.

Between the equator and latitude 10° N., in the belt known as the Sudan, there is much greater speech diversity than elsewhere in Africa. The languages of the Sudan fall into several families, perhaps into a fairly large number. Opinion conflicts or is unsettled as to their classification. They are, at least in the main, non-Hamitic and non-Bantu; but this negative fact does not preclude their having had either a single or a dozen origins. It has usually been easier to throw them all into a vague group designated as non-Hamitic and non-Bantu than to compare them in detail.

In Oceania conditions are similar to those of Africa, in that there are a few great, widely branching stocks and one rather small area, New Guinea, of astounding speech diversity. Indeed, superficially this variety is the outstanding

FIG. 15.   LINGUISTIC FAMILIES OF AFRICA

1, Hamitic. 2, Semitic (A, old; B, Arabic, intrusive in former Hamitic territory since Mohammed). 3, Bantu. 4, Hottentot. 5, Bushman, perhaps related to last. 6, Malayo-Polynesian. X, The Sudan, not consistently classified.

linguistic feature of New Guinea. The hundreds of Papuan dialects of the island look as if they might require twenty or more families to accommodate them. However, it is inconceivable that so small a population should time and again have evolved totally new forms of speech. It is much more likely that something in the mode of life or the habits of mind of the Papuans has favored the breaking-up of their speech into local dialects and an unusually rapid modification of these into markedly differentiated languages. What the circumstances were that favored this tendency to segregation and change can be only conjectured. At any rate, New Guinea ranks with the Sudan, western North America, and the Amazonian region of South America as one of the areas of greatest linguistic multiplicity.

All the remainder of Oceania is either Australian or Malayo-Polynesian in speech. The Australian idioms have been imperfectly recorded. They were numerous and locally varied, but may derive from a single mother tongue.

All the East Indies, including part of the Malay Peninsula, and all of the island world of the Pacific—Polynesia, Micronesia, and Melanesia, always excepting interior New Guinea—are the habitat of the closely knit Malayo-Polynesian or Austronesian family, whose unity was early recognized by philologists. From Madagascar to Easter Island this speech stretches more than half-way around our planet.

North and South America, according to the usual reckoning, contain more native families of speech than all the remainder of the world. The conventional conservative classification allots forty or more families each to North and South America. These families varied greatly in size at the time of discovery, some being confined to a few hundred souls, whereas others stretched through tribe after tribe over enormous areas. Their distribution is so irregular and their areas so disproportionate as to be impossible of vivid representation except on a large-scale map in colors. The most important in extent of territory, number of speakers, or the cultural importance of the nations adhering to them, in North America are: Eskimo, Athabascan, Algonkin, Iroquoian, Muskogean, Siouan,[2] Uto-Aztecan, Maya; and in South America: Chibcha, Quechua, Aymara, Araucanian, Arawak, Carib, Tupi, Gê. It will be seen on the maps (Figs. 16 and 17) that these sixteen groups held much the greater part of the area of the double continent, the remaining smaller areas being crowded with perhaps four times as many stocks. Obviously, as in New Guinea, such a multiplicity cannot well have been original; in fact, recent studies are tending to consolidate the New World families into fewer and fewer groups. But the evidence for such reductions is necessarily difficult to find and much of it is still incomplete. The large stocks named above have been long determined and are universally accepted.

[2] Iroquoian, Siouan, Muskogean (nos. 4, 5, 6 of map 16) are often united with Hokan, Caddoan, and others into a Hokan-Siouan "superfamily"—something like Ural-Altaic— which seems a probable historical unit in origin, but remains unproved as such.

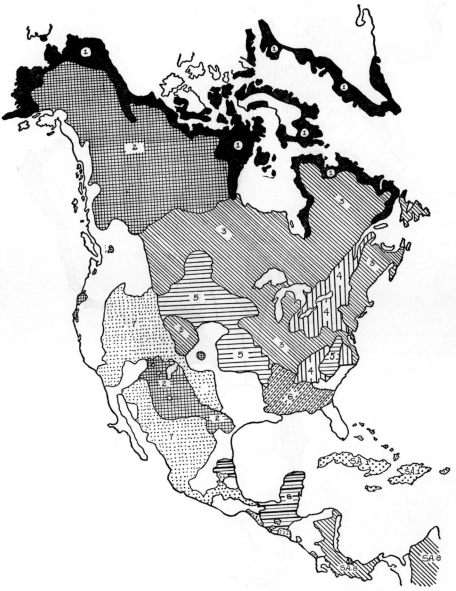

FIG. 16. LINGUISTIC FAMILIES OF NORTH AMERICA

1, Eskimo. 2, Athabascan. 3, Algonkin. 4, Iroquoian. 5, Siouan. 6, Muskogean. 7, Uto-Aztecan. 8, Mayan. SA1, Arawak = No. 1 and SA8, Chibcha = No. 8 of South American map (Fig. 17). The white areas are occupied by a greater number of smaller families, according to the usual classification.

FIG. 17. LINGUISTIC FAMILIES OF SOUTH AMERICA

1, Arawak. 2, Carib. 3, Gê. 4, Tupi. 5, Araucanian. 6, Aymará. 7, Quechua (Inca).
8, Chibcha. 9, Tucano. 10, Pano. 11, Diaguita. 12, Guaycurú. 13, Puelche. 14, Tehuelche.
Smaller families in unnumbered areas. Nos. 1 and 2 extend into the West Indies, No. 8
into Central America. (After Chamberlain and Jiménez Moreno)

About a third of humanity today speaks some form of Indo-European. Nearly a quarter talks some dialect of Sinitic stock. Semitic, Dravidian, Ural-Altaic, Japanese, Malayo-Polynesian, Bantu have each from about 50 to 100 million speakers. The languages included in these eight families form the speech of approximately 90 per cent of living human beings.

97. CLASSIFICATION OF LANGUAGES BY TYPES

A customary nongenetic classification groups languages or families according to their structure into four main types: inflective, agglutinating, isolating, and polysynthetic or incorporating. These classes are not logically co-ordinate.

An inflecting or fusional language expresses relations or grammatical form by adding prefixes or suffixes that cannot stand alone, or if they stood alone would mean nothing, and which therefore can be considered as fused into the word; or it expresses relations by internal modification of the stem. The *-ing* of *killing* is such an inflection; so are the vowel changes and the ending *-en* in the conjugation *write, wrote, written*.

An isolating language expresses relations by separate words or isolated particles. Words are always unexpanded, unaltered stems or radicals. English *heart of man* is isolating, where *man's heart* and Latin *cor homin-is* are inflective.

An agglutinative language "glues together" into solid words, or juxtaposes, elements for which a definite, exclusive, regular meaning of their own can be traced or felt. English does not use this mechanism for purposes that are ordinarily reckoned as strictly grammatical, but does employ it for the related purpose of derivation. *Under-take, rest-less, fore-go, moon-like,* are examples; *quick-ly,* for *quick-like,* is a border-line case.

Polysynthetic languages are agglutinative ones carried to a high pitch, or those which can unite words into equivalents of fair-sized sentences. *Steam-boat-propeller-blade* might be called a polysynthetic form if we spoke or wrote it in one word as modern German might. Incorporating languages are generally included in polysynthetic ones: they embody the object noun, or the pronoun representing it, into the word that contains the verb stem. This construction is totally foreign to English.[3]

Each of these classes evidently defines one or more distinctive linguistic processes. The mechanisms at work are different. But no one language operates wholly with one process. The instances given show that English employs most of them. Obviously, therefore, it would be arbitrary to classify English as being outright of one type. This is also the situation for most other languages. There

[3] Noun incorporation seems mostly to form compounds of nouns with verbs, or verbs with verbs, to form verbs: "to rabbit-kill," "to run-kill," and so on. This construction happens to be so alien to the genius of Indo-European that it has been singled out as notable. Pronominal incorporation is discussed below, in § 108.

are in fact dozens and dozens of mechanisms by which languages operate, and the combinations of these in particular languages are indefinitely numerous. To force these many different actual structures into four classes may be convenient, but is logically roughshod.

There are other difficulties. English, for instance, was mainly inflecting fifteen hundred years ago, but today more largely uses isolating processes. We still say *John's house,* but we use *heart of man* perhaps more often than *man's heart;* and *house's top* would strike a listener as so odd that he might think he had misheard. *Camest thou?* for *Did you come?* would still be intelligible as poetry, but in conversation it would be construed as a stilted attempt at a joke. Which pigeonhole, inflecting or isolating, does modern English go into? And how valid are compartments when languages can wriggle themselves like this from one into another compartment in a fairly short span of their history?

Any classification into types is basically logical; whereas a genetic classification that reflects development and relationship must be empirical. And the only genetic classification yet devised for languages is based on the kind of comparisons described, and yields speech families—certain, probable, or possible families, according as the data are more or less full, exact, and carefully analyzed.

Also, the type classification started with the idea that Latin, Sanskrit, and Hebrew were both inflecting and superior in kind. Chinese, whose literature is also ancient, made the isolating class respectable; but the other types were considered inferior. These implications of better and worse have tended to remain attached to the classification; and it is obvious that such judgments have no place in scientific analysis or description.[4]

98. PERMANENCE OF LANGUAGE AND RACE

It is sometimes thought that because a new speech is readily learned, especially in youth, language is a relatively unstable factor in human history, less permanent than race. It is necessary to guard against two fallacies in this connection. The first is to argue from individuals to societies; the second, to believe that because change is possible, it normally takes place.

As a matter of fact, languages often preserve their existence, and even their territory, with surprising tenacity in the face of conquest, new religions and culture, and the economic disadvantages of unintelligibility. Today, Breton, a Keltic dialect, maintains itself in France as the everyday language of the people in the isolated province of Brittany—a sort of philological fossil. It has withstood the influence of two thousand years of contact with Latin, with Saxon and

[4] Sapir has proposed a structural type classification into Pure-relational and Mixed-relational languages, each subdivided into Deriving or Complex and Nonderiving or Simple, and then qualified by the concepts here discussed. But the scheme seems never to have been applied in actual description; perhaps because the scale from concrete to relational values on which the classification is based is sliding, and not easily defined objectively.

Frankish German, with French. Its Welsh sister tongue flourishes in spite of the Anglo-Saxon speech of the remainder of Great Britain. Ancient Egypt was conquered by the Hyksos, the Assyrian, the Persian, the Macedonian, and the Roman, but whatever the official speech of the ruling class, the people continued to speak Egyptian. Finally, the Arab came and brought with him a new religion, which favored use of the Arabic language. After four thousand years, Egypt at last became Arabic-speaking; but until a century or two ago the Coptic language, the daughter of the ancient Egyptian tongue of five thousand years ago, was kept alive by the native Christians along the Nile, and even today it survives in ritual. The boundary between French on the one side and German, Dutch, and Flemish on the other has been accurately known for over six hundred years. With all the wars and conquests back and forth across the speech line, endless political changes and cultural influences, this line has scarcely shifted anywhere more than a few dozen miles, and in places has not moved the distance of a comfortable afternoon's stroll.

While populations can learn and unlearn languages, they tend to do so with reluctance and infinite slowness, especially while they remain in their inherited territories. Speech tends to be one of the most persistent populational characters; and "ethnic" boundaries are most often speech boundaries.

In general, where two populations mingle, the speech of the more numerous most often prevails, even if it be that of the subject nationality. A wide gap in culture may overcome the influence of the majority; yet the speech of even a culturally more active and advanced population ordinarily wrests permanent territory to itself only slowly, except where there is an actual crowding-out or numerical swamping of the natives. This explains the numerous survivals and "islands" of speech: Keltic, Albanian, Basque, Caucasian, in Europe; Dravidian and Kolarian in India; Nahuatl and Maya and many others in modern Mexico; Quechua in Peru; Aymara in Bolivia; Tupi in Brazil. There are cases to the contrary, like the rapid spread of Latin in most of Gaul after Caesar's conquest, but they seem exceptional.

As to the relative permanence of race and speech, everything depends on the side from which the question is approached. From the point of view of hereditary strains, race must be the more conservative, because it can change rapidly only through admixture with another race, whereas a language may be completely exchanged in a short time. From the point of view of history, however, which regards human actions within given territories, speech is often more stable. Wars or trade or migration may bring one racial element after another into an area until the type has become altered or diluted, and yet the original language, or one directly descended from it, remains. The introduction of the Negro from Africa to America illustrates this distinction. From the point of view of biology, the Negro has at least partially preserved his type, although he has taken on a wholly new language. As a matter of history, the reverse is true: pure English continues to be the speech of the southern United States, whereas the population now consists of two races instead of one, and the Negro element has been altered by the infusion of white blood. It is a fallacy to think that because an individual can learn French or become a Christian and yet is powerless to change his eye color or head shape, therefore the language or the culture of large populations is necessarily less stable than race. Speech and culture have an existence and a continuity of their own, whose integrity does not depend on hereditary integrity. The two may move together or separately.

99. THE BIOLOGICAL AND HISTORICAL NATURES OF LANGUAGE

It is a truism, but one important never to forget in the study of man, that the faculty of speech is innate, but that every language is wholly acquired. Moreover, the environment of which languages are the product is not a natural one—that is, geographic or climatic—but social. All words and speech forms that are learned—and they constitute almost the complete mass of language—are imitated directly from other human beings. Those new forms which from time to time come into use rest on existing speech material, and are shaped according to tendencies already operative although perhaps more or less hidden. The new or changed forms cannot generally be attributed, as regards origin, to particular individuals; in short, they present a history similar to that of inventions and new institutions. Language thus is a superorganic product, which fact of course does not contradict—indeed implies—that it rests on an organic basis.

The "speech" of the animals other than man has something in common with human languages. It consists of sounds produced by the body, accompanied by certain mental activities or conditions, and capable of arousing certain definite responses in other individuals of the species (§ 20). It differs from human speech in several fundamental particulars. First of all, the cries and calls and murmurs of the brutes appear to be wholly instinctive. A fowl raised alone in an incubator will peep and crow or cluck as it will scratch and peck. A dog reared by a foster cat will bark, or growl, or whine, or yelp when he has attained the requisite age and on application of the proper stimulus, as he will wag or crouch or hunt or dig, and no differently from the dog brought up in association with other dogs. By contrast, the Japanese infant turned over to American foster parents never utters or knows a single Japanese word, learns only English, and learns that as well as do his Caucasian stepbrothers. Evidently, then, animal speech is to all intents wholly organic and not at all "social" in the sense of being superorganic. If this summary is not absolutely exact, it departs from the truth only infinitesimally.

Further, animal speech has no "meaning," does not serve as a vehicle of "communication." The opposite is often assumed popularly, because we anthropomorphize. If it is said that a dog's growl "means" anger, and that his bark "communicates" suspicion or excitement to his fellows, the words are used in a sense different from their significance when we say that the term *red* "means" the color at one end of the spectrum, or that a message of departure "communicates" information. The animal sounds convey knowledge only of subjective states. They "impart" the fact that the utterer feels anger, excitement, fear, pain, contentment, or some other affect. These are immediate reflex responses to a feeling. They may be "understood" in the sense that a sympathetic feeling is evoked, or at any rate mobilized; and thereby they may lead or tend to lead to action by the hearers. In the same way, any man instinctively "understands" the moan of a fellow human being. But the moan does not tell whether the pain is of a second's or a week's duration, caused by a blow or by gas in the bowel, by an ulcerated tooth or by mental anguish. There is no communication of anything objective, of facts or ideas as distinct from feelings, as when we say *red* or *break* or *up* or *water*. Not one of these simple concepts can be communicated as such by any brute speech.

One consequence is the "arbitrariness" of human speech. Why should the sound cluster *red* denote that particular color rather than green? Why does the same word often designate quite distinct ideas in different languages—the approximate sound combination *lay* meaning "milk" in French; *lass* "a girl" in English, "tired" in French, "allow" in German? Such facts are physiologically arbitrary; just as it is physiologically arbitrary and organically meaningless that Americans live in a republic and Britons under a monarchy, or that they drive respectively to the right and the left on the road. Phenomena like these have other cultural or superorganic phenomena as their immediate antecedents and preconditions. In the light of these antecedents, viewed on the level of history, they are intelligible: we know why the United States is a republic, we can trace the development of words like *lay* and *lass*. It is only from the biological plane that such facts seem nonsignificant or arbitrary.

100. PROBLEMS OF THE RELATION OF LANGUAGE AND CULTURE

This association of language and civilization—or better, let us say the linguistic and nonlinguistic constituents of culture—brings up the problem whether it would be possible for one to exist without the other. Actually, of course, no such case is known. Speculatively, different conclusions might be reached. It is difficult to imagine any generalized thinking taking place without words or symbols derived from words. Religious beliefs and certain phases of social organization also seem dependent on speech: caste ranking, marriage regulations, kinship recognition, law, and the like. On the other hand, it is conceivable that a considerable series of simple inventions might be made, and the applied arts might be developed in a fair measure by imitation, even among a speechless people. Finally there seems no reason why certain elements of culture, such as music, should not flourish as successfully in a society without as with language.

For the converse, a cultureless species of animal might conceivably develop and use a form of true speech. Such communications as "The river is rising," "Bite it off," "What do you find inside?" would be within the range of thought of such a species. But the significant fact in this connection is that no non-human animal possesses even traces of such power of communication. Why? Possibly because such a language would lack survival value for the species, in the absence of accompanying culture.

On the whole, however, it would seem that language and culture rest, in a way that is not yet fully understood, on the same set of faculties, and that these, for some reason that is still more obscure, developed in the ancestors of man while remaining in abeyance in other species. Even the anthropoid apes seem virtually devoid of the impulse to communicate, as we have seen earlier (§ 29), in spite of freely expressing their affective states of mind by voice, facial gesture, and bodily movement. The most responsive to man of all species, the dog, learns to accept a considerable stock of culture in the sense of fitting himself to it: he develops conscience and manners, for example. Yet, however highly bred, he does not hand on his accomplishments to his progeny, who again depend on their human masters for what they acquire. A group of the best-reared dogs left to themselves for a few years would lose all their politeness and revert to the predomestic habits of their species. In short, the culture impulse is lacking in the dog except so far as it is instilled by man and kept instilled by him; and in most animals it can notoriously be instilled only to a very limited degree. In the same way, the impulse toward communication can be said to be wanting. A dog may understand a hundred words of command and express in his behavior fifty shades of emotion; only rarely does he even seem to try to communicate information of objective fact. Very likely we are only attributing to him in these rare cases the impulse we should feel in the same situation. In the event of a member of the family being injured or lost, it is certain that a good dog expresses his agitation, uneasiness, disturbed attachment; but it is much less certain that he *intends* to summon help, as we spontaneously incline to believe because such summoning would be our own reaction to the situation.

The history and the causes of the development in incipient man of the group of traits that may be called the faculties for speech and civilization remain one of the darkest areas in the field of knowledge. It is plain that these faculties lie essentially in the sphere of personality, and therefore of the body. Yet men and the apes are far more similar in their general physiques than they are in the degree of their ability to use their physiques for superphysiological purposes. Or, if the antithesis of physical and mental seems unfortunate, it might be said that the growth of the faculties for speech and culture is connected more with special developments of the central nervous system than with those of the remainder of the body.

IOI. PERIOD OF THE ORIGIN OF LANGUAGE

Is, then, human language as old as culture? It is difficult to be positive, because words perish like beliefs and institutions, whereas stone tools may endure as direct evidence. On the whole, however, it would appear that the first rudiments of what deserves to be called language are about as ancient as the first culture manifestations, mainly because of the theoretically close association of the two. The skull interiors of fossil men, which conform fairly closely to the brain surface, have been construed by some authorities as indicating that the speech areas of the cortex were sufficiently developed, even in forms as old as Sinanthropus, to suggest that these races talked.

Such findings may be accepted as highly tentative. What is more to the point, however, is that anthropologists are in general agreement that language grew up in correlation with culture, if indeed it was not its necessary antecedent. Cultural activity, even of the simplest kind, inevitably rests on ideas or generalizations; and such or any ideas, in turn, human minds seem to be able to formulate and operate with and transmit only through speech. Nature consists of an endless array of particular phenomena. To combine these particulars into a generalization or an abstraction, such as passing from potential awareness of the thousands of stones along a river bed into the idea of stone as a distinctive material—this synthesis appears to require the production of some kind of a symbol, perhaps as a sort of psychological catalyzing agent or point of crystallization: a symbol such as the sounds that make up the word *stone*. In short, culture can probably function only on the basis of abstractions, and these in turn seem to be possible only through speech, or through a secondary substitute for spoken language such as writing, numeration, mathematical and chemical notation, and the like. Culture, then, began when speech was present; and from then on, the enrichment of either meant the further development of the other.

This view is hardly demonstrable; but it seems pretty much to represent the belief of such anthropologists as have grappled with the problem.

I02. SPEECH, CULTURE, AND NATIONALITY

This assumption as to the rise of culture raises the question whether one ought to speak of language and culture or rather of language as a part of culture. So far as the process of their transmission is concerned, and the type of mechanism of their development, it is clear that language and culture are one. For practical purposes it is generally convenient to keep them distinct. There is no doubt that two peoples can share in what is substantially the same culture and yet speak fundamentally different idioms and therefore feel themselves to be separate nationalities; for instance, the Finno-Ugric Magyars or Hungarians among the adjacent Slavs, Germans, and Latins of central Europe, who are all

Indo-Europeans. British and Americans speak the same standard language; they are closely related, in fact derived, in culture; and yet their geographical separation has been followed by enough divergence of institutions and habits to have led to political separation, which in turn induces both populations to feel themselves as distinct nationalities. In fact, nationality is essentially a feeling of distinctness or unity, of sense of demarcation between in-group and out-group. Thus the concept "nationality" is fundamentally subjective, whereas both languages and cultures are objectively alike or unlike, unitary or distinct.

It is therefore logically inadmissible and risky in practice to infer from nationality to language or culture, or vice versa. It is unsound much as it is unsound to assume an identity of race, language, and culture for a given area, or to argue from the prevalence of one to the other (§ 80).

Nevertheless, speech and culture do tend to form something of a unit as opposed to race. It is possible for a population to substitute a wholly new language and type of civilization for the old ones, as the American Negro has done, and yet to remain relatively unmodified racially, or at least to carry on its former physical type unchanged in a large proportion of its members. On the other hand, a decisive change of speech without some change of culture seems impossible. Certainly wherever Sumerian, Greek, Latin, Spanish, English, Arabic, Sanskrit, Pali, and Chinese have penetrated as carriers of a religion, literacy, or an associated culture, there have also been established new forms of civilization (§ 169). In a lower degree, the same principle probably holds true of every gain of one language at the expense of another, even when the spreading idiom is not associated with a great or an active culture.

The linkage of speech and culture is further perceptible in the degree to which they both tend to contribute, ultimately, to the formation of the idea of nationality; and this in turn may contribute to a desire for a politically independent state or nation. What chiefly marks off the French from the Italians, the Dutch from the Germans, the Swedes from the Norwegians—their respective customs and ideals, or the language gap, or their political autonomy? It would be difficult to say. The cultural differences tend to crystallize around language differences, and then in turn are reinforced by language, so that the two factors interact complexly.

It is also important to recognize that nationality and nation are not necessarily the same, although they sometimes coincide. Usually we think of a nation as the population of a wholly autonomous and supreme political unit—what Europeans used to call "the state." Politically, state and nation are one: [5] as when

---

[5] While a political nation or body politic means a state in its most general and ordinary sense, a special historical accident of our manner of growth has brought it about that in the United States of America we call "national" whatever pertains to the total people and government, and by "state" designate constituted parts thereof. This is an anomaly in Western civilization. In our American term "Department of State," the word still has its original sense of referring to the whole body politic.

we speak of the United Nations. But an essentially single nationality can comprise several states that in modern political terminology are called nations: such as Australians, New Zealanders, Canadians, and British. Or again a century ago Germans formed as definite a nationality as they do now, with distinctive speech, customs, temperament, and ideals, but were broken up into some thirty self-governing units or wholly independent states or, technically in the political sense, nations. On the contrary, most large states, and especially empires, have comprised a variety of nationalities. Thus the mediaeval Holy Roman Empire included French, Dutch, Czechs, Slovenes, and Italians as well as Germans; and the original Roman Empire, particularly in the times of its greatness and peace, included still more nationalities, who became equal before its law in spite of their diversity. The reason for this variability of usage is the ambiguity of the word "nation." Its dictionary definition is double. First, nation denotes a people organized under one government, a "body politic." Second, a nation is a people of common origin, tradition, and language. Now the latter is just what a nationality is, by universal consent; and it would be fine if everyone would always use the word "nationality" when that was the meaning, and if "nation" on the contrary were restricted to denoting politically organized peoples.

Here are some contemporary cases of political nations that include two or more nationalities. Belgium is almost equally divided between Walloons speaking a French dialect in their homes and Flemings speaking a variant of Dutch. Switzerland is 72 per cent German-speaking, 21 per cent French, 6 per cent Italian, 1 per cent Romansh. Canada is one-third French, in origin and in speech. The Union of South Africa has a white population that is part English-speaking and part Afrikaans- or Dutch-speaking, plus the racially distinct Bantu Negro natives. India in 1947 set up housekeeping on its own, as two independent political nations, with dozens of nationalities and languages. Similarly in the Philippines there are seven major and many minor tongues. In the U.S.S.R. there are 78 per cent Russians (Great, White, and Ukrainian), plus forty-six other recognized nationalities. Some of these nationalities, such as Georgians, Armenians, Uzbeks, Kazaks, Moldavians, and Lithuanians, as well as the three Russian groups, have union republics of their own. Formally, therefore, these constitute politically autonomous nations as well as centers of nationality, and three of them have been so recognized in the United Nations organization; whereas the United States is reckoned as a single political nation, with its "states" mere subsidiary divisions.

It is evident from these examples what diverse things "nation" and "nationality" can and do mean. It is certainly clearest always to use the term "nationality" when the reference is ethnic, and to add the epithet "political" to "nation," or to substitute "government," when that is the sense, unless the context leaves no doubt as to meaning. Also it is clear that of the several objective factors which operate to produce nationalities, language is on the whole much the most important. Without the free intercommunication that common speech provides, it is very difficult for the "consciousness of kind" that is the subjective or psychological precondition of nationality to arise. Cultural conditions can either reinforce or thwart the effects of linguistic segregations, or be neutral. Thus the French of Quebec are further set apart by their Catholicism in Protestant Canada. In Switzerland, the Germans of some cantons are Catholics, of others Lutheran Protestants; the French are mainly Calvinist Protestants; the Italians, Catholics. There is a general understanding among the Swiss citizenry that neither religion nor linguistic consideration is to serve as a basis for political crystallization. In India, on the contrary, religious cleavage has proved a strong obstacle to political unity in the formative period. Language diversity was felt to be much less of a bar, perhaps because of the wide availability of English speech on upper educational levels. Should political intransigeance drive out English, the diversity of nationalities kept separate by speech might become a greater threat to the political cohesiveness of India.

All in all, anthropology is more immediately concerned with nationalities than with nations, with ethnic than with political groupings. And in nationalities and ethnic units, language is always a factor, and often the basic one.

103. RELATIVE WORTH OF LANGUAGES

One respect in which languages differ from cultures is that they cannot, like the latter, be rated as higher and lower. Of course, even as regards culture, such rating is often a dubious procedure, meaning little more than that the person making the comparison assumes his own culture to be the highest and estimates other cultures low in proportion as they vary. Although this is a subjective and uncritical procedure, nevertheless certain objective comparisons are possible. Some cultures surpass others in their quantitative content: they possess more different arts, abilities, and items of knowledge. Also, some culture traits may be considered intrinsically superior to others: metal tools against stone ones, for instance, since metal is adopted by all stone-culture peoples who can secure it, whereas the reverse is not true. Further, in most cases a new addition does not wholly obliterate an older element, this retaining a subsidiary place, or perhaps serving some more special function than before. In this way some cultures become richer and more differentiated. The old art may even attain a higher degree of perfection than it had previously, as the finest polish was given to stone implements in northern Europe after bronze was known. In general, accretion is the process typical of culture growth. Older elements come to function in a more limited sphere as new ones are added, but are not extirpated by them. Oars and sails remain as constituent parts of the stock of civilization after it has added steamboats and motorboats. In the senses, then, that a culture has a larger content of elements, that these elements are more differentiated, and that a greater proportion of these elements are of the kind that inherently tend to supersede related elements, the culture may be considered superior.

As regards languages, there are also quantitative differences. Some contain several times as many words as others. But vocabulary is largely a cultural matter. A people that uses more materials, manufactures more objects, possesses knowledge of a larger array of facts, and makes finer discriminations in thought, must inevitably have more words. Yet even notable increases in size of speech content appear not to be accompanied by appreciable changes in form. A larger vocabulary does not mean a different type of structure. Grammar seems to be little influenced by culture status. No clear correspondence has yet been traced between type or degree of civilization and structural type of language. Neither the presence nor the absence of particular features of tense, number, case, reduplication, or the like seems ever to have been of demonstrable advantage toward the attainment of higher culture. The speech of the earlier and the modern nations most active in the propagation of culture has been of quite diverse types. The languages of the Egyptians (Hamitic); Sumerians; Babylonians and Arabs (Semitic); Hindus and Greeks (ancient Indo-European); Anglo-Saxons (modern Indo-European); Chinese; and Mayas are about as different as any that exist. The Sumerian type of civilization was taken over bodily and successfully by the Semitic Babylonians. The bulk of Japanese culture is Chinese; yet Japanese speech is built on wholly different principles.

Then, it is impossible to rate one speech trait or type as inherently or objectively superior to another on any basis like that which justifies the placing of a metal culture above a stone culture. If wealth of grammatical apparatus is a criterion of superiority, Latin is a higher language than French, and Anglo-Saxon than English. But if lack of declensions and conjugations is a virtue, then Chinese surpasses English almost as much as English surpasses Latin. There is no reason favoring one of these possible judgments rather than its opposite. *Amabo* is no better or worse than *I shall or will love* as a means of expressing the same idea. The one is more compact, the other more plastic. There are times when compactness is a virtue, occasions when plasticity has advantages. By the Latin or synthetic standard, the English expression is loose-jointed, lacking in structure; by the English or analytic standard, the Latin form is overcondensed, adhering unnecessarily to form. One cannot similarly balance the merits of a steel and a flint knife, of a medical and a shamanistic phase of society. The one does really cut or cure better than does the other.

So, from the point of view of civilization, language does not matter. Language will always keep up with whatever pace culture sets it. If a new object is invented or a new distinction of thought made, a word is coined or imported or modified in meaning to express the new concept. If a thousand or ten thousand new words are required, they get developed. When it desires to express abstractions like futurity or plurality, any language is capable of doing so, even if it does not habitually express them. If a language is unprovided with formal means for the purpose, such as a grammatical suffix, it falls back on content and uses a word or a circumlocution. If the life of a people changes and comes to be conducted along lines that render it frequently important to express an idea like futurity to which previously little attention has been paid, the appropriate circumlocution soon becomes standardized, conveniently brief, and unambiguous, like *will* in *He will come*. In general, every language is capable of indefinite modification and expansion and thereby is enabled to meet cultural demands almost at once. This is shown by the fact that virtually anything spoken or written can be translated into almost every other language without serious impairment of substance. The aesthetic charm of the original may be lost in the translation; the new forms coined in the receiving language are likely at first to seem awkward; but the meaning, the business of speech, gets expressed.

104. SIZE OF VOCABULARY

The tendency is so instinctive in us to presuppose and therefore to find qualities of inferiority, poverty, or incompleteness in the speech of populations of more backward culture than our own, that a widespread, though unfounded, belief has grown up that the languages of savages and barbarians are extremely limited quantitatively—in the range of their vocabulary. Similar misconceptions are current as to the number of words actually used by single individuals of civilized communities. It is true that no one, not even the most learned and prolific writer, uses all the words of the English language as they are found in an unabridged dictionary. All of us understand many words that we habitually encounter in reading and may even hear frequently spoken, but of which our utterance faculties for some reason have not made us master. In short, a language, being the property and the product of a community, possesses more words than can ever be used by a single individual, the sum total of whose ideas is necessarily less than that of his group. Added to this are a certain mental sluggishness, which restricts most of us to a greater or less degree, and the force of habit. Having spoken a certain word a number of times, our brain becomes accustomed to it and we are likely to employ it to the exclusion of its synonyms or in place of words of related but distinguishable meaning.

The degree to which all this affects the speech of the normal man has, however, been greatly exaggerated. Because there are, all told, including technical terms, some hundred thousands of words in our dictionaries, and because Shakespeare in his writings is said to have used 24,000 different words, Milton in his poems 17,000, and the English Bible contains 7200, it has been concluded that the average man, whose range of thought and power of expression are so much less, must use an enormously smaller vocabulary. It has been stated that many a peasant goes through life without using more than 300 or 400 words, that the vocabulary of Italian grand opera is about 600, and that he is a person above the average who employs more than 3000 to 4000 words. If such were the case it would be natural that uncivilized men, whose life is simpler, and whose knowledge is more confined, should be content with an exceedingly small vocabulary.

But it is certain that the figures just cited are erroneous. If anyone who considers himself an average person will take the trouble to make a list of his speaking vocabulary, he will quickly discover that he knows, and on occasion uses, the names of at least 1000 to 2000 different things. That is, his vocabulary contains so many concrete nouns. To these must be added the abstract nouns, the verbs, adjectives, pronouns, and the other parts of speech, the short and familiar words that are indispensable to communication in any language. It may thus be safely estimated that it is an exceptionally ignorant and stupid person in a civilized country who has not at his command a vocabulary of several thousand words.

Test counts based on dictionaries show, for people of bookish tastes, a knowledge of about 30,000 to 35,000 words. Most of these would perhaps never be spoken by the individuals tested, would not be at their actual command, but it seems that at least 10,000 would be so controlled. The carefully counted vocabulary of a five-and-a-half-year-old American boy comprised 1528 understandingly used words, besides participles and other inflected forms. Two boys between two and three years used 642 and 677 different words.

It is therefore likely that statements as to the paucity of the speech of unlettered peoples are equally exaggerated. He who professes to declare on the strength of his observation that a native language consists of only a few hundred terms displays chiefly his ignorance. He has either not taken the trouble to exhaust the vocabulary or has not known how to do so. It is true that the traveler or the settler can usually converse with natives to the satisfaction of his own needs with a few hundred words. Even the missionary can do a great deal with this stock, if it is properly chosen. But it does not follow that because a civilized person has not learned more of a language, there is no more. On this point the testimony of the student is the evidence to be considered.

Dictionaries compiled by missionaries or philologists of languages previously unwritten run to surprising figures. Thus, the number of words recorded in Klamath, the speech of a culturally rude American Indian tribe, is 7000; in Navaho, 11,000; in Zulu, 17,000; in Dakota, 19,000; in Maya, 20,000; in Nahuatl, 27,000. It may safely be estimated that every existing language, no matter how backward its speakers are in their general civilization, possesses a vocabulary of at least 5000 to 10,000 words.[6]

105. QUALITY OF SPEECH SOUNDS

Another mistaken assumption which is frequently made is that the speech of nonliterary peoples is harsh, its pronunciation more difficult than ours. This belief is purely subjective. When one has heard and uttered a language all one's

---

[6] Jespersen, who allows 20,000 words to Shakespeare and 8000 to Milton, cites 26,000 as the vocabulary of Swedish peasants.

life, its sounds come to one's mouth with a minimum of effort; but unfamiliar vowels and consonants are formed awkwardly and inaccurately. No adult reared in an Anglo-Saxon community finds *th* difficult. Nor does a French or a German child, whose speech habits are still plastic, find long difficulty in mastering the particular tongue control necessary to the production of the *th* sound. But the adult Frenchman or German, whose muscular habits have settled in other lines, tries and tries and falls back on *s* or *t*. A Castilian, however, would agree with the Anglo-Saxon as to the ease and "naturalness" of *th*. Conversely, the "rough" *ch* flows spontaneously out of the mouth of a German or a Scotchman, whereas English, French, and Italians have to struggle long to master it, and are tempted to substitute *ḳ*. German *ö* and French *u* trouble us; our "short" *u* is equally resistant to Continental tongues.

Even a novel position can make a familiar sound strange and forbidding. Most Anglo-Saxons fail on the first try to say *ngis;* many give up and declare it beyond their capacity to learn. Yet it is only *sing* pronounced backward. English uses *ng* finally and medially in words, not initially. Any English speaker can quickly acquire its use in the new position if, to keep from being disconcerted, he followings some such sequence as *sing, singing, stinging, ringing, inging, nging, ngis.*

So with surd *l*—Welsh *ll*—which is ordinary *l* minus the accompaniment of vocal-cord vibrations. A little practice makes possible the throwing on or off of these vibrations, the "voicing" and "unvoicing" of speech, for any sound, with as much ease as one would turn a faucet on or off. Surd *l* thereupon flows with the same readiness as sonant *l*. As a matter of fact we often pronounce it unconsciously at the end of words like *little*. When it comes at the beginning, however, as in the tribal name usually written *Tlingit,* Americans tend to substitute something more habitual, such as *ḳl*, which is familiar from *clip, clean, clear, close, clam,* and many other words. The simple surd *l* has even been repeatedly described quite inappropriately as a "click," which is about as far from picturing it with correctness as calling it a thump or a sigh; all because its "unvoicing" comes in an unaccustomed position.

Combinations of sounds, especially of consonants, are indeed of variable difficulty for anatomical reasons. Some, like *nd* and *ts* and *pf,* have their components telescope or join naturally through being formed in the same part of the mouth. Others, like *ḳw* (*qu*), have the two elements articulated widely apart, but for that reason the elements can easily be formed simultaneously. Still others, like *ḳt* and *ths,* are intrinsically difficult, because the elements differ in place of production but are alike in method, and therefore come under the operation of the generic rule that similar sounds require more effort to join and yet discriminate than dissimilar ones, for much the same reason that it is on the whole easier to acquire the pronunciation of a wholly new type of sound than of one that differs subtly from one already known. Yet in these matters too, habit rather than anatomical functioning determines the reaction. German *pf* comes hard to adult Anglo-Saxons, English *kw* and *ths* to Germans. So far as degree of accumulation of consonants is concerned, English is one of the extremest of all languages. Monosyllables like *tract, stripped* (*stripd*), *sixths* (*siksths*), must seem irremediably hard to most speakers of other idioms.

Children's speech in all languages shows that certain sounds are, as a rule, learned earlier than others, and are therefore presumably somewhat easier physiologically. Sounds like *p* and *t*, which are formed with the mobile lips and the front of the tongue, normally precede back-tongue sounds like *k*. *B, d, g*, which are voiced like vowels, tend to precede voiceless *p, t, k*. Stops or momentary sounds, such as *b, d, g, p, t, k*, generally come earlier than the fricative continuants *f, v, th, s, z*, which require a delicate adjustment of lip or tongue—close proximity without firm contact—whereas the stops involve only making and breaking a jerky contact. But so slight are the differences of effort or skill in all these cases that as a rule only a few months separate the learning of the easier from that of the more difficult sounds; and adults no longer feel the differences.

106. RAPIDITY OF LINGUISTIC CHANGE

The rate of change in language remains a somewhat obscure subject. The opinion often held that unwritten languages necessarily alter faster than written ones, or that those of savages are less stable than the tongues of civilized men, is mainly a naïve reflection of our sense of superiority. It contravenes the principles just referred to and is not supported by evidence. Occasional stories that a primitive tribe after a generation or two was found speaking an almost made-over language are unconscious fabrications due to preconception and supported by hasty acquaintance, faulty records, misunderstanding, or perhaps change of inhabitants. Nahuatl, the language of the Aztecs, has probably changed less in four hundred years than Spanish; Quechua, that of the Incas, no more. English has apparently altered more than any of the three in the same period. Dozens of native tongues, some of them from wholly rude peoples, were written down in the sixteenth and seventeenth centuries by Spanish and other priests, and in most instances the grammars and dictionaries are usable today.

Cultural alteration would appear to work toward speech change chiefly in the following way: New things need new names; new acts mean new thoughts and new ideas require new words. These may be imported; or they may be made out of elements already in the language; or old words may undergo a shift of meaning. In any event, the change is mainly on the side of vocabulary. The sounds of a language are generally much less affected, its plan of structure least of all. The introduction of a new religion or the development of a new form of government among a people need not be accompanied by changes in the grammar of their speech, and usually are not, as abundant historical examples prove.

While the causes of grammatical innovation are far from clear, contact with alien tongues is certainly a factor in some degree. An isolated offshoot of a linguistic group is generally more specialized, and therefore presumably more altered, than the main body of dialects of the family. The reason is that the latter, maintaining abundant reciprocal contact, tend to steady one another, or if they swerve, to do so in the same direction. The speakers of the branch that is geographically detached, however, come to know quite different grammars so far as they learn languages other than their native one, and such knowledge seems to act as an unconscious stimulus toward the growth of new forms and uses. It is not that grammatical concepts are often imitated outright or grammatical elements borrowed. Acquaintance with a language of different type seems rather to act as a ferment that sets new processes going.

It is in the nature of the case that direct specific evidence of changes of this character is hard to secure. But comparison of related languages or dialects with reference to their location frequently shows that the dialects which are geographically situated among strange languages are the most differentiated. This holds of Amharic in the Semitic family, of Singhalese in the Indic branch of Indo-European, of Hopi in Shoshonean, of Arapaho in Algonkin, of Huastec in Mayan.

But it is also likely that languages differ among each other in their susceptibility to change, and that the same language differs in successive periods of its history. It is rather to be anticipated that a language may be in a phase now of rapid and then of retarded metabolism, so to speak; that at one stage its tendency may be toward breaking-down and absorption, at another toward a more rigid setting of its forms. Similarly, there is reason to believe that languages of certain types of structure are inherently more plastic than others. At any rate, actual differences in rate of change are known. The Indo-European languages, for instance, have perhaps without exception altered more in the three thousand years of historical record than the Semitic ones. And so in native America, while contemporary documentary record is of course wanting, the degree of differentiation within the two stocks suggests strongly that Athabascan is more tenaciously conservative than Siouan.

There are also notable differences in the readiness to borrow words readymade. English is distinctly more hospitable in this regard than German, which tends rather to express a new concept by a new formation of old elements. Certain South American languages appear to have borrowed more words from one another than have any of those of North America. In this matter the type of language is probably of some influence, yet on the whole cultural factors perhaps predominate. The direction and degree of cultural absorption seem to determine the absorption of words to a considerable measure. Here writing is certainly potent. The Latin and French elements in English, the Sanskrit and Arabic elements in the Malaysian languages, were brought in to a large extent by writing, and were fixed by being written. They would probably have remained smaller if the historical contacts had been wholly oral. This is perhaps an important way in which writing exerts influence on the development of spoken language, an influence that in other respects is often overestimated.

107. SPEAKING AND WRITING

Learning our mother tongue is a largely unconscious process which goes on until control has become automatic. The process or act of acquisition is imitative, and it fades quickly from our memories. Learning to read and write, on the contrary, is at least started by teaching, comes later in life, and is a conscious process. Writing of course is a secondary symbol system serving as a surrogate for the primary symbol system of spoken language; it has certain special purposes such as distant or anonymous communication, permanent record, and the like. By one method or another, and more or less accurately, the visible symbols stand for the audible ones. Their reconversion into audible symbols, or into actually silent but potentially audible ones, is what we call reading. This writing-reading process comes so much later than speech-learning in the life histories of each of us—as well as in the history of the species—that it remains much less automatic and much more in our awareness. Consequently we tend often to think and express ourselves in terms of writing-reading when we mean speaking. The common term "word" is ambiguous: it denotes both an element of audible utterance that we feel as having a certain isolable identity, and an element of writing or printing to which we give a formal identity by spacing it apart from others. But a "letter" is merely a visible silent sign for an audible sound. It belongs to a writing system, as sounds belong to a speech system. To say therefore that such and such a language lacks the letter *f* is undiscriminating nonsense, especially if the language is an unwritten one. Such a language does lack the *sound* which in writing English we *represent* by the character *f*. It is not so long ago that even writers of grammars made this confusion. Some educated and intelligent people who have never given much thought to linguistics still make it. If we are not on intellectual guard, this prevalent nondiscrimination tends to color all our thinking on linguistic matters. Popularly, we "speak" English spontaneously, but "language" is something foreign we are taught after we can read and write. Most language instructors still misplace the emphasis on writing and reading of, for example, French, instead of on hearing and pronouncing it and remembering it kinaesthetically with ear and tongue.

That the basic component always is the actually spoken or "living" speech is shown by the fact that spoken languages change in essentially the same way and at about the same rate, apparently, whether they are also written or unwritten. Speech alters; writing may or may not conform for a while. If the writing, through blind habit persistence or prestige of the past, refuses to change, the actual speech may alter and alter until it has become really a new and distinct language before an adjustment is made.

After Caesar's conquest, the Gauls of France rapidly gave up their Keltic speech and learned Latin instead. This was not the highbrow Latin that Cicero wrote and perhaps actually spoke in his orations, but the "vulgar Latin" which legionaries and nonliterary people spoke in their daily life. With the centuries this Latin progressively changed. In part it altered provincially, with the growth of Gallic peculiarities; in part, through the development of new features common to all late local Latins, in Italy and Spain as well as in France, such as the well-attested growth of articles alongside the shrinkage of inflections (§ 108). Also, with the centuries sliding into the Dark Ages, fewer and fewer people learned to write; but those who did spelled words as they used to be spelled in literary Latin, not as rewritten to conform to the contemporary pronunciation. Gradually the spoken language changed so much that it, and the Latin used to represent it in writing, had only very partial similarity. People probably still thought that they were dealing with only one language when they were really already speaking French but still writing Latin. Then suddenly the two pulled apart with a jerk. In the Strasbourg Oaths of the grandsons of Charlemagne in 842, we have the actual spoken French of the time written as French—very Old French, to be sure, but indubitable French, and no longer spelled at all as the Latin originals of the words were spelled. The document marks the birth of the French daughter of the Latin mother—as a written language. But for spoken French, who can set a birthday? It had been changing continuously through the nine hundred years since Caesar. This typical continuity of change is what characterizes spoken languages as being natural, spontaneous, underlying growths, in contrast with their superimposed and more "artificial" writing systems, which quickly tend to crystallize. The difficulty with any *spoken* language is to keep it the same; with its *written* expression, it is to keep it plastic. The writing will set and finally break in a sort of revolution, but it has great difficulty in conforming and adapting. Written languages that have survived for millennia, like Latin and Sanskrit, are dead as spoken languages.[7]

This relation results in revivals of dead or dying languages, such as the attempted revival of Gaelic and Hebrew (§ 181), which seem somewhat uncertain as regards successful outcome, though of extraordinary theoretical interest. These present revivals are highly original and conscious experiments, if sentimental ones, being made in the laboratory of history. Whatever the final results, they will illuminate our understanding of the nature of language, by establishing new principles or confirming old ones.

It would be going too far to say that writing is unable to react on speech and to influence it. For instance, we have taken from French the word *niche,*

---

[7] Classical Arabic is a thousand years younger than Latin and Sanskrit, but the relation to it of its living provincial dialects is beginning to approach the relation of French and Spanish to Latin around 800.

and pronounce it either "neesh" if we follow the original sound or "nich" if we follow spelling. Those who know French, and that the word is French, are likely to say the former; those who do not, the latter. That dictionaries "allow" us choice in such cases means only that there is not yet a decisive majority of quantity or quality lined up on either side. More recent but probably more often used in English is the French *chic,* which those who know French, or who associate with those that have heard how the magic word is pronounced in France, pronounce as "shick" (or "sheek," if very ultra), while the unilinguals, who perhaps learned the word from reading clothing advertisements in the newspapers, say "chick." Here the issue is between the socially more and less advantaged; between prestige and numbers. *Silo* comes to us from Spanish, where of course it is spoken "seelo," just as our pronunciation of it would be "sailo" in Mexican or Spanish. Interlanguage transfers are perhaps the most common cause of changes of this type. The written form of a word penetrates farther, is learned first by the majority, and its pronunciation is then adapted to the spelling as if this were native. The slightly varying pronunciations current for the names Illinois, Chicago, St. Louis, Des Moines, reflect greater or smaller degrees of attempted adhesion to the original French pronunciation, though they all deviate from it.

These examples suggest minutiae, or special points. And that is what on the whole the influence of writing on speech is: a very partial reaction. This we might expect from the fact that speech comes first, is spontaneous and automatic, and has less of the conventional about it, less of the arbitrarily agreed upon (§ 204), than writing.

The strength and independence of writing are at their maximum where the system is primarily ideographic by word units—"logographic"—and is phonetic only in supplementary degree. Chinese is the important living example. Here writing is essentially a self-sufficient code rather than a script of spoken and heard sounds. In consequence, North and South Chinese will read off the same passage of writing with so much dialect difference of utterance as to be mutually unintelligible. In fact, an old-fashioned Chinese scholar wants to read his classic poetry by himself. If he listens to it read aloud, even by a fellow scholar, he is disturbed by the possible ambiguities in the many homonyms. This is because in the historical development of the Chinese language many words that were once spoken differently are now spoken alike, so that there remain far fewer distinct sound words than there are distinct word characters. The apparatus of the written language has remained rich, though the spoken language has shrunk.

Still more different are the pronunciations of Chinese [8] taken over along with the system of written characters centuries ago by Koreans, Japanese, and Annamese. These were somewhat mispronounced by the foreign learners to

[8] Called Sino-Japanese, Sino-Annamese, etc.

begin with, and are more so now. In fact, wholly different-sounding words of pure Japanese origin, often polysyllabic, can be spoken for some of the written characters, which also have their imported imitation-Chinese "pronunciation." This is as if we used both the English word *five* and the French word *cinq* as alternative-choice words expressing the number and visible symbol 5.

All this development in the Sinitic sphere is obviously an illustration of the degree to which writing *can* become autonomous of spoken language—rather than being an example of its normal reflex action on speech. Indeed, as has been said, the actual pronunciations of all the East Asiatic languages have altered through the centuries while the script system maintained its crystallized identity or even grew. For that matter, it would be theoretically possible to divorce the Chinese writing from Chinese speech, marry it to a new set of English words, and have it function with reasonable adequacy. Or, going still farther, it could be successfully used, with certain extensions, as the ready-made core of an international or universal code "translatable" into any spoken language.

108. DIFFUSION AND PARALLELISM IN LANGUAGE AND CULTURE

A phenomenon that language shows more conspicuously than culture, or which is more readily demonstrated in it, is parallel or convergent development, the repeated, independent growth of a trait (§ 223).

Thus sex gender is an old part of Indo-European structure. In English, by the way, it has wholly disappeared, so far as formal expression goes, from noun, adjective, and demonstrative and interrogative pronoun. It lingers only in the personal pronoun of the third person singular—*he, she, it*. A grammar of living English that was genuinely practical and unbound by tradition would never mention gender except in discussing these three little words. That our grammars specify *man* as a masculine and *woman* as a feminine noun is due merely to the fact that in Latin the corresponding words *vir* and *femina* possess endings that are recognized as generally masculine and feminine, and that an adjective associated with ends respectively in masculine *-us* and feminine *-a*. These are distinctions of form for which English possesses no equivalents. The survival of distinction between *he, she,* and *it,* while *this* and *that* and *which* have become alike irrespective of the sex of the person or thing they denote, is therefore historically significant. It points back to the past and to surviving Indo-European languages.

Besides, Indo-European, Semitic and Hamitic also express sex by grammatical forms, although like French and Spanish and Italian, they know only two genders, the neuter being unrepresented. These three are the only large language stocks in which sex gender finds expression. Ural-Altaic, Chinese, Japanese, Dravidian, Malayo-Polynesian, Bantu, and in general the language families of Asia, Africa, and the Americas do without, although a number of languages make other "gender" classifications, as of animate and inanimate, personal and impersonal, superior and inferior, intelligent and unintelligent. Sex gender however reappears in Hottentot of South Africa and in the Chinook and Coast Salish and Pomo languages of the Pacific coast of North America.

How is this distribution to be accounted for? Indo-European, Semitic, and Hamitic occupy contiguous territory, in fact surround the Mediterranean over a tract largely coextensive with the Caucasian area. Could they in the remote past have influenced one another? That is, could grammatical sex gender have been invented, so to speak, by one of them, and borrowed by the others, as we know that cultural inventions are constantly diffused? Not many philologists would grant this to be likely: there are relatively few authenticated cases of formal elements or concepts having been disseminated between unrelated languages (though see § 109). Is it then possible that our three stocks are at bottom related and one? Sex gender in that case would be part of their common inheritance. For Semitic and Hamitic, a number of specialists have accepted a common origin on other grounds. But for Semitic and Indo-European, many linguists remain dubious: positive evidence is still scant. Nevertheless, the territorial continuity of the three speech groups possessing the trait is difficult to accept as mere coincidence. In a parallel case in the realm of culture history a common source would be accepted as probable. Even Hottentot has been considered a remote Semitic-Hamitic offshoot, largely, it is true, because of the very fact that it expresses gender. Linguists, accordingly, may consider the case still open; but it is at least conceivable that the phenomenon goes back to a single origin in these four Old World stocks.

Yet no stretch will account for sex gender in the three native American languages as due to contact influence or diffusion, nor relate these tongues to the Old World ones. Clearly, here is a case of independent origin or parallel "invention." Chinook and Coast Salish, indeed, are in contiguity, and one may therefore have taken up the trait in imitation of the other. But Pomo lies well to the south and its affiliations run still farther south. Here sex gender is obviously an independent, secondary, and presumably rather recent growth in the grammar. The application of the category in Pomo is limited as narrowly as possible: to human beings; whereas in Chinook, as in older Indo-European, all nouns are given a gender, usually "artificial."

In short, it remains doubtful whether sex gender originated three or four or five or six times among these seven language stocks; but it evidently did originate repeatedly.

Other traits crop out the world over in much the same manner. A dual number, for instance, is found in Indo-European, Malayo-Polynesian, Eskimo, and several American languages. The distinction between inclusive and exclusive *we*—between *you-and-I* and *he-and-I*—is made in Malayo-Polynesian, Hottentot, Iroquois, Uto-Aztecan.

A true nominative case-ending, such as Latin and other early varieties of Indo-European evince, is an exceedingly specialized and rare formation; yet is found in the Maidu language of California. Articles, in regard to which Indo-European varies, Latin for instance being without while its Romance daughter tongues have developed them, recur in Semitic, in Polynesian, and in several groups of American languages, such as Siouan and Hokan. The growth in Romance is significant because of its historicity. That is, French developed its articles independently and secondarily, a fact which makes it probable that many languages in other parts of the world, whose history we do not know, also developed theirs instead of inheriting them—"invented" them, in short, although unconsciously.

A trait found in a considerable proportion of the American languages is the so-called incorporation of the object pronoun (§ 97). The objective pronoun, or an element representing it, is prefixed or suffixed to the verb, is made a part of it. The process is familiar enough to us from Indo-European so far as the subject is concerned: in the Latin *ama-s, ama-t, ama-nt,* the suffixes express "you, he, they," and independent pronouns comparable to the English ones are usually omitted. The *-s* in *he love-s* is the sole survival of this same process in modern English. None of the older Indo-European tongues however showed an inclination to affix similar elements to the verb for its object, although there are some approaches in a few recent languages of the family: Spanish *diga-me,* "tell me," and *mata-le,* "kill him," for instance; or French *je le vois,* "I see him," pronounced as one word, "zhlvwa." Semitic, on the other hand, and Basque, do "incorporate" objective elements, whereas most Asiatic and some American languages do not. Many other instances of parallel or convergent traits could be cited.

That frequency of parallel developments is greater in language than in culture is perhaps in part due to easier demonstrability in the field of speech. But in the main the high frequency seems real. Two reasons for the higher frequency of parallel developments in language suggest themselves.

First, the number of possibilities is small in language, so far as form or structure is concerned. The categories or concepts used for classifying and for the indication of relations are limited, and so are the means of expression. The distinctions expressed by gender, for instance, may refer to sex, animateness, personality, worth, shape, position, or possibly two or three other qualities; but there they end. If a language recognizes gender at all, it must have gender of one of these few types. Consequently there is some probability of several unconnected languages sooner or later happening upon the same type of gender. Similarly for the kinds of number (singular, dual, trial, plural, collective, distributive), or of case, or of person expressed. And these categories, such as gender and number and case, are themselves not numerous. Then too, the means of expressing the categories are limited. Of such mechanisms there are: position or relative order of words; compounding of them; accretions of elements to stems—namely, prefixes, infixes, and suffixes; reduplication, the repetition of part or the whole of words; internal changes by shift of vowel or accent within words; and therewith the types of grammatical means are about exhausted. Again the number of possible choices is so small that accidental probability must cause some languages to hit upon the same devices.

A second reason for the greater frequency of parallelism or independent reinvention in language is that structural traits—that is, grammars—appear to resist diffusion by imitation to a considerable degree. Words are borrowed, sometimes freely, almost always to some degree, between contiguous languages; sounds considerably less so; grammar least of all. That is, linguistic content lends itself to diffusion readily, linguistic pattern with more difficulty.

At bottom, it is true, the same holds of culture in some degree. Specific elements of culture, or groups of such elements, diffuse very widely at times and may be said to be always tending to diffuse: the wheel, for instance, smelting of metals, the crown as a symbol of royalty, battleships, Buddhism. The relations of elements among themselves, on the other hand, tend to change by internal growth rather than by external imitation. Of this sort are the relations of the classes and members of societies, the fervor with which religion is felt, the esteem accorded to learning or wealth or tradition, the inclination toward this or that avenue of subsistence or economic development. By conquest or peaceful pressure or penetration one people may shatter the political structure or social fabric of another, may undermine its conservatism, may swerve its economic habits. But it is more difficult to find cases of one people voluntarily adopting such tendencies or schemes of cultural organization in mere imitation of the example of another than of its adopting specific culture content—the wheel or the crown or Buddhism—from outside. The result is that culture relations or patterns develop spontaneously or from within probably more frequently than as a result of direct taking-over. Also, the types of culture forms being limited in number, the same type is frequently evolved independently. Thus monarchical and democratic societies, feudal or caste-divided ones, priest-ridden and relatively irreligious ones, expansive and mercantile or self-sufficient and agricultural nations, evolve over and over again. On the whole, therefore, actual comparative culture history more often deals with the specific contents of civilization. In part, also, this is true because events like the spread of an invention can usually be traced more exactly than the complex evolutions of, say, two feudal systems can be compared. The result, at any rate, is that specific diffusions seem to outnumber precise and sure parallels in culture, as is set forth in several of the chapters that follow (Twelve to Fourteen).

In general linguistics, on the contrary, interest inclines to the side of pattern rather than content; hence it is the parallelisms or convergences, the independent similarities, that stand out conspicuously. If as much attention were generally given to words and their meanings as to grammar, and if they could be traced in their prehistoric or unrecorded wanderings as reliably as many culture traits have been, it is probable that diffusion would loom larger than it now does as a principle shaping human speech. There are words that have traveled almost as far as the objects they denote: *tobacco* and *maize,* for example. And the absorption of words of Latin origin into English was as extensive as the absorption for over a thousand years of Latin, Christian, and Mediterranean culture by the English people—in fact, went on as its accompaniment and result.

109. CONVERGENT LANGUAGES

Parallel development in speech is not restricted to special traits like sex gender and object incorporation. It may affect whole languages in their types. Chinese a long time ago became an extremely analytical or "isolating" language. That is, it lost all affixes and internal change. Each word element or item became an unalterable unit. Sentences are built up by putting together these atoms. Grammatical relations are expressed by the order of words: the subject precedes the predicate, for instance. Other ideas that in many languages are treated formally, such as the plural or person, are expressed by content elements; that is, by other words: *many* for the plural, separate pronouns instead of affixes for person, and so on. The now uniformly monosyllabic stems of Chinese accentuate this isolating character, which however does not depend intrinsically upon monosyllabism. In the Indo-European family, as already mentioned, for over two thousand years there has been a drift toward something of the Chinese type of structure. This drift toward loss of formal mechanisms and toward the expression of grammar by material elements, or by their position only, has been evident in all branches of Indo-European, but has been most marked in English. The chief remnants of the older inflectional processes in spoken English today are four verb endings, *-s, -ed, -ing, -en;* three noun endings, the possessive *-'s* and the plurals *-s* and *-en,* the latter rare; the case ending *-m* in *whom, them;* a few vowel changes for plurals, as in *man—men, goose—geese;* and perhaps two hundred vowel changes in verbs, such as *sing, sang, sung.* Compared with Latin, Sanskrit, or even primitive Germanic, this brief list represents a survival of possibly a tenth of the original synthetic inflectional apparatus. That is, English has gone approximately nine-tenths of the way toward attaining a grammar of the Chinese type. A third language of independent origin, Polynesian, has traveled about the same distance in the same direction. Superficially it is less like Chinese in that it remains prevailingly polysyllabic, but more like it in having undergone heavy phonetic attrition. This then is a clear case of entire languages converging toward a similar type.

It is further remarkable that this change, from a complex, close-knit, "synthetic" type of structure to a simple, loose-jointed, "analytic" one, occurs throughout Indo-European, though it has been carried somewhat the farthest in English. The same kind of form reduction took place in Latin as it transformed into

French or Spanish; between classical and contemporary Greek; between ancient and modern Persian; between Sanskrit and Hindi: it can be traced in every Indo-European branch language of which our historical record is long enough. Most of these languages have not been in contact with each other for the one to three thousand years that the change has been going on. Change by influence of one on the other, leading to imitation, is therefore excluded. In the first edition of this book, the phenomenon was called "secondary parallelism"; that is, parallelism of change of type in the same direction, persisting subsequent to and during the increasing diversification of the languages in content and specific form. Sapir has made the situation famous by citing it as "linguistic drift," a sort of "slope" or long-range secular trend; but he has not been able to put his finger on a cause. Possibly the change toward looser structure got under way early, in original Indo-European, before this stock had branched out into its daughter languages, and the impulse persisted in the latter in greater or less strength. That would make the process carry on by momentum from the past. Whatever the cause, the breadth of the continuous drift or trend over thousands of miles and thousands of years makes the phenomenon impressive.

Another instance of convergence or superficial secondary assimilation of form in originally wholly separate and diverse languages is found in the remarkable resemblances in plan of structure of Indo-European, especially in its older forms, and the Penutian group of languages in native California. Common to these two families are an apparatus of similar cases, including accusative, genitive, locative, ablative, instrumental, sometimes even a true nominative; plural by suffix; vowel changes in the verb according to tense and mode; a passive and several participles and modal forms expressed by suffixes; and pronouns either separate or expressed by endings fused with the tense-modal suffixes. Thus, the processes that make English *sing, sang, sung, song,* or *bind, bound, band, bond,* are formally similar to those which have produced in Penutian Yokuts such forms as *shoḳud,* pierce, *shukid-ji,* pierced, *shoḳod,* perforation or hole, *shiḳid,* piercer or arrow. In short, many of the traits usually thought to characterize Indo-European as typically inflectional reappear in Penutian; and of course they appear there quite independently as regards their origin and history.

These are linguistic phenomena comparable in kind to the growth of feudalism in China more than a thousand years earlier than in Europe, or the appearance of a great centrally governed empire in Peru similar to the ancient monarchies of the Orient.

We have seen that while words can diffuse freely from one language to another when social pressures are set in that direction, grammars have much greater difficulty in diffusing. Forms and relations as such are not easily taken over by the stranger. Either he keeps his own, or he accepts the whole of the impinging other language, word content along with grammar. There are innumerable cases of one language replacing another in a given society; but there is very little evidence of a population accepting any considerable part of the grammar of another language to embody in their own. That is why we can speak so confidently of linguistic parallels, convergences, and joint drifts. If there were free imitation, borrowing, and diffusion of structural form, the cases we have discussed might just as well be attributable to that process.

Yet to a limited extent, alien influence on structural form can now and then be established, as distinct from word-borrowing. There is a Balkan instance where several Slavic, Albanian, and Latin languages have taken over a series of grammatical and idiomatic traits from Greek, which as the old language of religion and higher civilization long enjoyed a prestige priority. Some of these features due to Greek influence are: articles, which the Slavic and Latin tongues did not originally have; disuse of the infinitive: *give me that I drink* instead of *give me to drink;* genitive case including the dative; suffixion of an unaccented pronoun, like *daughter-mine;* double pronoun on the plan of *me-seems to me;* similar tautology of pronoun and clause, as *she believed him that he was her brother;* substitution of co-ordinate for subordinate conjunction: *hardly I escape and I meet another;* and idioms like *he was of twenty years* (that is, old), and *he saw how fifty* (for about fifty). These Greek idioms and structure features recur in Latin-derived Rumanian and with equal frequency in Slavic Bulgarian; Serbian, which is also Slavic but more distant, has adopted about half of them. Most of the same features have been accepted also in Albanian, but more in the nearer southern dialect than in remoter North Albanian.

Herewith the principle is established that structural form can be taken over by one language from another. However, the dozen formal traits involved here constitute only a minute fraction of the total grammar and idiom of the Balkan languages. The amount or degree of grammatical imitation or diffusion influence is therefore small. This limitation seems to hold in other instances also. A general "wave theory" evolved by certain Indo-Europeanists maintains that a trait—even a new sound—which originates in one dialect, language, or group of languages tends to be propagated to other related ones, or at least to be diffusible. In proportion as this wave theory holds true, it tends logically to vitiate the evidence of phonetic law and comparability on which linguists have built their family trees and classifications of relationship during the past century and a half of study. This is because genetic descent is intrinsically a process of diversification, whereas wave influence leads to assimilation. The wave theory must unquestionably be accepted as true to some extent; but the extent is minor. Internal change of related languages away from one another appears to be much the more prevalent process. Assimilation by imitation in waves, convergent resemblances developing independent of relationship, are occasional secondary crosscutting influences. The wave principle has a certain theoretical interest because it establishes to some extent for language a factor or force which as diffusion by imitation is extremely influential in the development of culture.

110. UNCONSCIOUS FACTORS IN LANGUAGE AND CULTURE CHANGE

The unceasing processes of change in language are mainly unconscious or covert, or at least implicit. The results of the change may come to be recognized by speakers of the changing language; the gradual act of change, and especially the causes, mostly happen without the speakers' being aware of them. This principle holds for all departments of language: the sounds, the structural form, even the meaning of words. When a change has begun to creep in, it may be tacitly accepted or it may be observed and consciously resisted on the ground of being incorrect or vulgar or foreign. But the underlying motives of the objectors and the impulses of the innovator are likely to be equally unknown to themselves.

If this view seem extreme, it can easily be shown that the great bulk of any language as it is, apart from any question of change, is employed unconsciously. An illiterate person will use such forms as *child, child's, children, children's* with the same "correctness" as a philologist, yet without being able to give an explanation of the involved grammatical ideas of singularity and plurality, absoluteness and possession, or to lay down rules as to the manner of expression of these ideas in English. Grammar, in short, exists before grammarians, whose legitimate business is to uncover such rules as are already there. It is an obviously hasty thought that because grammar happens to be taught in schools, speech can be grammatical only through schooling. The Sanskrit and Greek and Latin languages had their declensions and conjugations before Hindu and Greek and Roman scholars first analyzed and described them. The languages of primitive peoples frequently abound with complicated forms and mechanisms that are used consistently and are applied without suspicion of their existence. It is much as the blood went round in our bodies quite healthily before Harvey's discovery of its circulation.

The quality of unconsciousness seems to be a trait not specifically limited to linguistic causes and processes, but to hold in principle of culture generally. It is only that the unconsciousness pervades speech farther. A custom, a belief, an art, however deep down its springs, sooner or later rises into social consciousness. It then seems deliberate, planned, willed, and is construed as arising from conscious motives and developing through conscious channels. But many social phenomena can be led back only to nonrational and obscure motives: the wearing of silk hats, for instance. The whole class of changes in dress styles springs from unconscious causes. Sleeves and skirts lengthen or shorten, trousers flare or tighten, and who can say why? It is perhaps possible to trace a new fashion to Paris or London, and to a particular stratum of society there. But what is it that in the winter of a particular year makes every woman—or man—of a certain social group wear, let us say, a high-collared coat, or a shoe that does not come above the ankle, and the next year, or the tenth after, the reverse? It is insufficient to say that this is imitation of a leader of fashion, of a professional creator of style. Why does the group follow him, and think the innovation attractive and correct? A decade earlier the same innovation would have appeared senseless or extravagant to the same group. A decade after, it appeals as belated and ridiculous, and everyone wonders that style was so tasteless so short a time ago.

Evidently the aesthetic emotions evoked by fashions are largely beyond the control of both individuals and groups. It is difficult to say where the creative and imitative impulses of fashion come from—which, inasmuch as the impulses obviously reside somewhere in human minds, means that they spring from the unconscious portions of the mind. Evidently, then, our justification of the dress styles we happen at any time to be following, our pronouncing them artistic or comfortable or sensible or what not, is secondary. A low shoe may be more convenient—or inconvenient—than a high one, a brown one more or less practical than a black or a white one. That that is not the reason which determines the wearing of low brown shoes when they are customarily worn is shown by the fact that at other times high black ones are put on by everyone. The reasons that can be and are given are so changeable and inconsistent that they evidently are not the real reasons, but are the false secondary reasons which are best distinguished as rationalizations. Excuses, we should call them with reference to individual conduct.

What applies to fashion holds also of manners, of morals, and of many religious observances. Why we defer to women by rising in their presence and passing through a door behind them; why we refrain from eating fish with a knife or drinking soup out of a two-handled cup, though drinking it from a single-handled one is legitimate; why we do not marry close kin; why we remove our hats in the presence of the deity or his emblems but would feel it impious to pull off our shoes—all the thousands of prescriptions and taboos of which these are examples possess an unconscious motivation.

Such cases are also illustrations of what is known as the relativity of morals (§ 116). The Jew sets his hat on to worship, the Oriental punctiliously slips out of his shoes. Some people forbid the marriage of the most remote relatives, others encourage that of first cousins, still others permit the union of uncle and niece. It would seem that all sociocultural phenomena which can be brought under this principle of relativity of standard are unconsciously grounded. This in turn implies the unconscious causation of the mores, those products of the social environment in which one is reared and which one accepts as the ultimate authority of conduct. As mores are those folkways or customs to which an emotional coloring has become attached, so that adherence to the custom or departure from it arouses a feeling respectively of approval of disapproval, it is evident that the origin of folkways generally is also unconscious, since there seems no reason why the emotions or the ethical affect enveloping a customary action should incline more than the custom itself to spring up unconsciously.

It has long since been recognized that the average man's convictions on social matters remote from him are not developed through examination of evidence and exercise of reason, but are taken over, by means of what used to be denominated the herd instinct and is now called social suggestion, from the society or period in which he happens to have been born and nurtured. His belief in democracy, in monotheism, in his right to charge profit and his freedom to change residence or occupation, have such origin. In many instances it is easy to render striking proof of the proposition—as in the problems of high tariff, or the Athanasian creed, or vitamin deficiencies, which are so technical as to their evidence or so intricate in their argument as to be impossible of independent solution by the majority of men. Time alone would forbid; we should starve while making the necessary research. And the difference between the average man's attitude on such difficult points and the highly gifted individual's attitude toward them, or even toward simpler problems, would seem to be one of degree only.

Even on the material sides of culture, undesigned motivation plays a part. In the propulsion of ships, oars and sails fluctuate as the prevalent means down almost to the period of steam vessels. It would be impossible to say that one method was logically superior to the other, that it was recognized as such and then rationally adhered to. The history of warfare shows similar changes between throwing and thrusting spears, stabbing and hewing swords, light and heavy armor. The Greeks and the Macedonians in the days of their military superiority lengthened their lances and held them. It no doubt seemed for a time that a definitive superiority had been proved for this type of weapon over the shorter, hurled javelin. Then the Romans, as part of their legionary tactics, reverted to the javelin and broke the Macedonian phalanx with their pilum. By the end of the Roman Empire, the infantry legion had yielded to heavy cavalry as the most effective military arm. After about nine centuries, around 1300, infantry began once more to come into its own, and then to dominate. Armor reached its perfection after gunpowder had begun to come into use; but firearms finally crowded armor out altogether. Yet the last few decades have brought the rebirth of the helmet.

These fashions in tools and practical appliances do not alter as fast as modern dress styles, and some of their causes can often be recognized. Yet as regards consciousness or intent there seems no essential difference between the fluctuation of fashions in weapons—or in navigation or cooking or travel or house-building—and, let us say, the fluctuation of mode between soft and stiff hats or high and low shoes. It may have been the open array of the legion that led to the pilum, ever more rapidly fired bullets that induced the abandonment of the breastplate, shrapnel and the machine gun that caused the reintroduction of the helmet. But these initiating factors were not deliberate as regards the effects that came in their train; and in their turn they themselves were the effects of more remote causes, such as improvements in general metallurgical arts. The whole chain of development in such cases is intricate and branching, unforeseen, mainly unforeseeable. At most there is recognition of what is happening; in general the recognition seems to become full only after the change in tool or weapon or industrial process has become complete and is perhaps already being undermined once more.

Of course purely stylistic alterations—and linguistic innovations—also possess their causes. When the derby hat or the pronoun *thou* becomes obsolete, there is a reason; only, we generally cannot cite a really convincing specific cause.

The common causal element in all these changes may be called a shift in social values, in attitudes, or in the configuration of the total culture; often perhaps a change in some other and remote part of the culture—or language. Perhaps practical chemical experience has grown, and gunpowder explodes more satisfactorily; or an economic readjustment has made it possible to equip more soldiers with guns. The first result is a greater frequency of bullet penetrations in battle; the next, the abandonment of the breastplate as hampering and useless. Increasing wealth or schooling or city residence or class differentiation makes indiscriminate familiarity of manners seem less desirable than at an earlier period: brusque *thou* begins to yield to indirect plural *you*. Or again, new verbs, all of regular conjugation like *love, loved,* are formed in English, or imported from French, until their number outweighs that of the ancient irregular ones like *sing, sang.* A standardizing tendency is thereby set going—"analogizing" is the technical term of the philologist—which begins to turn irregular verbs into regular ones: *shaped* replaces *shopen,* just as *lenger* becomes *longer* and *toon* becomes *toes.* Or, conversely, the analogy of *write-wrote, drive-drove, ride-rode,* causes *dived* to tend to be replaced by "colloquial" *dove.* There is much the same sort of causality in one of these phenomena as in another. The individual or community that leaves off the breastplate or the stiff hat may more likely be aware that it is making the change than the one that leaves off saying *toon* or *thou.* But there does not seem to be an essential difference of process. Linguistic and aesthetic changes may be most fully unconscious, social ones next, material and economic ones perhaps least so. But normally, change or innovation is accompanied by a shift of values that are broader than the single phenomenon in question, and that are held to impulsively far more often than they are deliberately planned. That is why all social creations—institutions, beliefs, codes, styles, grammars—prove on impartial analysis to be full of inconsistencies and irrationalities. They have sprung not from a premeditated system of weighed or reasoned choices but from impulsive desires, from emotionally colored habits, or from "accidents" happening in some other part of the culture.

The foregoing discussion may be summarized as follows. Linguistic phenomena and processes are on the whole less conscious than cultural ones, without however differing in principle. In both language and culture, content is more readily imparted and assimilated than form, and it enters farther into consciousness. Organization or structure in both cases takes place according to unconscious or covert or implicit patterns, such as grammatical categories, social standards, political or economic points of view, religious or intellectual assumptions. These patterns tend to attain recognition only in a last or sophisticated stage of their development, and even then continue to alter further even without the exercise of conscious control. The number of such linguistic and social patterns or forms being limited, there is some tendency for them to repeat in different cultures with a degree of similarity, though without historical connection or without attaining actual identity. Partially similar combinations of such patterns sometimes recur, producing languages or cultures of roughly similar type. But established patterns of form, and still more their combinations, replace each other with difficulty. Their spread therefore takes place mostly though the integral substitution of one language or culture for another, rather than by piecemeal absorption. This is in contrast to the specific content elements of which language and culture consist—individual words, mechanical devices, institutional symbols, particular religious ideas or actions, and the like. These elements absorb and diffuse readily. They are therefore imitated and imported more often than they are reinvented. But, as if in compensation, linguistic and cultural patterns or structures growing up spontaneously may acquire, through the accidents of convergence, considerable resemblance of general form that is not dependent on historical connection or spread.

111. LINGUISTIC AND CULTURAL STANDARDS

It does not follow that because social usages largely fail to spring out of purposive and deliberate reasoning, they are therefore unworthy of being followed, or that standards of conduct need be renounced because they are relative—that is, unconsciously founded and changing. The natural inclination of men being to regard their standards of taste, behavior, and social arrangement as reasonable, perfect, and fixed, there follows a first inclination to regard these standards as devalued as soon as their emotionality and variability have been recognized. Such a negative reaction is disappointing: it is a further result of the illusion. Once the fundamental and automatic assumption of fixity and inherent value of social patterns has been given up, and it is recognized that the chief motive power of behavior in man as in the other animals is affective and unconscious, there is nothing in institutions and codes to quarrel with. They are neither despicable nor glorious; no more deserving, in virtue of their existence, to be uprooted and demolished than to be defended as absolute and eternal. In some form or other, they are inevitable; and the particular form they take at this time or that place is always tolerably well founded, in the sense of being adapted with fair success, or having been but recently well adapted, to the conditions of the natural and social environment of the group which holds the institution, code, or standard.

That this is a sane attitude is sometimes more easily shown in the field of language than of culture. This is because language is primarily a mechanism or means, whereas in culture ends or purposes obtrude more. It is thus easier to view linguistic phenomena dispassionately. Grammars and dictionaries, for instance, are evidently the result of self-consciousness arising about speech which has previously been mainly unconscious. They may be roughly compared to social formulations like law codes or written constitutions or philosophical systems or religious dogmas, which typically begin also as representations of usages or beliefs already in existence. When moralists about language stigmatize expressions like *ain't* or *them cows* or *he don't* as "wrong," they are judging an innovation, or one of several established but conflicting usages, by a standard of correctness that seems to them absolute and permanent, but which is really only the hallmark of a class or a locality to which they choose to give priority. As a matter of actuality, the condemned form may or may not succeed in becoming established. *He don't,* for example, might in time attain to "correctness" —meaning social reputability—although *ain't* is perhaps less likely to become legitimized, and *them cows,* though old, to have still smaller prospect of ultimate general recognition. That a form departs from the canon of today of course no more proves that it will be accepted in future than that it will not. What is certain is that if it wins sufficient usage by the right people, it will also win sanction, and will become part of the standard of its time.

Linguistic instances like these differ little if at all in principle, in their involved psychology, from the finding of the Supreme Court that a certain legislative enactment is unconstitutional and therefore void, or from the decision of a religious sect that Sunday baseball is wicked. The chief point of divergence would seem to be that a court is a constituted body endowed with an authority that is not paralleled on the linguistic side, at any rate in Anglo-Saxon countries; although the Latin nations possess Academies whose dicta on correctness of speech enjoy a moral authority—though a sanctionless one—approximating the verdicts of a high court. And it is notorious that courts and religious denominations, like speech purists, may begin by condemning and yet end by tolerating or even accepting innovations, after actual usage of the times has drifted far enough. Witness the fates of the American income tax, Methodist dancing, and the rule that prepositions are not words to end sentences with!

It is also of interest to remember that the power of nullifying legislation was not specifically granted the Supreme Court by the Constitution of the United States, but that the practice grew up gradually, quite like a speech innovation that becomes established. Certain elements in the American population look upon this power as undesirable and therefore take satisfaction in pointing out its unsanctioned origin. The majority, on the other hand, feel that the situation on the whole works out well, and that a Supreme Court with its present powers is better than the risk of a Supreme Court without power. Still, it remains curiously illogical that the preservation of the Constitution should take place partly through the extraconstitutional functioning of a constitutional body. In principle such a case is similar to that of grammarians who at the same time lay down a "rule" and exceptions to the rule, because the contradictory usages happen to be actually established.

Codes, dogmas, and grammars are thus normally reflections, secondary rather than primary causes. Such influence as they have is mainly in outward crystallization. They produce an appearance of permanence. In the field of speech, it is easy to recognize that it is not grammarians that make languages, but languages that make grammarians. The analogous process evidently holds for culture. Lawgivers, statesmen, religious leaders, discoverers, inventors seem to shape civilization when actually they much more express it. The complex and often obscure forces that shape culture also mold the so-called creative leaders of society as essentially as they mold the mass of humanity. Progress, so far as it exists objectively, can be construed as something that happens rather than as something we make as we set out to make it. Our frequent assumption to the contrary is probably the result of a reluctance to realize our individual near-impotence as regards remodeling the culture we live in, as contrasted with the overpowering molding we receive from it. But how much does any one of us create or shape or alter his language? Culture no doubt is a bit more malleable; but the comparison with speech should make us cautious not to overrate our capacity for initiative.

Undoubtedly we do have social influence as individuals. It is an influence on the fortune and the careers of other individuals, sometimes on larger segments of society, and it is concerned largely with aims of personal security, relative dominance, or affection among ourselves. We also have many choices among the alternatives contained in our culture and in our speech. To some extent we can manipulate certain alternatives and ambiguities of the culture in our personal favor, or in the direction of our ideals. Now and then, perhaps, we succeed in establishing, with the support of others, some altered behavior or idea or idiom, some novel twist of custom or phrase. That seems to describe the range of our exertion of influence on the form or content of those mass products and mass influences which we call civilization and language.

CHAPTER SEVEN

The Nature of Culture

112. WHAT CULTURE IS

WHAT CULTURE is can be better understood from knowledge of what forms it takes and how it works than by a definition. Culture is in this respect like life or matter: it is the total of their varied phenomena that is more significant than a concentrated phrase about them. And again as with life and with matter, it is true that when we are dealing with the actual manifestations we are less often in doubt as to whether a phenomenon is or is not cultural than we are in deciding on what is includable in the concept of culture when we reason abstractly about it. Nevertheless, it will be worth while to consider some definitions briefly.

Tylor says that "culture or civilization is that complex whole which includes knowledge, belief, art, morals, law, customs, and any other capabilities and habits acquired by man as a member of society." Linton equates culture with "social heredity." Lowie calls it "the whole of social tradition." All three statements use the term "social" or "society," but in an attributive or qualifying sense. We can accept this: society and culture, social and cultural, are closely related concepts. There can obviously be no culture without a society—much as there can be no society without individuals. The converse—no society without culture—holds for man: no cultureless human society is known; it would even be hard to imagine. But it does not hold on the subhuman level. As we have seen (§ 6, 20), ants and bees do have genuine societies without culture, as well as without speech. Less integrated and simpler associations are frequent among animals. Even a pair of nesting birds rearing their young constitute a society, though a small and temporary one. Accordingly, so far as man is concerned, culture always has society as a counterpart; it rests on, and is carried by, society. Beyond the range of man there are societies, but no cultures. Cultural phenomena thus characterize man more specifically than his social manifestations characterize him, for these latter he shares with vertebrate and invertebrate animals.

Roughly, then, we can approximate what culture is by saying it is that which the human species has and other social species lack. This would include speech, knowledge, beliefs, customs, arts and technologies, ideals and rules. That, in short, is what we learn from other men, from our elders or the past, plus what we may add to it. That is why Tylor speaks of "capabilities and habits acquired by man," and what Lowie means when he says "the whole of social tradition," or Linton by "social heredity." The last term is unfortunate because heredity now denotes in biology precisely what is received organically or genetically to the exclusion of what is acquired socially or culturally. But if we substitute for "heredity" the more noncommittal near-synonym "inheritance," the phrase then conveys much the same meaning as Lowie's "social tradition."

The terms "social inheritance" or "tradition" put the emphasis on how culture is acquired rather than on what it consists of. Yet a naming of all the kinds of things that we receive by tradition—speech, knowledges, activities, rules, and the rest—runs into quite an enumeration. We have already seen in § 2 that things so diverse as hoeing corn, singing the blues, wearing a shirt, speaking English, and being a Baptist are involved. Perhaps a shorter way of designating the content of culture is the negative way of telling what is excluded from it. Put this way around, culture might be defined as all the activities and non-physiological products of human personalities that are not automatically reflex or instinctive. That in turn means, in biological and psychological parlance, that culture consists of conditioned or learned activities (plus the manufactured results of these); and the idea of learning brings us back again to what is socially transmitted, what is received from tradition, what "is acquired by man as a member of societies." So perhaps *how it comes to be* is really more distinctive of culture than what it *is*. It certainly is more easily expressed specifically.

In one sense culture is both superindividual and superorganic. But it is necessary to know what is meant by these terms so as not to misunderstand their implications. "Superorganic" does not mean nonorganic, or free of organic influence and causation; nor does it mean that culture is an entity independent of organic life in the sense that some theologians might assert that there is a soul which is or can become independent of the living body. "Superorganic" means simply that when we consider culture we are dealing with something that is organic but which must also be viewed as something more than organic if it is to be fully intelligible to us. In the same way when we say that plants and animals are "organic" we do not thereby try to place them outside the laws of matter and energy in general. We only affirm that fully to understand organic beings and how they behave, we have to recognize certain kinds of phenomena or properties—such as the powers of reproduction, assimilation, irritability—as added to those which we encounter in inorganic substances. Just so, there are certain properties of culture—such as transmissibility, high variability, cumulativeness, value standards, influence on individuals—which it is difficult to explain, or to see much significance in, strictly in terms of the organic composition of personalities or individuals. These properties or qualities of culture evidently attach not to the organic individual man as such, but to the actions and the behavior products of societies of men—that is, to culture.

In short, culture is superorganic and superindividual in that, although carried, participated in, and produced by organic individuals, it is acquired; and it is acquired by learning. What is learned is the existent culture. The content of this is transmitted between individuals without becoming a part of their inherent endowment. The mass or body of culture, the institutions and practices and ideas constituting it, have a persistence and can be conceived as going on their slowly changing way "above" or outside the societies that support them. They are "above" them in that a particular culture, a particular set of institutions, can pass to other societies; also in that the culture continuously influences or conditions the members of the underlying society or societies—indeed, largely determines the content of their lives. Further, particular manifestations of cultures find their primary significance in other cultural manifestations, and can be most fully understood in terms of these manifestations; whereas they cannot be specifically explained from the generic organic endowment of the human personality, even though cultural phenomena must always conform to the frame of this endowment.

An illustration may make this superorganic quality more vivid. A religion, say Roman Catholicism or Mohammedanism, is of course a piece of culture, and a typical piece or sample. Obviously Catholicism exists only in so far as there are Catholics; that is, when and where there are human individuals who have acquired the faith. Once established, however, the Catholic hierarchy, beliefs, rituals, habits, and attitudes can also be viewed as going on century after century. Popes, bishops, communicants succeed one another; the church persists. It certainly possesses a continuity and an influence of its own: it affects not only its adherents but the course of history. On a smaller scale, or for shorter periods, the same thing holds for smaller segments of culture—institutions, beliefs, or customs down to short-lived trivialities of fashion and etiquette. On a larger and more general scale, the same holds for the totality of human culture since it first began to develop. Big or little, then, culture affects human action. It is the accident of what culture happens to be in Occidental countries toward the middle of the twentieth century which determines that when I get up in the morning I put on a shirt and pants and not a chlamys or a toga or just a breechclout. Can we call this contemporary Western culture the cause of my shirt-wearing? In ordinary parlance, we might; the specific custom can certainly not be derived from anything in human hereditary constitution. Dialectically, the cultural causation might be challenged; it depends on logical definitions. But everyone will agree at least that the concrete cultural fact of habitual shirt-wearing is specifically related to or conditioned by other cultural facts, such as antecedent dress styles, manners, laws, or religion.

Again, the English language is a piece of culture. The faculty of speaking and understanding some or any language is organic: it is a faculty of the human species. The sounds of words are of course made by individual men and women, and are understood and reacted to by individuals, not by the species. But the total aggregation of words, forms, grammar, and meanings which constitute the English language are the cumulative and joint product of millions of individuals for many centuries past. No one of us creates or invents for himself the English he speaks. He talks it as it comes to him, ready-made, from his millions of predecessors and from his elders and age mates. English is obviously super-individual in the sense that it is something enormously bigger and more signifi-cant than the speech of any individual man, and in that it influences his speak-ing infinitely more than his speaking can hope to contribute to or influence the English language. And English is superorganic in that its words and meanings are not direct outflows or consequences of men's being human organisms—else all men would spontaneously talk as much alike as they walk alike. Instead, how they talk depends overwhelmingly on how the societies in which they were raised talked before.

A piece of culture such as the English language is therefore a historical phenomenon. This means that its specific features cannot be adequately ex-plained by the organic features of our species—nor of a race—but are most intel-ligible in the light of the long, complex, and locally varied history of the insti-tution we call English speech. In short, a cultural fact is always a historical fact; and its most immediate understanding, and usually the fullest understanding of it to which we can attain, is a historical one. To a large degree calling culture superorganic or superindividual means that it yields more readily to historical interpretation than to organic or psychosomatic explanations.

A simile that may further help the realization of what culture is and how it works is that of a coral reef. Such a reef may be miles long and inhabited by billions of tiny polyp animals. The firm, solid part of the reef consists of calcium carbonate produced by the secretions of these animals over thousands of years—a product at once cumulative and communal and therefore social. What is alive and organic in the reef is these innumerable little animals on its ocean-fronting surface. Without their ancestors, there would have been no reef. But the reef now exists independently of the living polyps, and would long continue to en-dure even if every polyp were killed by, say, a change in ocean temperature or salinity. It would still break the surf, would now and then wreck ships, and would bar off quiet water behind. While a coral reef is the accumulated precipitate of dead polyps, it is also a phenomenon affording to millions of living polyps a base and a foothold, and a place to thrive.

This parallel is incomplete. It breaks down in that a reef is actual physical matter, whereas only the artifacts and the manufactures of culture are material or physical, most of culture consisting of ideas and behaviors. Also, a reef determines that and where new polyps are to live, but not how they will live, not the specific way of many possible ways in which they will function, which on the contrary is just what culture does largely determine for men. Yet the simile is valid and suggestive on one point: the minute role played by the individual polyp or human being in proportion, respectively, to the mass of reef or of culture. Each of us undoubtedly contributes something to the slowly but ever changing culture in which we live, as each coral contributes his gram or two of lime to the Great Barrier Reef. In the main, though, it is our culture that directs and outlines the kind of life we can lead. There is left to our individual gifts and temperaments the relative success and happiness we attain in life; and to our own volition, the alternative choices provided by our culture—the choice, perhaps, between being doctor, lawyer, or merchant chief; or whether our next drink shall be water, beer, tea, or milk. Even this last set of choices would not be wholly free to the individual if he were a participant in strict Methodist or Mohammedan culture; and in old China the beer would not be available and the milk considered too nasty to want.

At any rate, the comparison may be of aid toward seeing things in perspective; with a consequence, perhaps, of somewhat deepened personal humility in the face of the larger world and human history.

113. COMPOSITENESS OF CULTURE

One general characteristic of culture is what may be called its openness, its receptivity. The culture of today is always largely received from yesterday: that is what tradition or transmission means; it is a passing or sending along, a "handing-through" from one generation to another. Even in times of the most radical change and innovation there are probably several times as many items of culture being transmitted from the past as there are being newly devised. Historians would be unanimous, for instance, that with all the important changes produced by the great French Revolution, France of 1780 and France of 1820 nevertheless still were far more alike than different. It would take a series of revolutions, or a quite long series of generations, before the changes equaled the persistences. Even French culture of 1520 would almost certainly be rated as more like than unlike that of 1820. We might have to go back to A.D. 820, or even to A.D. 220, before the alterations could safely be estimated as surpassing the transmissions. This does not mean merely that mankind is generally hidebound and unimaginative, and that its cultures are therefore inclined to be persistent. It means also, put in terms of process or dynamics, that on the whole the passive or receptive faculties of culture tend to be considerably stronger than its active or innovating faculties. This is something that seems to be pretty deeply ingrained in the nature of culture because it is deeply ingrained in the nature of man, something without which it would lose its continuity, and therewith its stability. And most participants in most cultures—most human beings, in short—seem to want a pretty high degree of social stability on account of the security and repose it gives them. A culture that was so unstable and novelty-mongering that it could continually reverse its religion, government, social classification, property, food habits, manners, and ethics, or could basically alter them within each lifetime—such a culture can be imagined. But it would scarcely seem attractive to live under, to most men and women; and it would presumably not survive very long in comparison or competition with more stable cultures, through lacking the necessary continuity. If what was on today were mostly off tomorrow, there would be little chance for institutions or sets of habit to be carried on long enough to develop to their most successful fruition. There would be conflicting ideas, ideals, and aims, in place of the at least partly coherent ideology which characterizes most actual cultures; and along with them, confusion, indecision, and a constant starting all over again. In short, we can see that it is profitable for cultures to carry a considerable degree of ballast in the shape of consistency and continuity, and that those which have fallen markedly short in these qualities have soon disintegrated and perished; quite likely that is why they are so inconspicuous in history. But to maintain a real continuity, a culture must put a genuine value on what each generation hands on to its children; it must, in short, be receptive to its own past, or at least largely acquiescent to it.

Now allied to this receptivity of its own past is a receptivity that every culture shows toward cultural material worked out by other cultures. Such acceptance of foreign elements and systems of course constitutes a geographical spread; and the designation most in use for it is "diffusion" (§ 171). Such spreads occasionally are rapid, but often they require a considerable time interval. Accordingly, much of what is acquired by diffusion from outside also has its origin in the past, much as what a culture receives by internal handing-on of traditions; but the characteristic of diffusion, the emphasis of the process, is on transmission in *space*. The amount of diffusion which is constantly going on between cultures that have contacts is impressive, and the amount of cultural material or content of foreign origin which gradually accumulates within any one culture may fairly be said to be normally greater than what is originated within it. Also, an integrating process, discussed again in § 122 and 171, brings it about that as soon as a culture has accepted a new item, it tends to lose interest in the foreignness of origin of this item, as against the fact that the item is now functioning within the culture. One might say that once acceptance is made, the source is played down and forgotten as soon as possible. So it comes about that a large proportion of every culture was not spontaneously developed by it, but was introduced from outside and fitted into it, after which the people of the culture were no longer much concerned about the fact of introduction. Probably the greater part of every culture has percolated into it.

We do not think of our American civilization as something that is particularly discordant or ill-assembled. Yet we speak an Anglo-Saxon form of a Germanic language that contains more original Latin than English words. Our religion is Palestinian, with its specific formulations into denominations made chiefly in Rome, Germany, England, Scotland, and Holland. Our Bible is translated partly from Hebrew, partly from Greek. We drink coffee first grown in Ethiopia and adopted in Arabia, tea discovered in China, beer first brewed in ancient Mesopotamia or Egypt, hard liquor invented in mediaeval Europe. Our bread, beef, and other meats are from plants and animals first domesticated in Asia; our potatoes, corn, tomatoes, and beans were first used by the American Indians; likewise tobacco. We write an Etruscan-Roman variant of a Greek form of an alphabet invented in or near Phoenicia by a Semitic people on the basis of nonalphabetic writing in still more ancient cultures; its first printing took place in Germany, on paper devised in China. It is needless to extend the catalogue. We no longer feel these things of foreign origin as being foreign; they have become an integral part of our culture. It is only when we pause for scientific analysis, for historical retrospect, that we become aware of their alien or remote source. They *are* a part of our culture, and are used as such.

This is not because modern American civilization is particularly polyglot, but because so far as we can tell such a condition is typical of all cultures. If ancient Egypt, Sumer, India, or China seems less flooded with import and more original, it is only because historical record fails, and we get no more than occasional indications of the alien and still more ancient sources of their culture content.

This is not to say that there are no resistances, strains, and dislocations when particular culture import takes place. They may or may not occur; they frequently do. We shall consider some of these resistances later (§ 172, 176). But in spite of them, in the long pull, absorptions and assimilations continue to take place. How far such assimilation is also an integration, or how far it may be simply a collocation of things that are treated as if they were functionally fitted together even though they are not—this is a complicating problem whose consideration we must also defer. But it is a fair question: Why is cultural receptivity so high, and the amount of diffusion and absorption so great?

There are several reasons. A steel knife or ax just is physically more effective than a stone one; a motortruck more so than a freight wagon. In other words, in the sphere of practical, mechanical things, there are objective superiorities, and the invention of a superior artifact in one culture anywhere tends to start the process of its adoption by other cultures as soon as they learn about it. Then, whatever comes from a society that is stronger, wealthier, cleverer, or has greater prestige comes with a favorable recommendation. Missionization may accentuate this process; and there often is conscious missionization for products and brands, for political and social ideas, as well as for religions. Finally, man is an animal who has a great faculty for getting bored, and many things are taken up just because they are new and different. Some of these will be dropped again for the same reason; but others will stick. There probably are still other factors at work; but those mentioned may suffice to make it reasonable that there should be so much cultural receptivity, diffusion, assimilation, and compositeness.

114. ORGANIC DIVERSITY, CULTURAL HYBRIDITY

It is a striking fact that on the organic level there is nothing parallel to this cultural assimilativeness. Animals and plants absorb and assimilate their food—note the identity of the words, but with the metaphorical connotation quite different—but they do so by breaking it down. It is no longer grass or seed or flesh; it has become muscle or blood or bone in a new organism. But Christianity and the Roman alphabet are still Christianity and the alphabet after our culture, or that of our ancestors or successors, has taken them in, has "absorbed" them. The counterpart of course is that no part of Christianity is destroyed or made over into something radically different on being taken into a new culture, as food is in the body. There simply is more Christianity in the world than there was before, instead of less. This is one way in which culture may be said to work cumulatively, in comparison with organisms.

Another comparison, or rather contrast, with the organic may be made. A cow and a bison can, with some difficulty, be crossed or hybridized, so that an intermediate form results. This is because they are both of the family *Bovidae;* that is, sprung from common ancestors from whom they have not yet diverged very far. A horse and a donkey will hybridize, but the offspring is sterile. It seems impossible to produce a self-perpetuating species of mules. If the divergence is a little greater, there will not even be offspring. Cows and horses simply cannot be amalgamated. In other words, the organic process, while it allows enormous persistences, is also, so far as its general or longer course is concerned, both diversifying and irretraceable. Once the genetic diversification or "evolution" has gone beyond a certain quite narrow degree, there is no more possibility of reversal and assimilation.

By contrast, cultures can blend to almost any degree and not only thrive but perpetuate themselves. Classic Greek civilization was a mixture of primitive Greek, Minoan, Egyptian, and Asiatic elements. Of the Asiatic elements, the alphabet, the zodiac, and the system of weights (§ 191, 208, 229) are only a few examples. Japanese civilization is partly autochthonous, whence its god-descended Emperor and Shinto ritual; partly Chinese, such as its writing and philosophy; Indian in its prevalent Buddhism; Western in its factories, export trade, telephones, and movies. It is needless to pile up examples: as has already been said, the greater part of the content of every culture is probably of foreign origin, although assimilated into a whole that works more or less coherently and is felt as a unit. However diversified or specialized a culture grows in its development, it can therefore always largely retrace its course; and it does normally do so, by absorbing more generalized content from other cultures, and thereby assimilating not only to them but to the totality or the average of human cultures. Cultures are always tending to equate themselves by imparting their characteristics to one another, even while another set of impulses pushes each of them toward particularistic peculiarity.

It is as if, let us say, a rabbit could graft into itself the ruminant digestive system of a sheep, the breathing gills of a fish, the claws and teeth of a cat, some of the tentacles of an octopus, and an assortment of other odd organs from elsewhere in the animal kingdom; and then not only survive, but perpetuate its new type and flourish. Organically, this is of course sheer nonsense; but in culture, it is a near-enough figure of what happens.

A result of this difference is that the course of organic evolution can be portrayed properly as a tree of life, as Darwin has called it, with trunk, limbs, branches, and twigs. The course of development of human culture in history cannot be so described, even metaphorically. There is a constant branching-out, but the branches also grow together again, wholly or partially, all the time. Culture diverges, but it syncretizes and anastomoses too. Life really does nothing but diverge: its occasional convergences are superficial resemblances, not a joining or a reabsorption. A branch on the tree of life may approach another branch;

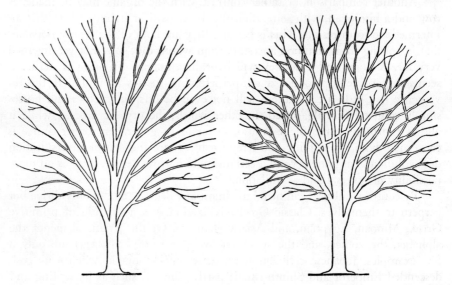

FIG. 18.   THE TREE OF LIFE AND THE TREE OF THE KNOWLEDGE OF
GOOD AND EVIL—THAT IS, OF HUMAN CULTURE

it will not normally coalesce with it. The tree of culture, on the contrary, is a ramification of such coalescences, assimilations, or acculturations. The schematic diagram in Figure 18 visualizes this contrast.

It is true that no figure of speech or of drawing will really prove a point like this. Nevertheless the illustration, both in words and in diagram, does validly represent something significant: that the specific processes of life and the specific processes of culture are drastically different.

115. THE CONTINUITY OF CULTURE

This unlimited receptivity and assimilativeness of culture make the totality of culture a continuum: the parts merge into each other without definite breaks. It is generally assumed that all life is also a continuum; but the continuity of life is traceable only by going back in its history and then reascending other branches. One moral of our diagram is precisely that culture is a far more closely and frequently interconnected continuum, in space and time as well as in developmental relations.

Perhaps this is why we have only the one word "culture," or its equivalent, "civilization," for its broadest as well as its narrowest exemplifications. We use the same term for the totality of human culture considered philosophically, and for the specific and distinctive culture of a little tribe of a hundred souls. This is because the English language, like other modern languages, has not yet evolved distinct terms for the big and the little, the general and the special aspects of culture. Nor have anthropologists and other social students managed to agree on any technical terms to help out the distinction—which is perhaps just as well, since sharper terms might help, but once the process of free coining starts, everyone prefers his own words and there are endless quarrels about them. But it is interesting to note how different this condition is from what we have in biology—even in popular biology. Everyone knows that life falls into two primary divisions, animals and plants, which can nearly always be distinguished without difficulty. The animals fall into phyla, of which the vertebrates are one,[1] among which the mammals constitute a class, and so on down the line to orders, families, genera, and species, like *Homo sapiens* or *Equus caballus;* and the species may have subspecies, and within these we get the near-repetitive individuals with only their individual or personal peculiarities. To all these different ranks of manifestation of life we have scarcely a counterpart in the terminology for culture. Such distinctions as are made are expressed in terms of societies or areas, such as tribal versus national, or local, provincial, national, and continental; and even these concepts intergrade somewhat in actual practice, precisely because their cultures intergrade.

---

[1] Popularly speaking; technically, of course, the vertebrates are only the largest and most important subphylum of the chordates (§ 9).

Let us run down an example. It needs no proof that total human culture shows a number of well-marked varieties, such as contemporary Western or Occidental or Eur-American civilization; the East Asiatic, the Indian, and the Islamic civilizations; and a number of cultures that are possessed by smaller societies and are often labeled "primitive" or "savage." Within each of these, subvarieties are recognizable without difficulty, such as Chinese and Japanese within East Asiatic. From the point of view of the outsider, Japanese culture is still very similar to Chinese culture, because so much of it has been derived from the Chinese or through the Chinese. Yet recent Japanese culture contained a native cult religion, Shinto, that was without counterpart in China; but Japan lacked any Taoist establishment. It provided for a ruler who was also a god— an institution lacking in Chinese culture; but it never accepted the women's foot-binding or men's queues which so long characterized the latter. And so on. Deviations of a roughly similar degree separate the main areas or nations within Occidental civilization: Italian from German, German from French, French from British, American from British, in ways that are familiar. Somewhat lesser are the differentiations we generally call regional: as of Bavaria within Germany, the Midi in France, Scotland in Great Britain. To the foreigner, these regional peculiarities may be a bit elusive, but a native is likely to be oriented about them. He will know roughly how New England and the South or the Middle West diverge in denominational and party affiliation, in degree of industrialization or agrarianism, in manners, temperament, and dialect. A step lower, and we come to what is usually called provincial distinctiveness, as of Normandy from Brittany. To this there might correspond the differentiation between North and South Carolina. Beyond this, there is the cantonal or local—Swiss Geneva being Calvinist, watchmaking, and international-minded; but Swiss Schwyz, Catholic, agricultural, home-centered. It was on this level that until recently peasant costumes and folk dances varied from valley to valley, or even from village to village, in much of Europe. At present in Europe, and almost from the first in historically shallow-rooted America and Australia, differences of the scope of these cantonal cultures are more likely to be expressed between economic classes or professions than locally; as between, say, doctors, barbers, printers, railroad men, and ministers, rather than between counties. There is no doubt that, quite apart from their vocational skills, the average culture of these professional groups differs slightly in dress, manners, standards, tastes, knowledge, habits, and amusements. We might call them professional subcultures or sub-subcultures.

This example shows how the same term is actually applied to the important cultures of great societies spread over large areas and to their more transient local or divisional phases. There even seems to be a degree of good reason for applying the same term. Occidental civilization no doubt represents something more generic and more important than the subculture of Midwestern clergymen. But it cannot possibly be defined as rigorously as the latter, because it is itself only a composite, a common denominator, of innumerable such phases, which have the greater definiteness. That is to say, it is the subcultures of clerical, sporting, transportational, and other such groups, and the Southern, New England, Midwest, Pacific-coast variants of these, which possess the sharper characterization, as against which total "American" culture is a slightly blurred composite or average. On the other hand, these local and divisional phases die out, merge, or get absorbed, like the cantonal cultures characterized by costume and dance. They are being obliterated by the spread of communications, by the rise of syndicated newspapers, by radio and films, and by ready-made-clothing factories. While the larger cultures are therefore less easily definable in terms of precise combinations of the traits characterizing them, they tend to be more durable in their main aggregations. There is thus a continuous transition from the greater to the minutest manifestations of cultures, with corresponding variation from more permanence to more precision; but all of them are significant.

Similarly, where sessile primitive populations live in small groups, it has been found that their local cultures vary almost exactly in proportion to distance. Thus the Pomo Indians of California lived in independent groups or tribelets of perhaps two hundred, each owning a tract of land and a main settlement. These settlements averaged possibly ten miles apart. A careful estimate, based on count of culture traits found present and absent, has shown that adjacent communities shared about 95 per cent of their culture, and that each was likely to have evolved perhaps 1 per cent of innovations or specific originalities. The other 4 per cent of their cultures consisted of a border zone of traits known to both communities but used by one only, or practiced by one for the other. In this cultural transition there might fall a ritual performed only by tribelet A but attended by B; a fishing harpoon known to all communities in the area and used by B but not used by A because the streams in A's territory were too small for fish of harpoonable size; and so on. Tribelet C—say twenty miles from A, beyond B—would differ from A more than B differed from A, but by the same ratio; D still more; and so on; the process continuing in all directions until perhaps a mountain range or an uninhabited tract, a radical change of speech, or some not too ancient movement of people or other accident of history, produced a slightly greater jump in the continuity. Where the situation of the tribelets or communities was linear, as along the coast from California to Alaska, the gradualness of the change is particularly striking, and renders it quite difficult to decide, except on the basis of speech, where one culture type ended and another began. Surprisingly, it seems to have made little difference whether adjacent communities were prevailingly friendly or hostile. All this seems very much like the locally variant forms of culture in Europe, especially rural Europe, of only a century or two ago.

A moment's reflection will show that a well-known historical phenomenon, the continuity of history, parallels in time this continuity of culture in space.

The fall of Rome did not mean that a former culture was completely obliterated in A.D. 476, or that a new kind of history first began then; it is just a convenient landmark. Culture in Western Europe, even in the city of Rome itself, almost certainly changed less in the decade enclosing 476—say from 470 to 480—than in the two decades before or the two after—say from 450 to 470, and from 480 to 500. At any rate historians would say that this is a fair example of normal historical change. The same thing is involved in what we have already seen in regard to cultural changeability (§ 113): while cultures practically cannot stand wholly still and do always alter, their prevailing behavior is one of inclination toward dominant stability, so that their normal change is gradual.

It is just that we are more familiar with the principle of continuity in historical time than we are with that in geographic space. Country L is red on the map, country M blue. Their speech, at least the standard or official language, changes abruptly at the frontier. The inhabitants pay taxes, in different currencies, to a nominal King directed by a prime minister in one capital, to a republican President in the other. The two states are sometimes at war, and in between times erect tariff barriers and require passports. The whole setup is calculated to emphasize the thoroughness of the break at a political frontier. Contemporary governments usually do their best to emphasize it; national prejudices often reinforce it; and finally the colors on the maps rub in an equally false visual image of it. There is never as great a uniformity within a national frontier as is aimed at or pretended, nor as deep a change across it.

The upshot of all of which is that human culture is a continuum or continuity, but a continuity gradually changing, and changing equally as it is followed through space and through time. We recognize, and for convenience label, culture periods like the Periclean age, the Renaissance, the Enlightenment or the Rococo in Europe, the Colonial period in America. We recognize also culture areas, such as the Occident, the Far East, India, the Nearer or Mohammedan East. Ethnologists recognize a good many more for illiterate native peoples outside the scope of documentary history; such as the Southwest of the United States, the United States Plains, the Arctic coast of America (again included in a larger Circumpolar Zone), Andean South America, western Polynesia, Congo-West African coast. An accidental difference is that culture periods are often named after something cultural that happened within them, such as reformation, enlightenment, exploration, colonization, increase of ignorance and rudeness; whereas culture areas are mostly named geographically. Nevertheless, they also really denote a particular culture rather than its mere geographical frame. "Southwestern" culture primarily refers to peaceful, maize-farming, heavily ritualistic Indians living in storied stone communal houses, only incidentally to the area this type of culture covered in New Mexico and Arizona.

Context alone, then, decides whether the word "culture" refers to *a* culture, a particular larger form or manifestation of it, such as Southwest Indian or

Korean; or to a subdivision thereof, such as Zuni; or to all culture seen as a whole, as a generalization, as when we say that culture is carried by society, or that it tends to change gradually.

116. FOLKWAYS AND THE RELATIVITY OF MORALS

In the eighteenth century of the "Enlightenment" in Europe it began to be widely recognized that the variety of national and tribal customs the world over was not merely a lot of strange oddities, but had certain significances. If Huron "savages" took their family line from their mothers, and if "Esquimaux" felt it their duty to dispatch their aged parents, this might well have some bearing on original man, as contrasted with members of the highly "polished" societies of western Europe. This original or "natural" man proved to be an effective club with which to pound contemporary civilization for its departure or corruption from an imagined condition of primeval purity. The motivation was variously anticlerical, antireligious, nostalgically daydreaming, or idealistically imaginative.

The nineteenth century came to adhere more and more passionately to the idea of progress. This idea forbade any looking backward and up to the "noble savage," but it was favorable to attitudes of relativity, instead of fixity or a perfection already achieved. There was accordingly a growing realization among intellectuals, during the latter part of that century, of what came to be called the relativity of morals. The Eskimo custom which obligated killing off one's old father was part of an ethical code as genuine as ours. If, in reverse of our way, the Jew put on his hat and the Moslem took off his shoes on entering a house of worship, that did not prove them "wrong," but did prove that there were many and even opposite ways of showing respect. The diversity in fact suggested that probably there was no absolute right or wrong in such matters: it was clear that the Arab and the Jew were as convinced as the Christian that they were doing right by doing the opposite from him.

Moreover, as soon as people were opposed, pressed, or cross-questioned on customs of this sort, they manifested resentment: it was evident that they held to their rules of conduct with emotion. When asked as to the reason for the observance, they either had none beyond the allegation that that was the way it had always been done (which belief could often be proved erroneous); or they gave a mythological justification that was obvious fantasy. All in all, comparative studies not only revealed great diversity, but showed that moral codes were essentially mere group habits or customs. They were nonrational, though often falsely rationalized; and they were emotionally charged. Moreover, the customs were "blind": those who followed them might be unconscious of them until the customs suffered infraction; and the followers were usually unconscious of any larger system of principles uniting the customs, or of partial contradictions of logic between customs.

The general effect of these nineteenth-century recognitions of course was in favor of tolerance and in diminution of ethnocentrism—that tendency to assume the universe as pivoted around one's particular people and to see one's in-group as always right and all out-groups as wrong wherever they differ. The realization that every culture is more or less right in its ways when judged in terms of its own premises, and that no culture is provably more right than others in the abstract, was achieved by a much wider circle of minds than the scattering anthropologists of the later nineteenth century. But anthropologists, being in most continuous contact with a wide series of highly divergent cultures, were perhaps most consistently impressed, and they came to take the principle for granted as underlying their work.

The most eloquent exposition in English of the point of view is Sumner's *Folkways* of 1906. A somewhat heterodox sociologist and economist freely using ethnographic and historical data, Sumner wrote brilliantly and exemplified vividly and abundantly. To him, folkways are ways of the folk, of the unsophisticated, unanalytic mass of mankind. They are, in short, customs, held to with much momentum but with incomplete rationality; and crossing them may cause a flare-up of fear or anger. They grow unconsciously; they are not creations of purpose; but they are basic societal forces. Mores,[2] Latin for customs and the origin of our word "morals," is a somewhat more special concept that Sumner helped to establish in nontechnical English usage. Mores are folkways which include a belief that they are desirable for social welfare and which people insist that their fellows conform to, though the mores are not derived from politically constituted authority. They are not laws, though they may produce laws, just as they result in taboos. "Folkways whose ethical sanctions have risen into consciousness" might be a fair definition of mores.

Similar ideas as to the nonrational and unconscious elements in culture were widely diffused throughout the field of later nineteenth-century social thought and studies. Marx, for instance, was certainly convinced that he knew the right understanding of past history as well as the solution of the problems of the future. Yet his economic determinism is tempered by considerable realization of the unconsciousness of social forces. He holds that it is not consciousness or purpose but methods of material production which determine the social, political, and spiritual processes of life—in other words, the noneconomic culture; and then, in turn, this socio-politico-spiritual culture "determines" or produces consciousness or recognition of itself.

Psychology has arrived at much the same basic concepts, largely by a route of its own—a route of reaction in some ways. Formally, psychology began as a branch of philosophy after this had become preoccupied with the problem of how we know things and what knowledge is valid. The early psychology was introspective, self-conscious, and rational. As it drifted, in the later nineteenth

[2] The little-used singular is mos.

century, from philosophical and deductive affiliations into inductive and exploratory aims, it worked on the one hand into objective experiment and test; on the
other, into the fields of the nonrational, the emotions and the subconscious,
where direct introspection pretty much breaks down. Psychoanalysis is one
special manifestation of this general psychological trend. The realm of the nonrational is also the realm of custom and morals, analytically viewed; and cultural, social, and psychological thinking have more and more approached and
reinforced one another. The element of relativity, of a new culture making a
new environment for the individual, came into psychology latest, because there
was nothing in the antecedents of psychology to suggest that differences of culture had much significance. Introspection in its nature emphasizes the ego and
underemphasizes environment, social or other. Also, the philosophy in which
psychology had its root was so completely concerned with universals and constants that it gave little notice to relativities and differences. Recent decades however have seen a thorough swing-over of psychology; and while as a science
directed at the individual it must operate quite differently from anthropology,
whose central concern is the superindividual aspect called culture, the two approaches now make essentially the same basic assumptions as to the relations of
individual and culture. They may therefore be said to be attacking the same set
of problems each from its own side—each in its own proper way, but with co-
operative understanding.

117. CULTURE AND SOCIETY

Cultures are products of human societies operating under the influence of
cultures handed down to them from earlier societies. This description illustrates
the close relation of culture and society: they are counterparts, like the two faces
of a sheet of paper. To each distinctive culture there corresponds, necessarily and
automatically, a particular society: to Hottentot culture, the Hottentot nationality, to Chinese civilization, the Chinese people. It is rather futile to discuss
which of the two phases or aspects is primary. It is obvious that if there were
no people and therefore no societies, there could be no cultures. But equally, if
there were no cultures, humanity would be merely another species of brute
animals. We should in fact in that event probably not even be organized in
tight societies like the ants, bees, and termites, because of lack of the highly
specific instinctual faculties of these animals, and of their altruistic devotion
to the hive.

Occasionally someone or other still attempts to assert that culture is secondary to society and therefore relatively negligible; or that within culture the
domain of social relations is primary over the fields of economics, technology,
knowledge, and belief. We have already seen (§ 6) that the first of these
opinions is arbitrary. The second is equally so. It is true that social structure of
some sort cannot be dispensed with in any culture. But neither can a sub-

sistence economy be dispensed with. And it is clear that the threats as well as the final victories of nations and cultures in the two World Wars depended on their technological capacities, which in turn are parts of their bodies of knowledge. And as to beliefs—ideologies and standards—how can these be relegated to a humble secondary place when they permeate and express all of human living? It is fair enough to select one aspect of this human living as a personal interest or for special study; but it is unwarranted to insist on its superior importance.

As a matter of fact, culture and society are so interwoven as actual phenomena that they are often quite difficult to disentangle. An upper class is certainly a significant feature of the structure of any society in which it occurs. Yet it is also a feature of the culture—an overt feature if the aristocracy has privileges in its own name; an implicit but perhaps no less important trait if the de-facto class is unavowed. There is a social and there is a cultural aspect to a situation like this, undoubtedly; but the phenomena actually constitute but a single cluster or nexus of facts.

When the philosopher Comte, "the father of sociology," coined its name more than a century ago, he appeared to be emphasizing the function of society. But as soon as he classified societies according to the "stage" they had attained, he rated them as mythological, metaphysical, and positive—in other words, according to their beliefs or type of thought; which is certainly first of all a cultural criterion, and not a societal one.

Conversely, it is impossible to give an adequate picture of any culture without including an account of its social structure, which almost inevitably ramifies into economics, government, law, religion, art—in fact touches almost every department of the culture.

It is customary to speak of social solidarity but cultural integration. The two are related, but not quite the same thing. A society can lack solidarity yet retain a fairly integrated culture. France during the Great Revolution is an example. England is socially a more class-conscious and class-observing country than the United States, but most non-Anglo-Saxons would probably agree that its culture is somewhat more stable and better-integrated. American culture is perhaps less differentiated, but the British differentiations seem more tied together and adjusted, probably because England has had longer to shake itself down.

Nevertheless, social solidarity and cultural integration tend to go together; and there is nothing against turning the terminology around, and speaking of social integration or even cultural solidarity.

It is obvious that each class in a society will possess a slightly different phase of the same culture, just as each regional section or district will have one (§ 115). The speech may differ a little, manners and dress are even more likely to, incomes and occupations almost inevitably will. Mediaeval Europe and East Asia had sumptuary laws to enforce class distinctions of dress. We do not usually consider class cultures as actual cultures, because they are parts of "one society" and this tends to correspond in modern life with the larger political unit of the nation, and it is to this that we are wont to consider a type of civilization as attaching. But if there is any need for it, it is just as legitimate intellectually to speak of "lower-middle-class English culture" as of French culture: the one is part of all-class English culture and shades off into it; the other, of western-European culture. For that matter, a class has as much right to be considered "a society," at any rate within one locality, as has the total population of a country. It is more homogeneous, can function more easily as a unit, may or may not have more solidarity. But it is also a lesser thing, and normally of less significance. In short, what has already been said about the range of inclusiveness of the word "culture," of its being determined by the context, holds equally for society.

In the United States, classes theoretically differ less than in most Occidental national societies. People do differ in income, but that is not supposed to put them into separate classes. In part this condition is actual, having been initiated by the newness of the country and the once nearly equal opportunities of start for everyone. But in part it is an unreal condition: social classes exist in America, yet our basic national ideology disapproves of them. Hence we disavow them as much as we can, or fail to be frank in admitting their existence. Our formal institutions have certainly long been geared against class segregation: for instance, the franchise and the public school—state-provided education for all. As if in conformity with the institutions and the ideals, a rather unusual degree of outward class uniformity has been achieved in America. This means relative cultural uniformity between the classes, or relatively similar participation of all strata and occupations in the benefits and pleasures held out by the culture. Owning cars, eating steaks, seeing films, and reading the funnies are more widely shared than in other countries, except perhaps New Zealand and Australia. Actually, the American standard of living certainly has a lot to do with this: the standard is high enough to enable more of the population to participate regularly in these desirables. Nevertheless, the range of American culture does get narrowed by the uniformizing, and the spread between our actual social classes is obscured by our approval of uniformity.

An interesting result of the American inclination to ignore or deny such social stratification as exists is that social anthropology took a particular turn in the United States under Warner. He set out to show that classes exist among us, how they are characterized, and how people operate in staying in their class or getting out of it into a higher or a lower one. The classification is basically in terms of the old common-knowledge recognition of upper, middle, and lower classes, more or less corresponding to the aristocracy, bourgeoisie, and proletariat of Marxian ideology. Following the suggestion given by the familiar British phrase "lower middle class" with its very definite connotations, each of the three levels is further subdivided, in the Warner scheme, into upper and lower. Individuals are put into the subclass to which the community assigns them: mostly, anyone in the community that knows a given individual agrees pretty well with everyone else as to his place in the scale. In an old but smallish New England town thinly disguised as "Yankee City," the percentage strength of the six classes from Upper Upper to Lower Lower is: 1.5, 1.5, 10, 28, 33, 25, with 1 per cent unknown. In this New England community the classes are also very well characterized culturally, by what clubs or organizations their members belong to, denominational affiliation, type of magazines read, and so forth; and social mobility—social climbing—is low and slow.

It remains to be seen how far this scheme is of general utility, even in other American situations. It is of course possible to slice any population into three or six levels; the question is: How far will these levels represent natural segregations, distinctions, existing de facto in the society and culture? It seems doubtful how far the seven million people of New York City could be easily allocated to the same six levels; or for that matter the members of a prosperous rural community in Iowa; and if it turned out that they could somehow be allocated, it is certain that the cultural criterion of each class would be very different. For instance, "Cottonville" in the Deep South proved no longer to contain any Upper Upper old aristocracy, though it was still definitely under the influence of the ideals and standards of that class. This recognition of a class existing outside the community would indicate that Cottonville was not a society complete in itself; that its culture is only part of a larger culture (§ 119). At the other end of the scale, its "poor whites" are set off as an essentially unitary Lower class; and everything in between them and the nonpresent aristocracy, from Lower Upper to Lower Middle, also seems remarkably homogeneous. All this is for Caucasians in Cottonville: the Negroes form a separate "caste"—really therefore a separate though interlocked society—with its own social classes. Of these the Upper, containing 5 per cent of the Negroes, is determined by sex morality, education, and professional occupation rather than by income.

"Plainville," as described by West, is an agricultural Missouri community with a small-town center. Just about half the population tends to describe itself as "good, self-respecting, average people," less frequently as "better," "middle class," "all right," or occasionally even as "upper class." This half would seem to correspond objectively more or less to Warner's Middle Class, probably Lower Middle. A few families among them are somewhat more prosperous and influential than the rest, and are occasionally referred to as "upper crust," "rich," or "think they're better." However, they do not differ in manners or in professed social claims, and West refrains from designating them as a distinct group. The whole upper half of Plainville lives overwhelmingly on prairie land, the lower half, on hill land. Of this lower half, somewhat more than the majority—say around 30 per cent of the total population—is described by the upper half as "good lower class." The remaining 20 per cent or so segregate in a ratio of about two to one respectively into "the lower element" and "people who live like animals"—these last not only poor but without pride, ignorant, and apparently often subnormal in intelligence. Both the groups above these two lowest groups are in full agreement as to which families are to be assigned there. The two lowest subgroups together would correspond roughly to Warner's Lower Lower; the 30 per cent above them, to his Upper Lower. Here we have another example of a community without an upper class within itself: if it has a top, that exists elsewhere, in the larger national society. In other words, the community is not self-sufficient, nor is the culture wholly intelligible in terms of community structure as such. This condition is probably true in some degree even of fairly large communities, but is increasingly conspicuous as their size is smaller.

Plainville also agrees with our previous American examples in that the bottom stratum is less numerous than those above it. The social classes do not form a broad-based pyramid, as social theorists have often proclaimed or assumed—and as may have been true until recently in countries of mediaeval retardation like China, Czarist Russia, and parts of Latin America. The better diagrammatic representation of social stratification in the United States is evidently by the figure of a lozenge or diamond stood on end, as West employs it for Plainville.

Religion was still socially significant in Plainville as of 1941. Nonchurch people easily outnumbered any one sect, but the five denominations together had perhaps twice as many adherents as there were nonchurch people. These denominations would probably have been somewhat different in the next town, but in Plainville they happened to be, in order of their strength: Baptist, next Holiness, then Christian and Methodist about even, and Dunkard last. The distribution in terms of social rank is however quite uneven. Membership in the Holiness Church is a full 95 per cent Lower Class. Dunkards are about half and half, and Baptist somewhat more Middle. Neither of these sects includes persons from the very apex of the local social structure; but Christians and Methodists do. Both these denominations, and especially the Christian, also penetrate only very slightly into the lower half of the society. By contrast, the nonchurch contingent reaches all the way up and down the Plainville social scale. It includes nearly half of the Middle Class apex, but a decreasing proportion as one descends the Middle ranks. Then it increases again toward the Middle border line and throughout the Lower half, finally taking in most of "the lower element" and nearly all of the "live-like-animals" segment. It is evident that the church denominations serve as symbols and instruments of social hierarchy, but that the distribution of the nonchurch population is due to other and less obvious factors.

In "Small Town," of less than 1000 souls in eastern New York, Hicks found only two classes, the upper one nearly twice as large as the lower. There is considerable difficulty in defining criteria of distinction between the classes, but no difficulty in assigning any resident to his class. Public opinion seems spontaneously unanimous on that. In fact, the largest factor in determining class affiliation in Small Town seems to be subjective admission of belonging. Some accept lower-class affiliation with a dour sense of frustration, but more do so with a sense of relief at being able to let themselves go instead of having to live up to responsibilities and standards.

Obviously there is no one class pattern that can be applied everywhere. Conversely, some class segregation can be expected in practically all societies except the smallest and poorest in culture. The most important effect of the Yankee City school of social anthropology is probably to prove to us that we Americans too are socially stratified in spite of wanting to believe that we are not. If the stratification proves to be locally variable, that only makes it so much the more interesting.

The trick of professing one thing and doing another is no doubt common to all societies. They vary chiefly in what they are inconsistent about. The habit of rationalization has been discussed (§ 81) and will be referred to again (§ 216). One need not feel too harsh about it. Professions after all mean standards and ideals; and it may be better for societies to have standards and fall short of them than not to have them. Obviously, the important thing intellectually is to recognize whatever discrepancy there is, instead of covering up to produce a sensitive blind spot.

118. INFLUENCE OF SIZE OF SOCIETY

It has long been recognized that the size of a society can be expected to exert certain effects on its culture. This influence appears to be most marked in the periods when higher civilizations first take shape. While reasoning on this matter is somewhat a priori, the drift of history and archaeology confirms it.

Assume a given population in a given area, but divided into a hundred tribes, each owning a territory yielding it subsistence, each independent, each jealous and suspicious of its neighbors. With a million people in the area, the tribes would average 10,000 souls. There might be a council or a chief or a kinglet to govern each of these tribes. There might be in each tribe some sort of a central settlement or market or town, but nothing like a real city, nor any serious accumulation of wealth. Most of the tribal members would be scattered over the land getting their subsistence. As in our wholly rural sections until quite lately, every man would be something of a jack-of-all-trades, able to farm, clear, build, fell, repair, or fight; his women would know how to cook, spin, weave, sew, milk, and thresh, or the equivalents of these in the local form of culture. There would be little need for writing or records, hence limited learning. Arts would most likely be home crafts. The priest and the doctor might function as such mainly in their spare time after making a living; a smith or two perhaps would work full time and professionally—if iron and tools were abundant enough to keep him busy. In short, the smallness of the social group would tend to keep it undifferentiated in its activities, and therefore culturally undeveloped.

Now let our hundred little tribes be united into one society acknowledging its unity—whether by voluntary conglomeration or by the conquests of one leader. The hundred councils or chiefs are replaced by a central government. The seat of this would tend to become a city; its house, the largest in the country, would now be a palace of sorts; its shrine, a national temple. To tend the shrine there might follow full-time priests, who would leave their offices to their descendants or to trained successors. Revenues and trade would flow into the capital; craftsmen could now expect steady custom and could become skilled. The ruler's resources and inclination toward show might lead to patronage which in turn would encourage the arts; the lifelong priests might pile up observations leading to the devising of a regulated calendar. All in all, the mere size of the society, now a hundredfold greater and with its parts in closer intercommunication than before—at least toward its center—would trend toward professional differentiation, accumulation of skills, new inventions, and an upsurge of cultural content.

To a greater or less degree this is what appears actually to have happened in ancient Egypt and Mesopotamia, China and Japan, Mexico and Peru, and again, with intensification, in Western civilization since 1650. The period was by or before 3000 B.C. in Egypt and Mesopotamia (§ 286); perhaps a thousand years later in China (§ 299); during the Christian era in the other countries. In each case there was more political unity than there had previously been, rulers of greater authority and sometimes with attribution of divinity, the beginnings of cities, development of metallurgical and other arts, and usually the formulation or the introduction of systems of writing and calendars. Any one of these advances tended to bring advancement in others. For instance, city life meant that there were classes no longer working the soil themselves: rulers, or craftsmen, or merchants, or priests. Wealth could accumulate; and temples or palaces called for new architectural endeavors. Similarly, writing opened a variety of new avenues: bookkeeping for taxes, history on behalf of the reigning dynasty, more exactly transmitted rituals, records for the calendar-framers. The entire complex process of forward movement may have been actually initiated by any one of its interwoven components, for all we know—by urbanization, or by metallurgy, writing, the divinity ascribed to rulers, or by some other factor. But the distinctive accompaniment in any one of these cases was the political unification.

That meant there was a much larger society, which could now diversify into a variety of classes and professions instead of being broken up quantitatively into a series of nearly uniform tribal units. And of course a society diversified qualitatively means a richer culture instead of a repetitively narrow one.

This summary of what actually happened in the protohistoric period in several parts of the world should not be construed as a universal "must." The successful development of Greek culture in a period of autonomous tiny city-states is enough to show that. Emphatically, the richness of civilizations cannot be measured in the abstract by the size of their societies. All that can be maintained is that, other things being equal, an integrated society large enough to be socially diversified has a better chance to produce a richly diversified culture than an equally large population broken up into many small units each with less diversification. This seems especially true at a certain level or stage; namely, after agriculture has made concentration of numbers possible, and when tribal, oral, folk culture is about to begin to convert into urban and literate culture. The Greek states remained minute in the period of their cultural efflorescence; but they were urban, and they had recently become literate.

Also, it is possible for a society to attain new peaks in its culture while many of its members are worse off than before through not sharing in the new attainments. This is a price that tends to be paid for the gains of specialization; and it can become fatal. This counterpart is discussed below under Participation in § 124.

119. SUBCULTURES AND PART-CULTURES

We have seen how each class in a society exhibits a more or less distinct phase, a subculture, of the total culture carried by the society; just as geographical segments of the society manifest regional aspects of the culture. This principle extends farther: to age levels and the sexes. Men do not practice the specific habits of the women in their culture, and vice versa. And though both sexes are generically oriented about these habits—they always know that certain peculiarly feminine (or masculine) activities exist—they may be so hazily informed about them that they could not adequately practice them or transmit them in their entirety if they would. At the same time these sex phases are never felt as constituting more than a side or an aspect of the culture—nor, indeed, do they constitute more. A unisexual society could no more exist among human beings than could a unisexual race; and neither are there unisexual cultures. The feminine component is always a complement of the masculine: the culture is not felt as complete, and is not complete, without both components. The same things holds, incidentally, for the class phases, and often for the regional phases, of well-integrated cultures. Scavengers and bankers will be recognized in such cultures as quite properly following diverse strains of life and making diverse contributions, but their coherence within the body politic of culture and society is felt to outweigh the separateness. They are both organs within the same body, like the patricians and the plebeians in the old Roman fable about the stomach and the limbs.

The cultural differences between age levels within a society follow a somewhat different pattern. The ages are inevitably continuous and overlapping, as sexes and many classes are not. Culture phases associated with age may be assumed to correspond to changes taking place in the culture, rather than to reflect chronic or static lines of segregation like those between social classes. Individuals above fifty will largely be trying to practice and maintain their established habits and status, and therewith a phase of culture some of which is just beginning to pass; those under thirty will be interested in the phase that is trying to arrive.

It is now well recognized that in contemporary civilization adolescents in the larger sense—the individuals between dependent childhood and full maturity with social responsibility—learn more about many things from age mates or near-age mates than from their elders. At any rate, they learn more willingly, often eagerly, from age mates, and are more conditioned socially by them. As for the effect of this fact on culture, that is an intriguing and little-explored problem. However, it seems that the constant change which is normal in every culture is chiefly initiated not by its adolescents, but by its mature individuals, especially by the younger half of these mature individuals.

What then do adolescents teach each other? It appears to be little in the way of substantial cultural content. This substantial content, if well established in the culture, would come of itself from the parental generation; if new, from the younger or more progressive section of the adult population as a whole. What adolescents impart to one another seems chiefly to be accepted cultural content stylistically modified as to its manner or form. This means fashions, mannerisms, ways of speaking, sitting, dancing, or reacting, and the like: special brands of slang, for instance, or of slouches and other postures; modifications of existing traits, in short, rather than brand-new elements of culture. The subadult age class goes in for certain choices among existing types of clothes, such as low flat shoes and sweaters for coeds, or even only a certain way of pushing the sleeves back; they do not ordinarily invent a new garment. This example seems typical of adolescent culture. Its quality is a special twist given to the standard culture; a conscious departure from some elements of it, or a sort of deliberately distorted reflection. Ordinarily there is no real revolt, no seeking a reform, but a basic conformity with the existing order, accentuated by an assertion of age-class independence at points of no great moment. By the time full social maturity is entered, most of the twists are abandoned by each individual. The whole phenomenon may be compared to the slight wave or bulge of water that the bow of a moving ship keeps pushing just ahead of it.

It must also be remembered that this kind of adolescent-culture phase is specially characteristic of modern city life and the leisure of prolonged education. In cultures or classes where economic responsibility is assumed early, the more usual adolescent urge seems to be toward acquisition of adult status and privilege in normal form.

It also seems possible that in our contemporary society the urge of each adolescent generation to set itself off as an age class is an unconscious compensation for the relative lack of sharp demarcation of overt social levels.

A particular kind of class is caste. Castes are closed classes. Individual mobility from one into another class is forbidden by the larger society. Naturally, each caste reflects one particular facet of a larger culture. This is true even where, as in most of the United States, the basic doctrine of democratic equality sets limits to the functioning of caste. American Negro culture may aim at being an integration into white culture or a repetition of it, but actually it is a variant and not a duplication. In a country like India, differentiations are so intensive, and so firmly entrenched, that the more extreme castes might almost be accredited as following distinct cultures, so much do they differ—not only in occupation and rank, but in food, manners, internal laws, education, amusements, worship, and standards. Essentially it is the less extreme intervening castes, plus intercaste community of regional speech, which succeed in holding the top and bottom levels within the frame of one society and one culture in India.

India is almost perversely unique in the degree to which it is caste-ridden, and the American color situation carries a high-voltage charge of emotion, so it may be well to examine a case that does not involve either race or a wholesale caste system. Through much of North Africa and Arabia smiths form an in-marrying profession. They may be respected, despised, or feared, but are set apart. Among the camel-breeding Beduin of northern Arabia, such as the Ruwala, smiths and the Negro slaves form the only separate castes not marrying with the main population. The smiths alone know how to shoe horses, repair guns, and the like, and get paid for their work, with which income they purchase their food and living, instead of raising camels as do the rest of the Beduin. They are uninvolved in the touchy honor system, vendettas, and raids of their tribes. If by oversight a smith is pillaged, the smiths in the raiding group arrange for his property to be returned to him. On the other hand, though they do not fight, smiths receive what may be described as a small fixed percentage of the spoils taken in battle. It is evident that the social and prestige system as well as the occupational and economic activities of the smiths is wholly distinct from those of the main body of the Ruwala Beduin. Yet the two form parts of one society. The Ruwala would be paralyzed without their smiths, and the latter of course could not exist at all without the Ruwala.

120. NOMADIC, CASTE, AND PARASITIC CULTURES

Much the same sort of relation holds, on a larger scale, between the Beduin and the neighboring settled Arabs. The livelihood of the nomads is in their camels, whose milk is their main food, whose herds are their wealth and their only salable produce (§ 165). Each midsummer when the water holes of the steppe and the desert go dry, it is with their camels that they buy, in the settled country, all their clothing and black tents, their carpets, their weapons and iron pans, barley to feed their prized brood mares, and virtually all their own non-milk food—wheat, rice, dates, and coffee. The very poor may have to do without this bought food; but the reasonably prosperous consume close to a pound of it a day per capita. Meat is too valuable to eat, ordinarily; a butchered camel is so much capital eaten up. It is clear that without what they secure from the towns and traders of the farming country, the Beduin would have so one-sided a culture that they could not survive by it: no clothing, shelter, weapons, few utensils, limited diet. In one sense, accordingly, their own culture is no more than a half-culture. At least they can produce only half of it, and are dependent on the Hadhar, the "dwellers in brick," for the other half. Yet the Beduin are not a mere occupational subgroup, nor a caste like the smiths. They are a full-fledged society, or series of tribal societies, independent, autonomous, each owning territory, waging war.

To some extent, this condition of possessing a "half-culture" holds for most nomads. Their range is from Arabia westward across Africa through and south of the Sahara; and eastward through Iran, Soviet Turkestan, Chinese Turkestan and Tibet, North China and Mongolia, to Manchuria—the great transcontinental arid belt of Africa-Asia. With insignificant exceptions it is only in this belt that true pastoral nomads occur: peoples making their living wholly off their flocks without settling down to plant. Alongside them, however, in rainier tracts and oases or on irrigated land within the belt, there normally are farmers, and often towns or cities. These agricultural populations are frequently the more numerous, though the herders loom large on the map because they need and have more of the low-grade land. In some areas the herding people are politically dominant, like the Masai and Bahima and Banyankole in East Africa, and the Fulah in West Africa. Elsewhere, the settled people are more often on top, though it may be difficult, or not very worth while, for them to control the roamers in the steppe. Jenghis Khan was a pastoral nomad Mongol when he and his sons and grandsons in the 1200's conquered out from Central Asia as far as to include Russia and China. But by 1600 Mongolia was again dominated by China. Nomads in general feel free, are proud, and look down on the sedentary groups, though they are fewer, poorer, and envious of the latters' luxury and wealth. The roaming life in the desert largely colored early Arabic poetry; but Mohammed, who launched the Arabs and their culture to greatness, was a townsman and a trader. Lattimore has even advanced a theory that East Asiatic nomadism developed secondarily out of the mixed farming and stockbreeding of China when increase of population began to push this mixed method of livelihood northward and inland into marginal steppe and then into submarginal desert. After a certain point was reached, it proved more profitable to renounce planting altogether in favor of wide herd range and human mobility. This is suggested as having begun to happen on the North China frontier only shortly before the Christian era; whereupon the power of the Hiung-Nu arose as the first of a succession of transient pastoral-nomadic states of which the Mongol finally became the greatest. This interpretation still remains hypothetical; but it is interesting because it does recognize pure pastoralism as a specialty secondarily segregated out of a more balanced economy by accentuation of one part.

In passing, it may be mentioned that the view of a succession of stages of human-culture evolution from hunting to herding to farming is now considered a completely antiquated theory. It was a pseudo-philosophical guess aiming to supersede actual history, and there are masses of scholarly and scientific evidence to the contrary. In fact, the theory has been traced back in its germs to speculations made by the Sumerians of lower Mesopotamia five thousand years ago.

All in all, while it would be an exaggeration to say that all pastoral nomad cultures would perish if they tried to become wholly self-sufficient in isolation, yet it is clear that they are particularly one-sided and limited, and tend to stand in a relation of complement to the richer and more varied cultures of adjacent or interspersed sedentary societies. This is what is meant here by calling them half-cultures or part-cultures. They would not have been able to specialize to the same degree if they were wholly isolated and independent. They exist in some degree of cultural and social symbiosis.

Our cowboy world of Western fiction and films is much the same sort of thing on a fantasy level. On that level, attention is directed toward romance, and away from the fact that this appealing world of the Bar-X ranch would collapse, or at least squalidly deteriorate, if it were really cut off from the rest of the United States. Riding range in actual life is just one occupation of many in our economy, and in everything else the cowpuncher is a participant in American culture and only in that. If he lived in the pastoral belt of Africa-Asia, the cowpuncher would often be set apart from the nonpastoral population in race or speech or religion also, and perhaps he would be politically independent. But his complementary integration with the nonnomadic culture would remain fairly similar to the cowpuncher's with ours. It is in his social consciousness that the nomad is free, separate, and proud. His specific culture may be almost as largely a part of a greater culture as the facet cultures of classes or castes elsewhere are only such parts.

There are several other populations, ranging from castes to small races, to whom something like half-cultures might be attributed—and disputed.

There are the Jews, whose culture differs from that of coterritorial Gentiles primarily in religion and ritual practices. When this religion loses its hold, Jews come to approximate Gentiles very closely, and generally tend to merge socially, or at least are willing to lose their group identity. Where the culture of Jews is distinctive in nonreligious matters, as in their occupations, it is most often because they are confined to these through being shut out from other callings; or through having been shut out legally from them until so recently that enforced habits still persist. The degree to which Jews are separate in their bodily heredity has been discussed in § 68. It can be at best only a quite minor factor in their culture determination. Their speech too is usually that of the country in which they live. If it differs, it is through recency of immigration, as in New

York. Or it is because of enforced migration, as of the Spanish-speaking Jews of Salonika, or the corrupt German called Yiddish which the Jews of much of eastern Europe spoke because they were driven there from Germany. Compulsory ghetto segregation, as in Czarist Russia, has kept dialects like Yiddish alive through the centuries. Biblical Hebrew was a dead language to about the same degree as Latin until it was resuscitated as a living national speech by some hundreds of thousands of Zionists in Palestine; but whether with historical success, only the future can tell (§ 107, 181).

All in all, the Jews seem to constitute a social quasi-caste based originally and mainly on a religion that of course is voluntary, not enforced. Their social segregation is markedly stronger than their cultural distinctness, though the latter is not absolutely lacking.

The Gypsy situation is a little different. Fundamentally, the Gypsies are an endogamous caste. They originated in India; and they show definite evidence of that fact in their blood type (§ 72) and in the Romany speech of which they retain remnants in addition to the language of whatever country they inhabit. In religion they are more or less professing Christians; and they specialize in certain occupations like horse-trading and tinkering. But what sets them off from the rest of the population is not so much positive cultural peculiarities as the inclination toward an unrooted and vagrant life. Their distinctness lies above all in an attitude, or orientation, which leads them to select a certain group of activities in Western civilization and to discard most of the others. They want a horse or an automobile, but not a house; silver jewelry, but not a bank account; music, but no education; and so on. In many of their attitudes they are like hobos: both elect to follow one particular vein of the many that make up our culture—the vein or line of freedom, irresponsibility, and instability. But of course hobos have no separateness of race or speech, nor are they strictly a caste, because without women and families they lack hereditary continuity and are merely an association group constantly rerecruited by adversity or temperament. Gypsies evince definite cultural distinctness; only, as they neither constitute a full society nor possess a complete culture, they serve as another example of half-cultures. They certainly have an ethos (§ 125) all their own.

At the extreme edge of this concept, we have peoples like the Seri Indians or the Negritos, whose attitudes are in part like those of Gypsies. Here we have indubitably distinct and autonomous social groups, each with its specific culture. The Negritos are even markedly distinct in their miniature racial type (§ 64), though they speak the languages of their neighbors.[3] The mode of life of both peoples is unsettled, and, in line with that propensity, the culture of both may be described as kept simple. It contains nothing specific that is not known in the surrounding richer cultures. The specializations consist of makeshifts like the

---

[3] The Negritos of the Andaman Islands are the only ones who have no immediate neighbors and who do have a language of their own.

single shaft that the Seri use interchangeably as harpoon, mast, or raft-poler; or like the Negrito bow, which the non-Negrito Filipinos have discarded as useless to them. Historically at any rate, cultures such as these are parasitic. They have contributed little or nothing, so far as we can judge, to the stock of human culture, while they have taken from other cultures what they do possess, and that with heavy reduction. The Seri, so far back as we know them, have also been outrightly parasitic on other groups, so far as they could, by force, cajolery, or sufferance, much like Gypsies. On the contrary, the Negritos are sturdily independent; so that the cases are not quite parallel. Moreover, the historical dependence or parasitism of one culture on another is by no means the same thing as the social parasitism of one group on another. Nevertheless, if all non-Gypsies were suddenly blotted out of Europe and North America and those continents left wholly to the Gypsies, it is reasonable to believe that the culture of the Gypsies in a few generations would fairly resemble that of Seris or Negritos in orientation, and perhaps ultimately in simplicity of substance or content also.

This matter of partial cultures or half-cultures needs more defining and exploring. It is evident that the relations between the larger or "enclosing" cultures and the special smaller ones vary a great deal—as much so as the relations between "whole" societies and their castes or classes or regional segments. Unconsciously we tend to think in terms of large ethnic units, such as the French, whose geographic boundaries are within a single color block on the map, and whose society, nation, language, and culture pretty well coincide. Actually of course France includes not only "Frenchmen" but Gypsies, Jews, Bretons, Walloons, Basques, hobos, and apache criminals, each of which groups has its variant form of French civilization, just as French officials and French dirt farmers have. And of course French civilization itself is only one phase or form of Western culture. Also we tend to think of the units as static, whereas they are constantly flowing, changing, and influencing one another. If we knew better the history of peoples like Negritos, Seris, or even Gypsies, or if we kept more in mind the total composite history of peoples like the French and the Bretons, we would realize more clearly the continuity of the material of culture, and how its segregations are never complete. In their origin and their history even the greatest and richest cultures are only parts of the great nexus of human culture as a whole.

121. RURAL AND URBAN—FOLK AND SOPHISTICATE FACETS

It is customary to distinguish rural and urban components in modern populations. There are of course corresponding rural and urban facets or aspects in the culture of such societies. Moreover, whole societies and cultures can be classified into those predominantly rural or predominantly urban. India, China, and Czarist Russia will serve as examples of the one; England or Massachusetts of the other—or even Australia, recent as it is, with the majority of its inhabitants living in its capital cities. In this familiar form, the rural-urban distinction is well enough known to need no detailed analysis—except for one comment on a fundamental though obvious fact. The rural condition is the underlying one, logically and historically: there must be a country area producing more food than it consumes before other people can live in cities.

On the widest consideration, the rural-urban differentiation is a somewhat special and modern form of a more general distinction of societies and cultures into those which are more folklike and those which are more sophisticated or "civilized." This is not an either-or segregation. Rather we must conceive of a line or an axis along which societies and cultures, or the part-cultures of segments of societies, can be ranged from the one extreme or pole of greatest folklike or tribal backwardness to the opposite pole of greatest sophistication. The concept is of some importance because it gathers in and subsumes a series of diverse but related recognitions that have gradually become established in social science.

A characteristic folk culture or tribal culture belongs to a small, isolated, close-knit society, in which person-to-person relations are prevalent, kinship is a dominant factor, and organization, both societal and cultural, is therefore largely on a basis of kinship—sometimes including fictitious kinship, as in many clans and moieties. By contrast, political institutions are weakly developed: "primitive democracy" is the characteristic form; but this denotes only a maximum of equality coexisting with a minimum of authority or control. Such a way of doing works because of the strong integration within the small group involved. Everyone knows everyone else, and many of them are blood or affinal relatives.[4] It has long been noted that there seems to be a spontaneous upper limit of tribal size: probably around five thousand souls, in many areas less than that. When this limit is transcended, the society breaks into two, often painlessly. Where "tribes" of fifty or a hundred thousand or a million persons are spoken of, they are either organized into a supertribal state, or they are really no longer tribes, but nationalities. Nationalities possess a culture and a speech that they recognize as common in essentials, but they may constitute many societies. This means that, in the case of a nationality, ethnically and culturally we are dealing with a single people, but politically often with multiple independent societies, each one autonomous and owning its own distinct tract of land. Such would be populations like the Lolo, the Ifugao, the Maya, all of whom are sometimes inaccurately called "tribes" when they really are multiple-society nationalities of nearly uniform culture. The mere fact of the narrowness of range of their social integration holds them near the folk end of the polar axis.[5]

[4] Related to the folk-sophisticate polarity are the distinctions made by Durkheim between "organic" and "mechanical" solidarity, and by Tönnies between "community" and "society," as his *Gemeinschaft* and *Gesellschaft* are approximately translated.

[5] The subject of nationality is discussed also in § 80, 102, 180-81.

It is also the smallness of the maximal social unit which keeps folk populations homogeneous and uniform, with only slight division-of-labor specialization, beginnings of class divisions, or slender concentrations of residence in permanent towns. Folk societies are attached to their soil emotionally by ties of habit, and economically by experience. Consequently they belong to that group of societies which identify themselves with their locality, in contrast to the sophisticated city dwellers who float without roots but take pride in living in their era and day and are therefore constantly subject to the play of fashion (§ 121, 164, 253).

Finally, it is folk societies that are specially dominated in their culture and their behavior by the folkways discussed in § 116. Their moral and religious sense is therefore strong. They believe in the sacred things; their sense of right and wrong springs from unconscious roots of social feeling, and is therefore unreasoned, compulsive, and strong.

Folk cultures afford their individual members full participation in their functioning—they invite and encourage such participation; their functioning, however limited and inadequate, is therefore personalized and saturated. The relatively small range of their culture content, the close-knitness of the participation in it, the very limitation of scope, all make for a sharpness of patterns in the culture, which are well characterized, consistent, and interrelated. Narrowness, depth, and intensity are the qualities of folk cultures.

Maturely civilized societies are inevitably large. A population that has become great, whether by its own growth, by absorption, or by the welding together of originally independent groups, inevitably becomes depersonalized on the one hand, individualized on the other. The kin group, of lifelong close associates bound by affective ties, has lost its force, except for the immediate or biological family, and often partly even within that. In consequence, each individual's relations with others take on an impersonal character. There are now numerous such relations, but most of them are special, limited, shallow, without emotional implications. We do not know our milkman, who in fact probably represents a corporation none of whose members we have ever set eyes on. And as for the actual delivery driver, if we do now and then see him, it is to extend a greeting or a comment on the weather: we do not invite him to dinner or seriously exchange views on religion or social problems with him. If we have real business with him, such as ordering an extra quart, we usually make sure of it by leaving him a note in an empty bottle—about as impersonal and unemotional a method as there is. In fact, most writing and all printing are inevitably indirect, remote, and "denatured" as regards feeling, compared with face-to-face contact. Writing, then, greatly reinforces population size as a joint cause of the growing impersonalization of higher civilization. So do large-scale urbanization and mechanical industrialization. The four constitute a set of interdependent causes, and of intercorrelated effects as well.

At the same time, kin and associative groups, which were dominant under tribal culture, have lost most of their strength and influence, and the large total society being only remotely and mechanically interested in persons, the individual has become relatively free. He is free to try to develop as he wishes, free to choose his own contacts and to change them. There is nothing to hold him in the course of his forefathers, nor even in his own original course. Individuals therefore become highly differentiated—not indeed in their inner personality, which the immense society and great culture have difficulty in reaching intimately—but in their behavior, their actions. This differentiation corresponds to the differentiation of labor and profession. With it also there tends to go a certain instability. This shows in the fluctuating careers of individuals: they may live here today, there tomorrow, with ever new associates but perhaps never close friends. On the sociocultural side it shows in the fluctuations of fashion, not only of dress but of fads, novelties, amusements, and the fleeting popularity of persons as well as things (§ 164, 253). The influence of the total sociocultural mass on the individual is probably as great as in the small folk society; but it is indirect, remote, "mechanical," because it is impersonal, extensive instead of intensive, and directed toward time co-ordination rather than toward association based on spatial contiguity.

With this diluting and spreading of the fervid intensities of attachment, it is inevitable that religiosity, piety, regard for the sacred things, should tend to evaporate with civilization. Shrines become show places rather than spots of worship. Criticism and rationalism grow. As beliefs fade that have rested largely on the social dictation of a homogeneous small group, empirical and actual knowledge comes to seem more desirable, and accumulates. Faith in the supernatural and the magical gives way to faith in science. The culture and the life are secularized. Here again dilution of the affective social group into impersonality goes hand in hand with rationalization, secularization, and urbanization: each tends to produce the others and to be further produced by them.

It is evident that our present-day Western civilization is near one polar end—the most urbanized, lay, depersonalized, sophisticatedly civilized end—of an axis that can be traced through all societies and cultures. Basically this classification or ranging on a scale is perhaps social in character, concerned with size and integration of the group. It is however expressed also in culture, and apparently more emphatically so; namely, as secularization, ceaselessness of the swings of fashion, and cultural instability. Even the rural-urban and tribal-state distinctions deal with forms that are cultural as well as social. And finally, there is a psychological expression of the polarity, manifest in affectiveness, depersonalization of relations, and the like.

Of course, intergradations occur all along the axis. China, for instance, and India are markedly less sophisticate-urban-depersonalized than Western countries, but much more so than most tribal nationalities.

An intermediate place is occupied also by peasantry. Peasants are definitely rural—yet live in relation to market towns; they form a class segment of a larger population which usually contains also urban centers, sometimes metropolitan capitals. They constitute part-societies with part-cultures. They lack the isolation, the political autonomy, and the self-sufficiency of tribal populations; but their local units retain much of their old identity, integration, and attachment to soil and cults. Peasantries persisted in probably every European country alongside growing urbanization and industrialization all through the nineteenth century, and they had been modified but were by no means extinct when the crash of World War II overwhelmed the Continent. In Russia, four-fifths of the population in 1917 consisted of ex-serf peasants. New countries rapidly settled by large-scale immigration, such as the United States and Australia, leave small room for peasant conditions or attitudes. There is too little rooting in the soil, too little stability or knitting together by kinship, for local particularity as expressed in folk custom or peasant art to develop. However, a close approximation to a true peasantry did develop in those Latin American countries like Mexico, Guatemala, Peru, and Bolivia where the Spanish conquest froze the bulk of the native population resident on the land into a depressed class living under its own partial or folk culture. In later prehistory, after food production had become established, a number of societies exhibit rather conspicuous peasantlike qualities: the Neolithic Europeans, for instance, including the Swiss lake dwellers (§ 283); also the Indian, Greek, and other early Indo-Europeans (§ 305). These are all peoples who had become settled but, either from newness or from remoteness, had made little progress toward urbanization. The Near East may have gone through a similar phase on which we are less well informed because it happened two to three thousand years earlier. And there were some interesting national differences in this regard; as between Mesopotamia and Egypt, for instance. In these two lands amorphous folk cultures grew simultaneously into early civilizations, with writing, towns, political organization, metallic industry. But during the last millennium before Christ, Mesopotamia had become sophisticatedly civilized, with a conquered empire, great cities of metropolitan character like Babylon, and prosecution of true science; whereas Egypt had stood nearly still for a thousand years. This difference was perhaps partly due to the fact that the population of Egypt consisted overwhelmingly of a rural peasantry, capped by little else than a governing bureaucracy.

The question fairly arises whether the trend from the rural to the urban, from folk to sophisticate culture, involves the gradual extinction of religion and morality, as might seem inferable from the strength that the mores and beliefs in the *sacra* retain in localized folk cultures, but tend to lose in civilization. In short, can we project this tendency, so apparent at the present day, and perhaps most strongly so in Western civilization, forward into the future to a vanishing point? In line with such a trend is the fact that as time has gone on, states or empires have been growing larger; and that "universal" states and churches—

universal in the Toynbee sense of aiming at totality—are regular and expectable phases in the growth of major civilizations.

However, any prophecy resting on the extrapolation or projection of a trend assumes that the trend is constant. There is no proof that such constancy holds throughout for the change from folk culture to sophisticate civilization. We know of pieces of history that show the change; our own American contemporary history is impressively so oriented; and over the total range of human culture the net drift is perhaps to the same effect. But the trend is not universal and is not irreversible. For instance, following Alexander the Great's conquest and the fusion of mature Greek and mature western-Asiatic civilizations, there first occurred a conspicuous development of many of the symptoms that characterize modern life: withering of the closer social ties, along with decay of beliefs and piety, democratization, growth of population, cities and larger states, industrialization, marked accumulation of knowledge, general sophistication. This culture period is known as Hellenistic; in the early Roman Empire its character was both accentuated and spread to the western Mediterranean. However, from the beginning of the breakdown of the Roman Empire in the third century, the drift was reversed in most respects. The international state fell apart; the fragments had little intercommunication; loyalties became ethnic, often tribal; outlooks were parochial, at best provincial, instead of metropolitan. Cities shrank tremendously; the self-sufficient economic unit now was the rural *villa*. Knowledge and education decreased; religious convictions under Christianity were far firmer and more influential than they had been in late paganism. The outcome was the western-European "Dark Ages" of rural custom, ignorance, piety, and folkway dominance, from which our own civilization made its first step of gradual emergence when it attained to mediaevalism. In the East, Constantinople and in a measure Alexandria indeed remained great cities of wealth and sophistication for some centuries longer. But they finally fell before the expansion of Islamic society, whose culture must in some ways be regarded as recessive also; it certainly aimed at simplification.

There have presumably been other reversals in history. The overturn from the Indus Valley civilization to that of the Vedic Aryans certainly signified the partial triumph of rural folkway living (§ 105). And even primitives vary considerably in the strength of their piety and animistic beliefs (§ 250). It may therefore be fairly concluded that movement along the rural-urban, folk-sophisticate axis is not necessarily one-way or predestined.

It is of interest in this connection that Soviet doctrine aims at bringing about a condition closely resembling one of the polar extremes we are discussing. The program includes a single world state with only one class of citizens, speaking a single language; what remains of other idioms and of regional customs will be harmless nostalgic remembrances of the order of folk songs and dances (§ 182). Life will be fully industrialized, according to the Soviet program; it will be lived urbanly even on the farm. Knowledge and enlightenment will be universal; religion will be defunct, rationalism in full control, the individual a willing, depersonalized cog serving the ends of the universal community. It is really rather curious how closely the goal of Communism approximates an anticipatory projection or sensing from the drift of the last two or three centuries: it is like a Lindberghian "wave of the future."

Finally, the folk-sophisticate polarity, especially when it is viewed not so much as a scale but as a one-way drift, definitely overlaps with the emotionally tinged idea of "progress" that is discussed farther on in this chapter, in § 127-128.

122. INTEGRATION—INHERENT OR INDUCED

The double proposition can hardly be overaffirmed that most of what is in any one culture was produced outside of it, but that the highly composite product nevertheless is regularly felt as something coherent and integrated, and normally is accepted as "right." It is so accepted because the average individual is so thoroughly under the influence of his culture, has been so molded by it in growing up and adjusting to it, that even its incoherences and contradictions tend to be taken for granted as if they were logically sound and a-priori evident. It must be remembered also that any "average" individual knows little or nothing through convincing personal experience of other cultures, so that his own must appear to him as being natural and inevitable. He accepts his culture, his social inheritance, as he accepts the surrounding atmosphere he breathes, or as a fish accepts water. What is fifty years old in this culture and what is three thousand years old touch him alike and affect him alike. So do elements that the culture originated, and elements which were introduced into it. Thus it is no wonder that his immediate reaction to it is as to a homogeneous unit. It is only dissective analysis and knowledge of history that reveal the compositeness of any culture.

As regards the historical origin of its contents, accordingly, every civilization is what Lowie has called it: a "thing of shreds and patches," a "planless hodge-podge"; but it does not ordinarily seem so to the people living under it, nor does it function as such. Every culture is an accretion to a far greater degree than any living organism. It is the end product of a long series of events occurring mostly in other cultures, accidents from its own point of view, but ultimately of influence upon it. Plan or pattern there always is—and in some ways its pattern is the most important thing about any culture—see the whole next chapter: nevertheless, as regards origin, plan or pattern is secondary. The plan modifies the cultural material that flows in, sometimes rejects it, fits it all, native and foreign, into something that is not too discordant, something that the majority of the society can get along under tolerably and some of them successfully and pleasantly. It is patternings that produce the internal consistency. But it is important to recognize that cultures do not start with a pattern or predetermined plan and then fill it in. That is what inveterate reformers and dreamers of

Utopias do. Actual societies tend to evolve the plan of their cultures as the content of these grows. And the plan changes as introduced content changes, although traits of internal origin—innovations—are likely to develop in accord with the way the pattern-plan stands at the moment.

In short, cultures are constantly and automatically acquiring or reacquiring a sort of integration. But this is a very different thing from the organic integration that holds together, say, a grasshopper or a rabbit. This organic integration involves a pattern of finished animal that is essentially predetermined when two germ cells unite to start a new individual. Cultural integration—or for that matter human social integration—is invariably of a much looser sort. It is an accommodation of discrete parts, largely inflowing parts, into a more or less workable fit. It is not a growth of parts unfolding from a germ in accord with a pre-existing harmonious master plan. Such an unfolding has often been assumed, insinuated, or asserted by writers as diverse as Frazer, Spengler, and Malinowski. But it remains wholly undemonstrated, and history shows it to be at least partly untrue.

The point sometimes made, as by Radcliffe-Brown, that every society is confronted by the constant problem of how it is to preserve or maintain itself, seems a false analogy with the organic world, where the struggle for existence mostly is indeed keen. But when one society incorporates another, it does not ordinarily destroy it, except perhaps as a conceptually separate entity. Its members go on living under somewhat altered conditions; the frame of the society has been enlarged; whereas if a society splits, there merely are two instead of one. Culture we have seen to be even more plastic than societies in merging, partly merging, or dividing.

Moreover, while animals make every effort to maintain themselves, they are evidently not aware of a constant need of self-preservation; nor indeed are men, who are the most conscious of organisms. Food is necessary to life, and animals get hungry and set about satisfying their hunger, with pleasure if successful; but they do not feel it as an unremitting *problem* of self-preservation. That is rather the intellectual attitude of philosophers, or emotionally of neurotics. When it comes to societies and cultures, the problem of preservation seems even more philosophical and remote. The normal attitude of the normal man probably is that his society and culture were, are, and will be. If anything, he is likely to assume more perpetuity for them than they possess. And not without reason. Most cultures do continue for quite a while. Sooner or later they may be superseded, or altered out of recognition; but ordinarily there is no immediate prospect whatever of that.

In fact, what has impressed most observers is the power of persistence of cultures. They always change, but they change slowly—too gradually to suit the reformer. Every nation or tribe has its conservative party, whether it is so labeled or not. There is nothing mystical in this faculty of cultures to maintain themselves and to resist overrapid alteration. Any culture, even the lowly one of a small society, is a pretty big thing, a complex of thousands of items and activities, each interconnected with many others. It just is a large mass to dent, or roll along, or do away with. And this holds even more for the great civilizations of great nations. There is so much to them that it is almost a wonder that they alter as much as they do. Even pieces of them are enormous. Take the government of the State of Pennsylvania, or the Presbyterian Church, or the educational system of Switzerland, or the commerce of England, and think of all they comprise, plus all that they touch or interlock with in addition. How can they be destroyed quickly, except by rare world catastrophes or revolutions? Big things at rest have great inertia, and if in motion they have great momentum. Such seems the way to look at the enormous superindividual aggregations that we call our greater civilizations. They change; they are always changing; but at any given moment the expectation is that they will go on, mainly as they are, though never wholly so. To fail to realize this is to disregard the total trend of history.

123. MOLDING THE INDIVIDUAL

Through being born into a society, every individual is also born into a culture. This culture molds him, and he participates in it.

The degree to which every individual is molded by his culture is enormous. We do not ordinarily recognize the full strength of this shaping process, because it happens to everyone, it happens gradually, it is satisfying at least as often as it is painful, and usually there is no obvious alternative open anyway. Hence the molding is taken for granted and is accepted, like the culture itself—perhaps not quite unconsciously, but uncritically. The formal or deliberate part of the process we call education: education through schools, in religion, and in manners and morals primarily at home. These agencies convey the mores and some of the folkways (§ 116). But perhaps a larger fraction of the cultural tradition is acquired by each individual at his own initiative. He is left to "pick it up," to grow into it. In this class are his speech, bodily postures and gestures, mental and social attitudes, which he imitates from his elders or from near-age mates, and a thousand and one activities, such as putting on shoes, splitting fire-wood, or driving a car, which a child "learns," often without any formal instruction, because he has seen others do these things and wants to do them too.

How much of all that a person knows how to do, and does do, comes to him from outside, from the cultural environment that surrounds him, and how much from within, from his independent personality? The former is surely much the larger mass. That he speaks, say, English and not Chinese is the result of "where he is born" or raised; that is, of which language forms part of the culture in which he grows up. Similarly with his being a Christian instead of a Buddhist, casting his vote in November, observing Sunday, celebrating New Year on January 1 instead of in February, eating with a fork and not with chopsticks, and bread and butter in place of rice, tucking his shirt in and not out (in Kipling's day at least), saying hello to his parents instead of using honorifics, steering a tractor and not a lightly shod wooden plow, writing with letters instead of a thousand logograms, and so on endlessly. In fact, the mass of what any person receives from his culture is so great as to make it look at first glance as if he were nothing but an individual exemplar of his culture, a reduction of it abbreviated to the scope of what one personality can contain. All there remains of him that is not induced by his culture consists of two sets of things. First are his innate general human capacities, and second, his individual peculiarities.

The capacities—already discussed in § 30-35, 87-89, 103-105, and again in 241—merely ensure, just because they are generic, that our normal person has the faculty of learning to speak, to read, to operate tools, to practice a religion of some kind or other. What the kind of speech, tools, religion is depends absolutely on the culture, not on him. In other words, his birth as a normal man gives him certain potentialities, but his birth in a culture determines how these potentialities will be expressed and realized.

Individual peculiarities comprise such traits as speaking with a lisp or a drawl, having a bass or a tenor voice, worshiping piously or perfunctorily, being naturally tidy or hasty or bright or the opposite. These are individual variations from the average intelligence, energy, or temperament. They range all the way from genius to imbecility, from superexcitability to ultrasluggishness; but of course the great majority of individuals depart only slightly from the mean in any one trait. These "individualisms" or idiosyncrasies do have a physiological and hereditary basis, in the main. Yet in part their qualities too can be culturally induced, as when a drawl is a Southerner's or a cowboy's, or the tidiness and phlegm are those of Hollanders. In such instances it is the occasional Southerner who doesn't drawl, or drawls infernally, the Dutchman who is precipitate and disorderly, who represents the individual variation from the norm that is characteristic of the culture or the subculture of his society.

This brings us to a second class of features in which individuals differ: roughly, those areas which are alternatives within one's culture. Shall I be a farmer or a storekeeper or a dentist, go in for tennis or baseball or golf, join the Army or the Navy, be a Methodist or a Presbyterian or a Quaker? Here the culture leaves several choices more or less open to the individual members, though it is well to remember that each culture has a different array of choices. In unwesternized China, for instance, there would be no choice of dentistry or baseball or Navy, and the religious denominations available would be altered to Confucian, Buddhist, and Taoist. Even among ourselves, not all choices would be open to everyone everywhere: golf might be only a theoretical possibility to a farm laborer or a sheepshearer on the Great Plains. In fact in rigidly segregated India only a few of all occupations, worships, amusements, and foods known to Hindu civilization would be open to the members of any one caste.

In summary, heredity gives us at birth certain generic human faculties. How we shall use these, and therefore how we shall mainly live, the culture in which we are launched thereupon decides. But it leaves us, theoretically at least, certain choices between alternatives in its total scheme; and it leaves us also a degree of freedom of departure from its norms in personal mannerisms, innovations, and successes.

This enormous influence of culture in molding the individual has a bearing on psychology. This science is set up to study particular individuals in order to reach understanding of human beings in general; that is, of what might be called the abstracted human person. But since all individuals as they actually occur in life are patterned by culture, and their behavior is full of culture, the task of psychology is made difficult. This was not clear at first. But then psychologists began to realize how great was the effect on individuals of their happening to be exposed to different influences, as these exist within our civilization; how the children of articulate parents generally come to be above-average in verbal facility; how the children of unhappy or broken marriages are more likely than the average to be emotionally unstable in their adjustments to other persons; and so on. So "conditioning" came to be one of the slogans of modern psychology where innateness of behavior had been assumed before. Then, as psychologists gradually came to be culture-conscious also, the variety of cultures was seen to increase enormously the range of the conditioning people are subject to. The abstract man, or what the psychologist felt he could properly say about him, shrank in proportion. This is why there is such great difficulty, as we have seen (§ 86-90), in deciding how alike or different the heredity equipment of races or descent groups is. It is not that psychological tests are unsound. The tests are valid enough, within limits, within the culture for which they were constructed. They show at any rate how much culture an individual has absorbed in comparison with other individuals. They are less good at showing, per se, whether greater absorption is due to greater exposure or to greater inborn capacity. And the tests break down, or become dubious, when they are applied interculturally. Hence it is that we do not yet know how different the races are in their endowment, while we do know that cultures differ enormously in content and orientation. And of course individuals differ both in their heredity and in what their conditioning has made them.

124. PARTICIPATION

Besides differing in heredity and conditioning, individuals also differ in degree of participation in their culture. How large a share does a given person hold in the stock company of his society, and what dividends of satisfaction does it pay him? It is evident that the complex culture carried by a large society is just too big for one individual to take an active part in, in all its many departments. It is only the exceptionally gifted or favored member of a large society who can hope to operate successfully in a number of its more important activities. The run-of-the-mill man is likely to be equipped to follow only one or two occupations out of hundreds or thousands of existing ones, and to have a run-of-the-mill income, wife, home, a run-of-the-mill seat in the church or at the game, run-of-the-mill tastes, thoughts, and habits. With a little bad luck, he may even come out below-average in all or most of these things. In a culture full of books he may not read a newspaper; in a land of wealth he may be ragged and half-famished.

This is the counterpart, the seamy side, of what has already been discussed in § 118: that large societies make for division of labor and specialization of function, therefore for professional training, advances in the arts, and inventions or at least improvements in the ways of living. But as the total culture is thereby varied and enriched, it also becomes more difficult for each member of the society really to participate in most of its activities. He begins to be an onlooker at most of it, then a bystander, and may end up with indifference to the welfare of his society and the values of his culture. He falls back upon the immediate problems of his livelihood and the narrowing range of enjoyments still open to him, because he senses that his society and his culture have become indifferent to him. If the society and the culture retain a degree of integration, the lower classes may participate vicariously: in imagination, by symbols or through pageantry. The British lower classes participate thus in the life of the aristocracy, which is so much richer than theirs, and even more in the doings of the royal court. No doubt Egyptian peasant-serfs of five thousand years ago got some similar satisfactions out of what went on in the god-king's entourage at Memphis, or even when they contemplated his pyramid tomb over which they sweated for years in a labor draft. In fact, one of the uses or values of kings and costly courts is precisely to serve as symbols increasing the integration of large societies. But vicarious participation at best is partial, and it may be lacking. Wherever there exists a true urban proletariat, or where the mass of country people are outright serfs, a large part of the population is participating very incompletely in their culture and being denied many of its satisfactions. This in turn means that those who are most largely supporting the culture economically are getting the least of its rewards; and, reciprocally, that the values of the culture are being continued in their development by only a fraction of the society.

Most revolutions, successful and unsuccessful, seem to be preceded by such a condition of imperfect participation. Only we must remember that there is no absolute scale of measurement. A sufficient discrepancy in one country between actual participation and what is considered possible participation will bring on efforts at remedy; whereas elsewhere there may be even less participation by most of the society in most of the culture, but the ideal of participation being also low, the condition is endured fatalistically. Thus the French Revolution was precipitated not because the oppression and the nonparticipation of the lower classes were extreme: as a matter of fact, their situation was better than in some other European countries which did not revolt, and on the whole it had probably improved in the generation before 1789. But just because France was the home of enlightenment and considered itself the most highly civilized country in the world, the gap between top and bottom was felt keenly and engendered the revolution.

The Russian muzhik had probably achieved even less participation by the early twentieth century. Nor is it probable that Russia left to itself would have achieved a deep-going social revolution at one stroke. But conscious Westernization, initiated by Peter the Great two centuries before, finally brought in its train also the Marxian ideology, which was organized to operate by revolution on the gap of nonparticipation, and had as its ultimate aim the abolition of the gap. Marxism completely missed its own prediction of first succeeding in the most highly industrialized countries of Europe. It did succeed in a marginal area of low industrialization, because the standard of living and cultural participation of the population in Russia had remained unduly low for twentieth-century-conscious Europe—and for twentieth-century-Europe-conscious Russian intellectuals.

The contrast of all this of course is with primitive cultures. Here societal units are small; skills, differentiations, and privileges are limited; and participations are reasonably equal. No one is evicted for nonpayment of rent, or left on the sidewalk to watch the prosperous stream into the opera. The simpler cultures have simpler and smaller problems to meet. Much of the eighteenth-century admiration of the romantic and unspoiled savage, and our own occasional hankerings after South Sea island idylls, stem from a vague sense of this fact. To be sure, it is well to remember that if the Ifugao and the Yurok and other nonliterate people did not evict, they did enforce debt slavery; and that others practiced war enslavement, human sacrifice, and cannibalism. Yet the total range of activities remained small enough so that even a slave might participate in more of the culture than a serf elsewhere, or than a free outcaste in India. Larger and richer cultures just do have bigger and harder social problems to solve.

125. CONTENT AND FORM; ETHOS AND EIDOS: VALUES

It is worth while to examine briefly certain overlapping distinctions among several aspects of culture. They are: content and form of culture; eidos and ethos; and material and nonmaterial culture.

The content of a culture is the sum of the items of which it is composed: things present in it—whether present or lacking in other cultures. For instance, kingship, hereditary titles of nobility, a state church, stringent libel and divorce laws, driving left on the road, spelling labor and honor with a *u,* are several big or little items contained in British civilization but not in its close American counterpart. However, British and American culture share as content steam engines and railways, alphabetic writing, representative parliamentary government, dairy foods, and many other items that until recently were wholly lacking in, say, China. It is content like these items which tends to increase and accumulate in the aggregate cultures of mankind, and to a certain extent even in one culture, and thus to give the impression of progress taking place (§ 127), though the process may actually be one largely of quantitative enlargement.

Cultural form is harder to describe or illustrate. We might approximate it by saying it is what is left over when we subtract cultural content from culture. What is this remnant? It may be a rearrangement, a transfer of an item or a group of items to other departments of the culture, to another of its jurisdictions. Thus education can be in clerical or in lay hands; schools may be parochial or public, as we say in America, parish or board in Britain. The education given may be very similar. In its elementary stages it is bound to be practically identical: *C a t* will spell *cat* and $3 \times 3 = 9$ whether the school and the teacher be democratic, religious, communist, or fascist. Yet we all know that the tenor or purport and the outcome of the schooling will be different—different enough to fight for, often. This is not wholly an affair of totalitarian propaganda aiming to thrive by liquidating everything else. Such extreme propaganda began to be developed chiefly some years after World War I. Yet even before then it obviously mattered who controlled the schools. Besides content, such as reading and arithmetic, education inevitably imparts an ideology, a *system* of beliefs and sentiments and values, which if accepted is all-important for its influence on conduct. An ideology or a system might also be called a pattern or configuration; that is, a way of arranging things.

Theoretically, one might conceive of two cultures whose itemized content was identical, and which yet differed in the form or arrangement or system or pattern of this content. Actually, form and content are far too interwoven for just such a situation to arise; but the hypothetical example will help point out what is meant by cultural form. A system or configuration is always, in its nature, more than the mere sum of its parts; there is also the relation of the parts, their total interconnections, which add up to something additionally significant. This is well recognized in "Gestalt" or configurational psychology. The "form" of culture may therefore be regarded as the pattern of interrelations of the contents that constitute it.

Somewhat related to the foregoing are a contrasting pair of aspects that have been called the *ethos* and the *eidos* of culture. Greek *eidos,* from which we have "idol" as a derivative, denotes form or appearance or likeness. The eidos of a culture would therefore be its appearance, its phenomena, all that about it which can be described explicitly. This would primarily coincide with cultural content as just discussed. The Greek word *ēthos,* from which we have "ethics," denotes first of all disposition. With reference to a people, it means their ways or customs, corresponding nearly to the Latin *mores*. Like that term, it carries an implication of what is sanctioned and expected. Hence the connotation of right or rightness, on which we have centered in our derivative Christian use of the words "ethical" and "moral" in their everyday sense. However, when we speak of the ethos of a culture, we revert at least part-way to the original Greek meaning, and refer not so much to the specific ethics or moral code of the culture as to its total quality, to what would constitute disposition or character in an individual; to the system of ideals and values that dominate the culture and so tend to control the type of behavior of its members.

Thus, we might say that the ethos of Italian Renaissance culture was sensuous and passionate, but that of the northern-European Reformation, puritan and ascetic. Hindu civilization is not only otherworldly but mystical, rationalizing, and extravagant in its ethos; Chinese, this-worldly, prosily moralistic, and matter-of-fact. The Japanese ethos differs from the Chinese in putting more emphasis on action, precision of form, and neatness.

It will be evident from these examples that ethos deals with qualities that pervade the whole culture—like a flavor—as contrasted with the aggregate of separable constituents that make up its formal appearance and are the eidos. The ethos includes the direction in which a culture is oriented, the things it aims at, prizes and endorses, and more or less achieves. We are here getting into metaphors that personify culture as if it had a will and a purpose of its own. That is a fault of the language of our day. Scientific thinking has penetrated so recently into these fields that it has failed as yet to work out its own more exact expressions. When we say that a culture aims at, prizes, and achieves certain ends, that is a shorthand way of saying that most of the members of a society, through having been molded by its culture, aim at, prize, and help achieve those ends. The ends or things referred to, the qualities that differentiate one culture from another, are undoubtedly distinctive, are genuine attributes of phenomena of history and nature. The difference between Western, Indian, and Far Eastern civilizations obviously consists of more than a diversity of content as exemplified by items of the order of eating with forks, fingers, and chopsticks respectively. Beyond these concrete facts, there is a pervading difference of character and outlook in the three cultures. That is what is meant by ethos.

It is evident that the ethos of a culture is pretty close to what a philosopher or a historian might call its system of values. This somewhat technical term denotes something that physical and biological scientists are agreed they cannot properly deal with by their methods, and therefore ought, as scientists, to leave alone—though most of them admit that there are such things as values, moral or otherwise, and personally try to live up to them. Whatever "values" are, it is clear that they have some relation to culture. Cultures differ in their values; each one shapes, or at least colors, its own. Values in this technical or philosophical sense might be informally defined as those things—cultural products, standards, or ideas—which men living in societies prize and hold as having a high importance, for them, for their group and descendants, and in themselves, over and beyond their practical utility. Christianity is one of the great values of our society and culture; so are the works of Shakespeare, and our democratic institutions and liberty—even the Liberty Bell, as a visible and tangible symbol. In China, Confucius would represent a similar value. No one would deny that these values influence human conduct and constitute real phenomena and effective forces in the world of history, and therefore of nature. This is true even though these same values have not been measured, and are regarded by the physicist and biologist as beyond the scope of their sciences. For the present, let us carry in mind that values exist and that they are tied up with culture. We shall be coming back to them again.

126. MATERIAL AND NONMATERIAL CULTURE

A distinction often made between material and nonmaterial culture is mentioned here only as probably having no first-rank significance. The literal difference is of course obvious: physical objects as against institutions and ideas.[6] But do they stand for something basically different? Do they function with significant difference in culture? The answer seems No. What counts is not the physical ax or coat or wheat but the idea of them, the knowledge how to produce and use them, their place in life. It is this knowledge, concept, and function that get themselves handed down through the generations, or diffused into other cultures, while the objects themselves are quickly worn out or consumed. It is the ax itself that is effective in chopping, the idea of the ax that is effective in getting axes made and available for use. In fact we can almost conceive of the ax as an institution, as we can certainly speak of lumbering and wearing clothes and grain farming in a sense entirely parallel to the institutions of marriage or churchgoing.

The attempt to segregate material from nonmaterial traits of culture perhaps derives from a white-collar distinction unfortunately long made in Germany between Naturwissenschaften and Geisteswissenschaften: sciences dealing with nature and sciences dealing with the human spirit. The latter corresponded to what we call the humanities and the social sciences. But there is nothing gained by implying that since humanistic and social studies have to do with the "spirit" or "mind," whereas natural science deals with tangible objects, the latter is therefore of a different and lower order. Such a point of view smacks of old-fashioned theology with its contrasting of body and soul. Genuine science is characterized first of all by its method, only secondarily by subject matter, except that this must be in nature and must consist of phenomena. My having learned how to write

---

[6] Material culture and content of culture partly overlap, but are conceptually different. Objects of material culture are part of culture content; but a lot of culture content is not material; monogamy, for instance, or mother-in-law avoidance, or belief in ghosts.

or being a Christian are phenomena; and equally so are the alphabet and Christianity and ax-using; and so are axes and clothes and chairs; and they are all parts of culture. Accordingly we may forget about this distinction between material and nonmaterial culture, except as a literal difference that it is sometimes of practical convenience to observe.

127. THE IDEA OF PROGRESS

One of the most widely held preconceptions is that culture is progressive. "The progress of civilization" is a familiar phrase—almost a trite one. Simple or primitive peoples are labeled "unprogressive." The implied picture is of a continuous moving forward and onward. Popularly, evolution is almost synonymous with progress; and progress means advance to something better.

Actually, the idea of progress is itself a culture phenomenon of some interest. Strange as it may seem to us, most of humanity during most of its history was not imbued at all with the idea. An essentially static world, a nearly static mankind, were most likely to be taken for granted. If there was any notion of alteration, a deterioration from the golden age of the beginnings was as frequently believed in as an advance. A definite system of belief in progress began to acquire strength only in eighteenth-century Europe. Reinforced by the French Revolution, it became a sort of article of liberal faith in the nineteenth century. It entered into the philosophy of Comte and Spencer. The latter saw evolution as a manifestation of progress. Darwin, who propounded a mechanism by which organic change might be explained—a mechanism about which the man in the street is mostly still a bit hazy—was popularly acclaimed as having "proved evolution"—that is, progress. The Unitarian profession of faith is interesting in this connection: "I believe in the Fatherhood of God, the brotherhood of Man, the leadership of Jesus, salvation by character, the progress of mankind, onward and upward forever." There is a certain nobility about this sentiment of liberalism; but it is as indubitably a sentiment and a dogma, and not a scientific conclusion, as are the Apostles' Creed and the Thirty-nine Articles. Progress has largely taken the place of Jesus in this most denatured branch of Christianity. But the concept of progress is far from being limited to that. If a poll were taken, devout Methodists and other Trinitarians would undoubtedly favor progress overwhelmingly and believe it to be enjoined by religion. So widespread is the modern attachment to the idea that even many strict fundamentalists would be shocked if told not to believe in "progress," in spite of some remaining inclination to balk at "evolution" as non-Biblical.

These instances are mentioned to show, first, that the concept of the progress of humanity is a special characteristic of contemporary Western civilization; next, that within this civilization it generally has the force of an a-priori assumption; and finally that, like most a priori's, it is adhered to with considerable fervor of emotion. All this does not disprove progress; but it does show that progress is something to be analyzed rather than taken for granted.

Now in a grand, over-all sort of way, there has undoubtedly been progress in human culture in the last quarter-million years. We are undeniably "higher" or "more advanced" culturally than the Acheulians, in much the same way that a mammal is higher than an Ordovician sponge or brachiopod. The real questions in this connection are: In what does progress consist? and, Is progress continuous and inevitable?

Let us consider these interrelated questions.

We have seen that, broadly speaking, the process of cultural development is an additive and therefore accumulative one, whereas the process of organic evolution is primarily a substitutive one. When men acquire flight, they add it to their former faculties; when birds acquired it, they converted a pair of legs into wings. One might thus fairly enough suspect that new culture tended to be incremental and not replacing; and that therefore the total stock of culture of any society, and of humanity as a whole, would show a normal inclination to grow. All in all, the verdict of history confirms such a judgment. There may have been occasional periods of stress for this or that society in which its total inventory of cultural items diminished. There is nothing to show that such hard times and shrinkages ever extended simultaneously to all the societies on earth. While one particular form of civilization is undergoing atrophy or decay, neighboring ones are usually coming into vigor. What Egyptian culture lost from 800 to 1 B.C.—if it did lose in total bulk—was more than made up for by the successive inventions and acquisitions of the contemporary Mesopotamian, Persian, Greek, and Roman cultures. The Dark Ages of western Europe, around A.D. 450 to 750, denote a period of breakup of an old pattern system before the patterns of a new system had been developed very far, with a resulting loss of political stability, intellectual and aesthetic achievements, urban refinement, and wealth; and in consequence very few superior men were able to realize themselves as "geniuses." But the historians most conversant with the era would probably find it difficult to say how much the total stock of western-European culture contracted during the Dark Ages, or to be wholly sure that it did contract seriously. Knowledge of Plato and Aristotle certainly was both less and rarer, and roads were not kept in as good repair; but useful and important new things like horseshoes and water mills (§ 183) became commoner. In any event, while Europe was perhaps receding, China was inventing printing and otherwise advancing.

Recessions in civilization, in short, either are local and likely to be compensated for elsewhere; or they primarily affect patterns or organization and the values of their products—cultural qualities.

And it does seem clear that in an over-all sort of way the sum total of culture of mankind has pretty continuously grown in bulk through history. As new artifacts and faculties are developed, the old ones tend to sink to a relatively more limited or humbler sphere, but rarely become entirely lost. Candles survive in the age of electricity, horses alongside motorcars, the bow beside firearms (§ 159); bronze has its special uses and virtues in the age of iron, and iron in that of steel. We use stone in more ways in modern civilization than Old Stone Age men did, although it was of primary significance to them but is only subsidiary to us.

Quantitatively, then, civilization advances because it tends in its nature to be accumulative; and to this extent the modern a priori of progress is justified. But will the admission of a mere swelling of bulk satisfy those who wish to believe in progress? Mostly, progress is taken to mean advance in higher qualities or toward more ideal values.

And there of course we get on subjective terrain. Is the philosophy of Plato or St. Thomas or Kant the highest and most valuable? Answers are obviously going to be colored by nationality and religion. A good Hindu might put all three of them lower than Sankara. Everyone will appreciate the values his own civilization has developed. Egocentricity in the form of ethnocentricity is inevitably injected into the problem, and makes the objective attack difficult. It is pleasant to believe in progress—which makes my times and my ways superior to all others—as it is pleasant to believe in the superiority of my nationality, my religion, my race, my language—my town or county even, my family, and myself.

Let us try, however, despite this emotional cloud, to discover something scientific or objective to justify a degree of acceptance of the progress idea. There are three approaches that seem to yield at least a partial standard of what constitutes "higher" or more advanced culture, apart from mere quantity of it.

The first is the criterion of magic and "superstition." In proportion as a culture disengages itself from reliance on these, it may be said to have registered an advance. In proportion as it admits magic in its operations, it remains primitive or retarded. This seemingly dogmatic judgment is based on the observation that beliefs in magic, such as are normal in backward societies, do recur in cultures that by profession have discarded magic, but chiefly among individuals whose social fortune is backward or who are psychotic, mentally deteriorated, or otherwise subnormal. When the sane and well in one culture believe what only the most ignorant, warped, and insane believe in another, there would seem to be some warrant for rating the first culture lower and the second higher. Or are our discards, insane, and hypersuggestibles perhaps right and the rest of us wrong?

For instance, a Lassik Indian woman in California lost and buried her baby. The next afternoon she heard a child crying overhead and fell over in a faint. She was revived, but she kept hearing the crying of the baby, and got progressively more ill. She engaged a shaman doctor to cure her, who finally said: "It is your own child's shadow (soul) coming back to urge you to accept him as a spirit helper aiding you to become a shaman yourself." This woman did not happen to want such supernatural power, and so she began to argue with her baby's shadow when its voice reappeared to urge her. She remained firm and told him to leave her alone, until finally he desisted, and she became well again.

To be a shaman is an honored and respected status among most of the Californian tribes, and many individuals accept such spirit offers. In this event they gradually learn to tolerate association with the spirit, therewith recover their own health, and then profess and try to cure other people with the assistance of their invisible helper. It is clear that in these societies there is complete social and cultural acceptance of spirits and their ability to talk and aid; acceptance also of the power of the shaman who is so aided, and of the place of the shaman in the community. But in our culture a person who falls sick, hears voices, communicates with shadows, and acquires special abilities from them is inevitably classed as deranged.

Thousands of similar cases might be cited. They provide a consistent criterion of distinction between primitive or folk cultures and advanced or high cultures, apart from the respective quantity of content. The backward cultures in their magic, shamanism, animistic ritual, recognize as objectively effective certain phenomena that the advanced cultures regard as objectively unreal and as subjectively psychotic or deranged. The limits of relation of personality and world are differently drawn in the two series of cultures. What higher cultures stigmatize as personal, nonreal and nonsocial, abnormal and pathological, lower cultures treat as objective, conducive to ability, and socially useful.

It will be seen that the difference is in terms of socialization as well as reality. Backward peoples assume as actual certain phenomena to which we grant only a mental or subjective existence that is not real in the sense in which tangible human bodies or animals or stones are real. Or perhaps it is more accurate to say that retarded peoples are also aware of a distinction but invert the emphasis. To them a child or a hawk or a stone seen or heard in a certain kind of dream or trance is much more important than a physical child or hawk or stone that one can touch and handle, because it is the possible source of much more power. Certain things we classify as unreal the primitive considers super-real—with the result that his world often seems "surrealistically" fantastic to us. From this follows the difference in socialization. To us a person who hears the dead speak, or who thinks that he can turn into a bear or a wolf, is socially subnormal, socially useless, and likely to be a burden and an upset to the community. But among primitives he is a personality of special, enhanced, and productive powers, which he may indeed abuse in witchcraft, but which ordinarily are believed to help the community to better health, surer food supply, victory over enemies, and similar benefits. So the primitive weighs and favors the magical where we reject and try to exclude it. Our values rather than our perceptions differ from his. He recognizes, standardizes, rewards certain psychotic or neurotic experiences—socially channels them—which we regard as well outside our socially approved channels.

It is important for a clear grasp of the foregoing view to realize that it has no reference to the supernatural as such. Belief in God is not a sign of backwardness. All that is contended is that the bestowal of social rewards for the inability to distinguish subjective experiences from objective phenomena, or for the deliberate inversion of the two, is a presumable mark of lack of progress.

In so far, then, as the mentally unwell in modern advanced cultures tend to correspond to the well and the influential in ancient and retarded cultures, at least in certain situations, we can accept objective progress as having taken place.

128. MORE ABOUT PROGRESS

There is a second group of traits that characterize backward as against advanced cultures. These have to do with the obtrusion of physiological or anatomical considerations into social situations, or with the related matter of the taking of human life. Some of these practices are: blood or animal sacrifice; segregation of women at parturition and menstruation as being contaminating to others; contamination by death or corpses, often with segregation of mourners until purified; puberty crisis rites, especially for girls at the onset of physiological puberty; preoccupation with the dead body, including mummification, skull preservation and skull cult, wearing of skull or jaw by widows, disinterment and reburial, eating of bits of the body or of cremation ashes; ritual prostitution and inversion; human sacrifice; retainer burial; head-hunting; cannibalism. These practices almost invariably contain an element of the magical or the supernatural, and so far as they do they are allied to the class of traits we have just reviewed as being apparently characteristic of cultural retardation. But they contain also a second element, toward which cultures that have once abandoned such practices react with aversion, disgust, revulsion, or the shame of bad taste. This other element has as its common denominator what strikes us as the gratuitous obtrusion into public recognition and the social order of physiological happenings, including blood and death and decay, which we tend to regard as matters best kept private and unemphasized, and their public obtrusion as unpleasant and useless. Deformation of the head by pressure, filing or knocking-out of the teeth, pattern scarifications, distention of lips and ear lobes and other anatomical mutilations, can perhaps be included here because they also have to do with the human body and tend to arouse shock or disgust in us; though mostly they affect anatomy rather than physiology and sometimes have little or no magical motivation. At any rate, they constitute a set of folkways allied to the class we are considering. It is true that our fashions have developed strange coiffures, cosmetics, corsets, and such, but they lack the element of permanent bodily defacement, of mutilation.[7]

All in all, retarded cultures seem infantile both in their unabashed preoccupation with bodily functions and in their disregard of other human lives as compared with the gratifications of the ego. In this sense, advanced cultures may be described as psychologically more adult. Hence their unwillingness to interest themselves in personal physiology, but their concern about humaneness. The latter is manifest also in trends like those of opposition to slavery, torture as a judicial procedure, beatings as legal punishment, execution with torture, slaughter of prisoners of war.

While, apart from deformatory practices, the primitive folkways enumerated almost always have ritual approval or supernaturalistic association, it is equally significant that the advanced "universal" or world religions, Buddhism and Mohammedanism as well as Christianity, have consistently and positively thrown their weight on the prohuman and anti-infantile side. In other words, what primitive religion approves or enjoins in this field, civilized religion forbids. This suggests that the role of religion is secondary in these matters: it tends to fortify such standards of decency, humanity, cleanliness, and propriety as each culture has attained or only partly attained. It sanctions the mores more than it causes them. The present class of criteria of progress, then, consisting of adult attitudes toward physiological function, in which the magical and supernatural elements appear to be only indirectly contributory, accordingly differs from the class discussed in the last section, in which the animistic and surrealistic element is basic and essential.

Of course, we are dealing here with exceedingly broad trends or drifts, which cannot be uniform in particulars. Retarded cultures form an enormous class, advanced ones another, and there is bound to be a deal of variation in each. For instance, the Eskimo, as nonliterate, nonmetallurgical hunters, are always reckoned as primitives. In fact it was long fashionable to begin the scale of civilization with Australians, Bushmen, Negritos, and Eskimo at the lower end. Yet the Eskimo do not possess in very emphatic form any custom of the class now being discussed, and lack some of them altogether. Judged by this criterion alone, Eskimo culture would have to be rated as more advanced than some high civilizations—possibly that of much of India. In short, what we are dealing with is not a handy yardstick, but a probability tendency that holds good on the whole or in the long run.

Among the North American Indians, the Western ones were particularly

---

[7] Chinese foot-binding seems to be the only case of serious mutilation practiced in a great recent civilization. Ear-piercing and circumcision are after all anatomically negligible. Foot-binding is rather a special phenomenon. It is consciously erotic with a tingeing of the perverse to the point of making overt discussion of its motivation taboo; and its disabling effect limited the practice to certain economic classes.

obsessed by notions of contamination through birth, menstruation, and death. The Eastern tribes took these fears more lightly, but, here and there at least, went in for retainer burial and human sacrifice, ossuaries and reburial, and scalping as perhaps a partial equivalent of head-hunting.

But the total trend of development in the area and the era of the great religions is unmistakable. The way in which the blood sacrifice of the ancient Mediterranean peoples, and of South and East Asiatic ones, is perpetuated among marginal primitives is discussed in § 165, 192, and 238. The hecatombs and libations and feasts of Achilles and Agamemnon survive as sacrifices and feasts of water buffalo, chickens, and palm wine among the pagan Igorot of the Philippines and in West African Dahomey. In China, ritual bloodshed and funerary deposit of valuables have long since been replaced by offerings of symbolic paper figures. In Japan, more distant from the advanced center, retainer burial went on until the early centuries of our era, when it was replaced, on avowed grounds of humanity, by pottery imitations of the living retainers. Leviticus, one of the later books of the Old Testament in date, is still full of blood sacrifice. "Whatsoever man of Israel that killeth an ox or lamb or goat . . . and bringeth it not unto the door of the tabernacle, to offer an offering unto the Lord . . . blood shall be imputed to that man . . . he shall be cut off from among his people. . . . And the priest shall sprinkle the blood upon the altar of the Lord . . . and burn the fat for a sweet savour unto the Lord." [8] These practices were still in full blast when Titus destroyed Jerusalem in A.D. 70. They did not differ, save in deity worshiped and place and detail of manner, from the sacrifices that Titus and his pagan Romans made. Graeco-Roman paganism died out; Judaism lived; but, after the obliteration of the Temple in Jerusalem, sacrifices quietly dropped off from Jewish cult: they were becoming contrary to the spirit and attitudes of the times. Since more than a thousand years ago the most orthodox Jews no more think of slaughtering animals on the altars of their synagogues than do Christians in their churches. A tacit dropping of this part of their law was no doubt a condition of their being able to survive at all within the pale of civilization.

The first great religion to break resolutely with all the ancient ritual obsession on physiology was Buddhism. [9] One of its cardinal injunctions is against the killing of animals, even for food. This was part of its fundamental revolt against its parent, Vedic Brahmanism, in which sacrifice and bodily purification were basic. Five hundred years later, Jesus seems never to have sacrificed on the altar nor to have mentioned such sacrifice; and therewith it was tacitly, but decisively,

---

[8] Leviticus 17: 3-6. For more on blood and burnt offerings, see Leviticus, Chaps. 1-9; for defilement and purification from childbirth see Chap. 12; menstruation, Chap. 15; death, Chap. 21.

[9] Jainism did so equally, is coeval, and still living; but it became an Indian sect instead of a world religion.

eliminated from Christianity.[10] Six centuries later still, Mohammedanism followed suit completely. Even the minor religions and hybrid sects of the period, such as Manichaeism, discarded the practice. The one exception was Mithraism, which stressed not only the sacrifice of a bull but baptism in its gushing blood. Mithraism, an offshoot of Persian Mazdaism, began earlier than Christianity, which is perhaps why it retained the blood feature. Up to the third century after Christ, it still competed with Christianity, but it weakened, lost out, was suppressed in the fourth century, and died without trace or survival: it was literally too raw for its times in the civilized parts of the world.

Illustrations could be multiplied, but these examples may suffice.

Finally, there is a third way in which the idea of progress in culture can be justified by objective evidence. This is in technology, mechanics, and science, whose accomplishments have definitely more cumulative quality than other civilizational activities. It is true that high scientific productivity appears to come in bursts or pulses as definitely as art (§ 136). But there is the difference that each art, or for that matter each philosophy or religion, very largely has to begin all over again, whereas each of the intermittent periods of discovery in science can begin, and generally does begin, just about where the last one left off. Science, and in the main technology, are evidently accumulative by nature, while philosophy, religion, art—and empire and nationalism too—tend strongly to be substitutive: a new product replaces an old one. Consequently, once technological or scientific achievements have been made, they are likely to be retained, even through long sterile intervals, until there is a new flashing-up of inventions. A pulley or a water wheel, geometry and the laws of the lever, do not usually get themselves wholly forgotten or abandoned, even in times of wrack and misery. There may be lost mechanical arts or lost branches of science; but they are certainly neither numerous nor important, as will appear in a following chapter (§ 156-160).

Here then is a third manner of progress of civilization. But with it we are back largely among aspects that are quantitative—like growth in population, growth in size of states and nations, growth sometimes in the number and complexity of their political subdivisions. Similar perhaps also is growth in stocks of wealth—more gold, diamonds, farmed acres, houses in the world: part at least of the old are physically preserved, and new ones added. But we have already seen that there is serious doubt whether magnification as such, mere quantitative swelling-up, can be legitimately construed as progress. Size is easy to boast about, but does it bring with it wiser living or greater happiness? Only so far as it does can quantitative increase of culture be considered as making for progress.

[10] The only mentions of sacrifice or offering in the New Testament, other than references to Jewish and pagan sacrifice, are symbolic: as when St. Paul says that Jesus "appeared to put away sin by the sacrifice of himself" (Hebrews 9: 26); or the "blood of the Lamb" in Revelation.

In summary, the quantitative expansion of the content of total human culture; the atrophy of magic based on psychopathology; the decline of infantile obsession with the outstanding physiological events of human life; and the persistent tendency of technology and science to grow accumulatively—these are the ways in which progress may legitimately be considered a property or an attribute of culture. They are the residuum supported by fact when the emotional and aprioristic idea of a continuous and inherent progress of civilization is subjected to analysis. More will be found on this in the discussion of cultural losses already cited. And of course the folk-sophisticate polarity considered in § 121 partly overlaps with the idea of progress.

129. FUNCTION

Function has been increasingly dealt with in cultural anthropology, as in other branches of study and science, in recent years. The basic meaning of "function" is activity or operation that is natural, proper, or characteristic, such as "secretion of bile and storage of sugar are functions of the liver." From this there is a shading into the popular meaning of purpose: such as the function of a broom is to sweep. Between is a whole series of vague and elusive meanings; consult any unabridged dictionary in confirmation. Through most of these meanings runs the idea of a relationship that is active but not causal.

Linton has tried to clarify these variable concepts by distinguishing form, meaning, use, and function in culture. The *form* of a culture trait or complex is what can be perceived by the senses and objectively described.[11] The *meaning* is its subjective associations in the culture, implicit and explicit. Its *use* is its relation to things outside the society and culture, as expressible in physical terms; its *function* is its relation within the society and culture. For instance, the form of an ax comprises the blade and the handle, the curve of the bit, the steel of which it is made. It is this sensory aspect of a trait or complex that obviously passes or diffuses most readily from one culture to another. The use of an ax, according to Linton, is to chop wood; its function, to keep members of the society warm by providing fuel, and to make carpentry possible by providing logs. It is evident that if consideration of purpose has not already crept into the statement of use and function here, it is not far distant. As to the meaning of an ax, while Linton does not expatiate on this, it is evident that this is variable, not only between different cultures, but according to context within one culture. An ax is not only a household and a vocational tool, but a weapon and the instrument

---

[11] Obviously, "form" as used here is that aspect of the *elements* of culture which has to do with their *sensory* appearance; whereas in § 125 "form" means the *organization* of the contents of a *whole* culture. A more discriminating terminology will presumably come into usage someday—perhaps "appearance" for Linton's "form," and "organization" for the form that is contrasted with content. At present, the context will usually leave no doubt as to which meaning is intended.

of the executioner. In the primitive parts of southeastern Asia and the East Indies, it has powerful meaning in connection with head-hunting. In ancient Rome, in Fascist Italy, in Republican France, the lictor's ax, in conjunction with the bundle of rods or fasces, is a well-known symbol of punishment, and therefore of governmental authority. In ancient Crete, the double-bitted ax or labrys was a sign of divinity and a cult object. Axes of bronze, jade, and polished stone have meant wealth or treasure to people emerging out of primitiveness, in ancient Greece and elsewhere.

The form of a ballot would comprise its material, size, shape, columns, arrangement of offices and candidates. Its meaning might be said to be popular freedom and sovereignty; its use, to elect officials; its functions, democratic and representative.

A song would have its form given by its melody and rhythm: it is a succession of particular notes. The meaning or association would be patriotic, sentimental, or religious according as the song was "The Star-spangled Banner," a blues, or a hymn. The use would similarly vary from opening a patriotic meeting, entertainment at a night club, or conduct of a church service. In fact, the national anthem has repeatedly been used to prevent incipient riots by compelling everyone to stand still at attention. The function of songs is, as usual, the vaguest aspect: to strengthen patriotism, make a drink more enjoyable, further piety.

The mother-in-law taboo of many nonliterate peoples is characterized as to its form—or its substance too, if one will—by silence, looking aside, moving away. Its obvious use is to prevent contact between in-laws of opposite sex and different generation. The meaning is, according to the usual testimony of those who practice the custom, an expression of respect, or conversely of shame if the respect were violated by familiarity. The function is usually believed to be avoidance or easement of social strain. However, it is well to observe that this functional relation is one-way: wherever the custom obtains, relief from strain is likely to be its function; but where it is not customary, its *practice* would immediately cause strain, of much the same kind and strength as would result from nonobservance of the custom where it is mandatory. Opposites can therefore fulfill the same function in different cultures, or in different situations. So can wholly diverse acts: making a gift, inviting to a meal, speaking politely or flatteringly, or tabooing one's mother-in-law, all can ease social strain.

A wreath may be defined as a ring of floral elements, either worn on the head or hung. We use bridal, funeral, and Christmas wreaths, whose connotations and meanings are certainly even more diverse than their materials or colors. Not so long ago, in Europe, the bridal wreath was definitely a prized symbol of virginity. The ancients wore chaplets or floral wreaths as a party dress, and hung them on sacrificial victims. They also gave laurel wreaths as honors, and called them crowns when they were imitated in gold. For wreaths, meaning and use are evidently pretty much coextensive. And the function of wreaths?

Can we say much more than that it is to express by a visible symbol an emotion of joy or sorrow appropriate to a given situation? But one might also wonder whether such a statement means anything more than that wreaths, like a hundred other kinds of things, serve as symbols of feelings.

It is evident from these examples that the function of a cultural act or trait differs from its form, use, and meaning in that these three all reside in the culture, but the function is something we read into the culture. The "meaning" of a trait may be literally "subjective," as that of a mourning wreath, or of "The Star-spangled Banner"; but everybody in the culture is agreed on it, so that the fact of the meaning can be ascertained objectively. Indeed many of us are none too sure of the whole tune or words of the American national anthem—that is, we often do not securely control its "form"—but no one doubts that its significance is patriotic. Similarly, we all know what a black or white wreath hung by the front door means, though many of us might be somewhat hazy as to the material it was made of, or wonder whether the "use" might be to express respect, to give warning that a corpse lay in the house, or to keep tradesmen and solicitors away. Still, everyone in the society is at least roughly informed as to such points. By contrast, function is something that the student or analyst of culture finds out about. Function is an interpretation, something in *his* mind, which he attributes to a culture; but the form, use, and meaning of artifacts and institutions are actually part of the culture.

This is not so different, in one way, from the role of physiology. A healthy body functions without awareness. True perception of physiologic function is the result of dissection, observation, test, experiment, and the laboratory. Even some highly civilized peoples have been quite random in distinguishing nerves and veins, let alone veins from arteries, and have variously associated emotions, feelings, and thought with the bowels, the liver, the heart, or the brain. The difference between physiological function and cultural function is that the physiologist has his laboratory and can experiment, and the student of culture has not this advantage. In many cases he can only guess as to function—as the Greek, mediaeval, and Chinese physicians largely used to guess as to physiological function.

Professedly functional studies of culture accordingly tend to contain a maximum of theory, interpretation, or opinion, often based on a relatively narrow selection of facts seen as significant. Their value as well as their weakness lies in this point.

130. PURPOSE AND NEED

At bottom, much of the preoccupation of anthropologists with cultural function seems to boil down to two things: concern with purpose, and concern with integration. Integration has already been considered (§ 122). It remains to consider purpose; or, as it is more fashionable to disguise it: need.

Preoccupation with purpose appears for one thing to be due to the fact that there are many cultural beliefs and institutions which serve no visible utility, or at least no utility that could not equally well be attained by other means, and which are adhered to merely because they are customary and "right," like the mother-in-law taboo just discussed; or which are destructive and unprofitable, like most war. Why are there exogamic groupings? Why are these often to-temic? Why is eating their totem often forbidden to members of a group, but perhaps enjoined in special cases? Why are uncles called fathers by many peoples? Why are adolescents initiated into the sacred mysteries of adults, where they learn that apparent spirits or gods are only disguised fellow tribes-men? Why does a Yurok not eat in a canoe while it floats on the ocean? To all these questions there is no obvious answer of the sort of answer there is to why an arrow is feathered or what use a fish net has. Moreover, the practices cited are all limited to certain societies and do not occur in others, including our own. Accordingly, the practices cannot correspond to any universal need, bodily, emotional, or social; at any rate, not to any real or objective universal need. A native may think his baby will die if he does not observe the couvade taboo restrictions (§ 225). But since the babies of non-couvading peoples also live and these nations manage to multiply, the quite genuine problem remains for the reflective student: What actual need is fulfilled, what good or purpose sub-served, by people's believing in the necessity of the couvade? Or for that matter, in the necessity of clans, totems, initiations, taboos, and all the rest.

The simplest and soundest answer is that the need, good, use, or purpose is often imaginary; that a lot of culture is irrational, and that collectively human minds are as full of aberrations as individual minds—or fuller. But most of these irrationalities are harmless, or at least not destructive. It may bore a man, or be inconvenient to him, to lie around the house inactive for days after his baby is born. But he has the compensating satisfaction of believing that he has strengthened the child's life; and there will normally be brothers or friends around to see that the needed household and living chores get done. What we call the more primitive cultures are full of such extravagances, of strange, unpre-dictable, exotic doings; variable, and suggestive of the habits of children, of neu-rotics, and even of psychopaths; sometimes highly charged with emotion, but quite unreasonable; often vehemently backed by the mores or ethical sentiments of society. Quite likely our civilization has its share of counterparts, which we cannot segregate off from the more practical remainder of the business of living because we are engulfed in this civilization of ours as we are in the air we breathe. Some centuries may be needed before the full recognition of our own nonrational couvades and totems and taboos becomes possible.

Obviously, it is going to be very difficult to explain all these extravagances and absurdities on the basis of any coherent system of specific needs that they satisfy or purposes which they serve. The phenomena are too variable, the pre-sumable motivations too diverse. Some nations follow the couvade, some do not;

some set up social groups to forbid intermarriage, some merely specify the forbidden kindred. Certain of the practices seem actuated by fear or lack of assurance, others by hope of a positive gain or reward; still others may spring from restlessness, from the pleasure and excitements of change (§ 166-167). Or they may have originated from one of these motivations in a particular, transient situation; but the situation having passed, the practice continues to be followed—without motivation, or with a new one. It is plain that any general explanation of phenomena as variable as these is bound to be thin, commonplace, and trite; it can be vivid and satisfying only as it is particular and special.

For instance, let us consider one of the most widespread of these "aberrations," the belief in and practice of magic. No culture has been free of it; in no two cultures has it been identical. An older view, that of Frazer, sees in magic an impersonal counterpart of religion, a sort of applied pseudo-science that deals with cause-and-effect relations; the supposed causal relations are untrue, but they contain a logic, in that, like the cause and effect of our science, they recognize and deal with similarities and with proximities or contacts. A later interpretation by Malinowski construes magic as a response to the human sense of helplessness in a world beyond control: we invent a control, however fictitious, to reassure ourselves and make living more endurable. Incidentally, the two interpretations are not contradictory; they differ in emphasis rather than in being exclusive. Malinowski goes on to assert that where people feel competent in a situation, they tend not to invoke magic. Pacific islanders fish inside the lagoon without bothering with spells, charms, and amulets; these are reserved for fishing beyond the reef, where boats can founder or be blown away, where sharks bite, and the surf pounds, where the prizes as well as the risks are greater.

This explanation may hold for some Pacific peoples but it is not a universally valid principle. In that event the Eskimo, who have to contend with far greater dangers from ice, currents, waves, drowning, freezing, and starving than the Melanesians, ought to make much more use of magic than the Melanesians; whereas, in point of fact, they use it less. They are far more practical, competent with tools, and self-reliant. They may make magic for a whale; they do so occasionally for seals if these leave them altogether in the lurch; perhaps never for fish. One might pick up the point of self-reliance and say that it is precisely there that the Eskimo broke loose from magic, relatively speaking: that their subsistence problems were so tough that no bolstering of their courage with magic would have sufficed for their survival. They had to find techniques that actually killed the seal and brought the hunter back alive, or perish; and with such techniques, they became self-reliant, and discarded much of their magic. But with this concession, the explanation by need is weakened. Magic is no longer a regular response to an automatic human need for assurance (§ 250). This need is itself a variable, dependent on degree of technological invention, and perhaps on other factors as well. Contact with a new people may result in the learning of new weapons, tools, or techniques, increased competence and self-assurance, and a falling-away of the cumber of magic. Contact with a new people is certainly among what we call the accidents of history; and if such accidents can influence the amount or kind of magic or animism practiced, it is plain that the explanation of magic as a function of a constant and imperative need, universally intrinsic to the human psyche, pretty much falls to pieces.

Of similar import is the fact that, in the same Pacific Ocean, Polynesians are on the whole less magic-ridden than Melanesians; and among Polynesians the Samoans are described as taking their animism with comparative lightness (§ 250), and the Hawaiians as having been bored with their religion to the point of wanting to discard it (§ 168). Here we are within the range of almost identical environments and therefore presumably very similar needs and problems.

Another irregularity is furnished by the Yurok and the Karok of native California. These tribes lived in a climate of no rigors, on a river that gave them abundance of salmon, in a land full of acorns that were their staple, and for centuries no foreign foes nor even pestilences invaded them. Their food supply was greater and their population denser than in most of California, yet they had hedged themselves in with a thousand do's and don't's of magic. You didn't drink river water because it might have been poisoned, nor drink in strange places; you didn't eat in a boat on the ocean, nor on the river-mouth spit, nor before going hunting or doing the day's heavy work. You did not eat deer and whale meat at the same time, nor bear meat and salmon. After eating venison, it was obligatory to wash your hands, but in a basket, not in a stream. You might sleep with your wife in the brush or in a camp, but not in your house, else your shell money took offense and left you. Your bow had to be made from that side of a yew tree which faced away from the river. And so on ad infinitum. Yet need cannot be invoked as cause, as we have already seen. The elaboration of all this magic and taboo system of the Yurok and the Karok is due to an orientation of the culture that has nothing to do with any necessities or actual problems. For some unknown reason the culture just had gone hypochondriac, and all members of the society, whatever their congenital individual dispositions, had fear and pessimism pounded into them from childhood on.[12] They were taught by all their elders that the world simply reeked with evils and dangers, against which one sought protection by an endless series of preventive taboos and magical practices. (See also § 253.)

We must conclude, accordingly, that there is no relation of simple function between specific organic needs rooted in the body and the mind or in the en-

---

[12] One might also try to explain such pervasive timidity by frequency of social fears or interpersonal strains. The Yurok had a good many person-to-person quarrels and enmities, but few class or communal clashes. It is difficult to say whether they experienced more social strain than tribes of courageous and optimistic outlook, such as the Dakota or the Mohave. Beyond this—is it a tense, hypochondriac disposition that leads to clashes with people, or is it actual enmities which make a people hypochondriac even toward nature? It would be hard to say. In most cases of this type, the causality tends to be circular: each effect tends to become a reinforcing cause.

vironment of man on the one hand, and his cultural activities, such as magic, on the other hand. Whether it be magic or art, mythology or elaboration of social structure, or what not, cultural activities differ so much, from people to people and from period to period, in their strength and in the forms assumed, that it is impossible to derive these activities from, or even to relate them rigorously to, any intrinsic organic necessities, which must in their nature be far more constant. Of course, organic factors are always present and operative. But as soon as we have culture at all, another set of factors also becomes operative: ideas, beliefs, and the practices and affects attached to them—cultural manifestations such as no subhuman animal shows. And these factors being highly variable, their expression in specific but unstable cultural traits and complexes must be variable and complex, with considerable play or give-and-take. The most immediate functional relations of cultural phenomena are to cultural variables and epiphenomena, not to organic constants such as physiological necessities or psychobiological imperatives.

CHAPTER EIGHT

Patterns

PATTERNS are those arrangements or systems of internal relationship which give to any culture its coherence or plan, and keep it from being a mere accumulation of random bits. They are therefore of primary importance. However, the concepts embraced under the term "pattern" are still a bit fluid; the ideas involved have not yet crystallized into sharp meanings. It will therefore be necessary to consider in order several kinds of patterns. We may call these provisionally the universal, the systemic, the societal or whole-culture, and the style type of patterns.

131. THE UNIVERSAL PATTERN

The *universal pattern* was proposed by Wissler, with the alternative designation of "the culture scheme." It is a general outline that will more or less fit all cultures. It is therefore fundamentally different from the other kinds of pattern, since these all apply either to particular cultures or only to parts of cultures. The universal pattern consists of a series of nine heads under which all the facts of any culture may be comprehended. The nine heads are: Speech, Material Traits, Art, Knowledge ("mythological" as well as "scientific"), Religion, Society, Property, Government, and War. These subdivide further, as desirable. Thus under Society, Wissler suggests marriage, kinship, inheritance, control, and games; under Material Traits, food, shelter, transport, dress, utensils, weapons, and industries; Government is divided into political forms and legal procedures.

It is apparent at once that this universal pattern with its heads and subheads is like a table of contents in a book. It guides us around within the volume rather than giving us the essence or quality of it. Except for minor variations, the universal pattern is in fact identical with the table of contents of most books descriptive of a culture, such as a standard ethnographic report on a tribe. The main heads are conventional captions for those classes of facts which common sense and common experience lead us to expect to be represented in every culture. We know of no people without speech, food habits, artifacts, property, religion, society, and so on. We can say therefore that these captions represent a sort of common denominators found in all cultures, and that the universal pattern consists merely of the series of these common denominators expectably represented in any culture—represented perhaps very variably but represented somehow.

It is evident that the greater the range of cultures considered, and the more diverse these are, the more will the universal elements or common denominators shrink or become vague. The proportion of universal or common traits in the total range becomes less and less as this total grows more diverse, while at the same time the concepts corresponding to the captions have to be increasingly stretched to accommodate the facts or traits. Thereby the most characteristic features of each culture get blurred out. The Yurok, and again the Ifugao, have a highly intricate legal system, but a minimum of political institutions— in fact it might be argued whether they properly have any. This is certainly an interesting situation in that it differs so radically from our own culture, where not only both law and government are highly developed but law is made to depend on government or to derive from it. This characterizing distinction, which is obviously significant for the understanding of Yurok or Ifugao cul- ture, and almost certainly significant also for understanding our own culture better—this and similar distinctions are lost in the degree that one does one's describing in terms of the common denominators of the universal pattern.

This universal pattern thus boils down to a rough plan of convenience for a preliminary ordering of facts awaiting description or interpretation. No one seems to have developed the idea since it was set forth in 1923, or to have made serious use of it toward deeper understanding. We will therefore pass on to other kinds of patterns.

132. SYSTEMIC PATTERNS

A second kind of pattern consists of a system or complex of cultural ma- terial that has proved its utility as a system and therefore tends to cohere and persist as a unit; it is modifiable superficially, but modifiable only with diffi- culty as to its underlying plan. Any one such systemic pattern is limited pri- marily to one aspect of culture, such as subsistence, religion, or economics; but it is not limited areally, or to one particular culture; it can be diffused cross- culturally, from one people to another. Examples are plow agriculture, mono- theism, the alphabet, and, on a smaller scale, the *kula* ring of economic exchange among the Massim Melanesians. What distinguishes these systemic patterns of culture—or well-patterned systems, as they might also be called—is a specific interrelation of their component parts, a nexus that holds them together strongly, and tends to preserve the basic plan. This is in distinction to the great "loose" mass of material in every culture that is not bound together by any strong tie but adheres and again dissociates relatively freely. As a result of the persistence of these systemic patterns, their significance becomes most evident on a historical view.

As we mentally roam over the world or down the centuries, what is impressive about these systemic patterns is the point-for-point correspondence of their parts, plus the fact that all variants of the pattern can be traced back to a single original form.

The alphabet is an example. Its history and variations are set forth in § 206-221. But we may anticipate here by pointing out that the alphabet was invented only once, by a Semitic people in southwestern Asia previous to 1000 B.C.; that it operates on the principle of a letter symbol for each minimal acoustic element of speech; that the letters for most sounds in any form of alphabet, no matter how specialized, always resemble the letters in some other alphabet, and through that, or still others, they resemble and are derived from the letters of the original alphabet; and that for the most part the order and often the names of the letters are the same, or where different, it is evident where and why they were altered. Thus Hebrew aleph, beth, gimel, daleth, correspond in sound, order, and name to Greek alpha, beta, gamma, delta, and to Roman and our A, B, C, D.

The pattern of plow agriculture comprises the plow itself; animals to draw it; domestication of these beasts; grains of the barley or wheat type sown by broadcast scattering, without attention to the individual seed, seedling, or plant; fields larger than gardens and of some length; and fertilization with dung, primarily from the draft animals. This system originated in the Neolithic period, probably in western Asia or near it, and by A.D. 1500 had spread from Morocco to North China—since then to the Americas and Australia as well. There are two other and parallel systems, both without plows originally: the rice and maize types of agriculture. The former involves small fields flooded by nature or irrigation, hand planting of seedlings and hand weeding; the associated animals, pigs and buffalo, were not formerly utilized in the rice-growing, though the buffalo is now put before the plow in some areas. This rice pattern began as a hoe-and-garden culture and still largely is such. Native American agriculture, centering around maize, also did not attempt to use the available domestic animals—llamas in the Andes—and therefore was also hoe farming, or even digging-stick farming. The planting was done in hillocks. Irrigation and fertilizing were practiced locally and seem to have been secondary additions. The plants grown in addition to maize were, with the exception of cotton, wholly unrepresented in the plow or rice patterns. The histories of the three systems have remained essentially as separate as their origins, except for some relatively recent transfers of draft animals and plows from the plow pattern into the two others where these began to be drawn into modern international, metropolitan civilization.

The exclusive-monotheistic pattern is Hebrew-Christian-Mohammedan. The three religions are outgrowths of one another and originated in a small area of southwestern Asia. The pattern comprises a single deity, of illimitable power, and exclusive of all others; so far as there are other spiritual beings, such as angels or saints, they are derivative from him; the deity is proclaimed by a particular human vessel inspired by the deity; and worship according to this revelation excludes and forbids any other worship. Cults and philosophies outside these three organized monotheisms have repeatedly attained to monotheism, or to a pantheism or a henotheism that would be hard to distinguish logically from monotheism. And many religions, even of backward peoples, recognize a supreme deity. But all these others regularly lack some of the features of the exclusive-monotheistic pattern, and their resemblances are thus only partial convergences of an analogical type. This merely analogical similarity of these "high-god" and miscellanously monotheistic religions goes hand in hand with their diversity of origin: they are not connected with the exclusive monotheisms, nor for the most part with one another. By contrast, the three exclusive monotheisms are homologous—structurally or part-for-part similar—and they are connected in origin: Jesus was a Jew, and Mohammed took his ideas from Jews and Christians.

The systemic type of pattern accordingly not only partakes of the quality of a system, but is a specific growth. It originates in one culture, is capable of spread and transplantation to others, and tends strongly to persist once it is established. It recalls the basic patterns of structure common to groups of related animals developed from a common origin, with the original pattern persisting through all superficial modifications as they occur under evolution. For instance, the basic vertebrate pattern includes a skull with lower jaw, vertebrate column, and, above the level of the fishes, two pairs of limbs each ending in five digits. Within the range of this pattern, there is endless variation. A snake has no legs, whales and some reptiles and amphibians possess only one pair. Birds have converted the front pair into wings; seals, into flippers; and moles, into "shovels." The digits carry claws in carnivores, hoofs in running mammals, nails in ourselves. They number five in man as in the salamander, never more than four in birds and in pigs, three in the emu, two in the ostrich and the cow, one only in the horse—not counting nonfunctioning vestiges. Not one of the thousand of species of amphibians, reptiles, birds, or mammals ever possesses more than two pairs of limbs or more than five digits; any six-fingered vertebrate is an individual malformation.

By contrast there are the arthropods, among whom the higher crustaceans have five pairs of legs (modifiable to claws or paddles), the spiders four, and the insects three pairs of legs and two pairs of wings; but none of the hundreds of thousands of species of arthropods ever show a five-digited limb. Such are the basic arthropod plans, which are endlessly modified according to order, family, and species. Thus many butterflies have only two pairs of legs; bees have two pairs of wings, but the related ants break theirs off after mating; flies have only one pair; beetles have two pairs but fly mainly with one, the other having become converted into a protective shell; worker ants, fleas, lice, and many others have long since become wingless. We might add that all arthropods have definitely segmented bodies, a skeleton on the outside, antennae, and pale bluish blood containing copper-protein haemocyanin, as compared with the nonsegmentation, inner skeleton, lack of antennae, and blood reddened by the iron-protein haemoglobin of all vertebrates.

It is true that these fundamental plans of structure of the subkingdoms of life such as the arthropods and the vertebrates, or of their classes like insects and mammals, constitute something very much bigger than the system patterns of culture. They are hundreds of millions of years old, expressed in thousands to hundreds of thousands of species and in trillions upon trillions of individuals. The culture patterns muster an age of only a few thousand years. Once established, the great biological patterns predetermine, as it were, the main frames within which evolution will operate. No arthropod can give rise to a vertebrate, or vice versa; their patterns are separated by profound, unbridgeable clefts. Evolutionary change takes place in the domains between these chasms—strictly speaking, between their subchasms. By contrast, cultural system patterns, such as exclusive monotheism, plow agriculture, the alphabet, pass from one race or society, from one major culture, to another, and rather freely. Each year men who otherwise remain in their ancestral culture are for the first time learning to plow, to read letters, to fixate on a single God. Such a transfer of pattern to new kinds of carriers is of course impossible in subhuman organisms, whose forms are dominated by irreversible heredity. But the transfer is characteristic of the very nature of culture, which is plastic, reversible, and capable of unlimited absorptions, anastomosings, and fusions. Hence the patterns within cultures impress us as shifting and often transient. They are so, in comparison with the grand patterns of organic life, just as everything cultural, being an epiphenomenon, something superadded to life, is relatively unstable, modifiable, and adaptable. What the present type of cultural pattern system shares with the fundamental organic patterns is that they both embody a definable system, in the repeated expressions of which, no matter how varied, there nevertheless is traceable a part-for-part correspondence, which allows each form or expression to be recognized as related to the others and derived from the plan as it originally took shape.

In fact, the peculiar interest of these systemic patterns is that, within the endless kaleidoscope of human culture, they allow us to recognize things that are actually related in origin as against things that appear similar but are not connected in origin. The patterns differentiate homologies from analogies, the biologist would say. Thus, the several examples of exclusive monotheism are both homologous and historically interconnected through derivation of one from the other. But the Chinese Heaven, the Indian Brahma, the Egyptian Aten, "god" in the abstract of the Greek philosophers, the supreme deities of many primitive religions, represent analogies or convergences. They are distinct, separate developments which led to results that seem similar. And so, Egyptian hieroglyphs, Mesopotamian cuneiform, Indus Valley, Mayan, and other ancient ideographic or mixed systems of writing, and the surviving Chinese system (§ 202-205) are like alphabets in that they function as more or less effective methods of visible-speech communication. But they are like them only in that functioning. All alphabets are genetically one—derived from a single source; the other methods of writing have separate sources, operate on different principles, are built on different plans. They resemble alphabets as a whale does a fish— both communicate or swim—but without genuine similarity of structure or meaningful relationship. But alphabet resembles alphabet as whale and porpoise and dolphin resemble one another.

It is in the working-out of these real relationships, structural and genetic relationships as against mere functional similarities, that the recognition of culture patterns of the systemic type finds one of its chief uses.

133. TOTAL-CULTURE PATTERNS

Next, there are patterns that relate to whole cultures. There is an Italian, a French, a British pattern or form of European civilization. There is an Iroquoian, Algonkin, and Siouan aspect or facies of North American Indian Woodland culture. This Woodland culture in turn has its own larger total pattern, which, together with the Southeastern, Southwestern, North Pacific Coast, Mexican, and other patterns make up the still larger native North American pattern (§ 326). It is evident that we are here dealing with culture wholes, not, as in the last section, with specific complexes or systems that form only part of any one culture but can be grafted onto others.

East is East and West is West, Kipling said in vivid allusiveness to the different physiognomies or qualities of Occidental and Asiatic civilizations. When he added that never the twain shall meet, he was technically overstating things, in that civilizations do borrow and learn from each other, do assimilate or "acculturate"—which fact he was perfectly aware of when he went on: "But there is neither East nor West, Border, nor Breed, nor Birth, when two strong men stand face to face." But the "never-meeting" is also a poetical way of saying that civilizations are vast things like great ocean currents flowing past each other, and perhaps of implying that the sets or trends of civilizations as wholes vary profoundly, quite apart from the sum total of the items which make up their content. Civilizations differ in "configuration," in modern scientific jargon; "spirit" would have been an earlier word, "genius" before that.

There is of course nothing new in the fact that civilizations are distinct. Innumerable items can always be cited, either of differential or of likeness. To engage a button, we cut a slit in the cloth; the Chinese sew on a loop; and so on. But what do a hundred or a thousand or ten thousand such items mean? What do they add up to that is of wider import or deeper significance? If the items just scatter with equal randomness in two or more cultures, their effect will be equivalent, in spite of the endless variation of detail. Obviously, the specific items must concentrate in some peculiar way in each civilization, must gather or weight themselves along certain lines, if they are to have a larger meaning. And therewith we have a pattern or configuration.

There remains a difficulty, however. Items like buttonholes are definite and are readily ascertained or established, but their significance is limited. The pattern or physiognomy or trend of a great civilization is certainly an important thing to know, but it is difficult to formulate accurately and reliably. Such a pattern has in it breadth and complexity, depth and subtlety, universal features but also uniqueness. In proportion as the expression of such a large pattern tends to the abstract, it becomes arid and lifeless; in proportion as it remains attached to concrete facts, it lacks generalization. Perhaps the most vivid and impressive characterizations have been made by frank intuition deployed on a rich body of knowledge and put into skillful words. Yet this does not constitute proof and is at best at the fringe of the approved methods of science and scholarship. These difficulties will explain why the formulation of whole-culture patterns has not progressed farther, though it is surely one of the most important problems that anthropology and related researches face.

A spirited depiction of the total pattern of any culture possesses much the same appeal and interest as a portrait by a good painter. Some cultures, like some faces, are more interesting than others, but all can be given an interest and meaning by the hand of the skilled master. This gift of "seizing" character, with its suffusion by insight, admittedly partakes as much of the faculties of the artist as of those of the scientist. Excellent delineations of culture patterns have in fact been presented by nonanthropologists, by historians and travelers. More than eighteen hundred years ago Tacitus gave to posterity one of the masterpieces of this genre in his analysis of German custom and character. So keen was his penetration that many qualities of his subjects are still recognizable in the Germans of today. Other notable examples are the mediaeval Persian Al-Biruni writing in Arabic on Indian civilization; and in the nineteenth century, Burckhardt's *Renaissance,* Doughty's *Arabia Deserta,* Codrington's *Melanesians.* The first was a historian, the second a crotchety Semitist, the third a missionary bishop. At the risk of making invidious distinctions, Malinowski, Benedict, Mead, Evans-Pritchard, might be cited among recent avowed anthropologists. Through the medium of fiction, Pierre Loti, Freuchen's *Eskimo,* Maran's *Batouala,* and Mofolo's *Chaka* have done something similar with exceeding vividness.

A requisite for the recognition of the whole-culture type of pattern, besides of course insight and articulateness, is willingness to see a culture in terms of itself, of its own structure, values, and style. There must be an interest in the culture for its own sake. Without this, the depiction tends to degenerate into a recital of oddments, or of those features in which the culture's standards differ from our own—to its own worsening, of course. The disengagement from the biases and values of the describer's own culture should be complete, at least for the time being. Such preconceptions should never block his sympathies for the culture he is describing, where its qualities call for sympathy. Of course the account must not be a laudation, but an appraisal of what the culture's own standards and valuations are, and how far they are adhered to.

This process is akin to recognition of style in art; to "appreciation" in the stricter sense of that word, before it acquired its popular meaning of mere liking. There too we do not judge Michelangelo by the standard of Rodin, or Mozart by that of Shostakovich; nor, for that matter, Shostakovich by the values of Mozart, though unconsciously that is what conservatives may tend to do. What is in question in such endeavors is the recognition of the art of a certain region and period as expressed by its best exponents, the evaluation of how far it achieved its aims, and the definition of what these aims and values were. Attempts to recognize and define whole-culture patterns are of the same kind, but are larger in that they try to grasp the totality of styles—the nexus of social, ethical, intellectual, and economic as well as aesthetic styles or manners which together constitute the master pattern of a culture.[1]

134. EXEMPLIFICATIONS IN LANGUAGE

As so often, language, which is one specialized part of culture, can be used advantageously here to illustrate the total cultural situation. An author's style—literally his "writing-rod" or pencil—refers to his consistent ways or habitual manners of expressing himself distinctively enough to be recognizable from others. We have also superindividual styles, such as that of Elizabethan and of eighteenth-century English as compared with that of contemporary English. Going still farther, we may say there is a Latin style, an Anglo-Saxon style, a Germanic style, in English; and beyond these, there are styles characteristic of the Latin, English, and German languages. These whole-language styles consist of more than degrees of elaborateness of sentence structure, or the posi-

[1] Kluckhohn proposes to distinguish patterns from configurations. Both refer to structural regularities of culture. But to him patterns are objective and explicit ("overt"), or readily brought into social consciousness, whereas configurations are implicit ("covert") sets or trends akin to attitudes or motivations, and have to be dissected out by analysts of the culture. In part, though only in part, Kluckhohn's "patterns" correspond to what are here called systemic patterns (§ 132), his "configurations" to total-culture and style patterns (§ 133, 137).

tion of the verb. By insensible degrees they involve the whole of what we ordinarily call the grammar of a language. Latin has six distinguishable cases, German four, and English two. Latin conjugates its verb by a long series of complex suffixes, whereas spoken English has only three living conjugating suffixes and performs its main business of conjugation by the equally effective mechanism of separate auxiliary words, as set forth in § 97, 109. What are such grammatical peculiarities but crystallized stylistic idiosyncrasies? The grammar of a language may be viewed as its total specific style compared with the styles of other languages, or as its total pattern of structure.

It is true that what we ordinarily call "style" in language is more limited, superficial, optional, and perhaps individual than what we ordinarily call "grammar," and for many purposes it is desirable to observe the distinction. But there is no absolute line between the two, and both are ways or manners or patterns of expression. Just as the grammar of a language is its total pattern of fixed forms, so we might conceivably refer to the total pattern of a culture as its cultural grammar. That is not usage; but the comparison may help clarify what we mean when we talk of total patterns. The trouble is that there is as yet no word in English, or in any other language, to express this concept except vague or metaphorical terms like "genius," "spirit," "style," "trend," "direction."

Comparison with language may also help clarify the difference between the systemic patterns (§ 132) and the total-culture patterns (§ 133). Much as grammar corresponds to total pattern, so lexical content corresponds in one way to system pattern and to miscellaneous unpatterned material. It is lexical contents, words, that are often borrowed by one language from another, as when English takes over *Gestalt* from German or *chic* from French, or thousands and thousands of earlier words from Latin or French or both—all without the form or grammar or pattern of English being appreciably changed. Similarly, innumerable items or traits of cultural substance, such as corn-planting or seasoning with curry or voting on Australian ballots, can be taken over into a culture without its basic pattern or "grammar" being affected in principle. Moreover, we have seen cases of a system pattern such as the alphabet passing over into culture after culture but its various forms there being recognizable as derived from one common source by their part-for-part correspondence. Well, just as in the alphabet aleph, beth, gimel, correspond to A, B, C, and help prove their joint derivation, so in the relationship of language. English *nose, tongue, two, three* correspond to Spanish *nariz, lengua, dos, tres,* and to German *nase, zunge, zwei, drei,* in sound as well as meaning; but none of them correspond to Japanese *hana, hita, futa-tsu, mi-tsu* in sound or form. Thereby these words help prove that English and Spanish and German speech have a common origin and relationship, which we call Indo-European, but that Japanese is outside the Indo-European origin and relationship. It is the parts or content of a system that can be used as evidence of this sort, and it is the parts or words or content of a language that can be used in the same way. Both kinds of content are receivable into larger entities—culture wholes or language wholes—without much affecting the forms or major patterns or styles or "grammars" of these.

On the contrary, resemblances in style pattern mean much less as regards connective relationship. The Japanese language compounds nouns, piles up and encapsulates subordinate clauses, and then finishes up its elaborate periodic sentence with a verb, in much the way German speech style does. English word separateness and English syntax or word arrangement in the sentence are much more like those of Chinese. It is evident from this example that these grammatical, stylistic, or pattern resemblances can grow up in languages quite independently of their historical connection. Of the four just mentioned, English and German are the only two related. In fact they are closely and recently related in origin; but both tie up in certain features of their style pattern with wholly unconnected languages at the far end of another continent.

As a cultural counterpart one might mention the sharing by early Romans and by Chinese of addiction to patriarchal authority in the gens or extended family, the strong economic functioning of this group, the use of gentile or family names, the cult of manes or ancestral spirits, the relative meagerness of other ritual and mythology, the high premium on sobriety, piety, self-control, and moderation. All these pattern resemblances of orientation or outlook or physiognomy are certainly not due to any specific or direct historical connection of Rome and China, which these two countries never had. The pattern resemblances are evidently convergent or parallelistic (§ 223). That is, the two patterns originated independently, and therefore their similarity is secondary, functional, and analogous only. For instance, early Roman culture put, and Chinese does not put, strong emphasis on bravery, on military training and success, and on a martial tribal god.

Again, the late Roman Empire, in its Byzantine phase long after the capital had been moved to Constantinople, shows interesting approximations to late Chinese civilization, say of the Ming and Manchu dynasties, roughly 1400 to 1900. In both instances there are present: a sense of old and thorough saturation in high civilization, leading to self-satisfaction and disdain of the achievements of other cultures; a competent and educated bureaucracy as the mainstay of the state and civilization; fatigue as regards war, coupled with tried defensive skill; a flagging of originality in the arts, science, and philosophy, side by side with real respect for learning and its quantitative reproduction in encyclopaedias, commentaries, and the like. Some of these shared trends may be the results of a sort of civilizational senility. At any rate, they could hardly occur except in cultures of some maturity. Nevertheless, whatever the causes at work, they do not include imitation influence of the one civilization on the other. And we have again a degree of physiognomic resemblance, of total-pattern similarity. And this is evidently analogous in kind to the patterning that makes the grammar of

English—and not of Latin, or Greek, be it noted—more like that of Chinese in its general character than is that of any other European language.

In summary, *systemic patterns* are blocks or pieces of culture or language sharing a content that is of common origin and is arranged in a common pattern persistent enough to be recognizable for a long time, even after direct historical record of the community of origin has been lost. (In the case of language, the block may be so large as to comprise the majority of the vocabulary.) *Total-culture patterns* are the over-all quality, set, cast, organization, or grammar of the whole of a culture or language—the direction in which it slopes, so to speak. The total patterns of separate cultures sometimes are perceptibly similar, even though differing considerably in their content; and they can become similar of themselves even though starting out independently and different. Or, conversely, they can begin by being alike and then diverge increasingly. Their value is thus low for tracing historical connections or proving relationships. Their significance lies in expressing the distinctive individuality and quality pervading a whole culture or language.

135. PSYCHOLOGICAL ASPECTS

It will be seen that the examples just cited of whole-culture patterns tend somewhat toward the psychological; they have psychological implications. This is inherent in physiognomic characterizations, whether these be of particular men, of racial types, of historical periods, or of cultures. A face may express sternness or majesty or raptness or serenity or benevolence or craftiness or intellectuality or sensuousness, or combinations of such qualities. In much the same way, in referring to a civilization or period or tribal culture or phase, we often use terms of psychological appraisal, such as fatigue, self-satisfaction, bravery, premium on sobriety, flagging of originality. Yet it is true that other characterizing concepts, such as family names, ancestor worship, bureaucracy, encyclopaedias, manual arts, obviously refer to specific institutions or concrete cultural phenomena. It would seem accordingly that formulations of the total pattern of cultures contain both strictly cultural and psychological characterizations. A formulation begins with the former, with institutions or folkways; and as these more and more weave themselves into a larger coherence, it gradually also becomes evident in what directions the culture is faced, what ends it looks toward, which qualities it is occupied with and prizes most. In short, its characteristic values and its characteristic attitudes or orientations become comprehensible. An attitude, or for that matter an orientation, necessarily implies psychology. Attitudes might be said to refer to the ways an organism sets or arranges or orients itself, adjusts inwardly and outwardly to its environment; anything in its merely internal physiological operations would hardly come under attitude and orientation. Where the boundary lies here between straight anthropology and straight psychosomatics has not yet been determined. We might venture that we are still within the jurisdiction or claims of anthropology if the environment—toward which human organisms react by an attitude or an orientation—is a cultural one, if it includes folkways or mores with societal pressure, or, in wholly untechnical language, institutions. If however the environment is unmitigatedly physical, like warm sunshine after exposure to cold, or the proximity of an angry bear when one is in the woods unarmed, the reaction toward the environment is primarily psychosomatic and outside the domain of anthropology.

In recent years attempts have been made to characterize cultures definitely in psychological terms. This does not mean that their cultural features were disregarded. On the contrary, their cultural traits were carefully studied for a selection and an enumeration of all those customs and institutions which would fit into a coherent pattern or plan expressible in psychological terms. In short, the procedure was to try to convert cultural phenomena into psychological formulations through the medium of total-pattern recognitions. This is of course the same procedure as we have been discussing, carried one step farther. Mead, Gorer, and Fortune have described cultures more or less along these lines, but the most comprehensive procedure has been that of Benedict. She began by contrasting two American Indian cultures, those of the Plains bison-hunters and those of the southwestern Zuni and other Pueblo farmers, as being respectively Dionysiac and Apollinian. The Dionysiac temperament—named after the god of wine—is outgoing, addicted to rushes of strong feeling and their expression in activity; the self is asserted. The Apollinian type of personality is calm, restrained, "classic"; it dislikes surges of emotion, vehement action, and insistence on the ego; this last should be muted in favor of group tranquillity. For example, among the Dakota each man was free to seek his own "vision" or inspiration from supernaturals, who instructed him in his personal ritual and made him a shaman. Among the Zuni, such personal experiences would be frowned upon, and personal rituals were socially taboo. Ritual was in the hands of priests holding established offices, transmitting traditional tribal lore and cults, and teaching younger priests to follow in their footsteps. The psychological formulation of Zuni culture as Apollinian is based on a large mass of cultural traits, such as these customs differentiating shamans from priests.

Later, Benedict went farther and passed verdicts on cultures outside her personal experiences: the Melanesians of Dobu Island, described by Fortune, and the Kwakiutl Indians of Vancouver Island, on whom elaborate reports by Boas were available. The Dobuan culture she found to be paranoid in its inclinations; the Kwakiutl, megalomanic. Individual temperaments tend to conform to the cultural set; they are molded by it. A Dobuan who may be suspicious and plotting by nature fits in with the trends of his society and becomes a successful member of it, a distinguished citizen. But one who has impulses to be confiding and amiable, and cannot overcome these impulses, will be taken advantage of by his tribesmen and be a social failure.

There is no doubt that these four cultures actually differ in the directions described, and that other cultures differ from one another in analogous ways. Also, the characterizations tend to be in more or less psychiatric terms, or at least clinical ones, partly because clinical psychology was the first recognized branch of psychology that attempted to deal with whole human beings, as distinct from their intelligence or learning ability or other parts or special aspects of the mind. Furthermore, terms like "paranoid" or "megalomanic" do not imply downright insanity in psychology, as they frequently do in laymen's speech. A man may have a definite megalomanic streak in him and yet be a "normal" and useful member of society. Most of us in fact can think of an acquaintance or two whom that cap just fits. Also, there are five or ten individuals with clinically recognizable paranoid or schizophrenic or manic-depressive tendencies for every one that actually breaks into such a psychosis. We speak of such persons, quite properly, descriptively and without stigma, as being for instance of manic-depressive temperament. Which is as much as to say that if they were to become insane, which they probably won't, their psychosis would take such and such a form; just as one man will show a phthisic constitutional type to a physician, and another an apoplectic one, and yet the betting is that both will ultimately die of some other disease, respectively, than tuberculosis and a stroke. So much then in validation of these translations of total-culture patterns into psychological "diagnoses."

However, there are limitations to this method. So far as it is valid, it ought to be applicable to any and all cultures beyond the four primitive ones cited. Benedict herself seems to think that only some cultures can be described in this way; the majority are not sufficiently "integrated" around a single psychological trend, not oriented exclusively in one direction. If that is true, then her Zuni, Dobu, Kwakiutl cultures are abnormal cases, and are of significance chiefly as showing to what degree of specialization culture orientations can be pushed. But it seems much more likely that every culture is psychologically characterizable; and that if only a few can be appropriately labeled, it is because our assortment of labels is inadequate, or our interest flags beyond the gaudy ones. Psychologists do not deny a personality to individuals who are complex, balanced, and well rounded, or allow it only to those who have warped themselves around a single impulse or idea. The same must hold for the personalities of cultures. Some will be more decisively one-sided than others. But all must have a psychological physiognomy of some kind corresponding to their cultural physiognomy.[2] This is because culture is itself the product of psychosomatic activity; because in turn it conditions and molds psychology, as we have seen (§ 123); and because its operation is necessarily accompanied by psychological functioning.

[2] Subsequent well-rounded characterizations of East Asiatic cultures made by Benedict during World War II (see § 245 for a Siamese example) avoid the single-label designation.

As a matter of fact all kinds of psychological emphases can be recognized in cultures, even though it is but a rare culture all of whose manifestations can be constellated around a single motif. For instance there are cultures, such as the Yoruba and the Dahomey in West Africa, that are marked by a passion for method and relational organization; others, such as the Nupe, also in West Africa, view the world matter-of-factly as consisting of an agglomeration of so and so many discrete events which they feel no impulse to order (§ 251). Acquisitiveness and retentiveness are certainly personality traits. Dobu culture is acquisitive and retentive as well as sensitive and paranoid; Ifugao, in the Philippines, is acquisitive but normally healthy in its outlook; Yurok, in native California, is highly retentive of property but neurotically timorous; the Polynesian and Australian cultures generally are not acquisitive, still less retentive, but geared to constant consumption. There is bound to be one pervasive psychology in a culture that puts a social premium on co-operativeness, but a quite different set of mental reactions when a culture really prizes and rewards ruggedly individual competitiveness. Still other colorings are reviewed in Chapter Fifteen, where this whole set of problems is examined more systematically.

There are thus all kinds of psychological concepts against which cultures can be graded, if not as yet by any system of measurements, at least by general consent. The recognition of some such psychic qualities flows almost inevitably out of recognition of total-culture patterns. Sound formulations are likely to involve various sets of concepts. Thus it might be maintained that there was a culture at one and the same time acquisitive, wasteful, competitive, intuitive, sanguine, and uninterested in relations and abstractions. Which one? Contemporary American civilization can be so appraised, perhaps without too much unfairness. At any rate it would be generally accepted that there are at least half a dozen distinct psychological strands involved in our national make-up. Such multiple-term characterizations as this, though less incisive, will in the long run be applicable to far more cultures, and are likely to be fuller and truer descriptions than the occasional instances in which a culture is so specialized that nearly everything in it can be disposed along one conceptual axis expressible in a single word.

There is a large field here waiting to be developed as more students of anthropology learn to make psychological characterizations, or more psychologists learn to deal with culture. In both sciences, the tools of method have been sharpened, for about the last two lifetimes, by pursuit of critical analysis. Apart from psychiatry as a branch of medicine, clinical or whole-personality psychology of more than mere introspective or guesswork caliber scarcely existed consciously, even in germ, before about 1920, and is still in its infancy; and the same is true of whole-culture or pattern anthropology. When both have grown farther, and interpenetrated each other more, the results are likely to be immensely interesting.

From what has been said about the conditioning or molding of men by their cultures, it is evident that to every total pattern or orientation of culture there must correspond a type of personality. In fact, strictly, all psychic action takes place not in the culture but in the people who participate in it, carry it, and are shaped by it. The culture, which from one angle is a sort of set of rules enabling a certain set of activities to go on, by its existence inevitably induces certain habits in the members of its society; and these habits aggregate, in any individual, into a particular kind of personality. This personality will tend to be more or less alike in all members of a society, though varied by their purely individual conditionings as well as by their individual heredities, which are never wholly the same. The average or type or mode of these personalities produced in a society by its culture is, strictly, what the cultural psychologist tries to recognize or describe; the culture that produces the personality type is, strictly, the anthropologist's first concern. A potlatch and a thousand-guest wedding are cultural facts; but if a culture favors and rewards them, certain psychological attitudes, such as those toward lavishness and personal ostentation, tend to be set up in most people living in that society under that culture. This idea, of a type of personality always having to correspond to a type of culture, at least on the average, is after all a quite simple one, as well as being seemingly unassailable. It is the basis of the relation of anthropology and psychology, and the reason why examination of whole-culture patterns or physiognomies inevitably suggests psychological implications.

This rather simple relation has sometimes been obscured by premature attempts to explain the full causality of cultures or persons—which no one is yet in position to do—and sometimes by technical jargon, such as "basic personality structure." This phrase seems to mean nothing more than the personality type corresponding to a particular culture—the kind of person normal or average to the culture, one might say. "Basic" is unfortunate, because to biologists "basic" means what is hereditary and congenital, whereas this kind of personality is induced by the culture, not primary. If "basic" refers merely to being typical or average, it would better be called that. "Structure" appears to be just a yielding to a word that has a perfectly good meaning but suddenly becomes fashionably attractive for a decade or so—like "streamlining"—and during its vogue tends to be applied indiscriminately because of the pleasurable connotations of its sound. Of course a typical personality can be viewed as having a structure. But so can a physiology, any organism, all societies and all cultures, crystals, machines—in fact everything that is not wholly amorphous has a structure. So what "structure" adds to the meaning of our phrase seems to be nothing, except to provoke a degree of pleasant puzzlement. Moreover, an impressive phrase like this one tends to provoke an illusion that somehow knowledge of life histories of typical personalities in a society will explain why the culture is as it is; whereas in the main it is the culture that has made these personalities what they are (§ 123). However, apart from such putting of the cart before the horse, and from the matter of technical verbiage, the idea of some certain kind of a person or type of mentality corresponding to each particular culture is both simple and important. It will be developed farther in Chapter Fifteen.

136. CLIMAXES OF WHOLE-CULTURE PATTERNS

If we consider how cultures grow, by reviewing the course of those civilizations we know best through their history or archaeology, we are soon struck by a familiar phenomenon. Successful growth, which in retrospect is judged to have been productive, tends to come intermittently, in pulses or irregular rhythms. The word "cycles" is sometimes used, but it denotes a repetitive return, and return is more than is really characteristic of the phenomena now in question, or at least more than is sure about them. The manifestations are more like unpredictable swells or waves than like any wheel-of-fortune action in which an idea of retribution is implicit, or of a fate that eventually levels all things out. The "rise and fall of nations" is the familiar phrase that refers to the phenomenon; but there is actually a good deal involved beyond the success or failure of national fortunes. There is included, it is true, politico-military achievement: that is, success of the society in outright competition with other societies. But, more or less associated, there are usually: a growth in population; an increase in wealth; technological advances; and bursts of productivity in the aesthetic and intellectual fields, all the way from sculpture to literature, from philosophy to science. The peaks in these several activities may come simultaneously, or overlapping, or in close succession. Sometimes the total rise is gradual, as was that of ancient Rome; sometimes it comes suddenly, or seems abrupt, perhaps because the initial stages have not got into the preserved record of history.

An almost supertypical example is provided by the ancient Greeks:

Military success: 500-250 B.C.
Politics: progressively democratic constitution building, 600-400
Population: increasing to probably 300, decrease by 200
Philosophy: 585-200; peak: Plato, Aristotle, 400-320
Science: 585-150; peak: Euclid, Archimedes, 320-220
Medicine: 500-100; peak: Hippocrates, 420
History: 500-200; peak: Thucydides, 420
Tragedy: 500-400; peak: Sophocles, 450
Comedy: 480-280; peak: Aristophanes, 420
Poetry: 650-200; peak: Pindar, 450
Oratory: 450-300; peak: Demosthenes, 340
Sculpture: 550-100; peak: Phidias, 450
Painting: 500-100; peak: Apelles, 330
Architecture: 600-100; peak: Parthenon, 450

It is evident that for a few centuries Greek cultural activities were much heightened in the quality of their values achieved: the near-concurrence of dates is striking.

The five centuries involved include everything the Greeks produced which the world since their time has thought important, with the following few exceptions: Around 850-800 B.C., well before the main growth, there were the Homeric epics. Under the Roman Empire, two or more centuries after the great growth, there occurred an aftermath of science, largely in the nature of codifications (Ptolemaic astronomy, Galenic medicine, A.D. 100-150); a philosophic revival (Neo-Platonism, A.D. 250); and a "silver-age" prose literature (Plutarch, A.D. 150). All the rest of the Greek contribution falls in the period 650-100 B.C.; much the most of it, in fact, is comprised in the three centuries 500-200, with practically all the peaks or climaxes between 450 and 300. And this happened in a quite small area, as well as in the quite brief time. To put it a little differently, there was an enormous concentration of culture energy and innovation, of production of high cultural values, and of flourishing of men of the first rank of genius, in a very limited space and period, in contrast with much less of the same that the Greeks did before or after or elsewhere.

Quite so intense a condensation was perhaps never again accomplished in history. But the number of less extreme examples is indefinitely large. In Rome, the "Augustan" age around the time of the birth of Christ corresponded to the Greek "Periclean" age. All the most notable Roman achievements cluster around this Augustan climax, within a century or two before and after it: Cicero, Caesar, Lucretius, Virgil, Horace, Ovid, Tacitus; the world's first truly realistic portrait sculpture fifty to a hundred years after Augustus; Trajan, the emperor who brought the Empire to its greatest extent; and the culmination of Roman architecture, road-building, engineering, and probably population and wealth, in the first two Christian centuries.

Sometimes such bursts come repetitively within one area and population, as in China of the Chou, Han, and T'ang dynasties;[3] or in Egypt of the Pyramid Age, the Middle Kingdom, and the New Empire, with an aftermath renascence.[4] Sometimes successful activities string along spottily and successively, or somehow fail to appear altogether. Thus England was musically productive until 1700, musically imitative or second-rate thereafter; but began painting successfully only after 1750; and never had a first-rank sculptor. Holland's great men all came in the 1600's: Spinoza in philosophy, Rembrandt in painting, Huygens in physics, Vondel in literature. This was also the century of successful Dutch aggression against Spaniards and Portuguese, of the founding of their colonial empire, and of an unusual accumulation of wealth. In a small country it seems to be easier for everything to pile up simultaneously. The much more numerous

[3] Most productive about 550-300 B.C., 200 B.C.-A.D. 200, A.D. 600-800.
[4] At peak around 2600, 1900, 1400, 600 B.C., respectively.

adjacent Germans toward 1800 had in Kant, Goethe, Beethoven, the greatest contemporary European philosopher, poet, and musician, respectively; but politically they were mediaeval and disunited, and militarily Napoleon buffeted them around. Their famous science was only just beginning to function successfully at the time. During the nineteenth century this science flourished, Germany became politically organized and strong in war, population and wealth increased faster than in most of Europe—but German philosophy, literature, and music were progressively on the downgrade. Nevertheless, on the larger view the significant thing is the close time association of these somewhat separate German culminations. Some merely happen to reach their peak a little before the others—some during 1750-1825 and some during 1825-1900.

It will be seen that there are two related aspects to the type of phenomena we are considering. One is the fact of the production of great men and great cultural achievements; the other is their normal concentration in time, space, and nationality.

It used to be customary to "explain" such happenings as these, especially literary ones, by referring them to the stimulating effect of great victories, or other national events. It was said, for instance, that Shakespeare was somehow helped to write great plays by the defeat of the Spanish Armada; Phidias, Sophocles, and the other Athenians similarly were pushed forward to higher achievement by Marathon and Salamis; Augustus at last ended civil war and brought peace. But in many cases closer examination of the facts shows that the literary or other burst had already begun before the political event. And even if the burst is wholly subsequent, it is hard to see why and how better painting, or a discovery like Harvey's of the circulation of the blood, should be "produced" by a victorious war. The present-day view is that this kind of working from specific cause to specific effect will mostly not hold water in these complex matters of civilization. Modern opinion sees correlations or functional interrelations between a group of historical phenomena, rather than saying that A "produces" B. The Armada, Shakespeare, the playwriters who preceded both, the poet Spenser, Harvey with his circulation of the blood, Napier and his invention of logarithms, the composers of madrigals, the freebooter Drake, Raleigh and his colonial expansion, are all interconnected in making the Britain of 1575-1615. Each of them represents or expresses part of a successful pattern; and the group of patterns together constitutes the national culture-whole pattern of England in its temporary "Elizabethan" phase.

These national spurts of success and concentrations of cultural productivity may accordingly be regarded as constituting a phenomenon that recurs through history—and presumably through prehistory—even though separate occurrences never manifest wholly identical forms. The bursts have considerable significance in illuminating the dynamics of style patterns, the nature of genius, and the causes of invention. Their bearing on these three matters will now be considered in turn.

137. STYLE PATTERNS [5]

The basic reason for the concentrations of productivity seems to be that for things to be done well they must be done definitely, and definite results can be achieved only through some specific method, technique, manner, or plan of operations. Such a particular method or manner is called a *style* in all the arts, as we have seen. And "style" is perhaps the best available word that will cover also the corresponding methods or plans in other activities. We can speak of styles of governing, of waging war, of prosecuting industry or commerce, of promoting science, even of speculative reasoning. For instance, all modern Occidental business is carried on in a style that includes banking and credit. But ancient and Byzantine and Islamic businessmen necessarily followed a quite different style or pattern because they did not seriously employ credit, and actual money had usually to be collected or moved for any and all transactions. A style, then, may be said to be a way of achieving definiteness and effectiveness in human relations by choosing or evolving one line of procedure out of several possibles ones, and sticking to it. That means, psychologically, that habits become channeled, facility and skill are acquired, and that this skill can then be extended to larger situations or to somewhat altered ones. This process may mount for a while, the original skill itself being developed farther or giving rise to subsidiary ones. Or it may mount through enlargement of the field to which it is being applied, and therewith the product achieved perhaps increases in quantity as well as improving in quality. But the process cannot go on mounting indefinitely, because it began with a limitation of choice, a selection among possibilities. Therefore every style is necessarily prelimited: it is an essential commitment to one manner, to the exclusion of others. Accordingly it cannot encompass everything. The range of its channeled skills will extend so far; beyond, they fail. Then we say that the style has exhausted itself, its characteristic pattern has broken down. Or the style may be able to maintain itself for a while, but without any longer increasing the range of its control or improving its achievements. When this termination has been reached, accordingly, there is either decline or a freezing. The style either loses its skill of touch and its products deteriorate; or it becomes frankly repetitive, which is usually equivalent to a slowed-up deterioration, interest and feeling having been lost when further change is eliminated. A pickup in quality will normally be possible only with a new start toward a new style. And the evolution of a new style is likely to be easier to outsiders or novices than to the group which has been reared in an old style. That is why nations replace one another in their achievements; or if one does repeat, it is usually after a considerable interval.

This course of development will be familiar to anyone who has ever followed through the history of any art style, whether in literature, sculpture, paint-

---

[5] This is the last of the four kinds of patterns listed in the introduction to this chapter

ing, architecture, or music. It is a commonplace that all aesthetic styles rise and fall and perish. All art has constantly to get itself reborn with a new set of impulses, and then run a new course. Why that is so is what has just been set forth. But, as has also been just said, the arts are by no means something wholly set apart from the rest of civilization. The same principles of style or method, and therefore of pulsation, tend to hold for most or all cultural activities except the basic day-by-day and year-by-year repetitive ones like plowing and reaping, making a living, cooking and eating, marrying and dying. And even in these day-by-day activities, style patterns do intrude: we certainly have changing styles of cookery—usually dignified as cuisines; of marrying—early or late, for love or convenience, and so on; of funerals and corpse disposals. However, let us consider a cultural activity that is obviously neither of the repetitive kind nor aesthetic, one that passes as cumulatively progressive: science.

We have seen that Greek science and mathematics came in a four-century spurt and then stood still. The Greeks never did achieve much in simple arithmetic, probably partly because their method of writing quantities—by letter symbols denoting certain specific numbers instead of by position numerals—made ordinary computations of any size difficult. Even less was accomplished by them in algebra, of which the imperfect rudiments began—or first appear to our view—some four hundred years after Greek general mathematical progress had stopped. The branch of mathematics the Greeks did wholly originate and develop was geometry—plane, solid, and spherical. Here they substantially "exhausted the pattern," fulfilled its possibilities, and left nothing for others to discover. Now geometry is a special way of doing mathematics—with a compass and rule and nothing more, the Greeks insisted. It visualizes properties and relations; it can be pictured, as algebra and arithmetic cannot be. Although already truly abstract, geometry easily retains the most concrete aspect of all branches of mathematics. This geometric approach was the Greek "style" in mathematics. One part of the style was the Greek emphasis on proportion, which can also be diagramed; and the Greek avoidance, where possible, of all but integral numbers, which can be handled like visible and tangible blocks; and the avoidance also of negative quantities and irrational fractions, which cannot be handled in this way. On the positive side again, the Greeks pushed on from their geometry into conic sections—dealing with plane cuts across cones, resulting in curves such as ellipses, parabolas, hyperbolas. This is a branch of mathematics which we still call by the original name of "conic sections," although we mostly express its concepts algebraically now. The further limitations of the mathematical style of the Greeks are shown by their failure to develop anything at all in the field of logarithms, analytical geometry, calculus, or the concept of function. What they could do with their geometrical and whole-number manner or style, they achieved. Other mathematical possibilities, like these mentioned, were simply left to be realized by other peoples and times—chiefly by western Europeans in the last three or four centuries.

A style of mathematics quite different from both the ancient Greek and the modern Occidental was briefly developed in China around 1300 but was soon dropped, then taken up in Japan around 1600, and carried farther there during the following two centuries. This was an algebraic approach, though quite different in detail from Western algebra and very likely unconnected with it. This method was used ingeniously enough; but as neither China nor Japan had ever discovered or learned geometry, their method or style of mathematics was subject to limitations as great as was the Greek method, though the limitations were in many ways almost opposite. For instance, the native Chinese-Japanese algebra handled negative quantities as freely as it handled positive ones, but it concerned itself very little with the properties of shapes, such as triangles, cylinders, or tetrahedrons.

In much the same way, the style of ancient Greek science as a whole and the style of European science are distinguishable. The Greeks observed, but without instruments and without standard measures; and they did not experiment. These aids to the prosecution of science were developed only after A.D. 1500, as part of the western-European method of science. Galileo's trials with bodies falling from the leaning towar of Pisa were made about 1590. The telescope, invented in Holland in 1608 (§ 140, 152), was used for astronomical discovery by Galileo within two or three years. The microscope was almost simultaneous. Since understanding of the subtler forms of energy and of the qualitative properties of matter seems to depend on systematic experimentation, the basic discoveries in electromagnetism and chemistry were made still later, about 1750 to 1800, after the modern European pattern or style of science was becoming mature.

We can assume, then, that the higher values of human civilization tend to be produced in bursts or spurts of growth. This is because their achievement is dependent on the development of specific methods or styles somewhat similar in kind to styles in art; and, like art styles, it is limited or exhaustible. Further progress, beyond the potentialities of a given style and pattern, normally requires a pause, followed by a fresh start with a new style or pattern—a new approach to the problem, we might say. This principle seems to apply almost equally to aesthetic activities, to intellectual ones, to politico-military or national fortunes, and even to major economic achievements. At any rate, such related items as machine versus manual manufacture, mass production, and credit suggest that industrial progress can also be due to the fact that a "style pattern" has been devised.

138. BASIC PATTERN AND STYLE VARIABILITY

Dress obviously is heavily involved in the matters under discussion. The first association of many women to "pattern" is likely to be the paper model from which dresses are cut and shaped. Vulgarly, the word "style" refers to dress first of all; and it is certainly plain that dress in general is heavily conditioned by style. But beyond all this, dress excellently exemplifies even basic pattern and its influence.

For instance, Occidental civilization, Ancient Mediterranean, and East Asiatic are each characterized by a distinctive, long-term basic pattern of clothing. In comparison with our fitted clothing, Greek and Roman clothing was draped on the body. While this statement is not wholly exact, it is true comparatively. Sleeves were little developed, trousers lacking, the waist of clothing was not fitted in to follow the body, the general effect accentuated the fall of drapery and the flowing line. The Roman toga was a wrap-around blanket. One did not slip into it like a coat, one adjusted it to hang in proper folds.

After prevailing for many centuries, this basic pattern of dress began to crumble and become transformed toward the end of the Roman Empire, when the old Hellenic-Latin religion had yielded to Christianity and the total Mediterranean civilization was disintegrating and at the point of gradually being replaced by the beginnings of our Occidental one. Trousers, in spite of protests and counterlegislation, were adopted from the barbarians. Sleeves came into general use. During the Dark Ages, the transition was gradually accomplished. The fitted clothes might be pretty well concealed under a long coat or cloak, as in the sixth-century mosaics of the Eastern Emperor Justinian and the Empress Theodora; but they were there. By the Middle Ages, they were in the open; and their pattern is still the fundamental pattern of our own clothing. The characteristic of this, in contrast with ancient clothing, is that it is cut and tailored, fitted to the figure. Our word "tailored" is from French *tailleur,* one who cuts, carves, or trims; and *taille* still denotes both the figure as a whole and the waist. The plan of Western clothing for men is that its parts follow the limbs as well as the figure. For women, on the contrary, the legs are withdrawn from sight in a skirt that during most centuries has been ample. From the hips up, however, the pattern of Western women's wear makes up for the loose skirt and has a bodice or an equivalent that follows waist, bosom, shoulders, and arms fairly closely.

How thoroughly this is our basic type of dress even today, underneath all local or national variations and fluctuations of period and fashion, is evident when we compare Western dress as a whole for the past thousand years with the East Asiatic in the same millennium. Chinese and Japanese dress is also cut and tailored, but it is not fitted. It is cut loose, with ample sleeves, or kimono style, to suggest a broad figure. Trousers are ample, so as to have almost a skirt effect. The use of clothing to model or suggest women's bust, waist, and hip contour is wholly outside the Far Eastern pattern. Witness the Japanese *obi* sash and bow intended to conceal these features, while European women for four centuries or more have worn corsets and girdles to accentuate them.

Of course dress is notoriously subject to fashion change. But it is remarkable how virtually all changes of fashion, alike in Classical, Western, and East

Asiatic costume, have consistently operated each within the basic dress pattern of its own civilization. Fashion creates a thousand bizarre forms and extravagances; but it never has produced, among Occidentals, a man's type of dress based on toga instead of trousers, nor a woman's with a Japanese silhouette. The matter of fashion changes. which represent a minor sort of restless and anonymous innovation or invention, is discussed elsewhere (§ 164), with emphasis on a concealed rhythm or regularity much greater than the participants in a fashion are ordinarily aware of. But there is another aspect of fashion change—what may be called the intensity of its alteration, its momentary degree of variability—that both defines the basic pattern and helps to explain variation from it. Variability is high when the fashion of one year differs considerably from that of the year before; it is still more so when a series of particular dresses, all of the same year, differ considerably from one another. Low variability of course is marked by small differences of this sort. Such variabilities are easily expressed statistically.[6]

The underlying fashion swings or trends change what might be called the total silhouette of dress rather than its details. These minor features may come and go quite rapidly, and are what give the impression nearly everyone has that dress fashions are highly unstable. On the contrary, the total silhouette shifts rather steadily for perhaps fifty years toward one extreme of proportion, such as a narrow skirt for women, and then for about fifty years toward the opposite, giving a wavelength of close to a century for the periodicity, which seems to be adhered to with fair consistency in case after case.

It might be thought that the basic pattern (for Occidental women's dress during the last hundred and fifty years) would lie somewhere between these proportion extremes. Occasionally it does. But mostly the basic pattern proves to coincide with one of the extremes. The other extreme then represents a sort of opposition or aberration from the pattern. One might describe these aberrant extremes as the proportions still just inside the pattern but as far away as possible from its center of gravity. Or one might say the aberrant extreme is antithetical—almost perversely antithetical—to the ideal or saturation point of the pattern, though still barely remaining within its range. Thus, as the permanent Western pattern aims at amplitude from the hips down but slenderness above, the silhouette-extremes conformable to the pattern would be: full or wide skirt, long or low skirt, narrow waist, and therefore waistline just at the waist proper. The antithetical extremes would be: narrow skirt, short skirt, wide or full waist, and waistline moved from the anatomically narrowest part up toward the broader breast or down toward the broader hips. In this last proportion— position of the waistline—pattern saturation evidently falls at the midpoint between extremes. In the three other proportions, pattern saturation coincides with one of the extremes.

---

[6] By the standard deviation or sigma, converted into a percentage of the mean as the coefficient of variability.

A glance at the silhouettes in the upper row of Figure 19, showing characteristic dress at twenty-year intervals during the latter and larger part of the nineteenth century, reveals what characterizes the pattern—its consant stable features underneath temporary fluctuations. The lower row gives two silhouettes from the period of the French Revolution and Napoleon, and two from the period of the World Wars—two eras of sociopolitical restlessness enclosing the relative calm of Victorian times. Here skirts are in evidence that are narrow or high or both, and waists that are thick or ultrahigh or ultralow—the aberrant extremes.

VARIABILITY IN EUROPEAN WOMEN'S DRESS SILHOUETTE DURING FOUR YEARS OF PATTERN CONFORMITY AND STABILITY COMPARED WITH FOUR YEARS OF PATTERN STRAIN AND INSTABILITY

Stable Pattern Years: Low Variability *

	1839	1859	1879	1899	Mean of 4 years
Skirt length	27	0	55	0	21
Skirt width	61	22	73	61	54
Waist height	53	40	53	53	50
Waist width	170	107	43	138	115

Unstable Pattern Years: High Variability *

	1789	1813	1916	1935	Mean of 4 years
Skirt length	164	492	219	109	246
Skirt width	61	235	151	162	152
Waist height	93	253	106	186	160
Waist width	277	107	128	256	192

* Figures express $100(V$ for year$)/($mean V for 150 years$)$.—$V = 100\sigma/M$

When we look at the statistical expression of fashion variability in the same selected eight years as given in corresponding position on the facing page, it is at once clear that the years and decades of pattern saturation or concordance are marked by definitely low variability, indicative of stability; and the years and eras of pattern antithesis or stretch are marked by a surprisingly great variability, indicative of instability. Stability and instability here refer to the dress style pattern and its behavior. Since the periods of dress-pattern instability were also periods of marked sociopolitical instability and churning, there is presumably a connection.

The connection or relation seems functional rather than causal. There is nothing to indicate that the mere presence of wars and revolutions will make designers deliberately plan consecutive dresses as different as is possible within

FIG. 19. BASIC STYLE PATTERN IN WOMEN'S CLOTHES

Transient fashions conforming to basic pattern in upper stagger contrast with intrinsic departures from pattern in the lower. Also, upper figures are accompanied by low
variability of fashion, and date from the calm Victorian era; lower figures show high
variability and date from Revolution, Napoleonic, and World War periods.

the mode, whereas in times of calm they design them as alike as they can make them and still keep them from being identical. What evidently happens is merely that in periods of general stress, when the foundations of society and civilization seem rocked, the pattern of dress is also infected and subject to strain. It expresses this strain by moving from stable saturation to aberration, antithesis, restlessness, and instability.[7]

This example may make more concrete the role of patterns—both style patterns and total-culture patterns—in cultural change and stability. Not that patterns are the beginning and end of everything about civilization. But practically everything in culture occurs as part of one or more patterns. Hence whatever happens in the way of accomplishment, alteration, succession, or persistence in any culture is likely to happen through the mechanism of patterns. We do not yet know too much about them, because awareness of patterns is relatively recent in anthropology. But it is already clear that understanding of culture as something more than an endless series of haphazard items is going to be achieved largely through recognition of patterns and our ability to analyze them.

139. THE CLUSTERING AND NATURE OF GENIUS

We have seen that the higher values of civilizations, their greater accomplishments, tend to be achieved spasmodically, in intermittent bursts. Also, these bursts can be associated with the growth and fulfillment of style-type patterns. Yet there is something else equally associated with the bursts of cultural productivity. This is frequency of genius, frequency of extraordinarily gifted individuals.

Personalities of the very highest ability—whether in ruling, thinking, imagining, innovating, warring, or religious influencing—have long been known to occur in concentrations of country and period. The list in § 136 is not only a tabulation of when drama, sculpture, war, philosophy, and other activities of culture flourished in ancient Greece; it is equally an enumeration of its great men, its outstanding geniuses. The philosophy, for instance, is *exemplified* by Plato and Aristotle, by their predecessors like Democritus and Socrates, by their successors like Epicurus and Zeno the Stoic. Or we can equally well say that it is these men who *produced* the philosophy. These are but two ways of describing the same phenomenon. Obviously, there is not going to be much important philosophy without able philosophers around, nor able philosophers without important philosophy to show for it.

---

[7] Literally, of course, it is the minds of designers of dresses that are affected and show strain in their creations. But since such individuals tend to be affected and to react more or less alike, it is their common behavior, and the common drift of their products, that are historically most significant. This significance in turn justifies the use of short-cut metaphors like "patterns being infected," "straining," "moving," "saturating," "freezing."

Of these two related aspects, the philosophy and the philosophers, the activity and product or the personalities, there is no doubt which is the easier to grasp: the concrete persons. All sorts of Athenian contemporaries saw, heard, and perhaps touched Socrates, and had quite definite reactions to him and judgments of his merits—Athenians who nevertheless knew little and understood less of his thoughts. Through the accounts of Plato and Xenophon, Socrates remains today a very living and real personality whom one can never quite forget even if one's interest in philosophy be zero or negative. Hence ordinarily we tend to think first of Socrates the man and secondarily of what new ideas he produced. To put it on a lower level, a child cannot comprehend a philosophy, but it can comprehend events like being married to Xantippe or drinking hemlock in prison. The first recognition of the two-faced type of phenomenon we are dealing with, accordingly, was in terms of great men and their near-simultaneity or clustering. This fact was already recognized by the later Greeks and the Romans. Velleius Paterculus, a historian contemporary with Augustus, has quite a little passage on it. No one since appears to have doubted it.

However, as long as the matter is viewed simply as one of persons, it remains rather meaningless—curious but inexplicable. It came to be accepted that there are golden ages thickly studded with great men achieving unforgettable products; silver ages with somewhat lesser men attaining smaller performance; and ordinary times when men of ability or talent are still available though the great lights of history just do not put in their appearance. But no reason was manifest, through many unstatistically minded centuries, for such fluctuations, which glaringly violate the principle of random distribution or accidental occurrence, and therefore suggest that there must be specific factors at work to produce the unevennesses.

Biologically we know that hereditary races are constant to the degree that if a thousand morons and one man of genius are born per million in this generation, the proportion is unlikely to be seriously different in the next generation or for a number of generations following. If Athens for a thousand years had no great men, began to have a few in the sixth century, produced an astonishing number of geniuses of absolutely first rank in the fifth and fourth centuries, tapered off in the third, then became sterile again and has remained so until now, there is no known mechanism of heredity which can explain this fluctuation of incidence of high ability; nor is it within the reasonable bounds of mere statistical possibility. Galton, who still argued for a change to inherent race superiority in the Athenians (§ 90), because little was known before his time about the heredity of intelligence and ability, already recognized that the brief upcurve could not be a statistical accident, but that it must indicate some factor at work. Nor is there any serious doubt now what that factor is, among the ancient Athenians and in similar cases. It is, in general, what is variously called the milieu, the social environment, the cultural context, the condition of civilization. More specifically, the involved factor may be supposed to be the nature and degree of development of the value or style patterns of the Greeks, and among them of the Athenians in particular, around 500 B.C. There was a style of tragedy, for instance, in the making then. Aeschylus developed this tragic style farther in the grand manner, Sophocles freed it from the last traces of archaism, Euripides introduced the final psychological finesses and tendernesses—and in this style of tragedy there was nothing essential or important left to be done. If there had been an unfinished remnant to be achieved, it is expectable that this remnant would have been contributed. With the exhaustion of the Greek tragic pattern, no very great Greek tragic poets could arise, it may fairly be argued. There was nothing left for them to do in the Athenian pattern. Nor could they, as children of their time and place, conceivably invent Elizabethan or Japanese tragedy, not even in Attic Greek language dress.

Now this explanation does not mean that the state of the dramatic pattern in Athens around 400 B.C. prevented the *birth* of men endowed by nature with high potential ability of expressing themselves in tragic poetry. Such a direct reaction of a momentary condition of culture on organic heredity would be an even more unreasonable belief than Galton's belief that the heredity turned itself on and off again within a dozen generations like a playful faucet. What the situation does warrant us in inferring is that when general cultural conditions and specific dramatic pattern conditions were at their optimum in Greece, there would be an average of one individual of the poetic potentiality and caliber of Sophocles or Euripides born among so and so many thousand or million Athenians; and also that these rare individuals would be able to realize or express their gift by writing tragedies. When the general and specific pattern conditions were not at optimum, there would continue to be just as many potential poetic geniuses born among the same number of Athenians, but they would not become tragedians, or if they stubbornly tried to, they would find that their say had already been said, and that instead of fame they were acquiring mainly a repute for being somewhat dull repeaters. Conceivably, if they had a somewhat different vein in them also, they might still become great comic poets, since Athenian comedy ran a somewhat later course than tragedy. Or if their gifts were not too narrowly specialized but were plastically adaptable, these potential geniuses might have become actualized geniuses in oratory or history-writing, or perhaps even in philosophy. Here we are at the border of certainty of opinion, because no one yet knows how far the high capacities that we call genius are congenitally specialized—say for poetry and not for prose—or on the contrary how far these capacities are general—like articulateness of expression, for instance, or originality of ideas—and it is a matter of conditioning after birth that determines whether the inherent genius is to become a writer of tragedy, comedy, lyrics, or prose.

In any event, within a very few hundred years there was no form of literature left active in Athens, and soon after that no form of cultural activity anywhere among Greeks, in which a congenital super-AAA genius could any longer hope to attain super-AAA rating. This was because the possibilities of Greek civilization were so used up, its pattern so exhausted, that no super-AAA achievement was any longer possible in that civilization. The same one-in-four-thousand or two-hundred-in-a-million births of top-flight ability presumably continued to take place in Greek society in subsequent times as before.[8] But these individuals simply no longer had any chance to become top-flighters. They very likely became the leaders of their day; but posterity would rate them only BBB instead of AAA, because what posterity can judge, or does judge, is accomplishment. What posterity cannot readily judge, of course, and ordinarily is too busy to try to, is how much of any accomplishment is due to innate or hereditary endowment and how much due to favorable cultural and environmental circumstance.

What we have in this whole matter, in summary, is first the fact that great men do constellate, or genius does cluster; and second, an explanation of that fact in terms of degree of development of patterns of the style type. A third consideration may be added; namely, the reflection that only a fraction of all the men congenitally equipped for genius ever actualize as such. Only a fraction are ever found out, or allowed the rank, by history. This fraction is the same as the proportion that the number of generations recognized as fruitful and genius-studded, in all lands, bears to the number of barren, geniusless generations. This proportion can hardly be reckoned as greater than one in four, and may be as little as one in ten, if we take into account all the regions and eras of the world in which it is customary not to recognize any geniuses as having occurred.

There is a point of impressive significance here. Human biological heredity runs good enough to produce, once in every so many hundred thousand or million births, an individual so highly gifted as to be capable of becoming one of the lights of our species, a benefactor or a creator whose work will live in history; and yet the nature of our culture manages to neutralize or frustrate from seventy-five to perhaps ninety out of every hundred such great geniuses, or to depress them into mere second-rank talents or transient leaders of soon-forgotten days. Ideally considered, this is a tremendous waste from the point of view of those concerned with human achievement. It certainly invites the consideration of eugenicists, to whom it offers the pessimistic prospect that even if they should succeed in improving the heredity of our species, three-fourths or more of the gain would be lost again by the shockingly wasteful way in which civilization to date has operated.[9]

[8] Galton computed 248 in a million, or 1 in 4032, as born in Attica 530-430 B.C.

[9] This over-all wastage of 75 per cent or more of the finest congenital talents born in the human species may seem to constitute a blasting indictment of human culture. But without culture, the waste would be a complete 100 per cent. Culture is admittedly still an imperfect instrument.

Logically, of course, what we have in this situation about genius is a distinction we have already considered in connection with race (§ 86, 90): that achievement and capacity for achievement are different things, and that they do not correlate in any outright one-to-one or other simple manner. We assume that achievement presupposes inherent capacity, though even here it is a problem to be investigated how close the correspondence comes to being a 100-percent one. We certainly cannot assume that capacity is always actualized in achievement.

One difference between the race problem and the genius problem is that differences in ability between races are still somewhat uncertain, and, being differences of averages, are likely to prove small; whereas individual differences within one race and culture are well substantiated as considerable by psychological and practical tests. Moreover, it is relatively easy to compare individuals of practically identical physique, culture, economic stratum, and social opportunities and yet find marked differences between them; whereas races are never the same in culture, social environment, and opportunities.

Recognition of the fact that potential capacity may not be inferred in regard to race outright from accepted achievement, especially not negatively, began to be well and widely established by 1900. But recognition of the parallel noncorrespondence as regards individual genius did not come until well along in the twentieth century. And the significance of the clustering of both genius and cultural florescence has at times even yet failed to penetrate where an unhistorical attitude of mind prevails.

One possible misconception will be guarded against by its mention. The naïve view of course is that great men do great things. The greater achievements of civilization are therefore "explained" by the great men's happening to come along. Why they come along when and where they do hardly seems to call for further explanation in a pre-culture-conscious period. But once we are aware of culture and begin to take note of its workings, the simultaneous clustering of genius and of style-pattern fulfillments is one of the outstanding manifestations of history, and seems to lead inevitably to the conclusion of the interrelation of genius and pattern. The admission of this interdependence may put some curb on our notion of genius. We can certainly no longer look upon genius as something wholly unaccountable, heaven-sent, exempt from the laws of nature, operative solely according to its own uncontrollable will. Genius is reduced to a phenomenon, and therewith relatable to other phenomena. But genius is thereby not abrogated or denied. The genius remains the superior man, even the supremely able one. But he is such at birth by the bounty of the variability of organic heredity; and he is such at death by the grace of the condition of his culture, which has allowed and helped him to realize his congenital potentialities. In short, understanding of how culture operates does not in the least "abolish" individual superiority. It merely helps to explain greatness while using it also to explain better the patterns of culture.

140. THE MEANING OF SIMULTANEOUS INVENTIONS

Allied both to pattern florescences and to genius clustering is the fact that many inventions have been made independently by two or more men, and often even simultaneously. If this happened just now and then, and were true of only a small minority of all inventions, it could be called coincidence and attributed to accident. But as soon as simultaneity and independence of origin characterize any considerable proportion of inventions or discoveries, it is evident on the basis of the law of averages that some specific factor must be operating in that direction. Now the number of cases is not small: Ogburn and Thomas as long ago as 1922 had listed 148 instances. It is therefore of interest to understand what is at the bottom of the phenomenon, and why it went unrecognized so long—until about the time of World War I.

The reason for the nonrecognition seems to have been the reluctance of our minds to see anything superpersonal in matters that involve persons. Acceptance of impersonal forces lying outside the individual, but driving him to this achievement or that failure, appears somehow to infringe on our personalities, to delimit our freedom. Particularly do we tend to resent such invasions when they concern great intellects.

After 1700, everybody who knew anything of the history of science was aware that Newton and Leibnitz had both devised the calculus, and each at first without knowing of the other's discovery. It was their respective followers and compatriots who fought over priority and insinuated bad faith.

In 1845, Adams and Leverrier separately predicted the discovery of the planet Neptune. Adams's computation was worked out a little the earlier, but Leverrier's was published first, and the planet was promptly seen where he had said it ought to be.

In 1858, Darwin and Wallace presented parallel papers at the same meeting of the Royal Society, setting forth the idea of natural selection as a factor accounting for the evolutionary formation and change of species. Darwin had had the germ of the idea twenty years before, but hesitated to commit himself publicly. When the same idea occurred to Wallace, who was exploring in the East Indies, he promptly wrote it out and sent it to London. This both forced Darwin's hand and strengthened his confidence, with the result of the companion papers as an immediate compromise fair to both men, and the publication of Darwin's *Origin of Species* the next year.

The year 1900 saw the discovery of the basic laws of heredity—it was really a rediscovery, but more of that later (§ 152)—by three several biologists: De Vries, Correns, and Tschermak.

These four instances, all of them relating to fundamental discoveries in science, will at least suffice to take the phenomenon of simultaneity out of the range of mere coincidence. The list on the next page, which could be increased indefinitely, will reinforce the principle. If practically all of the cases cited are from modern Occidental civilization, that is because invention records which are authentic, full, and exactly datable nearly all hail from that civilization. Also it will be seen from the list that technological invention, scientific discovery, and even geographical discovery all behave much alike in this matter of simultaneity—in line with their shading into one another otherwise, as set forth in § 145.

SOME SIMULTANEOUS DISCOVERIES AND INVENTIONS

Telescope: Jansen, Lippershey, Metius, 1608 (§ 137, 152)
Sunspots: Fabricius, Galileo, Harriott, Scheiner, 1611
Logarithms: Napier, 1614; Bürgi, 1620
Calculus: Newton, 1671, publ. 1687; Leibnitz, 1676, publ. 1684
Problem of three bodies: Clairaut, D'Alembert, Euler, 1747
Nitrogen: Rutherford, 1772; Scheele, 1773
Oxygen: Priestley, Scheele, 1774
Water is H_2O: Cavendish, Watt, 1781; Lavoisier, 1783
Steamboat: Jouffroy, 1783; Rumsey, 1787; Fitch, 1788; Symington, 1788 (§ 155, 186)
Theory of Planetary Disturbances: Lagrange, Laplace, 1808
Pepsin: Latour, Schwann, 1835
Telegraph: Henry, Morse, Steinheil, Wheatstone and Cooke, about 1837 (§ 187)
Star parallax first measured: Bessel, Henderson, Struve, 1838
Photography: Daguerre and Niepce, Talbot, 1839 (§ 187)
Planet Neptune: Adams, Leverrier, 1845
Surgical anaesthesia by ether: Long, 1842, results disregarded; Jackson, Liston, Morton, Robinson, 1846; N_2O, Wells, 1845
Sunspot variations correlated with disturbances on earth: Gauthier, Sabine, Wolfe, 1852
Natural selection: Darwin, Wallace, 1858
Periodic Law of Elements: Mendeleev, Meyer, 1869
Telephone: Bell, Gray, 1876 (§ 187)
Phonograph: Cros, Edison, 1877 (§ 187)
Liquefaction of oxygen: Cailletet, Pictet, 1877
Rediscovery of Mendel's Laws: De Vries, Correns, Tschermak, 1900 (respectively on March 14, April 24, June 2; see § 152)
North Pole: Cook,[10] Peary, 1909
South Pole: Amundsen, December, 1911; Scott, January, 1912
Flight orientation of bats due to hearing reflections of uttered sounds: Griffin and Galambos, U.S.A., 1941-42; Dijkgraat, Holland, 1943—during total severance of communications in war years

A list like this tends to instill a conviction that inventions may be inevitable, within certain limits; that given a certain constellation and development of a culture, certain inventions must be made. Such a conclusion involves

[10] That Cook's discovery was untrue varies the principle of simultaneity without invalidating it. Fifty years earlier it would probably not have occurred to anyone even to pretend the discovery; twenty, perhaps even ten, years earlier, the claim would have been received with such incredulity as to discourage a false claimant; 1909 was the psychological moment for a fake attempt—the whole world was agog for the discovery that Peary was actually consummating.

the recognition of superindividual forces—historical agencies or social currents transcending personalities. This is a matter which will be taken up again, and more fully, in connection with the nature of invention, in § 145-155, especially 152. Our more immediate concern here is with the clustering of able inventors around an important invention or series of related inventions, like the clustering of able or great men in a particular art or any phase of a nationally delimited culture growth. The two sets of clusterings are strikingly similar; and it is evident that they are both related to the development of culture patterns. The patterns must have a certain potentiality, and they must have reached a stage of "fruitfulness," before we can expect great men, great productions, or great inventions. But once geniuses, achievements, or inventions begin to arrive, they may be expected in bursts of concentration.

CHAPTER NINE

Culture Processes

141. CULTURE PROCESSES

BY PROCESSES of culture we mean those factors which operate either toward the stabilization and preservation of cultures and their parts, or toward growth and change. Changes, in turn, may consist either of increments, such as new developments, inventions, and learned traits acquired from outside; or of losses and displacements. Beyond these, there are minor alterations or fluctuations that are neither particularly additive nor deductive, as when the wheel base of automobiles is shortened, or the floor is lowered, or the engine is placed behind.

The main value of these formal distinctions of kinds of process is logical: they help us organize a large mass of facts into some sort of preliminary order. For that reason the topical sequence of consideration: persistence, invention, loss, in this chapter, and change in the next, will be followed here. But as cultures and their parts actually live, thrive, decay, and alter, and as they influence one another, these several processes, which in the abstract seem so neat and distinctive, are found to manifest themselves in association and interwoven. All of them are often at work at once, so that the same phenomenon may be seen as an example of two or three of them. This constant interrelation of processes is characteristic of culture. Their segregation has something artificial about it, and is justified chiefly by convenience.

For instance, one might expect innovations to cause displacements: for the steel knife to crowd out the stone knife. But the latter may survive in ritual; or the stone tool may have become associated with certain motor habits that it is awkward or unprofitable to change, as when the Yurok Indians eagerly took over our American knives for most purposes, but during a couple of generations retained their flint ones for dressing and splitting salmon. If there is such a retention alongside the addition, the culture of course now possesses two traits instead of one. Yet we may not assume that this always happens, else cultures would regularly grow additively or cumulatively. They do sometimes: our Western civilization undoubtedly has more content now than it had a thousand years ago. But it is probable that there are occasions when losses can and do exceed additions: for instance, in Italy during the first seven or eight centuries of the Christian era.

What happens in particular cultures may of course happen to their sum, to human culture in the aggregate. The total quantity of this probably does tend to increase, but certainly at uneven rates in different periods and areas, as already discussed in § 127. Variation and fluctuation of culture content are evidently more typical events than its steady increase. If any generic inherent force making for progressive cultural accumulation existed, it would be difficult to explain the fact that there still remain backward and lowly "primitive" cultures of meager content.

We may conclude that while innovations sometimes result in displacements, they sometimes do not; but that losses also can occur without gains. While there is a relation between the two currents, they are separate enough to justify their separate consideration.

Even changes and persistences blend into each other. The normal way in which culture continues is for one generation of a society to transmit its culture to the next generation, the process occurring in time, since societies and cultures are normally attached to an area. But when one culture transmits some of its content to another—when for instance porcelain or papermaking diffuses from China to Europe, or glass or surveying from Europe to China—the receiving culture has changed by acquiring something new, though the process of transmission is now through space instead of time. But from the angle of the total culture material in the world, there has been merely a continuance of a trait, accompanied by its geographical spread, conceivably without any change in the trait itself, or only minimal change. Ultimately a diffusing technique or institution or system may even die out or be displaced in its homeland, but survive where it was imported; as Christianity withered away in Palestine, and Buddhism in India, but they continue to flourish respectively in Europe and China. In Europe, however, Christianity crowded out all other organized religions; whereas in China, Taoism and Confucianism have maintained themselves alongside Buddhism.

These instances will indicate what is meant by the statement that conceptually distinct processes tend to come intertwined, and to interact, in the actual operations and history of culture.

142. PERSISTENCE

It has been asserted that the first problem of any culture is that of its survival or persistence, much as any society is always confronted by the problem of surviving. This allegation seems truer logically than important factually. If a culture perishes, there is an obvious end to its problems of adaptation and modification. But this does not by any means involve every culture's constant striving to avert disaster—least of all an awareness of being perpetually faced by a life-or-death problem. Nor are societies in chronically acute jeopardy. Their case is rather like that of individual organisms. These also have indispensable needs, but mainly they are organized to function as physiological successes, and on the whole they do so. The same with human societies and their cultures: normally they make a go of it, at least for a time. What is more, most peoples expect to make a go of it. They do not expect that they themselves and their institutions will have crashed to ruin by next year. Such overclouded, anxiety-ridden states of mind would have something of the abnormal about them. Perhaps the whole notion of their being usual is a reflection in the minds of some anthropologists of the uncertainties, strains, depressions, and threats of the period from World War I to World War II (cf. § 122).

What is true is that ordinarily societies cling with attachment to their cultures. Genuine revolutionaries are rare, the world over. They characterize particular periods and limited areas. Reformers are more numerous; but even these generally want particular improvements on top of a basic maintenance of the scheme of things. And a large part of mankind just is fundamentally conservative—which means that they like their culture and their personal stake in it. This personal stake and its rewards might well be bigger for the average man, and he is likely to be trying to make it a bit bigger; but mostly he does so without any notion of changing the rules, except perhaps at a spot or two. This is not a statement of what should be, but an attempt to summarize the attitude of most people, primitive, barbarous, and highly advanced, throughout history and all over the earth.

There are several reasons for this attachment of men to their cultures. One of course is habit adjustment. We have been molded by our culture until we fit it, more or less, have got used to functioning within its framework, and have channeled such functioning into habits. Then there is always education of the young, both spontaneous and deliberate. This inevitably exalts the ideals and values of the instructing generation. In most countries and times, these ideals of the elders are pretty generally accepted, without much criticism or serious revolt. The folkways tend to persist; the mores are held to firmly, with release of emotion if they are challenged. It must be remembered that the idea and ideal of progress, which we of modern Western civilization tend to accept as axiomatic

(§ 127), has not been in the least axiomatic to mankind at large. To most societies the notion has hardly occurred, at any rate not as a guiding principle. They rather take essential continuance for granted: the golden age is in the past, not ahead. There certainly is reassurance and comfort in the idea of continuance, unless one has been imbued with the contrary attitude that restless improvement is a desirable thing, or a sort of obligation.

The famous French sociologist Durkheim went so far as to maintain that what the "most primitive" people—meaning the Australians—really worship through their rites, sacrifices, and taboos is the bonds of their society and the institutions of their culture. The totems and the ancestors and their impersonations, the sacred spots and the hallowed paraphernalia of bull-roarers, the carefully screened mysteries—all these are not randomly worshiped ghosts, animals, rocks, and fetishes, but symbols of the total tribal society of the past, the present, and the future, and its successful adaptation in the universe through entering into mystic ritual relations with the universe. This interpretation perhaps fits the Australians more tellingly than it would fit most primitives and nonliterates, and is somewhat extreme even as regards them; but the view undoubtedly expresses considerable truth, and it would be more widely accepted today if Durkheim had not stretched it into a basic philosophy of all culture and society that savored almost as much of mysticism as did the beliefs of the savages. There is no doubt that most religious cults stress strongly the continuity with all the past, an accord or oneness of the individual or his group with the whole world, and the basic changelessness of these relations.

It is also necessary to remember how children—and adults—enter into assimilation and participation with their society and culture, as already touched on in § 123. One of two main mechanisms for this is voluntary adaptation— imitation, wanting to conform, learning from example. Some of this is conscious, or begins consciously; more of it is unconscious, or foreconscious. Perhaps it would be fair to say that normally there exists a strong emotional bent, which is latently conscious, toward participation, and therefore toward assimilation and learning, but that the actual imitating by the young is mostly done without much specific awareness.

The second mechanism making for participation of the young in their culture, and their fitting into society, is education, learning by being taught or trained. This is clearly in the main a conscious process, even though its implications may often be overlooked. In general, what elders teach the young is ways of becoming what they themselves are and have attained; or what they might have become and attained under the same cultural rules if their luck or their ability had been better. It is evident that both mechanisms are calculated to work toward perpetuation and persistence.

143. MOTOR HABITS

Among the factors that make for persistence of culture, in whatever form it happens to have anywhere, are motor habits. Such habits become established in all higher animals. Resting on congenital anatomical structure, they may be modified, and are channeled, in accord with the circumstances of environment. In the field of culture, motor habits become particularly conspicuous in the technologies and the arts. As long as these arts are studied chiefly through their products, such as museum specimens, the motor habits that went into the making of the objects do not obtrude. But if it is possible to give attention to production as well as to product, motor habits are quickly seen to be a definite factor. For instance, whittling, sawing, planing, and many other tool operations can be done either by pushing or by pulling. The Japanese carpenter pulls the plane toward himself, centripetally. The Western workman pushes it away from his body, centrifugally. Probably one method is as good as the other in most cases. But once a certain skill has become established in connection with pushing, it is impossible for a given individual to be equally skillful when he substitutes the pulling motion. He may attain such skill by deliberately trying to learn a new habit, but meanwhile his work is that of a novice. As there is usually no reward for a change, and likely to be an obvious penalty, because of temporarily decreased quality of performance, the change is not made, and the individual remains a lifelong addict to the particular set of habits that first became established in him. Just as he acquired these habits from older workmen, he is likely to transmit them to his apprentices or pupils. Thus not only does one habit prevail among a certain population, and the contrary or a different one among another population, but such habits may persist for hundreds or thousands of years. These habits are definite parts of cultures. The difference between pushing and pulling a plane is as much a culture phenomenon as the difference between smoothing with a piece of sandstone and with a carpenter's plane.

There are a great many situations in which one way of performing an operation is about as good intrinsically as the other; but it is frequently more efficient, or at least timesaving and effort-saving, to decide on one method and stick to it. Driving on the right or the left side of the road is a case in point. Where traffic is negligible or slow, it is quite possible to get on without any motor habit or rule. In proportion as traffic is heavy and swift, it becomes indispensable to make a decision once for all and then to establish the chosen habit as an individual automatic reaction, as well as a law of the society. It is notorious that since the nations of the world have felt it necessary each to enforce a choice in the matter, they have divided, some in favor of right-hand and some of left-hand driving. Any reasons for one being intrinsically preferable to the other are mainly rationalizations. What actually seems to have happened is that loose tendencies toward passing oncoming vehicles on one side or the other became crystallized as wagon traffic became heavier with the growth of population and the improvement of roads, and were then transferred to the automobile when the matter of uniformity of reaction had become imperative.

It is interesting that once such a rule becomes set among a population it may be easier to alter manufactured objects than to change the rule. The English began with the horse-driver sitting on the right side of the seat and turning to the left on meeting another vehicle. He could thus see whether the wheels of the two vehicles were clear. When horses and wagons and roads were introduced in British Colonial America, the driver presumably continued to sit on the right of the seat: he had an established motor habit on this point. Traffic, however, was at first so sparse that apparently any rules of passing fell into disuse; and when finally, with the increase of horse-drawn vehicles, a rule or custom became desirable, the right-hand pass of oncoming vehicles was somehow chosen. This put the driver away from his clearing wheel; but apparently this was felt only as a minor objection. Only after the automobile with its much greater speed came on the scene, was there seen to be an element of serious danger. Then the conflict was solved by altering the pattern of car construction so that the driver was now put on the left side of his seat. The rule of swerving to the right, in which instantaneous response to a motor habit is frequently vital, remained unaltered.

Even animals get their motor habits conditioned by human culture. In our civilization one mounts to the saddle by the left stirrup. Many horses become disturbed or alarmed by an attempt to mount them from the right. An animal taught to obey the jerk line in multiple-team plowing will not know how to respond to the rein, and vice versa.

Differences in motor habits are not necessarily between whole cultures or societies. They may exist between groups within the same society, or between the sexes. Among ourselves a man's coat or vest buttons from the left over the right. The buttons are on the right edge. The side that carries the buttonholes laps over this from the left. The rule in women's garments is the opposite. The left side carries the buttons and the right is laid over and outside it. The result is that men execute most of the business of buttoning with their left hand, women with the right. Habits get established, and transfer to the other hand would bring awkwardness and irritation.

In weaving cloth on a vertical loom it is possible to begin inserting the weft either at the top or at the bottom. In a basket the direction of progress of weave can be clockwise or counterclockwise. Here it is possible to set up explanations to the effect that most people are right-handed, and that it is natural to keep the defter fingers free for the insertion and pulling of the weft while the left hand holds or spreads the warps. A basket can however be woven at the near edge, with the worker facing its outside; or it can be woven across its hollow, facing the inside, in which case the progress of the same weft between the weaver's hands would be opposite. Ordinarily perhaps a basket is manufactured resting on what will be its bottom; but some tribes hang the foundation of the basket up on a cord and work downward toward what will be the rim. In the contrasting cases the same finger manipulations will yield progress in the opposite direction. These several variations in technical manipulation actually occur as standard among certain populations. They plainly are cultural differences, although they all preserve the normal supremacy of the right hand. In such instances, factors of organic equipment, such as normal right-handedness, must be recognized if the total situation is to be understood. Yet the direction of progress depends not on this alone, but specifically on how the basket is held. A particular congenital motor habit rarely suffices to explain the whole method of operation: this always remains partly or mostly cultural in origin. Motor habits have the limits of their range set by the human organic equipment, but their specific determination is overwhelmingly by culture.

144. OTHER HABIT CHANNELINGS

There are some persistences in culture that recall habit formations in individuals and into which the factor of habit channeling undoubtedly has entered through the constant overlapping of generations in every society. For instance, in ancient Peru the southern coastal districts early got into the habit of making their pottery vessels with round bottoms, whereas the northern areas favored flat bottoms. This difference was consistently maintained as long as native pottery continued to be made. Both Peruvian areas, as far back as we have archaeological record of them, developed tubular spouts: single, double, or united like a stirrup-shaped handle. This is a trait which persisted throughout the ceramic history of Peru.

On the contrary, in ancient southern Mexico and Central America, habit ran in the direction of providing bowls, pots, and even jars with three legs. This tripod arrangement has certain practical advantages when cooking vessels are to be set over the fire; but among the Mexicans it became a stylistic manner or trend, because the supports were put on vessels whose shapes or ornamentation shows that they were never set on the fire; and in some cases the legs have degenerated into functionless lugs or ornamental devices. Moreover, in this same Mexican region the idea of tripod support was extended to objects of totally different uses, such as the metate for grinding corn, and the stool or seat. The tripod habit was already established two thousand or more years ago in the earliest wares yet discovered, and it maintains itself today in the household inventory of Indians and peons.

Farther north, in the United States Southwest, whose archaeological history can also be carried back something like two thousand years, both spouts and tripods are characteristically absent. They do occur occasionally, as spouts occur sporadically in Mexico, and tripods in Peru; and these exceptions are significant because they prove that the ideas of spouts or tripods were not beyond the capacity or range of any of these pottery-making peoples. They were in fact tried, but did not take except each in the area where it became typical. In short, though traits like tripods and spouts are relatively unimportant, they can nevertheless be extremely persistent and characteristic. From the angle of the successful functioning of the native cultures of the three American areas, it was of course immaterial whether they went in for spouts or legs or neither. Yet, having made one stylistic choice or the other, they adhered to it over long periods during which more important features of government, technology, or subsistence were altered fairly drastically.

Such cultural happenings are comparable to the ordinary habits of a person— his nonessential mannerisms. An individual early in his life acquires a particular shrug or gesture, a posture or way of seating himself, a manner of articulation, of forming or spacing his letters in handwriting. He goes through periods of good luck and bad luck, his fortunes fall or rise; but the mannerisms persist. This is not to say that habits in persons and cultures consist entirely of insignificant idiosyncrasies. As a matter of fact, habit formation enters just as much into the bigger and more important features of human life and culture. But in such cases we think of habit as character or attitude system; and these, being large and complex things, not only are bound to be partially modified with the wear and tear of time, but their persistent core is less easily extricated and defined. The smaller habits, those of the type of mannerisms, are more easily traced just because they are discrete, and because, being of indifferent importance, their very neutrality sometimes enables them to go on practically unaltered for surprisingly long periods.

Further examples on the cultural level are teapot-shaped vessels, with a double-curved spout and a handle, which in Japan have an archaeological history stretching back of the introduction of tea into the early Iron Age and even the Stone Age; and pile houses in the regions around the Alps, as illustrated by the Stone Age lake dwellings of Switzerland, the Bronze Age terramare of Lombardy, and by modern Venice. The North American side of the Atlantic was a clam-eating coast in prehistoric Indian times, as attested by shell mounds, and is so today. By comparison the mussel was neglected as food, and still is, except for a partial change in tastes recently introduced by French and Italian immigrants. On the European side of the same ocean, on the contrary, the clam is little esteemed and the mussel is eagerly eaten; and this was true in the Stone Age as it is today. This difference may be due in part to the quality of the species available, or to environmental factors; but it cannot be wholly accounted for on such grounds because the same species of mussel, *Mytilus edulis,* occurs on both sides of the Atlantic—in fact has a nearly world-wide distribution. Hence it would seem that the factor of long-term taste habits has contributed to the picture.

145. INVENTION

The most incisive form of cultural addition is invention, the finding things out, or, etymologically, "coming into" something new.

In studies of culture the word "invention" is used with a somewhat wider meaning than its current popular sense. To the man on the street "invention" denotes a new machine or technological process. In anthropology and culture history it includes this and more. We can for instance speak of institutional inventions, such as the matrilineate, kingship, moiety organization, representative government, or written constitutions. If it seems that this is stretching meanings unduly, because institutions are social growths, usually accepted gradually, so are machines social growths, having antecedents and being accepted gradually, as we shall see. Then there is intellectual invention: a scientific discovery, a new philosophical idea. We can just as properly speak of the Copernican invention as the Copernican discovery; perhaps more properly, because if the theory should ever be found incorrect, it would remain an invention although disproved as a discovery of the truth. From here it is only a step to the discovery of a new planet, and from that to the discovery of the South Pole. The point is not that all these inventions are exactly identical in character, but that they grade into each other. Above all, that they behave much alike, as regards their causes, manner, and effects. It is thus wiser to direct attention to the common features of the behavior of societies when they do something new, rather than to spend much attention on distinctions that are mainly logical.

There is one idea it is necessary to be rid of in order to understand the process of invention in general. This is the assumption that our contemporary Western habit of seeking or planning inventions is at all normal. Deliberately planned or sought invention, in fact, is nearly lacking in most of the history of civilization. It began timidly to come up in Europe around 1300 or 1400, increased in the 1600's, but did not become systematic and important until the nineteenth century. It is therefore an exceptional feature of our own civilization. In fact it would have been extremely difficult to plan much invention until both theoretical science and practical technology reached a development, about the seventeenth century, such as had never before been attained.

146. NECESSITY

The old byword of necessity being the mother of invention must be heavily discounted. It is true only in so far as ordinarily there must be a need, or at least a use, for a new thing before it will be devised, and especially before it will be accepted by a society. Necessity may therefore be a spur; it is never a sufficient cause by itself. Above all, need is a relative and subjective factor. Your need may not be mine. We feel that we need three meals a day. Many ancients ate and primitives eat only two and are content. Some obtain food so irregularly that they may not average much more than one meal a day; when they get enough, it is eaten up. These same people will cheerfully eat three times if they are fed; but they hardly feel that they must or ought to have meals so often. Their circumstances and habits are different, hence their orientations and expectations also differ from ours.

A Negrito wants a little sloping roof over his head; it does not occur to him that he wants a house with walls. If a river is to be crossed and recrossed, he may build a suspension bridge that shows him possessed of mechanical ingenuity. But a house instead of a leanto windbreak would be extra work and would give him nothing that he really wants. His family is small, his possessions few, and in several days or weeks he expects to move elsewhere because food will be exhausted where he is now. So he does not sense a need that we might regard as imperative.

On the contrary, most primitives obviously desire certain things on which we are much less intent. They strongly want close and constant association with their kin. The floating laborer of our society who leaves his home folks, drifts about without ever seeing them again or without rearing a family of his own, is as good as unheard-of among them. If a savage leaves his home, it is to settle down and marry among another group.

Similarly with religion, which all primitive peoples evidently feel a need of, since they all possess one, and the overwhelming majority of individuals seem genuinely to believe in—not to mention the much greater number of men in societies that are beyond the primitive. Yet many Russians of today, and a fair number of people among ourselves, get along comfortably without religion. One might contend that the Soviet social program constitutes the prevalent Russian religion. But though a program that leaves no room for God or the soul, which does not recognize anything supernatural, may function emotionally as the equivalent of a religion, though it may surround itself with satisfying social rituals and with sanctions, it obviously does not quite constitute a religion.

In short, necessity is so largely a function of orientation, of goals already established by the extant culture, that it is too variable a factor to be invoked very often to explain invention. It is wants that determine what people do, and wants are states of mind, largely determined in their turn by already existing culture.

147. ACCIDENT

On the other hand, accident is unquestionably one factor in invention and discovery. There are a number of cases in the history of medicine. Sulfanilamid was first made as far back as 1908 as part of a dye fixative. In 1935, the dye was found to be powerful against streptococcus infections; research then isolated sulfanilamid as the active agent. Penicillin was "invented" as a result of Fleming's working with staphylococcus cultures and noting that where these became infected with mold the adjacent colonies of bacteria were dissolved away. The shock cure for dementia praecox was discovered through a schizophrenic's being given, by a nurse's error, an overdosed insulin injection for the diabetes that he also had. He almost died, but recovered improved, and the way was pointed. Pasteur was led to the theory and the method of immunization by happening to inject an overlooked and stale bacterial culture of chicken cholera and finding that it failed to kill. It then occurred to him that an attenuated culture might immunize. By contrast, it may be pointed out that for several generations medicine has felt the urgent need for a nonoperative, non-radioactive treatment of cancer, and has brought all the planned resources of several laboratory sciences to bear on the problem, without being able to find a solution.

Daguerre solved a crucial problem in the invention of photography through forgetting that he had an open vessel of mercury standing in a cupboard. Into this cupboard, because it was dark, he put away overnight an exposed bromide-coated silver plate. In the morning, the latent image had begun to develop. Daguerre, in a flash, suspected fumes from the mercury, and trial confirmed his suspicion. Other chemicals in time came to replace mercury vapor, but the essential and hitherto undiscovered factor of "developing" invisible images had been found (§ 187). Yet to see the situation in its entirety, it must be remembered that Daguerre was a conscious inventor, long seeking a way to a specific goal. That is why he was able to profit at once by his fortunate accident: he was alerted to take advantage of it.

Malus's discovery of the polarization of light came from his happening to be looking at a crystal as he turned it idly in his fingers against a reflection of the rays of the setting sun in facing windows; he noted that the refraction altered perceptibly with the turning. If he had held the crystal against un-reflected light—or even with reflection if the rays had not been coming in nearly horizontally—there would have been no alteration. Malus had his head full of refraction phenomena at the time, so he promptly verified his chance observation, and determined its meaning by experiments. Another physicist, preoccupied with different problems, might have filed the observation and only followed it up years later, or forgotten it. The average layman would probably have thought the phenomenon odd and have done nothing about it. It is evident that the degree of experience and the direction of interest of the person to whom the accident happens is at least as important as the accident itself.

Thus, one F. P. Smith was testing ship's screws. An unduly long one hit a snag, broke off, and the boat went faster. This accident might not have been profited by at all except for happening in the course of trials deliberately aimed at invention.

Similar was Goodyear's accidental discovery of hard or vulcanized rubber by heating with sulphur, a process he invented in 1839 and patented in 1844. Yet the "accident" only happened after Goodyear had been in the rubber-goods business and had failed because of the deterioration which articles of rubber underwent. He had in fact previously experimented to prevent this deterioration.

Farther back in the history of culture there are a number of instances on which direct evidence is lacking but which suggest the factor of invention by accident, or as a by-product of some other effort. Rye, for instance, is believed first to have been a weed in wheat or barley fields of western Asia. As the cultivation of wheat was carried farther north, or to higher altitudes, the hardier rye throve at the expense of the wheat. There are regions where the two are put in together: if the wheat fails in a bad year, there is at least a partial rye crop to fall back on. In still colder climates, rye, on account of its dependability, came to be sown pure as a crop in its own right. In the same way, oats seem to have begun as a weed in fields of emmer wheat.

So with the fire drill. It is an uncertain enough implement; in most primitive communities only the more adept individuals attempt to use it. It requires wood that is neither too hard nor too soft and is both seasoned and kept dry, and especially a rather delicate balance of manipulative strength and skill. This makes it unlikely that anyone who noted that friction produces heat, and who deliberately attempted to apply the principle in the fire drill, would have succeeded. Without previous experience or teaching, it would be perhaps a thousand chances to one that the trial would fail and that our putative inventor would discard his invention. It seems much more probable that in the boring of a hole not only would warmth be felt, but sooner or later the ground-out wood dust would collect in a little heap and send up a wisp of smoke and show a glowing spark; whereupon it would only be necessary to repeat the operation with a new purpose. Much the same holds for the other friction devices, fire plow, fire saw, and fire cord. While there is no proof that these inventions were actually made as unintended by-products, it is mechanically plausible that they were. In any event, it is inescapable that the "invention" had antecedents.

The occasional part that accident plays among apes in the solution of problems that are akin to simple inventions has been discussed in § 28.

That accident has an occasional hand in invention is certain, but its importance must not be overestimated. Without awareness of want or problem, favorable luck will be wasted. It is again true that states of mind determine inventions, in individuals and in societies. Only as against this background does accident become significant.

148. INVENTION AND PLAY

Inventions motivated by play impulses are fairly common. The old "high" bicycle, with a very large wheel, was purely an instrument of sport. When about 1890 the modern type, with two equal and smaller wheels, then called safety bicycle, began to appear, it was hailed with acclaim. Bicycle parades were held, bicycle racing became an intercollegiate sport, century runs were scheduled every Sunday, hundreds of clubs were organized, then federated into a great League of American Wheelmen. It was only later that the bicycle began seriously to be used as a means of getting around on business. From this position, in America, it was again partly displaced by the abundance and cheapness of automobiles; but in Europe, where relatively few people have been able to afford motorcars of their own, the bicycle has remained standard as a middle-class means of local transportation. In 1944, when the American forces re-entered a western Europe denuded of railroads and gasoline, it was about the only civilian means of locomotion.

The history of the automobile is parallel. It too began essentially as a vehicle of sport, luxury, and recreation.

Ballooning, the first form of aviation, commenced partly as a scientific demonstration and partly as an adventure. The practical and economic utilization of all aircraft came much later.

The first invention of the bow and arrow may fall into the same class. A bow must have passed beyond a certain threshold of effectiveness before it can have any utility as a weapon. It seems dubious whether any primitive, starting from nothing and thinking up a bow and arrow by insight, could give it the several points of efficiency needed for killing even a small animal. Besides, certain manipulative skills are required in addition to aim, such as an arrow grip and a string release. Our hypothetical inventor out of the blue would therefore quite likely have given up his idea as unworkable on first actually trying it out. On the other hand, a string on a bent stick is under tension and will twang. Just such a "musical bow" is used by many primitive peoples as a sort of "Jews'-harp" or jaws'-harp, set against the teeth. The same strung stick could also be bounced in a game, or have sticks bounced off its string. From that it would be a short step to sliding or shooting light sticks at a near-by mark. Now, with something to build on, both in the way of a working instrument and manipulative skill, a little more strengthening or improvement of both bow and arrow would much more easily result in a workable weapon. This reconstruction is wholly speculative, and no assurance can be put on any step in the process outlined. The suggestion is merely that something of the sort is likely to have been the development, because the invention in toto, at one stroke, seems over-difficult mechanically; and the play factor, perhaps aided by accident, seems the most likely to have entered into the transitional stages. The influence of pattern, of existing similar forms, must also be reckoned with, as antecedents: not only a musical or game bow, but the spring trap or noose holding down a bent-over sapling. In both cases taut cords and the elasticity of wood are utilized. Unfortunately, we have no more actual knowledge of the origin of the sapling snare than of the bow. We do know that the bow as a weapon is not really early in prehistory. Its first record is late Palaeolithic or Mesolithic (§ 274-276), and it was preceded in Europe by a well-developed spear-thrower in the Magdalenian (§ 269).

A second prehistoric instance is American. It has long been known that even the most advanced native cultures of the New World—Aztec, Maya, Inca—totally lacked several basic technological devices that had long been important in the Eastern Hemisphere. These included ironworking, stringed musical instruments, plows, and wheels.[1] In 1944 wheeled toys of pottery were reported from excavations in the Panuco River region in Mexico, near Tampico. They consisted of effigies of dogs with the paired legs perforated, presumably for insertion of a slender rod or reed, on the ends of each of which pierced pottery disks were jammed. The axles have decayed, but the baked clay figures and sets of disks remain. These are indubitable little four-wheel wagons in principle, though applied to toys (or possibly cult objects) on the order of the stuffed lambs or wooden horsies that our children drag around. Subsequently it was noted that similar pieces had previously been discovered scatteringly all the way from Michoacán to Panamá.

As compared with all the other instances here discussed, this case is incomplete. The principle of the device was achieved in play, but it failed to be applied for utility. Actually this nonuse of the wheel after its discovery makes native America stand out in sharper contrast with the Old World. Literally and mechanically, the ancient Mexicans made the invention; socially speaking, they refused it—threw it away.

Generically, all the discoveries and innovations of pure science and fine art—those intellectual and aesthetic pursuits which are carried on without reference to technology or utility—may be credited to functioning of the human play impulses. They are adult sublimations, onto a largely supermuscular level, of the sensorily exploratory and kinaesthetic activities that constitute play in children and mammals. They rest on the play impulse, which is connected with growth but is dissociated from preservation, comfort, or utility, and which in science and art is translated into the realm of imagination, abstraction, relations, and sensuous form.

149. ANTECEDENTS

The bow is of interest, not only because of its presumptive relation to play before utility, but also because it illustrates the necessity of antecedents to almost any invention. These antecedents, prerequisites, or conditions must be present—both before an individual can make a workable invention, and before a culture can accept it. These antecedents are of the utmost importance to recognize, because we men are by nature romantic and unhistorical-minded, and, except under intellectual discipline, we prefer and shape for ourselves emotion-

---

[1] There were indigenous spindle whorls, but these were only disk buttons or weights on a rod twirled free by hand. They might at best be called near-wheels. The axle did not spin in a bearing, and the wheel edge engaged nothing.

ally appealing stories of how inventions are brought about by sheer resolve, superhuman insight, dire necessity, or mere blind luck. On analysis every invention on which we have information proves to depend on antecedents, as regards both individual creation and social acceptance.

The essential feature of the modern automobile is the propulsion of a wheeled vehicle by an explosion engine. Wheels were known for thousands of years, the explosion engine for decades, before the combination was made. It is completely certain that the idea of combining a vehicle and an explosion engine occurred to hundreds of men long before any automobile ever ran. The problem was not to put one and one together, but to make them fit workably. This involved all sorts of complications, which had to be mastered gradually. We need not go into the mechanical complexities of transmission and gearshift; simpler features will illustrate the point. To be effective, the gas explosion must occur in an enclosed chamber or cylinder against a piston whose plunge outward moves the machinery. How introduce an intermittent flame rapidly into this tight cylinder? The most feasible answer is an electric spark, and this is what has chiefly been used in gasoline motorcars. It could be used when automobiles came along, because by then first static electricity, next current, and then electromagnetism had been discovered. Until these prior discoveries had been made, the *principle* or abstract idea of an automobile could have been invented, but hardly a car that ran.[2] The difference is like that between Leonardo da Vinci's dreams of flying machines and the Wright brothers' realization at Kittyhawk. Leonardo merits high credit for his imagination; but he was four centuries too early. His time could not have produced a machine that would fly. It possessed too few scientific and technical antecedents.

Patents, by the way, are not issued for an idea, but for a specific device, process, or machine that is presumably workable, and which is concrete enough so that it can be drafted or a model can be supplied. If the Patent Office believes a proposed device to be unworkable, it refuses the patent. It is true that if a device includes a new idea, this idea also becomes protected by its patenting; but only secondarily, by inclusion. It is easy to see why the law takes this stand. Without it, there would be a scramble to pre-empt all possible new ideas, largely by people incompetent to translate them into effective execution. Patents would be held by those working out combinations of words instead of working out parts of machines. The point is significant for the understanding of culture history.

Sometimes the prerequisite antecedents are indirect and unexpectedly remote. The really first automobiles did not have gas engines, but were steam-driven. This was as early as 1770 in France, soon after 1800 in England, long before the gas engine was invented. Some of these early road machines have been preserved and may be seen in the United States National Museum Annex. They

---

[2] Some progressive dates are: workable gas engine, Otto, 1877; Selden basic patent, 1879; practical automobile, Serpollet in France, 1889; first gasoline motor of present motorcar type, Daimler, 1892.

look something like monstrous steam rollers. Trevithick's car of 1803 ran on the streets of London with 10-foot drive wheels. By 1823 tubular boilers had been introduced. These road cars were not a practical success, and for several reasons; but one of the reasons was that roads were bad. Locomotives, which is what these contraptions really amounted to, were accordingly put on rails, where they no longer shook to pieces, could go much faster, and could better haul cars. Thus the steam railway was born about 1829; is really was a transfer from the idea of the free-ranging automobile, which was then dropped for nearly a century. The idea of rails was much older than that of self-moving engines. Wooden rails for hand-pushed cars are said to have been used in small-scale mining operations in Germany as early as 1546, and certainly were used before 1700 at Newcastle; iron-shod ones in 1716, and cast-iron ones in 1767, all these last in England. Passengers were hauled in horse-drawn cars on rails near London in 1801—the same year that Trevithick carried them in a steam-driven locomotive—a full twenty-eight years before Stephenson's steam locomotive proved practicable on the Liverpool-Manchester rail line.

It should be added that several factors were involved in the nonsuccess of the early road locomotives. In England, where industry had become heavier and more mobile than in France, and roads were far better than in America, the directors and promoters of steam railways exerted competitive pressure as soon as the railways had proved successful and were promising to make money. Beginning as early as 1832, they induced turnpike trustees to exact prohibitive tolls from road machines. When this was not sufficient, they got legislation passed which put a 4-mph ceiling on any road engine-vehicle—a rule that was not relaxed in England until 1896, when the gas-engine automobile was already successfully racing across France. Such blocking of the development of inventions by use of influence is not mere wickedness. The railroads did represent a growing investment, much larger than any for road machines; and money is like life in seeking self-protection. Indeed, the early railway-builders were genuinely farsighted in their fears, as the later automotive competition beginning in the decade 1920-30 was to show.

A weakness of railways is that they involve heavy capital for right of way, roadbed, track, and maintenance, and that they reach only a limited number of points. Recognition of the desirability of a mechanical vehicle that could range freely on all roads was therefore bound to recur. Shortly before 1900, the immediate ancestors of our modern automobile began to appear, in three forms. One used the newer explosion engine already discussed; another, the old steam engine, though in a shape extremely light for the power produced, with 1000-pound-pressure flash boilers; the third, a storage-battery electric motor. For years the three forms competed, until the gas engine won out through greater adaptability to most demands. One thing, however, helped the modern automobile, even in its infancy, as against its precursor of a century before: the solid rubber tire, which eased some of the jolts as speed increased. This tire had come in toward the end of the horse-and-buggy days for pleasure vehicles: "Bring out your rubber-tired hacks." Soon the hollow, inflated rubber tire took its place; this had developed with the low or safety bicycle a decade or so before, and had there proved its advantage and feasibility. Without rubber and pneumatic tires, the automobile would have had to take a racking pounding at speeds of more than six or eight miles an hour on most roads of that time; but now the automobile's tires were awaiting it. Undoubtedly if tires had not been ready, they would soon have been developed; but the progress of the automobile would in that case probably have been delayed some years.

A simple case of antecedents, though an ancient one, is the calendar, which could not have been devised without recorded observations and counts. Reference is to a genuine calendar that recognizes a specified number of days and of moon appearances within the year, and attempts to reconcile the three factors—days, moons, year—which are not related in integral numbers. Even if such a calendar is only approximately true, it must be preceded by observations whose cumulative count is carried on for many years, probably for several lifetimes. This in turn involves some system of notation or record. Hence any complex calendar can hardly be expected to have preceded writing by very long.

Greek astronomy underwent a splendid development for some centuries, then slowed and ceased progress. The Greeks had no real clocks with gears, pendulum, or escapement. They had only water clocks depending on drip, and sundials. They knew optics and the lens in principle rather than in practice, because they do not seem to have ground glass. Hence they had no telescopes. Their other observational instruments were of the simplest. Looking back now, it is evident that Greek intellect and imagination had developed astronomy about as far as they were able to until clocks and telescopes were available—and, let us add, until a mathematics with a computationally efficient number-symbol system like our positional "Arabic" numerals was also available. It was by lack of these antecedents that the further progress of Greek astronomy was necessarily checked. As a matter of fact, when basic progress in astronomy began to be made again, it was by Copernicus and his successors some centuries after clocks (§ 184) and position numerals (§ 189) and algebra were in use. Within another century the telescope was invented (§ 152) and was immediately utilized by Galileo and others. Similarly, contemporary astronomy builds largely on the photography and the spectroscope that the nineteenth century devised.

150. CUMULATIVE AND COMPLEX INVENTIONS

So important is this matter of antecedents that it is often difficult to determine reliably just what constitutes an invention or when it took place. The more the situation is analyzed, the larger do the antecedents loom, and by comparison the less outstanding does the new step or increment appear. This is contrary to the popular view, which condenses a complex and gradual process into a single dramatic act by one individual, with whom we can identify ourselves emotionally. Hence the anecdotes about Newton and the apple, or Watt and his mother's teakettle, which we are taught as children. We profess not to believe these stories seriously, but they nevertheless tend to influence our thinking.

It is true that there is always insight at work when something new is devised or understood. It is no doubt also true that usually it is great men, genuinely superior individuals, who have these insights. But there is also a long chain of antecedents involved, in every case of which we have knowledge, without which the insight and genius could have done nothing in the given situation. This intricate and largely impersonal build-up is precisely the anthropologist's or the historian's business to elucidate for true understanding of what happened; but it is horribly unromantic, and the lay mind shrinks from it, just as a child could not grasp it. The popular mind loves being off duty as regards criticism and skepticism, and has invested the whole matter of invention with an atmosphere of fascinating mystery. It imagines a great intellect rushing along out of nothing like a new comet out of space, and making a complete invention at one stroke. The more inexplicable this is, the more satisfying it is as a day-dream story. In reality, however, we may say that most so-called inventions are not a single act but a cumulative series of transmitted increments plus a series of new elements when these become possible in the culture in which they appear.

Kuznets neatly demonstrated this rule in a type study of the plow sulky. This is a plow with wheels. The addition of the wheels undoubtedly made it a new kind of plow, which we can define, and distinguish from other plows. Kuznets went over data extracted from United States patent records on the number of patents issued each year that had to do with plow sulkies—new parts, improvements, refinements. Each year after the initiating invention in 1865 the number of new patents grew more rapidly, then began to level off, reached a peak around 1882, then diminished, declined rapidly, and dwindled away by 1923. There was little more to perfect on the plow sulky, and inventiveness turned to replacing it by new types of plows. The year-by-year curve of additions to and improvements of the plow sulky suggests a somewhat skew "normal" frequency distribution.

Now it cannot be maintained that all inventions develop as regularly as this. A physical or an economic catastrophe may come along and chop off the curve; or a new and subversive invention may displace a still growing one. The line of development would also look different if one chose a wider category, say plows in general. In that case the line would be a composite of the curves for inventions of handled plow, share plow, plow sulky, disk plow, and so on; and it would presumably run more nearly level but with many minor fluctuations. Also, in the absence of Patent Office records, we cannot be sure of the precise growth of many inventions. Yet what analysis of the plow-sulky history does show is that many inventions are not single acts of mind, but cumulative results. They are social events, and therefore they usually are gradual events.

In the last analysis, the fundamental invention in the plow sulky was the combination of two antecedents, the plow and the wheel, and two very old antecedents at that. The rest of the history of the invention consists of improvements and modifications; in other words, developments or consequences of the original combination. A great deal of invention seems to boil down to just that.

The more analytically facts are gone into, the more difficult is it to isolate many really basic inventions. More and more do they resolve into combinations of old elements, or into modifications that are reapplications of other old elements. What is new is often a new function, which is culturally significant because it is socially accepted, and which we can name. Such are the plow sulky and the automobile, the bow and arrow, and the fire drill. Mechanically, it is often hard to delimit an invention. The mechanical principle or structure of the shooting bow is the same as that of the drill bow, the game bow, the mouth-harp bow. The bow becomes a bow when it is shot as a weapon. It is its use, its human function, that makes it a weapon, its name, "bow and arrow," that gives it entity. For most of us, other than engineers and inventors, the cultural history of the bow is more significant than its mechanical history. Similarly with the automobile. Mechanically, the early nineteenth-century steam road-locomotives were motorcars or automobiles, as much so as a White Steamer of 1908 or a Chevrolet of 1948. But they failed to be successful, they went out, and culturally the history of what we call the automobile begins in the decade before 1900 when flash-boiler steam models and gas-engine makes began to be produced.

151. SOCIAL ACCEPTANCE

This brings us to the matter of social acceptance of inventions. We may lay it down as a definition that, anthropologically, sociologically, and historically, an invention is not an invention until it is accepted in a culture. Until then it exists merely individually or mechanically; it actualizes historically only with its social acceptance.

It is notorious that a great many successful inventions have been claimed by and for different nations. Which is the right one is often difficult to decide. Where nationalism enters into the problem, it becomes still more difficult. Asked who the inventor of the steamship was, the average American will answer Fulton; the Britisher, Symington; the Frenchman, Jouffroy. A Spaniard may even propose Blasco de Garay, who is wholly mythical as regards the steamboat. Each is reacting to what he has been taught. But Fulton had well-known predecessors, both American and European. The story is set forth in fuller detail in § 185-186, but it might be said here that what Fulton really did was to build a steamboat which convinced people that it was or could be made economically successful. Historically, the definition of the inventor as the man who makes a utilitarian invention pay, or succeeds in persuading others that it will pay, has a great deal to be said for it, especially in our contemporary civilization with its heavy economic and technological slant. For all times and places the definition is a bit narrow, since some successful innovations do not yield a money profit, and some cultures have neither money nor profit. Broadened accordingly, the definition reads that an invention is only potential while its idea remains in the head of an individual, but that it becomes actualized when it begins to be socially accepted into a culture.

The bars to adoption are of several kinds. First there is the direct economic preventive. We know how to extract gold from the ocean, or power from the tides, but it costs more, in money, to extract them than the gold and the power are worth. Then there is the already discussed matter of antecedents, as with Leonardo's ideas of flying machines. In 1500 Europe was technologically not far enough along to execute his ideas. Next is the factor of resistance. A new religion usually encounters an established one. An attempt to induce Americans to eat taro meal for breakfast failed because they already had fixed eating habits and a sufficiency and variety of foods, so an unexciting novelty made no appeal. An efficient private express system may block institution of a public parcel post, or vice versa. The two are competitive in serving nearly the same ends, and economic, political, or monopolistic pressure will be directed against the newcomer. Finally, there are innovations that may seem intrinsically desirable to nearly everyone, but which are bound to exact a heavy toll of temporary confusion and disorganization: a radical reform of the calendar or the alphabet, for instance, as discussed in § 170 and 212.

Converse conditions of course further the adoption of changes. An established religion that has lost its hold, chronic food shortages, times of distress when reorganization is in majority demand—all invite reforms that normally include innovations and long-delayed inventions.

A cultural novelty always encounters existing cultural conditions, and it is these which determine whether, when, how, and in what form it gets adopted. These preconditions of course are so variable from instance to instance that it is difficult to attribute the acceptance of particular inventions to their intrinsic merit. In the realm of machines there certainly is something pretty close to intrinsic or absolute merit, in the degree of physical fitness, efficiency, and economy. But even as between machines, their acceptance is always in part conditioned by their relation to the local culture in which they are invented or into which they are introduced. Witness the story of the steamboat in § 185. In nonmechanical matters, innovations are of course even more influenced by the culture they are trying to enter.

In this matter of their fate, or at any rate their date, being determined by the cultural soil on which they fall, inventions from inside a society and diffusions from outside it (§ 171) are much alike.

152. SIMULTANEOUS INVENTIONS AGAIN

The frequent simultaneity of inventions has been discussed in § 140 as a manifestation of pattern growth, but it is obviously also a matter of antecedents. If the prerequisites for an invention are lacking, it cannot be realized, even if the idea should crop up. On the contrary, once the prerequisites have been supplied, if desirability of a contrivance continues to be felt, a whole series of individuals are likely to work on the problem, so that the prospects are considerable that two or more of them will find a feasible solution. In familiar metaphor, we say that the discovery is now in the air, or that the time is ripe for it. More precisely, inventions are culturally determined. Such a statement must not be given a mystical connotation. It does not mean, for instance, that it was predetermined from the beginning of time that type printing would be discovered in Germany about 1450, or the telephone in the United States in 1876. Determinism in this connection means only that there is a definable relation between a specific condition of a given culture and the making of a particular invention.

The history of science is full of instances. Sunspots were first discovered in 1611, independently and in different countries, by Galileo, Harriott, Scheiner, and Fabricius. The specific antecedent is highly definite: the telescope was devised in 1608. The telescope, in turn, has three claimants to its invention. All three were Dutch, probably because the manufacture of lenses was developed farthest in Holland at the time. Only a little later, Spinoza, now remembered as one of the great philosophers, was earning his daily bread as a lens-grinder. The compound microscope also originated in Holland; and the discoveries through it of animalculae, egg development, blood circulation, insect anatomy, and the like were made later in the 1600's by two other Dutchmen, Leeuwenhoek and Swammerdam. All this means that the culture of seventeenth-century Holland included a pattern in which lenses figured with more weight than elsewhere. In short, the Dutch were lens-minded and lens-making, which was the antecedent that led to the telescope, and this in turn was the antecedent to the discovery of sunspots.

To a certain extent we may even speak legitimately of the inevitability of inventions—provided we mean by this nothing more than that, given an existing sense of the desirability of a conceivable device, and the presence of the needed antecedents, the device will necessarily be invented soon. Given enough knowledge of optics, technological skill in making lenses, and astronomical curiosity, sunspots and the moons of Jupiter will be discovered promptly—if not by Galileo, then by someone else. Given knowledge of electric current and electromagnetic induction and of sound vibration—especially with telegraphs in successful operation for thirty years—and the idea of the telephone is bound to occur to a number of technicians. It is only a question of who will first work the idea out feasibly. Will it be Bell or Gray in 1876, or someone else in 1877 or 1878 or perhaps as early as 1875? To the individual inventor the "Who?" is all-important, because it means who is to get the prize. To his society, and to the world at large, the "Who?" is really a matter of indifference—except for sentimental partisanship—because the invention was going to be made anyway about when and where it was made. We cannot always see this fact at the moment, and still less can we judge in advance whether all the necessary antecedents have been gone through with and the economic requirements satisfied. But after the event, especially at some little perspective from it—provided it is not so long ago that the record has again begun to get dim or lost—we can recognize the piling-up of the antecedents until the invention or the innovation follows as their consequence. See for instance the histories of mills, of the steamship, of the telegraph and telephone, in another chapter (§ 183-187).

This view of the inevitability of inventions is now pretty generally accepted. That it is not yet common popular knowledge is due to the persistence of what may be called the "great-man theory" or fallacy. No one denies that there are great men and that they do great things. The fallacy is to infer from this that everything important in history must have had a great man as its specific cause. From the fact that the telegraph and the telephone are extremely important in the mechanics of modern living, it does not follow that Morse and Bell were outstandingly great men; though obviously they were more than mediocrities.[3] It is the personalizing, anthropomorphizing habits of nonscientific thinking that lead us loosely to assume not only that such men were supremely great, but that they were so much greater than all their contemporaries that we might still be doing without the benefits of their inventions if they had not been considerate enough to make them. This is patently absurd, since they had rivals treading on their heels, and in fact sometimes stepping out ahead. Let us examine another instance or two, where the circumstances are unusually clear.

We have seen (§ 140) that Alfred Russell Wallace was the independent co-discoverer in 1858 of the "Darwinian" concept or hypothesis of natural selection as a mechanism explaining the change and origin of species and therewith of continuous evolution. At that time Darwin had had the idea for twenty years, and had discussed it with a few of his friends; but, not sufficiently winning their approval, he hesitated to publish until his hand was forced by Wallace. Suppose that Darwin had died during his two decades of indecision. Wallace's would almost certainly be the name now on our tongues. Suppose he too had died, say in 1857. Does it seem more likely that in that event biologists would have gone on indefinitely believing in special creation for each species? Or that within a few years some third man would have had the concept of natural selection occur to him and have announced it? The idea of evolution was "in the air"—as a matter of fact it was more than that, Herbert Spencer having developed it before Wallace and Darwin. Their explanation after all is only that

---

[3] Morse was also an able portrait-painter.

of a specific mechanism by which the general process of organic evolution is supposed to have worked. Darwin's grandfather Erasmus, and Lamarck, had already had the idea of developmental transformation. It is evident that natural selection was really a link in a chain, one idea among several whose union made a broad system of evolutionistic thought possible. All of which together would seem to build up to this: that science and philosophy having got where they were in western Europe around 1858, it was inevitable that the notion of natural selection should be thought up by someone within a very few years of 1860 at the latest.

By contrast we have Aristotle actually imagining and mentioning the idea of natural selection as something logically thinkable, but immediately dismissing it as something not worth testing against evidence. The Greek way of thinking favored the finite and the definite; its world view was not evolutionistic. The set of the culture pattern—the "spirit" of the Greek times—was against anything like natural selection, and so it was rejected, and remained out for two thousand years. Incidentally, thinking of the idea when he did can be credited to Aristotle as a mark of his individual genius. But his rejection of it is not to his personal discredit, because that was the result of his Greek environment and social heritage.

The case of Mendel, founder of the science of genetics, is extraordinary because his genius almost did never get recognized. In 1866 Mendel published in the proceedings of a learned society at Brno an account of his experimental breeding of peas. In this he announced the basic quantitative laws of heredity, and correctly: they have been much elaborated since but still stand. Except for the Swiss botanist Nägeli, who went unheeded, no one took any notice. Darwin, Galton, and hundreds of other biologists were studying heredity, but they either missed seeing Mendel's paper or failed to realize its significance. Surely this is a case of the time being not yet ripe: Mendel was ahead of it. He died in 1884 as an abbot, but scientifically an obscure person. In fact, he was so discouraged by his failure to impress anyone with his discovery that he is said to have abandoned belief in it himself. Then, a generation later, in 1900, within three months three biologists, the Dutchman De Vries, the German Correns, the Austrian Tschermak, who were studying heredity, and evidently were now severally approaching the point of view that Mendel had reached in the sixties, made his discovery over again (§ 140), and clicked to its importance. Correns also rediscovered Mendel's forgotten publication, and announced it. Literally and personally, the Mendelian laws thus date from 1866; culturally and socially, from 1900. From the angle of understanding human history and the workings of civilization, which is the effective date?

This array of evidence may seem to depreciate the great man, to make him merely a function of his culture. This is both so and not so. As compared with popular thinking, it is largely true, because popular thinking wants to dramatize and build plots around conquering heroes. But recognition of cultural forces or drifts is obviously quite compatible with recognition of genius or individual superiority. They can and do coexist. We can be sure that no important invention is ever made by a dub. If he made one by accident, he would not know it; but some more intelligent person might see the significance and communicate it, thereby becoming the real discoverer. We can be just as sure that there are superior individuals, whom we call highly talented and geniuses, as that there are inferior ones who are incompetent and unintelligent. It is the talented and the geniuses who make inventions. But they make them only when and if their cultures permit; and they make only the specific inventions that their cultures allow, within a narrow range. Other inventions have already been made, and still others are as yet impossible, given the culture as it is. Biography is a recognized literary genre, which has usually been assumed to have a laudatory purpose, and of late has tended frankly to assume semifictional dress. Biographers thus are free to cut out any cultural analyses that would make the human interest of the plot drag, or again to admit bits of culture as picturesque background. If however our purpose is to understand the history of human civilization, the cultural factors loom as decisive, just because they are the larger determinants. They determine what, where, and largely when and how. The individual determines the precise date, the particular manner or coloring of the event, and the mnemonic label of his personality and name.

153. INVENTION OF INSTITUTIONS

At the bottom of every invention there is an idea or a principle, whether formulated or not. Fundamentally, therefore, invention is one in kind, whether it relates to implements and machines or to institutions and beliefs. When a concept like that of divine kingship first appears in human history, it is, in our sense of a new idea, an invention, though an anonymous one. We know nothing of the inventor or the circumstances that led him to originate the idea, but it exercised a profound influence on millions of men from ancient Egypt to modern Japan. Against this, its persistence into recent centuries in Europe is but a fragmentary survival. This king-godship became one of the bases of an extensive politico-economic-religious system or major type of culture in protohistoric times (§ 286). The first sure record of the invention's being accepted is in Egypt. It must have been a startlingly original invention—first to conceive that a human being was a god and then to persuade people to believe it.

Among modern institutional inventions may be mentioned the form of ballot that is officially prepared, marked in privacy, but deposited under control: a system devised to minimize intimidation and fraud. It originated in Australia, whence its name after its spread to the United States.

There are also the initiative and the referendum, which come from Switzerland. Their roots are mediaeval, in the small cantons where every citizen could personally participate in government, much as in a Greek democratic city-state or a New England town meeting. In modern form, the referendum was first worked out by the minute, rural, and conservative canton of Schwyz in 1848. The idea received impetus when larger, liberal, and urban Zürich accepted it in 1869. Five years later it was written into the Swiss federal constitution; and in 1891 the initiative followed. South Dakota in 1898 was the first American state to adopt both institutions.

An American contribution is the written constitution. There were Magna Cartas and the like before, but they were essentially confirmations of concession or privilege. The American constitution was an attempt not to modify or retain, but to create a new political order, and in unambiguous terms free from the interpretations of usage or custom. It took over from existing English practice certain features, such as the bicameral legislature. But it developed as a new feature the differentiation of representation in the two Houses of Congress—by political units and by population size. Also new was the explicit co-ordination of the executive, legislative, and judicial branches of government. But perhaps the most radical innovation of the American constitution was its outrightly creating the basic foundation of a political structure. By contrast, the English constitution is a cumulative growth. As such, therefore, it is unwritten: it is a sort of direction followed through centuries of development. The American constitution, on the contrary, being made up at one stroke, had to be explicit and written out. The parallel shows that conscious, abrupt efforts toward production of new culture form and content may have functions and results closely similar to semiconscious, gradual efforts, and that as processes the two may intergrade.

Analogous to these political inventions are socioeconomic ones such as banks, credit, double-entry bookkeeping, social security and old-age pensions, installment mortgages. There is no difference in principle.

All these institutional inventions cited spread widely. In fact it is their spread beyond the point of origin that has made them historically important. In thus showing invention and diffusion as closely associated, the cases are typical. Just as an invention becomes culturally significant only upon its social acceptance, so an innovation by one population obviously becomes significant in world civilization in proportion as it is accepted by other populations.

154. INVENTION BY STIMULUS DIFFUSION

There is one type of situation in culture history that is interesting because diffusion and invention enter into it equally. It can be called either stimulus invention or idea diffusion. In ordinary diffusion, as of the just-mentioned Australian ballot or the automobile, both the principle and its mechanism are taken over by a receiving culture from the inventing one. Occasionally, however, there are difficulties about acceptance of the mechanism, or the mechanism has not been fully learned. The idea or principle may then also fail to be accepted. But again, the idea may exercise an appeal that causes it to penetrate. An effort may then be made in the receiving culture to devise another mechanism that will produce the desired result. Thus an invention, or reinvention, is stimulated by contact transmission or diffusion.

It is in the nature of such events that they tend to leave little historical trace of the processes at work. But there is documented evidence of several cases, and there are a number of probable ones.

Porcelain is a pottery containing a feldspar clay, kaolin, which on high firing vitrifies all through the ware, instead of only on the surface like a glaze, and hence is brilliant, hard, and waterproof. The Chinese gradually evolved porcelain around 1100 after a long series of groping experiments. In these step-by-step inventions accident may well have played a part, as well as blind trials. By the time Europeans came into direct sea contact with China soon after 1500, the porcelain art was highly developed there. Its products were brought to Europe and admired; but they were costly. Attempts to imitate porcelain were made, but with only partial success. This was because European ceramics were still only in the stage of development of Chinese ceramics some centuries before: they operated with surface glazes. The seventeenth-century delftware, and similar developments, represent this incomplete European imitation. Finally deposits of the necessary ingredient kaolin were found in Europe, the techniques were mastered, and in 1708-09 true porcelain was reinvented by Böttger and Tschirnhaus in Dresden. That is why we eat off "china" plates today. But without a mark having been set by the previous Chinese invention, Europeans would have had nothing to shoot at, and conceivably they might not have devised porcelain until much later.

In the early nineteenth century a half-breed Indian called Sequoya in his native Cherokee, and John Guest by white people, realized the value of writing. He was illiterate. Perhaps this is what made it seem desirable to him that his people should possess an instrument comparable to that of the white man. Had he been sent to an American school he would probably have been content to write English as a substitute. He wrestled with the problem for years. Finally, about 1821, he evolved a Cherokee writing of which his fellow tribesmen were at first incredulous, but which proved to be entirely adequate and simple to learn, and which they adopted and used. The characters are derived from English: in fact Sequoya had in his house a spelling primer, which he could not read, but many of whose letters he used for his own purpose with entirely different values. Eighteen of the Cherokee characters are straight English capitals; some are modified or extended or inverted capitals; a few are lower-case letters or numerals; about a third or a quarter of the total of 86 are freely invented. That Sequoya's feat was however a genuine and singlehanded invention is shown by two facts. Not one of the characters has the same value as in English; and all the characters denote syllables, not letter sounds. Thus A is read as "go" in Cherokee, B as "ya," C as "tli," D as "a." We have thus a true and real invention, with a high degree of originality; and yet we also have the assurance that but for the influence and example of the alien culture, the invention would never have been made. It is another instance of "antecedents," though unusual ones.

An entirely parallel invention of writing was made by a West-coast African, shortly before 1849, for his native Vai language. He had had a bit of missionary schooling in his youth; but he made the invention in a dream, in middle life. It is also a syllabary, as against the alphabetic system of English that had stimulated him. But the number of characters is over 200, and they bear no resemblance to English, nor of course to Cherokee. The names of primitive inventors are rarely known, so this one is cited: Doalu Bukere.

Stimulus diffusion accordingly is also stimulus invention. Therein lies its interest.

This is perhaps not one of the most frequent processes in culture. However, its nature is such that its results look wholly novel and original even when they are not; and the factors involved tend not to get into the historical record and often become quickly forgotten. The number of occurrences of the process may thus be considerably larger than appears. Several instances can be cited in which derivation by diffusion has actually been suggested by one and another culture historian without their being able to find direct evidence of the derivation. Yet the resemblances and the space-time tie-up are such that the operative mechanism may quite possibly have been reinvention stimulated by previous foreign existence of the trait. Such possible examples are:

The seemingly independent invention of pottery by the early Basket Maker-Pueblo (Anasazi) in northern Arizona-New Mexico at a time when pottery surely was already being made in central Mexico (Archaic) and perhaps in southern Arizona (Hohokam; see § 323)

Monks in Christianity, some centuries later than Buddhist monasticism, with convents, celibacy, begging, and tonsure

Development of Greek grammar some centuries after Sanskrit grammar, and of Japanese two centuries after Latin and Dutch contacts

In converse direction, Sanskrit drama following the Greek

Quantitative meter appearing in Arabic poetry, and then by known transfer in Persian and Turkish, after it had long been established in Greek and Latin

None of these can at present be either proved or disproved as examples of stimulus diffusion, but there seems an inherent probability that some of them may turn out demonstrably to be such.

155. INVENTION BY REDUCTION-SEGREGATION

In general, more invention means more machines and more institutions—more physical and social apparatus to be handled. This somewhat dismaying prospect is partly relieved by a type of invention that works through simplification or reduction. Perhaps "extraction" or "segregation" more nearly describes the process. Metaphorically it would be a sort of curdling or clotting-out.

The most striking case is the alphabet (§ 206 and 207). Previous systems of writings consisted of idea signs, word signs, syllable signs, and, in the case of Egyptian, of sound signs also (§202-205). Moreover, a word might be spelled out according to its sound and then an ideogram for it be added, as if to make sure that one representation would be read if the other were missed—see the example in Figure 20. Not only was the writing of particular words cumbersome, but each method of writing required several hundred symbols. Thus Egyptian hieroglyphic comprised 460 characters, cuneiform Babylonian around 500, Indus Valley writing nearly 400. As against this, the true alphabet rests upon the realization that if pure minimum-sound symbols—true letters—are con-

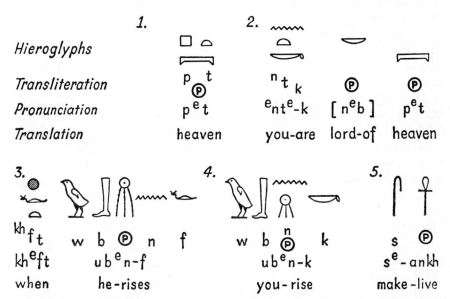

FIG. 20.   MIXED PICTOGRAPHIC AND PHONETIC ELEMENTS IN
EGYPTIAN HIEROGLYPHS

Phrases from a page of Egyptian hieroglyph papyrus. The circled **P** denotes a pictograph or ideograph; the rest of the writing is by pictorial *consonantal letters*. In 1, heaven is written alphabetically and confirmed by a conventionalized pictographic "determinative" (the vault of heaven); in 2, by pictograph alone. The first words of 2 and 3 are wholly phonetic: pictographs for the ideas of "when" and "you are" would be hard to devise. The grammatical suffixes -*f* and -*k* added to *uben*, "rise," in 3 and 4 illustrate another reason for the development of consonant letters. In the first of these, the confirming pictograph (sun with rays) is put in the middle of the stem *uben*; in the second, between it and the suffix. In the first words of 2 and 3, the letters in the word read downward; elsewhere, mostly horizontally. The true alphabet was devised by a process of *segregative reduction* out of mixed-method writing such as this.

sistently used, all the characters for syllables, words, objects, ideas, and "determinatives" or classifiers can be discarded; and anything that can be spoken can also be written, and with complete intelligibility, by means of from two to three dozen simple signs. It took two thousand years for this realization to be achieved. In one sense the cardinal quality required by the inventors of the alphabet was resolution, the courage to break with the multiple reinsurance of ways of denoting meaning that was characteristic of the older mixed pictographic-ideographic-phonetic systems. In a rough sort of sense, the invention was like a cripple's finding he could walk free when he threw his crutches away.

If the Egyptians missed a bet by failing to discard all their writing symbols except their 24 true letter-signs scattered among the rest, they did achieve another mental simplification: the invention of a pure solar calendar (§ 291). The "natural" tendency seems to be to take cognizance of time by nights and days, by moons and their phases, and finally by years and their recurrent seasons. The difficulty bred by this is that the moon's revolutions around the earth and the earth's around the sun do not gear. There are more than twelve lunations in a year, but considerably less than thirteen. They average a bit over 29½ days, so that a twelve-moon year is nearly 11 days short. A rough correction can be made by putting a thirteenth month into every third year. Yet not only does this have the inconvenience of the years being quite unequal, but the correction is still short by three and a fraction days. More elaborate intercalations are more accurate, but also more cumbersome. But no such system can be wholly accurate, because earth and moon revolutions are incommensurable. Hence the Chinese, Mohammedan, and ritual Jewish calendars, which really observe the moon, are always beginning the year at a different absolute and seasonal date. The simplification made by the early Egyptians consisted in disregarding what the moon was actually doing, and substituting months—arbitrary periods of thirty days. There were always twelve of these in the year, plus five supplementary days; and the Egyptian year accordingly always was of the same length and always began at the same seasonal or astronomical time—except for the few hours' gain that we correct by a leap day. We still follow the Egyptian plan of months' being independent of the physical moon and its phases, though we do not use the supplemental days, and we have our months of unequal length—"Thirty days hath September," and so on. The cardinal act in the devising of the Egyptian calendar, and a feature that we retain, was the *discarding* of the moon's revolution from any relation to the earth's revolution or year.

Another example of the process is the way in which astronomy and astrology were originally associated in one system in Mesopotamia, as discussed below in connection with the origin of the week (§ 196-197). It used to be thought that the segregation was effected wholly by the Greeks, who discarded the omens and portents and developed the pure science. It is now known that in late Mesopotamian days, after the fall of Assyria and especially after that of Persia, there was a school of genuine or pure astronomy in Babylonia on which the Greeks were more dependent—both for observation and for interpretation—than their self-centeredness had led us to believe. But however the credit may fall between the two nationalities, they did manage to curdle a purely naturalistic science out from a previous amorphous, naturalistic-supernaturalistic mass of knowledge and beliefs regarding the heavenly bodies. This astronomy maintained itself for a number of centuries; but about the time it stopped progressing, by Roman Imperial times, it was reinvaded by a new wave of magic. This was astrology, of the type still followed by a remnant of the mystically inclined and the credulous among ourselves. The earlier Mesopotamians had been concerned mostly with eclipses as portents. The later astrology crystallized chiefly at Alexandria and dealt with the continuous fortunes of men as determined by the positional relations of the planets, or rather of the seven moving heavenly bodies visible to the human eye. From then on until about 1600 astronomy was astrology-ridden, among ancients, Arabs, and Europeans. Occasional astronomers disavowed the astrological component, more accepted it, some were ardent over it. It was close to 1700 before scientists were once more unanimous in repudiating astrology as wholly nonscientific.

The relations of alchemy and chemistry were similar except that here there was no ancient attempt at autonomy of a self-sufficient science. The result was that a wholly naturalistic chemistry never emerged as a productive and systematic activity anywhere until in the most recent centuries of European civilization. The magico-mystic ingredients in alchemy were the elixir of life, the philosopher's stone, and the transmutation of metals into gold. The search for these transcendentals was not calculated to encourage preoccupation with ordinary "base" substances and their humble quantitative properties. In the West, alchemy first appeared in the turgid atmosphere of Imperial Roman Alexandria about contemporaneously with planetary astrology.[4] In the East, substantially identical beliefs were rampant in China apparently a little earlier, during the first half of the Han period of 206 B.C.-A.D. 220. Alchemy still had some repute in Europe as late as the sixteenth century.

The type of inventive change by reduction or extraction has been called "etherealization" by Toynbee. The connotations of that word seem inappropriate, and perhaps unfortunate. But it is evident that the process deserves a name. It is not a process of outright specialization, though it somewhat resembles differentiation by specialization. For instance, medicine begins with general practice, from which after a time eye-ear-nose-throat treatments separate off. With added knowledge, instruments, and skills, certain doctors begin to limit themselves to the eye and are called oculists. The remainder for a while go on as a unit, but in time the aurists perhaps again split off as specialists. In

---

[4] This is the usual version. Another interpretation makes the Alexandrians crude chemists concerned with producing deceptive imitations of gold. Both accounts may be true.

this medical specialization there is no discarding or repudiation of one element or ingredient; they are all developed further, and therewith it became advantageous and desirable for individuals to choose among the subspecialties. In the process here discussed, however, the essential step is that an encumbering ingredient, which is either unnecessary or false, is got rid of. There is accordingly a *reduction* of total compass of a system or activity through a segregation of its more valuable or efficient elements from its inferior or impeding ones.

Apparently, a process somewhat reminiscent of this reduction-segregation is observable in technology. In the main this technological happening is obscured by the fact that many machines grow more complex as they develop, because their functions and powers increase. But as each kind of machine approaches the limits of its inherent possibilities as a type, it tends to revert to simplicity, to emphasize economy of means, and to achieve what engineer and artist would agree in calling beauty of design and function. An example in point is the clipper ship coming to its peak in the very days when steam was beginning to supersede sails. The superb swords of Japan in an era of cannon are another instance. We have here a field of social process that has been inadequately explored, but in which interesting possibilities can be glimpsed.

156. CULTURAL LOSS

Popular romance maintains a half-belief in supposed lost arts of the ancients, such as hardening of copper to equal steel, miraculously lifelike embalming of mummies, and the like. Actually, it is likely that no art of serious consequence has been lost from total human civilization. Copper can be hardened by alloys most of which the ancients did not possess; it can be somewhat hardened by hammering, a quality which we know as well as they did but do not utilize precisely because we have very much harder steel. Lenin's body in Moscow is probably preserved much better than any Egyptian master embalmer would have known how to preserve it. And so on.

There is considerable cultural "loss" that is actual, but it relates to particular cultures rather than to human culture as a whole. Most of it, as will be seen presently, is displacement, properly speaking: a new custom, art, worship, or belief crowds out an old one. Utilitarian arts, such as hardening copper, dyeing with cochineal or with Tyrian shellfish, retire to a humble spot in the technological background as metallurgy improves steelmaking and chemistry devises anilines. Most of what we shall have to consider as cultural "losses" possess this character of replacement or displacement. In addition, particular societies do at times undergo genuine or downright losses of specific items of their culture, owing to environment, loss of materials or skills, shrinkage of population, impoverishment, and other or unknown causes. Some instances of both kinds will be briefly analyzed.

157. DISAPPEARANCE OF USEFUL ARTS

In 1912 Rivers demonstrated a series of convincing examples of the disappearance of useful arts in Oceania. The things given up were of unquestionable utility: canoes, pots, bows. The canoe went out of use in Torres Island in Melanesia, was replaced by sailing rafts in Mangareva. In a series of Melanesian islands—Malikolo, Pentecost, Lepers, Ambrym—potsherds are found in the ground, but pottery has not been made in the historical period. In several areas the bow was still known recently, but it was used only as a toy, in sport, or in small-game hunting of rats, birds, or fish—not in war. These areas of fighting without bow and arrow covered nearly all Polynesia except Tonga and Samoa; in Melanesia, most of New Britain, New Ireland, and the Admiralties; and some of the coast of New Guinea. The causes of the several disappearances were various. Lack of material was the least common cause. It would be applicable chiefly to canoes, but was not the reason for abandonment in either Torres or Mangareva. Sometimes the guilds or families of tohunga or craftsmen who had been taught magic as well as manual skills by their elders died out. This happened to the canoemakers in the Torres Islands, and to the stone-adz producers in Woodlark. Sometimes in Oceania a single community specializes in manufacturing one article, such as pots, and supplying it by trade to a large area. A catastrophe overwhelming such a village might result in the whole area's coming to use wooden vessels instead of pottery. As to the bow, there was generally no large game in the Oceanic islands to sustain one customary economic utility of the weapon. Of warfare there generally was enough, but it was sometimes ceremonial rather than waged for practical advantage. And in Polynesia war tended to be dominated by standards of bravery, chivalry, or manners of fighting: fashion exalted the hand-to-hand club.

All in all, the array of cases is significant in showing that the actual historical behavior of cultures cannot be predicted from an a-priori notion that practical utility—economic motivation—is invariably determinative.[5]

There also are conditions of natural environment under which particular utilitarian activities can wither away fast. In 1818 the explorer Ross discovered some two hundred Eskimo along the east shore of Smith Sound in northern Greenland—later also named Peary's Eskimo, or Eta or Polar Eskimo, because they live farthest north of any permanent human community, at Igita beyond latitude 78°. Ice and cliffs had long cut them off so effectually that they no

---

[5] One consideration that Rivers did not stress is that the Oceanian continent of native Australia also lacked canoes, pottery, and bows, and almost universally so. Australia seems to be a case not of having possessed and lost, but of never having had the inventions—in the main perhaps of not wanting them (see § 253, 310). Nevertheless, the proximity of Australia to New Guinea, Melanesia, and Polynesia makes it seem that the two negative distributions may be connected, according to the principles of distributional evidence set forth in § 223-224.

longer had clear knowledge of any other people. They possessed no kayaks—the decked-over boats of skins stretched on a light wooden frame which were so widely prevalent among the Eskimo that it is assumed that all once had them. This group lacked them because driftwood does not carry into Smith Sound. From 1818 on, they got wood from Ross, and from subsequent explorers and whalers; but still they made no kayaks: they no longer knew how. About 1868 a vigorous, restless Baffinland Eskimo took his family, pushed north with sledges, crossed Smith Sound on the winter ice, and found a new home among the Polar Eskimo. Then the kayak reappeared among them: this newcomer from a region of driftwood and knowledge of the kayak taught them how to make it. During the fifty years preceding this Baffinlander's coming the Polar Eskimo had again got the necessary material through the whites. But this had not helped them, because the design and art of joining a seaworthy frame had been forgotten in the preceding centuries of their isolation.

Technological skills can generally be taught only imperfectly by words. There must be visible example and, above all, manual practice. That is one reason why the teaching of chemistry and other science insists on laboratory periods. Useful technologies do not tend intrinsically to disappear faster than other parts of culture; the weak link in the matter of transmission of technologies lies in the acquirement of manipulative practice, the formation of motor habits. Interfere with these and the continuity of the art is broken and may be lost.

It was a deficiency of environment that was at the bottom of the Polar Eskimo's losing their boatbuilding ability. But having once lost the skill, the fresh accession of the needed wood did not suffice to cause them to reinvent the art. And meanwhile their lack of boats helped to pen them in their habitat.

However, nature gave the Polar Eskimo something else. Three large meteorites, now carried to New York City, had fallen in their habitat. From these they managed to whack off slivers of nickel-iron with stones; these they beat to an edge and set end to end in a groove in a bone handle and thus made themselves iron knives—something that no other Eskimo group had, except for rare pieces of drift or trade iron coming from Asia into Alaska. Here then we have both an invention and a loss connected with the same environment—an apt illustration of how complexly culture operates.

158. EFFECTS OF ISOLATION: SOUTHAMPTON AND EASTER ISLANDS

Small, isolated peoples are especially interesting because of the unexpected things that happen to them. While contacts remain open, complete losses are less likely to occur. Wholly localized increments, and fixations at an ancient level, are also less expectable under open contacts. because knowledge and customs have a chance to spread both in and out.

On Southampton Island, at the entrance to Hudson Bay, lived a second Eskimo group who had lost boats from their culture. They were therefore cut off from intercourse with the world unless other Eskimo, or subsequently whalers, ventured to them. They did have a makeshift substitute for alongshore hunting: inflated sealskins that they paddled, riding them like hobbyhorses. But with only these they could probably secure nothing more than occasional small seals. Their main dependence accordingly was on a large herd of wild reindeer that roamed the two-hundred-mile-wide island. With this herd once eaten up, reduced by disease, or impossible to get at, the Southampton Eskimo were doomed. In fact, this fate overtook them in 1902, when they starved to death. All in all, their tools were not those of the other eastern Eskimo, but represented a somewhat deteriorated form of what is called the Thule phase of Eskimo culture. This phase is estimated to have flourished quite widely in the American Arctic around A.D. 1000-1300, after which it became superseded elsewhere by the more modern or historical Eskimo culture. It looks therefore as if the Southamptoners, once they had settled down with their simplified and boatless version of the Thule culture, managed to get along and survived for centuries before disaster caught up with them.

The Polynesians of Easter Island, though they must originally have come in canoes, were also nearly boatless when discovered, because of lack of logs or planking. They had a very few small canoes, carrying from two to four persons, ingeniously sewed together of many patches and splinters of wood. The island is only ten by thirteen miles in size, is grassy and windswept, and very isolated. It lies sixteen hundred miles from Polynesian Mangareva, twenty-two hundred from South America. Tapa-bark cloth was nearly as scarce as canoes, because the paper mulberry withstands the cool winds of Easter Island only with considerable coddling. Breadfruit and coconuts are wholly prohibited by the climate; but bananas, sweet potatoes, taro, and yams were grown. All in all, the Easter Islanders had a purely Polynesian culture—as their speech was a pure Polynesian dialect—with its richness considerably thinned down by their small numbers and by environmental lacks and limitations. But the culture was thinned down more or less all over, without notable total losses at any one point. There were the usual Polynesian gods, chants, myths, kings or chiefs, wars, human sacrifice and cannibalism, houses, stone platforms, dress, foods, and the rest, in a somewhat meager provincial form.

What is really remarkable about this isolated culture is not so much what it had lost as certain unique positive increments that must have been local developments. Three of these stand out. The first was a peculiar bird cult culminating in a ceremonial race that was the great event of the year. The second feature was wooden tablets incised with lines of figures that look remarkably like a script and appear to have had some connection with prayers or chants, but which could not be read, and probably were not true writing but decorative symbols similar to large petroglyphs painted in connection with the bird cult.

The third specialty consisted of gigantic rude statues of tuff rock weighing from four or five to twenty or thirty tons. These statues have partial parallels elsewhere in Polynesia in small stone carvings or fair-sized wooden ones. Consequently they represent a heightening of degree—the largest statues occurring on one of the smallest islands—rather than a radically new idea. But the bird cult and the tablets are without real parallels elsewhere in the Pacific and are accordingly indicated as having been devised in the isolation of Easter Island. In this case, therefore, loneliness had several unique and conspicuous results, though they are probably balanced by many minor losses or impoverishments.

The period during which Easter Island was occupied is not known, but is estimated to have been less than a thousand years rather than more. Assuming an average population of 3000, for which there is warrant in the reports of early white voyagers, we must credit this small number of islanders with considerable originality in having evolved their specializations in perhaps from five to eight centuries. Withal, the originality puts no strain on credibility, as do some of the fantastic theories which blow up the Easter Island situation into extreme improbabilities—sunken land bridges, vanished prior races, or "writing" mysteriously preserved from the Indus Valley script of five thousand years earlier.

159. DISPLACEMENTS

On the whole, "loss" appears often to consist of a displacement by something new, rather than being an outright disappearance or a mere melting-away. And the displacement is often only partial. Thus we still have candles and oil lamps though gas came in a century ago and electricity in turn has been generally substituted for gas. The older elements survive, though with diminished or specialized scope. The total culture is thereby so much richer than before. Much of the enormous variety of our technology is due to this preservation of the old alongside the development of the new. The established culture trait loses most of its functions but retains part, or even acquires new ones. It is a use that is lost rather than the trait or item itself. There is, especially in contemporary civilization, a constant tendency for utilitarian devices that are dispossessed by new inventions to persist in art, sport, luxury, religion, or symbolism.

Thus, in North America the automobile has virtually displaced the horse for transportation of both passengers and goods. Yet the horse is still used considerably in certain situations, such as for small-farm plowing. It holds its own without diminution in racing, horse shows, rodeos, circuses, polo, and as a form of pleasurable exercise. All these serve the ends of sport or play.

Similarly the bow still exists in our culture, but archery has become purely a sport.

Woodcuts used to be the ordinary method of illustrating books; only expensive works had steel engravings. Photographic reproduction has entirely displaced the woodcut for practical purposes. Even apart from screen plates that render light-and-shade values with transitions, the ordinary pen-and-ink draw-ing, which can be done by the artist in a fifth of the time required for cutting a block, gives the same effect, and if necessary a much finer one. Has the wood-cut therefore disappeared? As a practical means of actually illustrating in print, yes. But it survives, in fact is having a bit of a cult, as an art form, as an aesthetic expression, as a conscious revival of what is antiquated and simple and com-fortable and rude, something like eighteenth-century furniture or imitations of primitive utensils. We do not live by utility alone.

The horn lantern was used when people were poor and glass was expensive as well as brittle. There was always a cow's horn available, and in winter there were evenings in which the farmer could steam and pare and trim it. Glass being much clearer, as soon as its price came down through industrial improve-ments and mass production, it drove horn out; except that occasionally we still buy sheets of horn for our electric bulbs to shine through with a "natural" mellow amber glow while we talk in the living-room. The glass that was once available only for the wealthy has now become universal; horn, once the poor man's refuge, has become an article of luxury. Many of the losses of civilization, especially in our own of the past century or two, are really displacements, or even inversions of function, like this.

A curious analogy is found in the history of the dog, the almost universal domestic animal. Except where he is of specific value for transport, hunting, herding, or watching, most cultures other than our own may be said to tolerate rather than to protect him; he fends for himself and becomes a scavenger. There are a few groups of primitive tribes that are exceptional in being dogless. There was at least one of these groups in South America and another in native north-ern California. In this latter area the dog was by no means unknown, but one might have to travel through several Indian villages to encounter one or two. These had been bought or traded from outside, and they were pampered, fed, allowed in the house at night, named, and given formal burial when they died. They were too soft and valuable to be used for hunting. They seem to have been so scarce as to have had no chance, ordinarily, to breed; so the supply had to be kept up by import from outside. This primitive luxury manifestation strangely parallels contemporary New York, where tens of thousands of child-less couples keep a dog in their apartment, and at night have the maid or a husband lead him about a bit to foul the public street. It is the attitude of over-cherishing a pet that is common to the two cases. How did these California Indians come to have their attitude? Evidently it was because they were essen-tially dogless and knew no practical use for dogs when they did get them. They may have been this way for one of two reasons. Either they had never in their past history acquired a full-scale dog-keeping habit, or they once followed it and it went into disuse—a case of loss, or more exactly of near-loss displacement into a luxury. The latter seems more likely in view of the near-universality of the dog among American Indians, and the fact that the few non-dog-raising tribes in California must for thousands of years have been in some contact and communication with the much more numerous dog-keeping tribes (§ 165).

Displacements involving both loss and innovation occur also in situations other than those of attitude or function. With cosmetics there may be substitutions of bodily topography. Many primitives paint the body as well as the face. The ancient Egyptians concentrated on the eyelids, the nineteenth century on the cheeks. Lipstick was unknown. After this had come in, interest shifted to the lips, at first timidly; but after a time the cheeks were toned or browned in order to exaggerate by contrast the vivid redness of the lips. Painting of the nails also developed—a new area that primitives seem to have overlooked; but at least it is a reversion to cosmetics elsewhere than on the face. We tend to think first, in all such cases, of the new or intruding item; it is what attracts interest; but of course every innovation ordinarily involves a loss too. The whole cosmetic custom went out once in our culture, with Puritanism. It might go out again, though perhaps next time possibly as a change of taste rather than from moral scruple.

160. KINDS OF LOSS

There remains the more general, seemingly philosophical problem of how large a factor cultural loss is or can be. For instance, can the loss be entire for one feature? Beyond that, could losses be universal, so as to lead to cultural death? Actually, the questions are ambiguous.

First of all, entire loss of features from what? From the particular culture of a particular people? In that case, the answer definitely is Yes. For instance, "we" have lost slavery in the past century. That holds for the United States. But does it hold for the totality of human culture, past and present, everywhere? Such a loss will obviously come more slowly: witness Ethiopia, which is still de-facto slaveholding. And in many cases, even if universal loss had occurred, it might be hard to establish. Things have a way of hanging on long in the remote places; or they persist undercover, in the subcultures of unsophisticated social strata at home: as astrology, crystal-gazing, voodoo, and magic do among ourselves. Then, as we have just seen, an item of culture may be displaced by a novelty from most of its uses, even from its primary use, but persist in one of its uses, or even acquire a new luxury or play use.

Second, it is necessary to narrow the question by defining what it is that is being lost. Is it culture content or culture form? A specific element, a system, a pattern, or an attitude? Or indeed do we mean that a whole culture may disappear? In the sections on progress (§ 127-128), we have seen that among those civilizations which by common consent are reckoned as higher there has been an indubitable drift to discountenance behavior motivated by magic and animism, as well as that which is psychically infantile and unsocialized in its inhumanity and its crude emphasis on the physiological. We may expect, and most of us will certainly hope, that this drift toward the gain of reason, taste, and humanity at the expense of practices based on more infantile motivations will continue. But we certainly cannot prove that it will continue indefinitely, nor can we assert that there might not be conditions which would reverse the trend and cause increase of what is now diminishing.

On the basis of a breakdown into more precisely defined questions, some generalizations can be made as to loss.

Specific items, such as painting the eyelids, or hammer-hardening copper, are more likely to be lost, by outright giving up or by displacement, in any one culture or in all human culture, and to be lost more rapidly, than broad, varied activities such as fishing or animal husbandry, or than large systems such as a religion or a method of writing. The counterpart is that the small trait generally also gets accepted more readily than a big complex. This is logically obvious; and the chief significance of the point perhaps is to help us guard against dealing alike with noncomparables—little things and big, isolated bits and ramified networks.

Replacements, modifications, and substitutions are, broadly speaking, more characteristic of the changes of organic evolution; additive increments are more typical of the changes of human culture (§ 5, 127). But this difference is probably most accentuated in artifacts, tools, and technologies, where a whole array of devices serving similar but not quite identical purposes can easily exist side by side with advantage and without conflict—say tenons, pegs, nails, screws, rivets, lashings, which all hold parts together. Religions, writings, or social systems may also coexist—witness the three "religions" of China and the two writings of Korea (§ 221); but between such there is likely to be strain or conflict, and time is required for an adjustment, if one is worked out at all. And particular items are likely to be rejected or forced out where they are in conflict with a dominant socioreligious system: blood sacrifice in Christianity or Mohammedanism, for instance, or cross-cousin marriage in our Western society. But it is hard to imagine any socioreligious system so averse in principle to crank handles or screws as to force their abandonment from its culture.

The contrast of the organic process as substitutive, of the cultural as additive, is broadly true, but it must not be forced so far as to mean that organic novelties occur *only* as substitutions—that is, as accompaniment of losses—while cultural novelties are regularly incremental. It is true that when birds evolved out of reptiles they gave up a pair of running limbs to acquire a pair of wings, whereas when men learned to fly in airplanes it was not by sacrificing arms—nor even wagons, railroads, and motorcars. From the point of view of the history of birds themselves it is true enough that they acquired flight by a transformative substitution. But from the angle of the evolution of life as a grand total there was also an increment: running reptiles and flying birds where there had been only running reptiles before. And much the same had happened millions of years before when some branch of the ancestral anthropods, having developed air-breathing and come out of the water, somehow got two pairs of wings and soared away as insects. The natural tendency in dealing with animals is to consider what happens to a particular line of descent in its evolution, but in dealing with man to view a cultural change as if it affected the totality of human culture. And not without reason, since an innovation may and sometimes actually does spread to all cultures, whereas the wings developed by birds remain confined to descendants of birds: they cannot possibly spread to non-descendants. In short, the contrast of basic process of organic evolution and cultural evolution is valid and fundamental; only it must not be pushed to exaggeration by comparison of a single line of organic development with the whole breadth of cultural development. Culture also has its substitutions, and therewith its losses—especially the single or particular culture as viewed separately.

161. PROBLEM OF THE DEATH OF CULTURES

When we come finally to the question of cultural death, it is particularly important to define the problem so as not to get enmeshed in what is really a metaphor. There is presumably no possibility of all human culture "dying"; that is, disappearing from internal causes. Of course, the cooling of the sun, the loss of our atmosphere, a collision of the earth or its atomic explosion—any such event that extinguished the human race—would automatically extinguish all culture with it. But that would not be an inherent or a spontaneous death. It may be assumed that culture has sufficient survival value for our naked, unarmed species so that if any branches of man, for whatever reason, got into the way of somehow consecutively diminishing or destroying their own stock of culture, they would inevitably be eliminated in competition with those branches which advanced or even only maintained theirs.

At the opposite end of the scale, as concerns culture traits or items—customs, techniques, beliefs—it is obvious that these get changed, replaced, and lost, but that there is no need of applying to these matter-of-fact happenings any term so metaphorical, so charged with emotional connotations, as "death."

The situation in connection with which the phrase probably arose and has a possible meaning is the passing away of particular national cultures. If there really is a "decline and fall" of civilizations or peoples, there might well also be a "death." What seems to be actually involved in such cases is the dissolution of a particular assemblage of cultural content, configurated in a more or less unique set of patterns belonging to a nation or a group of nations. Such particular assemblages and constellations do unquestionably "die out"; that is, they dissolve away, disappear, and are replaced by new ones. The elements of the content of such cultures may have previously spread to other cultures and survive there. Or their place may be taken at home by elements introduced from abroad. Or they may survive, with or without modification, at home, in the different configuration that gradually takes the place of the old one as a successor culture. All that goes out of existence or "dies" in such cases is a particular, characterized, over-all configuration or pattern grouping.

Thus there can be no question that the culture of ancient Egypt is "dead"— though a more precise formulation would be that its specific pattern assemblage has long since ceased to function or exist anywhere. We even know a good deal of the circumstances of the dissolution. Toward 1400 B.C. there was a last great flourishing of the Egyptian patterns. True, there had been a premonitory symptom a few centuries before in the irruption of the Hyksos, the first conquerors of Egypt, even though transient ones. But there had been recovery from this, and on the rebound the greatest military might, expansion, wealth, excellence of art, and development of thought were attained by the Egyptians. The inherent patterns of their culture may be said to have been fully realized or to have been saturated then. After that, with pattern potentialities exhausted, there could be only diminished or devitalized repetition; unless the patterns can be reformulated in the direction of a new set of values—which would be equivalent to recasting the civilization into a new one or into a thoroughly new phase of one. This latter did not happen in Egypt; so more and more sluggish, mechanical repetition within the realized but fully exhausted patterns became the universal vogue. After about 1200 B.C., general decline is evident. There were civil wars and rival dynasties, failure of art, and evidently of wealth, with only temporary checks. The last line of fairly successful rulers maintained themselves through Greek and other foreign mercenaries, while foreign ideas seeped in. From 700 B.C. on, Assyrian, Persian, Macedonian, and Roman conquests succeeded one another, with the upper classes increasingly Hellenized, and finally all classes Christianized. By A.D. 600 the old civilization had disappeared substantially as completely as now. No one worshiped Osiris or the hawk-headed Horus, no one could read hieroglyphs, no one mummified his dead, no one was Pharaoh. The Arab conquest and Islamization beginning a few decades later merely superimposed one more stratum on the cultural layers under which the old native civilization was already buried forever. The moment of "death" may be impossible to specify, just because the process of "dying" went on so long and is so continuously evident.

Egyptian culture as a unique nexus and entity thus went out of existence. But the society to which it had been attached went on. The Hellenized Egyptians of Cleopatra's time, the Hellenized Christian Egyptians of A.D. 500, the Mohammedan Egyptians of A.D. 1000, and those of today are no doubt mainly the bodily descendants of those Egyptians who first shaped their distinctive civilization around 3500-3000 B.C. Especially is this true as regards the mass of the population, the rural fellahin. The stream of biological heredity rolled on through the millennia with only minor alterations; above it, civilizations grew, dissolved, entered, and replaced one another.

The components of the old Egyptian civilization did not perish equally. Here and there bits of it persist into the thoroughly different culture aggregate of present-day Egyptian culture: perhaps a water-bucket sweep, an ass under his load. Other elements, like the hieroglyphs and burial pyramids, have long since been abandoned everywhere in the world. Other content traits still exist in one or another of the contemporary living cultures, including our own. If it is difficult to name such, that is only because the expansive phase of Egyptian culture productivity took place so long ago—it ended more than a thousand years before Western civilization began to germinate—that transmitted elements have reached us indirectly, at second and third hand, in much altered dress. Original Egyptian traits perhaps first became Asiatic, then Minoan, Greek, finally Roman, before they filtered into incipient Occidental culture, with reselection and remodeling all along the slow, devious route. But elements, ideas, or stimuli of probable Egyptian origin are recognizable in our own calendar, writing, religion (influences contributory to the concepts of monotheism, dying god, afterlife, Madonna with child), architecture, plant and animal husbandry; and others reappear in modern native African cultures (§ 311).

This picture seems typical of what ultimately happens to cultures. Their content is partly superseded and replaced; partly it diffuses through space and time, in ever new settings and with endless remodelings, selections, and recombinations. The ethnically or nationally individuated pattern aggregates of culture material—what we ordinarily call civilizations or culture wholes—also change, though slowly. But beyond a certain point it is no longer a matter of wear and tear with them, of better or worse fortunes, but of either gradual dissolution or gradual ossification of the nexuses which have held them into an active integrated whole. Even before they have become mainly loose pieces or skeleton, another and younger civilization is usually ready to step into their place; or, if there is none such in the vicinity, a new civilization may slowly integrate out of the debris of its indigenous predecessor.

At any rate, such is, in outline, what history tells us of the aging and death of past cultures. The corresponding societies, the culture-carrying groups, have a way of going on; much of the cultural content continues to exist and function somewhere, and may amplify; it is the particular set of patterned interweavings of content characterizing a civilization that breaks down.

The question that inevitably comes to our minds is whether such an end is necessary, or whether our own civilization may perhaps escape it. An honest answer seems to be that available precedent is pretty solidly one-way, but that history is never a sure basis for prophecy, since conditions can never be exactly repeated and precedents are therefore always only partial. For instance, there might be a new influence of culture-planning. Of this we have so far had only rudiments as by-products of contemporary social planning; for most social planning to date aims essentially to freeze most of the existing cultural values while trying to distribute their benefits more satisfactorily among the members of the society—or among all societies.

What is of interest in this connection is the contemporary trend of other cultures to assimilate themselves to Occidental civilization, of Turks, Arabs, Indians, Chinese, and Japanese to "Westernize" in their ways of life and standards. Mankind has never before been essentially unitary in culture. It is not yet unitary; but at the moment it is traveling fast that way. A good many persons, as diverse as ardent Christian missionaries, Communists, generalized idealists, until 1945 even Fascists and Nazis, look forward to the universality of civilization—implicitly their kind of civilization—as a goal and a boon. But there is this consideration: Suppose we attain a single, essentially uniform, world-wide civilization that has supplanted the many diverse ones of the past. And suppose that in attaining this one civilization we achieve its aims, realize the values potential in its patterns. What then when the exhausted, repetitive stage is reached, and there is no new rival culture to take over responsibility and opportunity and start fresh with new values in a different set of patterns—what then?

There is no precedent, and no answer, optimistic or pessimistic, can be proved for this future contingency. But the question is worth thinking about.

CHAPTER TEN

Culture Change

162. TYPES OF CULTURE CHANGE

SO FAR we have considered culture as if it constituted a kind of world of
Brahma, Vishnu, and Siva representing creation, preservation, and destruction: that being, in a sort of way, what invention, persistence, and
loss might be called. But in the actual physical world, as compared to a logical
one, there is a lot of change that ultimately is neither creation nor destruction,
but just change. In fact change is more frequent and more certain in the natural
world than either creation or destruction. Most physicists would deny both creation and destruction for energy as well as matter; but they would say that what
physics is concerned with is changes and redistributions of energy and matter.
So in culture too there are a great many happenings, such as the growth of swing
music, of informal manners and casual greeting, of sitting with legs crossed,
which are undoubted changes of recent decades and yet would be hard to fit with
sense into any rigid scheme of invention-persistence-loss. Nor are such changes
all trifling: drifts toward or away from totalitarianism or democracy, or funda-
mentalism or liberalism, or industrialism or laissez faire, are of the same order
as these examples, in that they are gradual and growthlike instead of happening
in jumps or steps.

We have accordingly to consider also cultural changes of the kind comparable to growths. For convenience of approach, we can separate off, among

such changes, those which are due mostly to internal factors and thus seem "spontaneous" in a culture, and those due chiefly to factors external to a culture and therefore induced in it.

Among changes from inside we have, first of all, alterations on the subsistence-economic-technological level such as the Neolithic Revolution (§ 262), the Industrial Revolution of recent centuries, the increasing urbanization of contemporary times, and many smaller shifts. These seem to be distinguished by what may be called a distinctive circular causality, about which more in a moment. Another large group of changes can be attributed to the biological play impulse in its cultural expression. These include fashion fluctuations, but also many that are not ordinarily classed under fashion. Affective factors—restlessness, strivings, boredom, repugnances, fatigue—are often involved in this group of phenomena. In fact, the emotional associations are sometimes quite disproportionate to the seriousness of the actual change, so that we are here skirting the field of social psychology. Finally, we have growth changes, leading gradually to new religions, different idea systems, social reconstructions, basically altered culture patterns. Revolutions, whether affecting one institution or a whole culture, form an extreme and special form of changes of this last class.

Changes from the outside relate either to culture elements or traits, the spread and introduction of which is usually called diffusion; or to the spread of larger pattern systems or complexes, such as the alphabet or Islam; or to the increasing contact of culture wholes, with attrition, penetration, and adjustments of these. This last type of externally caused culture change can be subsumed as *acculturation,* that word being construed as having outgrown its originally narrower meaning of assimilation—as will appear in the final sections of this chapter.

In the technical literature of anthropology certain similar features occurring in cultures of different periods, or of widely separated areas, are attributed to processes called independent parallel development and convergence; but other similarities are attributed to contact, dissemination, diffusion, or dispersal (§ 108, 109, 223). Parallels and convergences are due to internal or "spontaneous" growth factors; diffusions, as just stated, represent influences on a given culture from others outside it.

163. SUBSISTENCE AND POPULATION CHANGES

There is a group of basic factors that can have deep influence on the fortunes of societies and may affect the whole of their cultures. These factors include serious alterations in the environment, sufficiently heavy growth of population within a given territory, and fundamental changes in subsistence technique. It is evident that these factors are, strictly, subcultural, except for subsistence; and this, of course, not only is basal in culture, but in the case of farming and stockraising the subsistence provision amounts to the creation of an artificial or man-controlled floral and faunal environment.

An environment may alter with climate; or a people may abandon an old habitat, or be driven from it. If their new home is environmentally different enough to enforce a change in methods of subsistence, the rest of their old culture may alter profoundly. It does not follow that the new situation is inferior; it may be better or worse.

Changes in culture due to natural changes in environment undoubtedly occur. But this explanation for cultural change has probably been propounded ten times for every actual case of such change, especially in the long subarid belt from North China to southern and western Africa. Here there has been a mania or a fashion to posit pluvial periods followed by dry ones, with change from fertile lands to steppe and from steppe to desert, and with populations swarming out in consequence, or shrinking and impoverishing. If we go back far enough, there is no doubt that such climatic alterations have occurred. Yet it should always be recollected that ten thousand years is only a minimal unit in geology but an enormously long time in human history. Consequently, the two kinds of evidence barely meet; and it is where the evidential contact is poorest that the sparks of imaginative theory fly thickest. The explanation has certainly been worked hard, all the way from the Old Stone Age in Kenya to Jenghis Khan coming out of Mongolia, and there are very few scholars who really have enough control of all the data to separate the valid from the invalid guesses. There does seem to be general agreement that North Africa was moister about ten thousand years ago than it is now. But it is difficult to be sure of the extent of this change, or its precise effects on culture, which is infinitely more plastic and capable of rapid change than slow-moving climate is.

The transition from Palaeolithic to Mesolithic culture in northern Europe is now generally associated with the climatic change at the end of the last glacial period, which allowed forests to grow where there had been tundra, steppe, or grassland before (§ 276). The change in vegetation and fauna at the time seems well attested. That it was also the cause of the cultural change is plausible, but, in the nature of things, less certain: history is full of new culture phases without environment being involved.

More localized changes are sometimes well established. About 1425 the herring suddenly shifted their run and began to do their main spawning in the North Sea instead of the Baltic. The Holland fishermen profited economically, the Hanseatic Germans were the losers; and after about 1500, the Dutch, who till then had always trailed the Belgians in the Low Countries in prosperity and therewith in cultural productivity, began to draw abreast of them, and finally to forge ahead.

The general effect of increased population on culture has already been discussed in § 118 and 121. This is an expectable influence, a sort of reasonable a priori. It is validated at least partially by the fact that we find no very rich or advanced cultures among small populations.

That man-made new environment, the utilitarian domestication of animals and plants, which in prehistory is sometimes called the Neolithic Revolution (§ 281, 282), certainly provided a subsistence that for the long pull was more dependable than gathering and hunting had been, and it seems to have been followed by an increase of population. This new turn of culture became noticeable first in the Near East, the general region of southwestern Asia, and was followed there within a millennium or two by town life, building in brick, permanent structures for worship, metallurgy; and, in another millennium, by cities, rulers, states, writing, and records (§ 286). We are now, around 3000 B.C., at the beginning of history, in the narrowest sense of that word, as well as of higher civilization, in the Near East; but Europe of the time was only beginning to enter upon its first acquaintance with farming and the Neolithic. The regional difference is almost certainly due to the fact that ancestral grains and animals native to western Asia were first domesticated there. Here, accordingly, it was that the population gradually grew denser and that an advanced and partly urbanized type of civilization developed, while the diffusion of farming outward from this center was only commencing.

It is characteristic of this kind of culture change which advantageously affects subsistence that its causality tends to be circular,[1] or self-reinforcing, at least for a time. More and surer subsistence leads both to population increase and to specialization of skills and occupation. The specialization again makes for more stock of wealth, more varied and larger consumer demands, more concentrated productivity, and the chance for further population growth (see § 118).

Circular causalities similar to that of the ancient Near East seem to have been set going also in India and China and, more slowly, in Europe. Fairly soon after agriculture reached these areas, it was followed by metallurgical and other crafts, towns and states, and a population increase. In native America, again, massed populations, cities, conquest empires, and metallurgy characterize the areas between Mexico and Peru where farming was probably oldest and certainly most intensive. All these cases also are findings based on archaeological evidence.

However, these growth developments—except the American one—were all interconnected in some measure, as the identity of some domesticated plants and animals shows. They must therefore be construed as at least partly derived one from another. Consequently they cannot in fairness be counted as independent instances each reconfirming a law or generalization.

In fact, it appears to be the surety of ample food supply that is the primary factor in these circular situations, rather than farming as such. This is shown by the population of indigenous northern America, for which fairly specific estimates are available. These are easily highest for ancient nuclear Mexico with its intensive tillage: 7 to 8 people per square mile, or over 700 per unit of a hun-

---

[1] It might well be called spiral in many cases, but the technical term is "circular."

dred square miles. North of the Mexican high-density center, the figures drop to 26 souls per hundred square miles in the farming areas, and still further to only about 10 in the nonfarming areas as a total. So far we have corroboration. But from the nonfarming tracts there can be segregated out a narrow strip along the Pacific coast from Alaska to California, where the density was 65 per hundred square miles, as against less than 6 in the rest of the hunting-gathering areas. In this Pacific-coast strip the dependence was on sea and river fishing in the north, on gathering of acorns and seeds in the south. Neither procedure is likely to cut seriously into reproductive supply, whereas steady hunting on land does quickly exhaust game, as soon as the number of hunters becomes considerable. So population density was able to mount among the fortunate fishing and gathering tribes along the Pacific coast until it was two and a half times greater than the over-all among the farming tribes north of the Rio Grande. To be sure, most of the eastern groups were not too assiduous in their farming, leaving it mainly to their women, while the men hunted or warred. Also, farming had come to them out of the tropics probably not very many centuries before, and it was still unaccompanied by the cities, states, metallurgy, and calendars which had developed in Mexico along with, or soon after, agriculture. The relation of the farming Indians of the eastern United States of A.D. 1492 to those of Mexico was evidently quite like that of the Neolithic people of Europe around 2500 B.C.—when population was certainly not yet dense there—in comparison to the populous and literate kingdoms of contemporary Egypt and Mesopotamia. Left undisturbed for another thousand or two thousand years, these eastern and central United States farming Indians might have caught up; but when discovery overtook them, they were clearly less populous than the Pacific-coast fishermen. and probably not quite as far along toward a rich and diversified culture.

There is no doubt that, given time enough, and on the average, farming will lead to very much heavier concentrations of population than are possible under gathering, fishing, or hunting. Compare, again on the basis of 100-square-mile units: native Australia, gathering, 5 inhabitants; but Italy 39,000, Japan 50,000, Belgium 75,000 Kiangsi province 87,000, Java 90,000. In all of history there has never been a genuine city in a nonfarming culture. All that the foregoing citation on the northern Pacific-coast Indians proves is that the relation is not wholly automatic in favor of food-producers as against food-gatherers. Nonfarming at its optimum may be accompanied by heavier population than farming that is newly learned, indifferent, or inefficient.

164. FASHION CHANGE

A series of cultural activities seems ultimately rooted in the organic play impulses, which are most developed in the young of mammals—especially among the carnivores and the primates (§ 15). These cultural activities include, first of all of course, organized games and sports of all kinds; in addition, such expressions of play and relaxation and humor as may be more loosely standardized in the folkways. Definitely to be included, as nourished at least partly from the same organic root, are science and the arts and fashion—the sciences and arts perhaps more so in proportion as they are less colored by utilitarian purposes. Obviously, this is not saying that the fine arts and pure science are just play: they are serious endeavors and mostly hard work. Yet in their primary nature they are neither individually nor socially utilitarian, but are ends in themselves, and in a way pleasures in themselves, and in this respect they resemble play; just as the impulses toward, say, curiosity, or rhythm, which go into science or music, are also found in play. Science and art may be conceived as cultural sublimations, on the adult level, of hereditary physiological impulses whose manifestations in childhood we unhesitatingly class as play.[2]

Even more directly than science and art does the realm of fashion, with its constant seeking for something new, exemplify cultural play activity. While fashion change may be sought with considerable eagerness, it is generally regarded with a certain lightness—we might literally say with a playful attitude. Also like play, fashion is followed most actively when there is a surplus of food, energy, and leisure—wealth, in cultural terms. In connection with fashion we think first of variability in dress styles (§ 138); but it is evident that there are changing fashions in houses, furnishings, gardens, and automobiles. In fact, it is not difficult to recognize some degree of changeable fashions in political and religious beliefs and in institutions. The sciences, especially the newer ones, are subject to waves of fashion. The layman, standing respectfully outside, is likely to be unaware of this: the latest "edict" of science is to him the latest truth. Run-of-the-mill scientists may share this opinion: they are like the dressmaker who believes that this year's mode is at last the complete combination of beauty, comfort, and serviceability—forgetting that if it were, next year's fashion would have nothing left but to undo the ideal. The scholar with perspective of his subject is aware that ideas and methods come into vogue and pass out, in his field as in others, and that part of his business is to distinguish the evanescent fad from permanent progress. In short, there is hardly a field of culture that is not subject to some fashion variation.

It is difficult to say where fashion ends and where custom, or style in art, begins, because custom and style also change. A possible differential criterion would construe fashion as change for the sake of change, while style and custom alter respectively under the pressure of inner developments or of outer circumstance. But the concepts are continuous, and sure distinction can be made only at the ends of the scale.

[2] Not that any of these adult manifestations can be *directly* reduced to genetic and physiological causes. They always have cultural antecedents and their immediate determinants are sociocultural behavior. It is only their ultimate basis that is organic and comparable to play.

When some detail of dress is given a new cut this year, and already begins to be crowded out by a new cut or trimming next year, there is no doubt that we are wholly within the domain of fashion, in fact in its very froth. If, however, in the second year the new cut or color or embellishment comes back into stronger favor and is more accentuated, and for the next three or five or ten years it becomes increasingly emphasized or exaggerated, and only then begins to be soft-pedaled, until it fades away after another three or five or ten years—have we here a fashion growth or style growth? As a matter of fact, in § 137-138 we have seen that there are features of dress fashion, such as proportions of silhouette or figure, which trend in one direction for fifty or more years, and are as long in moving back. Underneath the inconsistent year-to-year fluctuations, or those of a few brief years, women's skirts, for instance, do steadily become increasingly fuller or increasingly shorter for a half-century at a time. Such drifts in duration are somewhat like the economist's "secular trends" which underlie the fluctuations of the few-year business cycle.

Such long-term fashion swings are also comparable to growth in art styles. In painting, neoclassicism, romanticism, impressionism, expressionism, cubism, have each lasted no longer, or less long, than some of these trends in Western dress; and the degree of change effected by them is no greater. The total form and effect of Occidental clothing in 1815, 1865, and 1915 seem about as different as canvases painted in the classic manner in 1790 are different from the romantic ones of 1840 and these from the impressionisms of 1890 and surrealisms of 1940. The main difference is that we like to think of picture-painting and art exhibitions as serious and dignified, and of clothes and fashion shows as frivolous. But the behavior manifestations of the two sets of phenomena are much alike, so that we are justified in assuming that the processes at work are similar. One might even suspect the genuineness of the greater formal or avowed respect accorded the painter's activity. Presumably for every ten people in our civilization really exercised about a change in the manner of paintings there are a thousand who participate personally in changes of dress style, and who would be intensely perturbed if poverty or a sumptuary law prohibited them from conforming.

Landscape design or gardening is in an intermediate situation, as regards the attitude of our culture. It possesses a certain dignity because it is an expression of luxury and requires at least a measure of prosperity as a threshold. The tenement dweller contents himself with two or three geraniums in tin cans on the fire escape. The reasonably well-to-do, when the city is not too crowded, have a garden. The wealthy go in for landscaping a park. The same changes however occur. In one century gardens are formal in the Italian or the French manner. In another they are informal or rustic on the English model. Yet even a small garden cannot conveniently be entirely made over each year like a dress, so annual fashions are lacking. But there are fluctuations that are measurable in relatively brief periods. Rock gardens have a vogue for a decade or so, and then people become tired and pull them up. Pampas grass had its day, but is now scarcely any longer to be found except on neglected or avowedly old-fashioned properties.

Dress-designing being an art, even though not a very highbrow one, has style as well as fleeting fashions. It is distinctive in that everyone in the society is affected by it, and in that its products wear out and must soon be replaced. It is perhaps for these reasons that there is in it a greater element of rapid minor change than in the other arts, and that we are attuned to being highly aware of these superficial changes. The processes at work in dress styles presumably are not very different from those in other art styles. A dress fashion is in its nature datable from its appearance. But so are sculptures and paintings datable to art historians—within a century if ancient, usually within a decade if modern. This of course not only implies change, but that the change is more or less regular in the sense of being steady.

Why it should be in the intrinsic nature of style to change, ordinarily, is a complex problem, which is still largely unsolved, though at least part of the answer lies in the domains of cultural pattern and its control or achievement by virtuosity. At any rate, the essential instability of styles strengthens the indication of the genetic relationship of the arts to physiological play impulses. Pure fashion of course is an even more immediate manifestation.

165. VARIABLE PATTERNS OF MOTIVATION FOR ANIMAL BREEDING

Akin to fashion changes in dress and art are certain striking variations in the purposes for which animals were presumably first domesticated and for which they are still often bred by nonliterate or retarded societies. The range of this variability from people to people through space is similar to the range of fashion changes among one people in time. Also, many of the manifestations of this variability resemble fashion in being dependent on nonutilitarian motivation.

We look upon stock-raising as part of farming, as an industry or a useful business. That it is such among ourselves is of course no proof that it began as such, that the original motivation in the keeping of animals was utilitarian. There are in fact grave doubts that it could have begun that way. Too many cultures disregard too many of the potential utilities. All of southeastern Asia uses no milk, butter, or cheese; also no wool, except for whole sheepskins in the fleece. In most of their early distribution horses were not ridden until long after they were driven. The pig was an unclean animal and was not eaten in ancient Egypt, by the Hebrews, or in Islam. Practically all Negro tribes keep cattle, wherever the climate and the tsetse fly permit; but none make cheese, some churn butter for body ointment instead of consumption, and the majority are so eager to build up their herds that they rarely eat beef.

All in all, the utilization of domesticated animals in ways that seem rational to us was so incomplete in ancient times, and is so incomplete today among backward peoples, that Galton, Hahn, Laufer, and others have stressed nonrational factors—affective or sentimental considerations—as dominant in early stages of this activity. The motivations range from desire for pets, companionship, or play to the needs of ritual and magic on the one hand and wealth symbolism and prestige satisfaction on the other.

Among the South American forest Indians, monkeys, parrots, and almost all and any kinds of small animals were freely kept as pets, though there were no species domesticated for utility, and in parts of Brazil even dogs were lacking. In some parts of native California dogs were valued for deer-hunting; in others, they were kept chiefly to be eaten; in still others, they were merely tolerated and allowed to fend for themselves. In another California region, we have already seen (§ 159) that dogs were rare, imported as articles of luxury, pampered, and watched over. This regional Californian diversity illustrates neatly the vagaries of which primitive culture is capable—the workings in it of fashion and fad by locale instead of by period, we might say—and how motives of utility, of affection or display, or of indifference, can replace each other.

Negro kings have been known to keep whole packs or menageries of the greater game animals. The Romans imported them largely for slaughter in their circus games. The wild elephant has long been tamed in India and Farther India for work and transport, but still more for war and royal show. In Burma and Siam albino specimens had almost sacred status as embodiments of supreme kingship. Farther India, by the way, is another area in which pets are in favor: monkeys and young gibbons. On the contrary, in this its presumptive original home, the common fowl is little esteemed for its eggs, which are few, or for its meat, which is tough; but since two thousand years ago its thighbones have been in demand for divination. Bristles are stuck into the blood-vessel foramina of these bones and the directions of protrusion throw light on the issue in question. In the pagan parts of Indonesia, chickens are in primary demand for ritual sacrifice, including divination from their bile sacs; in the Islamic and Christian areas, the pitting of the cocks in fights overshadows other uses. Indonesia and the adjacent southeast corner of Asia, so far as it is still pagan, perhaps contain the principal contemporary survivals of the once much more widespread identification of ritual sacrifice to the gods with meat-eating by the worshipers—an association once in force as far west as the Mediterranean (§ 128, 192). It would be too much to assert that people first bred cattle and pigs in order that they might sacrifice them. Nevertheless, over a large part of the domesticating area an early double custom grew up of eating ordinarily only such tame flesh as had been dedicated to the gods, and of consuming every offering so dedicated. The civilized nations of today might still be following this custom if it had not been displaced by Christianity, Islam, and Buddhism.

It is perhaps the fact that kept animals multiply which has led to their being prized as reserves of wealth—not only among pastorals who own little else, but among settled farmers, as among the Greeks and Romans. The word "pecuniary" is from the Latin *pecus,* cattle, just as "monetary," "money," derives from *Moneta,* an epithet of Juno, in whose temple the Romans happened to mint their coinage; the two terms illustrate the passage from a livestock to a money economy. Negro East and South Africa has not yet effected this transition. In favor of cattle as wealth is the fact that they are visible and conspicuous and lend themselves to prestige display and gifts. Thus it is that their social valuation is definitely greater than their actual subsistence utility, among many Negroes.

With the Ruwala of Arabia, mares have acquired a similar prestige position, while the camel and its milk is what these Beduin (§ 120) live by. Except for occasional raiding, horses are quite useless in the desert, and would perish if turned loose. But they are carried along with barley that has to be bought from alien farmers and which they share with the household. In dry times, water for them has to be carried in by camels. Their pedigrees are kept. They are an untold worry and trouble; yet a single mare is valued at perhaps twenty riding dromedaries, and many a man owns only a fractional share in one. Once more, this Ruwala situation is obviously an excrescence of development, rather than a condition typical of the origin of stock-raising. But with the attached affects and motivations so varied now, they are unlikely to have been solidly and uniformly utilitarian in the beginning.

Thus it is clear that men do not live by meat and bread only. They breed animals for their flesh and milk and hide and wool and traction, but they also breed them for religion and sport and social climbing and companionship and show. And from people to people, and from time to time, these ends intertwine and replace one another in almost endless recombinations: the changes are literally the play of culture. We can understand even the most alien of the attitudes, but we cannot explain more than a part of them from utilitarian need. The livelihood and profit motives have no doubt mainly sustained the continuity of stockbreeding through history. But its many other associations and motivations lend the greater interest to the changeable activity, as we view it in world-wide retrospect.[3]

166. LABILE SOCIAL STRUCTURES

When we pass from dress and animals and arts to institutions, we encounter a flood of impermanences and variabilities which suggest that we may still be at times within the sphere of the play-derived, though unconscious,

---

[3] And of course many of the innovations and shifts in respect to domestic animals can also be included among the play inventions of § 148.

activity of culture. Among primitives, such lability or instability is most often extreme in social structure; among lettered peoples, in political forms.

Consider for instance the situation among the several Brazilian tribes of the Gê family. Among the Canella or Ramkokamekra there are four separate and crosscutting moiety organizations—a moiety being a half of a society formally set off against the other half for whatever reason or purpose. This is very much as if among ourselves there were a compulsory segregation of the population into first Democrats and Republicans; next, Catholics and Protestants; third, people born in odd-numbered and even-numbered years; and finally, partisans of the American and National baseball leagues, with distribution so regulated that Democrats and Republicans would be about equally distributed between Catholics and Protestants, and similarly all down the line, so that the membership of one complementary pair of moieties would never coincide with the membership of another pair, but would crosscut all the other moieties as much as possible. The first pair of Canella moieties is matrilineal and matrilocal—follows the mother in descent and residence—and regulates marriage exogamously. The second pair of moieties is concerned with racing and hunting during the rainy season. It is not concerned with marriage but is totemic—that is, certain animals or natural objects are symbolically representative of each moiety. And membership in the moiety is determined by names given by older individuals, theoretically the cross-uncle or mother's brother for boys, the cross-aunt or father's sister for girls. The totemism of this second pair of moieties is conceptually extended over all nature. The third set of moieties consists of two pairs of age classes, each age class comprising all males jointly initiated within a given period of years. This third pair of moieties also functions in competitive sports, but in the dry instead of the rainy season. The fourth set of moieties has membership again based on bestowed names, but the names this time are the property not of uncles or aunts, but of three groups or subdivisions within each of the moieties, and of two clubs or four societies. The groups own assembly houses that occupy prescribed situations in the circle in which the village is built; and they and the clubs function ceremonially in connection with men's initiations. So far the Canella tribe.

Among the linguistically related Apinaye, there is only one set of moieties, matrilineal and matrilocal, whose houses are localized in the village circle, but who are not at all concerned with marriage. They compete in sports and are concerned with ceremonial, and are characterized by possession of a series of personal names bestowed by uncles and aunts. Marriage is separately regulated by four unlocalized *kiye* or "sides," where A marries B, B with C, C with D, D with A, for men; but for women, the rule is the reverse, or really, complementarily the same, A marrying D, and so on. These "sides" are not clans, because clan descent is the same for boys and girls but boys belong to the "side" of their father, girls to that of their mother. Moreover, the four "sides" group into two implicit or unavowed intermarrying moieties, one consisting of A and

C, the other of B and D; for A and C both marry with B and D, but never with each other.

Still another Gê tribe, the Sherente, have exogamous moieties that are patrilineal and patrilocal and are divided into six clans localized in the village circle, which seem to correspond partly, but only partly, to the six subdivisions of the Canella ceremonial moieties.

Still another tribe, the Kaingang, associate with their exogamous moieties the totemic division of nature that the Canella associate with their nonexogamous rainy-season moieties.

It is evident that a long array of social forms have been luxuriantly developed by these Gê tribes: the moiety, moiety subdivisions, their localization within the circular village, their seasonal functioning, totemism, exogamy, unilateral descent (both patrilineal and matrilineal, or even both simultaneously according to the sex of children), group ownership of names, bestowal of names by individuals of the uncle or aunt relation, competitive sports, ceremonial associations, and grouping of initiates into age classes. Underlying all these forms is the principle of grouping of persons, whether dual or multiple. However, the very luxuriance of kinds of groups has led to a variety of ways of combining them, and probably to the constant devising of new kinds of groups, which made possible still further combinations, or transfer of functions from one set of groups to another. It is difficult to review the structures of these Brazilian tribal societies without a strong impression of their instability: of remodeling, innovation, and experimentation having been active.

Inasmuch as the four tribes speak varieties of the same Gê language, they must be connected in their histories. The diversity of their modern social organization must accordingly represent changes after a period when they were more alike. They still share conspicuous remnants of an indubitably common original pattern, but each has enormously altered or rearranged this. Evidently, once the interests of a culture become weighted in the direction of social structure, the culture may make the most unexpected combinations and even inventions of social forms.

In scattered parts of native America there was practiced the custom of the ant ordeal. This was a ritual discipline or test of fortitude, and consisted of laying the victim or novice on a hill of biting ants. The act itself was uniform; its setting, context, and motivations were quite diverse. Thus, the South American Rucuyenne applied the ordeal to boys undergoing their ceremonial initiation. So did some of the Tupi tribes south of the Amazon—as did the far-away Luiseño in California. But back in South America, the Saliva administered the ant ordeal to their new chiefs on assuming office. The Arawak of Guiana used it in mourning; other Guiana tribes, in hunting ritual. It is evident that a distinctive and rather invariable unit of practice, the ant ordeal itself, must have a history of quite varied associations—it has been bandied about from one religious ceremony to another almost like a shuttlecock. Again we see lability prevalent: looseness of organization rather than stability, fixity, or permanence.

However, elaborate forms need not appear simply because a society is primitive. The Eskimo, the Great Basin Shoshoneans, and many other societies are instances of simple structures free from formal organizational features. The factors at work in producing these relatively unstructured societies may be connected with subsistence difficulties; they need not be. Extremely interesting is the discovery among the same clanless Shoshone of the custom of pseudo-cross-cousin marriage,[4] in semblance of the cross-cousin marriage favored by so many other peoples: the favored Shoshone mates are stepcousins, no blood kin at all. This was certainly a strange practice to think up. Relatives continue to be avoided, but imitation relatives are sought as mates. Who could deny inventiveness to primitives?[5]

In fact, the ingenuity and imaginativeness of the social structure of much of primitive life is the essential moral of such facts. Many of the institutions are true luxury products. They almost certainly serve some function; but it may be a minor one, while major ends are left formally unprovided for. A great deal of the picture suggests the play of earnest children, or the inventive vagaries of fashion. This in turn strongly suggests the high instability of many of these social constructs. This instability cannot ordinarily be absolutely proved, because our historical knowledge of primitives rarely has much depth; but it is indicated by the totality of the data.

Political organization, on the contrary, is something that primitives have in general not achieved to any notable degree. When unlettered peoples have achieved it, as in Africa and Peru, we tend to exclude them from our concept of what is primitive. By complement, high civilizations have throughout history regularly been accompanied by considerable degrees of political organization. The causes of the difference are probably complex. But weakness of technological controls and therefore of economic resources among primitives may be suspected as an important factor. If so, a generic nexus of technological development through economics with political organization can be inferred. Primitives being weak in the former, they remained weak in the latter. Instead, they threw their cultural interests and energies into the forms of social structure, into the institutions concerned with the nearer interpersonal relations.

In the grand vista of cultural growth, accordingly, technological and political developments, which characterize the successfully more complex civilizations,

---

[4] Cross-cousins are the children of brother and sister—whose sex differs or "crosses"—as contrasted with parallel cousins, who are the children of two brothers or two sisters. We do not make this distinction in our culture, either in law, inheritance, or reckoning of kin—in fact are usually unaware that it can be made. But among many nonliterates, and even in India and China, the distinction is important. Cross-cousins are often favored as spouses where parallel cousins are forbidden.

[5] Some African cases of luxuriation are mentioned in § 312: coexistence of patrilineal and matrilineal reckoning.

are secondary and late products reared upon social forms or devices centering immemorially around kinship. Some measure of these kinship forms persists into higher civilization because kinship is biologically inescapable and perhaps equally inescapable psychologically. But the kinship structures of complex civilizations are often reduced, almost always divested of excrescences and luxuriances of pattern; they have become humble, simple, subserving real ends. We no longer practice pseudo-cross-cousin marriage nor descend from our mothers into moieties in which we receive names from our uncles. Instead, we buy automobiles on the installment plan and elect officials to police and tax us. The inventiveness and instability so evident in the social forms of primitive societies are largely transferred in higher civilization to the technological, economic, and political fields.

167. AFFECT IN CULTURE CHANGE

Is it right for a man to marry his stepdaughter? Here again there is great variability between cultures and at times considerable change within cultures. Christian countries in which established religion strongly influences the law of the land have generally barred the practice. Sometimes the prohibition has persisted after disestablishment of the state church. For the forty-eight American states the situation in 1940 is shown in the diagrammatic map, Figure 21. A century or so ago probably all American communities ruled such marriage irre-

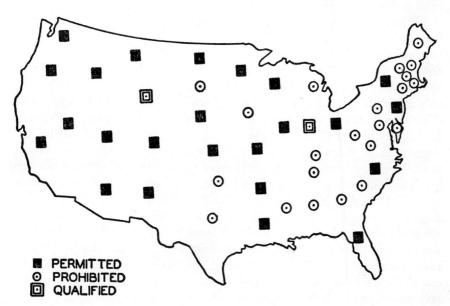

■ PERMITTED
⊙ PROHIBITED
▣ QUALIFIED

FIG. 21. LEGALITY OF MARRIAGE WITH A STEPDAUGHTER IN THE 48 UNITED STATES

ligious, immoral, and illegal. Most of the older and relatively conservative Eastern and Southern states still forbid it. But times have changed and twenty-six
of the forty-eight states no longer prohibit the practice—which means it is
legally tolerated. Yet two of these salve an uneasy social conscience by going
out of their way to specify extramarital relations with a stepdaughter as punish-
able.

Of 167 tribal and subtribal groups of Indians investigated between Vancouver Island and the Rio Grande, three-fourths definitely frowned upon stepdaughter marriage and presumably prevented it. Some 10 per cent disapproved,
but without attempting to do anything about occasional violations. About another 10 per cent of the tribes disliked but tolerated the idea; in other words,
were two-minded about it. Finally, perhaps 5 or 6 per cent of the groups admitted stepdaughter marriage as a recognized form; that is, gave it institutional
sanction. The custom is perhaps most common among the matrilineal and
matrilocal Navaho. If a man marries a separated or widowed woman who has
a small daughter, he often, with her mother's consent, adds the girl as wife
when she grows up. Each woman has less work, and yet the output of the
ménage is greater. The total tribal distribution of the custom, shown in Figure
22, is almost randomly scattering, with only slight tendencies toward areal segregation. Highly random local distributions of this scattered type can usually be
interpreted as the result of conflicting influences, and hence as indicating instability. While some tribes consistently banned the practice, others backed and
filled and kept changing their rules.

Why this variability and change? It seems to spring from a conviction that
is one of very few major premises common to all cultures: that one does not
marry close kin. But variation begins with the definition of who are close kin.
Some peoples bar even third cousins as wives; others permit aunts and half-
sisters. Some consider all clan mates kin, whether they are or not. Others not
only allow but favor the marriage of first cross-cousins, or again squeamishly
think they should be second cousins. Some religions, like the Greek Orthodox
Christianity, and until recently the Church of England, class affinals by marriage—such as sisters-in-law—as kindred, though they are not blood relatives
at all. This is reasonable enough because of the normally close association and
bonds with near affinal relatives; but it is scarcely logical, if incest has anything
to do with blood. It is of a kind with the Roman Catholic prohibition of marriage with a goddaughter, toward whom the relation is not even affinal, but
spiritual only. On the other hand, if the incest prohibition refers to blood kinship, permissibility of stepdaughter marriage is logical enough. Nevertheless,
many societies consider it unfit and shocking. Even where the practice is tolerated, there is often considerable individual repugnance to it; whereas in a few
polygynous groups it is institutionalized. The issue is evidently the sort of
problem one can argue and counterargue forever. In the end, it is settled by
some feeling or affect that one has or does not have. This feeling may be quite

strong, or it may be ambivalent. Being a feeling about ideas, it gets involved in logic. Nevertheless, the ultimate determination of the issue is affective, not intellectually realistic; and the motivation of affects is notoriously capricious. Culture features of this type are therefore likely to remain open problems, to which the answer keeps varying. Only when the point gets caught up in some larger organized system of feelings and ideas with big momentum is a consistent long-term answer expectable.

It is not to be assumed that strong affect necessarily produces stability and persistence. One can feel vigorously and yet have his feelings change. This is

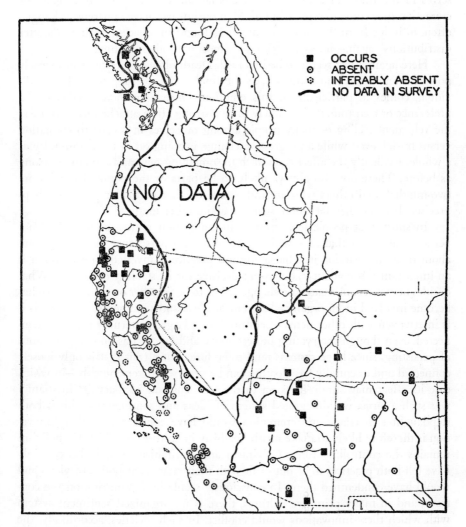

FIG. 22.   STEPDAUGHTER MARRIAGE IN WESTERN INDIAN TRIBES

true also of cultures. Disposal of the dead is a case in point. Human cultures have devised a great variety of methods: burial, cremation, water burial, setting away in vaults or canoes or houses, scaffold burial, exposure or simple abandonment, cremation with eating or drinking of the ashes by the relatives, temporary inhumation with either reburial or preservation of the bones—not to mention previous mummification, dismemberment, and other related practices. Now while some societies have adhered for long periods to one basic method of disposing of their dead—ancient Egypt to mummification and mediaeval Europe to churchyard burial, for instance—others have been changeable. We are ourselves in the midst of a drift toward cremation. This may die out again, or cremation may come to replace burial. Many primitives have apparently changed often, to judge from the variety of practices found in adjacent groups—"scatter distributions" again—in, say, Africa, or almost any other continent.

Here again affect seems to be involved. Death obviously releases immensely powerful emotions; and a funeral, as the final act of a group toward an individual, comes to participate in this emotion. Once a method has become a preference or a custom, there is likely to be a strong affect attached to it. Witness the vehement feeling of many people among ourselves in regard to cremation versus burial, even while a progressive change is going on in the community as a whole. Evidently the affect can attach to something new and remain as strong as before. There are also always likely to be parts of the population who are two-minded, and others who are indifferent on that particular point—perhaps precisely because they feel more strongly about other matters.

In short, that people feel strongly in connection with a custom does not per se mean either that they will adhere to it with persistence or that they are about ready to abandon it. That a cultural practice is invested with emotion is an important thing about it, but is not decisive for its stability or lability. What decides between continuance or change seems to be whether or not a practice has become involved in an organized system of ideas and sentiments: how much it is interwoven with other items of culture into a larger pattern. If it is thus connected, even though the rooting be secondary and late, it has good expectations of persisting, since large systems tend to endure. But a trait that is only loosely connected and essentially free-floating can be superseded very quickly—in which case its affect may simply pass on to the new custom. Mediaeval Christianity was such a large, well-integrated system of ideas and sentiments—with it both stepdaughter marriage and cremation would have conflicted. Neither innovation is therefore likely to make much headway in cultures in which Catholicism remains the controlling force. Calvinism and Puritanism would also certainly have felt both practices to be out of fit with their systems or points of view, and would have condemned them. In consciously secularized countries, on the contrary, and in many primitive cultures, there is no organized sentiment system with which these innovations would conflict. In such societies, accordingly, the practices may easily become established, only to be easily superseded again.

168. CULTURAL FATIGUE: TABOO IN HAWAII

In 1819 the Polynesians of Hawaii at one stroke abolished their religion. This was five months before the first missionary landed on the islands, and was therefore a voluntary act. To be sure, Captain Cook had discovered the islands some forty years before and had been followed by a number of explorers, traders, and whalers. Through these the Hawaiians had learned of the existence of Christian beliefs. But it is unlikely that they understood them at all well. They had however seen Europeans repeatedly violate religious prohibitions—taboos— without being even punished by the native gods, and that must have shaken Hawaiian faith. Among the natives, this taboo system had grown very power- ful and no doubt was sometimes felt as onerous. Women might not eat certain foods, such as bananas and coconuts. It was absolutely irreligious and shocking for men and women to eat together. The king let himself be carried over private lands because contact with his divine body would make the land taboo and un- touchable by its owner. There were religious festivals that the population cele- brated by remaining inactive indoors, so as not to break the taboo. The system was heavily loaded in favor of royalty, aristocracy, and priesthood, but ap- parently was coming to be felt as irritatingly restrictive by these classes also.

Some years after Cook's discovery, an able chief began to rise to power and finally fought his way to undisputed rule over the entire island group. This was the famous Kamehameha I. He died without having departed from the faith of his fathers or altered its regulations. His successor, Kamehameha II, was a young and easy-going man. The group that surrounded and swayed him now decided to do away with the taboo system. This group included his chief formal adviser or prime minister; his mother; and another widow of the preceding king, named Kaahumanu. The latter was a bold and ambitious person and per- haps the chief mover in the conspiracy. As a woman she unquestionably had much to gain by abolition of the taboo. Strangely enough, however, the high priest of the islands was also active in the coterie, and in fact subsequently took the lead in extending the movement from mere abolition of the taboo to the overthrow of the gods whose representative he was. This man seemingly had everything to lose by the change, and it is difficult to imagine what he could have had to gain. It is known that he did not profess to be a convert to the Christian- ity which was in the offing. He evidently represented, therefore, an element in the population that was psychologically ready for a breach with established re- ligion, from internal reasons. Whether such a frame of mind could have devel- oped before any Caucasian contacts, among Hawaiians who were beneficiaries of the existing system, seems doubtful. The old Hawaiians, knowing of no re- ligion but their own, would presumably have found it difficult to imagine or invent any radically different form of worship. Nevertheless it is also hard to un- derstand the high priest's motivation, unless he, presumably with many others, was tired of the established religious order to a degree that made him ready even for a switch to something unknown. In addition, the whites enjoyed prestige for their guns, steel tools, and big ships; and, by extension, their only vaguely known religion was probably accounted superior.

It was finally arranged by the conspiring royal entourage that the taboo should be publicly broken at a great festival. This would amount to a religious revolution from the throne. As the hour neared, the young king became increasingly uneasy; but he was coaxed and steered to the final act. After the royal ladies had first eaten forbidden foods in sight of the gathering, the king came over and ate with them. At first incredulous, the multitude finally realized what had happened. Shouts went up, and were carried over the island—"The taboo is broken!" The high priest himself mutilated the images of the gods and set fire to the temple. This action was imitated everywhere in a sort of frenzy. It is difficult to say now what the real reaction of the population at large was. They were certainly shocked and excited. Many of them must have been pleased. Some surely felt outraged, and others were more stirred than participant. The king was himself divine, so that the act must have resembled a sudden voluntary abdication by the gods themselves. However, the king's power was also absolute, and it is therefore likely that the mass of commoners received the event with some docility.

The only overt opposition came from high quarters. Kekuaokalani, a nephew of the late great king and next in line of succession to the high priesthood, when he could believe his senses rescued one of the god figures and strode with it from the assembly. He rallied a following of the pious and raised a revolt. His adherents were numerous and determined. It is evident that the innovation was not unanimously approved of by the population. Before long it came to battle. Kekuaokalani was defeated, his following scattered, and the conservative protest came to an end. However, the fight is said to have been decided by the Christian-made firearms which the king's side was able to muster. A few months later the first missionaries landed, were received with open arms and royal favor, and Hawaii as a whole rapidly became Christian.

There can be little doubt that we have here, in part, a culture change due to new contacts. It is also evident that at least some of the reformers were actuated by motives of personal advantage or convenience, though this does not apply to all of them. But the main factor seems to have been a kind of social staleness; the Hawaiians had become disillusioned, and tired of their religion. To this extent the incident is illustrative of what may be called cultural fatigue. It is no doubt an extreme case of such an attitude. But it is probably not wholly aberrant, and reactions of similar though milder type may be occasional factors in cultural change. French defeatism in 1940 was perhaps an example. Nor would it be difficult to make out a case for social fatigue or staleness having been operative in bringing on the French Revolution, in addition to exasperation over abuses and cultural lag and the ferment of new ideologies. The attitude of the

American people toward the depression of 1929 after it became profound suggests the presence of a considerable factor of the sort, with the New Deal as a reaction to it. Once an attitude of the kind develops sufficient strength, novelty as such may come to seem a virtue and a boon.

One other consideration is worth mentioning. The overthrow of the Hawaiian religion could not have been effected so rapidly and thoroughly if the impetus had not come from a strong and respected government. Without this, there would presumably have been prolonged civil war, and only a gradual giving-way of the old order to the new. The Japanese Emperor's sudden and successful renunciation of divinity in 1945 is a somewhat parallel case. In this respect both events resemble those alterations or reforms of calendrical, writing, and other pattern systems produced either by grand revolutions or by complete autocracies, usually in their first flush of power, as discussed in § 170 below.

169. CHANGE THROUGH ORGANIZED RELIGION

Organized religion has a way of being influential in the overturn and the reconstruction of major civilizations. It works first toward cultural change and then for conservation. Especially is this true of religions which set out to overrun the world because they alone are "true" and all other faiths and cults false and likely to taint even secular activities with which they have become associated. Most primitive and national religions have also started out, naturally enough, with the assumption of their own verity and importance; but alongside this they have had naïve tolerance of other faiths as being also more or less true, though of course not quite as good and true, or at any rate not as appropriate for their own nationals.

If one were asked to specify the most important single characteristic distinguishing Ancient Mediterranean or Classical from our own Occidental civilization—the culture of the Greeks and Romans from that of mediaeval and modern Western nations—it would almost certainly be Christianity. Our civilization is patently derived, in large measure even descended, from the Graeco-Roman; but it contains very few specific carry-overs from the preceding pagan cults or faiths. When the fourth-century Roman emperors, like Constantine and Theodosius, turned Christian, the end of the old order, of the former world view, was in sight. Within a century we have Rome "falling," and the continuous stream of history is renamed "mediaeval" instead of "ancient," as a symbol of the transformation.[6] The mythology and worship of the Greeks had of course been all intertwined with their literature, art, philosophy, learning, and even manners. Consequently Christianity in its three centuries of uphill fight tended to become hostile, suspicious, grudging, or at best indifferent toward Greek and Roman

[6] In fact, until not so very long ago, historical convention had "ancient" history ending not in A.D. 476 but in 325 with Constantine, the founding of Constantinople, and the Church Council of Nicaea.

achievements in these activities. So it was natural for the Dark Ages to follow the final supremacy of Christianity; and it was nearly a thousand years before Christian Europe could even begin to rival the pagan Mediterranean world in urbanity, knowledge, intellectual penetration, aesthetic performance, and the graces of life—including bodily cleanliness. This is not saying that Christianity was responsible for the long recession. These big historical situations are not adjudicated so simply as that. Just as soundly could one contend that Classical civilization had exhausted its patterns, was dying away within an empty shell, and that Christianity moved in to fill the void, but required time to grow a whole new civilization. However, this is sure: Irrespective of whether it was more largely cause or effect, Christianity was the pre-eminent point of crystallization for the civilization that superseded the Graeco-Roman one.

A very similar influence in change of civilization could be made out for Buddhism and Mohammedanism, the two chief competitors of Christianity as "world religions." The three share the following characteristics:

1. They are world religions not because they have encompassed the earth, but because they aim to encompass it, to be world-wide and supernational, in distinction from ethnic or tribal religions.

2. Each is attached to a transcending personality, from whom the name for the faith is taken. The usual view is that these personalities as individuals founded and made their religions. It is however also possible to see the founders more largely as symbols necessary to this type of religion. Certainly more of the total content of Christianity—as distinct from its "essence," which is in its very nature attached to his person—was evolved or contributed by his followers and successors more than by Jesus himself. St. Paul alone is sometimes said to have added as much as Jesus did. The same is unquestionably true of Buddhism, and quite possibly of Mohammedanism. Moreover, the fact that all three religions originated in southwestern Asia within little more than a thousand years, and followed outwardly parallel courses, suggests a pattern, and that something like them was "in the air"—that is, that the cultural set of the region and times was pointing that way.

3. All three religions are exclusive, in holding their truth to be incompatible with any other, so that cobelief and coworship in another faith are impossible (§ 132). This doctrine seems to have been first worked out in human history by the Jews as a gradual and hard-won attainment during that part of their history represented by the Old Testament, between 800 and 400 B.C. From Judaism the attitude worked over into Christianity and Islam. Buddhism has been the least intransigent of the three in this respect. It coexists in China with the state religion or Confucianism, and in Japan it even worked out certain accommodations with the native Shinto.

4. All three religions, and speaking broadly only these three, have been actively missionizing.

5. Each of the three world religions developed an ecclesiastical organization or church, which has been a potent factor in maintaining the religion and its gains. Culturally, the ideologies have probably had a much more profound effect than the churches; but the influence of the latter toward a firm anchorage through temporal fluctuations, and even within the developments of the mundane aspects of civilization, cannot be overestimated. Ethnic or national religions often had temples, but generally no church as a unifying organization.

6. Side by side with the features of world-wide aim, exclusiveness, and an authoritative church, there developed what may be called universal or world languages. In these were expressed the sacred texts of each faith; and each tongue became also the approved and classical medium of thought, learning, and often literature in a self-sufficient and largely self-contained sphere or "world" (§ 102). These languages are Greek for Eastern and Latin for Western Christianity— when northwestern Europe revolted against Catholicism in the Reformation, one of its most significant acts was the immediate substitution of vernaculars for Latin; Arabic—rigidly adhered to in ritual—for Mohammedanism; Sanskrit for the more numerous northern branch or Greater Vehicle of Buddhism, with Pali for the southern or Lesser Vehicle of Farther India. With each of these is associated also a distinctive alphabet. The only other language that functions today in its larger sphere in a way reminiscent of these "world" languages is Chinese, whose writing is nonalphabetic.

The foregoing is a summary formulation of an enormously large situation, whose exactly authentic description would require endless qualifications and requalifications. In particular, consideration would have to be given to certain crucial border-line cases, especially in the Iranian and Chinese religions;[7] since with enough transitions, the "world" type of religion just depicted would tend to dissolve away. Provisionally, however, the type seems to stand. And so far as it does, the influence of religion on total culture, in the direction of both formative change and fixation, is evident. The world of Islam has always been recognized as a separate sphere of cultural influence. European civilization, as we have seen, breaks primarily into a pre-Christian and a Christian phase. The culture of India changes similarly from the pre-Buddhist to the Buddhist to the post-Buddhist period. Even in China and Japan, where old native elements have persisted with unusual continuity and force, the greatest alteration perhaps is that between the early, purely native form of the culture and the later one with

[7] Iran had Zoroaster, probably a little earlier than Buddha; and China, Confucius, Buddha's contemporary. Zoroastrianism, also called Mazdaism or the Avestan or Parsi religion, differs from the big three in being nearly extinct, and in having never effectively established its supernational church and language. But some of its minor and later offshoots or divergences, like Manichaeism, and perhaps Mithraism, have tried to compete with the great religions by rivaling them in organization and missionary activity. Confucianism has a minimum of religious content and is a state cult instead of an ecclesiastical church; else it too might have grown into a world religion.

its Buddhistic absorptions. It is in the fundamental reorientation of civilization, in redirective change, that the great religions are outstandingly influential.

170. CHANGE BY REVOLUTION

Change by revolution may be construed as change suddenly precipitated, with more or less violence, affecting a considerable total portion of a culture, and due to an accumulation of arrears, or lag, in progressive change. Generally, it is one or two fields or departments of culture that do the lagging. Thus the lag was primarily economic in the French Revolution, in religion in the Reformation and Cromwellian civil wars, in politics and religion in England of 1688, and was due to war distress on top of economic disintegration in Russia of 1918. Once the revolution breaks through, however, other and neutral areas of the culture are flooded too, sometimes with most inconsistent results, both intrinsically and as regards permanence: the metric system is instituted, religion abolished, Lavoisier executed. This extension of area of overturn was practically lacking in the American Revolution, which is thereby characterized as atypical of revolutions. In fact its main immediate achievement was the formal and complete acknowledgment of a political independence that had been partial but unacknowledged before. This in turn was followed by the union of the colonies, and the "invention" of a written federal constitution (§ 153). But these latter were constructive rather than revolutionary acts.

Several other features are characteristic of revolutions. One is that change tends to be excessive, and is then partly given up again in early reaction. After the revolution the French kept their metric system, but gave up their irrelevant new calendar and the Goddess of Reason. These represented zeal for change in the abstract, but there was no real call for them and they provoked resistance and made for inconvenience. One of the first resolves of the Russian Revolution was to abolish the death penalty! Then three letters of the alphabet were dropped. This reform was not in the Bolshevik program, but it was a simplification and it has stuck. It is familiar history how the pure socialist doctrine began to be increasingly modified in Russia after about 1935 with property ownership, differential salaries, piecework premiums, fees for schooling, and the like creeping back. Free divorce and legal abortion were instituted early, but were discontinued after the peak of change was passed. At first there was a strong sense that all the older national literature, music, and art, except that produced by avowed revolutionaries, must be capitalistically tainted: the revolution would therefore produce its own proletarian higher culture. This attitude tended to persist while Bolshevik Russia felt itself an outlaw among nations and none too sure of internal solidarity. But once the revolution seemed a permanent success, and especially after the Germans had been stopped in their tracks and it had real allies among the Great Powers, Russian nationalism rearose stronger than ever, and great Czarist poets, novelists, and composers were proclaimed great once more. All these are type phenomena of what may be called the overswing and backswing of revolutionary change.

It is necessary to distinguish between the cultural and the social change of revolutions, though these tend to come intertwined. In every successful revolution there is not only an improved reformulation of rules, but in addition certain people get property, power, or privilege that others had before. This last is what causes most of the heartburnings. It whets the appetite of many a changer, and makes prospective changees bitterly resist reforms that they might accept as fair and desirable if they could be made other than out of their pockets and status. Protestantism arose as a religious revolution from the ranks, with an ideology of return to primitive Christianity, substitution of conscience and Biblical text for hierarchical authority, and the like. However, most of the converted rulers, in and out of Germany, were surely influenced also by the opportunity to confiscate extensive church properties and to strengthen royal power. And no less the peasants in Germany: the Reformation's change of ecclesiastical authority suggested to them the hope of politicoeconomic changes in their favor. They rose and were put down with bloody massacres—not as Protestants but as social revolutionaries. At least one group of Anabaptist sectarians extended their renewed primitive Christianity to include communization of property and redistribution of wives. It need hardly be added that this movement was premature and its leaders short-lived. Here we have both forces at work: personal advantage of new classes of individuals, and revolution spreading to additional aspects or sides of the culture.

There is a class of changes tending to be regarded as desirable in themselves by everyone but nevertheless difficult to effectuate except by revolutionary or totalitarian power. These are reforms in systems, such as calendar, spelling, measurements, or law. With the passage of absolute time, or change in speech, science, and customs, such systems get to be increasingly differentiated from the actual conditions to which they relate, and therewith increasingly inadequate, patched over, and complicated. Nevertheless, a change is upsetting and inconvenient, objectively as well as sentimentally, and therefore is deferred and redeferred until made by force, usually when long overdue. Everyone is agreed that the gulf between living English speech and English writing is so great that a reform which would make spelling coincide with pronunciation would save millions of hours—and probably even of weeks and months—of education annually. What blocks such a reform is the immediate cost. Grownups would have to learn reading and writing all over again—which many could not afford and few would want to do. The young would be cut off from everything now in print until it had been reprinted new-style. Newspapers and magazines would probably have to print everything two ways for a number of years—and run half as much matter. The crux of the difficulty would be that the acutest inconvenience would fall on us, now, for the first ten years; the clear benefit would all be reaped by future generations. People in the mass don't come as altruistic as that—and perhaps it is just as well.

But a Czar, a Pope, a revolution, a despot floated into control by a revolutionary period, can and sometimes do jam such reforms through. Thus there is the Julian calendar reform effected by Caesar in 46 B.C., the Gregorian by Pope Gregory XIII in 1582. Incidentally, since this latter correction came from the head of the Roman Catholic Church, Protestant and Greek Orthodox countries tended to hold off from it; England accepted the Gregorian calendar only in 1752, Russia in 1918.

Somewhat analogous is British and American resistance to the metric system, which in the abstract is undoubtedly superior to the irregular national systems, as shown by the fact that physical science, which is supernational, has never wavered from it. Continental Europe, and then Latin America and most of the world, soon accepted the system. The Anglo-Saxon nations, self-sufficient through being in the lead technologically and industrially, have not yet done so. To "go metric" would make for international uniformity and universal future convenience; but it would also entail a double standard and some confusion for a generation, or some years, in daily life and business in the United States and the British Commonwealth.

An ancient reform of spelling, if that term can be applied to a partly ideographic system, was supported around 1370 B.C. in Egypt by the Pharaoh Ikhnaton and his anticlerical coterie of the intelligentsia. They introduced monotheism, realistic sculpture, and "truthful" writing. Only the last stuck. As regards motivation, it may be added that the priesthood of the sun god Amen-Ra had become wealthy and powerful, and blocked the king and his reformist friends as hard as these fought the priesthood.

In most ancient and in most Oriental cultures, revolutions from above had much the better chance of succeeding. Apart from some cases in Greek and Roman history, successful and important revolutions from below seem to be a specialty of recent Occidental civilization. The great and effective Meiji modernization of Japan beginning in 1868 was engineered wholly by elements in the upper classes surrounding the young emperor. The Chinese revolution dating from 1911 did not emanate so clearly from those in power and has brought perhaps as much confusion as progress. The Bolshevik revolution was a symptom of Russia's having been drawn increasingly into the Occidental orbit, as its Marxian ideology was a direct import from western Europe. By contrast, Peter the Great, two centuries earlier, was Westernizing his subjects by force, like any good Eastern autocrat. He produced less profound changes than the Soviets, but also much less upset and clash. A revolution from below in Peter's day would have been foredoomed to fail.

One of the most drastic revolutions was that which Kemal Atatürk poured on the Ottoman Turks after World War I. Once the spearhead of the last Mohammedan penetration into Christian Europe, the Turks had for several centuries tried to remain stationary with Islam while Western nations changed and strengthened. Atatürk took over at the end of two and a half centuries of recession, with the last provinces of the Turkish Empire gone, his people defeated and reduced to their homeland. He deliberately led them out of the Islamic camp of culture into the Christian, in everything but formal religion. Western government, law, dress, calendar, were adopted more wholesale and more rapidly even than in Meiji Japan. Perhaps his most unparalleled overnight change was from the Arabic to the Roman alphabet. This happened also to be an immense improvement in its much better fit to spoken Turkish. But above all it marked a clear-cut break with Koranic law and attitude, and symbolized the transfer of Turkish allegiance from the defensive culture sphere of Islam to the expanding Occidental and international one. Like any capital operation, such a major set of changes had to be carried out decisively and swiftly, if at all.

Theoretically, revolutions, as redistributions of cultural structure and social rewards within a society, are due to internal strains accumulating until a sudden shift or tipover occurs. However, the cases just considered show in increasing measure external influences behind the internal strains, until, in the last instance, all the build-up of pressure is from outside and only the final climax of conversion is interior.

Therewith we can conveniently pass over to our second main group of changes, those from without.

171. EXTERNAL CHANGE: DIFFUSION

When something new has been evolved in a culture, whether a tool or an idea or a custom, there is a tendency for it to be passed on to the culture of other societies. This is much like the passing on of culture to the younger generation within the evolving society, except for being foreign-directed instead of domestic. In other words, new culture is transmitted geographically as well as chronologically, in space as well as in time, by contagion as well as by repetition. The spread in area is generally called *diffusion,* as the internal handing on through time is called *tradition*.

When an invention passes from the inventor to other individuals, we call that its successful cultural acceptance. Diffusion may be viewed as an extension of the process, on a much larger scale, by which an invention or innovation—or sometimes even an older culture trait—spreads from the society in which it originated to new societies and becomes established in their cultures.

Conceptually, the simplest form of cultural transmission is tradition: transmission within a society through education by the elders and imitation and learning by the young. Normally, education and imitation are not in conflict, and therefore reinforce each other. Also, neither education nor imitation in itself involves any element of innovation or change, both being aimed primarily at perpetuation of the culture.

In the case of areal transmission or spread of culture, the fact that the diffusion takes place between different societies somewhat alters the processes at work. Imitation or learning of course is still operative, but education mostly drops out. Missionizing may take its place, but the impulse to missionize occurs only in some societies. Moreover, it can scarcely hope to be as effective as education. Indeed it is chiefly when the missionary succeeds in controlling secular education of the young that he becomes really influential.

Even more important is the fact that, diffusion being cross-societal, new elements of culture are involved—new at least to the receiving or learning culture. This novel culture material may meet with anything from eager acceptance to bitter hostility. But since it does represent innovation and change, the traits that are being introduced will expectably encounter some resistance. After all, they are foreign to the pattern of the culture on which they are impinging; and while some of the imported traits will happen to fit into the native pattern, or be neutral, others will violate or upset it. Or their acceptance may have unforeseen consequences that prove to be upsetting. It will accordingly be evident that intra-society transmission of culture in time must normally tend toward persistence, but intersocietal transmission in space tend toward change.

This difference can also be viewed from the angle of total human civilization. When cannon and, later on, steam engines were invented, they represented a new increment in the whole of human culture as well as in European culture. When subsequently cannon and steam engines were introduced into Japan, both devices represented as much of an innovating increment there as they had in Europe, and their effects on war and industry were about as great. Yet from the angle of human development as a whole, there was no invention or addition whatever involved in the transmission to Japan, only a spread of things already in existence. In short, from the point of view of the world as a whole, diffusions can also be seen as continuations or persistences plus spread.

Similarly, though invention and diffusion certainly are distinct concepts, yet the resistance which an institutional invention or innovation often encounters at home, both as to being made and as to social acceptance, may be identical with the resistance set up against a diffusion from abroad.

These illustrations will serve to show how processes that as logical or abstract concepts are wholly distinct tend to appear intertwined and intergraded in the actual phenomena of civilization as history unrolls them. The very same cultural act or event can be construed equally as a continuance or an innovation, according as it is viewed from the angle of the trait itself or that of the receiving culture.

However, whatever else diffusion does or does not involve, it does always involve change for the receiving culture.

The total part played by diffusion in human culture is almost incredibly great. This is a corollary of what has been said before, in § 113, to the effect that all cultures are largely hybrid composites of material that once entered them from outside. Naïvely, human beings do not realize this to any great extent. It is of no advantage to a society, ordinarily, to have its members aware of the foreign source of most of their culture; nor is it a satisfaction to most individuals to be reminded of this debt to aliens. So the facts tend to be forgotten, perhaps more rapidly even than most events of history.

In addition, there is a precritical impulse in us to look upon foreign customs as things that flow spontaneously out of foreign peoples: Chinese "naturally" worship their ancestors and defer to their fathers, just as they "naturally" talk in singsong and naturally grow long black hair. This goes with the normal naïve assumptions on "race" differences and inferiorities (§ 80-81). So totems and couvade and bows and arrows and shell money and sympathetic magic were long construed as more or less "automatic" emanations of the "natural" human mind in its more "childlike" manifestations.

This older view, or rather assumption, has had to be largely abandoned under analysis. If our own civilization is due mainly to elements introduced into it from without, there is no reason to believe that backward peoples would be more spontaneously creative, especially since they obviously also incline to repeat one another in certain grooves. Above all, more accurate study of the forms of culture traits, of their related variants, and of their territorial distributions has yielded so many instances of proved or highly probable diffusion of things like totems and couvade and shell money that the explanation of spontaneous emanation is rarely invoked any longer.

In short, the usual intersocietal functioning of culture is somewhat like most interpersonal relations. We more often learn from others than devise original things ourselves. Therefore, when record has been lost of how culture traits were acquired, a specific, part-for-part resemblance between culture traits, coupled with evidence of sufficient other relations between the societies that possess them, is now mostly accepted as presumptive indication of their spread by diffusion, rather than of their wholly independent reinvention.

Like anything else, this working rule or hypothesis can be carried too far. On the average, it proves to be the soundest inference to make, in the present state of knowledge. Yet some diffusionists have gone so far as to deny altogether, or practically, the possibility of separate reinventions; all likenesses are claimed by them as due to diffusion. This stand seems arbitrary and unreasonable. It is perhaps motivated by an urge for rigor and simplification of process, comparable to the simplicity of the precritical "spontaneity" explanation. However, this ultradiffusionist view has also been pretty well abandoned.

Nearly all of the inventions discussed in § 147-149 and 183-187 also have a history of diffusion. Most modern technological inventions tend to show a rapid world-wide spread. New institutional devices, such as the referendum and the Australian ballot of § 153, often are not accepted the world over: these particular ones, for instance, obviously require democracy as a precondition. But so far as institutions do have a history of widespread success, this is one mainly of diffusion with adaptive modifications. The same is true of philosophies, religions, ideologies. In proportion as these are influential they tend to win an international following, at least for a time. Democracy, communism, fascism, are familiar examples.

To these illustrations from the full light of recent history, there can be added endless cases of more ancient traits or systems: Christianity or Mohammedanism, for instance, or printing. In the case of older technological inventions, the precise circumstances of the first origin have often become somewhat misty, although much of the spread is usually well attested. Such are the arch, gunpowder, tea-drinking, bells in towers, Arabic numerals, chess, the 360° circle, spectacles, water mills, clocks, and dozens of others. With these can be included a series of plants first domesticated in the Americas, such as maize, potatoes, sweet potatoes, tomatoes, Lima beans, and tobacco (§ 193), the cultivation and use of some of which spread rapidly to certain parts of the Eastern Hemisphere. The result is that we often speak of potatoes as Irish, and that whole archipelagoes in the East Indies have come to eat more maize or sweet potatoes than rice, and so on. Double diffusion is indicated by our name for the turkey: the domestication of the bird was native American, but it was carried first to Spain and the Mediterranean, and from there reached England and then its colonies. In consequence, North Americans mistakenly call an American bird after an East Mediterranean country. The histories of wheat, millet, and sugar cane, of chickens and horses, of pottery, of bronze, iron, and steel (§ 282, 284, 296, 298) are also clearer as regards diffusion than as regards origin.

Finally we come to elements of culture the beginnings of which may remain forever hazy to us but the coherent distribution of which argues strongly for a spread from one center of origin. Thus, none of the American Indian nations possessed any authentic record of how or when they had learned to plant maize. but it was found being grown all the way from central Chile to North Dakota and Quebec, by perhaps 500 distinct tribes. It would be intrinsically absurd to consider the possibility of each of these 500 tribes having made the domestication as an original invention of its own. Even if the notion were abstractly tenable, it would be refuted by the unusual "artificiality" of the cultivated maize plant, its inability to propagate and maintain itself in nature, our ignorance of a direct wild ancestor. But if most of the 500 tribes learned rather than invented maize-growing, economy of explanation inevitably carries us not only to 300 or 400 who learned it, but probably to 499. Invention in one tribe or region, then a spread to the rest, seems much the most economical and reasonable interpretation. This conclusion is fortified by a botanical consideration: Genetic mutations and hybridization, one or both of which are believed to have been needed to transform unknown wild ancestors into maize, are definitely rare in plant history—more likely to occur now and then only than over and over again.

The case for diffusion, rather than independent invention, of native American pottery, whose distribution is slightly wider than than of maize, though roughly correspondent, is similar, though not quite as firm. Theoretically it would be quite conceivable that there had been two or three or four independent inventions of the pottery art in America, each with its own history of growth and spread, until several diffusions coalesced and came to look on the map like a single bicontinental one. At any rate, there is no known physico-chemical reason, corresponding to the genetic-botanical one for maize, to weigh against such a view of multiple origin. Yet even if there had been four or five or six separate origins of pottery in the New World, the ratio of tribal diffusions to inventions would still have been about a hundred to one.

Even at the beginnings of all human record, from the early Palaeolithic well back in the Pleistocene, the discovered distributions strongly suggest diffusions of wide sweep. In western Europe, North and East Africa, Arabia and India, the earliest cultures we can define with thorough assurance are "core cultures" (§ 273) using massive, trimmed-down flints of bifacial "hand-ax" or "Chellean-pick" type. Contemporaneously, central and eastern Europe, and presumably northern Asia also, harbored "flake cultures," with tools of edged chips struck off from flint nodules. The indication is that the two technologies were devised separately, and that each had its own history of spread, though both spread intercontinentally. By the time of the last or Würm Glaciation, the two diffusions had met and overlapped in western Europe.

Similarly, toward the end of the Palaeolithic, the chipping of minute delicate blades of flint was evolved in North Africa during the Capsian period, spread to Spain, and in the following Mesolithic became characteristic of northwestern Europe from France to Scandinavia (§ 275-276).

As regards patterned systems of traits, the world-wide dispersal of several of these—the week, the alphabet, the zodiac—is outlined below in § 196-197, 206-221, 229.

172. RESISTANCE TO DIFFUSION

We can assume from the foregoing that any feature of culture once established will automatically tend to spread to the cultures of other societies, just as it will tend to persist in its own. The principle is empirical, but so great is the mass of experience, both contemporary and historical, on which it is based that it has the force of an axiom. However, the principle affirms not that there *must* be diffusion, only that there will be some impulse for it to take place. Roughly, we can assume that culture traits will spread unless there are specific factors to prevent spread, much as we assume that things once in a culture will continue in it until displaced or modified by some positive impingement. This is because, from the angle of the culture trait, spread is after all only a form of persistence: it is continuation in a new geography.

However, from the point of view of societies and their total cultures, the contrary is true, and is important enough to repeat: Diffusion is like invention in that it results in an innovation. When an invention is accepted, place is made for something that has just originated in the same society. When a diffused trait is accepted, a place is similarly made in a culture for something that previously originated in another society and culture. In both cases there normally are obstacles or resistance to acceptance. These may occasionally be actually greater for an invention or a home innovation, if this seems to threaten established economic interests or an ideology with active sanctions behind it, or even only bodily habits that have firm hold. But on the whole the edge is probably the other way, since the farther it travels, the greater the risk that the diffusing element will encounter wholly new settings which may contain something definitely antagonistic to it. Nevertheless, any difference between the resistances encountered respectively by invention innovations and diffusion innovations is more of degree than of kind, and, on the average, likely to be not very great in degree.

Of prime importance to the fate of either kind of innovation are the patterns it encounters in the culture at whose door it is knocking. There are going to be obvious difficulties about inducing Christians and Mohammedans to worship, say, river gods, or persuading Mohammedans and Jews to eat pork sausage—about equally so whether the prophet or the inventor of the idea be a native renegade or a missionary from another faith. This class of situations has been touched upon under invention (§ 151), and further instances are mentioned in § 185, 199, 221.

Sometimes the resistances are selective, as when the Japanese gradually took over most of Chinese civilization but resolutely refused to accept rhymed tonal poetry, civil-service examinations, foot-binding, and a number of other particular Chinese features. The reason for the first resistance is simple and in a way extracultural: The character of the Japanese language is such as to make a rhymed and tone-observing poetry almost impossible, whereas in Chinese, prose and poetry would be difficult to distinguish except by rhyme and tone. Civil-service examinations as the basis for officeholding, power, and wealth began to be developed in China when the aristocracy was crushed in the great national unification more than twenty-one hundred years ago. In Japan, however, aristocracy of descent always maintained itself, in fact has pretty consistently been the dominant power in the country, and never submitted to bowing to the yoke of a merit system of tests. In China, the emperor was the Regent of Heaven; but a dynasty that became wicked was thought no longer to represent Heaven and could justifiably be overthrown. The Japanese eagerly took over the idea of the Chinese emperor's absolute authority, which was much greater than that of their own early rulers. But with the native rulers claiming to be gods descended from the sun goddess, it would not do to admit that their line could become corrupt or that they might legitimately be deposed. So the dynasty has remained nominally unbroken, though most emperors have had little real power, and many have been edged into abdication.

Foot-binding is of interest because it seems to have clashed with an unconscious Japanese pattern to which anything like mutilation was repugnant. Thus eunuchism, which persisted at the Chinese court until this century, never got a foothold in Japan; and the Japanese avoidance of all body jewelry is perhaps related psychologically. In this way the Japanese nonacceptances of Chinese civilization seem quite spotty, and yet are characteristically Japanese. After 1931 it gradually became evident that the Japanese had been equally selective in taking over Occidental civilization. But we of the West had felt so pleased at being imitated since 1868, and thought so well of the Japanese for imitating us, that we were overlooking how much of Western culture they were also firmly rejecting.

Items of culture that are isolated, not much woven into a pattern, and therefore relatively neutral in their social functioning, and yet of an indubitable practical value, are least likely to encounter resistances to their diffusion: matches, for instance, or potatoes. In fact, the flint-and-steel strike-a-light has maintained itself, if at all, chiefly among very remote or very poor groups who could not secure matches regularly. And why not? Matches conflict with nothing institutional. Here and there a priest might insist that ritual fire continue to be made in the old way, or even by drilling; but such exceptions would not in the least impair the spread of matches for ordinary secular use, where the main motivation inevitably is the pragmatic one of getting a light as quickly, surely, and easily as possible.

Tobacco, as a relatively harmless indulgence, habit-forming but not leading to incapacity, and reasonably economical at that, has had a rapid, world-wide diffusion (§ 193). It is also essentially neutral toward the ideology or value pattern of most of the cultures it entered. In native America it did often have religious associations; but these promptly got lost when its travels began.

Now and then an autocrat or a religion attempts to freeze a culture as of a given moment. In the main, the endeavor is of course foredoomed. But it may cause some strange, spotty retardations of diffusions. Mohammedanism is the most striking example. It forbade images, wine, usury, and gambling; and the Koran, or the custom law it accepted or implied, was to be the basic civil law of Islam for all time. Among the consequences one is that the Arabs, who had had no previous representative sculpture or painting, never developed any, though the Mohammedanized Iranians, who had had these arts, managed in time to revive them. Playing cards diffused from China; they struck quick roots in Europe, but seem to have passed Islam by. Insurance has been difficult to introduce in Mohammedan countries. The pious conservatives could claim that it partook of both usury and gambling. Even coffee-drinking was in jeopardy for a while because it is not mentioned in the Koran; though Mohammedans at large soon became coffee-lovers. Tobacco has also at times been forbidden by the very strict. Printing was under graver and longer suspicion (§ 199). It is not sanctioned in the Koran; it would expectably be applied to the text of the Koran, which Mohammed had dictated for writing down by hand; and it was an invention of Chinese and Christian unbelievers. The first attempt to print in Mohammedan lands—a history of Egypt in 1729, nearly three hundred years after Gutenberg—led to riots and prohibiton. It was not until 1825 that a Mohammedan Arabic press was established in Cairo, though Christians had printed in Arabic type in Italy as early as 1512. Printing of the Koran in Islam was specifically forbidden in 1727.

These several Mohammedan blockings of diffusions are perhaps most interesting for the common resistance they encountered in spite of being inherently disconnected. There is neither logical nor intrinsic nexus between sculpture, insurance, coffee, cards, and book-printing. What made these so dissimilar introductions meet resistance was a psychological attitude: a timorous legalism or puritanism (§ 248) that tried to protect the accidents of a system or code adopted by the culture. Obviously useful novelties that were indifferent toward the spirit or the letter of Islam, like the compass, cannon, matches, and automobiles, met no such resistance. Like Christianity, Mohammedanism has generally been imbued with a characteristic feeling of superiority and has tended to manifest aggressiveness. But a counterpart of this quality has been an inferiority sense and self-protectiveness whenever the culture was unsuccessful—as it mostly has been, in competition with Christianity, since about A.D. 1100, except for the interlude of the Ottoman Turks.

The resulting defensive attitude of Islam is somewhat akin to that which led China, Tibet, Korea, and Japan to try for two or three hundred years to shut out all Occidental contacts. The Far Eastern societies had been unaggressive, and now tried to isolate themselves and their cultures altogether. Islam could not make the identical endeavor, both because of being unusually far-flung and exposed in geography, and because of its fundamental militancy. But it could and did try here and there to effect a protective exclusion of culture features that were tending to enter. This might be construed as a sort of seclusion in spots.

173. MARGINAL CULTURES

The important concept that cultures are retarded because of their peripheral or marginal position in geography rests largely upon the idea that diffusion is a more or less continuous process. It also assumes that it is in the higher centers of civilization that the most numerous inventions and the most generally adoptable advances will be made, on the whole. As these new increments tend to spread, they will however spread most slowly to those societies which are most remote or most difficult to reach. Further, the innovations and additions that do reach the edges and peripheries may fail of acceptance by the cultures there, because they involve requirements the receiving culture cannot fulfill. Thus a marginal culture might be quite eager to use metal tools, and advanced enough in manual skills to learn metallurgical processes, and yet be forced to pass by the opportunity of acquiring them because it lacked, say, the gross tools, or the habits of industrial perseverance, necessary for mining ores.

In this way a growing gap may be created, theoretically and often actually, between the culturally productive center and the cultural margin. This gap tends to increase as the center piles up additional increments and the margin receives or accepts only a fraction of them. In theory, accordingly, peripheral cultures would tend to drop farther and farther behind. Finally some center, besides enriching its culture, may also extend it geographically until part of its society is transported to the marginal lands, comes in contact with the marginal cultures there, and proceeds to extinguish these, absorb them, or brush them aside. This is what has been progressively happening to most primitive cultures since 1500 at the hands of the increasingly expansive Occidental civilization.

But there is no necessary sequence in these matters. The high centers may recede or shift, or new ones may come up—finally even at the edges—until what was peripheral has become focal, and perhaps vice versa. In 3000 B.C., for instance, all of Europe was certainly marginally retarded as compared with nearer Asia and Egypt. In 500 B.C., Greece was within the center, but Italy still lagging, and western and northern Europe even more so. By A.D. 100, Rome looked like the focus, and certainly was part of it. At some later period—just when is debatable, but certainly by A.D. 1650—the nucleus of highest productivity in European culture had shifted across the Alps. During the past three centuries England has surely been among the small group of northwestern-European nations that constitute the central hearth of Occidental civilization. But previous to 1550, England was, equally obviously, retarded and marginal to western continental Europe, and the more so the farther back we go in history: in 1000 B.C., or 3000 B.C., England was no more than a feather edge of high culture, a margin of a margin.

Similarly with the radiation of culture out of the great Far Eastern center that began to glow and spark in North China three to four thousand years ago. This culture expanded, diffused over South China and Annam, also eastward into Korea, and from there to Japan. Of two peoples in Japan about the opening of the Christian era, the Yamato or ancestral Japanese held the parts of the islands nearest Korea, from about Kyoto southwest; the Ainu held Tokyo and the northeast beyond. The archaeological remains suggest no great difference of cultural level between the two races. But for century after century elements of the long-established civilization of China dribbled into southwestern Japan, culminating, around A.D. 400-700, in a rush of import of writing, learning, Buddhism, political organization, and hundreds of other things. Yamato Japanese culture now became fundamentally Sinitic. At the same time it was so placed as to cut off the Ainu from all immediate contacts with the higher Chinese civilization. The Ainu thus remained barbarian, the Japanese did not. They were gradually conquered, absorbed, or pushed by the Japanese to the extreme northeast of the archipelago, where some thousands still survive as an interesting racial relict, in a cultural and ethnic status recalling that of reservation Indians in the United States (§ 65). It was their geographical position of being marginal to the marginal Japanese that no doubt mainly accounts for the Ainu retardation until the present. But just so, and to about an equal degree, was Japan retarded fifteen hundred years ago as against China. And for the same reason. China on the mainland, in more or less contact with the rest of Asia and Europe, was profiting by this contact; but Japan lay beyond the farthest edge of the continent, in a little island world of its own, virtually beyond contacts in an age of limited and difficult navigation. Japan off the east of Asia and Britain off the west of Europe thus were in corresponding situations, and remained retarded for correspondingly long periods.

As for the Japanese, they sought for Chinese civilization at various times, and absorbed and assimilated it with skill, yet always managed to give the borrowed product a distinctive national individuality, until now and then it would have been difficult to assert that the teacher still remained more advanced than the pupil. Nevertheless, the flow of diffusion continued one-way. Whether it was coining money or drinking tea or printing books or a different Buddhist sect or a new style of painting landscapes, it was always China that originated, Japan that followed (§ 303). The lag might be one century or two centuries or six, but it was always Japan that was behind. The Japanese did exercise option about their acceptance, and simply rejected a good-sized series of Chinese traits, as we have just seen (§ 172). Where they had something of their own, however, as in the native Shinto cult, or where they gave something of Chinese origin a new twist or value, as in fine swordmaking, these originalities of theirs never passed out of Japan back into China. This does not mean that Japanese products and devisings were invariably inferior. They could hardly all have been so, and assuredly were not. Essentially it was Chinese self-sufficience, quiet arrogance about the superiority of their own culture, that prevented important return diffusion. Here, then, it was an attitude which was effective as a block; whereas the long retardation of Japan, like that of Britain at the opposite end of the great Eurasiatic land mass, was due primarily to its extreme marginal position. The historical relation of Chinese to Japanese culture may well be described as one of dominance, similar to that of parent on child, or between most persons in habitual relation to each other, or even, according to the psychologists, between most primate individuals.

Until 1500, the prevailing contacts of the whole Far Eastern or China-dominated center with the rest of the world were overland. Then came the ship-borne Portuguese, followed by Spaniards, Dutch, English, and French. After some unpleasant and disturbing contacts, both China and Japan—in fact Korea, Annam, and Tibet also—tried to shut these contacts out by policies of seclusion. During the nineteenth century these policies proved manifestly inadequate, were given up, and Western influences were once more admitted.

Here a difference developed: The Japanese now sought cultural imports from the West, the Chinese accepted them much more slowly, often reluctantly. Over the seaways, Japan now was no longer more remote from the new center of the Occident. In fact, as an island nation Japan was more accessible to successful diffusions, and more quickly permeated by them, than China with its hundreds of millions living mostly in the interior of a great land mass. So now, when advance for a while had largely become equated to Westernization, Japan at last took the lead, and before long not only defeated China in war but attempted to guide and instruct it. The roles of the two peoples reversed when the conditions changed, although the same processes continued at work.

This whole Chinese-Japanese relationship can also be seen, just as legitimately, as an example of acculturation. But acculturation is a more complex thing, from which diffusion must always be analyzed out as one of the elemental processes at work, as will be seen below, in § 176-179.

Marginal backwardness is manifest in total culture rather than in particular traits: it is essentially a cumulative matter. It is occasionally traceable in specific complexes, as when the Asiatic composite or three-ply bow of horn-wood-sinew appears in northwestern America as the simplified "sinew-backed" bow of horn and sinew or wood and sinew; and the associated thumb ring of Asia—for releasing the bowstring—is also lacking in America. Similarly, resist dyeing (§ 235), supposed to have originated in India and still flourishing in three forms in Indonesia—pattern, knot, and fiber dyeing—is represented as far out in the Pacific as Melanesian Santa Cruz Island by merely the last of these three processes. In general, however, retardation is obviously going to show in the total culture accumulated, rather than in special traits.

174. MARGINAL BIOTAS AS PARALLELS

Biologists long ago observed that the large backward or relict biotas—both faunas and floras—were those of the Southern Hemisphere. Africa south of the Sahara harbors a Pleistocene-like association of animals that is extinct in Europe. South America was never reached by many important groups of mammals; but as if to make up for this, it evolved a specialized fauna, such as the platyrrhine monkeys, and the noncompetitive sloths, armadillos, and other edentates of the Patagonian extremity. Australia of course is much the most retarded of continents biologically, its native mammals being virtually all of the primitive marsupial type. As compared with these three southern continents, Europe, North Africa, Asia, and North America form a virtually continuous land mass,[8] "Holarctica," within which species could migrate without much hindrance; and any new successful forms were likely to spread over the whole

[8] Continuous except for shallow Bering Strait, and this was repeatedly a land bridge in the past; whereas the existing Panama land bridge was more often a barrier strait in geological time.

great area. By contrast, the three southern continents are like three blind alleys running off from the much greater Holarctica, which stretches east and west four-fifths of the way around the globe. Newly evolved forms of life got into these three southern projections late, or not at all; old forms found shelter there, were preserved, or even underwent further local development. The net result has been that the three marginal southern continents—marginal to central Holarctica—have been evolutionistically retarded.

The cultural parallel is interesting. No very high civilization has ever developed independently south of the equator. The most advanced was that of ancient Peru. The native Australians are often cited as culturally the most primitive large block of mankind. Ultramarginal to the margin that the Australians constituted were the still more backward Tasmanians. The tip of South America was occupied by primitive Yahgan, Alakaluf, Ona, Tehuelche. In the far south of Africa were the Bushmen; scattered south of the equator, the Pygmy tribes; and Bushmen and Pygmies constitute the only two ethnic groups in Africa that still live wholly by hunting-and-gathering. The cultural retardation in the three southern continental extremities certainly seems similar to the faunal one.

At its northeastern end, the great Eurasiatic continent pinches into a nearly waste, unfavorable, Arctic tip, beyond which lies Bering Strait, and then nearly equally arduous Alaska, before the temperate and desirable parts of North America are reached. Here then is a bottleneck between the Old World and New World halves of Holarctica, between Palearctica and Nearctica. In the millions of years available for their dispersal since the Eocene, many species of mammals passed through this bottleneck at times when Bering Strait was dry land and the climate perhaps less raw than now. Among such were elephants, horses, bisons, camels, tapirs, wolves, bears, beavers, and many others. Some spread eastward, some westward; a few probably even flowed back. But other groups never did effect the crossing. Lions, tigers, hippopotami, rhinoceroses, true cattle and water buffalos, the whole group of true antelopes and gazelles, did not get into America, which can therefore be construed as faunally submarginal to Europe-Africa-Asia: semiperipheral to it, but not wholly dependent.

It is interesting as showing the influence of basic geography that for thousands of years America was submarginal in culture also. When this condition began to change after 1492, it was through the expansion of European societies across the Atlantic, not through enlargement or easing of the Bering Strait bottleneck. But pre-1492 America was culturally only semimarginal, not definitely peripheral like Australia. There was a demonstrable flow of culture from Asia into the nearer parts—about half—of North America. This diffusion included traits such as the sinew-backed bow just mentioned (§ 173), slat armor, snowshoes, the toboggan, bark boats, bark dishes and pots, basketry hats, the tepee or conical tent of skin or bark, scapulimancy, bear ceremonialism, the "magic flight" story (§ 227), and some others. But in the main, the more advanced and complex cultures of native America as a whole, both North and South, seem to have been independently evolved in the hemisphere rather than received by diffusion. This was perhaps the result of the opportunities offered by the large favorable areas well away from the Bering bottleneck, areas where agriculture was developed, population multiplied, and the arts of life increased. Most students of native American history believe that this development, which culminated in the stretch between Mexico and Peru, was essentially autonomous. It attained to cities, kingdoms, most metallurgical arts, some astronomy and calendry, and extraordinarily complex rituals. It did not achieve ironworking, writing, or a "world" type of religion (§ 169). It was thus retarded in type or level, by perhaps two or three thousand years, behind the highest centers in the Old World. But the retardation was through a separate and delayed start. Slowness and incompleteness of interhemispheric diffusions constituted only a remoter factor underlying the lateness of the beginnings of American Indian higher developments.

The Greeks had a name for the central area of higher civilization: *oikumenē*. Literally, this meant "the inhabited world"; but it had also the connotation of "civilized world," or civilization as a whole; much as an oecumenical council of the Church still means a council of the whole of Christianity. This *oikumenē* of the Greeks, which stretched from Gibraltar to India and dimly known China, was the region in which people lived in cities in organized states, plowed their fields and raised cattle, worked iron, and knew letters. What was beyond this civilization the Greeks were hazy about; they considered it either wasteland or land occupied only by unstable savages: for they much underestimated the size of the southern parts of Africa and the north and east of Asia, and of course Australia and America were wholly outside their ken. This concept of the *oikumenē* of the immediate pre-Christian and post-Christian centuries has a modern utility as a convenient designation of the total area reached by traceable diffusion influences from the main higher centers of Eurasia at which most new culture had up to then been produced.

175. INTERNAL MARGINALITY

It is important to remember that all this discussion of diffusion from centers to margins refers to prevalent directions of drift, and not to any rigorous or one-way determinism. To conceive the diffusion of culture as radiating out in concentric circles, like sound waves from a bell, is schematic; actual history is almost never so simple. In fact, even physical nature is likely to have winds and obstructions and conflicting noises interfering with the regularity of its waves. In culture, one of these complexities is manifest in societies that remain retarded although they are situated within the sphere of higher centers. Such cultures have been called "internally marginal." This phrase is literally appropriate when the habitat is a desert or a mountainous or undesirable tract inside a generally favorable region. In other cases the phrase is just a telescoped way of saying that the culture in question is backward, like cultures whose geography is marginal; that it is an incomplete form of some richer culture elsewhere and perhaps not far away. Often both conditions apply: The culture is retarded and is also crowded back into undesirable terrain that may shelter it from active diffusions almost as effectively as would distant remoteness.

Asia is particularly rich in tribal societies with "internally marginal" cultures. Examples are: the very primitive Veddas of Ceylon; the Todas and other nonliterate tribes of the Nilgiri hills in southern India; [9] most of the Munda tribes farther north in India; Palaung, Kachin, Moi, Semang, Sakai, and many others in the states of Farther India and Malaya; Lolo, Yao, Man, and so on in South China. None of these nationalities is situated on an actual outer edge of the continent. All of them constitute enclaves within a larger area and population of civilized people. Most often these latter, whether Hindus, Chinese, Burmese, Annamese, or Malays, have taken up the fertile plains and valleys. The primitives may now and then have pushed in to where they are, but more often they are an obvious remnant, now contracted to the hills, ridges, plateaus, higher mountain valleys, jungle, or "bush." This whole culture type is equally interesting from the angle of acculturation, which will be touched upon in the next section.[10]

In the East Indian archipelagoes, above all among the larger Philippine Islands, migration, travel, commerce, and enlightenment have moved easily by sea lanes, while land penetration is difficult, on account of both terrain and vegetation. The remote and backward places regularly are the interiors of the islands; the accessible and advanced tracts are their physical edges, the shore-lands—as in post-Perry Japan. So we find, for instance, in Luzon the Negritos of simplest culture in the mountains most difficult to reach; next to them the pagan brown Filipinos in at least two distinguishable levels of culture and remoteness, exemplified respectively by, say, the Ilongot and the Tinggian; and then the lowlanders like the Tagalog and the Pampanga, long ago influenced by Hindu and then by Mohammedan and finally by Christian civilization.

It is evident that this Indonesian condition inverts the space relation of "center" and "periphery" with which we started. Culturally, centers are spots of high productivity; margins, spots of prevailing receptivity and retardation. Cultural centers may be geographically central also, or on geographical margins.

[9] They are sometimes misnamed "pre-Dravidian" in order to shunt the contamination of primitive affiliation away from the civilized Dravidian nations. Actually the Toda, Kota, and so on are fully Dravidian in speech, and their cultures seem to be somewhat specialized and retarded tribal or caste facets of general Dravidian or southern Hindu culture.

[10] Internal marginality is recognized also in the Smithsonian Institution's *Handbook of South American Indians,* and in the ethnographic classification of that continent developed below in § 319, 331.

Geography always enters into consideration in the matter, because it is diffusion that is at work and diffusion is geographical spread; but it is culture that is spread, or which fails to be spread and leaves certain societies retarded. Such retarded cultures are often spoken of as peripheral whether their situation be on the edges or in the interiors of land masses.

176. ACCULTURATION

Acculturation comprises those changes produced in a culture by the influence of another culture which result in an increased similarity of the two. The influencing may be reciprocal or overwhelmingly one-way. The resultant assimilation may proceed so far as the extinction of one culture by absorption in the other; or other factors may intervene to counterbalance the assimilation and keep the cultures separate. The process of acculturation tends to be gradual rather than abrupt. It is perhaps always gradual and long-range enough for acculturation phenomena to fall within the scope of history, even if the phenomena examined be contemporary ones. In fact, in so far as history is more than the story of particular events and particular individuals and deals with social and cultural changes, a large part of all history the world over, possibly more than half of it, deals ultimately with the results of intercultural influencing —that is, acculturation. This is clear as soon as we consider the findings of that part of history in which the role of particular events and persons is of necessity reduced to a minimum; namely, archaeology. Practically all the diffusion we have been considering either contributes to acculturation or can be viewed as an aspect of acculturation; and conversely, all acculturation is full of diffusion. The two are thoroughly interwoven in the phenomena: the distinction is a conceptual one of approach and emphasis of interest. When we follow the fortunes of a particular culture trait or complex or institution through its wanderings from culture to culture, we call it a study of diffusion. When we consider two cultures bombarding each other with hundreds or thousands of diffusing traits, and appraise the results of such interaction, we more commonly call it acculturation. Diffusion is a matter of what happens to elements or parts of culture; acculturation, of what happens to cultures.

In 1935, Redfield, Herskovits, and Linton, as a committee of the American Anthropological Association, formulated the following definition: "Acculturation comprehends those phenomena which result when groups of individuals having different cultures come into continuous first hand contact, with subsequent changes in the original culture patterns of either or both groups." They went on to distinguish acculturation from culture change, of which it is only one aspect; from assimilation, which at times is one of the results of acculturation; and from diffusion, which constitutes only one aspect of acculturation, but yet is always present when there is acculturation and sometimes when there is not.

In a concrete science like anthropology there is little gained by pushing conceptual distinctions very far, and some risk of sterility, because phenomena intergrade endlessly, especially in so highly plastic a thing as culture. A broad definition, centering on the core of the meaning involved rather than aiming at hairline logical definition of its edges, is therefore ordinarily the most useful. A definition of this kind for acculturation might be: the effect on cultures of contact with other cultures. In this would also be included the effect on the societies that carried the cultures. Viewed in this way, it is evident that acculturation takes in a lot of meaning. It has no doubt been operative since there have been separate human cultures. Ninety-nine per cent of all acculturation must lie in the past; and it involves the nature, the processes, and the patterns of culture as well as its changes.

If any modification of one culture by another culture is acculturation, why the sudden interest, almost excitement, beginning about 1920-25 and culminating perhaps in 1935-40, about a concept as wide, elusive, and protean as this? It must have had some special implications; some portion or corner of it must have been charged with particular connotations.

The principal factors that made for the whirl of vogue which acculturation studies were given for a while were the beliefs that such studies were immediately contemporary and that they were practically useful—plus, probably, a sense that they dealt with our own civilization as familiar to us and that therefore they involved less wrench to our natural ethnocentrism, by our not having to depart from it to examine other culture and times. With these considerations, there were mixed some subsidiary ones. For instance, as World War I closed, an "Americanization" movement swept patriotic, political, social, philanthropic, and educational circles in the United States. Poles, Italians, and other immigrants were to be amalgamated. The "foreigners" who were outside were to be kept out; those who were in were to be remolded, as quickly and effectively as possible, into reproductions of Anglo-Saxon Americans. Anthropologists and sociologists were to help appraise the methods and the degrees of their assimilation. In England there was a somewhat analogous movement, relating to the adjustments to European civilization that "natives" under colonial administration were facing or making.

Further, it had become an ethnological technique to study other cultures, especially backward ones, by investigating them in the field, on their own ground: perhaps the Arunta in Australia, the Toda in India, the Yoruba in Nigeria, the Dakota or the Hopi on their reservations in the United States. In every case, these primitive societies had begun to have their culture visibly invaded and affected by Western civilization; some only to a minor extent, others so far that the former native culture could only be recovered from memories of the older people, while the present-day population lived in a transitional hybrid culture—or sometimes a parasitic one—that was neither quite native nor quite Western. Often it was easier to describe this patent, obtrusive mixture than to reconstruct the native primitive culture before it went all to pieces. One could observe the workings of the hybrid culture instead of having to extricate or to infer the workings of the past. Further, the unconscious hold of ethnocentrism on all of us is strong; so that some students preferred dealing with a bastard partial derivative of their own culture to orienting themselves in one of radically different assumptions, patterns, and attitudes; the mental journey took them less far from home. Again, uncontaminated primitive societies still going their own way might possess fairly retarded cultures, but normally these would be adjusted fairly well to their own problems and making more or less of a success as going concerns. In contrast, when the much more massive and powerful Occidental civilization begins to impinge on backward cultures, it tends to disarrange or disorient these. Primitive societies in process of disappearance are therefore usually full of maladjustments, miseries, and unsolved problems. These sufferings stimulate students with philanthropic or reformist inclinations or those interested in social pathology, but tend to distract those whose interest lies rather in cultural patterns and their normal values.

At first, acculturation studies also held out an exciting promise of showing how the wheels of culture change go round. One saw what people had been, what they were, what they were turning into, and why. It was like catching the dynamics of culture change in the act, almost like setting up a laboratory. This is more or less true. Yet essentially the same thing holds for all culture changes due to contact, in the past as well as now, between two alien civilizations as well as when our own is concerned. The precise motivations of the people involved in these former and foreign situations will mostly not be as familiarly vivid; but in compensation the ultimate effect on their culture patterns will normally be much more fully visible after the act of acculturation has been completed than while it is still in progress; and the outcome should be more fully understandable in the perspective yielded by a more remote period or region. There is no difference of principle between the acculturation involved in the Hellenization of the Romans in Italy during the two or three centuries following 270 B.C. and that of the Americanization of Italians in the United States in the century following A.D. 1850. The chief unlikeness is that the ancient Italians were the dominant and majority group, the modern Italians a minority and socially dominated group. Which problem one prefers to investigate is largely a matter of taste and temperament. Those to whom foreign and historical phenomena easily carry a meaning, or do so only with difficulty, will respectively be interested in one or the other approach. The approaches are equally legitimate. Which alternative one chooses for himself is likely to be determined by the degree to which one is ethnocentric or allocentric, at home with a synchronic or a diachronic view, inclined to discharge ideas into action or to let them sink in deeper—rather than being a matter of better or worse scientific procedure.

At any rate, these reflections on method are of a certain importance because they show that the particular type of "acculturation studies" developed by anthropologists in the interval between the two World Wars does not so much represent the discovery of a radically new type of problem as the emphasizing of one special aspect of the long-recognized phenomena of culture change, and the application of investigatory techniques to somewhat nearer and possibly more "practical" situations.

What is distinctive in these special acculturation studies, as Linton has pointed out, consists of several features. First, they view acculturation almost wholly and one-sidedly from the angle of the impact of a dominant, prestige-laden society and culture upon a backward or dominated minority. Next, the changes investigated are almost invariably not spontaneous and automatic, but purposively directed or controlled, at least in part, by the superior society, through its Colonial Office, Bureau of Indian Affairs, Army, police force, authorized missionaries, and the majority public opinion behind these. Special attention has also been given to phenomena of nativistic revivalism. By this is meant defense efforts of the dominated culture to glorify its past and to re-establish at least parts of it. Finally, the acculturation has been studied as it is intended to work; namely, to result in ultimate disappearance of the minority—in its cultural and social fusion. Even where conspicuous racial differentiation and a sense of racial superiority tend to prevent social assimilation, as in the case of the American Negro, there is little doubt that the pressure of the majority population is in the direction of cultural assimilation. The studies made therefore incline both to take ultimate uniformity for granted and to accept it with a degree of equanimity.

All these characteristics of the conventional type of professed acculturation studies apply to only a selective part of the total phenomena of change resulting from culture contact, or acculturation in the broadest sense. The following sections will accordingly try to present some instances of culture-contact dynamics of a broader and more fundamental type.

177. ACCULTURATION WITH AND WITHOUT DOMINANCE AND ASSIMILATION

Since acculturation basically is the acceptance or borrowing of material from one culture by another, it always involves some approximation between the two cultures. But there is no reason why such approximation should continue into assimilation. Normally, we may expect assimilation only when the outlook of one society is inclusive and when this society is definitely the stronger and its culture the more advanced. In the majority of cases the populations somewhat balance each other in size, have separate territories, are mutually influenced, but expect to retain separate ways and customs, and do retain them. In other words, the acculturation is more or less reciprocal, but incomplete. Each people is also likely to be developing new peculiarities even while it is taking over culture from the other. This is perhaps the most common form of acculturation: across a frontier that remains a frontier, although not a closed one.

A familiar example is the boundary between Mexico and the United States, which is also the frontier separating the two principal facets of Occidental civilization in the Western Hemisphere: Latin American and Anglo-American. The border states from Texas to California show a series of influences from Mexico that are not found elsewhere: in names, architecture, foods, land grants, community-property marriage law, frequency of knowledge of the Spanish language, and understanding of Latin American ideology and attitudes. Complementarily for the Mexican states from Tamaulipas to Sonora, as compared with for instance Michoacán or Oaxaca or Vera Cruz: people and habits seem and are more like those of the United States. At the same time there is no question but that crossing the Rio Grande either way means entering a thoroughly distinctive form of modern Western culture.

This type of situation is exceedingly common. It recurs wherever Mohammedan and Christian peoples adjoin. Religion and language maintain a cultural barrier that may be stationary for centuries, but which is continually permeated by diffusion. Spanish civilization for instance has a larger heritage of absorptions from Islamic civilization than any other in western Europe. Witness as a sample just the following words with the article *al-,* which were among the many diffused from Arabic into Spanish, and from there passed through French into English: algebra, almanac, alkali, alcohol, alfalfa, alcove, cotton (*algodón* in Spanish), adobe. Primitive tribes who are neighbors are always partly accultured, as is evident from the fact that their cultures regularly resemble each other even though their speech affiliations may be quite diverse. But no two such tribal or national cultures are ever identical. Each people is aware that the other has some peculiarities which have not been accepted by itself.

Of course assimilation also takes place at times. The Norman and Saxon fusion after 1066 is a familiar instance. Within three centuries these two strains were assimilated in culture, speech, and mainly in blood. English civilization was greatly enriched by the infusion of the large Norman-French element into the Anglo-Saxon, so that by say 1400 it had come to approximate more nearly French culture in its level; but of course it remained definitely distinct from French. The Normans produced a decisive effect because their mainland culture was more advanced and more effective than the belated island culture of the Saxons; but their being fewer in numbers made the assimilation easy and natural. Also, they were in a sense professional "acculturators." Only a century and a half before, in fact, the Viking Norsemen had similarly conquered Normandy for themselves out of France; and they had since then been acculturing themselves into fairly close representations of Frenchmen.

The Manchu, the Mongols, and the still earlier Tungus conquerors of China lost their own cultures there. This was evidently because they were a small minority with a much more limited culture than the Chinese. The situation was almost as if the Apache or the Sioux had overrun the eastern United States seventy-five or a hundred years ago. We might in that event conceivably be paying taxes to a great Indian chief, while American civilization with its machinery, highways, schools, newspapers, movies, and slang would perhaps be going on not so very different from what it actually is. At least one might so infer from the repeated Chinese cases; and from the story of the Vandals, the Goths, the Lombards, and other tribes of the Germanic Völkerwanderung. This hypothetical example indicates that as regards what happens to civilization, the main results will be much the same, irrespective of who conquers or becomes "dominant," when a large population possessing a rich culture collides with a small, backward one. The difference between our imaginary Sioux Indians giving orders from the Capitol and collecting customs duties for themselves in New York, and the actual Sioux living submarginally beyond the Mississippi because they have made a poor go of farming and can't all join Wild West shows—this difference is one that affects very profoundly the success and fortunes of some ten thousands of Sioux. But that is the principal effect the imagined difference would have had. Native Sioux buffalo-hunting culture would almost certainly be as essentially disintegrated by now as it actually is, even if the Sioux had by some miracle conquered us; and American culture would perhaps have been modified only in minor respects.

Some United States Indians have worked out an interesting semiassimilation of their own. These are certain central tribes, such as the Winnebago, the Fox, and the Shawnee. They have accepted American money, dress, houses, furniture, and transportation—in other words, the tangibles and the economics of our civilization. But they have kept their old social institutions and rituals. This snatching of a half-preservation from the pervasive swamping which acculturation has meant for most Indians appears to be due to an intransigeant sense of superiority that these few tribes managed to retain even when defeated and crowded onto reservations: they never accepted spiritual dominance by the white man. The Shawnee have had an unusual history of migrating from west to east and then north and west again for three hundred years, and of repeatedly moving into contact with white men and a variety of Indian tribes, and out again. Exceptionally exposed in these long roamings to a multitude of possible diffusions, they have ended up by developing an anti-acculturation attitude, in order to preserve their identity. Thus they avoided or postponed the total assimilation with which their small numbers threatened them.

The Pueblo Indians of Arizona and New Mexico have also kept their society and religion intact, plus a good deal of their material culture and subsistence. This is because for two and a half centuries they were under Spanish rule, with enforced Christianity. They countered with an outward acceptance of this, beneath which they kept their old rituals and idea systems alive by a sort of semisecret passive resistance. They were aided in their conservatism by the sparseness of Caucasian immigration.

Somewhat similar is what happened in Latin American countries in which the Indian racial ingredient remains heavy, especially parts of Mexico, Guatemala, Ecuador, Peru, and Bolivia. Here the Aztec, Otomí, Maya, Quechua, or Aymará Indians were economically oppressed by their conquest, and were made Christians more effectively than on the remote Pueblo frontier of New Mexico. Hence their old religion was completely shattered and is now largely lost, even where they live in solid populations of hundreds of thousands. Mostly they are devout Catholics, but with considerable pagan absorptions. Their dress is not the old native one; but it often is distinctive of locality or class, like peasant costume. The rest of their life is a similar mosaic of indigenous and Spanish elements in complex and unpredictable combinations. There are millions of such "Indians" in these countries, with a culture that is not pre-Columbian, not Spanish or colonial, not modern Occidental, but some of each, plus local developments evolved from the mixture during four hundred years. There has been an enormous amount of acculturing going on here in these centuries. But the product is better characterizable as a hybridization than as an acculturation, if that word is allowed to retain its usual implication of assimilation into something superior or larger. These millions of Indians are not "assimilated," either nationally or culturally.

A third type of adjustment has been made by the Navaho, a branch of the Athabascan Apache, along with whom they entered the Pueblo territory in the southwestern United States an unrecorded number of centuries ago. For some reason, the Navaho took over more culture from the Pueblos than did the other Apache: corn-planting, cloth-weaving, probably matrilineal descent, certainly a great mass of ritual elements. Subsequently they borrowed sheepherding and silversmithing from the Spaniards. With these enrichments of their culture, they became definitely prosperous, by their own standards, in a habitat that is pretty meager in resources. But this very poverty of the land resulted in few Spaniards or Americans coming into it. Meanwhile the Navaho multiplied themselves severalfold in the eighty years between 1865 and 1945; so that instead of retracting as did so many other tribes, they overflowed their territory. The result is that they are largely self-sustaining, independent, proud, and willing to maintain their old ways. They are Navahos with Navaho habits, dress, and speech, not imitation white men; and the usual absorption by assimilation is not in the least in sight for them at present. The chief causes of this situation seem to be their old and skillful adaptation to a rather poor environment; their growth in numbers, which made them a regional majority instead of a swamped minority; and with this the preservation of assurance and even a certain sense of superiority.

This factor of assurance can be of the greatest importance if a minority wishes to maintain itself. The Gypsies were satisfied with themselves, wanted to remain separate, and did keep themselves intact in Europe for centuries. They changed in some measure along with the culture that enveloped them, as in shifting from horses to automobiles in the United States—but without thereby ever coming any nearer to social absorption, which they evidently did not desire. Perhaps the greatest dislocation of the semiautonomy of their caste society in the United States was due to WPA and other work-relief inducements of the 1930's. Since Gypsies ordinarily possessed only portable and tangible property, those who, previous to WPA, wished to escape could ordinarily have done so only at a low social level; for this it was hardly worth while trading their unshackledness. It was perhaps the half-realization of this fact which strengthened their old attitude of aloofness and professed self-satisfaction.

On the other hand, the fact that Jews remain a minority group is perhaps more largely due to Gentile majority pressure. As their enforced segregation and exclusion diminished cumulatively in the eighteenth and nineteenth centuries, the Jews began definitely to assimilate culturally, and even socially. They have been, on the whole, economically prosperous, so that those who wished to and did flow out of their old caste confinement had opportunity to do so on favorable social levels.

By way of contrast, it may be of interest to consider some cases where groups of Western origin have become minority populations.

178. JEWISH AND CHRISTIAN MINORITIES IN ASIA

In 1163 a colony of Jews from Persia settled at K'aifêng in Honan. Five hundred years later they were still there, as attested by a stone inscription, and had just rebuilt their synagogue under imperial sanction. Two centuries more, however, and they were preserving only a consciousness of being Jews and some scrolls of their Law. The last rabbi had died about 1830 and the synagogue was pulled down by 1850. The colony no longer knew Hebrew, could not therefore read their scrolls, were uncircumcised, had lost their pedigrees, and were indistinguishable in names, dress, and often in features from Chinese. They had become poor, and this may have contributed to the relative rapidity of their final assimilation.

Even older is a Jewish colony in Cochin in southern India, which was flourishing in 1020, as is shown by a grant of lands and privileges to one of its leaders, preserved on copper plates of that date. There are also Jewish tombstones dated 1269. Following the Hindu pattern, these Jews today are divided into three castes, which do not marry or eat together, though their religion and general culture are identical. The so-called "White" Jews number less than 150 and are all in one congregation, to which the "Black" are not admitted. These

Whites may include some descendants of the original Jewish settlers in India, but seem mainly to be of Spanish Jewish stock that arrived in the sixteenth century and kept itself separate. They are of about the same complexion as southern Europeans, and in blood they are very high in type A (§ 72), a distribution characteristic of the Iberian Peninsula. The "Brown" caste numbers only two or three dozen native servants or ex-servants of the White caste converted to Judaism. The Black caste is some ten times as numerous as the White and has seven synagogues. They resemble the Cochin Hindus in color and blood type, and in origin they must be either outright converts from the native population or the descendants of former cumulative intermarriages of Jewish immigrants with natives. The two main castes are old: in 1686 they were described much as now, and synagogues still in use by the Whites and the Blacks were built in 1568 and 1489, respectively. The Cochin Jews are at once well fitted into southern-Indian civilization and separate from it where they want to be, which is chiefly in religion and group identity. They live in a ghetto street, but from choice. They all learn to read Hebrew, the Blacks as sedulously as the Whites, for prayers and services, but talk Malayalam along with the rest of Cochin. Rice is their staple food, as it is in all southern India; but they will never mix curries of meat with those of milk, in conformity with the orthodox Jewish injunction. They chew betel, paint their nails, play rummy, but have preserved their Hebrew ritual and festivals scrupulously. There is much acculturation, but also a wholly successful maintenance of the integrity of a minority group and of a subculture around an intact nucleus of religion.

Equally interesting are the native Christians of Cochin, who legendarily stem from the disciple St. Thomas, and at any rate were found long-established when the Portuguese reached India in 1498. There are five sects of them. Two groups are Roman Catholics, one using Latin and the other Syriac as the ritual language. These both acknowledge the Pope, of course, but represent somewhat different degrees of secondary influence of Portuguese missionaries on the local Christians. The native Chaldaean Syrians are under the Patriarch of Babylon; the Jacobite Syrians, under the Patriarch of Antioch. From these latter, the fifth sect, the Reformed or St. Thomas Syrians, seems to have branched off, with its own local bishop as head, under the influence of immigrant Protestant missionaries; this sect rejects confession, relics, masses for the dead, and invocation of saints. To these five sects there correspond seven castes, which absolutely prohibit interdining and intermarriage, in conformity with standard Hindu custom. The Roman Catholics of Latin rite comprise three castes, whose basis of separatism is not clear. Otherwise, each sect is also a caste, except that the Jacobite and Reformed Syrians are jointly split—not on the basis of religious adherence, but of ancestral residence: the northerners, Jacobite and Reformed alike, claim to have arrived in India earlier, thus being superior, and accordingly refusing to marry with the southerners.

It is clear that the customary tolerance of Asiatics toward religions, strengthened by the dominant Hindu leaning toward caste particularity, afford minority groups of foreign origin an excellent chance to maintain themselves without being extinguished by assimilation, and yet to acculture, outside of their religion, as far as is convenient to them. At the same time, it is also evident that the Cochin Jews, and still more the Cochin Christians, have been aided in the preservation of their particularities by occasional relations with overseas co-religionists, resulting in their reinvigoration as minorities. The Jews in China, remote, inland, and secluded, were beyond such reinforcement, and both their social and their cultural identity washed away after some centuries.

179. VOLUNTARY OR SPONTANEOUS ACCULTURATION

It is true that much modern acculturation of minorities is directed by the majority culture, and that their assimilation is consciously furthered as something desirable. Uniformity has a way of commending itself to majorities. However, there is some importance in remembering that assimilation and standardization are not inevitable outflows from anything in the nature of man or his culture. A whole lot of human history has unrolled without any notable endeavors at uniformizing. The Persian Empire, the Hellenistic states, and Rome were all notorious for not attempting any total assimilation of their subjects. One obeyed the authorities, kept the peace, and paid taxes. Beyond that, one was free to follow the ways of his fathers or to abandon them. And there was a deal of acculturation nevertheless. Asia Minor and Syria largely turned Greek in culture and speech; the greatest Greek city in the world was Alexandria in Egypt; Gauls and Iberians became utterly Romanized—of their free will, because it was to their own advantage or prestige, not because a ruler or a majority put pressure on them.

Ethnically at least, the attitude of the Middle Ages was much the same. Conformity to the Christian doctrine and church was exacted, but little else. In fact, controlled acculturation came late. Not until well into the modern period of European history, along with the rise of consciously nationalistic programs, did the inclination become strong to improve people of other culture and speech by inducing or forcing them to accept one's own. China and India have always been notoriously tolerant or indifferent in these matters. The list of "internally marginal" backward peoples that have been mentioned (§ 175)—who are of course only partly accultured populations—is evidence.

A few cases to exemplify this generalization—that much human acculturation has been voluntary—will now be cited. One instance will be recent, one older, the third in the primitive field.

Since the Meiji reform of 1868, Japan has obviously been making its culture over to conform progressively to Western civilization, at least in most respects. Thus, following the charter oath, with its clause that "intellect and learning shall be sought for throughout the world," in 1871 feudalism was abolished. Then there followed these introductions:

1872: compulsory universal education
1872: first railroad and telegraph
1874: Gregorian calendar
1875: girls' normal school
1881: Bank of Japan
1889: constitution with a parliament
1890+: new law codes
1897: gold standard
1899: abolition of extraterritoriality
1902: Anglo-Japanese alliance

All this "Westernization" or adoption of Occidental culture was voluntary. Perry had used a mixture of persuasion and threats to open the door and establish relations; but none of the actual Japanese acculturation was due to compulsion or even to pressure from outside—no more than there had been in the similarly large-scale Japanese taking-over of Chinese civilization between A.D. 400 and 800 discussed in § 172-173 and 303. Neither, of course, was there the least diminution of Japanese social, racial, or national integrity. The whole matter of minorities and absorption was lacking, as was direction or control from outside the group. And yet what happened is one of the most sweeping and important acculturations in history, even though much too brief to be complete.

The Lithuanians furnish the contrary example of a people voluntarily submerging both their culture and most of their identity. By about 1200 Europe had been Christianized, and therewith brought into Occidental civilization, except for the barbarous, independent Prussi, Litva, Latvi, Kor, and other tribes along the lower Vistula, the Niemen, and the Dwina. These peoples, often mistaken for Slavs, were not Slavs, but formed in speech an independent, co-ordinate division of Indo-Europeans, the Baltic or Lettic branch. To their east, the Russians had previously been Christianized from Constantinople to the rites of the Greek Orthodox Church. To the south, the Hungarians and the Poles had been converted to the authority of Rome. So had the Germans on the southwest and the Scandinavians to the northwest of the Baltic peoples. From Sweden, Christianity had been carried to the peaceful pagan Finns off to the north of our Balts; the latter thus formed the one remaining island of heathenism in Europe —a typical "internally marginal" retardation.

Then, in 1226, the Teutonic Knights, a military monastic order, began a crusade for the conversion or extermination of the Borussians or Prussians. Gradually the whole coastal territory along the east side of the Baltic Sea as far as the Gulf of Finland was subjugated and appropriated by the Germans. Its inhabitants were either exterminated or Christianized by force. One group of tribes alone, the Litva or Lithuanians, a little farther inland than the rest along the Niemen, fought back for their freedom and managed to retain it long enough to learn about organized war and statehood from the encroaching Germans. Beginning with Mindvog in 1247, they developed a series of national leaders. They also commenced for the first time to found fortified towns such as Vilna. Soon they passed from holding their own to expanding, especially toward the south, where the recent Mongol storm had left the several Russian nationalities and states shattered. Gedymin overran White and Volhynian Russia; his son, Ukrainian Russia beyond Kiev; under the Grand Duke Jagiello, Lithuanian dominion reached down the Dnieper almost to the Black Sea. In 1386, the heiress to the Polish crown was persuaded to marry this Jagiello, on condition that he become Christian; and his people followed him. A personal union of rule thus bound together Poland, much longer civilized, and Lithuania, perhaps twice as large. The combination being voluntary and reinforced by joint successes against the German Knights, the Lithuanian higher classes eagerly Polonized themselves. They took over not only the Catholicism but the speech, manners, dress, customs, and education of the Poles; and by the diet of Lublin in 1569 they handed over the old Lithuanian conquests to Poland. That, incidentally, was the basis of the Polish-Russian disputes over eastern Poland after World War I and during World War II. The population of the disputed area still is prevailingly White Russian, as it was when annexed by Lithuania six hundred years before; but it had been under unchallenged and sole Polish rule for about two centuries. In the home district of Lithuania, the peasants and serfs continued to speak Lithuanian and to preserve Lithuanian folk customs; but the culture of the higher classes was Polish. A heavy proportion of eminent Poles in all fields of accomplishment were Lithuanian in ancestry, but thought of themselves as Poles. This was much as a Spaniard or a Tunisian of the early centuries after Christ would feel himself to be really a Roman in citizenship and civilization; his actual provincial origin was of no particular moment. All three of the Baltic states founded in 1919 had genuine difficulties to overcome in their careers, because they were really erected on a basis of the social submergence of their nationalities. The nationalities, as linguistic or ethnic groups, were unquestionably there. But their educated, prosperous, professional, and politically trained classes were prevailingly either Germanized, Russianized, or Polonized. Yet in the case of the Lithuanians, their acculturation and semiassimilation had really been thoroughly self-sought and self-imposed by a respect for an older civilization.

Another voluntary reorientation is that made by the Algonkin and Athabascan hunting and fishing tribes of the great transcontinental coniferous forest of northern Canada, as a result of European demand for furs. Their habitat was rich in fine pelts, though miserably poor in almost all other immediate resources. Deer, moose, or reindeer continued to be hunted for food by these tribes; but mink, marten, beaver, and ermine assumed a wholly new value in terms of what white men were ready to give for them: steel traps, firearms, tools and kettles, woolen blankets, trinkets, and tea, flour, and pork. A dependence of families, bands, and tribes on trading posts grew up. Caucasian contacts gave the Indians more comforts, but also entrenched them more firmly as hunters. Their canoes, snowshoes, and the like were retained because they had been successfully worked out to fit living off the country. Their present culture thus has a native foundation, but it also has a large Caucasian constituent and at least partial Caucasian motivation. And the acculturation was not due to conquest, to missionaries, or to dispossessing settlers swarming in, but to the fact that the Indians, who remain in the majority, changed their ways of their own accord (§ 327).

180. NATIVISM, REVIVALS, AND MESSIAHS

After two societies have come into sufficiently close contact for one to feel the other as definitely more populous, stronger, or better equipped, so that its own culture is in process of being supplanted by the other, a conscious preservation effort or defense is often produced. Such reactions have been called nativistic endeavors or revivals. They envelop with a sort of halo the culture that is passing away, and attempt to reaffirm or re-establish it, or parts of it.

An immigrant group in the United States or Brazil almost always forms an association of its nationals, not only to give its members aid, but to help preserve the folkways, customs, speech, and home life characteristic of the old culture. This may be done even though the immigrants are economically better off than they were in the homeland and would not think of returning to the conditions from which they emigrated. People in growing up do get attached to the ways of their culture, much as they become attached to their kinsfolk or their old home. By the time they begin to age, their memories of the culture have got tinged with pleasurable nostalgic sentiments and assume a symbolic value. Folk dances, for instance, or literary exercises thus may come to mean much more than they did in the old country.

Much the same effect may be produced when the territory of a more backward minority is being occupied by an alien dominant population; when a people is conquered and forced to change its ways; or even if it only feels its own culture peacefully giving way under the automatic weight of a neighboring larger and more successful one. Thus the ancient bardic gatherings called Eisteddfods were revived in 1798 for the conscious preservation and cultivation of Welsh speech, poetry, tradition, and music; these were almost all that remained of the national culture of Wales, since Welshmen had long been full participants in British citizenship, empire, and civilization.

With primitive tribes, the shock of cultural contact is often sudden and severe. Their hunting lands or pastures may be taken away or broken under the plow, their immemorial customs of blood revenge, head-hunting, sacrifice, marriage by purchase, or polygyny be suppressed, perhaps their holy places profaned or deliberately overthrown. Resistance is crushed by firearms or by superior military organization. Despondency settles over the tribes. Under the blacking-out of all old established ideals and prestiges, without provision for new values and opportunities to take their place, the resulting universal hopelessness will weigh doubly heavy because it seems to reaffirm inescapable frustration in personal life also. At this juncture a prophet is likely to arise and picture a wish fulfillment: a release from the human impasse by supernatural mechanism. The ancestral dead are to return and sweep the encroaching whites off the land. Bulletproof shirts will neutralize firearms. The game animals will pour out from the bowels of the earth whither they withdrew to evade the white man. The old customs, the old rituals, the old happy gatherings, will all be re-established. All that is needed, says the prophet, is faith in the impending miraculous event, and some slight token observance of faith, such as dancing, or destroying one's belongings of white manufacture. Therewith a revivalistic movement of return to the good old days is launched. The prophet's motivation may range from sincere delusion to desire for power, fame, or even money, or be compounded of these. His converts follow him because of the stress of their social unhappiness. Skeptical individuals or groups are ignored, or finally get caught in the mass infection too.

Some of these cults end in an armed clash and defeat. Such were, among American Indians, the Delaware Prophet's announcements of 1762 and the Shawnee Tenskwatawa's of 1805, which were followed by Pontiac's conspiracy and by Tecumseh, the Battle of Tippecanoe, and the Creek War, respectively. Other movements merely fade away when the date passes and the prediction is unfulfilled. More often they maintain themselves as a new, hybrid church combining elements selected out of the former tribal religion and out of Christianity—its hybridity conforming to the transitional character of the dissolving native culture as a whole. Of this character was the revivalistic cult established about 1884 by the Columbia River Sahaptin Indian called Smohalla, which ended in a permanent religion with church buildings, half after the Caucasian model.

In 1869 a Walker Lake Paiute of Nevada named Wodziwob began to preach locally the end of the world, destruction of the white man, and return of the Indian dead. This "First Ghost Dance" belief spread intertribally with increasing momentum. By 1871 it had the Indians of northern California in a ferment (§ 239); but from 1872 to 1874 it broke up into three movements. The first of these was the Earth Lodge cult, professing to protect the faithful from catastrophe by having them enter specially built subterranean houses. Next was the Bole-Maru, which arose after it began to appear that the world would not end just then, and which therefore relegated the impending catastrophe and return of the dead into the background; but its prophets or dreamers seized upon certain spectacular native dances, simplified these, and combined them with the use of patterned flags and modifications of white women's dresses. The third current was the Big Head cult, which drifted away to attach special importance to a certain type of feather headdress, which was passed on like a fetish to new converts. Of these three proliferations of the Ghost Dance, only the Bole-Maru lasted: it still was being practiced after seventy years at the outbreak of World War II. It thus represents a return from the convulsive character of a messianic revival or native millennium to the more stable adjustment of progressive acculturation.

Even more famous was the Second Ghost Dance of around 1890. This originated, in a sense, among the same Nevada Paiute that started the first one, the originating dreamer or prophet now being Wovoka or Jack Wilson, a son of the foremost convert of Wodziwob twenty years before. His doctrine was the same: cataclysm, reversion of the land to the Indians, return of their dead relatives. Because the First Ghost Dance had found its most ardent proselytes to the west among the California Indians, who were now disillusioned, this second movement stirred a new clientele of Indians to the east, mostly beyond the Rockies, among Dakota, Arapaho, Kiowa, and other Plains tribes. Its hysteria led to the battle or massacre of Wounded Knee, after which it subsided fairly rapidly, leaving as its chief relics a few symbolic games and a couple of partly new dance costumes and steps—besides of course a more profound despair or resignation.

It is interesting that the rapid and wide spread of these Ghost Dances was itself due to a set of acculturation phenomena that had greatly increased the communication possibilities of the Indians. These were: English as a means of intertribal communication; railroads; and enforced acquaintance of diverse groups with each other on reservations.

Analogous stirrings, upheavals, and outbreaks are on repeated record from South America and South Africa, in Nigeria and New Guinea, wherever Caucasians have sufficiently crowded natives as to their land, subsistence, folkways, or religion. Usually the revolt—or the attempted escape into the miraculous—comes after the invaded culture has had its really mortal wound, when the natives as a mass begin to despair of its survival. Until then, they are troubled by the progressive disintegration of their fortunes and institutions, but not yet driven to relying on the supernatural for hope fulfillment. A few years later, disillusionment is profound enough to keep them in apathy—at any rate until a new generation has grown up. There seem always to be some pessimists and skeptics, and some passive resignationists. But when the emotional pressure on the mass becomes strong enough, even these individuals get caught up in the hope beliefs of the majority, or temporarily retire into side-line conformity: it is often difficult to tell which, subsequently.

The Jews have been particularly prone to such nativistic revival attempts. In 722 B.C. and again in 586, conquest and deportation by Nineveh and Babylon had ended, realistically and historically, the Hebrew dream of a great prosperous national kingdom. They possessed by then, however, a unique religion, more and more centering on belief in an exclusive deity with special interest in themselves. This belief led them in two directions. In part, they broadened their national monolatry and monotheism into a universal conceptual monotheism, and therewith laid the foundation for Christianity and Mohammedanism. On the other side, the narrower and cruder among the Hebrews took increasing comfort in the idea of the Messiah, the anointed one, descendant of David, who would restore the Hebrew kingdom to glory and perhaps supremacy among the powers of the earth. For more than two hundred years of Roman dominance, this Messianic idea kept goading the Jews into hopeless rebellions, the greatest being that led by Bar-Kochba, who actually took Jerusalem and a thousand villages before being destroyed by Hadrian's generals in A.D. 135. Thereafter rebellions were fewer; but claims to Messiahship kept being put forward through mediaeval and modern centuries, their frequency being fairly proportionate to the degree of misery or hopelessness the Jews were enduring at any given time in western or eastern Europe or under Islam.

The expectation of a Messiah definitely entered into the making of Christianity. Jesus' own immediate Jewish disciples considered him to be such: the epithet *Christos,* the anointed, is the Greek translation of *Mashiach,* the one anointed with oil—*mashach*—as a sign of sovereignty. It was denationalized Jews like Paul, and converted Gentiles, who in the generation after the Crucifixion swung the emphasis of the faith away from that of a Palestinian Jewish minority sect onto a basis that could serve for a universal religion. Blood sacrifice, circumcision, the exact Levitical law, were eliminated or made noncompulsory; belief, baptism, and communion sufficed to make non-Jews equal members of the church; and therewith the teaching of Jesus became possible of acceptance the world over. And with that, of course, the historically underlying nativistic revivalism was wholly transcended.

181. ETHNIC REVIVALS

Non-Messianic but literally revivalistic is a late development of Jewish history: Zionism, the movement to re-establish an independent state in Palestine, to serve at least as a center or a token of Judaism if not as a home for all the Jews of the world. Incidentally, the Zionistic movement is only a particular example of a world-wide drift toward autonomous nationalism: an independent Finland and an independent Poland emerging and re-emerging from World War I, Iceland breaking away from Denmark, the cry of "Indonesia for the Indonesians," and dozens of similar cases. The only fundamentally peculiar element in Zionism is that its proponent Jews are not a full nationality and have not been one for two thousand years. It is religion and religious customs, not speech or general culture, that have at the same time held the Jews together and segregated them from the rest of the world.

Some of the Jewish Zionists went one step farther, however, and decided to restore Hebrew as a national language (§ 107, 120), though it had been only a language of ritual and literature—a "dead" language as compared with a "mother tongue"—twice as long as Latin. It is believed that already in Jesus' time Aramaic had replaced Hebrew as the everyday idiom of Palestine. Now engineering and economics are being taught in Hebrew at a Hebrew university in Jerusalem, and some tens of thousands of Palestinian Jewish children speak nothing but Hebrew.

That we are really dealing here with only an example of a generic drift of the times is shown by the attempted revivification of Gaelic in Eire, and by the creation of a Norwegian national language in recent generations. Gaelic or Irish, of Keltic derivation, had sunk in the later nineteenth century to being the speech of a fraction of a minority population. In general, it survived only in western Ireland, mostly among the rural, remote, little-educated, and uninfluential. It has now been enacted into one of the two official languages of Eire, is spoken in the Dail, and taught in all schools.

Norway, while politically a part of Denmark, got along with Norwegian folk dialects on the part of its farmers and fishermen, though people with schooling and social pretensions had learned Danish, or rather a Norwegian sort of near-Danish. After the separation in 1814, this modified Danish assimilated more toward the homespun or folk Norwegian, and became known as Riksmaal, or "language of the realm," in distinction from standard Danish. This was not enough to satisfy the more ardent Norwegians, however, and soon after 1840 a linguist, Aasen, constructed a synthetic pure Norwegian out of local dialects. This, the Landsmaal or "language of the country," was accepted by some, opposed by others, suffered some changes, but was finally adopted as a second official and standard Norwegian language.

These cases are of some theoretical interest because it has been widely taken for granted that while a language in its written form might be embalmed and used indefinitely, as a living speech it was dead and unrevivable once it had no more mother-tongue speakers. It is evidently unsafe to predict too sweepingly about what any culture or aspect of culture can or cannot do. However, it would also be rash to predict that Biblical Hebrew, Irish Gaelic, and Landsmaal Norwegian have struck deep enough roots to flourish permanently and independently of propaganda, subsidy, and official support. They do look like experiments that so far are partly successful—which is a pretty good resuscitation for the seemingly moribund.

182. ASSIMILATION AND UNIFORMITY

The recent tendency and desire to see group minorities and cultural localisms assimilated into complete uniformity is much accentuated by the recent burst of technological development. Not only does a better machine quickly displace a dozen previous ones, but ever improving transportation and communications leave to all particularisms very little isolation in which to shelter themselves. Such particularisms may get temporarily caught up as an interesting novelty and have their nation-wide or world-wide day of vogue: the dirndl costume, for instance. Otherwise, they certainly tend to get obliterated by the increasingly uniformized general culture. It is precisely Austrian and South German dirndl-wearers who gave up peasant dress. In a country like the United States, everybody dresses alike, rides in the same makes of cars, reads the same dispatches, columns, and cartoons in similarly headlined newspapers, dances to the same music, in any given year or month. Much of this uniformization has begun to spread internationally. It is certainly convenient to find the same foods, drinks, houses, clothes, amusements, and reading matter anywhere in the world —if one knocks about the world. But, equally surely, it is also monotonous. And when there is no more place left to find something different, or from whose localism to derive a new stimulation, the world may conceivably awaken to a situation like that of the ancient Hawaiians when they found that their religion had staled on them (§ 168).

It is an old recognition that nationalistic effectiveness resides in union. Whether it be a matter of survival, expansion, or economic prosperity, a united English-speaking America was bound to count for more than thirteen colonial states; a German Reich, more than the sum of its twenty-six kingdoms, principalities, and free cities. And next to political union—in national efficiency—is social and cultural uniformity. A hundred million people living, acting, speaking, thinking, and feeling alike can normally move with a trip-hammer effect, whatever the undertaking, such as could not possibly be attained by a union of fifteen groups of ten million each, differing in customs, outlook, occupations, manners, and ideals—except perhaps occasionally in a transcendent crisis. In a shrinking world, which is therefore inescapably more competitive, there is an obvious premium, first for national size; next for tightness of political unity; third for cultural uniformity—at least while other things remain equal. India and China have the size, but neither the unity nor the uniformity; Japan and Germany, by 1935, had each begun to enforce their unity and uniformity, and therewith to threaten the world. The unusual cultural homogeneity of our 140 millions undoubtedly was a great help to the United States in enabling us to sustain the storm of World War II and to pass rapidly from defense to attack. Yet it is well to remember that this homogeneity differed from that of Hitlerian Germany chiefly in being spontaneous and unenforced, although its degree, after the United States was well in the war, was not so very different. The cause and the motivation of our homogeneity were different from those of the Germans and the Japanese. But it remains to be judged by what the future brings whether the net effect on ourselves of having had to uniformize ourselves, especially if we have to repeat the process, may not include the development of some attitudes similar to German and Japanese ones. There seems to be little doubt that a degree of differentiation by locality, profession, or custom, with the impingement of their varieties on the whole, affords a provocative stimulation and a wider scope of experiment toward fruitful change of culture forms, as well as greater inclination toward tolerance of differences.

In this connection the Russian attitude on acculturation is of considerable interest for its bearing both on uniformity and on its control. As a left-wing party developing in an absolute monarchy, the original Bolsheviki were naturally in sympathy with freedom for national aspirations. As socialists, their planning for a new organization of international culture, and their program of control of change, both tended toward their favoring uniformity. When they came into power in Russia, they set up, gradually, a long series of soviet republics, one for each larger minority nationality—Ukraine, White Russia, Latvia, Georgia, Armenia, Azerbaijan, Uzbek, Tadjik, Kirghiz, and so on—plus the inclusion in the Russian Soviet Socialist Federated Republic of subautonomous units such as Altai and Yakutsk. At first, subject or included peoples, such as the Georgians, the Uzbek, the Yakut, were to be liberated and unsubmerged, much like the Russian proletariat itself—also, much as Woodrow Wilson conceived of Letts and Lithuanians as free and autonomous nationalities. Alphabets were devised for the peoples if they had none; literature was translated into their vernacular; and everything was done to encourage each people to work out its own culture in line with its own past and its aspirations.[11] It was Czardom, the absolute and exploiting state, which had been crushing minorities and subject nationalities, just as it deprived the masses of liberty and opportunity. It was assumed by the Bolsheviks that each such group would spontaneously respond to the grant of its cultural liberty, and gratefully reciprocate by embracing the political faith of its liberators and supporting them. Some notable experiments were made in this direction of tribal cultural development, most interesting perhaps when they were applied to wholly specialized and backward peoples like the Chukchi, or some of the almost pure pastoral nomads.

After some dozen years the official Soviet attitude on these matters changed. The causes may have been a growing sense of security as to survival of the Soviet regime; the tendency to rechannel the emphasis of the Communist program from world-wide revolution to internal strengthening; or still other factors—the situation is complex, and it is unnecessary to account for all the precise causes in the present connection. At any rate, there was a shift in official policy away from international and multinational to strictly nationalistic aims. This shift was enormously strengthened by the successful resistance to the German attack after 1941. The overwhelmingly leading nationality in the Soviet Union being Russian, and especially Great Russian, this new attitude in effect was one of Russian patriotism. With this majority patriotism the minority nationalisms might interfere; but they could hardly strengthen it materially. The later Soviet policy has therefore tended to revert once more to de-facto Russianization, to promot-

---

[11] Except in the domain of religion, any form of which the early Bolsheviks saw as an inevitable enemy. Therefore they did what they could to prevent even the shamanistic practices of their primitive populations.

ing uniformity and homogeneity. The cultural autonomy of Tadjik or Lithuanians or Yakut or Ukrainians is evidently slated henceforth to consist mainly of folk dances and sports and suchlike matters, plus the use of their own tongue in local and provincial spheres. That is, the minority nationalities will presumably be submergent once more.

Quite likely this process is inevitable. Political fractionation would be endless over the world if every group with a culture and language that could be distinguished as separate were to split off into complete political autonomy at will. There is no attempt here to indicate a solution, or to say what rightly ought to be. The Russian situation is pictured in order to outline, a little more fully than one is likely to conceive it from the angle of one's own majority nationality alone, some of the involvements of acculturation, assimilation, and homogenizing to uniformity.

CHAPTER ELEVEN

Some Histories of Inventions:
The Interplay of Factors

WE HAVE discussed the principles of invention and the factors entering into the process. The concrete exemplifications so far given have necessarily been selected to illustrate this or that particular point; and often only so much of an invention has been cited as is relevant to the principle or factor under discussion. But a great many inventions have a long history of step-by-step increments, in addition to the cardinal innovation. These histories are interwoven with the working of the greatest variety of influences. Once it is economic demands or sufficiencies that are dominant; now psychological factors such as motor habits or prestige values prevail; then historical accidents of new contacts and diffusion surge or trickle in; and so on. Nevertheless the history of any one device or machine has a certain coherent unity; and this unity gives the story a meaning that is more than antiquarian, because it is an aid to realizing the full extent of the interplay of the multiple factors that are normally involved in culture change. So a few such unit histories are outlined here. These case histories are mostly taken from the more advanced and literate civilizations; chiefly, in fact, from our own Western civilization, for which the records are most continuous.

183. MILLS

The history of mills begins with flour-milling—the grinding of wheat for our daily bread. Next in order historically, but much later, in the Middle Ages, came fulling mills which "fulled" or evened woolen cloth, and tanbark-crushing mills for leather shoes and saddlery, and soon after, sawmills for cutting the lumber for dwellings. Food, clothing, housing, thus was the sequence. There are several points to be kept in mind: the size or strength of mills, the sources of their power, and their structure or mechanism of power transmission.

Grinding grains by hand is or was world-wide, of course. Of the two principal hand methods, pounding on a mortar or rubbing on a slab, it is the second that seems to have led to revolving mills and thence to all other kinds of mills. The respective advantages of rubbing and pounding seem never to have been seriously investigated, probably because all methods of direct hand-grinding had become economically unimportant by the time science was developed enough to undertake such an investigation. The wheat-barley-rye-using peoples on the whole crushed by rubbing or grinding—though there was a phase among the Romans when stronger male slaves, pounding with pestles in mortars, replaced women bent over the grinding quern. However, this last may reflect a socio-economic change rather than a mechanical improvement: while small farms prevailed, the women of the household milled the grain their menfolk grew, but with the growth of larger estates and industrial slave capitalism, men displaced women. The nations to whom rice is basic have most often pounded it. The maize peoples in America generally ground—what in England is called a saddle quern in America is the metate, Hispanicized from Aztec *metlatl*. But, by exception, the farming tribes of the southeastern United States pounded their maize in mortars. Preagricultural customs of how to handle wild seeds or acorns may have established motor habits in one direction or another, which then persisted in each area through the generations into the farming period, because intrinsically one technique is probably very nearly as good as the other, with most grains; and the thing most difficult or repugnant for a population would be the seemingly gratuitous substitution of a new set of body motions, for hours daily, in place of those that had become familiar and automatic and seemingly easy in youth. Addiction to a material might be a factor, too. Rubbing devices are almost invariably of stone, but most mortars, whether for rice or maize, are wooden.

The mortar and pestle have remained hand apparatus, or have been slightly elaborated now and then by the addition of counterweights. It is from the grinding slab that mills have grown.

In the ancient Mediterranean world the rectangular saddle quern, hollowed toward the middle of its length, is shown in Egypt as far back as depictions go. The motion was back and forth, with a small handstone sliding over the base slab. There are some scattered instances, among recent gathering tribes here and there, of grinding being done with a more round-and-round motion on a circular base. But practically all agricultural populations with their heavy-duty grinding have stuck to the back-and-forth stroke, which is evidently the easiest or most effective hand motion in the daily long pull.

When rotary motion finally comes in seriously, it is a case of one circular "millstone" revolving on another of the same size—not merely a little stone being pushed around on a big one. In other words, direct manual action is now over with: the upper stone must be turned by a handle or bar, and men slaves, or an ass or two, are called for instead of a lone woman. This rotary millstone was surprisingly late in appearing. The first preserved mention is by that famous

Roman Cato who was so bent on destroying Carthage. The actual use of the rotating millstone probably began somewhat earlier—perhaps in the third or even fourth century B.C.; but it seems to have been later than Phidias and the Parthenon and Sophocles and Socrates. The mechanical principle of this new machine, as it may fairly be called—whereas the handstone was only a tool— of course is that of the wheel, which had by then been immemorially known both in transport and in pottery-making. Why there was the long delay in the application of the wheel to milling is obscure, except that it does not appear to have been on account of mechanical difficulties in the transfer. The cause of the change when it did come thus was presumably again economic: larger estates, more concentration of wealth, more slavery or cheaper domestic animals, greater specialization of labor—something of that kind.

The next step was to apply inanimate power: water. Two ways were open to secure this power. One was a horizontal paddle wheel set in a current of water and connected directly with the horizontal revolving millstones. This seems to have been in effect a sort of crude turbine. The other was a vertical wheel, which meant an indirect transmission of power or gear, since the rotary millstone could not well function off the horizontal. The gear was single, of two wooden-cogged wheels meshing at an angle. Such a geared wheel is described by the Roman architect and engineer Vitruvius about 16 B.C. as something known though not common. It is more than a thousand years before we have another pictorial illustration of this simple geared mill—1169 in Germany, to be exact. But there can be no doubt that mills of this angle-transmission vertical type, as well as of the simpler horizontal type, continued to be made in Europe during the long obscure interval. In fact we have plenty of mentions in law codes, charters, and the like of water-driven flour mills in the Dark Ages and the early Middle Ages; but often we cannot tell from them which type of wheel is being referred to.

The vertical water wheels in the geared mill were undershot in all cases at first, and probably in most cases for many centuries thereafter. Indubitable descriptions or illustrations of overshot wheels came late; and it was not until the modern period of history that the superior effectiveness of the overshot was recognized. By "undershot" is meant a wheel of which merely the bottom dips into the stream; it is only the force of the current that drives it around. In the overshot wheel, the water is fed in by a millrace or flume at the top of the wheel and falls into buckets or boxes, so that the weight of the water and its impact combine in effect; but the direction of turn of course is opposite from the undershot. The feeding-in above requires more construction: either the mill wheel must be set below a dam or a fall, or the flume must be carried on props for some distance; whereas an undershot vertical wheel—or a horizontal one, for that matter—can be set anywhere in a lively running stream. The idea of an undershot wheel as a source of power may be derived from a large irrigation wheel with buckets that the Greeks and Romans found in use in Egypt. This was usually and originally turned by manpower, or by donkeys, to lift water out of the Nile or out of canals and dump it into distributing ditches. It was therefore not a power producer at all, but a power applier or converter for lifting weight. But, set in a swift enough stream, and with simpler blades or paddles replacing its buckets, it became a power wheel.

Just how, when, or where either the horizontal or the vertical mill wheel was first used is hazily obscure, like the beginning of so many practical inventions: they are so practical and private that they do not get into the political and public record of history until long after, and then perhaps only through impinging on some matter of law or taxation. It has been thought that the horizontal wheel originated in Greek-dominated southwestern Asia in the first century before Christ and was established in Italy in the next century. However that may be, this practical invention seems to have been made well after the great burst of Greek fundamental science as typified by Archimedes in the third century B.C., and to have had little direct relation to this pure science.

It is probable that water-driven mills quietly multiplied and spread through the centuries, inside and outside the Roman Empire, undisturbed by the rise and fall of states, invasions, and conquest. In fact, while the Roman Empire was strong, and slaves abundant and cheap, we hear nothing much of water mills and may conclude they were not yet of much importance. But in the century or so before and after the fall of Rome—between 398 and 650, to be exact—the mills of that city are mentioned repeatedly. First there are edicts protecting the water supply of the mills from private encroachment; then we hear of a whole group of mills served by a timber aqueduct or flume; and when this was cut in a siege, of the mills being set on boats or rafts on the Tiber (which suggests a vertical undershot wheel); and finally of the mills being moved inside the city wall. By the same period the water mill had spread not only to those barbarians occupying the former western Roman Empire, like the Visigoths, the Franks, and the Lombards, but to those beyond. In fact the earliest known mill reference outside of Rome is in the Irish code called *Senchus Mor,* attributed to 438-441. The enumeration in this of the parts of the mill shows that the wheel was of the same horizontal or pseudo-turbine type.

Mills entered into law because, while privately built and owned, they were considered a public utility. Transportation generally was so poor that many small mills served better than a few powerful ones. Yet with a little and slow mill, it did not pay the owner to sit around. He just left it open for his neighbors to run as they needed to, and settled afterward for his fee or percentage of the flour. Later, with the growth of feudalism in the Middle Ages proper, there was a tendency for lords to insist that use of their mill by their tenants and other residents was obligatory; though this was also often contested. At any rate, as mills and fees grew larger, professional millers remained in attendance—witness Chaucer's "The Miller's Tale."

China is known, from pottery models in graves, to have had circular mill-stones in pairs since the Han period, 200 B.C. to A.D. 200. The upper stone was turned by a handhold. Similar stones are still in use, as community property of a village. The water-driven mill appears in China soon after the Han period, the invention being ascribed to Tu Yü about A.D. 260. This statement probably means that the invention was made or adopted by some anonymous farmer or artisan, and that Tu Yü was the scholar, and therefore the official, who found the contrivance in use in his district and included mention of it in an administrative report which happened to get into history. A fuller reference was made, or an improvement reported, by a Ts'ui Liang, who lived under the Wei dynasty, 386-532. Laufer, who first unearthed these items of history, believes that they are not inventions made independently by the Chinese, but transmissions that reached them, under the surface of recorded history, from the Asiatic provinces of the Roman Empire. The two to three centuries of interval between the appearances in West Asia and East Asia might presumably suffice for the spread. The derivation is by no means proved, since there is no direct evidence; but the situation is such that a derivation looks entirely possible. As a matter of sound historical reasoning, the degree of probability which this possibility can take on is proportionate to the number of other and independent instances of proven transmissions between West and East Asia: in other words, the total context.

The spread to China is supported by the reputed introduction of water mills to India by a Persian sent by Constantine the Great. The time, around 325, fits fairly well with the Chinese dates.

Let us return to Europe. From about the twelfth century on it appears that most larger mills were being run with vertical wheels; and considerably later, the overshot vertical began more certainly to encroach on the undershot. It is around the same period that we have the first definite records of mills other than for grain: for crushing tanbark in 1154, for fulling cloth in 1168, for sawing lumber in the next century, for breaking up ore still later. The crushing and pounding mills operated with drop hammers that were lifted by a cam on a wheel or a cylinder.

The mediaeval sawmill is anticipated by nine centuries in a reference to a marble-cutting sawmill in northern Gaul, written by a late Latin poet, Ausonius. But the nine-century gap of silence is so long, and the poverty and crudity of all Europe between the Roman Empire and the High Mediaeval revival were so great, that an independent reinvention in the thirteenth century may be indicated, rather than a continuity. Once started, however, sawmills spread fairly rapidly: at least ten charter authorizations in France and Germany have been preserved from the 1300's and early 1400's; and within a year or two after the Portuguese had discovered and occupied Madeira Island, they set up a sawmill there, in 1420.

Meanwhile, another "prime mover" had been harnessed for milling: air in motion. The windmill was not a Greek or Roman or European invention, but a western-Asiatic one in Islamic time. The Arabic-writing geographer Al Mas'udi saw windmills in Persia in the early 900's; and we have another Arabic reference within the same century. All European mentions are later: thus for England, the three or four earliest references cluster around 1190-1200. This was just a century after the First Crusade, and it may have been Crusaders who brought the idea from the Levant to Europe; but this is only supposition. The original European windmill was a small affair, hung or pivoted on one post, which was either sunk in the ground or propped by a tripod of timbers. The idea was to turn the whole mill around by a handle as the wind shifted until the sails properly faced the wind again. It was a sort of big box, therefore, rather than a house; and contained a single gear mesh, converting from the horizontal axle of the wheels or sails to the vertical axle of the revolving stone. After nearly three hundred years the turret type of windmill was evolved, as a response to bigger milling. The millhouse was now a real building, in fact a large tower, around which the sail frame could be shifted. This "Dutch" type of windmill seems to have originated in Italy toward 1500, but was worked out and perfected in Holland in the later 1500's, about the time the Dutch were successfully revolting against the Spaniards to gain their religious and political liberty. Holland, then rising to economic prosperity, no doubt felt a need for more power than its sluggish delta branches of the Rhine and the Meuse could supply; and beyond wind, water, or animals, there was as yet nothing in the way of power source—nor would be till Newcomen's atmospheric one-way steam engine of 1705. At any rate, the turret mill doubled or tripled the minimum power of the post mill—raising it from around two or three horsepower to six horsepower and up; whereas the post mill, while the wind blew strong and fair, about equaled what an eighteen-foot overshot water wheel would deliver, and surpassed the performance of an undershot or horizontal wheel. The estimated output was about a bushel of wheat ground in an hour per horsepower developed.

The windmill, contrary to the water mill, never reached China nor was it independently invented there.

A next step was to use water wheels to work force pumps to raise water so that it could be distributed in cities. There are records for such developments in 1526 at Spanish Toledo, by an Italian engineer; in 1548 at Augsburg; in 1582 at London (preceded by a windmill pumping plant at smaller Gloucester in 1542); and at Paris under Henri IV somewhat later than at London.

The turbine, after the great Swiss mathematician Euler had worked on its theory, was developed in France in 1822 and completed there ten years later. The confinement of water to the drum that holds the turbine blades allowed pressures, speeds, and volumes hitherto unheard-of in water wheels. Thus Fourneyron's 1832 turbine already developed fifty horsepower.

Several reflections emerge from this meandering story. First perhaps is a sense of the slowness of the development: the lateness of arrival of its several phases. It is scarcely two thousand years back to the devising of the first stationary machine driven by natural power. Even after the invention was made, human and animal power for some centuries tended to be used side by side with inanimate power, as if they were about equally cheap, or rather dear—which they probably were.

Next, the whole development has surprisingly little relation to science. Greek pure science had run its productive course before natural-power mills were invented. That they then spread through the Roman Empire, and to equally civilized China, is natural enough, though the spread over the Roman Empire was far from startling in its speed. The spread seems to have continued right on among the illiterate barbarians of northern Europe without diminution of rate into the depth of the Dark Ages. This period accordingly must be construed as one in which darkness descended on the propagation of abstract science, but in which people retained normal keenness for practically advantageous technologies within their means. This conclusion is strengthened by the fact that it was in the same Dark or Protomediaeval period that stirrups, horseshoeing, and improved draft harness became established in educationally benighted Europe. The same lack of relation of pure science to technical industry is again evident at the other or enlightened end of the Middle Ages. The dominance of the vertically set and then of the overshot wheel; the extension from grain-grinding to fulling and stamp mills and sawmills; the addition of wind as motive power—all these were under way by the twelfth century, whereas modern science scarcely began its active growth till the fifteenth. Spectacles, printing, cannon, cast iron, spinning wheels were developed in this same Late Mediaeval period while pure science was making little progress.

The specific mechanical factor that did most to retard a rapid development of power milling seems to have been the difficulty of preparing smoothly functioning gears for transmission of power. Mesh gears were hand-wrought, either of hardwood or of blacksmith's iron. Even the best engagements must have been somewhat uneven, and there appears to have been no satisfactory lubrication. A single mesh per mill unit seems to have been the limit. Presumably attempts at more meshes had failed to work satisfactorily; the principle of cog and screw gears had been theoretically understood since the time of the Greeks. It appears then to have been technological rudeness of execution of apparatus that long rendered progress in milling accomplishment so slow.

184. MECHANICAL CLOCKS

Timekeeping devices are as characteristic of modern Occidental civilization as is power development. Clocks permeate our activities to such a degree that we take them for granted, and only by an effort can we imagine a style of life in which the time factor is indefinite, unimportant, or lacking. Take away exactness of time from the railway train, the factory whistle, and the eight-hour day, from radio programs and sporting events, from physics, astronomy, navigation, and aviation, from classroom and "date" even, and what confusion would we be in! Perhaps our institutions would not crumble to pieces; but there would be utter breakdown of living at first, followed by a readjustment to a basis of much rougher approximations and far more resultant waste. So our civilization ticks by the clock; but the first mechanical clocks were made less than seven hundred years ago, in Europe. The ancients, the Chinese and the Hindus, the Egyptians and the Mesopotamians, judged by the sun or by shadows and sundials, or followed their unconscious sense of elapsed time, or now and then had a water clock—a drip affair on the order of an hourglass. They divided day and night into twelve hours; but mainly they guessed what hour it was. Their civilizations must all have been very different from ours in being so loosely oriented, so slack and full of wobbly play, as regards "when."

The essential parts of a mechanical clock or watch are: first, the power, now usually a coiled spring, originally a weight descending from a pulley, as in our cuckoo clocks; second, a series of meshed wheels, at least three in number but usually more, which transmit the power and successively slow the motion, and the last of which carries and turns the hour hand (minute and second hands are later additions); and third, the escapement, which finally slows and regulates the clock's motion to the needed tempo. Each of these three systems, respectively concerned with power, transmission, and regulation, which together make up a mechanical timepiece, has its own history and cultural significance.

As to power, it was almost inevitable that this should at first be supplied by falling weights: both on the analogy of falling water or sand, and because the pulley had been familiar in Europe and the Near East since the time of the ancients. The first mechanical clocks were set high, in palace or church towers, serving as they did a whole city. Here their weights had plenty of the needed drop; and there would be an attendant to come around daily and crank back up the great load that was necessitated by the crudeness with which the rest of the mechanism operated. Thus the clock completed by de Vick in Paris in 1370 was driven by a quarter-ton weight that descended thirty-two feet daily. The weight for the strike mechanism was almost three times as heavy. In mills, where power is unfolded, the development has been from modest to larger and larger machinery. In clocks, the development has been downward from tower to table and wrist-band size.

The transmission, which dilutes the power into slow motion, is the most constant feature of mechanical clocks. It consists today, as it did in the beginning, of a series of cogged gears, the greater wheels engaging small pinions on the axles of the other large wheels. The question arises why this principle, which was perfectly well known in antiquity, was so late as the Middle Ages in being applied to clocks. One reason is the imperfection of mesh in gears made by carpenter's or blacksmith's manipulation, an imperfection that has already been recognized as a factor in the slow development of power mills. A second reason is that the ancients, though they perfectly well understood the principle of the cogwheel, were not accustomed to operate with it. It took, as we have seen, centuries for the vertical water wheel to triumph over the horizontal, largely because it required a single mesh to convert from its vertical motion to the horizontal motion of the millstones. The longest "chain" of transmission recorded from antiquity is a cyclometer—a sort of speedometer to record distance traveled by a cart or wagon—which consisted of five wheels and four screw pinions. The problem was one of converting wheel revolutions into recorded miles; power was provided by the harnessed beasts, and the question of speed was not considered. Even at that, this "hodometer" seems to have been only an occasional luxury gadget, something like the "south-pointing" chariot devices of ancient China. When the most comprehensive application of a mechanical principle is in a toy or sport, it is evident that the principle is not yet firmly rooted in the associated utility techniques, or has already been largely displaced in them.

The first clock escapements, large and heavy, were of the type called "foliot balance and verge escape." This means that the saw teeth of the third and last wheel alternately engaged and pushed aside projections on the verge rod, turning this part-way back and forth. Across the verge rod, and swinging with it, was a bar weighted at the ends, the foliot balance, which slowed and more or less regulated the escape movement. In fact, it swung with momentum enough not only to recoil the wheel at each check, but each time actually to raise a little the quarter-ton driving weight at the other end of the transmission. Instead of a steady tick-tock, the sound of such a mechanism must have been a slow whirrrr-bang—almost more like a small pile-driver than like a modern clock.

Just when the first mechanical or geared clocks were constructed cannot be specified with precision because there is a century, from about 1230 to 1340, during which the accounts are incomplete and confusing. There may have been true mechanical clocks then, but there were also water clocks. A good many of the earliest of these devices were brought into Europe from Mohammedan countries, and seem to have consisted of weight-and-pulley arrangements for striking hours or presenting puppets. Others were made in Europe, but were primarily orreries or astronomical models—such as machines by which "an angel pointed his finger at the sun." Some were probably true clocks with gears but without escapement, or with no more escapement than the weight rope's being periodically checked by being pressed between a wheel and a post. There must have been a lot of interest in these attempts, a good deal of groping experiment for a century.

Soon after 1340 the evidence is decisive for the balance-and-verge escape being known. Within less than thirty years, from 1344 to 1370, there is record of no less than twenty-one true mechanical clocks in as many European cities—

the greatest number in Italy and Germany, but France and England also being represented; in short, all of western Europe participating simultaneously. The specimen we are best informed about is one built from 1364 to 1370 in the Palais de Justice at Paris by a German named von Wick whom the French called de Vick. His clock was preserved, and ran almost unaltered until shortly before the French Revolution, when careful drawings of it were made. This was the apparatus with the quarter-ton weight and a chain of three gears. The very first and still cruder true mechanical clock may have been made anywhere from a generation to a century earlier.

As might be imagined, the early clocks were too coarse both in principle and in execution to keep time with precision, especially for short intervals; over longer periods, they probably averaged out to reasonable accuracy. It was more than a century, in 1484, before we hear of clocks being used for astronomical observations. As late as 1590, Tycho Brahe, rather than depend upon one clock, took the mean time of two or more—averaging their errors; or, for real precision, he weighed the mercury he dripped through a water clock.

The next important step was the replacement of weights as the source of power. Even a small cuckoo clock must be hung close to the ceiling so that its cast-iron pine cones may have space to descend to the floor. This change meant that clocks could come down from their high towers and enter domestic life and private use. The replacement was by a coiled steel spring, and occurred by 1500: the customary ascription is to Peter Henlein at Nuremberg in the decade 1490-1500.

The metal spring is another device that the ancients knew but employed astonishingly little, and the Middle Ages no more. Of course an ordinary bow for shooting depends on elasticity; and the Greeks would use little strips of springy horn to return the keys of a water organ to position after they had been pressed. The ancients also knew of steel swords that were tested by being bent far sidewise and snapping back perfectly straight. But the only use they seem to have made of a metal spring was in what the Romans called the fibula and we the safety pin. And this, in fact, goes back to the pre-Greek, Minoan Bronze Age. Some time between 400 and 300 B.C. the catapult was invented. This had a groove for the projectile, and windlass, ratchet, and trigger for winding and release: but its power came from twisted thongs. There are ancient writers who suggest leaf springs (of bronze, not steel!) as usable for such war engines, as they also suggest compressed air. But these seem to have remained idle speculations.

The Dark Ages and the Middle Ages did no better. The crossbow, also with groove and trigger, a weapon powerful enough to be outlawed in Christian Europe in 1139, was not given a steel bow until after 1300. In fact it is only in the fourteenth and fifteenth centuries that we find the beginnings of any serious use of the elasticity of metals. In the 1400's spiral springs began to be introduced in locks; in the later 1500's there was the first use of leaf springs. (The first coaches

—four-wheeled spring wagons—date back to 1457, but seem originally to have been hung, like the thorough-brace stagecoaches of Buffalo Bill's days, on long leather straps.) The whole metal-spring development appears to have been part of a general metallurgical growth in Europe that had been centering in Germany after the later Middle Ages and which resulted in rock-boring and other new mining and smelting methods and in the discovery of zinc, brass, cast iron, cobalt, type metal, and so on.

Well, a ribbon of steel wound up tight in a little drum inside a clock was compact enough, and the "Nuremberg eggs" soon became famous. In size, they were somewhat between a pocket watch and an alarm clock—they are the ancestor of both. They were about three inches high, spherical or somewhat oval or flattened, with a foot; they were made wholly of iron or steel, with holes cut in the case to allow the dial to be seen. Glass crystals did not come in until after 1600, and pocket sizes—true watches—later in the 1600's. Until then, there had been a gradual differentiation toward smaller models, first intended for the purse, or as pendants, which finally ended up as watches; and again toward larger ones for the mantel or table, which usually carried a strike. There was evidently a whole new craft of delicate, precise ironmongery that had to be developed before these radically diminutive Nuremberg timepieces could be even attempted.

But there remained some problems. As the spring uncoils and runs down, it loses power and the clock slows. This difficulty was first met by a device called a stackfreed; and after about 1525-40 by the fusee, invented by Zech, a Swiss in Prague. This last is a driving barrel of increasing diameter connected with the spring case by a belt. It can be extremely effective, and while it has dropped out of watches, it is still retained in chronometers, where requirements of space are subsidiary to that of accuracy. What most hampered the development of an early movable clock was retention of the foliot-balance-verge escape, which works true only while it is kept in a horizontal plane. For a century and a half, accordingly, stationary weight-driven clocks remained the more accurate.

The rest of the story essentially concerns new escapement devices. The first was the pendulum, whose beat controlled the regularity of the verge rod more evenly than could the swing of the foliot balance. Here was another device, and an absolutely simple one, which the ancients appear not to have made use of: it gives no power, but does control its rate of flow. Now at last the science of physics was directly contributing to technological invention. Both Galileo and Huygens were concerned with the theory of the pendulum and its application to clocks. Huygens completed or corrected Galileo's theory, and by 1661 he had not only invented the pendulum clock, but had also devised a form of it for marine use. Physics by now had entered a phase in which speed or rate of movement became part of its problems, as it had scarcely been among the Greeks.

A little later, around 1680, invention of the "anchor recoil" finally began to replace the centuries-old verge escape. This is a little piece shaped like the two prongs of an anchor, hung from its middle, and swinging its hooked ends alternately in and out of the saw teeth of the control wheel. Its invention is in dispute as between Clement and Hooke, the physicist contemporary of Isaac Newton. This device still operated with a degree of recoil, but about 1715 Graham invented an improvement called the deadbeat, in which the two engaging points are cut off blunt at an angle that eliminates recoil. It will be seen that we have now arrived at a point in the story where steps in invention are being made by individuals whose names are known; by individuals who are physicists or at least trained in science; and some of whom are—for the first time—Anglo-Saxons.

About the same time the balance spring was invented as a regulatory device in place of the pendulum, which of course is practically feasible only in stationary clocks and those of some height. Therewith the way was opened for true pocket watches, which could be moved and carried in any position, and of course for freely portable clocks. The balance spring is a small bar, weighted at both ends like the original foliot balance but ever so much smaller, and attached to the center of a fine coiled spring. It still shows in the regulatory apparatus of our watches of today. Its invention was claimed by Hooke, Huygens, and Hautefeuille—three H names from as many western-European countries. Hooke was perhaps a shade the earliest, but all three seem to have worked independently and essentially simultaneously; Hautefeuille anticipated Huygens in his application for the French patent. This is another example of concurrent inventions as discussed in § 140 and 152.

By this time also it had been recognized that a spring-driven clock movement accurate enough to allow of the computation of longitude at sea would be a great help to navigation; and prizes for its perfection were offered in England, France, Spain, and by the maritime republic of Venice. Between 1714 and 1728 England alone paid out, through its Board of Longitude, the then enormous total of £101,000 for improvements. Here then at last in our story we have entered the realm of conscious, planned, and subsidized invention which is so rare in the history of civilization as a whole.

Much refinement has gone into the making of clocks, watches, and chronometers in the last two hundred to two hundred and fifty years, and time is being kept with increasing precision. However, this seems to be the result of constant minor improvements along established lines of plan rather than of any basic innovations or new principles. This means that after some thousands of years of measuring time by water drip or shadow-casting, mechanical clocks had their basic patterns evolved in a succession of fundamental inventions made in western Europe between about 1300 and 1700. Since then effort has been directed at enhanced convenience, serviceability, and precision instead of revolutionizing of structural design. We go in for jeweled watches, thinner watches, rectangular wrist watches, waterproof and shockproof watches, and the like; but they are still watches on the same well-proven mechanical plan of spring drive, geared transmission, and escapement. Even electrically driven clocks retain two of these elements.

Meanwhile it is worth remembering, as regards the principle of abandonment or loss (§ 156-160), that we still decorate estate lawns and public places with bronze sundials, which we consider ornamental and pleasantly nostalgic; and we fabricate, if not hourglasses, at least three-minute sandglasses, ostensibly to help time our breakfast eggs, though their short active life is likely to be as toys in the hands of children. This is the obverse of the lingering of water clocks into the 1600's, and of a late revival spurt, in the same century, of sundials, now of pocket size, as a species of early competitors or anticipations of pocket watches.

185. INVENTION OF THE STEAMBOAT

The steamboat belongs to a type of invention in which the elements of fundamental insight and imagination are of a fairly low order, and the problems to be solved are overwhelmingly practical, industrial, or economic. Once the steam engine was established, it required no great originality to conceive of setting one up in a boat and having it turn something like the familiar mill wheel or a pair of mill wheels, simply reversed from being a source of power to being an application of it. As a matter of fact it was about eighty years from the original Newcomen steam-and-atmospheric engine to the first steam-propelled boats, and just over a hundred to the first commercially successful ones.[1] What follows is essentially an account of the practical, not scientific, difficulties that had to be overcome, and why and when they were overcome.

The first steamboats were French. In 1773 the Count d'Auxiron built a steamboat on the Seine, which sank before it ever ran. In 1775 Périer launched at Paris a one-horsepower boat, which is said to have moved, but would not run against current, and was broken up. Next year the Marquis Jouffroy designed and more or less ran a steamboat with a folding webfoot on the Doubs, an upper tributary of the Rhone, near Switzerland and Alsace, of all places. The webfoot failed to open as soon as the boat gathered speed or was turned upstream. This was seven years after the appearance of Watt's condensing engine; but when after another seven years, in 1783, Jouffroy put a 140-foot steamer on the Saône, it was still with the old-fashioned Newcomen atmospheric engine, but with paddle wheels this time. This vessel ran well against the current for a quarter of an hour. Then the seams of both hull and boiler opened from the pounding of the heavy engine, and the boat had to be beached. Jouffroy did not get his expected monopoly rights and gave up. A long lull followed. France was traversed by canals and towpaths and had then the most and the best roads in the world, but its rivers were shallow and crooked. Steamboats might run, but they

---

[1] It was over forty years from Watt's first condensing steam engine to the operation of the *Clermont* on the Hudson. In the Newcomen engine steam pushed one way; when it was chilled back to water, atmospheric pressure pushed the piston back.

could not compete with horse-drawn transportation—not until they became a lot more efficient. In 1803, Napoleon, on the advice of a committee of experts, turned down a boat of Fulton's that developed three or four mph. Therewith, steamboating was dead in France for another spell. Only in 1816, when there already were steamboats in Russia and Java and 5000 tons of them on the Hudson alone, did poor Jouffroy organize the first steam-vessel company in France, forty years after he had sailed one on the Doubs—only to fail once more. It was another decade before steam navigation began to prosper in France: geography and competition were against it.

In Britain, canal and river conditions were similar to those of France, and the first efforts were followed by a parallel period of complete cessation, during which the United States forged ahead. In 1788, Symington ran a 25-foot steamboat on a Scotch lake, and next year a 60-foot, five-to-seven mph one on a Scotch canal. During the 1790's there was a whole series of vessels that actually ran in Scotch and English waters, designed by Clarke, Lord Stanhope, Smith, Hunter, Dickinson, and the American Rumsey, who used his favorite jet mechanism; but none of them paid, and the inventors kept losing their financial backers.

In 1802 Symington found a new sponsor and perfected the *Charlotte Dundas,* an efficient vessel, which however was soon barred from the Forth-Clyde Canal because it was washing away the banks, or because horse-towed competitors alleged that it might wash them away. For a time British investors, like the contemporary French ones, became convinced that profitable operation was impossible, and laid off completely. In 1812 there was a resumption by Bell, an innkeeper, who built the *Comet* to carry excursionists on the Clyde to his hotel. The next year saw improved vessels; and then came a rapid development and acceptance, which was extended to the North and Irish seas by 1815 and 1818. In the development, from then on, of the heavy-tonnage, sturdy, open-ocean steamship, the British, with their world-wide commerce, took the lead.

In the United States, conditions were much more favorable for success of the weak craft of the early experimental period. There were good-sized rivers with prosperous towns on them, but not crowded with boats; there were no canals or towpaths, few and bad roads. It was on these waters—the Connecticut, Hudson, Delaware, Potomac, Savannah rivers, with Lake Champlain and the St. Lawrence—that the American steamer, a true river boat, worked its way to economic success in the very period of 1803-13 when navigation in Europe was in a lull of discouragement—in fact in suspension.

The first American efforts began soon after the Revolutionary War, a little after the earliest French experiments and a shade before Symington's in Scotland. Rumsey worked on the principle of steam-driven stern water jets. He is said to have tried such a boat on the Potomac in 1786 and 1787; it worked, but then failed. He was constructing a larger one on the Thames when he died in 1792. This boat later made four knots an hour, but was adjudicated not to have fulfilled its contract. Fitch, at Philadelphia, after a proving boat in 1786, built a paddle-wheel steamer that worked in 1787, and a better one in 1788. In 1790 he put a stern-wheeler of six to eight mph on a regular run on the Delaware from Philadelphia to Trenton. It traveled some two or three thousand miles during its life, and came near paying at least for its operation. This was seventeen years before Fulton; but the route was short, for once was paralleled by good roads, and Fitch was a difficult, restless person, who antagonized partners and sponsors. Stevens ran a high-pressure, steam-turbine, propeller-screw boat in New York Harbor in 1802; but American engines being still of bad workmanship, he reverted to low pressure and paddles, and built the famous *Phoenix* in 1808. This was probably as good a vessel as Fulton's *Clermont* of 1807, but Fulton had been given a monopoly of the Hudson River. So the *Phoenix* sailed, timorously and with stops and waits during thirteen days, the hundred and fifty miles from New York to the Delaware—the first steam voyage on the ocean—and ran the Philadelphia-Trenton route from 1809 to 1815.

Fulton came at the critical moment when, after thirty years of experiment, pioneering, and outlay, success was at last around the corner for someone operating in favorable American waters. Fulton had the advantage of knowing nearly all previous inventors, ships, or their plans. He had personality and charm, utilized these to form good connections, as with Livingston; and this connection not only financed him but secured the monopoly of New York State waters. This gave him the straight, deep, well-populated Hudson River, its hundred and fifty miles flanked by hills instead of roads, as a proprietary right of way. His United States patent claims on his steamboats fell to pieces, as they deserved to, because as an inventor Fulton was belated and was more versatile than profound. The *Clermont's* Watt engine was imported bodily from England, and the main reason for her success was the engine. There was then no plant or shop in America that could produce a steamtight engine operating smoothly and reliably: that was Britain's contribution. Fulton had what was worth more to him than an invention—a virtual patent on a great river that nature had made as it were to order for steam transportation. So the *Clermont* finally made money, or convinced investors that steamboats would make money; and therewith the battle was definitely won for the now twenty-odd-year-old invention. By 1811 Fulton had a steamboat on the faraway Mississippi—while the whole of Europe was still in the phase of having given up the problem.

It is clear that in a case like this of the early steamboat, the term "invention," as generally used, includes a mass of factors—economic, geographic, and what not—that have nothing to do with science. Even on the wholly mechanical side, the real problem was the gradual overcoming of a long series of side-issue difficulties, such as perfection of an engine that would not rock or sink the boat, and would not give out. This overcoming of minor obstacles was the actual crux of the invention, and not the imaginatively obvious putting together of one and one to make two. That in fact had been done early in the 1700's, soon after the Newcomen and long before the Watt engine. English patents were granted to Allen in 1729 for a jet-propulsion steamboat and to Hulls in 1739 for a paddle-wheel steamboat.

The question remains: Why the singling out of Fulton from among dozens of competitors as the outstanding hero of the occasion? Why is he the recipient, in American popular history, of from nine-tenths to ten-tenths of the glory, when his intrinsic earned credit, merely as inventor and engineer, could not have been over one-tenth? The basic reason is one we have already encountered (§ 140, 152): that naïve thinking refuses to deal with abstracted, generalizable factors, but demands a personalized, anthropomorphic story. It must be Caesar that wins the battle, not the myriad anonymous legionaries, still less their wholly impersonal armament or drill. So with inventions: an inventor must be found, or fabricated if necessary, on whom the dramatized tale can be hung.

That brings us to the specific question: Granted the emotional need for a hero, why was Fulton selected to be cast for the role? Here the answer is that he was the first obvious success-boy in the story, in a way which a schoolchild, a shopkeeper, and a millionaire could all understand. He did make money, he did make headlines, he did get into the grammar-school histories and the Hudson-Fulton Centenary, and he was a fellow patriot American. So he must have been a great man—which he was; and therefore, folk reasoning runs, he must have been *the* great man, *the* inventor—which he was not.

Underneath this fairy tale, we can see the process of actual invention as something manifold and complicated, with no one individual really dominant, but with impersonal and economic factors like presence or absence of roads influential, reaching down even into geographical conditions, and determining within narrow limits both when and where the invention would become effective. Not that Fulton lacked ability: he had it; but without his predecessors, and Watt's engine, and his social connections, and the gift of the Hudson, most of us would never have heard of him, and the same success story, in only a slightly different version, would have been attached to some other name. Suppose Fulton had died in 1806. Even with nothing more to go on than the facts here skeletonized, we can scarcely doubt that someone else, perhaps Stevens, would in 1808 or 1809 or by 1810, in the United States and almost certainly in the vicinity of New York Harbor, have got far enough to be acclaimed as the finally successful inventor. Or, with some imaginary catastrophe blotting out America, it seems reasonably safe to believe that by say 1815 it would have been an Englishman.

It is in this sense that inventions can be said to come with inevitability (§ 152). Not that their date and place and nationality are predetermined through all time, or are immanent in some great design of world predestination. What is meant by inevitability is that, given enough information on a certain status of a certain culture, it is possible to understand why particular inventions or innovations were made when, where, or how they were made, and not in other times, places, or contexts; and to understand this without denying personality but also without bringing into the argument any unique, God-given qualities of it. With sufficient knowledge, such explanations in social or cultural terms can be reasonably reliable in retrospect.

Predictions before the event would be less certain: first, because the facts of the whole story are not yet in; second, because there is bound to be less perspective and more emotional involvement while matters are still in the making.

186. INVENTORS OF STEAMBOATS

In the last section we have traced the principal factors that entered into the invention and the delayed invention of steamboats. These factors consisted of the antecedent conditions of technology, science, transportation, economics, and even legal and political considerations, such as patents and monopolies. All such factors are historical and are generic conditions; namely, they are or can be viewed as impersonal or superpersonal. Thus, good roads in France, canals in England, both lacking in America; recognized engine-builders in England, none in America; prevalent enthusiasm over the possibility of steamboats in America, equally prevalent skepticism or opposition in England—these are all broader than individual personalities.

However, every cultural step in advance, every move made, had of course to be made by some individual. It is therefore possible, and legitimate, to arrange and view the facts on the history of steamboat invention also as they relate to the individual persons involved. This procedure would mean that we consider what Fulton did, or failed to do, and what qualities in him made him succeed or fail—and the same for Fitch and Rumsey and Symington and Stevens—instead of concerning ourselves, as we have so far primarily done, with national development of canals or skill in engine-building in 1786 or 1806. Let us try this approach and break the larger social story up into smaller ones told in terms of evaluations of the personalities involved.

Fitch was Connecticut farm-bred and uneducated. He was cheated out of learning from his clockmaker apprenticeship, but became a competent silversmith. He clearly possessed mechanical skill and originality, but remained so ignorant that he never knew the reason for his failures or successes, hence was unable to improve his work cumulatively. He was tall, twitching-faced, careless of his appearance, brusque with people, alternating between self-depreciation and boasting. He was unable to inspire the least confidence in Benjamin Franklin. He was thoroughly unsure of himself, and intermittently withdrew from all companionship. He got on well in the Western wilderness and as an Indian captive; one of his few happy periods was in a British prison camp. A thorough Puritan, he ever mortified and humbled himself, and then turned around to assert his claims and to challenge the world. He pamphleteered vehemently against Rumsey. In an interview with Washington, he succeeded chiefly in disconcerting that most just of men. He abandoned wife and child. Bred a Calvinist, he needlessly acquired an atheist's repute, traded his Kentucky lands for an annuity of board and whisky, and committed suicide at fifty-five with hoarded sleeping pills. Kindly at heart and upright, he mismanaged human relations by his fanaticism and lived and died disappointed and embittered. He was obviously a personality that, starting from nothing, could build the first steamboat that ran all summer—and yet fail and die in complete frustration.

Rumsey, a Marylander of Southern ancestry, was blacksmith, miller, housebuilder, and innkeeper until at the age of forty he met Washington and won his confidence for a boat planned to work itself upstream by the force of the current. Steam entered his invention later. He also secured the interest and protection of Jefferson, Franklin, and other prominent men, and was financed in 1788 by a Rumsean Society to push his fortunes in England. There, however, after losing, through suspicion and exorbitance, the chance at an invaluable partnership with Watt's firm of engine-builders, and other ups and downs, he died in debt in 1792. Rumsey was practical and mechanically gifted, but fundamentally an adventurer. He was exceptionally handsome, of distinguished but easy manners, and always made a brilliant impression. Wholly without fanaticism and a thorough realist, he seemed open, but was consistently secretive. A free spender and a gambler at heart, he was at once suave and sharp. His greatest asset was his ability to win confidence—as Fitch consistently failed to do; his drawback, inability to maintain or justify the confidence.

Fulton was born in Pennsylvania twenty-one years after Fitch and Rumsey, was apprenticed to a Philadelphia jeweler, and from that drifted into miniature-painting. At the age of twenty-three, financed by subscriptions, he went to London to make his fortune as an artist, as the great Benjamin West had done before. After half a dozen years, Fulton gave up painting for the invention of canals, submarines, torpedo mines, and incidentally steamboats. He began with grandiose claims and impractical ideas, but had the faculty of correcting his mistakes and profiting from other men's half-successes. He knew Rumsey well and seems to have had some access to the plans or products of nearly all previous steamboat inventors. His technically successful submarine was partly reinvented from Bushnell's of 1776. After twenty years in England and France, Fulton returned to America with a little money, considerable repute, and, most important of all, a superior Boulton and Watt engine that was to make the *Clermont* a mechanical and economic success the next year. He was partner in this venture with the magnate and statesman Livingston, who had got from the New York Legislature the monopoly of state waters when Fitch's permit for them lapsed. Fulton promptly married Livingston's heiress cousin. Fulton's appearance and manners were strongly in his favor. His character was plastic. He always professed ideals and lived up to them as he found it expedient. He had associated long enough with the great to lose any earmarks of the adventurer; in fact he was sent abroad for development of his talent, not as a promoter. He was not spoiled by success but improved under it: he became somewhat haughty but remained kindly and was often generous. Fulton's outstanding qualities were not so much originality as adaptability to situations, adeptness in dealing with people, and interest in feasible results. It is by these primarily social gifts that Fulton finally won out.

Morey, a New Hampshire artisan and a gifted inventor, seems to have built three separate steamboats that ran with paddle wheels—fore, aft, and side—between about 1791 and 1797. His efforts came to nothing because of a fertility of mechanical imagination that led him to turn to other inventions when his steamboat promotion struck economic snags. He was apparently the artist type, so absorbed in working with his own hands as to lack business interest or persistence.

Another mechanic associated with the steamboat was Nicholas Roosevelt of New York City, who in 1794 established in New Jersey the first plant in America for building engines—with the help of former employees of Boulton and Watt. Against his better judgment, he was browbeaten by Livingston into building for him a steamboat operating by a jet propelled from a box by a paddle wheel! It finally ran, but not fast enough; and then Livingston bullied him out of the steamboat game. Evidently Roosevelt was too subservient to his social superiors to succeed even as a contributing inventor.

The Briton Symington was able both as an engineer and as a mechanic, and his inventions worked superbly by American standards, but only moderately well by the more exacting British ones of the time. His noblemen backers therefore cut off support, and with a certain docility Symington switched to other undertakings.

We turn now from men able to use their hands to gentlemen unused to doing so.

Jouffroy was an ancien-régime aristocrat with powerful enthusiasm for a hobby idea, but helpless in the face of initial failure.

Livingston was a grand seigneur who wanted also the fame of being a great inventor. His ideas were visionary, his executions impractical. He really enters the picture because of his partnership with Fulton, to which he contributed money, political influence, and monopoly.

Stevens was another educated rich man untrained with his hands. He and Livingston were brothers-in-law and for a while partners in trying to invent. Stevens had engineering ability, and as we have seen, in 1802 built a boat with high-pressure pipe boilers, steam turbine, and propeller screw. This was structurally the most advanced and perhaps most sound engine yet put aboard any ship, though it failed practically because fittings and packings could not then be made sufficiently tight for high pressure. Had Fulton not just anticipated him with his imported Watt low-pressure engine and monopoly, Stevens would certainly have had vessels running in New York waters within a year or two.

It is evident that a matter like the origin of steamboats can be viewed primarily from the angle of the personalities concerned, if one so wishes. Brief as are the character analyses presented here in outline, they suffice to show essentially in what and why each man failed or succeeded. Viewed as a competition between individuals, the invention of the steamboat makes sense in terms of personal character and psychology; just as, viewed as a piece of culture history, we have seen it to make sense in terms of sociocultural situations, conditions, and antecedents. They are two different sets of interpretations: both significant, but neither excluding the other from being "true." If the aim is psychology and personality understanding, determination of why one individual rather than another in the same society was successful, then examination of the personalities is the obvious approach. If one's interest is in culture, if the objective is to learn why the invention turned up in one society, time, and place rather than in others, then analysis of the essentially impersonal cultural antecedents and factors is evidently indicated.

It is important to remember that both sets of data always coexist in the phenomena. They are necessarily intertwined, because no culture is ever operative except through and in human beings. But human beings also operate or behave only under the influence of some one culture; and their behavior has cultural effect. This inevitable double-faceting of all social or historical phenomena should never be forgotten. Yet this does not mean that as scientists we should forever remain attached to the raw phenomena to the degree that we deal with them only as they occur in mixture. Scientific progress begins with devising methods of separating diverse data and extricating consistent findings out of the welter of confused brute phenomena. It is obvious that to the personality psychologist the segregated line of facts on the involved people, viewed as individuals, must mean more than an analysis in terms of culture situations or history. And vice versa for the anthropologist, for him whose first concern is culture. By comparison a mixed consideration, explaining one event psychologically and the next culturally, necessarily leads to indecisive and ambiguous results. Such an unsegregated approach may be entailed as long as we remain unable to apply differentiated methods to the data. After differentiation is possible, the unsegregated approach is still justifiable literarily, but becomes superseded in culture study as conceptually blurred and increasingly ineffective. It remains an undifferentiated tool.

187. PHOTOGRAPHY, TELEGRAPH, TELEPHONE, PHONOGRAPH

Photography is another of the important arts that was discovered independently by more than one inventor. In this case the necessary antecedent that conditioned the simultaneity was the development of chemistry. Two Frenchmen, Daguerre and Niepce, became associated in the search as early as 1827. Niepce died in 1833, but Daguerre continued, perfected the work, and in 1839 the discovery of photography was publicly announced on his behalf by Arago. In the same year Talbot, an Englishman, announced an equivalent invention, which he had made in principle in 1833. Both processes depended on silver bromide or iodide; but Daguerre's formed a film on a silver plate, was developed with mercury fumes, and yielded a positive, whereas Talbot coated paper with iodide, developed it with gallic acid, and obtained a negative. This diversity of course proves the complete independence of the two inventions.

In the invention of telegraph and telephone, Americans took a leading part, no doubt both because of the longer distances in the New World and of the greater premium on time in daily civilian life—this latter in turn being connected with higher wages and higher cost of living. In theory, the telegraph was invented as early as 1753 by Morrison, an Englishman, immediately after it became known that the static charge of a Leyden jar would flow along a wire. This of course was an "invention" in the same sense as Leonardo da Vinci's airplanes, and many other such "discoveries" that were really only prophecies; but it shows that the basic idea is often the simplest and least important thing about an invention. The familiar hero who gets nearly all the popular credit in this case is Morse, who was a portrait-painter. Returning from England in 1832, and hearing his fellow passengers discuss electricity, he conceived and sketched out his telegraph; but it was 1837 before it was worked out, with the help of two skilled assistants and the writings of a gifted and trained physicist. The latter was Henry, who had prosecuted studies toward a telegraph as early as 1831, and who later engaged in controversy with Morse over their respective parts in the invention. Cooke and Wheatstone patented a telegraph in England in 1837, and Steinheil is credited with relevant findings as to induction in the same year or the next. The contribution that is wholly Morse's, and which in some ways proved of decisive importance, is not the specific instrument or the electrophysics involved, on which others were working, and in which they were probably more competent; it is the dot-dash code, which of course is a quasi-literary device. The practical significance of this Morse code appears in contrast with earlier suggestions or attempts to use pith balls or fluttering papers as receiving signals.

The telephone dates from 1876. Gray filed a United States patent caveat on February 14 of that year, but was anticipated by Bell—by a matter of hours only, according to story. Gray was an American who contributed to the development of the multiplex telegraph. Bell was born in Edinburgh, came to Canada to teach his father's "visible speech" to defectives, went on to Boston, devised his telephone in 1872, and exhibited it at the Philadelphia Centennial in 1876. In his case, it was preoccupation with speech that led to interest in the problem; whereas in Gray's case it was concern with electric message transmission, and the sound reproduction was discovered unexpectedly. The simultaneity was thus a convergence rather than a parallel. But it was probably well-nigh inescapable that this particular invention should be made in the United States. Its enormously rapid adoption there suggests the existence of a latent or conscious demand before 1876 that helped precipitate the invention.

A sort of nonreproducing phonograph—if such could be called a phonograph—was devised in 1857 by Scott, a Frenchman in spite of his name. Twenty years later another Frenchman, Cros, described a recording and reproducing phonograph in a sealed letter filed with the Academy of Sciences. In the same year Edison made a workable phonograph. Being industrial-minded, he did not send a letter to the Academy but got a patent. The records were cylinders covered with tin foil and turned by a foot treadle. It was eight years more before Bell and Tainter devised "wax" cylinders, and yet two more—1887—before Berliner, a German, introduced the first disk record. The chief superiority of the disk however proved to be the incidental one that the sound tracing was now for the first time cut by a sideways motion of the needle, whereas the tracing on the cylinder was a compound of vertical needle motion and of vertical grooving by weight of the diaphragm piece. Modern phonographs thus retain nothing of Edison's original invention except the quite generic idea of the sequence sound-diaphragm-needle-impression and its reversibility. The specific Edison features of foot power, cylinder, tin foil, and vertical groove have all been discarded. Yet Edison remains the inventor justifiably enough, since it was he who first made the phonograph a social fact.

188. THE FIRE PISTON

The fire piston is a device for lighting fire with the heat engendered by the sudden compression of air. This compression is effected by striking a plunger piston into a hollow cylinder. This cylinder must be true, and the piston must be packed airtight and yet move freely. It is also necessary to admit free air to the inflamed tinder as soon as possible after the compressing blow is struck, so as not to suffocate the spark. All this makes a device that is far from obvious. It is hard to believe that any inventor could have first imagined the implement and then have proceeded to work it out. It must have been a by-product of something else.

The distribution is as peculiar as the utensil. It occurs first in and near southeastern Asia from northern Burma to Luzon and the Flores Islands, in at least fourteen different tracts (see Fig. 27, § 234), which however comprise only a small minority of the square miles in the total area. This broken distribution is discussed again in § 234. Second, the fire piston was invented in France early in the nineteenth century and had a temporary vogue in western Europe. It was reported from remote spots in southeastern-Asiatic territory early enough in the nineteenth century so that it could not well have spread from France to there, and only to there, in the few decades intervening. Moreover the diversity of shapes, decorations, and materials is so great as to indicate that the piston must have had several centuries of development in Farther India and Malaysia. For instance, the material varies from wood to bamboo to horn, bone, or ivory to brass, lead, pewter, and lead-lined brass. In reverse, there is nothing to indicate that any knowledge of the East Indian tool had reached France to serve as a stimulus or a suggestion for the invention there.

There are however three other machines known in the southeastern-Asiatic area that are cylindrical and are used to compress air: the blowgun for poison darts, the piston bellows to fan the smith's fire, and a popgun with piston plunger. Moreover, Southeast Asia-Indonesia is one of the only two areas in the world in which the blowgun occurs (the other being eastern native America), and is the center of the single area of dispersal of the piston bellows. A pattern or precedent was therefore given in that region for the compression of air in a tube. Whether it was accident that led to the lighting of tinder, which had been introduced into the cylinder by chance, or whether the noticeable heating of the popgun or repeated use was discovered and tinder then deliberately inserted, no one can say with assurance. But almost surely it must have been one or the other. Moreover, the peoples of the region have evidently been given to playing with fire-lighting in their history, since it is among them that the greatest variety of fire-making methods occurs: the fire saw with rattan, with split bamboo, with rod against rod; the fire drill; and, among culturally related peoples like the Polynesians, the fire plow. We have therefore an attitude of mind favorable both to experimenting in this field and to seizing a workable novelty if luck happened to present it.

In Europe, the fire piston was discovered in 1802, either by a physicist in Lyon operating a compression air pump, or by a workman in an arms factory near Lyon who was charging an air gun—a modern mechanical cousin of the Indonesian blowgun, by the way. This is probably another case of independent and simultaneous invention—which was certainly "on the line" just then, since Dalton only two years before had reported that air was heated by compression. Both the mechanic and the professor, however, were primarily doing other things when they made their observation and succeeded in lighting their tinder. The French invention was therefore clearly a case of accident profitably taken advantage of; and it was independent of the same principle that had been operative in Indonesia earlier.

The European fire piston was used chiefly, as Tylor expresses it, as a scientific toy, or as a demonstration apparatus in the teaching of physics. It was patented in England in 1807; but in no European country was it able seriously to rival in practical use the long-established strike-a-light of flint and steel. Three or four decades later, both were swept aside by friction matches.

This device accordingly illustrates with high probability: (1) invention by "accident"; (2) influence of pre-existing patterns of implements and manipulations; (3) repeated independent invention in quite different sorts of culture; and, quite likely, (4) invention made simultaneously by individuals within the same culture.

189. ZERO

One of the milestones of civilization is the symbol cipher or zero. This little sign renders possible the unambiguous designation of a number of any size with a small stock of figures, and permits arithmetical operations to be made with a minimum of difficulty. It is the zero that enables the symbol 1 to have the varying values of one, ten, hundred, thousand, and so on. In our arithmetical notation, both the number symbol itself and its position count: 1234 and 4321 have different values, although they contain the identical symbols. Such a system is impossible without a sign for nothingness: without it, 11, 101, 110, 1100, and 1001 would be indistinguishable. Our zero, along with the other nine digits and the principle of position value, appears to be an invention of the Hindus approximately twelve or fifteen hundred years ago. We call the notation "Arabic" because it was transmitted from India to Europe by the Arabs. "Zero" and "cipher" are the same word in origin: Arabic *sifr*, "naught," from *safara*, "empty"; the two words reached English respectively through Italian and through Latin and French.

Without a zero sign and position values, two methods are open for the representation of higher numerical values. More and more signs can be added for the high values. This was done by the Greeks and Romans. MV means 1005, and only that. This is simple enough; but 1888 requires so cumbersome a denotation as MDCCCLXXXVIII—thirteen figures of seven different kinds. A simple system of multiplying or dividing numbers expressed like this is impossible. The unwieldiness is due partly to the fact that the Romans, not having hit upon the device of representing nothingness, employed the separate signs I, X, C, M for the quantities we represent by the single symbol 1 with from no to three zeroes added.

The other method is that followed by the Chinese. Besides signs corresponding to our digits from 1 to 9, they developed symbols corresponding to "ten times," "hundred times," and so on. This was much as if we should use the asterisk, *, to denote tens, the dagger, †, for hundreds, the paragraph, ¶, for thousands. We could then represent 1888 by 1¶8†8*8, and 1005 by 1¶5, without any risk of being misunderstood. But the writing of the numbers would in most cases require more figures, and mathematical operations would be more awkward.

A people other than the Hindus who invented a zero sign and the representation of number values by position of the basic symbols was the Maya of Guatemala and Yucatán. Some forms of their zero are shown in Figure 23. This Maya development constitutes an indubitable parallel with the Hindu one. So far as the involved logical principle is concerned, the two inventions are identical. But, as usual, the concrete expressions of the principle are dissimilar. The Maya zero does not in the least have the form of our or the Hindus' zero.

Also, the Maya notation was vigesimal where ours is decimal. They worked with twenty fundamental digits instead of ten. Their "100" therefore stood for 400, their "1000" for 8000.[2] Accordingly, when they wrote, in their corresponding digits, 1234, the value was not 1234 but 8864.[3] Obviously there can be no question of a common origin for such a system and ours. They share an idea or a method, nothing more. As a matter of fact, these two notational systems, like all others, were preceded by numeral word counts. Our decimal word count is based on the number of our fingers, that of the Maya on fingers and toes.

It is interesting that of these two inventions of zero, the Maya one was the earlier. We possess date inscriptions preserved (8:14:3:1:12 and 8:14:10:13:15) in the "long-count" arithmetical and calendrical system of which the Maya zero forms part, which are construed to correspond to our A.D. 320 and 328; and it has been thought that the devising of the system may go back five or six hundred years farther to the third or fourth century B.C. The Hindus seem to have possessed the prototypes of our numerals as early as the second century after Christ, but as yet without the zero, which was added probably during the sixth century—first as a dot, and later as a small circle. The idea of nullity, called *sunya,* "void," seems to have occurred to Hindu mathematicians earlier than a symbol for it.

Incidentally, the priority of the Maya must weaken the arguments sometimes advanced that the ancient Americans derived their higher culture from Asia. If the zero was their own product, why not the remainder of their progress also?

It has only recently become clear that zero as a position numeral was invented a third time, and that the earliest of all. This was in Mesopotamia, among the Semitic Neo-Babylonians, centuries before either Hindus or Mayas. These people reckoned sexagesimally: 60 was their unit of next higher order, instead of 10 or 20 (§ 191). The idiosyncrasy of this system is enough to assure the historical separateness of the Mesopotamian invention. Thus the symbol for 1 might denote 1 or 60 or 3600; or $\frac{1}{60}$ or $\frac{1}{3600}$; and 3 might denote 3 or 180 or 10,800 or $\frac{1}{20}$. How this sexagesimal method came to be developed is not altogether certain. Most likely it was a transfer, to the written numeral designation, from the existing system of measures (§ 191), and especially of weights used for money. In these, a larger unit like the pound or mina or maneh was made to contain 60 shekels, probably because 60 is divisible by 2, 3, 4, 5, 6, as well as by 10, 12, 15, 20. This mensuration and numeration system, as well as the associated cuneiform system of writing, was the product of the pre-Babylonian Sumerians of southern Mesopotamia; and their beginnings can be traced beyond 3000 B.C. However, the Sumerians and the subsequent early Babylonians did not yet work by position in designating numeral values, nor did they feel the need

---

[2] Or 360 and 7200 respectively in calendrical notations.

[3] $(1 \times 8000) + (2 \times 400) + (3 \times 20) + (4 \times 1) = 8000 + 800 + 60 + 4 = 8864.$

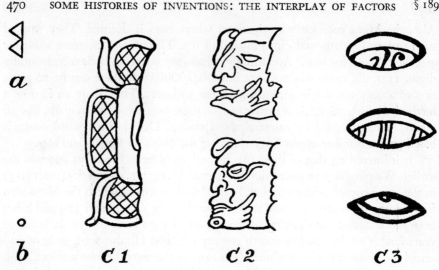

FIG. 23.   ANCIENT SYMBOLS FOR ZERO

a, Babylonian cuneiform; *b,* India; *c,* Maya: *c1,* monumental inscription style, *c2,* face inscriptions, *c3,* written in books.

of a zero symbol. They would write 1 and let the reader guess, or infer from the context, whether 1 was meant or 60. It was not until about the period when Babylon had fallen under the rule of the Persians (528-330 B.C.) that we begin to find documents containing 0: such as 1-0-4, which denotes 3604.[4] The Neo-Babylonian sign for 0 is two adjacent little triangles, one above the other, both pointing left. However, even these late Mesopotamians wrote their zero only when it fell "internally," as in the 1-0-4 just cited—not when it was external, as in our 50 or 770 or 0.3. Thus, to be systematically consistent, they should have written 3840 as 1-4-0 [5]; but actually they wrote simply 1-4, leaving the -0 to be inferred, and failed to distinguish in their representation between 3840 and 64 [6] or $1\frac{1}{15}$.[7] The Neo-Babylonians thus genuinely invented zero, but only half applied it. So it is no wonder they let it slip again, and failed to impart it to other nations or later times. They were in a sense too early to profit much by the invention and make it stick.

This half-success is like the failure of the Maya zero to be taken over by the Aztecs and other nations of Mexico, although the calendar system of the Mexicans has a common origin with that of the Maya and indeed probably was derived from it. Also this calendar system operated somewhat like the Mesopotamian weight measures in providing a scheme of multiplied ranks or orders, which must have gone far to suggest position values for numbers. Thus, much as in Mesopotamia 180 grains made a shekel, 60 shekels a mina, 60 minas a

[4] $(1 \times 60^2) + (0 \times 60) + (4 \times 1)$.   [6] $(1 \times 60) + (4 \times 1)$.
[5] $(1 \times 60^2) + (4 \times 60) + (0 \times 1)$.   [7] $(1 \times 1) + (4 \times \frac{1}{60})$.

talent, so with the Maya 20 days made a "month," 18 months a "year," 20 years a "lustrum" or katun, 20 katuns a cycle. This regularity inevitably engendered habits of designating by position instead of by name, especially when there was abundant numbering or calculating to be done—much as in British bookkeeping with £ s. d. The situations were really quite parallel when a Neo-Babylonian wanted to designate a weight of 2 talents 6 shekels; a Maya, two "years" and six days; or a Londoner, 2 pounds sixpence. And from these situations it is only a step, so far as manner of operation is concerned, to our writing the abstract value 206, or a Babylonian writing his "206" to denote 7206.[8] While we do not know too much about how the Maya carried out their calculatory operations, we can assume as likely that when they wanted to add several time intervals, or when they subtracted one date from another to learn the length of the elapsed period, they put the days, months, years, and so on in columns, one under the other, much, say, as when we want to subtract 206 from 773. Therewith we have what we may call actual "positional operation"; and if there is very much of this going on, it seems likely to tend to force the hand of the operator toward devising some means of designating absence, especially of internal units—of minas or months or shillings or sixties or tens, as the case may be.

Corresponding somewhat to the Babylonian addiction to operations with a multiplicative scale of monetary weight units, and of the Maya with time units, as the antecedents of their respective inventions of zero, is the Hindu use of the ancestral "Arabic" digits from 1 to 9 for several centuries before they added a dot as a sign to denote that a certain position was vacant.

Zero is of special interest because the invention, though repeated, has evidently always been made against considerable psychological resistance. The "natural" or spontaneous thing, after there are signs to indicate each quantity, is not to go on and add one also for nullity, but to let nothing denote nothing. To treat absence of quantity as if it too were a specific quantity, by providing it like the positive values with a symbol, is a tour de force, a highly intelligent thing to do, but a completely arbitrary one. That it is "unnatural" is shown by the fact that nations as culturally developed as Egyptians, Greeks, Romans, Christian Europeans, and Chinese failed to do it for themselves.

On the other hand, the value of the invention is hard to overestimate. Without some kind of a zero, there can be no position numerals, and without these most operations with numbers are tremendously complicated and slowed. It is no meaningless accident that the Greeks were able to develop fully geometry and those branches of mathematics such as conic sections which are derivable from geometry, but remained definitely backward in arithmetic, which we consider merely an elementary-school study. Their reckoning system of letter numerals just made arithmetical computations unpleasantly difficult. And with-

[8] $(2 \times 60^2) + (0 \times 60) + (6 \times 1)$.

out the antecedent of arithmetic, their algebra also developed late and imperfectly.

It will be noted that all three inventions are anonymous. History has not thought it worth while to confer fame in the matter of zero, to preserve or invent a name, to record circumstances or the exact dates. All we know is the inventing people, the era, something of the accompaniments. However, these are known well enough to render it as reasonably sure as such things can be in history that there was no connection or interinfluence between the several cases, but that these represent three genuinely separate inventions made in far-apart countries at intervals of about five centuries, under varying stimuli and embedded in diverse context. Thus:

THE INVENTION OF ZERO

Area	Shape of Symbol	System	Influencing Factor	Date
Babylon	Two triangles	Sexagesimal	Monetary weighing	500± B.C.
Maya	Nucleated lens (shell?)	Vigesimal	Calendar	A.D. 1±
India	Circle (dot)	Decimal	Arithmetic(?)	A.D. 500±

CHAPTER TWELVE

Culture Growths and Spreads

THE LAST chapter outlined the history of some inventions: how they came to be made and how they grew more comprehensive and effective. In the present chapter some further inventions and innovations are considered, this time with special reference to what happened to them as they spread to new peoples or traveled over the world.

With the emphasis put in this chapter on exemplification of the process of diffusion of cultural ideas and devices, which has already been discussed as a principle in § 171-173, it may seem strange that there is so little mention of *migrations* both in those sections and in the present chapter. The reason is that migrations of peoples are a rather special mechanism of cultural spread and not its most frequent means. They form the crass instances of the process, easily conceived by a simple mind. That a custom travels as a people travels carrying it along is something that a child can understand. The danger is in stopping there and invoking a national migration for every important culture diffusion, whereas it is plain that most culture changes from without have occurred through subtler and more gradual or piecemeal operations. The Mongols overran vast areas of Asia and Europe without seriously modifying the civilization of those tracts. The accretions that in turn most influenced them, such as writing and Buddhism, came to them by the quieter and pervasive process of peaceful penetration, in which but few individuals were active. We are all aware that printing and the steam engine, the doctrine of evolution and the habit of rhyming verses, have spread through Western civilization without conquests or migrations, and that each year's fashions flow out from Paris in the same way. When, however, it is a question of something remote, like the origin of Chinese civilization, one need only point out that the early forms of Chinese culture bear certain resemblances to the early culture of Anau or Mesopotamia, and we are sure to have someone producing a theory that marches the Chinese out of the west with their future culture packed away in little bundles on their backs. That is far more picturesque, of course, a more vivid concrete image, than to conceive of a slow, gradual, hesitant, and partial transfusion stretching over a thousand years. In proportion as the known facts are few, imagination soars unchecked. It is not because migrations of large bodies of men are rare or negligible in their influence on civilization that they have been touched so lightly here. In fact, both Americas are overwhelmingly populated today by the descendants of people who immigrated there from Europe. Yet unconsciously we tend to think more exclusively in terms of migrations than the sober truth warrants. It is in culture history as in geology: the occasional eruptions, quakings, and other cataclysms stir the mind, but the work of change is mainly accomplished by quieter processes, such as uplift, erosion, and deposition in geology, or diffusion in culture, going on unceasingly and often almost imperceptibly until their results accumulate.

190. THE DOUBLE-HEADED EAGLE

An unexpected story of wandering attaches to the symbol of the double-headed eagle. One of the great gods of Egypt was the sun. The hawk and the vulture were also divine animals. A combination was made showing the disk of the sun with a long narrow wing on each side. Or the bird itself was depicted with outstretched wings, but with the sun disk constituting its body. These were striking figures of considerable aesthetic and symbolic appeal. From Egypt the design appears to have been carried in the second millennium B.C. to the Assyrians of Mesopotamia and to the Hittites of Asia Minor. A second head was added. Just as a wing and a foot went out from each side of the body or disk, so now there was a head facing each way. This double-headed bird symbol was carved on cliffs in Asia Minor. Here the picture remained, no doubt wondered at but uncopied, for two thousand years. In the twelfth and thirteenth centuries after Christ, Turkish princes of Asia Minor began stamping the symbol on their coins. The later Crusaders brought these coins, or the idea of the pattern, back with them to Europe, where the mediaeval art of heraldry was flourishing. The double-headed bird, now slightly like an eagle, was a welcome addition to lions and griffins. The meaning of sovereignty remaining attached to the figure, the device before long became indicative of the imperial idea. This is the origin of its use as a symbol in the late empires of Austro-Hungary and Russia.

Under Charles V, King of Spain and Holy Roman Emperor of Germany, Cortés and Pizarro conquered Mexico and Peru. On coats of arms and perhaps coins, the double-headed eagle was carried into the New World. Indians became conversant with it and introduced it into their textiles and embroideries: the remote Huichol, for instance. Since no pre-Columbian representation of the two-headed eagle seems to be known from Mexico, this modern Mexican Indian use of the figure probably traces back to an Asiatic origin three thousand years old.

This is one story of the double-headed eagle or hawk. Another is the story of its independent devising—we do not know under what circumstances or how—in the coastal plain of southern Peru in the Nazca culture. The latest possible dating of this culture is A.D. 1000, because several cultures intervened between it and the coming of the Spaniards in 1532. In fact, most Peruvianists put the Nazca period five hundred or more years earlier than A.D. 1000. In any event it is clear that the occurrence can have nothing to do with the Egyptian-Hittite-heraldic-Hapsburg one; it far antedates the Spanish transfer to the Mexican Indians. The Nazca symbol shows the two-headed condor instead of the eagle, and is not an angular textile design but a curvilinear, semirealistic one painted on pottery. Both these minor differences only fortify the case for independence.

This two-sided instance is typical of how culture develops. There is practically nothing in the history of civilization of which we can affirm that it must happen, and which we can therefore predict, except perhaps occasionally on the very threshold of an event. Each case has to be worked out for what did actually happen or is happening; and even with enough ascertained cases in hand, we are able to infer safely no more than generalizations as to tendencies, preponderances, or probabilities. To date, such rigorous laws as are known emanate from the sciences which can conduct controlled experiments.

191. DUODECIMAL AND SEXAGESIMAL MEASURES

A surviving increment of civilization due to the Sumerians of Mesopotamia is a series of metric standardizations. These include the division of the circle into 360 degrees, of the day into 24 (originally 12) hours, of the hour into 60 minutes, of the foot into 12 inches, and the pound—as it survives in our troy weight—into 12 ounces. The system is based on the numbers 6 or 12 and their multiple 60. The weights current in the ancient Near East also increased by 60's. On these weights were based the ancient money values. The Greek mina, Hebrew maneh, approximately a pound, comprised 60 shekels (or 100 Athenian drachmas), and 60 minas made a talent. A talent of silver and one of gold possessed different values, but the weight was the same. This system the Greeks derived from Asia, as evidenced by the borrowing of the names, as well as by close correspondence of the actual weight of the units.

The duodecimal method of reckoning was carried west, became deeply ingrained during the Roman Empire, and has continued down through the Middle Ages to modern times. It would be going too far to say that every division of units of measure into 12 parts can be traced directly to Mesopotamia. Now and then new standards were arbitrarily fixed and new names given them. But even when this occurred, the old habit of reckoning by 12's was likely to reassert itself in competition with the decimal system. Modern coinage systems have become prevailingly decimal, but it is only a short time ago that in Bavaria 60 copper kreutzers made a gulden, and that elsewhere in Germany an imperial thaler contained 30 silver groschen. The 12 pence of the English shilling obviously suggest themselves.

Certain of these metric units became fixed more than two thousand years ago and have descended to us by an unbroken tradition. The Babylonian degrees, minutes, and seconds, for instance, became an integral part of Greek mathematics and astronomy, and thus entered Roman, Arab, and mediaeval European science. When a few centuries ago, beginning with the introduction of the Copernican point of view, astronomy launched forward into a new period of progress, the old system of reckoning was so deeply rooted that it was continued without protest. Had the first truly scientific beginnings of astronomy taken place as late as those of chemistry, it is doubtful whether we should now be reckoning 360 degrees in the circumference of the circle: the decimal system would almost certainly have been applied.

If stress is laid here on names and numbers, it is not because they are more inclined to diffusion, or are most important, but because their diffusion is more easily traced. They sometimes provide an infallible index of historical connection in a deficiency of historical record. If not only a thing but also its name are shared by distinct nations, doubt is removed, since it is obvious that peoples speaking unrelated languages will not coincide one time in a thousand in independently using the same name for the same idea. In fact the name is the better touchstone. An invention may be borrowed and given a homemade name like the English days of the week (§ 197); but a foreign name would scarcely be adopted without the acceptance of the object itself. Much the same obviously holds for sets or combinations of specific numbers.

192. DIVINATION

Another Mesopotamian invention is the pseudo-science of predicting the outcome of events by examination of the liver of animals sacrificed to the gods. A system of such divination, known as hepatoscopy, was worked out by Babylonian priests soon after 2000 B.C. Their rules are known from the discovery of ancient clay models of the liver with its several lobes, each part being inscribed with its significance according as it might bear such and such appearance. This system, or parts of it, were carried to western Asia and Greece, and to the Etruscans of Italy. These last, addicted to priestly magic, practiced this liver divination alongside another method, that of haruspicy or foretelling from the flight or action of birds. Both systems were learned from them by the Romans, according to Roman tradition itself.

With the spread of Christianity, hepatoscopy and haruspicy died out in the West. But meanwhile they had been carried also in the opposite direction, evidently became established in East Asia, and finally, in somewhat modified form, among distant uncivilized peoples. The pagan priests of the remoter interiors of Borneo and the Philippines even today are foretelling the future by observing the flight of birds and examining the gall bladder—an organ intimately associated with the liver—of sacrificial animals. If these primitive Malaysian peoples had always remained uninfluenced by higher cultures, their divinatory customs might be imputed to independent invention. They are, however, known to have been subjected to heavy cultural influences from China, Arabia, and especially India (§ 308). With these streams of culture flowing into the East Indies, the only reasonable conclusion is that the arts of liver and bird divination were also imported. In fact, it seems probable that the broader custom of sacrificing animals to the gods and spirits and of the worshipers then eating the flesh—a custom to which the pagan Malaysians still adhere—is a part of the same wave of influence from the Nearer East that has so deeply stamped the Homeric poems and the Old Testament. Although theoretically it is not surprising that hepatoscopy and haruspicy still flourish among some backward and marginally situated peoples, yet, in the concrete and at first blush, it is striking to find that an institution that was active in Babylonia three or four thousand years ago should still maintain an unbroken life in Borneo. Evidently the diffusion principle reaches far and long.

Another method of foretelling, which has spread equally far, although its flow has been mainly from the East westward, is scapulimancy, divination from the cracks that develop in scorched shoulder blades. This seems to have originated in ancient China with the heating of tortoise shells; at least it is known in detail there from Shang-dynasty times before 1000 B.C. It had spread by the third century after Christ to Japan, where deer shoulder blades were employed, and it is found today among the Koryak and the Chukchi of northeasternmost Siberia, who utilize the same bones from seals and reindeer respectively. Elsewhere domestic animals, above all the sheep, furnish the proper shoulder blade. All the central-Asiatic nations as far south as the Tibetans and the Lolos are addicted to the custom, which had official status with the Mongol rulers in the thirteenth century, but must have been older, since it was reported by the Byzantine Greeks two hundred years earlier as in vogue among some barbarian nations. The practice spread over practically all Europe, where it flourished in the fifteenth and sixteenth centuries and still lingers among belated rural populations; to Morocco and other Islamized parts of North Africa; and in Asia to southern Arabia, Afghanistan, and westernmost India. The European and African practice omits scorching: it observes shape, thickness, or veining of the bone. Scapulimancy was not known to the ancient Mesopotamians, Egyptians, Hebrews, Greeks, Etruscans, and Romans; it seems not to have penetrated far into India and not at all into the countries and islands to the east of India, which are sheepless regions. The custom did obtain a foothold in aboriginal North America, where sheep and other tame animals were not kept. It was practiced, by scorching of moose, reindeer, and other bones, by all the Athabascan and Algonkin tribes of the American transcontinental subarctic coniferous belt, though not by any on the immediate Pacific coast, nor by the Eskimo. In summary, it appears therefore that the custom, after a period of somewhat wavering formation in East Asia, crystallized into two subvarieties. The Western form abandoned the use of heating, and became associated with domesticated sheep, forming an arbitrary complex, and was diffused almost as far as this animal was common. The Eastern form retained the practice of scorching, but at some unknown time it passed to the nonherding hunting tribes living across Bering Strait in northerly America.

193. TRAVELS OF TOBACCO

The speed with which inventions sometimes diffuse over large areas is in marked contrast to the slowness with which they travel on other occasions. The art or habit of smoking originated in tropical America, where the tobacco plant is indigenous. From this middle region the custom spread, like agriculture, pottery, and weaving, in both directions over most of North and South America. Originally, it would seem, a tobacco leaf was either rolled on itself to form a rude cigar, or was stuffed, cigarette-fashion, into a reed or a piece of cane. Columbus found the West Indians puffing at cigars. In the southwestern United States, the natives smoked from hollow reeds. Farther into the United States, both to east and west, the reed had become a manufactured tube of wood or stone or pottery. This tubular pipe, something like a magnified cigarette-holder, has the bowl enlarged at one end to receive the tobacco. It has to be held more or less vertically. This form has survived to the present day among the California Indians. As the tubular pipe spread into the central and eastern United States, it was elaborated. The bowl was made to rise from the top of the pipe, instead of merely forming its end. This proved a convenience, for the pipe had now no longer to be pointed skyward to be smoked. Here, then, was a pipe with a definite bowl; but its derivation from the straight tubular pipe is shown by the fact that the bowl was most frequently set not at the end of the stem, as we "automatically" think it should be in a pipe, but near its middle. The bowl evidently represented a secondary addition which there seemed no more reason to place at the end than in the middle of the pipe; and the latter happened to become the fashion.

All this evolution took place a long time ago. Elaborate stone pipes with animals carved on platforms have been discovered in the earthworks left by the Hopewellian Mound Builders of the Ohio Valley, a people whose very existence had been forgotten when the white men first came. Californian tubular stone pipes occur well down toward the bottom of high shell mounds. Their age must be a thousand years, and may be much more.

Here and there this slow diffusion suffered checks. In the Andean region of South America tobacco came into competition with coca, a plant whose leaf was chewed. The effect of the contained alkaloid is to prevent fatigue and hunger. Of the two, coca triumphed over tobacco, possibly because its action is more druglike. In North America, on the other hand, tribes that had not adopted maize and bean agriculture sometimes tilled tobacco patches. With them, tobacco cultivation had outstripped the spread of so important an institution as food agriculture. In the extreme northern parts of North America, climatic factors checked the growth of tobacco, either wild or cultivated. Where the supply was scarce, it was either diluted with pulverized tree bark, as by many tribes of the central United States, or it was eaten, as by a number of groups on the Pacific coast. These mixed it with lime from burnt shells and chewed or swallowed it. Taken in this form, a small quantity produces a powerful effect. In the farthest north of the continent, even this device had not obtained a foothold. The development of intertribal trade was too slender and intermittent for anything but valuables, let alone an article of daily consumption, to be transported over long distances. The result was that the Eskimo, when first discovered, knew nothing of tobacco.

The use of tobacco was quickly carried to the Old World by the Spaniards, and before long all Europe was smoking. Throughout that continent, irrespective of language, the plant is known by modifications of the Spanish name *tabaco,* which in turn seems based on a native American name for cigar, or perhaps "snuffing tube." By the Spaniards and Portuguese, and later also by the Arabs, the habit of smoking was carried to various points on the shores of Africa, Asia, and the East Indies. Thence it spread inland. Native African tribes, and others in New Guinea, who had never seen a white man have been found not only growing and smoking tobacco, but firmly believing that their ancestors from time immemorial had done so. This is a characteristic illustration of the short-livedness of group memory and the autocentricity of attitude.

In northeastern Siberia, where the Russians introduced tobacco, a special East Asiatic form of pipe came into use. It has a narrow bowl flaring at the top, which, seen from above, looks like a disk with a rather small hole in the center. In profile the bowl is almost like a capital T, set on the end of the pipestem. This stem may be straight or flattened and curved. This form of pipe, along with tobacco as a trade article, crossed Bering Strait—probably carried by the Russians—and was taken up by the Alaska Eskimo. That this pipe is not of Eskimo origin is shown by its close resemblance to the Chukchi pipe of Siberia. The fact that it is impossible for the Eskimo to grow tobacco corroborates the late introduction, as does the Alaska Eskimo name: *tawak.* In short, smoking reached the Eskimo only after having made the round of the globe. Originating in Middle America, the custom spread very anciently to its farthest native limits without being able to penetrate to the Eskimo. As soon as the Spaniards appeared on the scene, the custom started on a fresh career of travel and rolled rapidly westward and northward—Mexico to the Philippines to Fukien to North China to Amur tribes to Russians in Siberia—until it re-entered America in the hitherto nonsmoking region of Alaska.

A second invasion of America by a non-American form of pipe occurred in the eastern United States. The old pipe of this region, as already stated, had its bowl set well back from the end of the stem. The whole object thus had nearly the shape of an inverted capital T, whereas the European pipe might be compared to an L laid on its back. After the English settlers had become established on the Atlantic coast, a tomahawk pipe was introduced by them for trade purposes. This was a metal hatchet with the butt of the blade hollowed out into a bowl that connected with a bore running through the handle. One end of the blade served to chop, the other to smoke. The hatchet handle was also the pipe-stem. The combination implement could be used as a weapon in war and as a symbol of peace in council. The heads of these iron tomahawk pipes were made in England. They became so popular that those Indians who were out of reach of established traders, or who were too poor to buy the metal hatchet-pipes, began to imitate them in the stone their forefathers had used. In the Missouri Valley a generation ago, among tribes like the Sioux and the Blackfeet, imitation tomahawk pipes, which would never have withstood usage as hatchets, were being made of red catlinite alongside the standard, native, inverted-T pipes. One of the two coexisting forms represented a form indigenous to the region for a thousand years or more, the other an innovation developed in Europe as the result of the discovery of America and then reintroduced among the aborigines. Diffusion sometimes follows unexpectedly winding routes.

194. LINTEL AND CORBELING IN ARCHITECTURE

Two principal methods have been followed in the solution of the architectural problem of covering large free spaces. The first is the method of the wall with superimposed roof beams, or column and lintel; the second that of the arch or vault.

Most early architecture developed the column. Even so superb an architecture as that of the Greeks did not grow beyond it. The aesthetic value of the Parthenon lies in the balance and the feeling with which a fundamentally simple and quiet plan has been developed, not in the daring way in which an inherently ambitious engineering problem has been met.

On account of its essential simplicity, columnar architecture grew up among several historically unconnected nations. In some, there can be distinguished an early stage of building in wood when the column was the trunk of a tree, and a later stage in which the post was replaced by a monolith, or by superimposed drums of stone. It has been thought that Greek architecture was derived from Egypt, but there was probably little more than a transmission of stimulus, since Greek temples were wooden-pillared several thousand years after the Egyptians were rearing huge stone columns. Furthermore, if the Greeks had borrowed their column outright from Egypt, they would probably have copied it slavishly at the outset, with Egyptian lotus capital, relief decoration, and the rest. Here, then, there was parallel development, as also in Mexico.

The failure of the Greeks to pass beyond column and lintel architecture may seem strange for a people that showed so unusual an artistic faculty and so bold and enterprising a spirit in many departments of civilization. The cause appears to lie not in any internal arrest of their artistic evolution, but in the conditions that prevailed in another field of their culture: their particularity. The Greek state remained a city. All attempts to establish larger political aggregates, whether on the basis of confederation or of conquest, failed miserably and speedily. The Greek was ingrainedly addicted to an outlook that was not merely provincial but literally municipal. The result was that really large co-operative enterprises were beyond him. Paved roads, aqueducts, sewers, and works of a like character were scarcely attempted on any scale of magnitude. With the rather small numbers of individuals which at best the Greeks assembled in one spot, such works were not necessary. Consequently Greek public buildings were, by the standards of many other nations, mediocre in size of ground plan, low in height, without endeavor to impress by sweep of clear space. This fact illustrates the interconnection existing between the several sides of the culture of any people; it illustrates also the importance of knowing the whole of a civilization, and its basic patterns, before trying to provide an explanation for any one of its manifestations.

The arch is a device for carrying construction over an empty space without horizontal beams. But it may take two principal forms: the corbeled or "false" arch, and the "true" arch. Both are arches in form, but the blocks that form the curvature of one are not self-supporting; in the other they are.

The corbeled arch achieves its span through a successive projection of the stones or bricks that abut on each side of the open space. The stones at the end of the second course of masonry extend part of their length beyond the end stones of the first course. What keeps the projecting stones from toppling into the clear space? Nothing but such weight as is put on their inner or embedded ends. Obviously, there will be more counterweight needed the higher the arch rises. The same principle holds for the vault, which is a three-dimensional, barrel-shaped extension of the flat façade of the arch. The hollow or half-barrel of the corbeled vault has to be flanked or covered by a volume of building material. Hence the clumsy massiveness of, for instance, Maya architecture, which, so far as it employs the vault, often contains more building material than spanned space.

The corbeled arch and vault and dome were independently devised and have also diffused. They were employed in gigantic Bronze Age tombs at Mycenae in Greece—the so-called Treasure House of Atreus—in Portugal, and in Ireland. These developments seem historically connected. On the other hand, the Maya also built corbeled arches, which presumably constitute a separate invention. And there are some hesitating approaches in ancient Peru, which appear to be separate from the Maya cases.

This parallelistic development of corbeling differs from that of the true arch, which seems everywhere to be derived from a single original source.

195. HISTORY OF THE TRUE ARCH

The true arch differs from the corbeled in needing no counterweight. The blocks that form the undersurface or soffit of its span are self-sustaining. The true arch thus yields an aesthetic satisfaction that can be attained in no other way, especially when it soars in magnitude. The fundamental principle of the true arch is the integration of its elements. The constituents fuse their strength. Each block has a shape that is predetermined by the design of the whole, and each is useless, in fact not even self-supporting, until all the others have been fitted with it. Hence the figure of speech as well as the reality of the keystone: the last block slipped into place, locking itself and all the others. The feature of the blocks or voussoirs which makes possible this integration is the taper of their sides. Each is a gently sloping piece of wedge instead of a rectangular block. When bricks replace dressed stone, the mortar takes the place of this shaping, being thinner toward the face of the vault and thicker toward the interior of the construction.

While the exact circumstances attending the invention of the true arch are not clear, the earliest specimens yet found occur in mud brick in the eighth stratum down from the top at Tepe Gawra in northern Mesopotamia, which is of Jemdet Nasr period of the fourth millennium B.C. (see table in § 286). It becomes more common in Sumerian lower Mesopotamia, as at Nippur and at Ur in the period of the Royal Tombs, soon after 3000 B.C. Thence the principle spread over the whole area. The Mesopotamian peoples employed the arch chiefly on a small scale in roofing doors and in tunnels. It remained humble and utilitarian in their hands; its architectural possibilities were scarcely conceived. They continued to rear their monumental structures mainly with an eye to quantity: high and thick walls, ramps, towers ascending vertically or by steps, prevailed.

The true arch and the vault are next found in northern Italy, among a prosperous city-dwelling people, the Etruscans, several centuries before Christ.[1] All through the civilization of this nation runs a trait of successful but never wholly distinctive accomplishment. The Etruscans were receptive to new ideas and applied them with energy, usually only to let them degenerate in the end. Whether they discovered the arch for themselves or whether knowledge of it was carried to Italy from Asia is not wholly clear, since history knows little about the Etruscans, and archaeology, though yielding numerous remains, leaves the question of their origin dim. A number of features in Etruscan civili-

---

[1] The estimates of period vary from the seventh to the fourth century B.C.

zation—such as liver divination—as well as one ancient tradition, connect them with Asia. It is therefore probable that the principle of arch construction was transmitted to them from its Sumerian source—though the route and the circumstances are not positively known. The Etruscans also failed to carry the use of the arch far into monumental architecture. They employed it in tombs, gates, and drains rather than as a conspicuous feature of public buildings.

From the Etruscans their neighbors, the Romans, learned the arch. They too adopted it at first for utilitarian purposes. The great sewer of Rome, for instance, the Cloaca Maxima, is an arched vault of brick. Gradually, however, as the Romans grew in numbers and wealth and acquired a taste for public undertakings, they transferred the construction to stone and introduced it into their buildings. By the time their polity changed from the republican to the imperial form, the arch was the most characteristic feature of their architecture. The Greeks had built porticos of columns; the Romans erected frontages of rows of arches. The exterior of their circus, the Colosseum, is a series of stories of arches. Much of the mass of the structure also rests upon arches, thus making possible the building of the huge edifice with a minimum of material. On the practical side, this is one of the chief values of the arch: it eliminates a large percentage of brute labor. Earlier peoples would have felt it necessary to fill the space between the interior tiers of seats and the outer wall of the Colosseum.

Once the fever of architecture had infected them, the Romans went beyond the simple arch and vault to the dome. Their engineers put domes on their Pantheon, the tomb of Hadrian, and other buildings. In the centuries in which the Mediterranean countries were Romanized, the dome and the arch, the vault and the row of arches set on pillars, became familiar to the inhabitants of the civilized Western world. After Roman power crumbled, the architectural traditions survived. Even when there was decadence of execution and little monumental construction, the principles once gained were never lost.

With the emergence from the Dark to the Middle Ages, architecture in western Europe revived with an application to churches instead of temples, circuses, and baths. In southern Europe adherence to the old Roman model remained close, and the style is known as Romanesque. In northern Europe the Roman principles found themselves on newer soil, tradition bound them less rigorously, and the style underwent more modification. The arch became pointed at the top. Vertical building lines were elongated at the expense of horizontal ones. The dominant effect became one of aspiration toward height. This is the so-called Gothic architecture, developed from the twelfth century on, most notably in northern France, with much originality also in England, and undergoing provincial modification in the various northern-European countries. In fact, the style was finally carried back into Italy, as in the famous cathedral of Milan, to compete there with the Romanesque order.

As an artistic design a Gothic cathedral is as different from an imperial Roman building as the latter is from a Greek temple. Yet it represents nothing but a modification of Roman methods. Its essential engineering problems had been solved more than a thousand years earlier. The effect of a semicircular arch associated with low round columns, and of a high pointed one soaring from tall clusters of buttresses, is almost as diverse as can be obtained in architecture. But so far as plan or invention is concerned, there is no decisive distinction between the two orders.

In the East, Roman architectural tradition was sustained without rupture and even carried forward in the Byzantine Empire. The great church of St. Sophia at Constantinople—Istanbul now—is a sixth-century example of a splendid dome set on four great arches and intersecting with smaller domes at its corners. From the Byzantine Greeks—or Romans, as they long continued to call themselves—and perhaps from the neighboring Sassanian Persians, who had made pointed arches, the principle of arch and dome came to the Arabs when this people underwent their sudden expansion after the death of Mohammed. In many of the countries overrun by the Arabs—Mesopotamia, Syria, Egypt, North Africa, Sicily, and Spain—they encountered innumerable old public buildings or ruins. It was not long before they were emulating these. Fashion did not stand still. The Arab sometimes twisted his columns and bulged his arch to horseshoe shape. But he too added no essential structural element.

Among the countries in which the Arabs built is Spain. Hence their architecture, in the form known as Moorish, influenced that of the Spaniards. The Spaniards in turn carried the style to Mexico; from there it was transported to New Mexico and California, where converted Indians made and laid the adobe bricks of their mission churches according to the plans of the padres. Since the American occupation, the buildings and ruins of the Spanish period have stood out as landmarks and have set the model for a type of architecture: the Mission style, which in essentials is nothing but Spanish Moorish architecture, as this again is only the Arab modification of the Roman original.

Along with Mohammedanism, the Roman-Saracenic architecture spread eastward also to India. In the sixteenth century, Mohammedan conquerors of Mongol origin, known therefore as the Moguls, carved out a great empire in northern India. Prosperity followed for several generations, and its memory was embellished by the erection of notable buildings. Perhaps the most famous of these is the tomb near Agra known as the Taj Mahal. Set in its sunlit environment, built of white marble, and its surface a maze of fret and inlay in polished stone, this structure seems unrelated to the grim, narrow, upward-stretching cathedrals of northern Europe with stained glass filling the spaces between their buttresses. Yet the central feature of the Taj Mahal is a great dome on the identical plan of that of St. Sophia or the Pantheon, and derived from them. What then one is wont to regard as the triumph of Indian architecture is not Indian at all, any more than Gothic architecture had any connection with the Goths. The one is Mohammedan, designed by a Persian or a Turk; the other is French. Both represent the working-out in new countries and in later centuries of an invention the Romans had borrowed from the Etruscans and they perhaps derived ultimately from Mesopotamia. The device diffused from Asia into Europe and Africa and returned after several thousand years, to flourish once more near its source of origin, modified, expanded, and enriched aesthetically.

196. THE WEEK: HOLY NUMBERS, PLANETS, AND ASTROLOGY

The history of the week is a meandering one. Its origins go back to a number cult. Many nations have a habit of looking upon some one number as specially lucky, desirable, and holy, or perhaps unfortunate—at any rate endowed with peculiar virtue or power. The numbers 3 and 7 at once rise to mind, with 13 as unfortunate. But the particular numbers considered mystic are very diverse. Most American Indian tribes, for instance, exalted 4. Seven was devoid of special meaning in Egypt, but it did have such significance in Mesopotamia.

The Mesopotamians, together with the Egyptians, were also the first astronomers. The Egyptians turned their interest to the sun and the year, and devised the earliest accurate solar calendar. The Mesopotamians adhered to a more cumbersome lunar-solar calendar. But they acquired more information as to other heavenly phenomena: the phases of the moon, eclipses, the courses of the planets. They devised the zodiac and learned to half-predict eclipses. It is true that their interest in these realms, at first and for a long time, was not scientific in the modern sense, but sacerdotal and magical. An eclipse was a misfortune, an expected eclipse that did not "come off," a cause for rejoicing. Yet this superstitious interest did lead the Babylonians to genuine astronomical discoveries.

Among these was the observation that five luminaries besides the sun and the moon move regularly across the heavens, visible to the naked eye and independent of the host of fixed stars: the planets we call Mercury, Venus, Mars, Jupiter, and Saturn. This impressive fact must have significance, they felt, and anthropocentrically they found the significance in the influence of these bodies on the fortunes of men. This was the beginning of astrology, which mystics and dupes still practice among ourselves, but which in its youth represented one of the triumphs of civilized knowledge. The planets were identified with gods by the Babylonians, at any rate were named after gods.

After the conquest of western Asia by Alexander in 331 B.C., the Hellenistic Greeks took over the Neo-Babylonian astrology-astronomy, and the two interacted. The distance or order of the seven luminaries from the earth was determined as correctly as was possible so long as it was assumed that our earth formed the center of the universe. Saturn was placed as the most outward, next Jupiter, Mars, Sun, Venus, Mercury, with the moon nearest the earth.

This scientific advance the western-Asiatic astrologers again took hold of and brought into connection with the hours of the day. For this purpose they employed not the old Sumerian division of the day and night into twelve hours—

which had long since passed over to the Greeks—but an Egyptian reckoning of twenty-four. This was possible because later Greek science centered in the Egyptian city of Alexandria.

Each of the twenty-four hours in turn was assigned by the astrologers to a planet in the order of remoteness, beginning with Saturn. As there were only the seven planets, the permutation cycle began over again on the eighth hour, and in the same way the fifteenth and the twenty-second were "dominated" by Saturn. This gave the twenty-third to Jupiter, the twenty-fourth to Mars, and the twenty-fifth—the first of the next day—to the sun. This second day was thought to be specially under the influence of the planet of its initial hour, the sun, as the first was under the influence of its initial hour, that of Saturn. With continuance of the same count, the moon would become dominant of the first hour of the third day, and so on through the repeated series, the remaining planets emerging in the sequence Mars, Mercury, Jupiter, Venus; whereupon, the cycle having been exhausted, it would begin all over again with Saturn's day—Saturday, as we still call it—and its successors sun's day and moon's day.

This was the week as we know it, evolved perhaps somewhat more than a century before Christ in nearer Asia, soon carried back into Alexandria, and there imparted to Greeks, Romans, and other nationalities. By the time Jesus was preaching, knowledge of the planetary week had reached Rome. Less than a century later, its days were being scrawled on walls in Pompeii. In another hundred years it was spoken of by contemporaries as internationally familiar.

197. NAMES OF THE DAYS, THE SABBATH, AND THEIR TRAVELS

As yet, however, the week was more of a plaything of the superstitious than a civil or religious institution; and it was pagan, not Christian. The names of the days were those of the gods the Babylonians had assigned to the planets centuries earlier; or, in the Western world, they were "translations" of the Babylonian god names. The Greeks had long before, in naming the stars we know as Mercury, Jupiter, Venus, substituted their Hermes, Zeus, Aphrodite, for the Babylonian Nabu, Marduk, Ishtar, on the basis of some resemblance of attributes. Thus, Nabu had to do with learning or cunning, like Hermes; Marduk, like Zeus, wielded thunder; Ishtar and Aphrodite were both goddesses of love. The Romans, in turn, "translated" the Greek names into those of their divinities Mercury, Jupiter, Venus, which survive for instance in French *mercre-di, jeu-di, vendre-di.*

In the passing on of the week to the Germanic barbarians, still another "translation" was made, to Woden, Thor, Frija, whence English Wedn-es-day, Thur-s-day, Fri-day. It is true that these northern gods were not equivalents of the Roman ones, but that mattered little. The reckoning of the week was growing in frequency, and some sort of familiar and pronounceable names for its days had to be found among the new peoples to whom it spread. So a minimum of resemblance between two deities answered for an identification. Moreover, the ancients, because they believed in the reality of their gods but not in the infinity of their number, were in the habit of assuming that the deities of foreign nations must be at bottom the same as their own. Therefore a considerable discrepancy of attribute or worship troubled them no more than the difference in name.

For the days of the week, then, which the public came more and more to deal with, these translations were made. Astronomy, however, was in the hands of the learned, who knew Latin; and hence scientists still denote the planets as Mercury, Venus, and so on, instead of Woden and Frija.

Jesus observed the Sabbath, not Sunday, which he was either ignorant of or would have denounced as idolatrous and polytheistic. The Sabbath was an old Hebrew institution, a day of abstention and cessation from labor, evidently connected with the Babylonian Shabattum. These Shabattum were the seventh, fourteenth, twenty-first, twenty-eighth, and also nineteenth days of the month, the first four probably having reference to the phases of the moon, and all five being "days of rest of the heart," inauspicious for undertakings, and therefore unfavorable for work. They were thus tabooed, supramundane days, and while their recurrence chiefly at seven-day intervals, like that of the Jewish Sabbath, provided a sort of frame for a week, this week was never filled in in Mesopotamia. The influence of the Babylonian-Hebrew Sabbath on the development of the week was chiefly this: it provided the early Christians with a ready-made habit of religiously observing one day in seven. This period, coinciding with the seven-day scheme of the week that was coming into use among pagans, ultimately reinforced the week with the authority of the church.

Christianity however felt and long resisted the essential paganism of the week. The Roman Catholic Church in its calendar recognizes the Lord's Day, the second to sixth days, and the Sabbath, but none named after a heathen god. In Greece the influence of the Orthodox Church has been strong enough to establish a similar numbering in civil life; and the Slavic nations, also mostly Orthodox, follow the same system except that our Monday is their "first" day and they close the week with Sunday.

Sunday, instead of Sabbath-Saturday, became the religious day of the week in Christianity because of the early tradition that it was on this day that Jesus rose from the dead. An unconscious motive of perhaps greater influence was the desire to differentiate the new religion from its Sabbath-observing mother religion, both in the minds of converts from Judaism and in the opinion of the pagans. The Romans for about a century confused Jews and Christians, no doubt to the irritation of both.

Meanwhile, the pagans themselves, perhaps under the influence of the popular sun-worshiping Mithraic religion of the second and third centuries, had come to look upon the sun's day instead of Saturn's as the first of the week. At any rate, in A.D. 321 Constantine ordained "the venerable day of the Sun" as a legal holiday from governmental, civic, and industrial activity. Constantine

perhaps issued this decree as high priest of the state religion of the Roman Empire, but he was also the first Christian emperor, and his action must have been
wholly acceptable to the church. Before long, Church and State were in accord
to discountenance work on Sunday; and thus Christianity had adopted the
heathen planetary week in all respects but the names of its days. Protestantism
finally withdrew even this barrier and accepted the planet-god names that had
so long been popularly and civilly established.

The Mohammedan week is that of Judaism and Eastern Christianity, and
was taken over bodily from one or the other of these religions. Sunday is the
"first" day, and so in order to Thursday. Friday is "the meeting," when one
prays at the mosque, but labors before and after, if one wishes. And Saturday is
"the Sabbath," though of course without its Jewish prescriptions and restrictions.
The Arabs have spread this form of the week far into Africa.

But the planetary week of Babylonian-Greek-Egyptian-Syrian origin spread
east as well as west and north and south. It never became so charged with
ritual meaning nor so definitely established as a civil and economic institution
in Asia as in Europe; but it was used astronomically, calendrically, and in divination. By the fifth century, it had been introduced into India. For a time after
the tenth century, it was more used there in dating than among European nations. Again "translations" of the god names of the planets were made: Brihas-
pati was Jupiter, and Brihaspati-vara Thursday.

From India, the week spread north into Tibet, east to the Farther Indian
countries, and southeast to the Malay Peninsula, Sumatra, and Java. In the
former lands, it was employed in calendrical record, as well as for fortune-telling;
among the Malaysians, chiefly astrologically, with preservation in strongholds of
relict Hinduism like Bali (§ 230), but partial supersession elsewhere by Mohammedan forms.

This history of the week is one of the more striking instances of institutional system diffusion. An ancient western-Asiatic mystic valuation or magical
cult of the number 7 led on the one hand to an observance of taboo days, on the
other to an association with the earliest astronomical knowledge, polytheistic
worship, and divination. A European people learned the combination and built
on it for further scientific progress, only to have this gain utilized for new playing by the astrologers. The planetary week, the permutation of these mathematical diviners, was reintroduced into Europe and became connected with the
calendar and civil life. Christianity recontributed the old idea of regularly recurring holy or taboo days. Mohammedanism took over this concept along with
the period, but without the polytheistic and astrological elements. East Asia, on
the other hand, was chiefly interested in the latter. With us, the significance is
becoming increasingly economic and social. Names have changed again and
again, but their very variations evidence their equivalence. About two thousand
years from its definitive establishment, the institution of the week has by now

spread over the whole earth, for even China and Japan have accepted it secularly along with the Western calendar. The planetary week provides a neat case of a systemic pattern as discussed in § 132.

198. DIVERSE ORIGINS OF OTHER KINDS OF "WEEKS"

Contrasting with the single history of the specific seven-day planetary week is the independent development of other periods, signalized by divisions of the lunar month or by markets or by supernumerary days. Such "pseudo-weeks" have sprung up in many parts of the world, independently but only partially parallel. They have no specific content or associations built up into a system with recurrent names. Consequently, if their several occurrences were connected, this fact would be difficult to trace. Except for such as characterize a limited or provincial area, their instances appear to be unconnected: they express some astronomical, mathematical, or psychological fact, or an economic reflection, not a genuine system-pattern growth.

For instance, a ten-day period, apparently having reference to the beginning, middle, and end of lunation, was more or less recognized in ancient Egypt; ancient Greece; parts of modern central Africa; China, Japan, and Farther India; and Polynesia. No historical connections are known between the customs in these regions; their official and religious associations are everywhere slender, and intervening nations either employ other periods or none at all. It looks, therefore, as if these might be cases of true independent origin or parallelism.

Regular market days among agricultural peoples have frequently led to a reckoning of time superficially resembling the week. Thus, in central Africa, south of the sphere of Islamic influences, markets are observed by a number of tribes. Most frequently these come at four-day intervals. Some tribes shorten the period to three days or lengthen it to five. Six-, eight-, and ten-day periods appear to be doublings. The fairly compact distribution of this African market week points to a single origin. The early Romans observed a regular eighth-day market and semiholiday. This might be connected with the African institution, but cannot be historically linked with it.

In the less advanced populations of Farther India and in many of the East Indian islands, even as far as New Guinea, fifth-day markets are common. The entire tract has many internal culture connections, so that within its limits diffusion has evidently again been active.

In ancient America, markets were customary every fifth day in Mexico, every third day in Colombia, every tenth day in Peru. These variable American instances establish beyond serious cavil that some of these "market weeks" are truly independent local evolutions. For it is only the idea, the outline of the institution, that is similar; its concrete cultural execution, as expressed in the length of the period, differs in Asia and Africa, and in the three American regions. That the Mexican and southeastern-Asiatic weeks were both of five days means nothing but the sort of coincidence to be expected when the choice of duration is limited to a small range, such as between three and ten days.

Finally, there is a correspondence between the Egyptians and the Mexicans in recognizing the solar year as composed of 360 + 5 days. The Egyptians counted the 360 in twelve months of thirty days, the Maya and the Aztec in eighteen groups of twenty days; both agreed in regarding the five leap days as supplementary and unlucky. This last fact looks like a close correspondence, but analysis dissolves much of the likeness. The solar year consists of 365 days and a fraction. There is nothing cultural about that phenomenon except its recognition, and careful observation continued for a long enough period inevitably yields that. But 365 is indivisible except by 5 and 73; 360 is much "rounder"; that is, divisible by many numbers, and these "simple" like 6, 10, 12, 18, 20, 30, and therefore easier to operate with. This again is a mathematical, not a cultural, fact. As to the five leftover days being considered unlucky, that is unquestionably cultural; but it cannot be construed either into a generally valid law or into a historical connection. The ancient Hindu calendar, being directly lunar, had about twelve days left over each solar-year end at the winter solstice: these twelve were looked upon as prophetic and portentous, but not as specifically evil. The Persian and Armenian calendars, seemingly derived from the Egyptian, had the same five supplementary days. But in the former the first of its five is reckoned as lucky, only the third as unlucky; and in the latter, none of the five has any special value or observance. Our own twenty-ninth of February is supplementary and we hold a half-serious pseudo-superstition in regard to it and its year.

In short, the human mind may attach some sort of unusual value to any day in the calendar that is in any way peculiar. This observation is a psychological one, and could be predicted from what is known of the principle of association in individual psychology. When it comes to the cultural expression of this psychological tendency, regularity ceases. The special days may be lucky, unlucky, or indifferent. Their value varies because there is no specific cultural common origin or historical connection.

199. PAPER AND PRINTING

The story of paper and printing is a tale partly of invention, partly of amplifications and improvements, partly of diffusion—but at different rates, and with strange starts and checks. Paper was invented as a material for writing, and its primary function is still to carry visible words, though it has achieved a variety of other uses in both the Orient and the Occident. Printing, a means for mechanical reproduction of writing, serves two purposes: multiplication of copies, or authentication of them—ensuring that they are correct. The latter motive was to the forefront in the first Chinese grapplings with the problem.

And authentication still remains an active aim in certain special situations, such as the printing of paper money.

It is curious that the original basic inventions of printing and its main accessories were all made long after the true alphabet was in existence, but in a culture that did its writing by a form of the older mixed or phonetic-ideographic method: Chinese. Whether this is a coincidence—that is, one of the accidents of history—or whether there was an inverse causal relation, is not altogether clear.

Paper is a virtual prerequisite to printing of the manifolding or multiplicative type, in that it fills the need for a material which is both serviceable and cheap. The ancient Chinese scratched their writing on strips of palm leaf or on harder materials like the famous oracle bones of An-yang (§ 299). Around 220 B.C. a new script came into use: the Lesser Seal; the characters were written with a new quality of stroke. The new quality was due to their now being painted, with a "hair pen" or brush, instead of being cut. This new method rendered finely woven silk cloth—necessarily silk in China, which otherwise had only hemp fiber, and neither cotton nor linen—a splendid material, and it came into occasional use; but of course it was far too costly. Attempts were evidently made to utilize silk waste or scrap; and by the beginning of our Christian era something like an expensive near-paper of silk fiber was in production. The famous invention of true paper, of shredded rags and nets and bark and hemp fibers, is the one conventionally attributed to Ts'ai Lun in A.D. 105. This was a great boon to a nation of littérateurs and archivists, and its use spread rapidly. Paper estimated to have been fabricated within a half-century of the invention has been found preserved in arid northwestern China, at Tunhuang in Kansu, and a piece dated within about another century (A.D. 264) has been preserved in East or "Chinese" Turkestan.

The westward march of paper has been traced in detail. Regularly, it would first be imported as a luxury novelty, then in increasing quantity, until it became a need. Within one to three centuries, introduction of local manufacture usually followed. Here is an outline of the successive stations reached by the art of making paper:

DATES FOR PAPER MANUFACTURE

    105. "Invented," China
  (264. In use in Sinkiang, Chinese Turkestan)
    751. Samarkand, Russian (then Arab) Turkestan
    793. Baghdad, Iraq
  c.900. Egypt
 c.1100. Morocco
 c.1150. Mohammedan Spain
  1189. France
  1276. Italy
  1391. Germany
  1494. England (introduced after printing)
  1690. Philadelphia

For the repeating of writing, the earliest devised mechanism is the seal, a flat or cylindrical surface cut with the inscription or the symbol of a name, for stamping or rolling impressions. Seals are very early in the Near East. They occur in Mesopotamia and the Indus Valley as early as the devising of any writing, if not before; at any rate by 3000 B.C. Strangely enough, seals are very late in the Far East, where printing was ultimately to originate. Their first mention in China is only in 255 B.C., when writing had been in use well over a thousand years. Thereafter they came into more general use; but for a long time this was confined to impressing clay: seal-stamping with ink was six or seven centuries in developing. All sealings anywhere were originally marks of validation or authenticity; mostly they remain so today. They are like trademarks on the one hand, like signatures on the other. Many ancient kings, especially outside of China, probably could not write: their orders were therefore validated by their seal. Whoever got a king's seal away from him was on the fair road to successful revolution.

The seal thus first defined an individual or an authority; its use as a labor-saving device, or for economical, rapid reproduction, was not thought of for thousands of years. The first large-scale reproduction of a body of writing, other than by individual copying by hand, occurred in China. This was some four-odd centuries after seals began to be used there, and it concerned the great classic books of the country. These were carefully cut on stone slabs and set up publicly so that any scholar might bring his handwritten copy and compare it for correctness. It need hardly be pointed out that, with continual recopying of manuscripts down the generations, early errors tend to be perpetuated and new ones to be introduced, and that mistakes thus accumulate. The purpose of these inscribed slabs accordingly still was authentication of what Confucius and the other sages of the past had really said. However, within a generation after setting them up, by about A.D. 200, the Chinese found that if they pressed moist paper against the slabs and into the grooves or cuts of the inscribed characters, and then slid an ink pen smoothly over the paper so that it blackened the surface but did not enter the countersunk strokes of the writing, they got a reversed, white-on-black, exact copy or impression of the text on the stone. They really were almost printing, though they did not know it because they were not yet thinking in terms of manifolding for the public.

The step of multiple production in quantity was first taken not by high scholars but by eager missionaries of religion, Taoists and Buddhists, who were competitively spreading their faiths among the unlearned masses. In the 500's and 600's after Christ, prayers and charms were manifolded for this pious, humble public, large parts of which could not read but would therefore all the more prize possession of a parcel of holy words. The Taoists fell back on seals, which they now made large and cheaply, of wood. The Buddhists used not only seals but small rubbings, on the principle of those of the scholars, pouncing stencils, and even printed cloth. From these it was only a step to block prints, and a step involving no radically new methods. Block prints are smooth slabs of wood, usually from pear trees, of the size of the page or two pages desired. On these a flimsy transparent sheet of writing is placed, to show through in reverse. The background of the block is then cut away, leaving the strokes of the characters projecting. These are inked; and paper is then laid on the block, usually being patted down with a brush to ensure even contact. It is not pressed with a lever or a machine as in the Western printing press. When enough impressions have been made, another block is treated the same way, to make page 2—or pages 3 and 4—of a book. It is plain how close the technique is in all essentials to the classic slab-rubbings of five centuries earlier. The wooden blocks are smaller and much cheaper to cut, but this is a difference only of degree; and the characters are now cut in right-to-left reverse; and in the main the change is one of purpose; from authenticity to multiplication—from aristocratic to democratic motivation.

The date of the first block prints may be estimated as some time not long after A.D. 700; the time is not known exactly because the blocks do not represent a cardinal invention, but were slid into, as it were. We do know this: that by 770, they were being used in Japan, which of course had got them from China. In that year, more than a million copies of a one-sheet Buddhist charm of about 150 characters were printed in the island empire by order of the Empress Shotoku. The language was Sanskrit, the writing Chinese. Probably very few laymen in Japan, and only some priests, could actually read and understand this Sanskrit imprint. But its words were very sacred and desirable, and to have it manifolded was a deed of merit that would prolong the life of the Empress. We know about it because several copies were preserved and still exist.

The oldest whole book extant is nearly a century later (868). It is the Buddhist *Diamond Scripture,* printed in China, and found in the ruins of Tunhuang, Kansu. It undoubtedly had predecessors that did not get preserved. About the same time (883) printing is mentioned in the literature of the day. Szechwan in the far interior is referred to as the center and perhaps the origin of the industry, and some secular as well as popular religious books were being issued. Within another fifty years the whole series of Chinese literary and historical classics were being issued under the sponsorship of Fêng Tao, at the capital Sian, beginning in 932.[2] About the same time, paper money was being issued in Szechwan by a number of banking families; and by 970 the printing of this "convenient money" had become an imperial privilege. For more than four centuries the Chinese used paper money, now and then yielding to the temptation of a loose press and running themselves into an inflation. No other mediaeval country followed them in this practice more than transiently; they were perhaps either not advanced or not stable enough. The Mongols in Persia

---

[2] Not all the printing was now classical. Beginning in 972, there was a 130,000-page edition of the *Three-Basket* scripture, the Buddhist *Tripitaka.*

tried paper currency, and so did the Japanese; but both soon withdrew their issues. Besides Marco Polo, seven other late-mediaeval Europeans reported home about the Chinese printing of money, which evidently impressed their imaginations. But not one of them had anything to say about printed books, which in the years before 1440-50 were equally lacking among their countrymen. Possibly the European travelers were so overawed by the strangeness of Chinese script that they failed to distinguish between its handwriting and its printing. Or perhaps they knew, but the demand for books was still so limited in Europe that the possibility of their cheap mass production did not appeal to the travelers as being so interesting or important as the making of money out of paper.

Some three centuries after block printing began, the Chinese developed printing with movable types. This is accredited to Pi Sheng, 1041-49. He molded his types of clay and baked them to pottery. To assemble them he set them up on a gum base within an iron frame. Later the types were cast of tin, with holes through their bases by which they were wired together and held in a frame of pottery. Still later, bronze and lead were experimented with as type metals; and there was also a reversion to wood. In the far northwest, at Tunhuang, wooden types of about A.D. 1300 have been found preserved, each of which prints a whole word, although the words are Uigur Turkish and are spelled out in alphabetic letters! These word types are a strange hybrid, among a neighbor people, between page-size blocks and loose types for single characters. It is evident that the whole process of printing with separate or movable types had a fluctuating history in China. Types never did supersede printing from whole-page units, which in fact retained its ascendancy; whereas in Europe ten years sufficed to tip the balance decisively in favor of the loose types. The primary reason is that Western alphabets have only about 25 letters, but a font of Chinese characters sufficient for books contains thousands of different characters. The initial outlay in equipment therefore is relatively enormous in China; in the long run only the state has been able to afford good type printing. Private shops found it cheaper to hire skilled labor to cut blocks page by page as they went along. The Japanese never used movable types at all, except between 1596 and 1629—which means that they either temporarily learned from the Koreans, or bodily stole their types from Korea when they were invading that country in 1592-98.

Another difficulty was that the most satisfactory single types were of metal, and this did not print well with the water-and-lampblack ink which the Orient remained addicted to because it worked well both with wooden blocks and for handwriting. Europeans got in the way of using oil ink about the time they began to make metal types. This is a satisfactory combination, and we still use it.

The one successful and large-scale employment of movable and distributable types in the Far East was in Korea. Following the expulsion of the Mongols from China by the Ming rulers, the Koreans also acquired a new and vigorous dynasty, which signalized its prosperity and nationalism by having a great font of sand-cast bronze types of Chinese characters set up in 1403. Some of these types are still in existence, and so are some of the books printed from them. In 1484 and 1770 new fonts were cast; and in 1662 the Imperial Manchu government of China did Korea the honor of imitating it, making a fine metal font by the Korean process, primarily for the printing of an encyclopaedia. There is likely also to be a connection of attitude and motivation between the Korean type-printing activity of 1403 and the devising of the native Korean true alphabet in 1446 (§ 221). At any rate, both have to do with writing, were nationalistically colored, and were inspired from above.

The diffusion of the art of papermaking took nearly eleven centuries to traverse its country-by-country course from China to Europe. Block printing appeared in the West six centuries and type printing four centuries later than in China. Were they also diffused from China? For block printing the answer is almost certainly Yes; for type, a hesitant Not proven.

We have seen that by A.D. 900 Egypt was making its own paper. From 1200 on, for about two centuries, Egypt was block-printing little one-page charms; books were not printed anywhere in Islam until many centuries later (§ 172). There was a resistance to printing because Mohammed had not authorized it, and there was an especial fear of impiety if the Koran were printed. But these cheap little charms, of which several have been preserved, were amulets, not literature, and it probably seemed immaterial whether they were written by hand or pressed off a block. And from 1307 we have an Arabic description of the method of Chinese printing. Thus the process was known in Islam, even if not used seriously.

Around 1350, as nearly as can be estimated, single-sheet block prints began to be made in Europe; the earliest datable one preserved happens to be from 1423. These prints are devotional. Their specific content of course is different from the Arabic Egyptian ones; but the general idea and nature are similar; and they overlap in time. It is reasonably certain that they represent an adapted imitation of the Egyptian precedents, as these were imitated from China. There is the more reason to believe this because printed playing cards, which are first mentioned in China in 969, suddenly appeared four centuries later (1377-79) almost simultaneously in several European countries—Spain, Italy, and Germany; and incidentally, they were accepted with unbounded enthusiasm. Geographically, either the Mongols or the Mohammedan nations might have been the transmitters to Christian Europe; but since Islam forbids all gambling (§ 172), it left no evidence if it was involved: transmission would have been black-market and off the record if it did occur. More likely, travel between the several Mongol overlordships or khanates was the medium of transmission.

After about 1400 there was evidently a growing public in western Europe that wanted to read a great deal but could not afford enough hand-copied books.

The block-printers undertook to supply this demand, and in the decade from about 1440 to 1450 had begun to provide a number of block-printed books, in addition to their single-sheet, posterlike ephemeral products. Type printing is so much more effective with alphabetized languages that once it was developed around 1450, it quickly killed off the older block method.

The conventional name, date, and place for the invention of type printing are: Gutenberg, about 1450, at Mainz. But there is much dispute about every detail: the people who knew most about the event were trying to keep it a trade secret. There is no direct proof whatever of connection with China or of derivation from it. Carter, on whom the present account is chiefly based, weighs the possibility of derivation from China, but ends up with a verdict of no direct evidence. Nevertheless, Pi Sheng's four hundred years of priority over Gutenberg, coupled with the fact that paper, block printing, and playing cards did travel all the way across Asia into western Europe, keep the suspicion alive that somehow, underneath the incomplete record of history, something of the idea of separate, single-character types was also transmitted; enough, at any rate, to give Gutenberg or his predecessors the assurance that their problem of invention was soluble because it had previously been solved, though so far away that they did not know the precise method. In short, European type printing was a reinvention; but it is not certain whether the reinvention was wholly independent or was induced by subsurface stimulus diffusion (§ 154). How the latter might have operated is plausibly suggested by Hudson. It was not Pi Sheng's Chinese type of bygone centuries that Gutenberg would have heard of, but the molds for casting type which the Korean royal printery had developed successfully and on a large scale only some few decades before. The khanates into which the Mongol Empire of Jenghis had broken up stretched from the near-confines of Korea to the Grand Duchy of Moscow; and, say at Kazan on the Volga, a Tatar caravan trader, or possibly a Russian escaped from slavery in the Far East, might easily have met a German Hansa merchant and conceivably have told him about books marvelously made from movable foundry-cast types. Routes of communication that could *not* have been followed in a diffusion are more certain than those which might have been. The Mohammedan phobia against printing of books blocked out the Islamic lands; and direct connections by sea between Europe and China were not established until the next century.

The invention of printing took like wildfire in Europe. For more than a century the compact, narrow frame of High Mediaevalism had been ready to burst by internal growth of European civilization. People wanted wider horizons, a chance to learn and explore, fuller knowledge and new ideas. Books that private citizens could hope to afford to own went far toward filling this need. Within twenty-five or thirty years the invention of book-printing had been taken up even in the remoter European countries like Poland, Spain, and England; and Greek and Hebrew books were being issued. A little later copyright was instituted in Venice, then in France, and elsewhere. Within about a century semibarbaric Russia was printing. From there on the development is familiar.

200. THE FLYING GALLOP

The flying gallop is the name given to a way of representing in art a horse or other quadruped running at full speed. The front legs are stretched out together forward, the hind legs similarly extended back almost horizontally, with the soles of the hoofs vertical, or even up. No horse ever actually assumes this position or one like it, in a gallop or in any other gait: the motion camera has put that beyond dispute.[3] In fact a horse that somehow got itself into flying-gallop posture would either fall or have a bad spill when its legs reached the ground again. The position is therefore a wholly conventional or symbolic one, used in art because of its suggestion of great speed. Its objective falsity was no bar to its acceptance by artists, because the human eye and brain are not quick enough to "freeze" most of the shifting positions of the legs of a running animal.

In fact, nearly all the gallop postures in nearly all arts—until the cinema came to the rescue—are visual lies. This makes their history interesting. Being inventions of unrealities, we can trace their genealogies. If they corresponded to reality, they might derive anew from that, every so often, instead of being, as unrealities, obvious imitations of other artists' unrealities. The belief that geese hatch from goose eggs can hardly have its first origin run down because the actual observation is constantly repeated. But the mediaeval belief that geese hatch out of barnacles is such a fantastic unreality that all versions of the story may safely be considered as deriving from one original invention.

The most common method of picturing a running animal, the world over, is with its hind legs on the ground, the front legs either pawing the air in a somewhat bent position, or stretched forward. This is a rearing or prance, like that of a goat when it is rising to stand up to butt. Something like this prance is momentarily assumed when a horse is about to leap over a hurdle; but it would completely interfere with a gallop. A running horse (Fig. 24a-e) does the very reverse of what the prance suggests: it gives its final push off the ground for its spring through the air with one and then the other of its *fore-feet*, and lands first on its hind legs (Fig. 24a).

This landing position is the only one revealed by the camera that any art has managed to use. Its earliest known appearance is in Greek coins from

---

[3] A greyhound and a deer at full speed do momentarily assume a position something like that of the flying gallop. But they are light animals, and their foot sequence in galloping is "rotary," instead of "transverse" as is that of horses, cattle, and most other mammals.

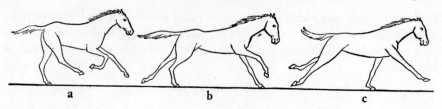

a   b   c

FIG. 24 *a-e*.   CAMERA VIEWS

The five basic positions: *a*, alighting from leap on a hind leg—the only actual posi
cessive pushing forward; *d*, the final spring or push with front leg; *e*, the horizontal leap,

Corinth. Phidias then popularized it (Fig. 24*f*), and it had a vogue alongside
the prances in the best Greek period; but then it got rarer, and from about
A.D. 200 on it disappeared from Greek, Roman, and Western art. The usual
representation of this posture by the Greeks was with the body and neck of
the animal rising, as if it were loping in a slow canter, or were being pulled
back in its pace; whereas the actual running horse has its back level and its

f

FIG. 24 *f*.   AN ART REPRESENTATION
WHICH IS TRUE TO LIFE

From the Parthenon frieze, Phidias: corresponding to 24*a* in the leg positions, though the
horse is checked back or reared too much.

neck stretched. It was probably this effect of checking or slowness that caused
the later Greeks and Romans to abandon again the depiction of this one posture of the gallop that really occurs.

Following Mesopotamians, Egyptians, and Greeks, the Romans, Byzantines,
peoples of the Middle Ages, Renaissance, and Modern times (Fig. 24*g-l*) until
the nineteenth century, all used only one or the other form of the prance; although the masters in more recent centuries, such as Raphael, Leonardo,
Rubens, Velásquez, usually concealed the monotony of this stance by favoring
foreshortened views of their animals (Fig. 24*k*).

The flying gallop has an entirely separate history. It appears full-blown in
the Minoan art of Crete and the derived Mycenaean art of the mainland, of say
1600-1100 B.C (§ 293), and is therefore pre-Greek (Fig. 24*m-n*). This art was
interested in vehemence and rapidity; the device of stretching out the body
and the limbs is evidently the result of this inclination: the posture suggests
the speed of flight. The flying gallop did not get adopted into the main current

d   e

OF RUNNING HORSE

tion caught by artists' eyes, and used by Phidias, but lost again by later artists; *b, c,* suc-
all legs off the ground and gathered under.

of Greek art, which really began pretty much over again centuries later than
Minoan-Mycenaean art, with quite crude, stiff, and static forms.

Next we find this same flying gallop, and other contorted animal postures,
in Scythian and Siberian art. The Scythians lived in the steppes of the Ukraine,
where they had trading contacts with Greek cities on the north side of the
Black Sea. They were mainly a horse-riding pastoral people, not skilled in the
arts, but often wealthy; and from the sixth century B.C. on, they fancied luxury

g   h   i

j   k   l

FIG. 24 *g-l.*   THE PRANCE—AN UNREAL INVENTION BY ARTISTS

The prance has been favored in most art to represent running. It does not actually
occur in the gallop, but is the take-off for clearing a hurdle. *g,* ancient Egypt; *h,* Assyria;
i, Mediaeval France; *j,* Giotto, Italy; *k,* Raphael; *l,* Vernet, early 19th-century France.

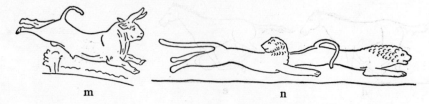

m   n

FIG. 24 *m-n*.   THE FLYING GALLOP—ANOTHER INVENTION OF AN
UNREALITY

It appears first in Minoan-Mycenaean art. Though unnatural, it does suggest speed
of motion. *m*, bull, *n*, lions: Vaphio and Mycenae.

products of foreign manufacture, among which occur the flying-gallop examples.
There is a time gap here, since by the sixth century Minoan-Mycenaean art
had been extinct in its homeland for half a millennium. But it is probable, or
possible, that certain of its traditions had been carried to the Black Sea and survived there, and that the flying gallop, appealing to the horse-loving barbarians,
got preserved in articles made for them, or imitated by them. The alternative
would be to assume that the flying gallop was independently reinvented by
the backward nomadic Scythians only five hundred years later and five hundred miles away from the seats of the technologically skilled Mycenaeans. The
lapse and the distance are somewhat short in the vista of culture history, and
the circumstances unfavorable, to make an independent recurrence seem
likely, as compared with a transmission and carry-over of which the actual
record happens not to have been preserved.

From the Ukraine, this Scythian style with the flying gallop spread to
Hungary; to the Goths who at various times ranged between the Baltic and
the Crimea; to the Caucasus and the Caspian Sea; and to southwestern Siberia
(Fig. 24*o*), where a related art maintained itself long after the Scythians were
extinct, in fact until around A.D. 500. From this general region our device was
communicated to Sassanian Persia (226-641; Fig. 24*p*); all earlier Persian art
lacks the device, as did the Assyrian and Greek arts by which Persian art was
influenced. A farther spread was to China, where depiction of the flying gallop
had become installed by terminal Han times, in the second post-Christian century (Fig. 24*q-r*). The Han dynasty repeatedly sought Western connections,
especially in order to obtain heavy cavalry horses from Ferghana in modern
Soviet Uzbekistan, so that an avenue was open for import of the stylistic
influence.

The Chinese, and following them the Japanese, adopted the flying gallop
in their art and have kept it to the present time, though it was not their only
method of representing running animals. Also, in conformity with the bent
of their styles, the Chinese and Japanese gallop is mostly not very much stretched

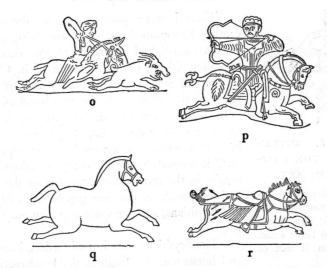

FIG. 24 *o-r*.   INTERNATIONAL TRAVELS OF THE FLYING GALLOP

o, Early Siberian art; *p*, Sassanian Persia; *q*, Han China; *r*, T'ang China. (Note stirrup in *r:* it is one of the earliest pictures of a stirrup, soon after 600 A.D.).

—the legs flex more than elsewhere; but the hind hoofs leave no doubt as to
what it is.

This diffusion to China and Japan was the last but one of the travels of the
flying gallop. In 1794 it suddenly appeared in an English engraved print of a
race horse by Stubbs, followed three years later by a woodcut in the *Sporting
Magazine*. It was about twenty-five years more before the new posture made
its way into British high-art oil painting. This timidity of acceptance shows that
it probably was popular and aristocratic predilection for horse-racing in England, and not any aesthetic originality of its academic painters, that led to the
innovation's being made in Great Britain. In France, where thoroughbred track
racing was first introduced from England
in 1781, the painters were more receptive:
the first examples of the flying gallop in
sketches date only from 1817; but within
four years Géricault established it in exhibited art with his Epsom Derby—painted in
England (Fig. 24*s*). The flying gallop soon
overshadowed or crowded out the older
rears or prances, except in equestrian statues, where contact with the ground was
necessary for support. In Germany the flying gallop seems first to have been sketched
as late as 1835, and painted in 1840.

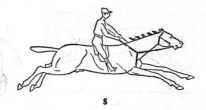

FIG. 24 *S*.   THE FLYING GAL-
LOP BREAKS INTO EUROPEAN
ART

From Géricault's 1821 painting of
the English Derby.

**FIG. 24 t. INFLU-
ENCE OF THE CAM-
ERA ON ART**

The painter's eye be-
gins to borrow from the
photographic film. From
Morot's 1886 battle scene.
The position is that of
24*e*.

There is some question whether the nineteenth-century European depiction of the flying gallop represents an original invention of this deceptive but appealing falsity, or an imitation of it. Chinese ceramics and other works of luxury and art had been reaching the West freely for two hundred and fifty years before 1794, so that European eyes, especially the eyes of overseas-trading Englishmen, may have become gradually accustomed to the representation until it seemed "natural" enough to adopt. The two breaks in the record, for singleness of the invention and its spread, are the time gap between Mycenaeans and Scythians, and the space gap between China and England.

The Scythians were horse-breeders, horse-milkers, and horsemen; the English, the horse-racers par excellence of modern times. These orientations probably had something to do with the parts of both in the story. This would be so equally whether the role of the two far-separated nations was that of being alert to receive an innovation or that of making it.

The history of the flying gallop was as brief in the Occident as it was long in human civilization. In 1879 Muybridge made his famous photographs (see Fig. 24*a-e*) of horses in motion—on soil that is now part of the Stanford University grounds—a sort of nonreproductive pre-cinematograph. Within seven or eight years, in 1886, the Frenchman Morot first portrayed in a painting the four-legs-gathered-under leap through the air of the actual running horse (Fig. 24*t*, corresponding to 24*e*). This soon became standard in art, and we now see it as natural. But it is interesting that this posture is copied from the camera film: the unaided human eye had not been able to extricate the position from out of the whirl of four legs.

FIG. 24 *u-v*. THE BUSHMAN EYE AND A FAST CAMERA

Bushman painting of galloping cattle (*v*), compared with position of racing horse from a newspaper photograph (*u*). This actual position falls between basic 24*b* and *c*. The Bushman eye may have been quick enough to seize the position—or the likeness may be a coincidence.

Did the Bushman eye seize what all civilized eyes failed to seize? Reference now is not to the all-legs-gathered-together position, but to another posture momentarily occurring in the gallop: one foreleg pointing out forward and most the weight of the body on the other, as in Figure 24*u-v*. Or is this just a coincidence, or randomness of representation, which the Bushman stumbled on in varied attempts to indicate speed and vehemence, without having actually seen it thus?

201. NEW GODS TO THE KOTA

In South India, interdigitated on the Nilgiri plateau, live four unlettered tribes, Toda, Badaga, Kota, and Kurumba. Though outside the recognized Hindu caste system, they might be called castes except for speaking different Dravidian dialects or languages. The polyandrous Toda are buffalo dairymen with elaborate rituals. The Badaga, much the most numerous of the four, are mainly farmers. The Kota are artisans and musicians; the Kurumba, jungle dwellers and hired sorcerers. The Kota live in seven separate villages. Each village has three associated little temples—not much larger than shrines—for a trinity of gods: father, mother, and younger brother.

In each Kota village these gods have the same names and parallel, though separate, shrines, priests, and rites. Each trinity is served by a priest—or sometimes two: there may be a separate one for the goddess. These priests conduct the appropriate rituals. The shrines are also oracles, where the gods answer questions of public welfare or private import. They do this by speaking to the assembled villagers through the mouths of their diviners. These diviners shake convulsively while possessed. Whether consciously or unconsciously, they behave as if in a trance. There is one of these potential "mediums" for each god. This makes four or five religious officials in each village: one or two priests and three diviners. All these ministrants are men, but none may be widowers. The offices are not inherited. Instead, they are believed to be bestowed by the will of the gods. When a priest dies or retires, the village assembles at the stated time, a diviner shakes and becomes possessed of his god, and in this condition takes hold of a man and leads him forward: this man becomes priest. When a diviner's position is vacant, there is a similar assembly, at which after a while one or more men begin to shake; that one who first dances up to a certain post and touches it in his trance is believed elected by the god to be his new spokesman. We have here, then, a well-established Kota religious institution, seven times manifolded, apparently functioning steadily, and with a specific mechanism for smooth self-renewal.

Now let us get acquainted with some personalities that were to be influential when change of institution came to Kolmel, one of the seven Kota villages.

First was Kakn, a man not outstanding except for his perfect love for and memory of ritual. He could always help out when others bogged down in ceremony; in this he was distinctive and for it he was appreciated. He was not specially bright; when opinions differed, he was likely to have his way by sheer tenacity and shouting.

Next, Kusvain was shiftless, poor, unstable, and not respected. He had once been a diviner, and as such held a certain status and power in the village; but on his wife's death, he had had to resign as no longer eligible.

Third, Sulli was the government schoolteacher and the only Kota who spoke English and could read. He came of an exceptional ancestry. His grandfather was the first Kota to replace his thatch roof by tiles, his father, the first to own a horse. The utility of these innovations was probably slight for any Kota, but their prestige value was great—perhaps proportionate to the shock they caused the Kota community. Sulli showed his radicalism as a boy by insisting on becoming a Christian. This would not do at all, and the Kota rescued him by force from the missionaries. But Sulli did go to school, and learn English, and become in many situations the mediating link between his people and the British Raj; all of which enhanced his sense of importance and success. He remained a consistent agitator for reform, particularly on specific points that seemed symbolic of Kota inferiority: long hair, prolonged childbearing taboos, meat-eating, and serving as professional musicians. To Sulli, these were stigmata of group inferiority, which the Kota in their provincialism did not feel as such, or at least accepted without shame; but Sulli's contacts were wider and he did feel shame and inferiority.

Here, then, we have a little society with a stable, well-adjusted culture, and within it one man who was comfortable with what the culture gave him and therefore conservative about it; another weak and unstable, without fixed direction, and out of the one status job he had once had; and a third whose prestige and success had been wrung from his reluctant society by innovations of the culture's value standards. That is the setting. Now for the drama.

In 1924, an epidemic struck the Kota. Kolmel village, the hardest hit, lost the majority of its population, including both its priests and all three of its diviners. During the epidemic, the dead were cremated without stinting the customary expensive ceremonies. Sulli suggested unritualized burial as an expedient alternative; but there was no disposition to listen to any proposal of change, in spite of all the suffering and cost. At the first village assembly after the plague, there was no priest to officiate, no diviner to transmit a god's will or to select a new priest, no one to indicate by his shaking that the possession of divination was coming on him—not one person left to administer the extant paraphernalia and rules of the worship or its orderly succession. Only a woman, Nidj, an accepted diviner for ghosts, but too defiled by her sex to be entered by a god, began to tremble and come forward at the assembly. Evidently she was tempted by the opportunity of the gaping vacancy before her to aspire to more than any Kota woman had yet been allowed to attain. But the innovation was too shocking. Magaly, a headman and friend of Kakn, told her to stop, then took a stick and beat her away.

Soon after this annual assembly, which was the standard time for filling vacancies among priests or diviners, another ineligible offered himself. Perhaps he had needed time for his ambition to come to a head, for a way to suggest itself to him. It was Kusvain, former diviner, but debarred by the death of his wife. He began to tremble and talk. But the voice was not that of one of the old village gods. It was the voice of a god Ranga worshiped by civilized Hindus near the foot of the Nilgiri plateau. And it announced, conveniently enough, that until shrines had been built for him and one male and one female associate, there would be no priests or diviners for the three old gods. This was radical procedure, relegating the immemorial gods to second place, and unheard-of. And Kusvain was so little respected in his own person as to be a poor medium for a god's will when that will was so upsetting. No one was convinced; the message went unheeded. Only Sulli, the professional reformer, urged acceptance of the revelation.

But when the next god assembly rolled around, it was nearly a year and a half since Kolmel had had officiants for its deities, and the need was dire. So when the Hindu god Ranga again announced through Kusvain's mouth that shrines for new gods must precede priests for the old, the villagers began to yield. Kakn the conservative led the resistance; but when Kusvain in trance seized hold of a red-hot iron and challenged him to do likewise, Kakn was forced to desist. Kusvain led the villagers to a site where the new god commanded his shrine to be built, and ordained the offerings. These were coconuts and plantains of the lowlands—now obtainable because a railroad had climbed the Nilgiri plateau; they were to be presented on brass platters before lamps such as are usual in lowland Hindu temples. Then two more men began to shake and announced themselves as mouthpieces of the Hindu goddess Betdamn and deity Rama. One of these, like Kusvain, was a former diviner unfrocked by the loss of his wife and thus ineligible to be spokesman for the old gods. So new shrines were erected—somewhat poorer than the old ones, but sufficient for worship. Then at last Kusvain's prophecy came true. With the invading gods satisfied, the old ones finally spoke again from out of shaking men who became their present diviners, and who led forward new priests to serve the old gods as before.

Now Kusvain's poor judgment led him too far. His god ordered the group of new-god diviners and priest to dress themselves like the higher-caste Badaga and go to the neighboring Badaga to demand tribute for the new worship. However it might be with the deities, to the Badaga this was just insolence coming from low-caste Kota. A mob formed and mauled the delegation—all except Kusvain, who promptly fell back on his usual weapon of the possession trance; this religious state was respected by the Badaga. Among the Kota at large, even conservatives like Kakn resented this assault on their tribal dignity. All Kolmel boycotted Badaga festivals. More beatings brought in the police, and the incident was finally closed by the Badaga's paying a token fine for violence committed, but no tribute to the gods of the low-caste.

This settlement, however, allowed disunion among the Kota to rearise, and the conservatives, led by Kakn, once more expressed their dissatisfaction freely. Some of them, now that they had their accustomed old gods back and functioning, refused to have anything to do with the new. Thus, fourteen years after the epidemic, the new cult was firmly established; it too had become a custom— for the majority. Yet a minority had deliberately dropped off again. These were mostly elderly men; and unless they managed to gain adherents also among the young, time was against them: their side was scheduled to die off first. However, the new deities still enjoyed the lesser prestige: they were almost bound to stand lower, with two of their three diviners disqualified from acceptance by the traditional gods. But though it might be a bit second-rate, the new cult seemed secure in Kolmel, as another item of general Hinduism diffused to the backward Kota. Whether from Kolmel the cult would spread to the six other Kota villages; or whether it would remain the local uniqueness of one village to puzzle the historian of custom some centuries from now; or whether, indeed, when the prime movers Sulli and Kusvain have passed on, the uniformizing inclinations of the other Kota villages might not undermine the Kolmel aberrancy and lead to its being allowed to lapse—on all this only the future can pronounce.

In terms of culture history the episode boils down to a small piece of diffusion, partly and perhaps permanently successful against definite resistance, but with the specific import made to conform at most points with the existing pattern. It may be doubted whether the epidemic had broken down Kota faith in their religion. But the unprecedented death at Kolmel of all their functionaries at once had left them at a loss how to start the machinery running again. As a group, they were paralyzed for action. That gave one of them a personal chance, which he would otherwise not have had. Debarred from reattaining the one status he had ever possessed, Kusvain invented a new god who did accept him. Sulli gratified his own compulsion toward reform at all costs by supporting the religious claims of Kusvain, for whom as a fellow citizen he felt only contempt. The puzzled villagers finally assented: not because they thought the new gods better or finer, but because the modest demands of these seemed, in their bewilderment, to be the condition of getting the old ones back. Kakn, proud of his part in the old worship, saw no chance for glory in the new. So he resisted stubbornly, conceded when he had to—red-hot iron is very real to a stable, practical man—but fell off again as soon as he could. The individual motivations are highly personal, selfish if one will, but thoroughly human and intelligible. Kusvain, Sulli, Kakn, all manipulated their culture for their personal ends, to satisfy inward drives and pressures of which they were largely unconscious. Even the woman Nidj tried, but against too great a handicap.

These personal participations in an act of culture change accordingly were personally motivated, not culturally motivated. We may assume they always are largely so. But our episode is also typical in another way. In manipulating their culture for their personal ends, the participants often produce a cultural effect that may be enduring, as well as attaining their individual goal or tension reliefs. And yet because they have been conditioned by and molded in their particular culture, whatever kind or degree of change they may accomplish in it is bound to remain overwhelmingly within the system of basic patterns of that culture. There may be new specific gods, shrines, priests, and offerings at Kolmel, but they remain gods, shrines, priests, and offerings: even to trinities, prostrations, trance utterances, and other quite precise details of established Kota pattern. And such innovations as are accomplished—what are they: products of wholly unbound imagination by the manipulators? No; they are likely to be liftings from the culture of the adjacent lowland or whatever other region: spreads of institutions existent and ready-made. Or if they are not bodily imports but are internal in origin, the alterations consist of a development, a carrying-on further, of potentialities resident or implicit in the existing patterns of the home culture.

The whole process—fairly transparent in a select, incisively analyzed, microcosmic episode like this Kota one, but enormously complex for the important swings in a great civilization—the whole process is essentially double conceptually, though the phenomena coexist in undifferentiated association. If we are interested in persons and personal motivations, we can follow out the interplay of these, viewing the culture only as a starting point and a limiting frame—as before in regard to the invention of steamboats—and construing the cultural effects essentially as by-products of interpersonal activities. Yet if we are interested primarily in social man and his accomplishments, we can take the motives, needs, and tensions of individual men and women for granted as more or less constant and familiar antecedents. We can direct our attention to the interrelations of the forms and values and patterns of the culture involved in the given situation. There is no clash, no conflict, between the two approaches. Each gives a clear picture, a coherent understanding, consistent in terms of itself, on its own plane. The one level is oriented toward psychology and biography and social relations, the other toward anthropology and culture history—or philosophy of history, if one will. Nor are the planes intrinsically unrelatable. There is every reason to believe that they can gradually be brought into increasing correlation: theoretically, culture is ultimately reducible to psychology as psychology is reducible to physiology. But to have such a correlation really meaningful involves our first understanding personality and its mechanisms as such, and culture and its mechanisms as such. To force insistence on the correlation so long as our concepts of personality and of culture remain mixed and blurred is a short-circuiting. Through prior ability to deal with our phenomena in two ways and to interpret them doubly—as physics and chemistry have done in their field—there should result a deeper ultimate understanding of the relation of the two sets of interpretations.

CHAPTER THIRTEEN

Story of the Alphabet

THE ALPHABET is a tightly knit system, as systems are defined in § 132. It is highly specific in both form and function. Invented only once, it has traveled all over the world, displacing all other writing systems but the Sinitic. More exactly, it is the altered derivatives of the original alphabet that have had this spread. The alterations are partly due to the recurrent need of fitting old alphabets to new languages with different sounds, or of keeping them fitted as languages change. But transformations have resulted also from the desire to differentiate or to simplify, to reform or to preserve, to embellish calligraphically or to get by sloppily, from stylistic fashion and from mere wear and tear. The history of the alphabet thus illustrates at one point or another the principles of basic invention, supplementary invention, diffusion, acceptance, refusal, modification, survival, loss, patterning, and function—and the interweaving of all these. It illustrates these interacting mechanisms with unusual clarity because as a system it is as limited as it is definite, and because its high specificity usually allows connections between deviant alphabets to be traced with confidence even across the gaps in recorded history. At the same time the story with all its ramifications is a coherent unit: as much so as the story of, say, the evolution of mammals. It is presented here as one of the most precise chapters in the international history of civilization.

The first four sections give the foundation of other methods of writing on which alphabetic writing was reared. These sections (§ 202-205) are schematic— logico-analytic. The remaining sections (§ 206-221) are actual history with commentary of interpretation.

202. KINDS OF WRITING: PICTOGRAPHIC AND MIXED PHONETIC

Three stages are logically distinguishable in the development of writing. The first is the use of pictures of things and actions, and, derived from these, pictorial symbols for qualities and abstractions. This is the pictographic and then the picto-ideographic method. In the second stage the representation of sounds begins, but is made through pictures or abbreviations of pictures; and pictures or ideographs as such continue to be used alongside the pictures whose value is phonetic. This may be called the mixed or transitional or rebus stage. Third is the phonetic phase. In this, the symbols used, whatever their origin may have been, no longer denote objects or ideas but are merely signs for sounds— words, syllables, or the elemental letter sounds.

The first of these logical stages, the picto-ideographic one, has generally been assumed to flow spontaneously out of the human mind. This assumption is unproved. Many cultures have got along without efforts at any graphic representation, and some even without graphic symbolism. All we can honestly affirm is that if a culture had the habit of drawing pictures, especially schematic pictures, and then came to feel some need of communicating information to a distance or to the future, it would presumably have evolved a more or less standardized pictography as its first halting step, and then a more elaborate and more symbolic picto-ideographic system as the first full method of writing.

The second or transitional stage makes use of the principle that pictures may either be interpreted directly as pictures or can be named. A picture or suggestive sketch of the organ of sight may stand for the thing itself, the eye. Or the emphasis may be on the word "eye," its sound; then the picture can be used to represent that sound even when it has a different meaning, as in the English pronoun "I." The method is familiar to us in the form of the game which we call rebus, that is, a method of writing "with things" or pictures of things. The insect bee stands for the abstract verb "be," two strokes or the figure 2 for the preposition "to" or "too," a picture of a house with the sign of a tavern— that is, an inn—for the prefix "in-," and so on. This charade-like method is cumbersome and indirect enough to provide the difficulty of interpretation that makes it fit for a game or a puzzle. But what to us, who have a system of writing, is a mere sport or occasional toy is also the method by which peoples without writing other than pure pictography made their first steps toward the writing of words and sounds. The principle of reading the name instead of the idea of the thing pictured is therefore a most important invention. It made possible the writing of pronouns, prepositions, prefixes and suffixes, grammatical endings, articles, and the like, which are incapable of representation by pictography alone. There is no difficulty in drawing a recognizable picture of a man, and two or three such pictures might give the idea of men. But no picture system can express the difference between "a man" and "the man." Nor can relational or abstract ideas like those of "here," "that," "by," "of," "you," "why," be expressed by pictures of their meanings.

203. DEFICIENCIES OF TRANSITIONAL SYSTEMS

Important, therefore, as the invention of the designation of words or sounds was, it was at first hesitant, cumbersome, and incomplete as compared with alphabets. For one thing, many symbols were required. They had to be pictured with some accuracy to be recognizable. Thus, to go on with our fictitious English-language exemplifications of the type of problem facing some ancient people groping its way toward script, a picture of a bee would have to be made with some detail and care to be distinguishable with certainty from that of a fly or a wasp or a beetle. An inn must be drawn with its sign or shield or some clear identifying mark, else it is likely to be read as house or barn or hut or shop. The figure of the human eye is a more elaborate character than the letter I. Then, too, the old pictures tended not to go out of use. When the writing actually referred to bees and inns and eyes, pictures of these things continued to be written and read as pictures. The result was that a picture of an eye would in one passage stand for the organ and in another for the personal pronoun. Which its meaning was had to be guessed from the context. If the interpretation as pronoun fitted best—for instance, if the next character meant "tell you"—that interpretation was chosen; but if the next word was recognized to be "brow" or "wink," the character would be interpreted as denoting the sense organ.[1] That is, the same characters were sometimes read by their sense and sometimes by their sound, once pictographically and once phonetically. Hence the rebus system was really transitional or mixed, whereas an alphabet, and a true syllabic system, both of which represent sounds only, are unmixed or pure in principle. Owing to the paucity of sound signs at first, the object or idea signs had to be retained; after they were once well established, they continued to be kept alongside the sound signs even after these had grown numerous.

The tenacity of most mixed systems is remarkable. The Egyptians early added word signs and then syllable and even elemental sound signs—pure letters in the strict sense—to their object signs. After they had evolved a set of letter signs for the principal sounds of their language, they might perfectly well have discarded all the rest of their hundreds of characters, as has been discussed

---

[1] Context is also the usual mechanism for distinguishing words in spoken language, such as *pine* (tree) and *pine* (languish), or *like* (love) and *like* (similar). But in face-to-face communication supplementary words, gestures, answers to questions, and so on are available in addition to context, whereas they are usually not available for written words.

in § 155. But for three thousand years they clung to these multiple characters, and wrote pictographic and phonetic characters jumbled together. They would even duplicate to make sure: as if we should write e-y-e and then follow with a picture of an eye, for fear, as it were, that the spelling-out was not sufficiently clear. Actual and translated cases of this method of "overinsurance" of writing have been shown in Figure 20, § 155.

From our modern point of view it seems at first quite extraordinary that the Egyptians should have continued to follow this plan a thousand years after nations with whom they were in contact, Phoenicians, Hebrews, Greeks, Romans, were using simple, brief, accurate, pure alphabets. Yet psychologically of course they were only following the grooves of crystallized habit, as when we write "weight" or "piece" with unnecessary letters, or employ a combination of two simple letters each having its own value, like *t* and *h,* to represent a third simple sound, that of *th*. With us, as it was with the Egyptians, it would be more of a wrench and an effort for the adult generation to change to new and simpler characters or methods than to continue in the old cumbersome habits. So the advantage of the next generation is stifled and the established awkward system goes on indefinitely—if indeed habit allows the awkwardness to come to public consciousness at all.

204. ABBREVIATION AND CONVENTIONALIZATION

This mixture of pictographic and ideographic with phonetic characters, and its long retention, were substantially as characteristic of Sumerian-Babylonian cuneiform, of Chinese, and presumably of Indus Valley and Maya writing, as of the Egyptian. In all these systems there was more or less tendency to abbreviate the pictures, to contract them to a few strokes, to reduce the original representations to conventional characters. Cuneiform and presumably Chinese underwent this process early and profoundly. In Egyptian it also set in and led to hieratic and later to demotic cursive script, which consist of signs that are meaningless to the eye, although they resolve into standardized reductions of the pictures which during the same period continued to be made in the monumental and religious hieroglyphic. Such conventional abbreviations made possible a certain speed of production, rendered writing of greater use in business and daily life, and thereby contributed to the spread of literacy. In themselves, however, they introduced no new basic principle.

In addition to this conventionality of form of characters, there is to be distinguished also a conventionalization of meaning that is inherent in the nature of writing. Conventionalization of form accompanies frequency or rapidity of writing, conventionalization of meaning must occur if there is to be any writing at all. It must develop in pure nonphonetic pictography if this is to be able to express any considerable range of meaning. An outstretched hand may well be used with the sense of "give." But the beholder of the picture writing is likely to interpret it as "take." Here is where conventionalization is necessary: it must be understood by writers and readers alike that such a hand means "give" and not "take," or perhaps the reverse, or perhaps that if the palm is up and the fingers flat the meaning is "give" whereas the palm down or the fingers half-closed means "take." Whatever the choice, it must be adhered to; a standardized, conventional union of form and meaning now exists. That is why one customarily speaks of "systems" of writing. Without the system, there can be not even picture writing, but only pictures, whose range of power of communication is far more limited.

When the phonetic phase begins, conventionalization of meaning is even more important. An inn must be distinguished from a house by its shield or signboard, a house from a barn by its chimney, and so on. The shield will perhaps have to be exaggerated to be visible at all, be heart-shaped or circular to distinguish it from windows, and so forth. So with the phonetic values. A syllable like English *per-* might be represented by one scribe by means of a cat with a wavy line issuing from its mouth to denote its *purr;* by another by a *pear;* by a third, by something that habitually came as a *pair,* such as earrings. Any of these combined with a *sieve* symbol would approximately render the word *perceive.* But someone else might hit upon the combination of a *purse* and the setting sun at *eve.* Obviously there has got to be a concordance of method if anyone but the writer is to read his inscription readily. This correspondence of representation and interpretation is precisely what constitutes a set of figures into a system of writing instead of a puzzle.

205. PRESUMPTIVE ORIGINS OF TRANSITIONAL SYSTEMS

For such a set concordance to grow up among all the diverse classes of one large nation would be very difficult. In fact, it is likely that transitional systems of writing have usually originated among small groups with common business or purpose, whose members were in touch with one another, and perhaps sufficiently provided with leisure to experiment: colleges of priests, government archivists, possibly merchants with accounts. It is also clear that any system must reflect the culture of the people among whom it originates. The ancient Egyptians had no inns or purses, but did have horned serpents and owls. Still more determining is the influence of the language itself, as soon as writing attempts to be phonetic. The words expressing *pair* and *sieve* are obviously something else in Egyptian than in English, so that if these signs were used, their sound value would be quite otherwise. Yet once a system has crystallized, there is nothing to prevent a new nationality from taking it over bodily. The picture values of the signs can then be wholly disregarded and their sounds read for words of a different meaning. Or the sounds could be disregarded, but the idea value of the characters be carried over into the other tongue. Thus the Semitic Akkadians or Earlier Babylonians and the Assyrians took the cuneiform writing from the Sumerians, whose speech was wholly distinct; and later it was transferred to the Hittites, whose language is now known to have been allied to Indo-European.

It is also well to distinguish between such cases of the whole or most of a system being taken over bodily, and other instances in which one people may have derived the generic idea of the method of writing from another and then worked out a system of its own (§ 154). Thus it is hard not to believe in some sort of connection of stimulus between Egyptian and cuneiform writing, because they originated in the same part of the world almost simultaneously. Yet both the forms of the characters and their meaning and sound values differ so thoroughly in Egyptian and cuneiform that no specific connection between them has been demonstrated, and it seems unlikely that one is a direct or even a modified derivative of the other. So with the hieroglyphs of the Minoans, which appeared in near-by Crete somewhat later. Consequently, although the Cretan forms are distinctive and, so far as can be judged without our being able to read the system, Cretan values are distinctive also, it would be dogmatic to assert that the development of Cretan writing took place without any stimulation from Egyptian or cuneiform. Something of a similar argument would perhaps apply even to Chinese (§ 299), though on this point extreme caution is necessary. Accordingly if one thinks of the invention of the first *idea* of part-phonetic writing, it is conceivable that all the ancient systems of the Old World derive from a single such invention, although even in that event the Maya-Aztec system would presumably remain as a wholly separate growth. If on the other hand one has in mind the content and specific manner of transitional-type systems, Egyptian, cuneiform, Cretan, and Chinese are certainly distinct and constitute so many instances of parallelism.

206. PHONETIC WRITING: THE PRIMITIVE SEMITIC ALPHABET

The last stage of basic invention in writing was that of purely phonetic writing—the expressing only of sounds, without admixture of pictures or symbols. Perhaps the most significant fact about this method as distinguished from earlier forms of writing is that it was invented and permanently accepted only once in history. All the alphabetic systems that now prevail in nearly every part of the earth—Roman, Greek, Hebrew, Arabic, Indian, as well as many that have become extinct—can be traced back to a single source (§ 132). The story in this case is therefore one of invention, spread, and adaptation, not of more or less parallel reinvention.

What circumstance it was that caused this all-important invention to be made is not known, though time may yet bring knowledge. There is even division of opinion as to the particular system of mixed writing that was drawn upon by the first devisers of the alphabet, or that served as jumping-off place for the invention. Some have looked to the Egyptian system, others to a cuneiform or Cretan source of inspiration. Nor is it absolutely known who were the precise people responsible for the final invention; though it is clear that they were a northwestern Semitic nation, and probably were the Phoenicians. But the discoveries of recent decades furnish an outline of the story.

For a long time the earliest extant example of the primitive Semitic alphabet was on the famous Moabite Stone of King Mesha, and it is still the longest and most important alphabetic inscription of its age. It is also remarkable how similar, considering the remote time and place of the Moabite Stone, many of its letters are to our own corresponding capital letters (Fig. 25). It was in the ninth century, around 860 B.C., that Mesha erected this monument to commemorate his successful defense of Moab against the invading Hebrew kings of Judah and Israel, an event touched on also in the Bible, in Chapter 3 of the Second Book of Kings. The speech of these three realms, and of the Phoenicians, whose name is most often associated with the invention of the alphabet, differed only dialetically; and it was written with the same 22 consonantal letters in two runs of 11; namely, in modern equivalents:

'	b	g	d	h	w	z	ḥ	ṭ	j	k
l	m	n	ṣ	'	p	tṣ	q	r	s	t

This, the Phoenician or Primitive Semitic alphabet, is the first which survived and had descendants. Scraps of inscriptions carry its age back to 1000 B.C. or a bit beyond—say 1200 B.C. But experiments or endeavors to devise alphabets are now known to have been made in the same general region of Palestine, Phoenicia, and Syria for a number of centuries before.

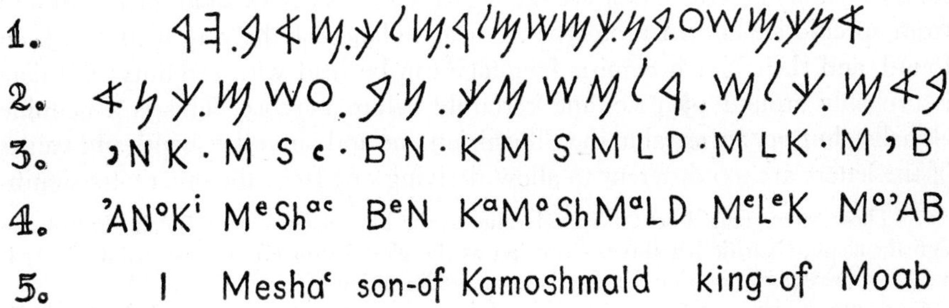

FIG. 25.   INSCRIPTION ON MOABITE STONE, 860 B.C.

1, First line of actual inscription, read right to left. 2, Same, reversed, left to right, words slightly spaced. 3, Transliteration into modern Roman capitals. 4, Unwritten vowels supplied, to give full pronunciation. 5, English translation.—Note resemblance of letters of line 2 with those of 3 and 4, slightly disguised by originals facing opposite from ours (B, D, K), lying on side ('A, S), extra stroke or lengthening of a stroke ('A, D, M).

207. ENDEAVORS AND ANTICIPATIONS OF THE INVENTION

The earliest of these anticipations are the Sinai inscriptions discovered in 1905 by the British Egyptologist Flinders Petrie at ancient Egyptian copper mines in the desert peninsula just south of Palestine. On Egyptological grounds, these workings are dated before 1500 B.C., possibly as early as 2000, most likely around 1800. The sixteen short inscriptions are supposed to have been cut by local Semites, and have been read as a Semitic dialect. They show enough resemblance to the Moabite-Phoenician letters to make them look like earlier forms of these. But the inscribing was hasty, time has tended to obliterate the characters, and the legends are very brief, averaging only about ten letters each, so that lack of context makes verification of readings difficult. A degree of doubt therefore still attaches to the interpretation of the Sinaitic writing as an ancestral form of the Phoenician alphabet, even though partial confirmation has been found in three short phrases in similar writing on a dagger, a bowl, and a potsherd from Canaanite Lachish and Gezer, estimated to date from between 1800 and 1500 B.C.

A second pre-Phoenician alphabet is clearly not ancestral to the Phoenician. But for that very reason it is of double interest, in that as an independent endeavor to write with element-sound letters, it shows that there existed a sense of need and problem before the final invention was achieved. This alphabet is known as the Ugaritic, after the ancient Semitic-speaking city of Ugarit or Ras Shamra, near Latakia on the coast of Syria, a scant hundred miles north of the farthest Phoenician city. There are about 28 letters formed by impressing wedge-shaped strokes on clay.[2] This technique is of course taken from the cuneiform writing of Babylonia; but that writing is a mixture of ideographic and syllabic characters without element-sound signs or true letters, while the Ugaritic system consists wholly of letters. Nor are the Ugaritic letters derivable in form or sound from specific cuneiform prototypes. An abundance of the clay texts has been found, and their North Semitic language can be read with certainty; the date is probably around 1500 B.C. and certainly before 1365 B.C. This is a genuine alphabet, but *not* ancestral to the Phoenician one and ours: the shapes and values of the letters are too different to allow deriving one from the other.[3] Its signifi-

[2] These correspond closely in sound value to the Phoenician letters. But instead of one sign for aleph, Ugaritic has three, according as the glottal stop (') is associated with A, I, or U. This seems just outside the threshold of the invention of vowel signs.

[3] Another view makes the Ugaritic alphabet to be a sort of "translation" of the scratched or carved Phoenician characters into new characters evolved by Syrian Semites who were familiar with the manipulations of Babylonian cuneiform, and hence wanted to continue to write with wedge strokes impressed into clay, and running from left to right instead of right to left, although they were ready to adopt the alphabetic idea from the Phoenicians. If this view is correct, the independence of the Ugaritic achievement would be limited to the devising of wholly new character shapes, instead of being an autonomous preinvention or reinvention of the fundamental alphabetic principle.

cance lies in its being a parallel invention, working on the same basic principle, but wholly distinct in execution and happening to die out while the Phoenician invention lived.

It is thus clear that a period of experimentation in alphabetic writing, lasting from perhaps 2000 B.C. or at any rate 1800, to say 1400 or 1300 B.C., preceded the use of the definitive or stabilized "Phoenician" alphabet from around 1200 or 1000 B.C. on; the intervening two or three centuries perhaps being the time when the definitive alphabet was being shaken down into an increasingly settled system.

It has previously been shown (§ 155) that the essence of the invention of our alphabet was a process of reduction, of extrication from the unnecessarily elaborate accretions of ideograms, word signs, syllable signs, and sound signs in the previously prevalent mixed systems of writing. The cardinal point is that new and superior efficiency was attained through people's having the courage to rid themselves of an established inventory. This would be easier for outsiders or late learners to do than for the confirmed descendants of the originators of a system. Hence it came about that it was not the Egyptians who invented the alphabet. Although they had attained to true letters, these constituted only around 4 per cent of their total system, and they would have been shocked to throw away the equally hallowed other 96 per cent. The neighboring Semites, with a different language and no settled or universally accepted method of writing, could begin by devising letters without having to discard anything. In this they were evidently helped by the system of acrophony: namely, using a simple form of a word sign as the letter for the first sound of that word. The Egyptians had already done that for their 24 letters, as *l* from *labo*, lion; but they appear to have remained unaware of the principle as such, perhaps because their few letters were so buried in the mass of their system. But the Semitic inventors seem to have used acrophony deliberately. Thus the letter which in Hebrew is still named *'aleph* or "ox" denotes the sound ' and was originally an abbreviated picture of an ox head; *b* is from *beth,* house; *g* from *gimel,* camel; and so on.

208. THE GREEK ALPHABET: INVENTION OF THE VOWELS

The Phoenicians founded Carthage, and consequently the Carthaginian or Punic writing until after the extinction of that great trading city was also Phoenician.

More important was the spread of the Phoenician letters to an entirely foreign people, the Greeks, whose language was largely composed of different sounds and possessed a genius distinct from that of the Semitic tongues. The Greeks' own traditions attest that they took over their alphabet from the Phoenicians. The fact of the transmission is corroborated by the form of the letters and by their order in the alphabet. It is also proved very prettily by the names of the letters. As we speak of the ABC, the Greeks spoke of the alpha beta—whence our word "alphabet." Now *alpha* and *beta* mean nothing in Greek; they are obviously foreign names. In Semitic however, the similar names aleph and beth were used for the same letters A (or ') and B, and meant respectively "ox" and "house," as we have just seen. From these names alone, then, even if nothing else were known about the early alphabets, it would be possible to prove the correctness of the Greek legend that they derived their letters from the Phoenicians.

The Greeks however did more than take over the alphabet from the Phoenicians. They improved it. An outstanding peculiarity of Semitic writing was that it dispensed with outright vowels. It represented the consonants fully and accurately. In fact it had carefully devised letters for several breath and "guttural" sounds that Indo-European languages either do not contain or generally neglect to recognize. But, as if to compensate, the Semitic languages slurred the writing of vowels—perhaps because one of their distinctive traits is a great variability of vowels. When a Semitic verb is conjugated, when it is converted into a noun, and in other circumstances, the vowels change, while the consonants remain the same, much as English "sing" becomes "sang" in the past and "goose" changes to "geese" in the plural. Only, in English such changes are comparatively few, whereas in Semitic they are the overwhelming rule and quite intricate. The result of this fluidity of the vowels was that when the Semites invented their letters they renounced the attempt to write the vowels. Apparently they felt the consonants, the only permanent portions of their words, to be a sort of skeleton, sufficient for an unmistakable outline. So, with their ordinary consonants, plus letters for J and V (*y* and *w* sounds) which at need could be made to stand for I and U, and the consistent employment of breaths and stops to indicate the presence or absence of vowels at the beginning and end of words, they managed to make their writing readily legible. It was as if we should write: *'n Gd w' trst* or *Ths wy 't*. Even today the Bible is copied and read in the Jewish synagogue by this vowelless system of three thousand years ago.

In the Greek language more confusion would have been caused by this system. Moreover, the alphabet came to the Greeks as something extraneous, so that they were not under the same temptation as the Phoenicians to follow in the precise footsteps of the inventors. They felt freer to discard or alter, as the Phoenicians in their day had felt freer than the Egyptians. As a result, the Greeks took the novel step of adding vowel letters.

It is significant that what the Greeks did was not to make the new vowel signs out of whole cloth, as it were, but that they followed the method which characterizes most inventions in their development and spread. They took over the existing system, twisted and stretched it as far as they could, and created outright only when they were forced to. While the Phoenician alphabet lacked vowel signs, the Greeks felt that it had a superfluity of signs for breaths and stops. So they transformed the Semitic breaths and stops into vowels. Thus they satisfied the needs of their language; and incidentally added the capstone to the alphabet. It was the first time that a system of writing had been completely worked out on the basis of a letter for every sound. All subsequent European alphabets are merely modifications of the Greek one.

The first of the Semitic letters, the aleph, stood for the glottal stop, a check or closure of the glottis in which the vocal cords are situated; a sound that occurs, although feebly, between the two *o*'s in *co-ordinate* when one articulates overdistinctly. In the Semitic languages this glottal stop is frequent, vigorous, and etymologically important, wherefore the Semites treated it like any other consonant. The Greeks gave it a new value, that of the vowel A. Similarly, they transformed the value of the symbols for two breath sounds, a mild and a harsh H, into short and long E, which they called epsilon and eta. Their O is made over from a Semitic letter for a "guttural" sound, while for I the Semitic ambiguous J-I was ready to hand. U, written Y by the Greeks, is a dissimilated variant form of F, both being derived from the Semitic vau or sixth letter with the sound value of W or U. The vocalic form was now put at the end of the alphabet, which previously had ended with T. Its consonantal double, F, later went out of use in Greek speech and was dropped from their alphabet.

209. SLOWNESS OF THE INVENTION

The Greeks did not make these alterations of value at once. The value of several of the letters fluctuated in the different parts of Greece for two or three centuries. In one city a certain value or form of a letter would come into usage; in another, the same letter would be shaped differently, or stand for a consonant instead of a vowel. Thus the character H was for a while read by some of the Greeks as H, by others as long E. This fact illustrates the principle that the Greek alphabet was not an invention that leaped, complete and perfect, out of the brain of an individual genius, as inventions do in film plays and novels. One might imagine that with the basic plan of the alphabet, and the majority of its symbols, provided ready-made by the Phoenicians, it would have been a simple matter for a single Greek to add the finishing touches and so shape his national system of writing as it has come down to us. In fact, however, these little finishing touches were several centuries in the making; the final result was a compromise between all sorts of experiments and beginnings. One can picture an entire nationality literally groping for generation after generation, and only slowly settling on the ultimate system. There must have been dozens of innovators who tried their hand at a modification of the value or form of a letter. It is the point that we have met before (§ 151, 187): inventions are social as well as individual events.

Nor can it be denied that what was new in the Greek alphabet was a true invention. The step of introducing full vowel characters was as definitely original and almost as important as any new step in the history of civilization. Yet it is not even known who the first individual was that tried to apply this idea. Tradition is silent on the point. It is quite conceivable that the first writing of vowels may have been independently attempted by a number of individuals in different parts of Greece.

210. THE ROMAN ALPHABET

The Roman alphabet was derived from the Greek. But it is clear that it was not taken from the Greek alphabet after this had reached its final or classic form. If such had been the case, the Roman letters, such as we still use and call English, would undoubtedly be more similar to the Greek ones than they are, and certain discrepancies in the values of the letters, as well as in their order, would not have occurred. In the old days of writing, when a number of competing forms of the alphabet still flourished in the several Greek cities, one of these forms, developed at Chalcis on Euboea and allied on the whole to those of the western-Hellenic world, was carried to Italy. There, after a further course of local diversification, one of its subvarieties became fixed in the usage of the inhabitants of the city of Rome. Now the Romans at this period still pronounced the sound H, which later became feeble in the Latin tongue and finally died out. On the other hand the distinction between short and long (or close and open) E, which the Greeks came to recognize as important in their speech, was of no great moment in Latin. The result was that whereas classic Greek turned both the Semitic H's into E's, Latin accepted only the first of these modifications, that one affecting the fifth letter of the alphabet, whereas the other H, occupying the eighth place in the series, continued to be used by the Romans with approximately its original Semitic value. This retention, however, was possible because Greek writing was still in a transitional, vacillating stage when it reached the Romans. The western-Greek form of the alphabet that was carried to Italy was still using the eighth letter as an H, so that the Romans were merely following their teachers. Had they based their letters on the "classic" Greek alphabet, which was standardized a few hundred years later, the eighth as well as the fifth letter would have come to them with its vowel value crystallized. In that case the Romans would either have dispensed altogether with writing the sound H, or would have invented a totally new sign for it and probably tacked it onto the end of the alphabet, as both they and the Greeks did in the case of several other letters.

The net result is the curious one that whereas the Roman alphabet is derived from the Greek, and therefore subsequent, it remains, in this particular matter of the eighth letter, nearer to the original Semitic alphabet.

There are other letters in the Roman alphabet which corroborate the fact of its being modeled on a system of the period when Greek writing still remained under the direct influence of Phoenician. The Semitic languages possessed two K sounds, usually called kaph and qoph, or K and Q, of which the former was pronounced much like our K and the latter farther back toward the throat. The Greeks, not having both these sounds, kept the letter kaph, which they called kappa, and gradually discarded qoph or koppa. Yet before its meaning had become entirely lost, they had carried it to Italy. There the Romans seized upon it to designate a variety of K the Greek dialects did not possess, namely KW; which is of course the phonetic value the symbol Q still has in English. The Romans were reasonable in this procedure, for in early Latin the Q was produced with the extreme rear of the tongue, much like the original qoph.

211. LETTERS AS NUMERAL SIGNS

In later Greek, qoph remained only as a curious survival. Although not used as a letter, it was a number symbol. None of the ancients possessed pure numeral symbols of the type of our "Arabic" ones. The Semites and the Greeks employed the letters of the alphabet for this purpose, each letter having a numeral value dependent on its place in the alphabet. Thus A stood for 1, B for 2, C or gamma for 3, F for 6, I for 10, K for 20, L for 30, and so on. It will be noted that the extra symbols are needed because of the lack of a zero sign (§ 189). As this series became established among the Greeks, Q as a numeral denoted 90; the Greeks, long after they had ceased writing Q as a letter, used it with this arithmetical value. Once it had acquired a place in the series, it would have been far too confusing to drop it. With Q omitted, R would have had to be shifted in its value from 100 to 90. One man would have continued to use R with its old value, while his more new-fashioned neighbor or son would have written it to denote ten less. Arithmetic would have been as thoroughly wrecked as if we should decide to drop out the figure 5 and write 6 whenever we meant 5, 7 to express 6, and so on.

Just such a change did happen in the transmission between Phoenician and Greek, when the letter TS, tsade, value 90, got lost. This was too early to affect the majority of the Greeks. But the Semitic number values ran: P 80, TS 90, Q 100, R 200, and were thus preserved in Hebrew, as against Greek P, Q, R for 80, 90, 100. A shift in order between the languages would disturb only those few individuals concerned in effecting the difference. It is at such intercultural points of connection that nonconformities of system are most likely to occur.

But with a sequence of system once accepted within a society and culture, habit in cases like this is almost insuperable. No matter how awkward an established system becomes, it normally remains more practical to keep it with its deficiencies than to replace it by a better scheme. The wrench and cost of reformation are greater, or are felt to be greater, by each generation, than the advantages to be gained.

212. REFORM IN INSTITUTIONS

This last fact is one reason why radical changes are so difficult to bring about in institutions. These are social and therefore in a sense arbitrary. In mechanical or "practical" matters people adjust themselves to the pressure of new conditions more quickly. If a nation has been in the habit of wearing clothing of wool and this material becomes scarce and expensive, some attempt will indeed be made to increase the supply of wool; but if production and import fail to keep pace with the deficiency, cotton is substituted with relatively little reluctance. If, on the other hand, a calendar becomes antiquated, the simple act of will, the mere exercise of community reason, needed to correct it is resisted vigorously. Time and again nations have gone on with an antiquated or cumbersome calendar long after any mediocre mathematician or astronomer could have devised a better one. It is usually reserved for an autocratic potentate of undisputed authority,[4] a Caesar or a Pope, or for a cataclysm like the French and Russian revolutions (§ 170), to institute the needed reform.

As long as men are concerned with their bodily wants, those which they share with the lower animals, they appear plastic and adaptable. In proportion however as the socially systematized products of their intellects are involved, when one might most expect foresight and reason and cool calculation to be influential, societies seem swayed by a conservatism the strength of which looms greater as we examine history more deeply. Some of this conservatism is mere stubborn addiction to the folkways, the established, the habitual. Some of it is due to societies' getting enmeshed in their institutions and not seeing a way out, like the Egyptians with their hieroglyphs; some to realistically counting the cost of extrication as too burdensome on the reforming generation (§ 203).

Of course, each nation and generation regards itself as the one exception. But irrationality is as easy to discern in modern institutions as in ancient alphabets, if one has a mind to see it. Daylight-saving time is an example near home. For centuries the people of Western urban civilization have gradually got out of bed, breakfasted, worked, dined, and gone to sleep later and later, until the middle of their waking day came at about two or three o'clock instead of noon. The beginning of the natural day was being spent in sleep, most relaxation taken at night. This was not from deliberate preference, but from a species of procrastination of which the majority were unintentionally guilty. Finally the wastefulness of the condition became evident in World War I. Everyone was actually paying money for illumination that enabled him to sit in a room while he might have been amusing himself gratis outdoors.

A rational free individual would have changed his habits—blown the factory whistle at seven instead of eight, opened the office at eight instead of nine,

---

[4] Through Kemal Atatürk, the Osmanli Turks changed summarily from Arabic to Roman letters in 1928, as part of an enforced process of Westernization.

gone to the theater at seven and to bed at ten. But we are all social rather than free individuals, and therefore herd conformity is necessarily strong. The individual who departed from the custom of the mass would have been made to suffer. The first theater opening at six would have played to empty chairs. The office closing at three would have lost the business of the last hours of the day without compensation from the empty hours prefixed at the beginning. The only way out was for everyone to agree to a self-imposed fiction. So the nations that prided themselves most on their high civilization solemnly enacted that all clocks be set ahead. Next morning, everyone had cheated himself into an hour of additional daylight, and the illuminating plant out of an hour of current, without anyone's having had to depart from established custom—which last was evidently a course so difficult as to be avoided at all hazards. With the emergency over, the same nations changed back to natural time and natural procrastination. Twenty-five years after, World War II sent us all back to daylight-saving—some of us even to double daylight-saving—only for the most part to disestablish it as quickly as possible in 1945.

Of course, most individual men and women are neither idiotic nor insane. The only conclusion is that as soon and as long as people live in relations and act in groups, something wholly nonrational is often imposed on them, something that is inherent in the very nature of society and civilization. There appears to be little or nothing that the individual can do in regard to this limitation except to refrain from adding to its irrationality the delusion that it is rational.

213. THE SIXTH AND SEVENTH LETTERS

Letters such as Q, in which the Roman alphabet is in agreement with the original Semitic one and differs from classic Greek writing, might lead, if taken by themselves, to the conjecture that the ancient Italians had perhaps not derived their alphabet via the Greeks at all, but directly from the Phoenicians. But this conclusion is untenable: first, because the forms of the earliest Latin and Greek letters are on the whole more similar to each other than to the contemporaneous Semitic forms; and second, because of the deviations from the Semitic prototype that the Latin and Greek systems share with each other, as in the vowels.

The sixth letter of the Roman alphabet, F, the Semitic waw or vau, is wanting in classic Greek, although retained in certain early and provincial dialects. One of the brilliant discoveries of classical philology was that the speech in which the Homeric poems were originally composed still possessed this sound, numerous irregularities of scansion being explainable only on the basis of its original presence. The letter for it looked like two Greek G's, one set on top of the other. Hence, later when it had long gone out of use except as a numeral, it was called di-gamma or "double-G."

The seventh Semitic letter, which in Greek finally became the sixth on account of the loss of the vau or digamma, was zayin, Greek zeta, our Z. This, in turn, the Romans omitted, because their language lacked the sound. They filled its place with G, which in Phoenician and Greek came in third position. The shift came about thus. The earliest Italic writing followed the Semitic and Greek original and had C, pronounced G, as its third letter. But in Etruscan the sounds K and G were hardly distinguished. K therefore went out of use; and the early Romans followed the precedent of their cultured and influential Etruscan neighbors. For a time, therefore, the single character C was employed for both G and K in Latin. Finally, about the third century before Christ, a differentiation being found desirable, the C was written as C when it stood for the "hard" or voiceless sound K, but with a small stroke, as G, when it represented the soft or voiced sound; and the seventh place in the alphabet, that of Z, being vacant, this modified character was inserted. Thus original C, pronounced G, was split by the Latins into two similar letters, one retaining the shape and place in the alphabet of gimel-gamma, the other retaining the sound of gamma but displacing zeta.

But the letter Z did not remain permanently eliminated from Western writing. As long as the Romans continued to be rude and self-sufficient, they had no need of a character for a sound they did not speak. When they became powerful, expanded, touched Greek civilization and borrowed its literature, philosophy, and arts, they took over also many Greek names and words. As Z occurred in these, they adopted the character. Yet to have put it in its original seventh place, which was now occupied by G, would have disturbed the position of the following letters. It was obviously more convenient to hang this once rejected and now reinstated character on at the end of the alphabet; and there it is now.

214. THE TAIL OF THE ALPHABET

In fact the last six letters of our alphabet are additions of this sort. The original Semitic alphabet ended with T. U was differentiated by the Greeks from F to provide for one of their vowel sounds. This addition was made at an early enough period to be communicated to the Romans. This nation wrote U both for the vowel U and the consonantal or semivowel sound of our W. To be exact, they did not write U at all, but what we should call V, pronouncing it sometimes U and sometimes W. They spelled *cvm,* not *cum;* and they spoke *weni,* though they wrote *veni.*

Later, they added X. An old Semitic s-sound, *samedh,* in fifteenth place in the alphabet and distinct from the S or *sin* in twenty-first position which is the original of our S, was used for both SS and KS. In classic Greek, one form of *samedh,* with KS value, maintained itself in its original fifteenth place. In other early Graeco-Italic alphabets, it was the second form, the one with SS value, that kept the fifteenth place, and the X or KS variant was put at the end, after U. This SS letter later dropped out because it was no longer pronounced.

The Y that follows X is intrinsically nothing but the U which the Romans already had—a sort of double of it. The Greek U, however, was pronounced differently from the Latin one—like French *u* or German *ü*. The literary Roman felt that he could not adequately represent it in Greek words by his own U. He therefore took over the U as the Greeks wrote it—that is, a reduced V on top of a vertical stroke. This character naturally came to be known as Greek U; and in modern French Y is not simply called "Y," as in English, but "Y-grec," that is, "Greek Y."

With Z added to U (V), X, and Y, the ancient Roman alphabet was completed.

Our modern Roman alphabet is however still fuller. The two values V had in Latin, those of the vowel U and the semivowel W, are so similar that no particular hardship was caused through their representation by the one character. But in the development of Latin from the classic period to mediaeval times, the semivowel sound W came to be pronounced as the consonant V as we speak it in English. This change occurred both in Latin in its survival as a religious and literary tongue, and in the popularly spoken Romance languages, such as French and Italian, that sprang out of Latin. Finally, it was felt that the full vowel U and the pure consonant V were so different that separate letters for them would be convenient. The two forms with rounded and pointed bottom were already actually in use as mere calligraphic variants, although not distinguished in sound, V being usually written at the beginning of words, U in the middle. Not until after the tenth century did the custom slowly and undesignedly take root of using the pointed letter exclusively for the consonant, which happened to come most frequently at the head of words, and the sounded letter for the vowel, which was commoner medially.

In the same way I and J were originally one letter. In the original Semitic this stood for the semivowel J (pronounced *y* as in *yet*); in Greek for the vowel I; in Latin indifferently for vowel or semivowel, as in Ianuarius. Later, however, in English, French, and Spanish speech, the semivowel became a consonant just as V had become one. When differentiation between I as vowel and as consonant seemed necessary, it was effected by seizing upon a distinction in form that had originated merely as a calligraphic flourish. About the fifteenth century, I was given a round turn to the left when at the beginning of words, as an ornamental initial. The distinction in sound value came still later. The forms I and J were kept together in the alphabet, as U and V had been, the juxtaposition serving as a memento of their recency of distinction—like the useless dot over small *j*. Had the people of the Middle Ages still been using the letters of the alphabet for numerals as did the Greeks, they would undoubtedly have found it more convenient to keep the order of the old letters intact. J and U would in that case almost certainly have been put at the end of the alphabet instead of adjacent to I and V.

The origin of W is accounted for by its name, "double-U," and by its form, which is that of two V's. The old Latin pronunciation of V gradually changed from W to V, and many of the later European languages either contained no W sound or indicated it by the device of writing U or some combination into which U entered. Thus the French write OU and the Spanish HU for the sound of W. In English, however, and in a few other European languages, the semi-vowel sound was important enough to make a less circumstantial representation advisable. Since the sound of the semivowel was felt to be fuller than that of the consonant, a new letter was coined for the former by coupling together two of the latter. This innovation did not begin to creep into English until the eleventh century. Being an outgrowth of U and V, W was inserted after them as J was after I. It is a slight but interesting instance of convergence that its name is exactly parallel to the name "double-gamma" which the Greek grammarians coined for F long before.

215. CAPITALS AND MINUSCULES

The distinction between capitals and "small" letters is one we learn so early in life that we are wont to take it as something self-evident and natural. Yet it is a late addition in the history of the alphabet. Greeks and Romans knew nothing of it. They wrote wholly in what we should call capital letters. If they wanted a title or a heading to stand out, they made the letters larger, but not different in form. The same is done today in Hebrew and Arabic, and in fact in all alphabets except those of Europe.

Our own two kinds or fonts of letters, the capital and the "lower case" or "minuscule," are more different than we ordinarily realize. We have seen them both so often in the same words that we are likely to forget that the A differs even more in form than in size from *a*, and that *b* has wholly lost the upper of the two loops which mark B. In late Imperial Roman times the original "capital" forms of the letters were retained for inscriptional purposes, but in ordinary writing changes began to creep in. These modifications increased in the Middle Ages, giving rise first to the "uncial" and then to the "minuscule" forms of the letters. Both represent a cursive rather than a formal script. The minuscules are essentially the modern "small" letters. But when they first developed, people wrote wholly in them, reserving the older formal capitals for chapter initials. Later, the capitals crept out of their temporary rarity and came to head para-graphs, sentences, proper names, and in fact all words that seemed important. Even as late as a few centuries ago, every noun was written and printed in English with a capital letter, as it still is in German. Of course little or nothing was gained by this procedure. In many sentences the significant word is a verb or an adjective; and yet, according to the arbitrary old rule, it was the noun that was made to stand out.

Today we still feel it necessary in English to retain capitals for proper names. It is certain that a suggestion to commence these also with small letters would be met with the objection that a loss of clearness would be entailed. As a matter of fact, the cases in which ambiguity between a common and a proper noun might ensue would be exceedingly few; the occasional inconvenience so caused would be more than compensated for by increased simplicity of writing and printing. Every child would learn his letters in little more than half the time that he requires now. The printer would be able to operate with half as many characters, and typewriting machines could dispense with a shift key. French and Spanish designate proper adjectives without capitals and encounter no misunderstanding, and all telegrams in English are sent in a code that makes no distinction. When we read the newspaper in the morning and think that the mixture of capital and small letters is necessary for our easy comprehension of the page, we forget that this same news came over the wire without capitals—not to mention *archy* and *mehitabel*.

216. CONSERVATISM AND RATIONALIZATION

The fact is that we have become so habituated to the existing method that a departure from it might temporarily be a bit disconcerting. Consequently we rationalize our cumbersome habit, taking for granted or explaining that this custom is intrinsically and logically best, although a moment's objective reflection suffices to show that the system we are so addicted to costs each of us, and will cost the next generation, time, energy, and money without bringing substantial compensation.

It is true that this waste is distributed through our lives in small driblets, and therefore is something that can be borne without seeming inconvenience. Civilization undoubtedly can continue to thrive even while it adheres to the antiquated and jumbling method of mixing two kinds of letters where one is sufficient. Yet the practice illustrates the principle that the most civilized as the most savage nations tend to believe that they adhere to their institutions after an impartial consideration of all alternatives and in full exercise of wisdom, whereas analysis frequently reveals them as equally resistive to alteration whether it is for better or for worse.

If our capital letters had been purposely superadded to the small ones as a means of distinguishing certain kinds of words, a modern claim that they were needed for this purpose could perhaps be accepted. But since the history of the alphabet shows that the capital letters are the earlier ones, that the small letters were for centuries used alone, and that systems of writing have operated and do operate without the distinction, it is clear that need cannot have been the true motive. The employment of capital letters as initials originated in a desire for ornamentation. It is an embroidery, the result of a play of the aesthetic sense; it is genuinely justifiable only on the ground that it makes writing more interesting and attractive. It is the use of capitals that has caused the false sense of their need, not necessity that has led to their use.

217. GOTHIC

Another exemplification of how tenaciously men often cling to the accustomed at the expense of efficiency, is provided by the 𝔟𝔩𝔞𝔠𝔨-𝔩𝔢𝔱𝔱𝔢𝔯 or "Gothic" alphabet used in Germany and Scandinavia. This is nothing but the Roman letters as elaborated by the manuscript-copying monks of northern Europe toward the end of the Middle Ages, when a book was as much a work of art as a volume of reading matter. The sharp angles, shadow lines, double connecting strokes, goose-quill flourishes, and other increments of the formal letters undoubtedly possess a decorative effect, although an overelaborate one. They were evolved in a period when a copyist cheerfully lettered for a year to produce a volume, and the lord or bishop into whose hands it passed was as likely to turn the leaves in admiration of the black and red characters as to spend time in reading them.

When printing was introduced, the first types were the intricate and angular ones then customary in Germany. The Italians, who had always been halfhearted about the northern forms, soon revolted. Under the influence of the Renaissance and its renewed inspiration from classical antiquity, they reverted as far as possible to the ancient shapes of the characters. Even the mediaeval small letters were simplified and rounded as much as possible to bring them into accord with the old Roman style. From Italy these types spread to France and most other European countries, including England, which for the first fifty years had printed in black letter or 𝔒𝔩𝔡 𝔈𝔫𝔤𝔩𝔦𝔰𝔥. Only in north-central Europe did the mediaeval forms continue to prevail, although even there all scientific books have for some time been printed in the Roman alphabet. Yet Germans sometimes complain of the "difficulty" of the Roman letters, and books intended for popular sale, and newspapers, go into old style. There can be little doubt that in time the Roman letters will dispossess the national ones in Germany and Scandinavia except for ornamental display heads. But established ways die hard; and the formal, decorative letters may linger on as the "old-style" calendar with its eleven-day belatedness held out in England until 1752 and in Russia until 1918.

218. HEBREW AND ARABIC

Only a small part of the history of the alphabet was unfolded in Europe (Fig. 26, § 219), where the seemingly so different forms of writing that have been discussed are after all only fairly close variants of the early Greek letters. In Asia the alphabet underwent more profound changes.

The chief modern Semitic alphabets, Hebrew and Arabic, are considerably more altered from the primitive Semitic or Phoenician than is our own alphabet. The Hebrew letters evolved in a religious setting—Hebrew had begun to change from a living to a ritual language—around the time of Christ, under stylistic influences that have turned most of them as nearly as possible into parts of squarish boxes. B and K, M and S, G and N, H and CH and T, D and V and Z and R, are shaped as if with intent to look alike rather than different. Arabic, on the other hand, runs wholly to curves: circles, segments of circles, and round flourishes; but several of its letters have also become similar—in fact identical except for diacritical marks. If we put side by side the corresponding primitive Semitic, the modern English, the Hebrew, and the Arabic letters, it is at once apparent that in most cases English observes most faithfully the three-thousand-year-old forms. The cause of these changes in Hebrew and Arabic is in the main their derivation from alphabets descended from the Aramaean alphabet, a form of script that grew up during the seventh century B.C. in the region of Damascus or Aram immediately inland from Phoenicia. The Aramaeans were Semites and therefore kept to the original sound value of the Phoenician letters more closely than did the Greeks and Romans. On the other hand, they employed the alphabet primarily for business purposes and rapidly altered it to a cursive or running form, in which looped or enclosing letters like A, B, D were opened and the way was cleared for a series of increasing modifications. Greek and Roman writing, on the other hand, were at first used largely in monumental, dedicatory, legal, and religious connections, and preserved clarity of form at the expense of rapidity of production.

The square or modern Hebrew developed directly out of Aramaean; Arabic, out of Aramaean via Nabataean, the writing of the Semites of the Sinai-Jordan area in the earliest Christian centuries. Arabic writing spread widely not only with the Koran and the use of Arabic speech, but through adoption for the writing of the important modern Persian, Turkish, and Urdu languages.

There is one feature of primitive Semitic that most Asiatic alphabets retained for a long time: the lack of vowel signs. In the end, however, representation of the vowels proved to be so advantageous that it was introduced. Yet the later Semites did not follow the Greek example of converting dispensable consonantal signs into vocalic ones. They continued to recognize consonant signs as the only real letters, and then added smaller marks, or "points" as they are called, for the vowels. These points correspond more or less to the grave, acute, and circumflex accents French uses to distinguish vowel shades or qualities, é, è, ê, and e, for instance; and to the double dot or diaeresis German puts upon its "umlaut" vowels, as to distinguish ä (= e) from a. There is this difference, however: whereas European points are reserved for minor modifications, Hebrew and Arabic have no other means of representing vowels than these points. The vowels therefore remain definitely subsidiary to the consonants; to

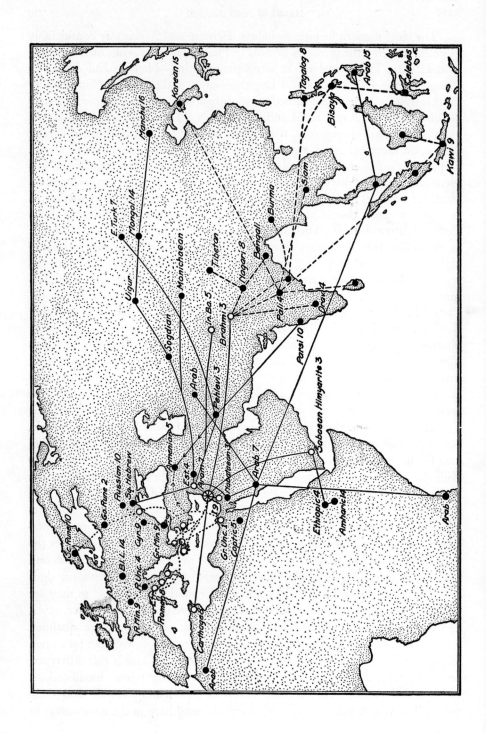

the extent of this deficiency Hebrew has adhered more closely to the primitive Semitic system than have we.

The reason for this difference probably lies in the fact that Hebrew and Arabic have retained virtually all the consonants of ancient Semitic. Hence the breaths and guttural stops could not be dispensed with; or at least such was the feeling of their speakers. In the Indo-European languages, these sounds being wanting, the transformation of the superfluous signs into the letters needed for the vowels was suggested to the Greeks. The step perfecting the alphabet was thus presumably taken by them not so much because they possessed special originality, or unusual imagination, as because of the accident that their speech consisted of sounds considerably different from those of Semitic. Perhaps the Greeks once complained of the unfitness of the Phoenician alphabet, and adjusted it to their language with grumblings. Had they been able to take it over unmodified, as the Hebrews and Arabs did, it is probable that they would cheer·fully have done so with all its imperfection. In that case they, and after them the Romans, and perhaps we too, would possibly have gone on writing only consonants as full letters and representing vowels by the Semitic method of subsidiary points. In short, even so enterprising and innovating a people as the Greeks are generally reputed to have been may be assumed to have made their important contribution to the alphabet less because they wished to improve it than because an accident of phonetics led them to find the means to a better fit.

219. THE SPREAD EASTWARD: THE WRITING OF INDIA: SYLLABIC TENDENCIES

The diffusion of the alphabet eastward from its point of origin was even greater than its spread through Europe. Most of this extension in Asia is comprised in two great streams. One of these followed the southern edge of the continent. This was a movement that began some centuries before Christ, and in part traveled by water routes. The second flow was mainly post-Christian and affected most the inland peoples of central Asia (Fig. 26).

FIG. 26.   SPREAD OF ALPHABETIC WRITING

Course of Occidental alphabets in dotted lines; West Asiatic, continuous lines; Indic, broken lines. The numbers stand for centuries: with hollow circles, before Christ; with solid circles, after Christ. Spoke circle, point of origin, Phoenicia, 11th century B.C. *Abbreviations:* Aram, Aramaean; Bl L, Black-letter (Gothic); Cyr, Cyrillic; Drav, Dravidian; Est, Estrangelo; Etr, Etruscan; Go, Gothic (Runes); Gr Min, Unc, Greek Minuscule, Uncial; In Ba, Indo-Bactrian (Kharoshthi); I, Israelite; R Min, Unc, Roman Minuscule, Uncial; Sc, Scandinavian (Rune). The flow was often back and forth; compare the 2000-year development from Phoenician to Ionian to Athens to Alexandria (uncial) to Constantinople (minuscule) to Russian; or from Phoenician northward to Aramaean, thence south to Nabataean and Arabic, east to Pehlevi and back west to Armenian.

India is the country of greatest importance in the development of the southern-Asiatic alphabets. The forms of the Sanskrit letters show that they and the related Hindu alphabets are derivatives, though much altered ones, from Phoenician or some kindred primitive northern-Semitic writing. Exactly how this was carried from the Mediterranean to India has not been determined; but it appears as the Brahmi alphabet in the inscriptions of the famous Buddhist King Asoka around 250 B.C. From this Brahmi are developed all later and still living Indian, Farther Indian, and East Indian alphabets. Besides this main importation, there was another, from Aramaean sources, which gave rise to a different form of early Hindu writing, the Kharoshthi or Indo-Bactrian of the Punjab, which spread for a time into Turkestan but soon died out in India.

One trait of Indian alphabets leads back to their direct Semitic origin: they did not fully recognize the vowels. The Hindus, speaking Indo-European, were confronted with much the same difficulty as the Greeks when they took over the vowel-less Semitic alphabet. But they solved the difficulty in their own way. They assumed that a consonantal letter stood for a consonant plus a vowel. Thus, each letter was really the sign for a syllable. The most common vowel in Sanskrit being A, this was assumed as being inherent in the consonant. For instance, their letter for K was not read K, but KA. This meant that when K was to be read merely as K, it had to be specially designated: something had to be done to take away the vowel A. A diacritical sign was added, known as the virama. This negative sign is a "point" just as much as the positive vowel points of Hebrew; but it was used to denote the opposite.[5]

There are of course other vowels than A in Sanskrit. These were represented by diacritical marks analogous to the virama. Thus while this is a diagonal stroke below the consonant, U is represented by a small curve below, E by a backward curve above, AI by two such, and so on.

Only for initial vowels, as in *Asoka* or *Indra,* did the Hindus have special vocalic characters. These, like the Greeks, they partly made over from useless Semitic consonants—the aleph glottal stop again becoming A—and partly devised anew.

If a syllable had two consonants before the vowel, these were condensed into one, the essential parts of each being combined into a more complex character. This was much as if we were to write *try* by forcing *t* and *r* into a special character showing the cross stroke of the *t* and the roll or hook of the *r,* and superposing a diaeresis for the vowel.[6] This process reduced every syllable to a single though often compound letter. If the syllable ended in a consonant, this carried over as the beginning of the next syllable. Even the end consonant of a word was

---

[5] Psychologically, this invention of a symbol for an absence parallels the Hindu invention of a symbol for zero (§ 189).

[6] We have a few faint efforts at such ligatures in English. The printer sets with a single type the complex characters fl and fi, not "f l" or "f i": *fine flavor,* not *f ine f lavor.*

written as the first letter of the next. According to the Sanskrit plan, *the dog is mad* would be rendered *the do gi sma d-*.

Obviously, there is something unnaturally regular, a systematic artificiality, about such a scheme. Love of system cropped out otherwise. The Hindus devised a new symbol—mainly by differentiation of old ones—for every sound that they had and Semitic lacked. Thus they more than doubled the number of their letters, to 48. Then they rearranged the order of these on a phonetic and logical basis. All sounds made against the back palate were brought into one group; those formed against the forepalate, gums, and teeth came after; the lip sounds came last. Within each of the groups the letters followed one another in a fixed order according to their method of production—voiceless stops always first, nasals always last. All this is obviously the work of sophisticated phoneticians and grammarians, as compared with the rule-of-thumb order of Phoenician, Greek, and our own letters.

The result of these innovations was that the Hindu alphabets diverged much more from the Semitic original than did ours. This perhaps was really to be expected, since writing entered India by long leaps between peoples who were not in intimate relations. Also, by the time the alphabet first reached them, the Hindus, in the isolation of their remote peninsula, had already worked out an advanced and unique type of civilization. This fact must have predisposed them to make over any imported invention in conformity with their established habits. In particular, it seems that they were well on the way to becoming competent analytic grammarians—the earliest in the world—before they wrote at all.

The Hindus' reshaping of their alphabet back in the direction of a semi-syllabic system also carries a theoretical interest. This is because of several independent parallel developments of wholly syllabic methods of writing. These include the Cherokee and Vai systems already mentioned in § 154 as nineteenth-century inventions of purely syllabic writings stimulated by knowledge of the alphabet. In the twentieth century, around 1900, Njoya, the Mohammedan sultan of Bamun in the French Cameroons, invented a writing system of about 1000 ideographs, which was repeatedly revised until by 1918 it had become essentially a phonetic syllabary of 70 symbols. The Japanese kata-kana and hira-gana consist of purely phonetic characters—respectively block and cursive in shape—of 47 syllables, supplementary to the thousands of Chinese phono-ideograms with which Japanese in general is written. The syllabaries are used for grammatical endings, foreign proper names, and other elements of the language that do not per se contain a meaning. Theoretically, either of the kana would have sufficed to write everything Japanese, and might accordingly have crowded out the Chinese phono-ideograms altogether; but they did not do so. On the contrary, the Lolo in southwestern China (§ 175), instead of taking over Chinese symbol writing, did derive from it a purely phonetic syllabic script for their own shamans. With a dramatization of the essential historical source of this writing, the Lolo say that it originated in "Confucius's left-hand script."

These examples of a repetitive tendency toward development of straight syllabic writing evidently rest on a trait of the human psychosomatic constitution. This trait is the fact that in deliberately slow and clear pronunciation, as for the benefit of learners, most people spontaneously break words or sentences into syllables. But they find it more difficult to break the syllables farther into their constituent elements such as *t* or *f* or *a;* this ultimate analysis, which underlies true alphabetism, has generally to be taught before it is grasped. In the recurrent syllabification of many writing systems we have, therefore, not a law of culture, but a fact or near-law of psychology.

220. THE EAST INDIES: PHILIPPINE ALPHABETS

The spread of the Hindu alphabet within India, over southeastern Asia, and into the East Indian archipelago, cannot be followed here because it is an intricate story, interwoven with the history of Brahmanism and Buddhism and their sects. It may be said that in general, with the chief exception of China and Japan, Hindu writing followed where any form of Indian religion penetrated. But it may be illuminating to touch briefly on one of the extensions.

In the early centuries after Christ, Hindus began to reach the East Indies, especially Sumatra and Java. Here they established principalities or kingdoms, and their religion. Many arts were also imported by them, such as ironworking, batik dyeing, sculpture, drama, and writing. From perhaps the sixth to the fifteenth centuries, the Malaysian population of Java lived under a heavy layer of Hindu culture (§ 308), and literacy gradually became fairly widespread. Greater or less portions of this culture were transported to the other East Indian islands, and with them went writing. In the Philippines, the Spaniards of the sixteenth century found several related alphabets, one to each of the principal nationalities, which seem to have derived from the Bengal or Telugu region some seven or eight hundred years before.

The Malayan languages are unusually simple in their array of sounds. Hence the greater part of the elaborate Sanskrit alphabet was discarded by them. But the salient characteristics of Sanskrit writing were retained. A consonant was read as consonant plus A. Points were provided if the consonant was to be read with other vowels. Of such points, the Philippine alphabets employed only two. One, put above the consonant, served indiscriminately for I and E; the other, below, for U ond O. The position of the points connects them with the Sanskrit vowel signs. In this way the Philippine languages were adequately rendered with a set of about 12 consonantal letters and 3 letters for independent or initial vowels, plus 2 vowel points.

At the time of the Spanish discovery, the native Philippine alphabets were already meeting Arabic writing, which had shortly before been introduced in the southern islands with Mohammedanism. The Spaniards of course brought the Roman alphabet. Under this double competition the use of native writing soon began to decay. The most advanced of the Filipino nationalities, such as the Tagalog and the Bisaya, have long since given up their old letters. Yet it has been discovered that two varieties of the native writing still survive—both of them among backward tribes: the Tagbanua of Palawan and the Mangyan of Mindoro. Here in the jungle, among half-clothed people living under rude thatches and without firearms or machines, the most remote descendants of the ancient Sanskrit alphabet linger—for charms and love letters.

Three widely different descendants of the primitive Semitic alphabet have therefore met in this archipelago. One, beginning its journey some twenty-five hundred years ago, traveled via northern India, probably reaching the Philippines around A.D. 800. The second evolved in the Semitic homeland, finally poured out of northern Arabia with Mohammedanism, was carried past India to Sumatra and the Malay Peninsula, and thence leaped across the sea to Borneo and the Philippines about A.D. 1400. The third followed the longest journey: from the Phoenicians to the Greeks, to southern Italy, to Rome, to Spain, and, after Columbus, to Mexico, and then across the Pacific Ocean to Manila shortly before A.D. 1600.

221. NORTHERN ASIA: THE CONFLICT OF SYSTEMS IN KOREA

The history of the alphabets of central and northern Asia is complex. It may be summed up in the statement that Aramaean derivatives of the primitive Semitic writing, evolving in and near Syria in the six or seven centuries before the birth of Christ, were carried not only south to the Arabs but east and northeast across Asia. One line led from Aramaean to Middle Persian or Pehlevi, which became perpetuated among the refugee Parsi of Bombay of today, but also long ago mingled with Greek influences to give rise to the Armenian alphabet. A second line leads from Aramaean to the Estrangelo alphabet of the early Syrian Christians and thence to the writings of the Christian Nestorian and non-Christian Manichaean sects in Iran and Turkestan in early mediaeval centuries. The third line of development is: Aramaean—Iranian Sogdian—Uigur Turk—Mongol—Manchu, the end of this traverse of five thousand land miles being accomplished only in 1599, by order of the ruler of the rising Manchurian state.

The farthest extension of the alphabet in Asia was to the shores of the Pacific Ocean, in Korea. Korean writing, however, seems to be derived directly from an Indian source, probably through Pali, the sacred language and script of the southern branch of Buddhism; hence it is only a remote collateral relative of the neighboring Manchu. Already in the seventh century the Koreans devised for themselves a phonetic syllabary based on Chinese. But this broke down; and in 1446 the önmun alphabet of 14 consonants and 11 vowels was constructed by order of the king.

The adoption of this quite effective Korean alphabet was limited, however—not through any inherent flaws or weakness of age, but by the competition of a totally different system of writing: the Chinese.

Chinese writing of course is not alphabetic at all. It represents the sounds of syllables or words, and it uses them only in a quasi-rebus combination with semi-ideographs, of which some are stylized pictographs. In a conflict between such a primitive system and a truly alphabetic one, the latter should expectably prevail on account of its much greater efficiency and simplicity. Actually, however, the Korean alphabet did not triumph, but for centuries barely managed to maintain an existence alongside Chinese. The cause was social conservatism as to prestige values.

When the native alphabet obtained its start in Korea, it was confronted by an overwhelming Chinese influence. The court, the government, the institutions, official religion, all activities of people of fashion and importance, were modeled after Chinese examples. The man who could not write and read Chinese characters was eliminated from polite society and advancement. This was only natural. The civilization of China is one of the most ancient and greatest in the world, and the Koreans were a smaller people and close neighbors. Western civilization was thousands of miles away, and it was only later, and rarely, that a driblet from it penetrated to the eastern edge of Asia. On one side, then, stood the undoubted simplicity and practical effectiveness of the alphabet; on the other, the momentum of the whole mass of Chinese culture. The outcome was that the nationally Korean true alphabet became something that shopkeepers and low people made use of, a thing easy to learn and therefore almost contemptible. But laws and documents and books of higher learning were written in Chinese characters, which upper-class Koreans for generation after generation spent years of their lives in mastering, and which therefore rated much higher.

Two principles beyond mere inertia are operative in this Korean situation. One is ascendancy rating or prestige. The other is the tendency of culture traits that have for some time been associated by historical accident—such as the geographical nearness of Korea to China—to form an interlocked aggregation or system of civilizational value. Once such a system or cluster has acquired a certain coherence, it survives with a tenacity independent of the degree of inherent or logical connection between its elements. The fact that ideographs were associated with Chinese religion, literature, and institutions constituted them part of what may be called the Chinese complex. On the higher social and cultural levels in Korea the mass of this Chinese complex overbalanced the less organized native influences. The alphabet originated in Korea as an isolated unit, under a combination of nationalistic and remote alien stimulus, but was borne down by the weight of the elaborate and high-ranked culture aggregate of Chinese origin.

This brute fact, and not any superior reasonableness or intrinsic merit of one system or the other, determined the issue between them.

In the same way the heterogeneous aggregate we know as Western civilization—Christianity and collars, science and picture films, factory labor and democracy, fine and base all tangled together—is today crushing the breath out of many ancient and exotic cultures in the name of progress.

CHAPTER FOURTEEN

Distributions

222. PROBLEMS WITHOUT RECORD EVIDENCE

ANTHROPOLOGY is not always so fortunate as to be able to study culture processes from historical sources documented by written records, as in many of the cases reviewed in preceding chapters. Even formal history has its gaps: there is likely to be more recorded about reigns, revolts, and battles than about customs. And primitive people are above all nonliterate people, and therefore leave no history at all, in the usual sense. Occasionally, more advanced nations record something about them, but that is likely to be one-sided as well as intermittent. Archaeology of course is a sort of unwritten history; but on some cultures nothing has been found. Also, the archaeological record necessarily is always imperfect. Ordinarily only tangible objects of nonperishable material have even a chance of being preserved; and while social structure, religion, and attitudes can now and then be inferred from these, it is never more than very partially that this is possible.

This means that there are hundreds of the humbler societies, and thousands of institutions and cultural items, such as the couvade or the safety pin or the spring snare, which history proper scarcely touches at all. Nor does any other branch of study concern itself systematically with them: they are unanimously left to anthropology. The result is that a considerable part of the endeavors of anthropology consists of a groping into these dimly lit realms, of collecting shreds of evidence and partial orientations, and of construing them into the best probability attainable. The task is to some minds thankless; to others it is fascinating; but if anthropology refuses to accept it, no one will have illumination on a large part of the total story of mankind.

This chapter accordingly reviews a number of problems to which only partial or probable answers can be given—reviews them as a sample of the type of approach that anthropology mobilizes in avowedly inferential situations. A certain method is common to all the findings of this class. In lack of documented history, historical-probability conclusions are reached by the use of data on geographical occurrence coupled with analysis of the structure and features of the phenomenon or institution being investigated. Put briefly, distributions and typology replace written documents as the materials of study in these cases.

223. SINGLE ORIGINS AS AGAINST PARALLEL AND CONVERGENT DEVELOPMENTS

One type of problem that recurs over and over in the historyless parts of the story of mankind is that of independent multiple origin as against single origin or connection. A custom or a tool is found in two or more separate parts of the world. There is no preserved record of the history of either occurrence. Did it originate independently in each area, owing to something in the constitution of human nature? Or to some law that ever tends in a certain direction? Or as the result of mere accident? Or was there some connection now forgotten and obscured that resulted in a transmission from the single originating point to other regions? In more technical phrasing, is the case one of parallel or convergent development or is it a case of diffusion? This is a perennial type of problem in anthropology. It is no longer, as it once seemed to be, its most fundamental problem; but it keeps insistently recurring in all those domains of human culture which recorded history does not cover.

If things are connected by spread or persistence, they obviously go back to a single origin. The spread of Christianity or the alphabet would be an example. If however origins are separate and multiple, as perhaps for writing systems or female-descent reckoning, the similarity attained is due either to "parallelism" or to "convergence." These two terms are metaphors based on geometry. Of course parallel lines do not converge, and vice versa. Logically, therefore, parallelism and convergence are quite separate processes. Parallel developments are supposed to grow spontaneously out of human nature, much as grassblades all grow upward out of a running root stock. Fifty years ago this type of assumption was in active vogue. Sir James Frazer of *Golden Bough* fame was its last eminent representative. Since his time it has been increasingly realized that this type of explanation tends to be verbal. Specific phenomena are not really explained by being referred to a vast, vague, catchall cause.

Usually the alleged explanation is only a redescription of the recurrent phenomena, under the cloak of an ill-defined or undefinable principle beyond them. Thus we have just seen (§ 219) that syllable denotation is historically documented as having been repeatedly and independently evolved in writing systems. We infer from this that it comes easy to men of all or most languages to break their sentences and words up into syllables when they have occasion to. We can label this the "syllabifying tendency," and readily confirm it by simple trials with illiterates. But professional psychologists hardly recognize any such psychological law of syllabification: they have never got around to it. It remains a sort of homespun induction by anthropologists on a particular point of human constitution. Most cultural parallels, even if indubitable, show this quality of loose rooting in a more or less amateur psychology; and the similarities are themselves loose and vague—such as that most peoples can syllabify, or have some sort of chiefs or rulers, for instance.

By contrast, convergences are things that start out differently and subsequently assimilate. Here the phenomena may be quite sharply defined; and the factors that go to make them alike may also be definite. The independent invention of zero signs by Babylonians, Mayas, and Hindus (§ 189) is a good example. It will be recalled that the antecedents, forms, and contexts of these three zeros remained quite diverse. It is only in their concept and function that the three zeros became alike. Moreover, convergence has abundant precedent in organic evolution, as in insects, birds, bats (and extinct reptiles also) all acquiring flight. The structure of the wings in these several classes of animals is quite different, in accord with the fact that the classes are widely separated in their origins. It is in the function of the wing organs, their similar use by the animal, that the resemblance lies. Convergence is in its nature a secondary process; but it enjoys perfectly good repute in both culture history and natural history because the similarities with which it is concerned are usually precise and definable.

In practice, usually, too much attention need not be paid to the distinction between parallels and convergences. In some situations, both may enter in, as perhaps in the development of writing from pictures. In more cases, knowledge is too scant to allow of a distinction. In any event, the first phase of all problems of undocumented development always is whether we are dealing with basically one phenomenon seemingly multiplied by having spread and diversified, or with separate and multiple phenomena due to either parallel or convergent development. Sometimes it is impossible to proceed beyond this primary stage. Consequently no attempt will be made in the rest of this chapter at consistent distinction of parallelisms from convergences.

Obviously, in spite of an undercurrent of theoretical involvements, this whole matter is not so much a large problem of principle as it is a series of special problems, each of which has to be answered on its own merits. No one can deny derivation by diffusion, because it is going on all around us. It would be equally fanatical to deny independent development, with history full of examples before us, such as rebus writings, fire pistons, representations of two-headed birds, lintels and corbeling, market weeks. The quarrel, except for amateurs and extremists, is not about which principle is the only one or the dominant one; even if an answer could be given to that, it would be a meaningless statistical average. Rather, the problem is: What happened in such and such particular case, and in this other, and in the next? The story of human development consists of an endless series of such specific problems, to some of which history gives us the answer, to some, archaeology; but for the remainder we can only make the best inference possible from the incomplete data.

224. DISTRIBUTIONS AS EVIDENCE

The strongest evidence is generally in distributions—in the knowledge of where the cultural phenomena under consideration occur. This placing of phenomena in space is an indispensable need in all the historical sciences—astronomy, geology, palaeontology, evolutionary biology, geography, as well as in history and anthropology. Geology may attain to a generalized theory of vulcanism and its processes, but it has to begin with an examination of particular volcanoes and their geographical relations to other volcanoes and to nonvolcanic formations. History absolutely brings in the space or place factor unceasingly. Napoleon was born in Corsica, became emperor of France, marched as far as Moscow, was defeated at Waterloo, died in St. Helena, his bones rest in Paris. Can we imagine his career without reference to place and area? It would be a meaningless thing in a vacuum. As a matter of fact, that Waterloo lies in Belgium and not in France or Germany is as significant as that the battle was fought in 1815 and not in 1810 or 1820.

It is often said that the specific quality of history is its dealing with time sequence. Why the time factor should be singled out for this distinction is hard to understand, except that the equally important space factor is so much taken for granted as to be overlooked. Perhaps also, humans being verbalizing animals, we take easily to places, which have names, and which in addition can be visualized and even visited, but resist the more abstract numbers by which we designate dates. Waterloo, once we have heard of what happened there, has specific connotations; whereas 1815, which might as well be a telephone number, usually has a historical association only for those steeped in history. Hence, by reverse, we tend to think of the time element as specially characteristic of history. Nevertheless, place obviously counts in history as much as time.

Now in the field of the nonliterate cultures and cultural items, where dates are totally lacking, and where archaeology can hope in general to give us only relative time sequences, it is also interesting to know whether an institution goes back a thousand or ten thousand years, or is older or younger than another institution. But how shall we learn? Now and then some other science comes to our rescue: geology and palaeontology in remote prehistory, botany or tree-ring dendrochronology in a few particular situations (§ 322). Such outside aids are however rare and unusual. In general, cultural anthropology has to help itself.

Its main method, broadly speaking, is to organize the space data of its phenomena and then infer time relations from them. This is a laborious method, is beset by several pitfalls, and is easily abused, especially if one begins with a bias to prove one thing rather than another. But it is a method of indirect and circumstantial evidence, such as the rest of science uses; and at least there are no witnesses to lie or distort testimony—any distortion is by the investigator. The mechanisms of the method will be set forth in a moment. At this point, it need only be added that in this method we have the reason why to an anthropologist a cultural phenomenon unaccompanied by its "distribution," by its occurrence in geography, is as nonsignificant a fact as an unplaced and undated event would be to a historian. As Lowie has said, an unplaced cultural phenomenon is not yet an anthropological fact.[1] That an unknown people somewhere practiced cannibalism or used the spear-thrower is as meaningless for science as the statement would be to a historian that at some place sometime some man established and lost some empire.

225. TYPOLOGY: THE COUVADE

In conjunction with distributional knowledge, typological comprehension is necessary. This is obtained by analysis and comparison. A sound typology ensures that only such things are brought into relation as are actually similar.

For instance, any and all stone axes are essentially one unit as against iron axes, in their developmental or historical meaning. When however we are investigating in a premetal area or age, stone axes are not all of a kind. Some are hewn, others are ground into shape, and it is precisely these differences which are likely to be significant of period, of cultural change, of development. For an archaeologist to equate chipped and polished axes would be silly.

In the ax we have a relatively simple implement, easily and abundantly preserved from antiquity. We also have accumulated by now a great mass of archaeological knowledge about it, so that no one would any longer use a typology so crude that it failed to discriminate hewn stone axes from ground ones; though it is well to remember that it is less than a hundred years since any scholar thought the distinction significant enough to coin generic names for Palaeolithic and Neolithic. Other phenomena, however, are not so simple.

The couvade (§ 130) is a custom formerly attributed to the Basques of the Pyrenees, under which on the birth of a child the mother got up and resumed her household duties, while the father went to bed in state and lay in. This piquant habit attracted even more interest when it was found that a good many primitive and backward peoples did more or less the same thing in South America, in Africa, in India and China. These all believed the child would suffer if they did not observe the custom. However, most of them did not go quite as far as the Basques are said to have done: the father lay in, but so did the mother. Cessation from labor by both parents was demanded for the child's health. In

---

[1] "When we do not know the distribution of a phenomenon, we know nothing that is theoretically significant."

still other tribes, both parents refrained from work and certain foods, but the mother refrained more strictly and longer than the father. Among others, the mother alone was under restrictions. And finally, among the southern Ute, where the mother lies still on a bed of hot ashes for thirty days, the father lies with her only for four, and then, after a good meal, must run and hunt as actively as possible for one or several days.

With all this gradation, what constitutes the couvade typologically? The most that it would be possible to give as a definition is: the participation of the father in the period of rest and recuperation that is physiologically natural for the mother after childbirth. In other words, the idea is expressed that it is his child too. Superimposed on this is an endless variety of things prohibited and things required, for the good of the child or for the good of the parents, for a few days or for a full month. And above all, there is every intergradation from the father's sole role, through a joint one, to the mother's alone. No wonder ethnographers have come to talk about "classical couvade," "semicouvade," "pseudo-couvade," and the like, without being able to define the couvade forms so that all specific tribal customs fall unqualifiedly into one or the other class. In short, we have no satisfactory typology for the couvade. Hence in a comparative study we would sometimes be comparing part-comparables, perhaps even noncomparables. The common factor is the name, plus a vague and extremely plastic concept. An exhaustive monograph on the couvade would be almost as near to a train of related but free associations as to a scientific treatise.

The question of whether the couvade has been diffused from a single origin or has had several independent origins can therefore not be answered at present. It is not yet a scientific problem, because the couvade is not a definable recurrent phenomenon but a variable or series of intergrading phenomena.

This case will illustrate why precise typology is as indispensable as knowledge of distributions in the comparative study of nonliterate culture undertaken to ascertain what happened and how and why. More or less, what is true of the couvade is true also of polytheism, of totemism, of caste systems; of throwing-clubs, which shade into knives on one side and into boomerangs on the other; also of masks, of windbreaks and beehive huts, and of many other material and nonmaterial things in culture, including probably some so broad and fundamental as animism. These are logically valid concepts; but the typology of their forms and functions is so variable as to preclude clean-cut, rigorous classification.

226. PROVERBS

The custom of uttering proverbs has a significant distribution. Most African tribes possess a stock of them as abundant and as pithy as those current in Europe. Not that the proverbs are identical. The Negro lacks too many articles, and too many of our manners, to allude as we do. But he does share with us the habit of expressing himself on certain situations with brief current metaphors of homely and instantly intelligible nature, that put a generality into specific and concrete form. Thus: "One tree does not make a forest"; "Run from the sword and hide in the scabbard"; "If the stomach is weak, do not eat cockroaches"; "Distant firewood is good firewood."

The proverb tendency seems sufficiently general to suggest its independent origin in both Africa and Europe. One's first reaction to the parallel is likely to be something like this: The Negro and we have formulated proverbs because we are both human beings; the coining of proverbs is natural or instinctive in humanity. However, as soon as the distribution of proverbs the world over is reviewed, it becomes evident that their coining cannot be spontaneous, since the native American populations appear never to have devised true proverbs. On the other side are Europeans, Africans, Asiatics, and Oceanians who are addicted to the custom. Degree of civilization evidently has nothing to do with the matter, because in the Old World primitive and advanced peoples alike use proverbs; whereas in the New World lowly tribes as well as the advanced nations like the Maya and the Inca had no proverbs.

The only inference the facts allow is that there must have been a time when proverbs were unknown anywhere—still "uninvented" by mankind. Then, somewhere in the Old World, they came into use. Perhaps it was a genius that struck off the first sayings, to be repeated first by his associates and then preserved by his more remote environment. At any rate, the custom spread from people to people until it extended over almost all the Eastern Hemisphere. Some cause, however, such as relative lateness of the invention, or geographical isolation, prevented the extension of the movement to the Western Hemisphere. The American Indians thus remained proverbless because the habit was never transmitted to them. Here is a case of the very incompleteness of a distribution going far to illuminate the history of a culture trait. The lack of agreement between the hemispheres disproves the explanation by spontaneous independent origin. This negative conclusion, in turn, tends to establish some presumption that the custom may have been derived from a single source in the several Eastern continents.

227. THE MAGIC FLIGHT

There is one folklore plot with a distribution that leaves little doubt as to its diffusion from a single source. This is the incident known as the magic flight or the obstacle pursuit. It recounts how the hero, when pursued, throws behind him successively a whetstone, a comb, and a vessel of oil or other liquid. The stone turns into a mountain or a precipice, the comb into a forest or a thicket, the liquid into a lake or a river. Each of these obstacles impedes the pursuer and contributes to the hero's final escape. This incident has been found in stories told over a continuous area comprising Europe, northern Asia, and northerly

North America. In Japan it enters into official Shinto mythology, first put into writing in A.D. 712.

There can be little doubt as to a common source of the incident, because of the coexistence of the three separate items that make it up. If the story merely were that water was spilled on the ground and magically grew into a vast lake, it would mean little as to historical connection, because belief in the virtue of magic is world-wide, and from this common soil the same episode of a drop enlarging to a lake might have sprouted independently. But the linkage of the three specific items—stone, comb, and liquid—much decreases the possibility of any two peoples' having hit upon the particular combination separately. It would be stretching coincidence pretty far to believe that each people independently invented the triple complex. In other words, the structure or typology of the tale makes its many occurrences properly comparable.

In addition, the distribution is favorable to unitary origin: a unitary or continuous area, though so large a one as to stretch over parts of three continents.

228. FLOOD LEGENDS

Flood myths are told by probably the majority of human nations. Formerly this wide distribution was thought to prove the actuality of the Biblical Flood, or to be evidence of the descent of all mankind from a single nation that had once experienced it. Refutation is hardly necessary. Yet a categorical interpretation is not easy. Much of the difficulty is caused by the fact that the various flood myths are not wholly comparable. Some peoples have it that the flood came after the earth was formed and inhabited, and that it almost destroyed the human race. Other nations begin their cosmology with a "flood." For them, water was in existence before there was an earth, and the problem for the gods or creative animals was to raise or to make the world. This, according to some American and Asiatic versions, they finally accomplished by having one of their number dive to the bottom and bring up a few grains of sand, which were then expanded to constitute terra firma.

The first type of story is evidently a true "flood" myth; the second might better be described as two concepts, "primeval water" and "earth diving." The difficulty is enhanced by the fact that the two types are sometimes found side by side or amalgamated. Thus the Old Testament begins with the primeval waters in Chapter 1, but in Chapter 6 the deluge covers the earth. So, according to some American tribes, the flood came after the earth, but the waters remained until after the diving. It is clear that flood stories are more shifting than the magic-flight episode. Several distinct concepts—primeval water, flood, the diving animals, an ark—may have evolved separately, traveled, and met and blended with others. The typology and the classification, or units with which we operate, are not clear; and hence it is difficult to reach conclusions as to what happened.

229. THE ZODIAC

The zodiac is the concept of dividing the path of sun, moon, and planets around the heavens into twelve equal parts, each named after a constellation of fixed stars. Inasmuch as the apparent celestial sphere of the stars makes a complete revolution in twenty-four hours, each of the twelve units of the zodiac can also denote the time period of a double hour. The series runs: ram, bull, twins, crab, lion, virgin, scales, scorpion, archer, goat, water-carrier, fishes. The specific arrangement of these twelve constellations as a measure of the movement of the heavenly bodies seems to have made its first appearance among the Chaldean Babylonians in the thousand years before Christ. From them the Persians, and then the Greeks, learned the zodiac; and with its introduction to the Roman Empire it became part of the fund of knowledge common to the whole of Western civilization. It does not appear to have been accepted by the Egyptians until Roman Imperial times. Knowledge of the zodiac also spread eastward to India. It seems to have been carried as far as China by Buddhist missionaries, but failed to be seriously adopted in that country until its reintroduction by Jesuit missionaries in the seventeenth century.

The Chinese long before this had invented another series of twelve signs that has sometimes been called a zodiac. At any rate it may have been they who devised it, and it came gradually to be shared by them and by Japanese, Koreans, Mongols, Turks, and Tibetans. This scheme is of independent origin from the Western or Babylonian zodiac. It appears to have been devised to designate periods of time—hours and years—and to have been applied secondarily to the heavens. Its path through the sky is the reverse of the Western zodiac; and its signs are specifically different: rat, ox, tiger, hare, dragon, serpent, horse, sheep, monkey, hen, dog, and pig. At most, therefore, it would seem that there might have penetrated to China from the West the generic or abstract idea of dividing time and celestial space into twelve units and assigning to each of these the name of an animal. The working-out and the utilization of the idea were native to the Chinese or some northern-Asiatic people.

Already in ancient times the pictures of the twelve constellations of the Western zodiac began to be abbreviated and reduced to symbols. These gradually become more and more conventional, although evidences of their origin are still visible. The sign of the ram, for instance, as we employ it in almanacs, shows the downward curling horns of this animal; that for the ox, his rising horns; for the archer, his arrow; and so on. These cursive symbols, once they became fixed, underwent some travels of their own which carried them to unexpected places. The Negroes of Togo on the West coast of Africa make gold finger rings ornamented with the twelve zodiacal symbols in their proper sequence. They seem ignorant of the meaning, in fact do not possess sufficient astronomical knowledge to be able to understand the use of the signs. It also remains uncertain how and when they learned the set of symbols. Nevertheless it is the true zodiac they portray, in its proper order, even though only as a decorative pattern.

No zodiac is known from native America, in spite of occasional claims to the contrary by those interested chiefly in unities. There does appear to have been one series of animal signs used by the Maya in some astronomical connection, though what the use was is not clear. The Maya series runs: an undetermined sign, rattlesnake, tortoise, scorpion, king vulture, marine monster, bird, frog (?), deer (?), two more undetermined signs, death, peccary. The number of symbols is thirteen, not twelve, and they do not agree with the two Old World lists. Even if this Maya series is an astronomical device, which is uncertain, it therefore represents an independent origin.

A few elements are common to the three systems. We and the Maya share the scorpion; the Maya peccary might be the equivalent of the Chinese pig, the rattlesnake, of the serpent; and we and the Chinese share the ram and the bull (sheep and ox). It is these partial similarities that are seized upon by those who are obsessed with the impulse—often mystically colored—of uniting everything possible. The process is then extended: the bird *might* be the hen, the deer a substitute for the sheep, the lion for the tiger, and so on. A few more stretchings, some sort of explanation for the difference of order, and everything is reduced to one origin, either in the vague depths of the human mind, or at some remote place—perhaps in Atlantis.

Genuine evidence for connection would be clean-cut in a closed system like this. It would consist of the number of symbols being the same; at least a majority of the symbols also being patently the same; and the order of symbols being the same, or mostly the same. The Maya series fails to agree with the others on all three counts, the Chinese and Western series on the last two. In fact, the Chinese list consists altogether of animals, half of them domesticated; the Western, of three domestic animals, four wild animals, four human designations, and one artifact. It is part-for-part structural correspondence that counts for proof in such cases; and that is conspicuously lacking here.

Use or function also counts in such situations, though for less. That the Babylonian zodiac related primarily to the heavens, the Chinese animal series to hours and years, is relatively unimportant, because the two functions are related in the physical world. Even if the Maya series were known to be both astronomical and calendrical, we would continue to give it a separate origin because its content is different. On the contrary, we accept the Togo Negro designs as derived from our zodiac, although the Negroes have neither astronomy nor time measures, because the symbols and their sequence are the same.

Incidentally, the same criterion of evidence is exacted in biology in problems of relationship. Part-for-part agreement in structure is required (§ 132). Functional resemblances contrary to structure—like that of bats to birds in flying, or whales to fish in swimming—have only secondary, adaptive, or analogical significance. But the part-for-part similarity of bat, whale, and dog structure makes them related as mammals.

230. TIME COUNTS BY PERMUTATION

We divide the year into months, the months into days. Or it might be said that we group days into months, months into years, years into centuries. There is however another method of counting time by permutating two series against each other. This can be illustrated by the simile of two cogwheels in gear. Suppose one has eleven cogs, the other four. Let us mark the two cogs that mesh, and start the wheels turning. How long before the two marked cogs mesh again? Evidently forty-four cogs must pass the mesh point before these two meet again: four revolutions of the big wheel, eleven of the little one. We may call this a cycle. But if the larger wheel has ten cogs, the cycle will not be forty, but twenty, because 4 times 10 must now be divided by the common denominator 2.

To apply this principle to time-reckoning, we need only two unequal series of equal time units, be they hours, days, or years. Say one series is named, the other numbered. As an example, we can take the twenty letters A to T, the numbers from 1 to 13. Starting with a day A1, the next will be B2, then C3, D4, and so on. When we come to M13, the letter series goes on, the number series begins over again: the fourteenth day is N1, the fifteenth is O2. The twentieth is T7. Now the numbers go on, the letters begin over: the twenty-first is A8, the twenty-second B9. The permutations are exhausted when one series has run thirteen times, the other twenty; that is, in 260 days the cycle is completed, and we begin over again with a new day A1; just as in our calendar each year begins with January 1.

This, with substitution of names of things for letters, is the basis of the time count of the Aztec and the Maya, who called this 260-day cycle tonalpohualli (tonalamatl) and tzolkin respectively. The Aztec day-sign series runs: crocodile, wind, house, lizard, snake, skull, deer, rabbit, water, dog, monkey, grass (or herb), cane (reed), ocelot, eagle, vulture, motion, flint (knife), rain, flower. How they came to choose these objects, and to put them in that order, is not known.

However, the Maya and the Aztec had also determined the length of the year, by recorded observations. They now went on to permutate, or mesh, the 260-day tzolkin with the 365-day year. This, in the same way, gave them a longer cycle of 260 times 365 days, divided by 5, the common denominator of these two numbers; or 52 years. This 52-year cycle is as far as the Aztec went, and part of the difficulty of unraveling the history they and their local predecessors recorded is that they had neither a fixed starting point, nor a supercycle, nor any method of numbering or designating their cycles. The Maya did go farther, in several respects, but these specializations of their calendar need not be considered here. It should however be added that the 260-day tzolkin, and to a certain extent the whole calendar system, had heavy religious and astrological import; they were more than a mere timekeeping device. For instance, people were often named after the tonalamatl day on which they were born: for example, Seven-Deer, a famous character in native manuscripts.

The Chinese also have a permutation calendar, which a legendary emperor is said to have invented for them. One series, the twelve terrestrial branches, consists of the twelve animals already mentioned under the zodiac, beginning with the rat. The other, the ten celestial stems, uses the five elements—fire, air, water, wood, metal—each in two forms. Geared against each other, this 12-list and 10-list gave a cycle of 60 years, this being the product 120 divided by the common denominator 2. This 60-year cycle was used historically: it is now the 77th cycle. Also, to indicate his age, an illiterate Chinese tells the animal year of his birth, such as tiger, and this places him within 12 years: if he looks too old to be 25, and too young for 49, he must be 37.

Another system is found in the East Indies. The island of Bali, for instance, has the Hindu year, called *saka,* of 12 lunar months plus an extra month after two years and a half. Concurrent with this there runs a native or Javanese "year," called *wuku,* of 210 days. This is not divided into months, but into weeks or *wukus,* whence its name. In fact the *wuku* year comprises a whole series of concurrent weeks of different lengths. Thus there is a 3-day market week, a 5-day week, one of 7 days, and several others of less importance, except that every so often the coincidence of day *m* in week *x* with day *n* in week *y* is specifically lucky or unlucky; this indeed seems to be the main function of most of the many kinds of weeks. The 7-day week is the same as ours, the days having the same sequence of planetary names derived from India, like Wrespati or Jupiter for Thursday (§ 197). There are of course 30 of these weeks in the 210-day "week-year." Each of these 30 weeks possesses a name of its own, in addition to its 7 repetitively recurring named days. When a certain day *klion* of the 5-day week also falls on Saturday of the 7-day week, it is accounted a specially lucky day. This of course happens every 35 days. This little 35-day permutation cycle might be considered a sort of month—and indeed the Balinese often say loosely that a month has 35 days; and six of these do actually fill up the 210-day year. It will be seen that we have here an intricate system of many ingeniously interlocking permutations, full of name series as well as number series, and perhaps serving magic and divination as much as time-reckoning.

Finally, our week, as already told (§ 196), originated through a permutation of the names of the planets or 7 visible moving heavenly bodies, with the 24 hours of the day, each day being named after its first hour. This is the same in principle as that part of the Maya-Aztec system which designates each year in a cycle by its first day: thus, one-reed. Only four of the Aztec twenty day-signs happen to enter into this new-year's day combination with all thirteen numbers; so these four signs are known as year-bearers.

We would be having a permutation cycle now through the meshing of our week with our day-month-year count if our months, and our years, were equal in length, instead of varying from 28 to 31 and from 365 to 366. This accident prevents any regular or cyclical recurrence of a combination. If it did happen, we should in all probability be recognizing and signalizing it.

Between these several cases of time counts we can be reasonably sure that there was no direct historical connection. They are independent parallels. They use different number values, different series of names, arrive at different cycle-results, and operate with different time units ranging all the way from hours to years. What they have in common is three features. First, they operate with permutating series, whose resulting cycles can be discovered by empirical trial, without knowledge of algebra. Second, the permutating series include name lists as well as number sequences. Third, there is a connotation or function which can be called divinatory or astrological; that is, it is based on the belief that the passage of time or of the heavenly bodies affects, or at any rate can indicate, the fortunes of men. The first feature is basically a mathematical fact. The second is cultural indeed, but the specific names and numbers are highly diverse. The third is also cultural, but is a fairly broad exemplification of belief in magic. This means that what is common to the several cases is generic, but that what is most specific in them is highly differentiated. Thus there is scarcely room for doubting as many separate origins.

Could it be maintained, however, that the belief in divinatory magic of the astronomic-calendrical type is psychologically founded to the point of being compulsive? That by some law of the human mind such a belief must sooner or later eventuate? Hardly, because there are too many cultures that have never developed or accepted astrology: those of most primitives, for instance, as well as those whose science is most advanced. Anything innate ought to be breaking out normally, instead of at certain times and places only.

231. PATOLLI

Another case also involves Mexico, but interpretation is more baffling.

The word "dice" calls up in our mind cubes, with a different number value for each face. Instead of two (or more) cubical dice, one can however play with six (or more, or fewer) two-sided dice. These would be flat billets or staves or disks of wood or bone or shell, with the opposite sides distinguished by color or marking. In principle this corresponds with tossing up half a dozen coins. They will occasionally, but rarely, fall all six heads up, or tails up. Somewhat more often the combination five and one will turn up; most frequently, a three-three. This is simply the law of chance expressed through the algebraic law of combinations. Now scores can be affixed to each cast; as, 6-0 counts ten, 5-1 five,

4-2 two, 3-3 nothing; or any other score that may be agreed upon. Herewith we have a perfectly effective game of luck equivalent to our cubical dice. Such games of multiple two-faced dice are actually played in most continents, both where cube dice are known and where they are unknown.

Now in Mexico a form of this game was played called patolli by the Aztec. Besides the dice, there was a scoring board or circuit with marked spaces on which the players moved men forward according to the cast. The circuit was not a simple circle or square, but a Greek cross. If you overtook an opponent's man and landed on the same space, he was "killed" and had to go back to the starting point. Also there were specially marked spaces that incurred a penalty, or perhaps brought safety. Aztec gamblers played this game passionately.

The reader will by now have thought of parcheesi, which he played as a child, though with a pair of cubical dice. This in turn is nothing but the pachisi recently imported from British India. Are pachisi and patolli connected? The great British anthropologist Tylor, in 1896, thought so; and for a very good reason. There are five or perhaps six specific features in which pachisi and patolli agree: flat dice, scoreboard, cross-shape, several men, killing opponents, penalty or safety stations. The mathematical probability of two games invented separately agreeing by chance in so many quite specific features is very low. On a bet, long odds could be laid against so complex a coincidence, long odds for its not being a coincidence, hence an influence or a connection.

The trouble is that another set of facts show contrary probability. If pachisi was anciently imported from India to Mexico, as it was later carried from India to England and America, it is extremely unlikely that the people who brought it would have brought that and nothing else; or that only pachisi survived as patolli, but practically everything else brought with it failed to be accepted in Mexico, or died out, or was so altered as to be unrecognizable. To be sure, just this *might* conceivably have happened: but it would admittedly be extraordinary; on the basis of chance, improbable. As a matter of fact, the same stream of influence that brought pachisi from India to the West also brought polo and curry and Paisley shawls and theosophy; and more ancient connections brought chess and position numerals. There are few such possible counterparts, and no unquestionable ones, in native Mexico. In short, the context probability is against connection.

There we must leave the problem. One logically sound probability is for diffusion, another for independent origin. Fuller and more accurate knowledge may some day resolve the dilemma.

It will be observed how much weight is put in the argument on probability in terms of the total situation. One identical feature in two games means nothing; half a dozen do mean something. One identical game or trait in two cultures also means nothing; a number do have meaning. A chemist or a physiologist in a comparable situation repeats his experiment, or devises a new one that bears on the situation. We cannot experiment on past events; nor can we ordinarily experiment, at least not scientifically, on present and future social and cultural situations. Hence the leaning on probability. Sometimes it is so overwhelming as to leave no doubt. Sometimes the balance tips and we find "likely but not proven." When probability is nearly even, the only honest thing is to leave the question open. The reason there are many such hesitant answers is that many difficult questions with incomplete information fall in the sphere of anthropology. The historian sticks to his records, and they tell him unanimously that American independence was declared in 1776 in Philadelphia, and not in some other year or city; the laboratory scientist has his experiments; the anthropologist usually has neither records nor experiments.

It cannot be too much emphasized that for probability findings to be worth anything they must be in terms of the total situation. The difference between the sound and the unsound anthropologist is that the former takes in all possible relevant context; the latter, as much as suits him or as helps him prove what he wants. Negative evidence is particularly likely to be overlooked, both by the biased and by the inexperienced. We are so constituted, as primates, that occurrences impress us more than absences. The business of science is to train us in being critical enough to see both positive and negative evidence.

232. GAMBLING

Quite puzzling as to meaning, also, is the distribution of gambling. By "gambling" we here denote the playing of games for serious amounts of money or property that the winner keeps—irrespective of what the game is. Playing for "love" or the fun of playing is a different matter, has a wider distribution, and is not included in this discussion. Puritanical religions, like the stricter sects of Protestantism and Buddhism and the main stem of Mohammedanism, may sanction athletic sports and tolerate the "innocent" playing of games as harmless, but they consistently oppose the emotional involvement that comes from playing for stakes.

Outside the range of the organized world religions, there are perhaps as many peoples who gamble as those who do not. In many cases there is no very clear reason why these peoples line up as they do. Nongamblers, for instance, are: the native Australians, the Papuo-Melanesians, most of the Polynesians and Micronesians, and a good many of such Indonesians as have not been too heavily subjected to historical Hindu, Chinese, or Malay influences. Of this array, the Australians are in general indifferent to property; the Melanesians, on the contrary, spend much of their lives acquiring or retaining wealth. In Asia, the chief nongamblers were the remoter peoples of Farther India and most of the Siberians, both nomads and hunters; in Negro Africa, the eastern peoples from the upper Nile to Capetown; whereas West Africa and the Congo Basin gambled. In the native Americas, most of the northern continent gambled, most of the southern did not. The significant exceptions, both ways, were the following: North American nongamblers consisted of peoples in parts of the transcontinental subarctic belt, where hunters had to live scattered most of the year; and the tribes south of Guatemala, who went in this matter, as in many others, with the southern continent. South Americans who did gamble comprised, roughly, the natives of Peru, highland Bolivia, Chile, Argentina, and Paraguay. The strongest addiction to the habit in the New World was west of the Mississippi. In this region lived some tribes to whom wealth was the outstanding symbol of success in life, and others who wanted property chiefly in order to acquire repute by being liberal in using it up for others.

No consistent world-wide correlation of gambling with subsistence economy, wealth system, or type of religion seems to work out. We can only conjecture that cultural attitudes favorable or hostile to gambling, tolerant of it or uninterested in it, have grown up somehow; and, once established, such attitudes have got themselves accommodated to whatever attitudes the same cultures had developed as regards wealth. The result would be that both avaricious and thriftless peoples were inveterate gamblers; and that elsewhere, both kinds might be nongamblers, either from lack of interest or from overt disapproval. The areas of gambling and nongambling are both, on the whole, rather large and compact. We must therefore conclude that they are both due to consistent diffusions. What is of interest in this matter of gambling is that these seem to have been diffusions of attitudes as such, or of failures of interest to develop, rather than ordinary diffusions of culture content such as specific games or devices.

233. INTOXICANTS

As regards alcoholic intoxicants, cultures are of three kinds: those using fermented liquors, those using both fermented and distilled liquors, and those getting along without any. In the past two centuries, many of the last-named cultures have been seduced as the result of increasing Occidental expansion. But there still are peoples, such as most of the Pueblo Indians, who prefer to remain unstimulated by alcohol. This is the continuance of an old attitude: the neighboring Pima and Papago tribes were drinking—once a year at a great festival—when the Spaniards first came among them, but the Pueblos had not then taken the habit over, nor have they done so since.

Distilled liquors—brandy, whisky, rum, cordials, and the like—are recent in the history of the world, first appearing in Europe at the end of the Middle Ages, although small-scale experimental distillation of a number of substances had long been practiced by the early chemists and pseudo-chemists known as alchemists. The one long history of alcohol for human consumption is the history of simple fermentation or brewing. This goes back, in Egypt and Mesopotamia, at least five thousand years, and quite likely six thousand. It may be equally old elsewhere, but decipherable records are lacking.

There would thus seem to have been ample time for alcohol-making to diffuse pretty much over all the world; but it did not do so. The main basis for both spread and nonspread seems evident: they are correlated with presence or absence of cereal farming. Whether the staple grain grown was wheat and barley or millet or rice or maize does not seem to matter. Nearly all grain farmers were brewing in A.D. 1500—and most had been doing so from time immemorial. Practically all peoples who were not growing cereals did without alcohol. (This generalization allows for some recent exceptions due to the prohibitionist attitude of Mohammedanism where this is actually lived up to.) A possible reason for the correlation is that while alcohol is produced immediately from sugars, under simple conditions of technology these sugars are most often and regularly available by change from starch, which in turn is likely to be most ready to hand in quantity in the cereal grains.

Of course, once knowledge of the process of fermentation was established, it was found that other substances than cereals might be used; in the West, above all, the grape. Vines, unfortunately, do not leave much archaeological record, such as cereals do occasionally leave in the shape of charred grains, husk impressions in clay, sickle blades, millstones, or pictures of plows. Consequently the beginnings of vine cultivation and wine-making fade out in the haze of prehistory at a time when barley and beer are already discernible to us as marching sturdily through the most ancient Near East. Nevertheless, while the proof is not absolute, the priority of barley or millet beer over wine is highly probable from the world-wide close coincidence of grains and alcohol. Other substances used for intoxicating brews have been: honey for mead; milk for kumiss; sugar cane and nipa-palm sap in the East Indies; coconut-palm sap in India; the sap of the date palm in the Near East. A few of these substitutes are occasionally employed in areas beyond the range of farming; others, like the grape and cane, were used alongside barley or rice.

The correlation with grain agriculture is neatly shown by the fact that alcohol is drunk as far east as rice is grown; namely, through Indonesia. Beyond, in New Guinea, Melanesia, Micronesia, and Polynesia, the natives are still all farmers, but grow starchy root crops such as taro, yams, sweet potatoes, or starchy tree fruits such as coconuts, breadfruit, bananas. And yet they lack alcohol, apparently merely because of the historical pattern association of this—it is not a chemical dependence—with rice or other grain.

Native American farming is generally held not to be derived from that of the Old World, because of distinctness of the plants grown as well as absence of associated animals, the plow, and fertilizer. If this is correct, the brewing of intoxicating drinks should also have had a separate origin in the New World. This conclusion is confirmed by several pieces of indirect evidence.

1. There exists a great gap, of nondrinking as well as nonfarming peoples, in northeastern Asia and northwestern America. This gap separates from each other the two blocks of nations farther south in each continent who do drink.

2. It is in the Americas that more serious departures from the alcohol-grain correlation occur than they do in the Old World, suggesting that the two histories have been separate. All the many maize-growing tribes from Arizona to Quebec did *not* drink! On the contrary, there are two other areas, farther south and also large, in which maize was known but alcohol was made mainly from other plants: from agave (century plant, mescal, maguey) in central and northern Mexico; and in much of the South American forest and savanna, from the root of the manioc (cassava, manihot), which in much of this region was primary to maize as a staple food.

The reason for the failure of the alcoholic-drink habit to penetrate the aboriginal United States area along with maize may be the following. It has just been said that central Mexico departed from the usual pattern in that it ate maize but drank fermented agave sap, called octli by the Aztec and pulque in modern Mexico. But by the time the North Mexican frontier was reached, as among the Pima and the Papago, cultivated agave had been further replaced, first by the cooked root stock of the wild agaves; then by the fruit of the wild cardon or organ cactus; and finally by the fruit of the sahuaro or giant cactus, also a wild plant, limited to the ultrahot desert. The maize-alcohol association was therefore now trebly weakened. A step beyond, the nearest farming tribes, such as Yuma, Hopi, Navaho, and Zuni, still were confirmed maize-growers; but the grain failed to carry the association of alcohol; and the giant cactus they might have learned to associate with it did not grow in their cooler and moister habitat. In short, the prevalent association pattern of alcohol with maize had been broken up in Mexico before it could reach the United States and get established there as a unit or a complex.

3. In Latin America other than Mexico—in other words, from Central America to Argentina—fermentation is started by chewing some of the mash and spitting it into the liquid. In the Old World, this process is unknown,[2] with one exception in Formosa, and yeast is either introduced or allowed to introduce itself. This consistent difference between the hemispheres in process of preparation seems to rule out the explanation of a single origin followed by world-wide spread—as well as the explanation of repeated multiple origins the areas of which subsequently coalesced in each continent. In the latter event, it would be likely as a matter of mathematical probability that fermentation both with and without mastication would have been independently discovered in both hemispheres.

The pattern difference, its hemispheric consistency plus the hemispheric gap, suggests two and only two inventions, each followed by a broad diffusion, which however rarely managed to get far beyond its original and fundamental pattern of grain association.

[2] At any rate as a means of producing alcohol. In the South Seas, kava root is prepared for consumption by mastication.

This example demonstrates once more that it is the combination of "typology" or pattern analysis with geographic distribution which leads to insights of some probability; whereas typology alone, or distribution alone, usually provides nothing but a jumping-off place for uncontrolled speculation.

234. THE FIRE PISTON AGAIN

In § 188 the fire piston was considered from the angle of its invention, with the finding that it was devised independently twice: in France in 1802, as a by-product of physics and industrial technology; and in Farther India-Indonesia as the by-product of a pattern of air-compression devices such as the blowgun and the piston bellows, plus a second pattern of experimentation with fire-producing apparatus. It is worth while to consider further the distribution in this Oriental region.

Balfour has found the southeastern-Asiatic fire piston occurring in at least fourteen separate tracts scattered in Burma, the Philippines, and the Lesser

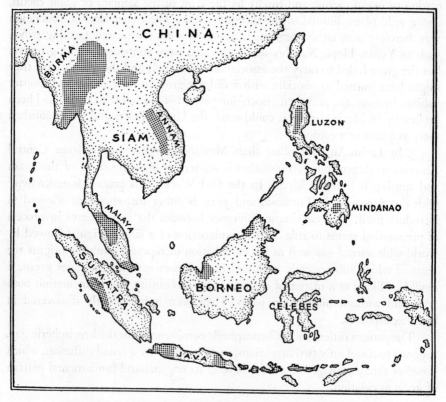

FIG. 27.   THE FIRE PISTON IN SOUTHEASTERN ASIA
(After Balfour)

Sundas. This highly broken distribution is shown in Figure 27. The fourteen areas together comprise only a small fraction of the square miles in the total range. What can we conclude from this sprayed distribution? Fourteen separate inventions among as many peoples is unthinkable, particularly for so specialized and tricky a gadget as this. Two or three inventions are barely within the range of possibility; one is much the most likely. This would then have spread. Such a spread presumably would have taken a few centuries, if not more. The local diversity of fire pistons in shape, size, and decoration is great enough to fit this inference. Thus the material varies from wood to bamboo to horn or bone or ivory, and from these to brass, lead, pewter, or lead-lined brass. A very recent novelty that had only just swept the area as a fad would presumably still retain greater uniformity.

The question remains: Why did not most of the Farther and East Indian populations hang onto the piston, knowledge of which must, according to the above explanation, at one time have reached them or their next-door neighbors? The answer lies in the unusual variety of fire-making devices rampant in the area: fire cord, fire saw, fire drill, flint and steel. There was too much competition for any one type to win out completely. Moreover, the piston is not easy to make: it must be true or it will not work; and while it is quick when it works, it takes a special knack to operate it. It is the most tricky and toylike of all the devices. Here and there, accordingly, we may suppose that it was kept up by individuals who liked playing with it—exhibiting it as a luxury article requiring skill. Elsewhere it came in but died out again in the face of simpler and more reliable apparatuses.

If this hypothesis is correct, the Far Eastern fire-piston distribution would have been, as regards its detailed irregularity, mostly the result of nonacceptance or of loss, of secondary disappearance.

235. TEXTILE PATTERNS AND PROCESSES

Rather strikingly similar diagonal and diamond-shaped patterns are woven in twilled baskets in parts of North and South America, in Asia and the East Indies, and in Africa.[3] Such a wide distribution for a type of design looks like parallelism; and it probably is parallelism. But it is presumably an implicit secondary consequence of the twilling process, as this in turn flourishes most vigorously where woody monocotyledonous plants—cane, bamboo, palms—are available to furnish hard, durable, flat, pliable splints. The technique of the weave is such that if materials of two colors are used, characteristic diagonal patterns evolve almost spontaneously; and diamonds or lozenges are two-way diagonal figures. The twilling process itself may have been invented independently in

---

[3] Twilling is distinguished by having the cross elements of weaving pass over or under two or more of the lengthwise elements at a time, with their insertion in successive rows or courses overlapping or staggering.

several of the regions using it, or it may have been devised only once in the world's history: it is too simple and ancient a technique for us to choose between these alternatives. But the patterns themselves are more likely to have been developed on the spot, as implicit derivatives from the more fundamental process of twilling.

The coiling technique for making baskets [4] looks from its distribution in Africa and about the Mediterranean, in East Asia and northwestern America, in Indonesia and Australia, and in the southern half of South America as if it might have originated independently several times, and there is partial confirmation in the fact that slightly different varieties of coiling usually characterize each area. If however increased knowledge fills most of the gaps between the areas, the art would then have to be regarded as possibly due to a very ancient diffusion. In that case, special varieties, such as half-hitch coiling in both Tierra del Fuego and Tasmania, and single-rod coiling common to the East Indies and California, would remain as instances of secondary parallels, as variations arose and rearose within the generic process. This would suggest that if any one of the varieties of coiling exists among a people, any of the other varieties stands a chance of being developed "spontaneously" by the same people, because all varieties are much alike in their basic distinctive principle.

A blending of diffusion and parallelism is apparent also in other textile processes. The fundamentals, as embodied in simple woven basketry, mats, and wiers, were perhaps already carried into America by the first immigrants. Weaving from suspended warps and in an incomplete loom frame may possibly have been similarly transmitted by diffusion, or may have been developed locally. The complete loom for fine cotton or wool threads, and the heddle shed, were quite likely devised in the middle region of native America independently of their invention in the Old World, as indicated by their absence from the connecting areas of North America and Siberia. But the treadle shed, the next step in efficiency in the Eastern Hemisphere, was never invented in the Western, so that at this point the parallelism ends.

Again diffusion and convergence both enter into the history of what is known as resist dyeing, that is, the covering of portions of textile patterns before immersion into the dye. Batik, when wax is used as the protecting medium, is one form of resist dyeing. Another method is to tie little bunches or knots of the cloth with a cord that has either been soaked in clay or wax or is spun from a fiber that has no affinity for the colors, and then to dip the tied web into the pot. This is tie dyeing. The third method, ikat, consists of respectively protecting and exposing measured spaces on the warps, so that a pattern appears after

---

[4] Coiled baskets are made with an awl or a needle. The continuous foundation progresses spirally. The "weft" or sewing element, which is also continuous or "single" in principle, lashes together successive courses of the foundation, or parts of courses. The foundation may contain a single rod, two rods and a splint, three rods, a package of splints, a bundle of straw, and so on.

weaving. In the Old World, resist dyeing is of Asiatic, probably Indian, origin, and was in use by the seventh century, perhaps earlier. Either Hindu colonization or Mohammedan conquest may have carried the art east to Indonesia on the one hand; Islamic influences almost certainly did carry it to North Africa and to Spain on the other; thence it was transmitted to the Indians of Guatemala after their subjugation by the Spaniards—like the double-headed eagle (§ 190). The Peruvians, however—also as in the case of the double-headed bird—had independently hit upon tie dyeing, as is attested by textile remains in graves of the Tiahuanaco period, several centuries earlier than the Inca Empire and the Spanish conquest. Here then, on the basis of the distributions, we have a wide and long-enduring diffusion of the general resist-dyeing process, and a locally limited instance of independent invention for one phase of it.

236. PAN'S PIPES

A startling parallelism has been alleged between the Pan's pipes of the Solomon Islands in Melanesia and those of the northwestern-Brazilian Indians. The odd pipes differ, each from the next, by the interval of a fourth. The even pipes give notes halfway in pitch between the adjacent odd ones, and thus form another "circle of fourths." But the similarity does not end here. The absolute pitch of some examined instruments from Melanesia and Brazil is the same. Thus, the vibration rates in successive pipes are 557 and 560.5; 651 and 651; 759 and 749; 880 and 879! This is so close a coincidence as to seem at first beyond the bounds of accident. The data have in fact been offered as evidence of a historical connection between the western Pacific and South America. Yet the connection would have had to be ancient, since no memory of it remains nor is it supported by resemblances in race, speech, or by anything very obvious or general in culture. The instruments are perishable. Primitive people, working by rule of thumb, would be unable to produce an instrument of given absolute pitch except by matching it against another, and perhaps not then. Moreover, it is not known that absolute pitch is of any concern to them. It is therefore incredible that this correspondence rests on an ancient diffusion: there must be an error in the record, or the one coincidence in a thousand has happened in the particular instruments examined.

The identity of scale, or intervals, however remains, and may be true parallelism. Only, as so often, it boils down to a rather simple matter. The circles of fourths evidently originate in the practice, in both regions, of overblowing the pipes. This produces overtones, of which the second one, the "third partial tone," is the fifth above the octave of the fundamental, so that successive notes in either the odd or the even series of pipes would, on the octave being disallowed, differ by fourths, which are the complements of fifths. The basis of the resemblance, then, is a physical law of sound. The cultural similarity shrinks to the facts of pipes in rows, the intercalating odd-even series, and the use of over-blow. These resemblances are striking, but they are generic enough to seem within the range of probability of separate, recurring origin.

237. BRONZE

A striking case of an independent development that is almost certain is offered by the history of bronze. Bronze is copper alloyed with from 5 to 20 per cent of tin. The metals form a compound with properties different from those of the two constituents. Tin is a soft metal, yet bronze is harder than copper, and therefore superior for tools. Also, it melts at a lower temperature and expands in solidifying from the molten condition, and thus is better material for castings.

In the Eastern Hemisphere bronze was discovered early—in the fourth millennium b.c.—and used widely. For two thousand years it was the metal par excellence of the more advanced nations. A Bronze Age is recognized as one of the great divisions of archaeological time in southwestern Asia, Europe, and China (§ 284, 294, 299).

In the Western Hemisphere bronze was invented much later than in the Eastern, and spread less extensively. It was discovered in or near the Bolivian highland, which is rich in tin, probably not until about a.d. 1000, because early Andean remains lack bronze, though containing copper. From there its use diffused to the Peruvian highland, then to the coast, then north to Ecuador and south to interior Argentina. The result is that a limited area in the New World attained to bronze about fifteen hundred to two thousand years after much of the Old World began to pass from bronze to iron weapons and tools.

Theoretically, it might be queried whether knowledge of bronze had possibly been carried to the Andes from the Eastern Hemisphere by some now forgotten migration or culture transmission. Against such a supposition there stands out first of all the isolated and restricted distribution of the South American bronze art. It is ten thousand miles by land from the metalworking nations of Asia to the middle Andes. A people or a culture wave that had traveled so far could hardly have failed to leave traces of its course by the way.

The theory of a Chinese or a Japanese junk swept out of its course and washed on a South American shore might be invoked. But the original South American bronze culture occupies an inland mountain area. Further, while Asiatic ships have repeatedly been wrecked on the Pacific coast of North America, and probably at times also on that of South America, there is everything to indicate that the civilizational effects of such accidents were practically nil. The highest cultures of Mexico and South America were largely evolved in interior mountain valleys or plateaus. Not one of the great accomplishments of the American race—architecture, sculpture, mathematics, metallurgy—shows specific or original localization on the actual shores of the Pacific.

Further, it is hard to understand how the arrival of a handful of helpless strangers could initiate an enduring culture growth. It is easy enough for us, looking backward through the vista of history, to fancy the lonely Indians standing on the shore to welcome the strangers from the west, and then going with docility to school to learn their superior accomplishments. Actually, however, people normally do not feel or act in this way. Nations are far more often imbued with a feeling of superiority. They look down upon the foreigner. Even where they admit his skill in this matter or that, they envy rather than admire him. Thus, there is historical record of Oriental and European vessels being wrecked on the Pacific coast of North America, during the last century and a half, among tribes that were still almost wholly aboriginal. In no case did the natives make a serious attempt to absorb the higher culture of the strangers. Generally these were enslaved or killed, their property rifled; sometimes the wreck was set on fire. The greed for immediate gain of the treasures in sight proved stronger than any dim impulses toward self-improvement by learning.

As one conservative author has put it, occasional visits of Asiatics or Pacific Islanders to the shores of America would be, from the point of view of the growth of the vast mass of culture in that continent, "mere incidents." On the basis of archaeology the accumulation of American culture, after its first primitive start, seems so consecutive and step-by-step a process as to leave a strong impression that it was overwhelmingly determined from within—metallurgy along with the rest of it. More on this in § 315-317.

238. AGE AND AREA

The age-and-area or age-area principle, first applied in palaeontology and in historical or evolutionary biology, has had some use in historical anthropology also. It is a method of inferring probable reconstructions of what happened in particular situations that resemble other situations in which the principle has actually been known to be operative. It includes the idea of the survival of old forms of culture at the remote margins, as already discussed in § 173-174.

For instance, until the British changed conditions in Australia by settling it, that continent contained only marsupial mammals, no placentals [5]—although contrariwise a few marsupials survive in the overwhelmingly placental faunas of the other continents, such as our North American opossum. These occasionals however are evidently relicts, nearly smothered out by competition with the more intelligent, aggressive, and adaptive placentals. Australia, on the other hand, has through most of geological history been cut off from the other continents. It was connected once, very early in the history of the mammals, long enough to receive some marsupial invaders, but became separated again before

[5] Except bats, and the dingo, a feral dog almost certainly introduced by man.

any placentals reached it, with the result that its marsupials luxuriated without competition. Where the later and more advanced placentals originated is not known, and does not matter in the present connection, because the other continents have all at one time or another, or repeatedly, been interconnected by land bridges. Europe, Asia, and North America together form "Holarctica" (§ 174). Consequently, whatever new and successful mammals one continent originated had a chance to spread to the others.[6] Thus, the horse and camel families originated in America but reached Eurasia-Africa; in fact, the whole horse tribe had died out again in America before 1492, while Asia and Africa still have wild horses, asses, and zebras. By contrast, felines and bovines as classes are Old World groups originally, but the jaguar, the mountain lion, and the bison are American in specific origin.

The upshot of all this is twofold. First, Australia is, geologically, precariously marginal to the other continents, and therefore possesses a mammalian fauna that is a living relict from an ancient phase of mammalian evolution. Second, the other continents as a unit have progressed by developing a variety of new forms with increased adaptability and survival ability, while Australia stood still.[7]

The same situation holds for native Australian culture, and for the same reason: it has been the most nearly cut-off and therefore remote of the continents during the tens or hundreds of thousands of years that man and his culture have been spread over the earth—comparable to its millions of years of isolation since the early mammals. Native Australia lacks not only all agriculture, metals, and structures other than brush huts, but it lacks even simple-culture features such as the bow, pottery, and for the most part boats, as well as gambling and alcohol (§ 157, 232, 233). Its tangible culture is so rudimentary and meager as to have provoked the theory that it is a modern survival of the Mousterian. This last hypothesis is wrong in singling out this specific European phase of the Palaeolithic as ancestral specifically to Australian blackfellow culture. But it is sound in designating the Australian general level as retarded by thousands of years behind the Eurasiatic or even the African and native-American levels of culture. The voids left in Australian indigenous culture by this unusual retardation were partly filled by luxuriations of what it did have: complex social

[6] Of the other continents, South America was oftenest or longest separated from the rest by water gaps at Panamá, and has therefore the most specialized fauna—sloths, armadillos, platyrrhine monkeys—as well as the most conspicuous lacks, such as all bovines, antelopes, wolves. In degree of marginality, South America thus is next to Australia; and it stands next to it also in the relict quality of its mammals, including the greatest number of marsupial species outside of Australia.

[7] Such major standing-still however allows special luxuriations to take place among what there is. Among such luxuriations are the great array of eucalyptus trees in Australia, and the diversification of its marsupials into functional hunters, burrowers, climbers, and so on.

groupings and marriage laws on a kinship basis, and these in turn connected with a primitive but rich circular system of totemism, myth, and magic ritual (§ 310). There is even one concrete originality that must be accredited as particular to Australia: the curved and warped throwing-club that we call the boomerang. But in the main the broad correlation holds that Australia, the most remote and isolated of the continents, is also the most rudimentary and backward in culture.

Divination from viscera and birds, as discussed in § 192, can also be seen as an age-area exemplification. Borneo and Luzon are certainly geographically at the edge of the Eastern Hemisphere land mass, and their pagan tribes, within a region to which Brahmanism, Islam, and Christianity have penetrated, are obvious cultural relics; whereas southwestern Asia and southern Europe, from which we have the first recorded occurrences of liver divination and bird augury, have certainly moved on in cultural level in the last three to four thousand years.

Blood sacrifice—the slaying of domestic animals and the shedding of their blood as gifts to the gods—is a clear case of perpetuation of ancient practices at the remote margin. We have already seen (§ 128, 192) that it is a contemporary custom of the West African and other Negroes beyond the sphere of Islamization. It survives sporadically in India; among the same pagans of Borneo and the Philippines that practice ancient divination; among some of the non-Buddhist tribes of Farther India and interior China, such as the Lolo; and, until recently, among the Manchu. Even farther out, the Chukchi sacrifice both dogs and reindeer, and the Gilyak and the Ainu keep bears to slay them ritually. This is certainly a marginal line along the south, east, and north rim of the mass of territory held by the great "world religions."

These three religions—Christianity, Islam, and Buddhism—superseded the earlier sacrificing religions, and were all three definitely set against blood sacrifice, even though for somewhat different reasons. Formerly, in all the great central area, blood sacrifice was an integral part of religious cult, whether among Greeks, Romans, Etruscans, Druids, Egyptians, Mesopotamians, Indians, or Chinese. The Book of Leviticus is full of prescriptions for sacrifice (§ 128), as Genesis relates cases of it—Abraham and Isaac and the ram, for instance. Down to the sack of Jerusalem in A.D. 70, there was a stream of victims brought to the high priests there. It was only after the destruction of the Temple and the Diaspora or scattering of the Jews, and as a parallel to the giving-up of sacrifice by the inhabitants of the Roman Empire as they become converted to Christianity, that the Jews tacitly dropped the practice, disobeying Old Testament injunctions. Similarly, in India sacrifice was basic among the Vedic Aryans and the earlier Brahmans, but Buddhism repudiated it, and the higher forms of later Brahmanism more and more abandoned it. Just so, the older national cults of China in Chou times included animal sacrifice, especially of a boar, a ram, and a bull, agreeing exactly with the Roman offering known as suovetaurilia. But the more rationalized and sophisticated official recent religion that is the gradual precipitate of the B.C. rituals, and which we call Confucianism and ancestor worship, confines itself to tablets and inscriptions—paper or verbal substitutes for images, victims, magic, and blood.

It is clear that this very ancient institution of sacrifice has been preserved mainly at the remote edges of its occurrence. Equally important is the point that this ancient bloody practice, in having got displaced by something more symbolic in the central regions of advancement, also illustrates one of the ways in which progress takes place, as is more fully discussed in § 128.

239. RECONSTRUCTION OF THE GROWTH OF A PRIMITIVE RELIGION

The age-and-area principle is concretely illustrated by the cults and ceremonial dances of the Indians of California, with a broad spread shown by the presumably old rites, and a localized distribution characterizing the specializations that seem late. The situation is in no way unusual; it is chosen as an example because of the accident of the writer's familiarity with the data.

All over native California and for long distances beyond in every direction—in fact, over western North America generally—the Indians practiced a Girls' Adolescence Rite at the onset of physiological puberty. In spite of numberless local variations in detail, the rite possesses constant features, based on the belief that the girl who is at this moment passing from childhood to maturity is undergoing a critical transition. A girl who at this period did not show fortitude to hardship would be forever weak and complaining: therefore she fasted. If she carried wood and water industriously, she would remain a good worker all her life, whereas if she defaulted, she would grow up a lazy woman. So crucial, in fact, was this moment that she was thought extremely potent upon her surroundings, as constituting a latent danger. If she looked abroad upon the world, oak trees might become barren and the next year's crop of acorns fail, or the salmon refuse to ascend the river. Among some tribes, therefore, the maturing girl was covered with a blanket, or set under a large basket, or made to wear a visor of feathers over her eyes. Others had her throw her hair forward and keep her head bowed. She was given the benefit of having ancient religious songs sung over her, and dancers revolved around her night after night. Recurrent rules are that she must not eat meat, fat, or salt; must not scratch her head with her fingers, but use a stick or bone implement made for the purpose; must not look at people; and must be sung over, or danced with.

What can be inferred from this essential near-uniformity and broad spread? It seems fair to try the presumptive conclusion of antiquity, to assume that this girls' rite is representative of an old stratum of native religion.

Less widely distributed are the Mourning Commemoration or Anniversary and the First-Salmon Rite. The Mourning Commemoration was practiced in southern and central California (Fig. 28, overleaf). It was a custom of bewailing each year, or at intervals of a few years, those members of the tribe who had died since the last performance, with the burning of large quantities of wealth— shell money, baskets, and the like—in their memory. Each family made offerings for its own dead, but people of special consideration were honored by having crude images of them constructed, and consumed with the property. Until the anniversary rite had been performed, the relatives of the dead remained quasi-mourners. After it, they were free to resume normal enjoyment of life; and the name of the deceased, which until then had been strictly taboo, might now be bestowed on a baby in the family.

In northern California and for a considerable stretch of the Pacific coast beyond, a leading shaman or chief of each locality conducted the First-Salmon ceremony at the beginning of each year's run. Until he had done this, no one fished for salmon or ate them. If any got caught, they were carefully returned to the river. When the medicine man had gone through his abstinences and prayers, he caught and ate the first fish of the year. After this, the season was open. To eat salmon no longer brought illness or antagonized the salmon and drove them away. The prayers recited propitiated them and caused them to run abundantly. There is clearly a communal motive in this "first-fruits" type of rite, even though the performance was entrusted to an individual.

Still more restricted in distribution are four sets of religious performances limited to as many areas of characteristically individuated native culture, and in their most developed and special forms restricted to a focus or climax in which each culture culminates. Thus:

Northwestern California: Esoteric ceremonies by a priest knowing the requisite formulas and acts to *renew* or *re-establish the world* for another year. He fixes the earth firmly against earthquake and flood, also protects it against famine and pestilence. Sometimes he lights new fire. Then the people celebrate by dancing, bringing out the family heirlooms of rare skins, fine featherwork, giant flint blades, each of the rich men vying to display the greatest wealth of such treasures. The height of these customs is localized among three tribes who alone make the splendid and precisely regulated deerskin and jumping dances.[8]

North-central California: The characteristic rituals are those of the Kuksu Society, in which boys or young men are initiated and learn to disguise themselves and impersonate Kuksu, other gods and spirits, or ghosts of the dead. The most elaborate and sumptuous of these dramatic performances was the *hesi* dance, performed only by a few of the most prosperous tribes.[9]

[8] Yurok, Karok, Hupa.

[9] Strictly, only Patwin and northwestern Maidu made the *hesi,* but some of the Nisenan had in the *akit,* and some of the Pomo in their *dama.* an equally elaborate performance.

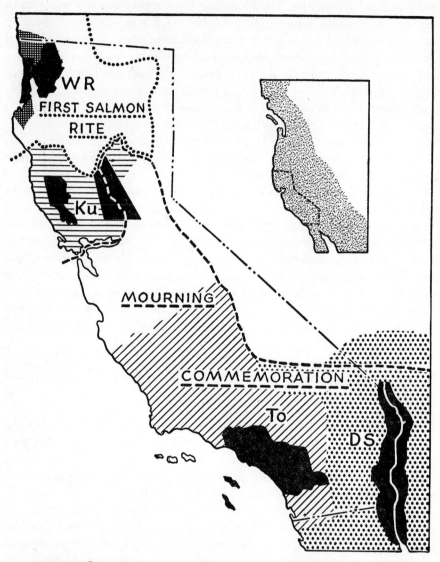

FIG. 28. HISTORY OF CALIFORNIA INDIAN RELIGIONS

Inset, range of Girls' Adolescence Rite, presumably extremely ancient. Heavy dotted and dashed lines in main map, First-Salmon Rite and Mourning Commemoration, with next widest distribution in California. Shaded areas, total range of World Renewal (WR), Kuksu (Ku), Toloache (To), and Dream Singing (DS) cults; with the region of highest development or climax of each shown in black. These are almost certainly relatively recent.

Southern and south-central California: Initiation of youths with *toloache* or jimson-weed drug (*Datura* species). The narcosis is accompanied by visions, which were considered sacred. Nearly all the dances of these southern tribes are made by men who have been initiated with *toloache,* though they are not disguised as spirits. The localized and presumably late specialization of the Toloache Initiation is the Chungichnish cult, named after a powerful, supreme, rather spiritually conceived high god. This Chungichnish cult was so late that it was still spreading in the nineteenth century. Its source was among the Gabrielino of Catalina Island,[10] and it is just possible that it originated from a reflex in the native mind to what the first missionaries had preached about the Christian God in the late eighteenth century.

Southeastern California: Characteristic cults of the desert region are long *cycles of dreamed songs,* sketchily narrating a mythological story. These cycles are sung both at celebrations, such as over the scalp of an enemy, and as a "gift" in honor of dying or dead kinsfolk. The greatest specialization is among the farming tribes along the Colorado River,[11] who maintain the extraordinary belief that their singers have actually witnessed the myth they sing about, through having projected their prenatal souls out of their mother's womb back into the beginning of the world. The same tribes have further "spiritualized" their religion by giving up practically all visible ritual, such as shrines, temples, and regalia, and even nearly all dancing except that done for entertainment.

The total distributional situation is shown in Figure 28: the very wide spread of the Girls' Adolescence Rite, the lesser extent of the Mourning Anniversary and the First-Salmon Rite, the definitely restricted four areal cults, and the highly focal specializations within these. That these four sets of developments also represent four stages in time cannot of course be demonstrated from distribution alone: historical or archaeological evidence would be needed for proof positive, and may be difficult ever to bring completely. However, it does seem reasonably probable that the general course of development in time is successively represented by the narrowing distributions. This succession would not necessarily have to hold at every point. Conceivably, for instance, the Mourning Anniversary might have begun later, or reached its full spread later, than the first rudiments of either the Kuksu or the Toloache Initiation, without seriously invalidating the general trend toward specializations' having occurred later in proportion as their recent distribution is more restricted.

When we pass from religion and cults to other aspects of native culture, the same sort of variation can be expected: from wide and presumptively old distributions to narrow and relative recent ones. It would be going too far into the minutiae of Californian ethnography to discuss these additional traits in

[10] It spread to the Juaneño and the Luiseño.
[11] Notably the Yuma and the Mohave.

detail. But the diagram on the facing page shows the distributional range of a few important technological, social, and intellectual features characteristic of the increasingly localized subcultures, in addition to the religious captions in bold-face type.

It may be objected that this sort of scheme of inference leaves no room for the occasional swift, convulsive spreads, which might come late but diffuse far; and that if any such occurred in our area, they would disrupt the argument. This is true. But there are two reasons why it is unlikely that any such spasms of a serious order occurred.

First, there is in native California no evidence of anything irruptive, of ends of great movements flowing in from elsewhere. The introduction of a higher religion such as Buddhism or Islam, or even of a powerful one like Mexican human sacrifice, would easily have upset the regular, slow, steady development we have tried to trace; but there are no remnants or traces of such influences. Cultural growth evidently was unusually autonomous and uninterrupted in and about the historically remote backwash of indigenous California. The quite slowly changing archaeological remains confirm this (§ 324).

Second, the coming of the Caucasian caused some flare-up reactions that did spread rapidly. But they also died again almost as rapidly; and they contain features that stamp them as intrusive reaction formations. Such was the "California Ghost Dance" of 1870, a precursor of the more famous Ghost Dance which wildfired the tribes west of the Mississippi around 1890—both of them typical "nativistic" revival attempts (§ 180). This world was to end, the white men were to be swept away, the Indians to be restored to their dead kin and their old way of life. Such a cult originates when a culture is felt to be disintegrating, not while it is still in orderly growth. Then there is the modern Peyote religion, built around the alkaloid-drug effect of a Mexican-Texan cactus, which spread intertribally in the United States for over sixty years, until it finally reached the edge of California and got itself established there in 1936. Even if we lacked all historical knowledge of this cult—or if we tried to assume that a similar cult had originated and had spread centuries ago, and some of it survived among the present Indians of California—we could probably soon discern it as being recently intrusive into the steadily progressive normal California development. First, by the peyote cactus itself, which would constantly have to be re-imported from Texas-Mexico. And second, by the Christian features absorbed into the modern anti-Christian nativistic Peyote religion: God our Father, references to Jesus, universal peace and goodwill, meetings from Saturday to Sunday night.

240. SUMMARY

The following recapitulates the argument of this chapter as it has wound its way among a diversity of exemplifications.

Information is incomplete on the history of many customs, institutions, and

Northwestern Subculture Area   Central Subculture Area   Southern Subculture Area   Lower Colorado Subculture Area

IV

Northwestern	Central	Southern	Lower Colorado
Property Law Deerskin Dance	Feathered Basketry Hesi Dance	Soapstone Carvings Chungichnish Cult	Loss of Sweat House Loss of Dances

III

Northwestern	Central	Southern	Lower Colorado
Plank house Nontribal Society Concept of Prehuman Race World-Renewing Wealth-Display Ceremonies	Mother-in-law Taboo Nameless Tribelets Concept of Creator Kuksu Society	Coiled Cap Basketry Water Bottle Plain Pottery Concept of Dying God Jimsonweed Society	Agriculture Tribal Cohesion, War Decorated Pottery Concept of Dying God Dream Singing

II

Hoppered Slab Mortar, Overlay Twined Basketry, Sinew-backed Bow

First-Salmon Rite

Mortar, Bow, Coiled Basketry, Totemism

Mourning Anniversary

I

Fire Drill, Metate, Twined Basketry, Self Bow, Sweat House

Girls' Adolescence Rite

RECONSTRUCTION OF SUCCESSIVE PHASES OF RELIGION AND CULTURE IN NATIVE CALIFORNIA AS TENTATIVELY INFERRED BY AGE-AND-AREA PRINCIPLE APPLIED TO DISTRIBUTION AND TYPOLOGY OF PATTERNS AND TRAITS

implements, and even more so on their origin. This is obvious and expectable for peoples without writing; but it holds also to considerable degree for nations with a written history, because annalists and historians tend to take such things as customs and tools for granted. Archaeology sheds a flood of light into some dark corners, little or none into others. Recorded testimony of direct eyewitnesses being lacking, methods of making inferences from indirect evidence have been developed by ethnologists and culture historians to take their place. While these methods cannot in principle claim certitude, they do in favorable cases attain high probability. Even where they result in findings of only moderate probability, this is often the best we have.

In these half-lit domains where illumination is being slowly increased, the first question about any cultural feature, be it institutional or technological, is likely to be whether its several more or less similar recurrences among several peoples or in several parts of the world go back to a single origin or to several. This is by no means always the first answer to be given about the feature in question, and it may be the last one found. But it is an aspect of the problem in which interest is perennial until satisfied, and one which is likely to be interwoven with any other results of interest ascertained as to the matter.

If the origin is multiple, the subsidiary problem may arise whether the developments of the several occurrences really ran parallel courses from the beginning, or whether they originated quite differently and later became more or less assimilated, and why. In practice the distinction cannot always be observed, for lack of evidence. Convergences have some precedent in organic evolution, and, as there, the resemblances are expressed chiefly in function, the structures remaining diverse—and incidentally proving the course of development to have been the convergent one from greater dissimilarity to partial similarity.

Even though the origin prove to be single, first appearances may be to the contrary because of the magnitude of changes that took place in persistence over long periods and spread over wide areas. All Indo-European languages, all alphabetic writings, all use of tobacco, go back to a unitary beginning, though this would hardly be suspected on superficial acquaintance with the facts.

It is also possible for both processes to take place in the same feature at different times or places; for instance, the probably separate origins of the use of metallurgy and intoxicants in the two hemispheres, but with an intraconnected, varied history in each.

Of the indirect evidences used in analysis, typology and distribution are the most important. Typology involves dissecting the institution or the implement in its several forms to ascertain its essential structure. Distribution is the total record of occurrence of a trait in geography, and if possible in time. The necessity of understanding structure is obvious: without it, noncomparables may be equated, or comparables not associated. The need for distributional knowledge is evident as soon as it is realized that the questions of ethnology and culture history are not abstract problems of principle to be solved by reasoning from structure alone, but specific problems of what happened when and where and how. All the precedent of evolutionary biology is to the same purport.

A special and extreme case of these methods is the age-and-area procedure, also based on biological precedent. This procedure employs typological analysis and distribution data, and adds to them the principle of development, spread, and central-marginal differentiation. Employed mechanically, the method can lead to absurdities; but if used with discretion, it can yield outline or summary probabilities. It is a process of reconstruction, as, fundamentally, is all doing or "finding-out" of history. Such a process is more difficult than ordinary formal history, because in history the time and the order of events are factually given by documents as a sort of external skeleton, and the historian's main task is to reconstruct what really happened in this framework, and why, and its significance. But in age-and-area reconstruction, even the order of events must be built up by inference from the results of the events. The task is therefore longer and more intricate than in conventional history, and results of equal precision and reliability cannot be expected.

CHAPTER FIFTEEN

Cultural Psychology

241. PSYCHIC UNITY OF MANKIND

IT IS self-evident that in every cultural situation there also necessarily inheres biopsychic activity: without men and minds there would be no cultural forms, activities, or changes. Cultural activity might be described as bodily-mental activity—"psychological" functioning—specially directed and shaped by impinging past and present culture. Students of cultural phenomena, whether anthropologists, sociologists, or historians, have always recognized that their material contains psychological aspects. But they leave these implicit, or make them explicit only at points; at any rate, they do not reduce their data to psychology. Reciprocally, all modern psychologists recognize that the total picture of any natural or spontaneous human situation always contains a cultural ingredient. They never actually encounter a "pure" unconditioned mind; that is a concept or abstraction: culture has always affected human minds—before the psychologist can examine them. The business of psychologists, however, is to try to hold this cultural factor constant in a given situation, to account for or to equalize it, and then to proceed to their own specific problems of investigating the mind *as if* it were "pure," of investigating the psychic aspects of the behavior of individual human beings, and after that of man in general.

In a corresponding way, anthropologists and historians normally begin with the tacit assumption that human nature,[1] in the gross and in the mass as it

---

[1] "Human nature" is here understood in its everyday sense, not with the technical sense—almost the opposite meaning—which some psychologists give it, of that which is

occurs in societies, is sufficiently uniform to allow of its being treated as a constant. Transmission of culture from generation to generation could not take place without loss or serious modification if the hereditary strain of the human culture-carriers varied considerably. Nor could culture material be diffused in space from population to population, often with ease and rapidity and sometimes with very little modification, if in its spread it encountered fundamentally diverse genetic strains, races with definitely distinctive endowments of faculty. We can infer from one human society to another, as regards capacity for essential interchange of their cultural functioning, as we cannot infer about capacities or behavior from dogs to cats or from cats to sheep.

The involved doctrine is the famous "psychic unity of man." This cannot be considered to be either a proved fact or an axiomatic principle; but it is so overwhelmingly borne out by the run of total experience that the anthropologist or the sociologist feels warranted in assuming the principle of essential psychic unity as at least a sufficient approximation to truth, and to employ it as a working hypothesis, or at any rate as a convenient symbol. He proceeds *as if* the principle were proved. He may be not conscious of this, just as the average historian constantly makes the assumption implicitly but might balk at an explicit avowal of it. The anthropologist continues to make the assumption because if he is impartial he finds that with it his work on culture leads to coherent and productive conclusions, but without it he bogs down before he has begun.

This does not mean that the question of panhuman psychic unity or equivalence is a settled one. For biology and psychology it remains a very real problem, and one of great interest. Only, it is a difficult and a complex problem because of the cultural factors that also enter it; and anthropologists obviously cannot suspend all study of culture until this tough nut has been cracked to their complete satisfaction, as well as to that of biologists and psychologists. It is indeed probable that the groups of men we call races are not absolutely identical in their make-up and faculties (§ 91). But it is clear from a great preponderance of the evidence that the differences between races are sufficiently minor to allow the essentially free flow of culture from one population and one generation to another, and to permit us to study the nature of these flows, and the nonracial changes and permanences of culture, with reasonable reliability. If this were not so, we should have to consign most of history, anthropology, and sociology to the scrap heap and begin over again with a psychosomatic genetic interpretation of man and his varieties.

Here, then, we have right at the outset a point where psychology and anthropology are in contact and in reciprocal interrelation.

---

wider or more common than the uniquely individual, but narrower than the universal (see § 246). This strange usage appears to be due to an ultrascientific leaning-back of some psychologists against the imputation of naïvely believing that we know anything about unconditioned human nature or that they would derive anything from it.

242. PERSONALITY IN CULTURE

Recognition of interpersonal relations, and hand in hand with them the recognition of individual personality qualities and differences, also have an important function in anthropology. Interpersonal relations may refer to the competitions and co-operations and adjustments between individuals in the same social group. In that event the term refers to a particular kind of psychology that emphasizes interindividual relations under proper consideration of the cultural frame. But again, study may be directed toward the effect that different kinds of culture have in producing different kinds of personalities and therewith coloring the interrelations of individuals in their societies; plus the reciprocal influence of such personalities on the maintenance or exaggeration or modification of their culture.

The recognition of personality and personality relations is of real significance in enhancing the understanding of culture by giving it body and reality—a stereoscopic sense of depth. We have seen (§ 6) that in one sense culture is an abstraction, a generalization inferred from many individual behaviors, statements, and happenings. One might query, if so minded, whether reality of existence can properly be ascribed to such an institution as marriage. One might say that the institution is a concept, only particular marriages between individual men and women possessing actual reality as phenomena. The "institution" comprises a set of rules and folkways, or laws and expectations, which rarely occur quite identically as we pass from one specific instance to the next. Among ourselves, among the rules or expectations are monogamy, being of age, the license, the wedding, its registry, the obligation to support, property claims, contingent rights to divorce; plus the expectation of love, fidelity, children, and so on. No deep argument is needed to prove that the expectations as well as the outcomes vary from couple to couple, from person to person; and that there are options or alternative choices at a great many points—whether to have a church or home or justice-of-the-peace wedding, or whether one bequeaths to his wife the legal minimum or his whole estate.

Any broad account of the institution is bound to suppress as much as possible the highly variable roles of the actual individual men or women concerned, and to become a catalogue of institutional features. It can even become a dry and lifeless listing, a bit like a law code. A half-dozen case histories of marriages are much more interesting, especially if the personalities are seized and rendered with spirit—why he married Joan and not Marjorie, and why then and not a couple of years before. Such anecdotes not only are vivid; they can also be extremely illuminating, like most gossip by intelligent people. But they are obviously not going to be very informative scientifically unless one compiles a great many cases and generalizes them.

To one who does want to learn about a custom, in order to compare it with the corresponding customs of other societies on the way to arriving at an inductive generalization of customs and culture, too much case history can be interminably delaying. It is a question of how far our interests are purely intellectual, or are diluted with aesthetic proclivities that insist on tempering the abstractions of science with portrayal of concrete, gossipy particulars. It is evident that an institution yields more of the "feel" of living reality when it is merely a background for the interplay of persons; but that it serves generalized understanding usefully in proportion as the colorful individualities and personalities are subsumed in the socially common features involved. It is much the same in history: the essentially literary historian puts us in constant touch with lifelike people; the profoundly intellectual one reveals rather the underlying drifts and major forces, and brings in personalities much less, and chiefly as exemplifications of situations and trends rather than as primary moving forces.

A less rigid construction is also possible: to see anthropology as dealing with culture expressed through and in persons. On this view, the subject matter of anthropology would be not merely culture as an abstraction, as a set of rules, as a series of depersonalized events, but culture with human beings living under and through it, conditioned by culture, adjusting to it, trying to manipulate it, now and then influencing and changing it a bit. From this angle, the skeleton of culture may be said to function, and to be fully understood, only as it is clothed by the flesh and blood of living personalities. This is an attractive way of presenting the situation: particularly to the outsider and the program-maker.

The working anthropologist is likely to receive it with a certain caution. He will ask himself whether we would know the larger things that we do know about the development of culture, about its processes and patterns, about the broad outlines of its history, if we had at every point tried to bring into the picture the fluctuations and clashes, the motives and variabilities, of the personalities concerned. Is it not essentially because on the whole anthropologists have abstracted from these individuals, have risen above them to a more generalized level, that we do know something of the forms and mechanisms of culture? The answer on the whole is Yes. If we had tried to bring in the full psychology of all the human beings involved in culture, we should have bogged in their endless welter. Specific progress in organized understanding is normally made by singling out certain aspects of the phenomena being studied and concentrating on these; by selective strategy rather than by an over-all, indiscriminate rush at the objective. After results have been attained, going back for reintegration and consolidation is in order. Anthropology is now in a position to call such a halt and review the tie-up with psychology. That is why this chapter is here. But it would hardly be in the book, or would be pretty empty talk, if anthropologists had not for the past generation or two pretty much forgone the temptation to psychologize, and had thereby discovered culture as such and piled up a gratifying amount of understanding of it.

The separateness of the two aspects—cultural forces and personalities—has been illustrated in a previous chapter, where the invention of the steamboat as a culture historical event has been outlined in § 185 and then followed in § 186 by a sketch of the personalities of the inventors. And, conversely, the interplay of the two is exemplified by the account in § 201 of how the Kota got themselves new gods.

The whole problem of the double aspect of our phenomena can also be seen as hingeing on how far we wish, in any given study, to carry or not to carry what might be called intellectual reductionism. In so far as we construe cultural happenings as personal ones, we explain them in psychological terms or "reduce" them to psychology. In the same way psychological happenings in individuals can be explained—actually only in part, but in theory and expectation wholly so—in physiological and biochemical terms, and psychology thereby reduced to physiology and biochemistry. One step further, and our physiological-biochemical findings are translated, or are theoretically translatable, into straight physicochemical factors. Such a reduction to the more underlying set of explanations has a great fascination for some minds, because it leads to the picture—or vision—of a seemingly unitary and simplified universe. The other side of the matter is that direct explanations regularly account for more phenomena than the reducing ones; and that they preserve certain qualities which get lost in the reduction process. Anger and fear can both be produced by adrenalin effecting vasomotor constriction. But anger and fear are actually quite different experiences, and can lead to opposite behaviors—without these differences' being explainable by the biochemistry of adrenalin. And so psychology can perhaps help us understand Fitch and Rumsey and Fulton, but it can never explain why France had the best roads, England the canals and good engines, but the United States the big empty rivers crying to be navigated. Reductionism is fine in its place. It interrelates the sciences, gives us a view of them as a larger whole, holds out the prospect of a grand unification. But it will not do the separate business of the several sciences, will not carry on their daily work. Reductionism is science straining at an ultimate philosophy, not a science doing its job. That is why psychologists continue to study anger and fear and other emotions in life histories, or by experiments, or with animals, instead of rushing to give adrenalin injections. And it is why anthropologists analyze cultural events and situations first of all in cultural terms—but remember always that cultural happenings are also personal and psychological happenings.

The ability to comprehend character and personal motivation is of course a psychological gift. But it is not necessarily formal scientific psychology: it may be allied rather to Thackeray or Shakespeare or Gibbon. It can plant the more arid stretches of the presentation of cultures with refreshing trees, and dot them with oases for which we must be grateful. But it is not in itself a theoretically intellectual activity. The intellectual discipline charged with dealing with personality and motivation and behavior is the science of psychology; and that is by no means a continuously lush oasis. Perhaps the strongest insistence yet made in anthropology on the "rights of the individual" was by Sapir, who was unusually sensitive aesthetically. But Sapir was and remained a superb ethnologist and contributor to the theory of culture, as well as one of the all-time great scholars in linguistics; and he who studies language inevitably deals with its patterns as a sociocultural phenomenon. Language, serving intercommunication, must be superpersonal to function at all. Language allows a final, slight personal touch of nuance, of style; but a greater injection of individuality than this cannot but lead to increasing unintelligibility and malfunction of speech. The linguist studies something that is in its nature overwhelmingly superindividual and anonymous.

Occasional anthropologists, inclined to anticipate the future by putting main emphasis on personality, may be assumed to be de-facto psychologists satiated with culture or uninterested in it from the beginning, so that they use it chiefly as a springboard. They are like the occasional psychological-laboratory workers specializing in brain anatomy or fatigue poisons who are actually doing physiology.

It is true, as Linton points out, that at present it is equally impossible to explain culture in terms of individual psychology and to understand it without some reference to psychology. After all, culture exists only through persons, in or by their behavior. Yet when we study culture, we concern ourselves primarily with those aspects of their behavior which are more than individual. Our generalizations, and therefore our specific scientific findings, are obviously on a more-than-individual level. But the individual and personalized substratum is still there. So far as we remain aware of the substratum, our depictions and analyses of culture retain a certain color and body and impression of life. So far as we are unaware of the underlying psychology, or indifferent to its suffusion, our cultural findings may be exact, but they tend to be arid, mechanical, and lacking in interest.

243. PSYCHOLOGICAL CONSIDERATIONS ALREADY ENCOUNTERED

Before proceeding farther into the psychology of culture, let us draw together in review the principal instances that have already been touched on in the course of this book.

Tradition on which culture rests for its continuance, and diffusion by which it spreads, viewed psychologically, are of course only imitation and learning (§ 123, 142). Imitation can be conscious or unconscious; learning, taught or untaught. Modern psychology gives much attention to learning, both animal and human. Imitation, and the related function of suggestion, were more in vogue a couple of generations ago, when the jurist-historian-philosopher Gabriel Tarde wrote his famous *Laws of Imitation*. Tarde is rich in illustrative cultural data, was translated into English by a social anthropologist, and his influence seems to have been greater on sociologists and anthropologists than on formal psychologists. Contemporary social psychologists appear to think that Tarde only described when he thought he explained—not realizing that this is characteristic of the historical as distinct from the experimental approach. Some of them say that the word "imitation" has become a cloak for ignorance, and ought to be replaced by "learning by human example." This sounds a bit like the corrective the ancient Chinese philosophers used to call rectification of names. Whatever we call it, we have here a good illustration of the relation of psychology and anthropology. The psychologist studies the mechanism of learning or imitation, as such. The anthropologist deals with what is learned or not learned; to wit, culture, and its structure or patterning, and the interrelations of cultures.

Since psychology entered its stimulus-response phase, it has been so concerned with conditioning, so impressed by its total influence on the plastic personality, that it is difficult to get psychologists to admit any genetic—inborn—differences between individuals; at any rate, any specific congenital differences. It is not that they deny the potential existence of such differences. But they cannot establish them with certainty; yet they can prove and measure a great deal of conditioning. The result is that they often proceed professionally *as if* individuals differed only in their environmental exposure and life experiences and not in their genes. This is a striking parallel to the attitude and procedure of anthropologists on race differences, as set forth in Chapter Five. Races may differ in their heredity, but the indubitable and ever present overlay of conditioning prevents us from proving it. So we proceed—must proceed when driven to it— *as if* race differences were wholly due to their historical conditioning.

Physiological needs and psychological "derived imperatives," already touched on in § 130, have been emphasized among anthropologists especially by Malinowski in an attempt to construct once and for all a complete and final theory of culture. It is now pretty well recognized that it is a perpetual snare to try to account causally for the endlessly varied forms of culture by tracing them back to a few organic needs or drives. Everyone agrees that physiological sex impulses underlie love and marriage. We even know something of the biochemistry as well as the effects of sex hormones. The real problem involved begins to be faced when it is realized that on the fairly simple sex-hormone situation there rest thousands of diverse forms of marriage and nonmarital sex customs, as just pointed out in § 242; much as there are hundreds of cuisines and kinds of table manners which obviously cannot be accounted for from the fact that all people have to eat to live and therefore get hungry. Even below the level of socialized culture, psychologists long since realized that the erotic psychic life of individuals varies enormously according to the conditioning and experience to which they have been exposed, and that only the simplest denominators of the phenomena can be explained by the organic sex equipment. A fortiori for the cultural phenomena.

Similarly, to account for, say, the art production of men under culture by invoking the "derived imperative" of an "aesthetic impulse" is a mere restatement of the facts, and barren except verbally.

The theoretical weakness of this position is revealed by the fact that at the same time that Malinowski thought he could derive culture from physiological needs and psychic imperatives, he was proclaiming culture "a reality *sui generis*" —as having an independent existence.

Conscious need of self-perpetuation as a basic drive of societies and cultures has been discounted in § 142. Not that societies do not wish to survive; but ordinarily they take for granted that they will. The whole matter of security about which we hear so much these days, both in psychology and in world affairs, has been tremendously magnified in our awareness as compared with our grandfathers. Perhaps our ancestors felt equally insecure, but they certainly let on about it less. The shift looks like a fashion change in social feeling that has invaded scientific thinking.

Psychological bases for certain specific and recurring cultural inventions have been invoked for: difficulty in invention of a zero sign (§ 189); tendency toward syllabic writing (§ 219); and doubt whether pictographic representation arises spontaneously (§ 202). These bases are not findings by psychologists but psychological inferences by anthropologists and historians from the forms and circumstances of the inventions.

Folkways (§ 116) underlie institutions and are customs, and customs may be called social habits. Social habits are also habits shared by individuals, and like these are acquired by conditioning, which in turn is a matter of repeated stimuli resulting in channeled responses.

Technologies involve manual or bodily activities, usually repeated, which establish motor habits (§ 143), which are perfectible to the point of virtuosity. Reciprocally, an extinction of technicians, or the enforced suspension of certain motor habits and skills for a generation, can lead to the loss of arts and technologies by a society (§ 157).

Several psychological factors enter into invention. On the primate level, control of emotion is of great importance in inventive problem-solving; but so is competition (§ 28); and impulses to destroy must be taken into account. The quality of insight, and of ability to profit by fortunate accident, which are recognized as close to the core of cultural invention (§ 147-148, 187), are sometimes perceptible among the more gifted anthropoids (§ 28). Play activity (§ 15, 29), direct or rechanneled, unquestionably enters into human inventing: occasionally perhaps into mechanical devices such as the bow and the wheel (§ 148); certainly at times into customs and institutions such as animal domestication (§ 165) and labile social and religious superstructures (§ 166-167).

The whole range of fashion, in style, in dress, and otherwise, not only crystallizes play impulses but undoubtedly expresses restlessness, tensions, surplus of energy, desire for change rather than for security (§ 137, 164). The cultural "fatigue" manifested by the pagan Hawaiians about their religion (§ 168) may be a metaphor, but it undoubtedly refers to an instability of attitudes.

Historical ambivalence of attitudes in intrinsically border-line situations is illustrated by the discussion of stepdaughter marriage (§ 167), both in primitive societies and in the contemporary United States.

Related to the changeableness of fashion is the sense of pride in the fleeting moment which in metropolitan and urban populations cumulatively replaces the pride of spot felt by peasant and rural peoples (§ 121). This change in turn involves a weakening of the strong sense of apartness and potential hostility that primitive and retarded groups regularly feel between their in-group and all out-groups, and which is an expression of strong identification with the in-group. This identification with a group, at any rate with a locally limited group, is what the cosmopolite and the sophisticate tend to replace by sense of immersion in a mass, with consequent loss of affective participation, of rooted attachment (§ 124). This matter will be touched on again in § 253.

This loss of the sophisticate is a loss of social attachments. There is an opposite condition, in which attachment to the group and to persons is strong, but attachment to possessions weak. The freedom of being unencumbered is prized, as among Australoids and Negritos (§ 120, 146). These attitudes in turn lead to a lack of interest and stunting of technologies which serve to manufacture possessions; and to a hand-to-mouth, reserveless subsistence economy.

The degree to which populations—and individuals too, mostly—are unconscious of their culture and take it for granted, or are only "foreconscious" or potentially conscious of it, has been stressed particularly in regard to language (§ 110). In language, sharply patterned form structure and unconsciousness of this structure coexist to a remarkable degree. In the fashionable terminology of the day, grammar is covert in speech. To a somewhat less marked and variable degree, the same holds for the other manifestations of culture (§ 116, 215).

Allied are the sensitive blind spots often covered by false rationalizations, in which societies indulge much like individuals (§ 116, 212, 216). Related to these, in turn, is the tendency of societies to forget the increments to and the changes made in their culture, largely even those occurring within living experience, and almost wholly as regards the farther past. This convenient forgetting makes possible a strong conviction of the functional integration of the culture. Such a conviction is evidently more useful to the society—as well as more pleasant—than active historical-mindedness. Folk history and popular history regularly minimize change and overemphasize integration and stability.

In proportion as stability is actual, especially in those parts of culture which necessarily function best as closed systems, like calendars and alphabets, strains sooner or later arise as other parts of the culture or the language change. "Reform"—that is, adjustment of the lag—is difficult in proportion as the system is tightly knit. Resistance to reform is in part affective attachment to habits; in part, realistic perception that the cost of change will fall largely on the present generation, its benefits accrue to future ones. False rationalizations find a favorable breeding-ground here, as well as subterfuges to cushion change that cannot be avoided. Sometimes conservatism is so entrenched in ramifications of sentiment that the violence of revolution or total authority is needed to break its resistance (§ 151, 170, 212, 216).

The dominance of social conditioning also accounts for the slowness with which certain inventions have been made whose essence is simplification of method or "reduction segregation"—Toynbee's etherialization (§ 155, 206-207). As might be expected, the reduction is more easily made by a population coming fresh to the problem than by the one that has accumulated and lived with the unnecessary accretions.

By no means all prohibiting puritanism of cultures is due to such tendency to innovate by reduction; but that it can be a factor seems to be established by the case of Islam (§ 172, 199).

Prestige considerations can be powerful advancing and retarding agencies in culture dynamics, as is evident from the competition of alphabetic and ideographic writing in Korea (§ 221) and of changes in Kota worship (§ 201).

The heart of the quality of culture resides in its patterns (§ 132-139), which represent its structuring or organization with relation to values (§ 125). The term "values" is here used in its current sense, which however also has some philosophical usage. It corresponds pretty well with "human values," provided that phrase is employed without its usual primary emphasis on common or universal values as if culture were uniform or consisted largely of common denominators. The common denominators are there, but all cultures also have particular qualities, and to allow for these we would have to expand our popular-term definition to "human values, both common and distinctive." To every value there is attached, or there corresponds, as Thomas long since pointed out, an attitude; and an attitude is an organization of responsiveness, an orientation of interest. At any rate, with attitudes we are admittedly in psychological territory: psychologists recognize and deal with them.

This whole important subject has only recently moved into the conscious consideration of students of culture and psychology, and will undoubtedly be developed further. Some exemplifications of its nature and scope have been given in § 125, 136-139.

Finally, there are the outright endeavors to represent whole cultures qualitatively by organizing them around the focus of a psychological or psychiatric concept, such as Apollinian or Dionysiac orientation, megalomania or paranoia. The virtues and limitations of this particular approach have been discussed in § 135.

The foregoing constitutes an unsystematic array, because the various psychological considerations have come up incidentally during a more or less orderly presentation of the nature and behavior of culture. From here on we can proceed somewhat more systematically in considering psychology.

244. NATIONAL TEMPERAMENTS OR TYPES

First of all, it is possible to take societies and cultures as they come, leave them whole, but try to characterize or describe their total cast or ethos in psychological instead of cultural terms. The terms or concepts would necessarily be those of individual psychology—at any rate in the beginning of our consideration.

Beyond this descriptive procedure, it is possible to try to seek out the psychological mechanisms at work in sociocultural situations in general; or to trace them comparatively as they appear in varying strength in the array of cultures that have existed in the world. These later procedures will be followed beginning with § 246, whereas the present section and the next will be concerned with characterizing descriptions.

Such characterizing descriptions can take two principal forms. Either a system of psychological types is set up, and cultures are fitted to these; or cultures may be empirically evaluated for the strength with which particular psychic factors or traits are represented in them. Both methods, as just admitted, involve a transfer from individuals to social groups. But this transferring should have validity, at least up to a certain point, because of the strong molding effect the culture of any social group has on its members, and because in turn the group consists of individual men.

We shall consider first the characterization by psychological types.

A number of type classifications devised for individuals are available: into extravert and introvert; into reasoning, feeling, intuitive, and sensory, according to Jung; into Dionysiac and Apollinian as taken over from Nietzsche; and so on. Scientifically, these types rate much like the constitutional bodily types discussed in § 79. They are open to the same limitation, that only a minority of cases correspond neatly to any conceptual type; the majority are intermediate or typologically indefinite. In short, there are good fits to the typological scheme, but they are only part of the total. With transfer of the method to the psychology of societies, this defect may be somewhat accentuated, and is certainly not removed.

The oldest of the type classifications—for individuals—interestingly enough is a strictly psychosomatic one. It is the famous classification according to "humors" by Hippocrates, the father of medicine, in the fifth century B.C. Bodily fluids and secretions, such as blood, mucus, bile, were supposed to give rise to dispositions or characters, of which four were recognized: sanguine, phlegmatic, choleric, melancholic. Methodologically, these four types are perhaps as arbitrary, and certainly as speculative, as the contemporary Greek selection of fire, air, water, and earth as the four "elements" of which everything material was thought to be composed. But chemistry has progressed farther than psychology, and the Greek elements are superseded by a set of 92 or more of a wholly different nature; whereas the Hippocratic characters are indeed sedulously avoided by modern professional psychologists, but without psychology's having evolved a notably better scheme for replacing them. Also, prescientific as both the Hippocratic dispositions and their supposedly causative humors are, the dispositions at any rate possess a degree of shrewd, empirical validity. We all can think of individuals who are splendid exemplifications of the sanguine or melancholic or choleric or phlegmatic type; though there are always more individuals who are only partial fits, or nondescript.

The types can of course also be applied nationally as well as individually, and sometimes have been so applied: though not, to be sure, by modern professional psychologists. Thus, the French and the Italians and the Irish would generally be described as sanguine; Scandinavians, Poles, and perhaps Russians as melancholic; Spaniards would probably come nearest to being choleric; Dutchmen and Germans are considered phlegmatic in Britain, whereas continental Europeans would put the same label on the British. Note however that these are all peoples belonging to one and the same larger society and civilization; they appear to differentiate sharply in temperament for the very reason that they are compared within the same European frame of reference, like the members of a family, a club, or other limited group. Americans might be harder to tag appropriately with one of the four labels, presumably because, though adhering to the same culture as Europeans, they live under new circumstances in another continent. Nations of antiquity, such as Romans, Greeks, and Hebrews, are also hard to characterize, and so are peoples of basically different cultures, such as Arabs, Hindus, Chinese, Japanese.

The philosopher Kant—for whose empirical characterizations in his *Anthropologie* see the next section—still accepted and dealt with the four Hippocratian temperaments, and grouped them. The sanguine and melancholic are temperaments of feeling, he says; the choleric and phlegmatic refer primarily to tension and action. In cross grouping, sanguine and choleric go together in that the affect or emotion comes and goes rapidly, melancholic and phlegmatic in that it rises slowly but persists. Kant denies composite temperaments; but he is silent on what to do about the temperamentally undifferentiated or subdifferentiated whom we would today assume to be in a majority.

Sapir has suggested applying Jung's individual personality types to nations. Apart from a primary division into extravert and introvert, which is now generally familiar through having seeped down to the man on the street, Jung recognizes four types prevailingly dominated by sensation, intuition, feeling,[2] or reason. The first two, in Sapir's translation, are considered less organized and the last two more organized. Feeling is thus as systematizing an activity as reason. Jung himself classed intuition along with sensation as "unorganized"—

[2] "Sensation" refers to sensory experience, "feeling" to emotion—cf. "feeling fine."

what is here called unsystematic. This was because he considered intuition as a mechanism for solving suspense by "irrational" or blind guessing; whereas Sapir construed intuition rather as a telescoped or stenogram-outline form of reasoning, the formal successive steps of demonstration being subconsciously perceived but overtly leaped over.

In this modified version of the fourfold Jung classification, Sapir sees the Latin nations as more sensory than northern Europeans. They indulge and culti-vate their senses; their ready aesthetic sensibility is due to the weighting with sensation. It might be added that they are often passionate in their actions be-cause they have few inhibitions; but they distrust and dislike prolonged feeling as a means of formulating thought. By contrast, Germans and Russians live much more largely in feeling, and much of their thinking is done essentially through it. In Americans the sensory elements are again lightly stressed; but intuitional propensities are strongly developed as compared with feeling. This of course would not mean that the characteristic American is callous, but that he is not at home with feelings and prefers not to operate with them if avoid-able. Like the Britisher, he is afraid to be thought guilty of gush and is uncom-fortable in the presence of it. He certainly tends to refrain from the uninhibited and immediate expression of feeling, and is averse also to prolonged reveling in it, to the *Duselei* of the German, or the "mooning" of the pre-Soviet Russian.[3]

Appraisals by this approach also become more difficult when extended to cultures different from our own. The ancient Hebrews were pretty surely of feeling type; but what were the Greeks and Romans? And how about still more remote India, China, Japan? Even there some measure of general agree-ment might perhaps be reached. The ascetic Hindu is presumably not sensory; or is his asceticism really a reaction formation to strong sensational develop-ment? As a mystic and a romantic he might be classed as of feeling type; but he is also an inveterate rationalist and arguer. And mysticism participates in intuition as well as in feeling. By common consent the Chinese are more sensory than the Hindus, and they tend to distrust feeling somewhat like Anglo-Saxons. But what is their basic ingredient? And how do they differ from the Japanese?

245. EMPIRICAL DESCRIPTIONS OF NATIONAL CHARACTERS

Perhaps one gets farther in these matters of national characters and cultural temperaments if one operates pragmatically from case to case with all the variable resources of description, instead of trying to force a fit to a scheme. Thus the Spaniard is individualistic and proud; the Frenchman has a passion

[3] How much national dispositions depend on culture is shown by this example. With the Bolsheviki coming into power, Russian culture was deliberately reoriented, and Russian temperament with it. One would not describe the contemporary Soviet character as a moon-ing one.

for clarity, reason, and money; the German alternates between sentimentality and throwing his weight around; the Russian is fatalistically resigned but cheerful and dogged. Of this nature, too, is the old Arab saying, seemingly first Englished by Gibbon, that God endowed the Arabs with excellence in the tongue, the Greeks in the brain, the Chinese (whom the Arabs knew better from their manufactures than in their institutions) in the hands.

Such appraisals may look like the "stereotypes" or derogatory labelings of ethnic groups about which modern social psychologists (§ 246), following the publicists on current affairs, have so much to say. But these appraisals differ from stereotypes in that they attempt an answer to a genuine intellectual problem, whereas stereotypes are emotional expressions of self-superiority used as substitutes for ascertaining the facts. That certain adjectives have now and then been applied in abuse does not remove them from scientific vocabulary. Anthropologists need hardly feel that they are going to be confused with hate-inciters because they see a problem in these matters of cultural and national psychology.

Popularly, national dispositions tend to be assumed as innate, but it is evident from the discussion of race in Chapter Five that heredity cannot be the principal factor, and that the dispositions must be due largely to cultural and historical causes. Thus, there is no doubt a temperamental difference between Englishmen and Americans as a whole, with Canadians pretty fairly intermediate. Yet Americans are descended in the main from Britons, and the non-British constituents in the American populational make-up are so diverse, and each of them is such a minor element in the total, that it is hard to see how these non-Anglo-Saxon elements could have pushed us away from the British prototype in any one consistent direction. They would rather neutralize one another and therewith leave Americans as slightly less characterized Britishers. That is certainly not the whole story of what happened. The typical Britisher appears to Americans slow in thought, speech, and action, and they in reverse seem volatile and vehement to him. There can be little doubt that Americans in general enjoy concentration of effort, instant decisions, quick mobilization, and all-out effort, even to exaggeration, where the English want to take their time, drift into commitments, and resent being hurried. The difference shows even in such supposedly physical activities as athletic sports: Americans excel in sprints and in field events that call for the crowding of supreme effort into a moment, whereas the British tend to surpass them in the grind of long-distance runs.

Many such appraisals, nonprofessional though they be, seem to rest on sound observation. The differentiations spring in the main from varying total-culture patterns that tend to impose different attitudes and habit formations on the majority of individuals of the population. The difficulty with the subject is that we cannot yet satisfactorily deal with it by accurate methods. To date, the approach has remained essentially subjective, intuitional, and common-sense. There is neither check of measurement nor control of experiment; and it is notorious that the topic can hardly be approached without a bit of coloring by our prejudices. This does not mean that considerations of the sort should be tabooed. They possess an undying interest for the student of man, and rightly so, because they touch what is supremely important in culture, its basic patterns and the value systems and orientations of these. It is better to proceed to some psychology by intuition than to have no psychological ideas at all—provided we realize our stabs and guesses to be only such.

Formal social science tends to be averse, as Sapir said, to characterizations of culture in psychological terms, but in the long run they are inevitable and necessary. They will no doubt continue to be made until some more verifiable approach is devised. Mostly, too, separately formed judgments agree surprisingly. For instance, in 1789 the greatest modern philosopher, Immanuel Kant, published his last work, which dealt with psychology, as we should call it, but which in line with the usage of the times he called *Anthropologie*. One of the final sections of this deals with the "character of peoples"—or as we might translate it, ethnic psychology.

His characterization of his own German countrymen remains of interest today. The German, he says, is home-loving; solid but not brilliant; industrious, thrifty, cleanly, without much flash of genius; phlegmatic, tough in endurance, persistent in reasoning; intelligent, capable, but lacking in wit or taste; modest, without confidence in his own originality, therefore imitative; overmethodical, pedantic; without impulse toward equality, but addicted to a painstaking hierarchical grading of society that sets title and rank above natural talent; docile under government, accepting despotism rather than resisting or altering the established order of authority. This was written more than a century and a half ago, when Germany was politically divided and impotent; but even after World War II most of it is still a surprisingly happy diagnosis. Or take this sketch of the Spaniard: ceremonious, grave, imbued with a sense of personal dignity and national nobility, though cruel; grandiloquent, but temperate in habits; devout and legalistic; unwilling to learn, resistive to reform; behindhand in the sciences; looking upon work as an evil or a misfortune. It is evident that these characterizations are made far more in terms of psychology than of institutions or culture. Nevertheless, Kant derives national temperaments partly from "culture," and partly from the diversity of ethnic origins. In this distinction he seems to be referring respectively to somewhat consciously directed cultivation, and to relatively spontaneous growth, both of them being within what we today call culture.

Characterizations or physiognomic judgments such as these may be regarded as attempted shorthand translations of the more general patterns of a culture, and especially of its ethos or values and standards, into terms of the psychological behavior of the generalized or averaged individual of the society to which the culture belongs. The judgments are subjective, but reasonably unprejudiced observers arrive at fairly concordant descriptions.

The following is what Morley of Chichen Itzá has to say on the modern Maya of the Yucatán Peninsula. They are industrious and hard-working even on a poor diet; cleanly in their persons but untidy with belongings; seemingly insensitive to suffering, fatalistic, and unafraid of death. They are conservative, and disinclined to lead or to assume public responsibility, but individualistically independent, though not at all competitive. They are talkative, sociable, cheerful, fond of practical jokes; are not highly sexed, but inclined to promiscuity; are strong on family ties, but not given to showing their affection. They have respect for law and a sense of justice; are honest, averse to thieving and begging; are not quarrelsome but do harbor revenge. And they are not religious, but strongly "superstitious"—which probably means that they do not bring much piety or feeling to their religion except the emotion of fear.

This characterization is based on thirty years of acquaintance. How much of a picture or conviction does it give to anyone who does not know the Maya or other American Indians? To the writer it seems an adequate rough description of Indians in general, even as far away as the United States, except for being somewhat sunnier; and this last characterization might be due to the fact that the Maya are a long-adjusted and a majority population, as compared with our Indians. Yet the question arises: How far would Morley's total characterization have applied also to the Maya of a thousand years ago, when their indigenous religion, art, architecture, astronomy, and hierarchy were flourishing? Most of the characterization perhaps would have held good at that time also, though both the content of the culture and its orientation would have been very different from that of today, when the Maya in effect are Catholic peasants or peons.

And that fact brings us to a consideration of some consequence. It seems possible, theoretically, for two peoples to show much the same psychological character or temperament and yet to have different cultures. The reverse seems also to hold: namely, that culture can be nearly uniform while national character differs. Western Europe, for instance, has basically much the same civilization all over, yet the temperaments of its peoples are sharply distinguishable. At any rate we are in the habit of distinguishing British, French, Spanish, Italian, and German national characters; even the smaller Irish, Dutch, Swiss, Portuguese, have their recognized distinctiveness in typical personality response. And to those who know Scandinavia, the Danes, the Norwegians, and the Swedes certainly present different temperaments. So do South English, North English, Welsh, and Scots among Britons. Are all these distinctions only the stereotypes of prejudice? Or mere conventional badinage? That hardly seems possible. And if so, then the normal or typical personalities of these several nations appear often to be more distinct than the cultures of these same nations. Or at least, to put it with less assumption, the psychologies seem in part to vary independently of the cultures.

If this is correct, then recent attempts to assign each culture a strict counter-part in a "basic personality structure" or "modal personality" type (§ 135) go too far. There can be little doubt that some kind of personality corresponds to each kind of culture; but evidently the correspondence is not one-to-one: it is partial. If this is so, we are not yet quite ready to describe exactly how a culture forces into a narrow mold each of its individual members, who then, in growing up, reperpetuate the culture. There is probably more play, more give, than that in the process. And part of our problem thus would be to ascertain how much of such give there is, how close the correspondence of culture and psychology is or is not, rather than to assume the correspondence as complete and confine our-selves to tracing out its detailed workings.

Let us consider some further cases.

Among the Papuanoid Indonesians of Alor in the Lesser Sunda Islands, the modal personality is described as that of teased, frightened, tolerated, half-abused children who have become adults full of fear, suspicion, spite, and tricki-ness. According to DuBois, the Alorese are wary, aggressive, touchy, given to chicane and hard dealing, but basically frustrated and confused. They are also greedily hopeful of people and always disappointed in them; this is inevitable, since they are ever exploiting them. They dispute with acrimony, shout, grasp weapons, swear curses—as readily toward spouses, affinals, or kin as to others. Then they sulk; but soon they eat together again or remove the curse by a sacrifice: they have no reserves of deep hate. Violence is feared, fortitude not highly prized, war carried on chiefly by treachery, bravery reckoned by success. Only lack of assurance and self-reliance keeps them from ruthlessness. There are no outstanding successes or accepted heroes in their society. Lacking internal conscience, they are sensitive to ridicule and derogation, and shame becomes the chief social sanction. Lying is taken for granted. A neighbor's disaster provokes pilfering of his effects. All skills, technological, ritual, or social, are at a low level for lack of prestige recompense; their execution is slovenly and slight; training for them is as inconsistent as their reward. When sick, the Alorese be-come depressed and give up; they have impulses toward suicide but rarely commit it and have not devised any institution for its occasions or forms. They are uninterested in intoxicants. All this suggests low and prevalently negativistic toning of affects. The chief symbol of euphoria is feeding: and that in super-natural as well as social relations. Women's power lies in control of food, which is grown chiefly by them; but they receive no corresponding status. Men have the status, but lack power and security. And as the children are exposed to whims instead of steady affection, everyone manages to seem chronically un-happy. The Alorese are discontent, distrustful, and exploitive of human beings and spirits alike; only danger makes them placatory.

This characterization seems one-sidedly repellent. Can any people actually be so unmitigatedly disagreeable and contemptible? The appraising observer comes from a culture that values internalization, conscience, reliance, scruple, courage, consistency of feeling and relations, dignity, and achievement—qualities that are underdeveloped in Alor. Hence the picture is black. We see no positive values in the culture, and therefore no virtues of character in the typical personality. So far as the culture seems to have values, it is for food, power, and prestige on a wholly infantile or even primate level—irrespective of how they are acquired. That the prevailing slants of behavior in Alor are as represented can hardly be doubted; but a more picaresque-minded observer might have drawn a somewhat more sympathetic portrait of Alorese personality. Subjectivity is difficult to eliminate wholly from these psychological characterizations of cultures.

It will be of interest to compare recent temperament characterizations for two neighboring nationalities of very similar culture, the Burmese and the Siamese.

Among the Burmese, according to Gorer, who moved from psychoanalysis into anthropology, women are good-humored, cool, impersonal, kindly, firm, efficient, and helpful. They manage the household, do most of the business, control the family money, and generally dominate, but without claiming dominance. As girls they act coy, but as wives and mothers they take the initiative in teasing, loving, and protecting.

By contrast, Burmese men are described as vain, lazy, pampered, primping, and gossipy; generally passive and unmanned, but when active, destructively violent. They fly into uncontrolled rages in which they are cruel and criminal: temptation is felt as something irresistible. Acts like arson, murder, and looting are common and are not causes for shame, but are freely confessed and are thought wiped clean by punishment. Such violences do not deprave Burmese men, nor lead to professional criminality. There is a similar irresponsibility toward money, which is prized as the means of adornment, indulgence, and social show, and is sought after without compunction through the easy ways of bribes, gambling, and confidence tricks. Excitement is found in competitive games like cockfights and boat races. Then too, men are vain of their bodies and dress, though boyishly so rather than effeminately. They are also theatrical, given to strutting in public; they are fond of professional plays and of amateur acting. In public station they are irresponsible and capricious. Sexually, they seem puritanical, or at least given to extreme bodily modesty. They use almost no opium, and alcohol infrequently, but drunkenness tends to be pursued to stupefaction. The quality in which men consistently claim to surpass women is "patience"!

According to Benedict, whom we have already encountered in § 135, Thai or Siamese women possess their own property, are more purposive than men in acquiring and retaining it, handle the day-by-day family money. They go in more than men for jewelry and display. Ideal wives are thought to be like sisters or mothers, cherishing and submissive; others are considered contentious or even "audacious."

Thai men are cheerful, easy-going, jolly, gay, indolent. They accept subordination to higher rank or power without either resentment or servility; they do not cringe. They respect and obey authority without demanding return or assistance from it. There is a minimum of discipline in the family, as in public relations: the Thai are a quiet people; their gatherings are convivial instead of unruly. They are self-reliant in a quiet, careless way—without much sense of responsibility for others. They enjoy resting unworried, at ease, preferably eating, chewing, drinking, or smoking. They like gambling; they trouble little over laying by money, but are fond of spending it. They dislike quarrels, rarely offer violence, are not easily irritated; in disputes, the better man tends to leave off first; anger is felt to be disadvantageous; and they incline to be forgiving. There is much festive drinking, which renders them happy and noisy, but releases no hostile aggressions, nor do they often continue to the stage of passing out; drunkenness is not a serious social problem, nor is opium. They tend to disregard property rights as children might, evade debts, do much petty pilfering, but commit few crimes of violence. Sincere in their Buddhism, they however practice no asceticisms and seek no mysticism or Nirvana, but aim to achieve merit in this life, which they appreciate as good. With all their gentleness, they are worldly-minded. Anger heats the heart, they say, disturbs life by leading to grudges and foolish actions, is disadvantageous; it should be curbed while still small. The "cool heart" is without anxiety, rests at ease, surveys and weighs the situation, accepts cheerfully what it must, and takes advantage of circumstances, including the stupidity or the emotion of others. Successful guile is admired, as successful force is not. Security is achieved through patience and in not being duped. "Patience"—of which women pass as having less than men, though they are more reckless—involves calm circumspection and acting with worldly wisdom; it gives peace as well as success. Patience really is self-control over disturbing emotion, and leads to a species of self-reliance.

Psychoanalytically, the Siamese are obviously "oral" in type (§ 255).

It is evident that the Burmese and Siamese cultures not only tend to mold their members alike by custom, as in making women the family budget managers, but are alike in their value appraisals, as in judging men more "patient" than women, contrary to ourselves. In contrast, it is evident from the foregoing accounts that there are indubitable differences between the two nationalities in their modal temperaments. This holds even if we allow for some degree of subjective difference between the two judgments cited. Other observers corroborate that the Burmese are relatively touchy, proud, theatrical, and violent; the Siamese relaxed, amiable, easy in their dignity, pleasure-loving, and serene. The normal degrees of tension differ, as do the "personas" assumed, the roles one tries to play. This reinforces at least that part of our previous finding which said that modal personalities or temperaments may vary characteristically while cultures remain much alike.

Indeed, national temperaments evidently become most distinctive when peoples are contrasted whose cultures are basically alike: such as Frenchmen, British, Germans, Scandinavians, Spaniards, whose cultures are only subvarieties of the general European phase of Occidental civilization. By contrast, to compare French national character with Chinese, or Italian with Japanese, seems random and somewhat futile. Part of the futility would appear to be due to a fact already noted; namely, that the categories of psychological characterization developed among Occidentals for Occidentals break down, tend to lose their meaning, when applied to Asiatics. A counterpart of this fact is the highly characteristic special meaning which Siamese and Burmese evidently give to their words for "patience"—and Chinese and Japanese to "sincerity"—meanings that obviously include a lot that our translating terms do not cover.

We may conclude therefore that the most fruitful and sound way in which national temperaments can be studied is as between related groups partaking of the same basic culture. Wherever the modal personalities of two such groups differ, there will expectably also be some subcultural differences in customs and institutions. But these will be known or readily ascertainable, and should be measurable or definable. Therewith the accompanying psychological differences may perhaps be explained. At any rate their associated variables will be clear. When this sort of systematic and partly controlled study has been made, say for Europe and another for East Asia, comparisons of a higher order should be successful: for instance, inquiry into how far the common denominators within European and within East Asiatic basic civilizations agree or differ.

The investigation could then be extended to the psychological aspects of the indigenous American cultures, the Negro African ones, the Islamic peoples, and so on. When Maya, Otomí, Yaqui, Navaho, Zuni, Yurok, Shoshone, Dakota, and Eskimo psychologies have been investigated for their common qualities as well as their distinctivenesses, and the relation of these to their cultural uniformities and peculiarities is known—when all this has been done, then comparison with the results of similar studies on the interrelations of, for example, Burma, Siam, Annam, Java, Bali, and Tagalog, and of China, Korea, and Japan, ought to be extremely illuminating. At present, while we are still limited to the matching of Zuni with Bali, of Samoa with the United States, of the Lepcha with the Navaho, of Germany to Japan, the situation is really pretty haphazard and random.

It is probable that we already possess a good many valid findings in this field of the psychological physiognomies that correspond to cultural physiognomies. But until the field is more systematically organized, there is little way of knowing which of the findings are relatively sound and secure and which represent chiefly personalized reactions of observers. With organization once achieved, it is also to be presumed that the validity and the limits of the concepts and categories used will become defined—whether these be "patience" or "aggression," "sincerity" or "frustration." And finally, it should then be possible to answer the further question of how far genuinely similar or homologous psychologies can appear in peoples of different cultures, either through accidental convergence or through recurrence of stages, castes, or classes.

246. SOCIAL PSYCHOLOGY AND CULTURAL PSYCHOLOGY

Social psychology began to develop soon after 1900, largely through sociologists who had been influenced by Tarde's *Laws of Imitation* (1890), and also by Le Bon's *Psychology of the Crowd* (1895), which in turn reflected the findings of the psychiatrists Charcot and Janet on suggestion. Professional psychologists, until then, had been essentially concerned with the individual. As they gradually took over social psychology from the sociologists and the philosophers, they gradually increased emphasis on critical caution, definition, and experiment. Social psychology is now a fairly well delimited subject. Among its specialties are in-groups and out-groups, social adjustment, attitudes, dominance, leadership, audiences, morale, public opinion, group prejudice including stereotypes, propaganda, revolution.

Personality is recognized as acquired, as being a product of socialization. Its consideration therefore falls within the scope of social psychology. Some go so far as to distinguish between "inherent nature," which refers to what is universal in men; socially conditioned "human nature," or the qualities of the personality that make it like other personalities within the same society; and individuality, or qualities that make it unlike others. Thus Japanese and Americans have differently conditioned "human natures." Apart from this special and somewhat confusing usage, it is evident that social psychologists recognize culture for what it is. But they scarcely deal with it as such, as something having a specific content. Instead, they deal with certain generalized or abstracted psychological processes operative in culture, such as drives; factors in learning, formal education; overt versus covert responses and symbolic versus direct behaviors; prestige influences; conventional, institutional, or formal situations; pressurings; and the like.

It will be seen from this that social psychology does not explain or even touch any concrete existing culture or part of a culture—which it would call "a cultural situation." It deals only with certain abstracted psychological mechanisms or attributes that are or can be operative in culture. In fact, what we have just considered as psychologically expressible types of culture or national temperaments (§ 245) social psychology tends to dismiss as unscientific, linking them with emotional "stereotypes" of ethnocentric, depreciatory, or abusive origin. Then, social psychology is more specific about society than about culture, and deals at length, and sometimes concretely, with interpersonal relations, such as social adjustment, leadership, propaganda; and interpersonal relations as such of course are social relations.

It is evident that social psychology deals consistently with what its name implies; but also that it scarcely touches culture as the anthropologist ordinarily concerns himself with it. Since about 1935 some anthropological work has been increasingly and avowedly aware of a number of the concepts of social psychology, such as covertness, prestige, symbolism, socialization of the individual. This widening is all to the good. Yet any attempt to consider culture only or primarily through the medium of concepts such as these would mean that the specific field of anthropology—culture content and cultural form and pattern— was being virtually abandoned for psychologizing. It does remain true that all the knowledge in the world about who influences whom, and how, tells us nothing of what people are influenced to—of their culture. And culture—pure culture as distinct from that mixture of persons, events, and institutions which is called history, and distinct also from the part-culture manifestations with which economics and government are concerned—culture is the specific subject of all the nonbiological part of anthropology, and of no other study or science, except perhaps sociology if it chooses to make the choice. If anthropologists do not study cultural manifestations as such, no one else will.

In short, social psychology is a developed and still developing field of importance, adjacent to that of anthropology and related to it, dealing with the interactions of human beings as social animals and therefore as culture producers and carriers. But to date this psychology has not been seriously concerned with the *different* behaviors of men under different cultures, nor with the explanation or even the characterization of different cultures in psychological terms. So far as this latter task has been undertaken—namely, what we might call the psychology of cultures, or of culture as such—it has been attempted, though as yet in piecemeal fashion, chiefly either by anthropologists or by inquirers influenced by psychoanalysis. The psychological description of cultures would necessarily underlie their psychological explanation. Such description would comprise, first, the characterization of whole cultures in terms of psychological attributes; and second, it would go on to comparison of the degree of development of such attributes in a variety of cultures. Neither line appears to have been developed very far, else we should presumably be recognizing a subscience or field of cultural psychology comparable to social psychology.

In the last two sections (§ 244-245) we have reviewed some of the endeavors at psychological characterizations of whole cultures. The eight sections which follow (§ 247-254) will pursue the complementary approach: namely, that of examining certain psychological qualities or attributes as they manifest varying strength and varying relationships in diverse cultures. It will be found that both approaches reveal quickly that cultures differ strikingly if somewhat elusively in their psychological qualities or physiognomies. But neither approach can yet be said to have yielded a notable body of theoretical conclusions. This means that such a field as cultural psychology evidently exists, but that it has not yet been developed and organized into an autonomous branch of science. If what follows, or in fact if this whole chapter, appears unsystematic, it is due to this condition of immaturity of the subject; this however may be partly compensated for by the stimulus inherent in the very awkwardnesses of youth.

The qualities or proclivities of cultures with which we shall from here on be dealing are evidently similar to the special orientations, attitudes, or weightings, the interests and preoccupations, that all cultures manifest and which have been discussed in connection with culture and its patterns in Chapters Seven and Eight. The difference from these patterns is that an orientation or an interest involves preoccupation with something specific, like horse-racing, or cattle, or dreams, or legal procedures, or funerals, and can therefore be described as cultural. But the psychological bents we shall be concerned with from here on are in themselves devoid of concrete cultural content: for instance, co-operativeness, or cleanliness, or aggression. While no wholly sharp line can be drawn between the two approaches, the cultural one is the more behavioristically descriptive as well as more concrete; the psychological one, the more dynamic and concerned with abstracted process.

247. CO-OPERATION, COMPETITION, AND INDIVIDUALISM

We have one comparative study, instigated by Mead, which classifies a series of nonliterate cultures as to their co-operative, competitive, and individualistic orientations, and inquires how far these may correlate with other trends in the same cultures. The individualistic category was introduced secondarily to cover certain cultures, such as the Eskimo, which are not organized co-operatively but at the same time hold out no social rewards for competitive success. It is a case, in them, mainly of each man for himself, or at any rate for his biological family group. In genuinely competitive societies, such as the Ifugao and the Kwakiutl, the social premiums definitely go to those who can outdo or outclimb others. Co-operative cultures tend to accord prestige in proportion as the individual's efforts benefit the lineage, the village, or the community. Thus there is little credit accorded him for acquiring property, but much for giving it away with honor. In extreme cases, as with the Zuni, the communal sense is so strong as to set public opinion against endeavors at leadership or conspicuous personal success as presumptuous and presumably antisocial. The diagram shows the grouping of the cultures (Fig. 29).

Certain traits, which were found by Mead to correlate pretty regularly with either predominantly co-operative or competitive tendencies, may be eliminated at the outset because they are implicit in the concepts of co-operation and competition. Thus "emphasis on rising in status" and "interest in property for personal ends" are contained in the definition of social competition; similarly,

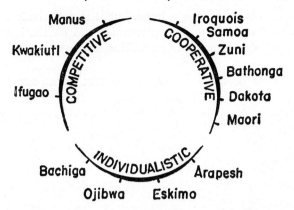

FIG. 29.   STRENGTH OF CO-OPERATIVE, COMPETITIVE, AND INDI-
VIDUALISTIC ATTITUDES IN 13 TRIBES
(After Mead)

"closed social system," "high security for the individual," and perhaps "faith in an ordered universe" are implied in co-operativeness. These come near to being verbal or spurious correlations.

There remain several other traits that either are outrightly cultural, like agriculture and institutionalized suicide, or which are at least culturally determined, like conscience and ego development. The distribution of these traits is shown in the tabulation; and it is evident that none of them evinces any very close correlation with any of the three orientations.

First of all, geography, a people's particular place in the world, has nothing to do with competitive, co-operative, or individualistic trends. The six American cultures examined, and the five Oceanic ones, belong to all three types. This rules out any major historical developments characteristic of grand areas. A given culture is, say, co-operative not because all the cultures in its continent have had a common development toward co-operation, but because of particular circumstances experienced in its peculiar national history. To put it the other way around, any one culture in an area may gradually become increasingly co-operative or competitive or individualistic. On the basis of probability, therefore, some cultures are likely to have changed at some time from one class to another. This in turn indicates that sets toward co-operation, competition, and individualism are not necessarily among the more permanent trends of development; and this suggests that they are secondary rather than deep-seated characteristics. Our own society has undergone considerable shift from a competitive-individualistic to a co-operative orientation in the last forty years, without fully equivalent change in the basic content of its culture.

One might expect that agriculture, with its settled life and its numerous tasks best performed by people working together, would induce co-operative attitudes. There probably is such a trend, but it is not wholly determinative. The co-operative Dakota were nonagricultural; and on the other side, there are three farming tribes among seven individualistic or competitive ones.

CORRESPONDENCES OF CULTURE TRAITS TO THE TOTAL SET OF CULTURE

Based on Mead

(All capital letters denote the presence of the trait in question; dashes, its absence)

Type	Tribe	Continent	Agriculture	Institutionalized Suicide	Forcing Education	Ego Development	Status Emphasis	Conscience (Internal Sanction)
Competitive	Manus	Oc	—	—	F	E	S	C
	Kwakiutl	Am	—	I	F	E	S	—
	Ifugao	Oc	A	I	F	E	S	—
Individual	Bachiga	Afr	A	—	—	—	S	C
	Ojibwa	Am	—	I	F	E	—	C
	Eskimo	Am	—	I	F	—	—	C
	Arapesh	Oc	A	—	—	—	—	—
Co-operative	Maori	Oc	A	I	—	E	S	C
	Dakota	Am	—	I	F	—	S	—
	Bathonga	Afr	A	I	—	—	S	—
	Zuni	Am	A	—	F	—	—	—
	Samoa	Oc	A	—	—	—	S	—
	Iroquois	Am	A	I	—	E	—	—

Institutionalized suicide (§ 254) means that occasions and forms for it— such as hara-kiri—are provided by the society. This trait shows so even a scatter as to indicate that it lacks correlation.

"Forcing or hastening education," to prod the young toward adulthood as fast as possible, is one of a set of habits that expectably would be well developed in definitely competitive societies. So would ego development. A boy that re- mained immature, yielding, docile, unstrenuous—given to play instead of work after he was able-bodied—would get off to a bad start in his career of living in such a society. It will be seen that all the frankly competitive societies do speed up education and instill self-regard. On the contrary, six of the ten noncompeti- tive cultures also show at least one or the other of this pair of traits; so that the correlation may be described as lopsided, complete for one kind of culture, partial for the other kind.

Status emphasis occurs in all three competitive cultures, and in five of the six co-operative ones—all but super-Apollinian Zuni (§ 135). This is no doubt because competition and co-operation both are concerned with interpersonal relations, and thus are sensitive of them, though with opposite weighting—one positively, the other negatively. The contrast accordingly should be between the two types jointly as against the individualistic type in which by definition people are attuned to self-sufficiency rather than to their relations with others. It does work out this way. Three of the four individualistic societies are classed as uninterested in status. The East African Bachiga are rated as status-concerned; but they are on the edge of the individualistic type, verging toward the competitive; and they are described as anarchistic, touchy, and contentious.

Five of the thirteen cultures are judged as showing definite development of "feelings of internal sanction"; that is, conscience. Three of these five are from the individualistic class. This is as might be expected, since when competition is accepted as the normal way of living, it will tend to stifle certain kinds of scruple; whereas in a co-operative setup, it would seem natural for internal sanctions to be replaced by social approvals. Nevertheless, the correlation is not complete, since one of the individualistic cultures fails to develop conscience, whereas one each of the co-operative and competitive ones does develop it. The latter, Manus, probably owes its conscientiousness to its puritanism (§ 248). It is interesting that the faraway Yurok of California also can be described as characterized by competitiveness, shrinking puritanism, conscience (sense of sin relieved by confession), strong emphasis on status, and a sensitive ego. In fact, except perhaps for less speeding of their children into adulthood, the Yurok psychological profile, in terms of the traits here dealt with, simply repeats the Manus one; and certainly without any specific historical connection between the two cultures.[4]

In summary, it appears that where the present set of correlations are not spurious through being implicit, they mostly are only partial. There seems to be surprisingly little tendency for broad psychological trends to co-occur regularly with either specific personality traits or with cultural institutions. This in turn suggests that cultures, like personalities, are psychologically plastic. They probably do not often permanently harbor directly conflicting trends; but they may and do include almost any combination of compatible trends. Thus the psychological structure of cultures, as of individuals, may be complex, and perhaps normally is complex, in the sense of being a composite, a more or less successful or viable integration, of factors that have no intimate or necessary relation to one another, but which do possess the faculty of working out an adjustment and being able to co-exist.

It is evident that we need more studies of the type of this one by Mead.

248. INHIBITION AND PURITANISM

Inhibition, asceticism, and puritanism can be recognized in societies as well as in individuals. Inhibition is the impeding of the free flow of expression, the checking or blocking of one impulse by another and contrary one. The blocking may be conscious and voluntary, in which case it may approach closely to the guiding power of "control"; although inhibiting definitely involves the halting

---

[4] This reinforces what has been said in § 245 on the possibility that cultures of unlike content can be alike psychologically; or their content may be similar but their psychology dissimilar. In other words, eidos and ethos (§ 125) may go together but do not have to.

or suppression of an impulse, whereas control, fundamentally, steers or directs without the implication of check or conflict. But the blocking may also gradually become habitual and unconscious, as well as widely spread or chronic in the personality, as when we speak of someone as an inhibited individual. This passive sense is the one most to the fore in recent psychological thinking.

Asceticism is always an act of will: the deliberate practice of austerity, abstinence, and self-mortification. It is the sensory gratifications of one's own body that are suppressed by asceticism in the interest of some standard of morals, religion, or inner development. Puritanism got its name from a cultural phenomenon, the ethics of a British group of sects three centuries ago, and it carries connotations varying from commendatory to adverse, with the latter gaining ground in contemporary usage. Puritanical aims are also ascetic; but the special quality of puritanism seems to be the wish to apply asceticism to others as well as to oneself, to enforce it socially. The Hindu prizes asceticism, the New Englander was a puritan. Continued puritanism tends to build up inhibitory systems, thus completing a circle of linkage; though puritanism and asceticism primarily prohibit and punish—others or oneself—while inhibition is basically protective and is derived from caution or fear rather than from misprizal or hate.

Not only Anglo-Saxons are puritanical: Protestantism in general inclines that way, and its strongest inclinations to puritanism seem to have developed under the influence of Calvinism, which originated on the continent of Europe. Early Christianity and then mediaeval Christianity put a high value on asceticism, at first for hermits and later for monks, but did not exact it of laymen; they cannot properly be described as puritanical. India, seat of asceticism, past and present, developed Buddhism and Brahminism; but like early and mediaeval Christianity, these religions asked asceticism only of their clergy, the monks or priests. With the laity exempt from mortification, and with abstinences such as from eating flesh being only recommended, Buddhism as a whole, though ascetically inclined, cannot be classed as puritanical. On the contrary, the third world religion, Mohammedanism, contains a definite puritanical element, and that in spite of its permitted four wives and promised houris which loom so large in our popular conception of it. Alcohol in any form, the eating of pork, gambling, representation of men and animals in art, are all forbidden in Islam; even coffee and tobacco had a hard time getting by, and are discountenanced by the strict, who also long opposed fire insurance and life insurance as being a form of gambling on decisions made by God, and who denounced printing as an unauthorized innovation (§ 172, 199). It is interesting, psychologically as well as culture-historically, that sex, on which later Protestant puritanism perhaps centered its repressive interests—"immorality" means nonmarital sexual indulgence in ordinary American English, as "passion" is coming to mean sex appetite—this same sex is the principal field of activity which Mohammedanism excepts from its puritanism.

Ascetic practices of one sort or another are widely spread among non-literate peoples also. Chiefly this is in connection with acquiring supernatural power or mana, which is conceived of as nonsensory, spiritual, and mental, and thus somehow to be heightened by repression or punishment of the body. The means of ascetic practice vary from abstentions—from food, drink, sleep, sexual gratification—to inflictions of pain—winter bathing, whipping, piercing, blood-letting. Some measure of asceticism in religious situations is so nearly universal as to need no further comment; variation is chiefly in kind.

Now and then a primitive people goes on beyond self-asceticism and becomes puritanical in its generic attitudes. The Melanesians of Manus are so described: censorious, joyless, vindictive, burdened with a sense of the world's wickedness. Something of this temperament is discernible among most Melanesians, though often it is difficult to be sure just how much of the quality inheres in the society or enters through the observers' eyes. Two things give Melanesian puritanism a special interest. It is not founded on well-developed religious practices of asceticism, such as punishing one's body; and it seems wholly lacking from the national temperament of the Polynesians farther out in the Pacific, as well as among the Indonesians on the other side of Melanesia. It seems to spring from a sense of sin rampant in the world and necessary to guard against.

A sense of something akin to sin appears to be involved wherever a regulated confession mechanism occurs. But it is clear that peoples can feel themselves guilt-ridden or sin-ridden without setting up confession as an institution. The Melanesians are a case in point: Manus has confession, near-by Dobu and Trobriand do not. Protestant denominations unanimously and strongly turned against confession when they broke away from Roman Catholicism; but in most of them sin was probably more to the forefront of consciousness than it had previously been in Catholicism (§ 253). The occurrence of institutionalized confession among nonliterate peoples the world over is spotty. Thus in North America it is a well-developed practice with Eskimo, Yurok, Aztec, and Maya, who certainly differ drastically among themselves in culture as well as temperament; besides, it occurs more incidentally among Carrier, Iroquois, Pueblo, and others. The acts confessed may range from breach of taboo to malevolent witchcraft, as at Zuni, or incest as at Manus. This variety, together with the distribution, indicates more or less parallel, separate developments for many of the institutions of confession. Common primitive features are that retribution for wrongdoing may befall the sinner's children or kinsfolk rather than himself; that the confession neutralizes the evil; but that to be effective it must be made publicly.

A generic inclination toward an inhibited temperament seems to characterize most the Mongoloids of Asia and America, but with definite exceptions, such as Eskimo and Polynesians and perhaps Indonesians. American Indians certainly cultivate restraint. They preach self-control, as well as constant pleasantness of manner to others. When they erupt into anger or cruelty, it is in the manner of the inhibited: with a break, or jerk. Negroids in Africa would probably be classed among the noninhibited, but in Oceania among the inhibited. Australians also would be on the noninhibited side. Accordingly there is the usual lack of clear-cut correlation with hereditary race.

249. CLEANLINESS AND ORDER

One attitude in which cultures differ is that toward bodily cleanliness. Allied to this is the sense of neatness and order in dress and personal effects and surroundings. There is immense variation in these matters, both between different nations and in the same nation at different times.

The Greeks built no great baths, but they did build gymnasia and they did prize athletic sports. In these they stripped: the word "gymnasium" originally meant a place in which one went naked, *gymnos;* and they used strigils to scrape the body, and then oiled or anointed it. They despised the Persians and other Asiatics for their false modesty in keeping the body covered at all times. The Romans took over much of this Greek cult of the body, and carried it farther by building enormous public baths, where people with leisure spent hours daily. This habit, incidentally, reached its peak after Rome had lost its republicanism and had become a despotic empire.

The early Christians felt themselves increasingly in conflict not only with the established pagan religion but with many of its attitudes and trends, its luxuries, art, philosophy. Baths were part of Roman Imperial culture; therefore they soon became construed as instruments not only of paganism but also of vice. Baths cultivated and softened the body instead of saving the soul; and before long overcleanliness, and then what we would consider minimum cleanliness, came to be considered one of the roads to ruin. After Christianity came into control of the government and culture of the Mediterranean, baths and bathing went out with slavery, gladiators, temples and altars, animal sacrifices, mythological and erotic poetry, nature worship and sensitivity to natural beauty, and a lot else both callous and gracious. The ascetic saint neglected his body and was indifferent to filth: keeping oneself scrupulously clean was now perhaps not exactly a sin, but it certainly bred suspicion that one might not be too good a Christian, especially if one were a man. Among the barbarian Christians, feelings smacked of the lumber camp, with piety reinforcing he-manness.

Things went more or less this way through the Dark Ages and the early Middle Ages. The Crusaders must have seemed an unwashed barbarian swarm to the Oriental Saracens from whom they took away the Holy Land. And to the first Crusaders the Mohammedan baths were but another expression of the effeminacy and decadence springing from a false religion.

A change came over Europe after it had passed through the peak of the High Middle Ages in the thirteenth century. By the 1400's, people had begun once more to like to wash, and public baths sprang up. This turn of sentiment after a thousand years was accompanied by many related changes. Established religion was losing its hold. The genuinely pious were fewer, the skeptical and curious-minded more numerous. It was the period of Popes at Avignon instead of Rome, of the great Papal schism, of widespread complaints against the irreligiosity and wealth of the clergy; also of awakening interest in foreign lands, then of exploration; and of new inventions like printing, clocks, iron-casting.

In the 1500's a reaction began. The Protestants aimed to return to primitive Christianity; the Church tried to hold its lines by tightening and purifying them. Moralists and the pious in both camps turned ascetic, once more condemned the baths, and began to demand their suppression. For over two centuries cultivated Europe did not, it is true, exactly glory in dirt, but it washed little and looked on bathing as rarely needed and as likely to be dangerous to health. If we of today had personally met great sovereigns like Elizabeth or Louis XIV, we should probably have been aware of their body odor.

This phase passed away with the slackening of religious intransigeance, with the growth of enlightenment, with the increase and spread of wealth and therewith of comforts, with the rise of the bourgeoisie. But the refinement of social manners on which the late seventeenth and especially the eighteenth century prided themselves definitely preceded the revived manners of bodily cleanliness. It was the countries in which the new wealthy middle class became specially influential that took the lead in the new direction; hence the scrubbing of Dutch doorsteps and the proverbial Englishman with his portable bath. The French Revolution stood for republicanism and increased the power of the bourgeoisie. Before long a mental association grew up, and prosperous democracy became a rough index of frequency of bathing and vice versa. Americans pride themselves almost equally on both, and take for granted that there is an inherent connection: "cleanliness next to godliness."

Other cultures differ equally. Tanks, pools, and bathing evidently figured much more in ancient Egypt than in the coeval and parallel Two Rivers civilization of Mesopotamia; but the Indus Valley civilization again built large baths of brick. India today is full of cow dung and filth, but the higher castes wash their bodies and clothes sedulously. This habit, most accentuated in the priestly Brahmans, is inculcated by religion. Above all, the Brahman must keep himself uncontaminated and pure. Physical cleanliness is the first step toward cleanness of soul, a physical expression of it. This Hindu attitude will prevent any hasty fallacy that religion and cleanliness are in their nature antithetical. Many religions have insisted on clean bodies as symbolic of a clean and holy mind. Japanese Shinto, for instance, uses bathing, washing, and sprinkling as a constant means of purification. Primitive tribes frequently insist on bathing or head-washing as a preliminary to ceremonial. It was especially the great world religions, Buddhism, Christianity, Mohammedanism, with their aim at a deeper theology, that felt physical symbolic acts to be insufficient—too easy, as it were—for spiritual attainments, and emphasized the separation of body and soul rather than their likeness and undifferentiation. From this sprang the frequent ascetic neglect or contempt of the body in order to elevate and free the soul; this in turn was likely to end by making obtrusive cleanliness suspect.

Neatness, daintiness, orderliness are allied to cleanliness. Animals differ so strikingly in these traits according to kind—as the cat from the pig—that we must consider their tendencies genetic by species; that is, inborn. How far impulses toward neatness or slovenliness are congenital in individual human beings is not known. Individuals can at any rate be strongly conditioned in one direction or the other fairly early in life. Human populations presumably average much the same inherently, and the differences between them can be assumed as habitual; that is, determined by their cultures. These differences are great. Witness this traveler's account of the confusion and filth in which one tribe lives, and that one's surprise at the neatness of the homes, belongings, and bodies of another group of "savages."

More orderly cultures as compared to less orderly ones, or better-organized in contrast to little-organized, are shown by the Colorado River Yuman cultures as against the Arizona-plateau Yumans; by the Pueblo as against the Apache; by the Plains Indians as against those of California and the northwestern coast of America—though these last probably had a fuller culture, one containing more items, than the tribes of the Plains. Neatness and order are conspicuous around the homes of the supposed Negrito—or dwarf Papuans? —of Dutch New Guinea, as against all other Negritos. Orderliness can be shown in the management of physical living, in systematized organization of ritual or society, in a coherent concept of the world. Even the way a native presents information to an ethnologist can be organized and orderly or haphazard and mixed. And tribes seem to differ as much as individuals in this respect.

The cleanliness of the Japanese is proverbial and almost obsessive. Equally compulsive are their neatness and orderliness. There are no incomplete performances, no rough edges or loose ends left, in Japan: the poorest object is finished. The contrast is marked with China, where seamy sides are common, but where the great profundities and humanities of East Asia were also worked out. By general consent, the Japanese lost something of these internal qualities in their taking over Chinese civilization; possibly because of their very perfectionism toward cultural neatness, finish, order, and efficiency.

250. ANIMISTIC ATTITUDES

Just as one person feels his religion deeply while his neighbor merely goes through the forms, so do cultures differ. One society is genuinely pious, another worldly-minded; or the same society may change from one attitude to another in a few hundred years. Our Western civilization took its religion hard in the seventeenth century, loosened increasingly in the eighteenth and the nineteenth, and in the twentieth has, though unavowedly for the most part, de facto replaced faith in revealed religion to a considerable extent by faith in science. In this period, the Church has been completely divorced from the State in many countries, and religion has largely been segregated off into a special sphere of its own. In Soviet Russia, under extreme conditions of ruthless revolutionary control, religion was in fact virtually outlawed for two decades.

Similar differences occur among nonliterate peoples. These mostly possess little available history of change, but their contemporary differences point to a similar variability. Thus Polynesians in general appear to be less animistic-minded, less driven by religious compulsion, than Melanesians and Australian blackfellows. We have seen (§ 168) with what lightness the Hawaiians voluntarily broke their taboo system and threw away their ancestral cults. Even if this strange revolution was a result of "cultural fatigue," it indicated that religion must have lost much of its hold if the population was tired of it. Similarly, the Samoans are described by Mead as retaining many Polynesian supernatural beliefs and practices, but as adhering to them perfunctorily, with little fervor of feeling. Religion is not an important actuating force: interest is turned toward social mechanisms and relations. The Samoans are pragmatic and realistic. The feeling tone of their life lacks intensity. They are a placid, pleasant people, inclined to be concerned with small, immediate objectives, averse to being stirred deeply.

Another people to whom a partial lack or lapse of animism might be attributed are the Eskimo, especially in contrast with the Indians of their continent. They retain of course a share of the taboos and the supernatural beliefs of all primitive cultures; but their primary and dominant orientation is realistic. They differ from the Samoans in that they have a minimum of social mechanisms and statuses to distract their attention. Their relations are personal, man to man, with little in the way of institutions as a framework. Nor can they be described as emotionally low-toned. While affable and ready to laugh, they are volatile, quick, and passionate, and when they dare, express anger as well as pleasure with little restraint.

The cause for this orientation can perhaps be sought in the extraordinarily trying circumstances of survival in the Arctic. The Eskimo must be mechanical-minded, able-bodied, manually skillful, and practical. Too many taboos or rituals would tie his hands, limit his resourcefulness, take up time that must be given to survival activities to a visibly greater extent than among almost any other people. Supernaturalism thus tends to drop into the background, relatively.

This explanation runs rather counter to a more general theory advanced by Malinowski which holds magic and animism to be man's response to his sense of insecurity in the world (§ 130). Magic appears when there is a hiatus in knowledge or power yet man has to proceed. His emotional state of instability results in substitute action—magical practices or worship—which have at least subjective value: they reintegrate the individual and organize society. In fishing or voyaging on the ocean, according to Malinowski, Melanesians feel insecure, and hence use prayers, charms, and avoidance taboos; but for fishing in sheltered lagoons, they dispense with these.

The contrary Eskimo example cited (also in § 130) shows that as a universal this theory is not watertight. In fact the contradiction is a good example of the difficulty of determining strict laws in the field of human behavior. We may grant a degree of validity to the insecurity theory, but must recognize that it has limits. Magic may be a fantasy response of men in situations of strain, but if the insecurity becomes too immediate and acute, magic may cease to be felt as the primary aid, and there is a return to organic self-reliance, to meeting problems with realistic means. Such a modified interpretation is also supported by the luxuriant development of animism and magic often found among peoples normally not confronted by great difficulties. All along the North Pacific coast of America, for instance, there were no serious rigors of climate, and food was abundant; nevertheless all the tribes here had developed a richer system of magic, rituals, and myth than the Eskimo. The same may be said of the Melanesians: these unquestionably had an easier time making a living than the Eskimo. Yet many of them did not trust themselves to such simple efforts as planting yams without the aid of magic.

For a general explanation in psychological terms, one might thus fall back on this: that marked excess or deficiency of security is prejudicial to the development of belief in the supernatural. The optimum condition for religion and magic would be a middle one, in which the total environmental and social situation gave people some uneasiness but not too much. This rather tame conclusion at least derives support from the undoubted facts that most cultures are religious, and that most of them have recurrent worries but not crushing ones. But the specific causes that make cultures vary in their religious set or orientation are evidently numerous. We cannot predict either the strength or the kind of religion and magic in a given culture from knowing how great the security of life is, nor how advanced the arts are, how much wealth has been accumulated, how militaristic or pacifist the inclinations are.

Some weakening of religious attachments seems generally to occur in the transition from rural to urban life, and is an inherent part of the change from folk to sophisticate cultures (§ 121).

251. SYSTEMATIZING TRENDS

Like individuals, cultures differ in their ability to systematize. Whether the systematization be by reasoning or by feeling and guessing, its essential quality perhaps is a habit of recognizing and dealing in relations, of generalizing. By contrast, the unsystematic-minded tend to take each fact of experience as separate: it remains an event, an item in itself. Like children, they are usually exact in perceiving and remembering the isolated fact, and perhaps its exact absolute place, without awareness of its relation. It is a matter-of-fact attitude of detailed sensory accuracy as compared with the more imaginative and constructive one of seeing significances.

Now certain West African cultures, such as the Ashanti and the Yoruba, have struck all observers as definitely systematizing. Their social structure, law, and beliefs are intricately organized. Other West African groups, like the Nupe, show much less of this tendency: their society is simpler, their religion without a hierarchy of higher and lower gods, their art frankly ornamental; whereas the Yoruba go in for the representative and the symbolic—the meaningful.

It also happens that we have an experimental psychological verification of these trends by Nadel. A short story was told to both Yoruba and Nupe children and they were then asked to retell it; pictures were shown them and they were asked to describe what they saw. The results evinced a tendency of the Nupe children to reproduce rather faithfully the details of what they had heard or seen. Things like the particular time of day were likely to appear in the retelling whether they were significant for the story or only incidental. By contrast, the Yoruba were concerned with the general plot of the story, or the main event or prospective result in the picture. Minor details had a way of being discarded, or misremembered. Motivations, why things happened, whether they ought to have happened, whether an action was good or bad, were accentuated or even invented. Not only was there more reasoning, but also more emotion, in the Yoruba versions. The Nupe remembered in a manner that was more matter-of-fact and externally more orderly in a step-after-step fashion. They catalogued or reproduced: what it was all about did not interest them so much. In the Jung classification, they would be predominantly sensory-minded, the Yoruba more of the rational and feeling type.

A similar difference was found to exist between the reactions of Arizona Hopi and Navaho children to pictures shown them as a stimulus.[5] The Hopi tend to carry the pictured situation through to an outcome, usually a reassuring or happy ending. This may include a moral judgment. The Navaho reactions are less consecutive, and mostly without statement of outcome. Mainly they redescribe the facts of the picture; feelings may be attributed to the people depicted, but ethical judgments are rare. In a general way, the town-dwelling Hopi react like the Yoruba, the Navaho somewhat like the Nupe; and of the two total cultures, the Hopi one is by general agreement somewhat more rationalized, organized, systematized, and sophisticate than the Navaho.

While we have few confirming psychological tests, the cultures of other peoples sometimes obviously differ according to the same criterion. California and Northwest-coast Indians tend to enumerate facts in presenting them to

[5] Technically, the Thematic Apperception Test was used, the pictures having been drawn by a local Indian.

ethnographers, Pueblo and some Plains tribes organize them. The organization may be rudimentary and not seem very significant to us, as when it is by cardinal directions or colors; but it is nevertheless an attempt to see things in relation instead of haphazardly. As these cultures function, the organization of ideas is effected especially in ritual and myth. And it is evident that a ritual of the Zuni Pueblo has much more motivation than one of the California Yurok. Its purpose is explicit, its parts are meaningful, it is full of easily grasped symbolism.

The Eskimo, again, are very sensory, immediate, concrete, and discrete in their ethos.

It would appear that all advanced cultures are relatively systematizing. We might say that if they were not, they would not have been able to advance far. And, complementarily, further organizing capacity is probably a product of higher civilization. Such circular causation is common in human history and affairs. We have already encountered it in the inter-reinforcement of enhancement of subsistence, population growth, specialization of skills, improved technology, and increase of wealth (§ 163).

The great world religions are obviously strong agencies of organization, in that they provide a basic philosophy, with a scheme of causality and motivation. Christianity may at first have been actually narrower, intellectually, than the Hellenism it supplanted; but its scheme was certainly more unified. In the same way Buddhism got rid of thousands of Brahman idols, of sacrifices, of rituals that had become meaningless, of taboos, and of other clutter of detail; with the result that its basic creed, its program of life, stood out much more clearly and coherently. To the sophisticated philosopher who was able to rise above the endless and jumbled items accreted through the centuries, Brahmanism may have provided an equally good base; but the average man could much more easily see a meaningful plan in Buddhism.

It may well be that the degree to which science has of late become for growing numbers a de-facto religion, or equivalent of religion, is due to the fact that with all its intricacy it possesses a coherence, a master plan that organizes innumerable items. This is true also of other successful faiths, notably the world religions. But the plan or system of all of these was devised a long time ago, when the content of culture was considerably simpler. Science on the contrary has largely grown contemporaneously with the growing wealth and complexity of Western civilization in the last few centuries, so that its system may well be more conformable with the total civilization.

252. SADISM

Almost any trend or inclination familiar from individual psychology might be recognized in culture. For instance, for cruelty, or sadism, peoples like the Aztec and the Assyrians immediately come to mind. Both built up conquest empires with imposition of heavy tribute. The Assyrian kings in their inscriptions boast not only of their victories but of their cruelties—whole populations slaughtered, impaled, or otherwise tortured. Their art expresses sternness, and is particularly addicted to scenes of battle or the hunt. Its greatest triumphs were attained in the portrayal of wounded and dying animals. The Aztec are notorious for the bloodiness of their religion. Hundreds of human beings were sacrificed annually by having the chest cut open and the heart torn out. Another device was to flay the victim, and to dress the priest in the victim's fresh skin. Self-penance was by piercing the tongue or other parts of the body. The captor of a war prisoner ate of his flesh at a formal banquet after his sacrifice. Skulls of the victims were kept in huge cribs in the public plaza in front of the temples. Aztec art portrays these scenes over and over again with the utmost unconcern, or rather, with pleased predilection. Death, skulls, flayed skins, rattlesnakes, and jaguars are among its favorite symbols. We think of Roman gladiatorial exhibitions as an example of cruelty; but the Romans, except for some degenerate emperors, were limited in their sadism as compared with Aztecs and Assyrians; they were only callous and brutal.

It would be possible to arrange the cultures of the world roughly according to a scale of the degree of sadistic manifestations. However, any such ranking would of course be wholly one-sided from the angle of the total inherent psychology. If any other trait were chosen, such as imaginativeness, or piety, or sensory predilections, the ranking would come out quite differently. In other words, any classification or ranking from one angle invariably crosscuts classifications made from others, and to that extent is arbitrary.

It is also clear that the extreme cases, as of Assyrians and Aztecs, represent local and temporary exaggerations. Historically related cultures usually show similar but less developed features. The Assyrian cruelties occurred also among neighboring and preceding and subsequent peoples, such as Babylonians and Persians, but without being carried so far. Human sacrifice with flaying and tearing out the heart was a practice common to all southern-Mexican peoples; but it was reserved for the Aztec to riot in the practice. The Maya followed the custom, but much less frequently; and it was only occasionally that they expressed it in their art. The difference accordingly was one of weighting; it was a relative or quantitative one. If consideration is given merely to the presence or absence of features like human sacrifice, without reference to their frequency or integration in the culture, important psychological differences of interests and accentuations are lost. Such relative differences between cultures are socially comparable to those which set off one individual human mind from others within the same society and culture.

253. OTHER PSYCHOLOGICAL BENTS

There is an indefinitely large number of further qualities according to which cultures can be oriented—as many, perhaps, as can be recognized in individuals. It is unnecessary to examine each of these; but a few may be touched on, so as to reinforce the idea of how psychologically plastic and variable the cultures of man are.

Acquisitiveness. Avarice, possessiveness, retentiveness, enter into the goals of societies in quite varying degree. Most primitives look upon Western white men as both greedy and stingy. Of course our highly developed economic system would break down, bringing distress on everyone in the community, as soon as production and maintenance of property ceased. We are therefore compelled to think fairly constantly in terms of acquisition, preservation, and accumulation. Nevertheless, the judgment of primitives that we are obsessed with our possessions probably reflects a fact that is descriptively true. On the contrary, certain primitive cultures also have their interests largely dominated by wealth: property makes for status, rank depends on wealth, and economic exploitation is limited only by opportunity. This is true of nearly all Melanesians, some Indonesians, all the Indians of the northwestern coast of America. In Africa, too, economic considerations are much to the fore. At the opposite pole of this axis are Australians, Negritos, Seri, and other peoples whose customs make them prefer being unencumbered with property and its care (§ 120, 146, 155). This bent cuts down both their responsibilities and their opportunities; but it does leave them untrammeled. Acquisitiveness also enters into the anal character type of the psychoanalysts (§ 255).

Mechanical and Verbal Developments. There are great individual differences in mechanical interest and ability, as well as in verbal fluency and capacity. These differences sometimes begin to be manifest within the first two or three years of life, and between siblings in the same home environment. This suggests that they may be partly congenital. There is ordinarily rather little in the affective relations to which small children are exposed, or in their training within one household, to make one brother more interested and skillful in driving nails or turning nuts on bolts, and another in throwing a ball, or perhaps chattering. So far as there are congenital individual differences, they would normally be heavily reinforced by selective opportunities of practice and training within each culture. As between populations, it is possible that there are true racial differences of significance, but the enormous divergences in cultural emphasis must far outweigh these differences. This conditioning would hold for verbalization as well as for muscular co-ordinations of both the athletic and the mechanical types (§ 88). That this is so is further indicated by the genuine mechanical gifts often suddenly displayed by a large proportion of nonliterate populations when guns or automobiles or motorboats are made available to them. From all precedent in these matters, it is probable that racial averages of congenital faculty vary less than individuals within the same race.

The same may hold for faculty of quantitative apperception and judgment in estimating numbers. Simple cultures may enumerate, but stress on quantitative valuations is largely a specialty of our Western civilization.

Desire for a Closed or an Open World. These affective inclinations are allied to agoraphobia and claustrophobia; and perhaps to bents toward the security of fixity and shelter, and the adventure of restlessness and unattachment, respectively. They probably tend to tie up with attitudes toward possessions. It is clear that strong habits in either direction can be acquired through socialization and experience, and that interference with these habits can cause acute discomfort. Many primitives have a strong urge to die where they were born, so as to close their life cycle by rounding it out. Other groups have become more interested in freedom of movement at will, even though the range be small. The previously cited Yurok and allied tribes of California are at the opposite extreme: they feel most comfortable in a tiny, snug world—one that a man with wings could fly around in a night. In their cosmology they set the ends of the earth, where the sky keeps descending to meet the horizon, only some fifty or sixty miles beyond their own last villages. At times they encounter members of tribes from beyond, and know something of their cultures; but they prefer to ignore this knowledge, and in the fantasies of their mythology and ritual they draw the boundaries of the human world closer in. About where their own highly characterized culture ends is where they like to believe the land of the immortals and everlasting dances begins—the Ultima Thule across the sea. The population adhering to this culture was somewhat under 10,000 at its maximum. The smallness of the society, coupled with the strong specialization of the culture, may have helped build up its restrictive inclination.

Essentially, such tendencies are retractile; and for these there is larger historical precedent. For instance, the Far Eastern cultures, headed by China but also including pre-1868 Japan, have generally been self-sufficient and unexpansive. In the 1500's they began to be reached by ships, traders, missionaries, and adventurers from five western-European nations—Spain, Portugal, Holland, England, France—that had entered an expansionist phase—the "era of discovery and colonization." By the 1600's, the resulting contacts had been sufficiently unpleasant and disturbing to make China, Japan, Korea, Annam, Siam, and Tibet all adopt the well-known policy of exclusion and seclusion. This attitude of nonintercourse and withdrawal some of them supported by refusing to readmit their own nationals who had left home. They all maintained it as well as they were able until forced to yield by threat or force in the nineteenth century.

This seclusion was defense against pressure. But Europe itself underwent a phase of partial cultural self-restriction after its first expansionism was over. This movement was most marked in manners and art in the France of Louis XIV. It represented an endeavor at order, clarity, fixity, centralization; it was a reaction against previous stirrings, tumult, and unsettlement. Regulatory Academies for literature, art, and sciences were established. There were rules for correctness, canons of propriety. Nearly all were negative and restrictive. The alleged aim was polish, refinement. Only elevated subjects were to be dealt with in plays, for instance: noble actions expressed in a limited, purged vocabulary were in the single, most stately meter. The result, whether in drama, poetry, painting, or sculpture, was a classicism that grew more and more elevated and more and more apart from real life. It no longer offended taste, but it had lost vividness and interest. In the early eighteenth century this movement spread to other European countries. In England, for instance, it produced the cold, correct, regular, narrow poetry of Pope, which contrasts so markedly with the earlier Elizabethan and later Romantic exuberance, irregularity, and vitality.

Though this French manifestation is different enough from those of the Chinese and the Yurok, what the three have in common is the impulse to limit or contract activity.

Fixity or Looseness of the Social Structure; Place and Time Mindedness. Here we would have on the one hand a complex of attitudes comprising acceptance of tradition, authority, and status, social docility, class-consciousness, relative permanence of institutions, conscious and desired rooting in the past, perhaps also fixity of residence and generic pessimism. India would be an example: the caste system embodies all these traits and tries to perpetuate them. The opposite pole among nations would be occupied by the United States and modern Australia, with their grudging acceptance of authority, diminution of status, emphasis on individualism, social and geographical mobility, relative lack of interest in the past or in tradition, exaltation of the contemporary moment, and unworried optimism as to the future.

This is an axis of polarity which is only partly psychological, and yet it involves a set of attitudes toward institutions rather than institutions themselves. It is allied to Tarde's distinction between place-minded and time-minded populations; and through this to the familiar rural-urban dichotomy (§ 121). Cultures that are primitive, of peasant or folk type, or definitely slow-changing, tend to be humble about their own moment but proud of the past and attached to their spot. They look down on their neighbors because these are different from them; but they look up to their ancestors. If there is a golden age, it is behind them. On the other side are metropolitan capitals, the later Graeco-Roman society, and increasingly our own modern Western society. Here pride is in up-to-dateness; origins are unimportant. It is the true atmosphere in which fashion and conformity to fashion flourish; but deviations according to locality are looked down upon as provincially backward.

Within a given society, its rural and urban components tend to differ in much the same way, relatively to each other; or again, the provinces and the court. But it would be erroneous to look upon the phenomenon as merely a by-product of country and city life. There have been large cities in India and

China for thousands of years with but little of the metropolitan outlook. On the contrary, pride-in-the-moment outlook is almost as characteristic of rural as of urban United States. Even our small towns participate in the era of streamlining. They drive the same cars, wear clothes of the same cut, see the same films, and read the same features, dispatches, and magazines. Free and rapid communications help bring this about. In fact the twentieth-century American town is likely to be much more exercised over its participation in universal modernity than in its sense of superiority to the neighboring town, which sense is usually pretty negligible except as an occasion for jokes.

One feature is shared by the socially fixed, the proud-of-locality, and the rural and folk cultures: religion remains a genuine influence and sanction, much more than in the cultures of opposite type.

If we try to formulate the most constant general features in this set of contrasts, to get away as much as possible from culture content into attitudes, from eidos to ethos, it would seem that the attitudes under consideration deal with social relation to time, with individual relation to society, and through this to culture. This set of attitudes toward relations comes near to meaning attitude toward tradition; not only in the popular but in the specific socio-anthropological sense of the word "tradition" as denoting social heritage or cultural transmission. In cultures of the folk type, the group or society with which conformity and identification are sought is relatively small, both areally and numerically; but its time dimension aims to be long, its consciousness of conformity with the past is strong. In "civilized" or metropolitan cultures the group is much enlarged—whence the almost frightening degree of areal and numerical conformity—but at the expense of the time dimension. Such a culture and society are like a vast, flat, quivering surface; folk cultures, rather like a long, tough, firmly clasping root.

The theoretical question arises whether there can also be cultures short in both the space and the time dimension, and others large in both. It may be that certain small, lowly, close-to-nature cultures actually approximate the former type; say Andamanese and other Negritos, Tasmanians, possibly Bushmen and Eskimo in some degree. These would have little sense of the past and little attachment to place. Life would tend to be lived in the moment and in the spot. There is no clear example in history of a civilization as extensive as ours but also deeply rooted; such a one just has not happened yet. But there are civilizations, like those of China and of Middle Ages-Renaissance Europe, which approximate such a condition. They have been much larger than most societies in size and area, have been as it were supernational in scope, have also been well integrated and reasonably uniform internally, and at the same time have had vital and conscious relation with their past. With somewhat greater uniformity and more mobility for somewhat more millions, but no other essential change, they would have conformed to the theoretical suggested fourth type, cultures at once vast in their even extent and deeply rooted in time.

The foregoing are descriptions of how cultures actually—and possibly—behave as regards their "social dimensions." The differences are in orientation; but this has psychological involvements.

Sin and Shame. A domesticated animal or a very small child probably does not feel either shame or sin in doing something forbidden. If the child or infant looks guilty, it presumably fears punishment or at least hostile reaction. Shame, of which all normal adult humans are capable, is defensive reaction against social disapproval or expected social disapproval. How far shame is felt spontaneously or is socially determined is a problem for the psychologists. But shame is partly externalized: it is a feeling with reference to others. Sense of sin, however, is internal. One can feel sinful in solitude, over an act involving no hurt to others. Sin implies a disapproving conscience at work within oneself; shame, the knowledge that others disapprove; though shame can also be superadded to sense of sin—perhaps normally is so added. The distinction is not hard and fast; but it is polar.

Of late years, with conscious effort to define the ethos of cultures, a whole array of observers have made a similar finding on culture after culture. They encounter plenty of shame, but little or no sense of sin. Other people's opinions, their remarks, their ridicule or laughter, are what the average man, in most cultures, is sensitive to, are what deters him. This has been remarked equally for nonliterate tribes and for literate nationalities. The Chinese are guided by "face-saving"; the Japanese lack the sense of "contrast of real and ideal" and "do not grapple with the problem of evil."

But the findings about the importance of shame as a social force are a bit too consistent. They leave little explicit sin sense to any culture but our own Occidental one; and within that largely to its Protestant portion (§ 248), in fact outstandingly its Calvinistically influenced sector. It is true that sin and guilt, sin and trespass, sin and evil, were rather imperfectly distinguished in Europe until the Reformation. It seems to have been this religious movement that internalized guilt and shame into sin, and reared conscience on a great pedestal. We took the word "conscience" from French, but then differentiated it from "consciousness"; the French *conscience* still denotes both. It looks therefore as if the reputedly independent and separate verdicts of Anglo-Saxon anthropologists on Asiatic, Oceanic, native American, and African cultures, that shame is a far more influential motivation in them than sense of sin, does not really specifically characterize these cultures nearly so much as its opposite—conscious sinfulness—characterizes Anglo-Saxon and Protestant culture. Shame as a deterrent factor and a social force is probably operative in nearly all cultures. It is perhaps generally expectable except in the special cases—like our own or Manus civilization (§ 248)—where it has been overlaid by some special development such as masochistic preoccupation with evil—preoccupation with other people's sins or our own.

254. SUICIDE

Naïvely, one might assume that suicide was a personal, not a social, matter: that individuals chose death when going on living became too hard for them, and that it was specially tender-minded individuals, or pathologically depressed ones, who reached that limit of endurance sooner than optimistic, tough-minded ones. These differences due to situation and personality make-up un-questionably occur, and largely account for the selection out of any one com-munity of the particular individuals who take their own lives as against those who do not. Suicide can be described as due to the internalizing of hate, shame, or fear, instead of the normal externalizing or projection of these emotions upon others. The internalization takes place either because the possibility of projec-tion is cut off by circumstances, or because inner disturbance or deterioration makes it seem cut off. Except in the case of disease, suicide thus always contains an element of relation to the individual's social environment.

However, there is also such a thing as institutionalized suicide, condoned, approved, or even exacted by a code and therefore by the culture. In that case, the culture not only defines certain situations that call for suicide, but often indicates the correct way to execute it. In large, complex societies, these specified situations and techniques are likely to be restricted to certain situations, classes, or castes, outside of which the attitude toward suicide may be indifferent, re-gretful, or disapproving.

The Japanese hara-kiri or seppuku immediately rises to mind. This, with its special form of disembowelment, was formerly confined to nobles and war-riors. From these it was transferred after 1868 to the new conscript peasant army, to become an obligation, as against the disgrace of surrender, when vic-tory or escape were both impossible. In that case, suicide was mandatory: those who evaded it were ostracized—obliterated by their society; and officers could kill men to prevent evasion. In this way the almost incredibly high suicide rate of from 90 to 99 per cent was built up among cornered Japanese troops in World War II. This of course is not only institutionalization, but enforcement by ultimate sanctions. And the enforcement, in turn, is a carrying of earlier and more widespread attitudes to their extremes.

One of these is the generic East Asiatic idea of suicide as a protest for the right and against the oppressor. By suicide, the oppressor is put in the wrong with public opinion, as having gone too far; a principle must be right, or must at any rate have something in its favor, if people will die for it. Suicide in this situation is well recognized in China, though much less frequent. In the hands of the Japanese, it seems to have led further to the practice of political assassi-nation: the murderer's convictions, it is thought, must be strong, and therefore likely to be right or at least noble, because his presumptive death sentence—he does not try to hide or flee—is equivalent to suicide. Another element that originally went into the making of hara-kiri as an institution has Western parallels: people of rank who had been condemned were formerly allowed to do away with themselves, instead of having low hands violently laid on them. Similarly, more fallen Roman emperors or claimants to the throne killed themselves, probably, than were executed.

Linkage of suicide to aristocracy as a conditional obligation of caste is fairly frequent. Suicide was expected of nineteenth-century European army officers who got into certain disgraces of dishonor: their colleagues would silently leave a loaded revolver for them. Analogous was the attitude of Cato, Brutus, Cassius, Seneca, and other Roman stoics, who considered themselves an aristocracy of the spirit.

Hindu suttee or widow-burning—abolished a century ago—was optional with the widow, and was often chosen because of its halo of extreme merit, social, moral, and religious. Not only was the dead man's memory enhanced by the act, but his family also participated in the prestige; and this tended to build up strong pressures on the widow; not to mention the economic advantage to the family of being rid of her and her dower rights. However, only high castes practiced suttee. It was not expected in low castes, and probably would have been censured as presumptuous.

These are cases of definite institutionalization, verging on the compulsory. At the opposite pole are prohibitory attitudes, as of Christianity, which ever since St. Augustine has branded suicide as a grave sin, and has retaliated with exclusion from hallowed burial. The laws of a few American states still reflect this mediaeval conception in providing punishment for the attempt, though altered public sentiment prevents much rigor of enforcement. Through the sentiment of Mohammed, Islam also took a strongly condemnatory stand against suicide. The same is true of post-Christian Judaism, though the Old Testament seems to have had no particular reaction to suicide one way or another and mentions only four cases. To these three interrelated religions of exclusive monotheism there may be contrasted the basically pessimistic and agnostic one of Buddhism, which views suicide with moral equanimity.

That fewer Catholics than Protestants kill themselves may be attributed to the fact that Catholicism is on the whole the socially stronger institution; that the rate among Jews has risen sharply for some decades appears to be correlated with their withdrawal from both orthodoxy and the close-knit ghetto life.

Between compulsory institutionalization of suicide and its prohibition there lies a range of attitudes: social disapproval, indifference, or sanction in particular situations. Here would fall the Japanese shinju, the joint suicide of hopeless lovers by casting themselves into the water tied together. Later, this old custom was often superseded by the railroad track; and a variant of it, suicide at the Kegon waterfall, reached a temporary peak of fashionable vogue around 1903. Here the stimulus situation is personal instead of class or social, and the government forbade and tried to prevent the practice, although public sentiment tended to condone it.

All sorts of situations are singled out by different cultures as being permissive of suicide; if there is also a standard or favorite technique of carrying it out, we can be sure that there is cultural channeling. Thus in Melanesia, jumping from a coconut palm is a response to a published charge of incest in the Trobriands; but aggrieved, accused, or jealous spouses are likely to vent their self-pity by eating poison, trying thereby to throw the onus on their mates. In near-by Dobu, this latter is the usual motivation and method; but the poison is uncertain, emetics are administered, and many of the suicides fail; which perhaps increases the frequency of trials, especially since the attempt often suffices to bring a readjustment. But the shame of incest is profound and ineradicable, and the Trobriand palm leap is usually fatal.

The Wintu of northern California had a quite special type of self-destruction. Losing gamblers, returning home to be upbraided by their wives, or refused food by them, dived repeatedly into a deep pool and finally failed to come up again. It is hardly conceivable that enough instances of this sort could happen in a small tribe for the cases really to fall into so definite a pattern; but as an imaginary pattern which had worked through to consciousness as a sort of favorite daydream or story theme, this suicide type is perhaps still more interesting.

The Eskimo show a heavy incidence of suicide, especially in the high Arctic, where life is mostly hard and always precarious, and where the old and the incapacitated are so obvious and unwelcome a burden that they often ask to be dispatched. Thus, at Ammassalik in eastern Greenland, an elderly woman whose legs remained swollen from frost "grew tired of life" and drowned herself. This was spontaneous; but another woman threw herself into the sea only after her son-in-law, on whom she was dependent, wondered aloud why anyone so old and useless did not die. A younger woman drowned herself, in this same little community of less than 400 people, from shame, or perhaps jealousy, at her husband's taking her own mother as cowife. A man was so shamed at his sister's going to live with strangers instead of their father that he slept outdoors until it killed him. In addition to starvation, always around the corner, there is no government whatever among these Eskimo, strength prevails, women are taken by force, murders are common and go unrequited, and life in general is in the raw, so that frequent suicide might be thought expectable. Yet if these cases are typical, three suicides follow upon a stimulus of shame,[6] or other feeling trauma, to only one resulting from direct despair of survival. Underneath the emotional hurts, however, there may well exist a habitual sort of trigger balance in a great many Eskimo individuals—due to chronic and widespread

[6] Compare the remarks on sin and shame in § 253.

privations, uncertainties, and shocks to personality. Most such situations are usually more complex than they seem on the surface.

As to racial propensities to suicide, there are differences, but, as usual, these may either be due partly to heredity and partly to culture ("environment"), or wholly to culture. In Oceania, Melanesians, Micronesians, and Polynesians clearly have a high suicide rate, Australian blackfellows a very low one. The Eskimo stand out among the other American Indians. The African rate is definitely low as compared with other continents, for Sudanese and Bantu Negroes as well as Bushmen-Hottentots. This might conceivably be a matter of inborn racial temperament; but, as usual, it is not provably so. Only about two-fifths as many American Negroes commit suicide per million as American whites. But the Negroes are also more largely rural and poorer, two conditions making for a lower suicide rate in most countries. It thus remains uncertain how much if any of Negro lack of inclination toward suicide can be attributed to racial inheritance. The Eskimo are generally accepted as a distinctive subrace of the Mongoloid Americans; this may or may not involve a perceptibly distinctive inherited temperament; but it is obvious that their living conditions keep them uncertain as to outcomes, and their strongly individualistic social code puts few restraints on self-destruction.

In the last analysis, the motivations and methods of suicide seem very largely to be part of cultural patterns. The frequency is less influenced by culture: age, sex, even season, are statistically proved determinants. So undoubtedly are the personality, and what may be called the provocation, the individual circumstances. Race may or may not be a contributory factor to frequency. It may well be; but proof is difficult to bring, because of the inescapable sociocultural overlay.

255. PSYCHOANALYTIC INTERPRETATIONS—AND SUMMARY

Psychoanalysis is a systematic theory of personality development and functioning formulated by Freud, notable for stressing unconscious processes and sexual psychology. Psychoanalysis includes also a therapeutic practice, which operates through the patient's gradually uncovering the portions of his life history of which his memory has become unaware but whose effects are still active and disturbing to him. The therapy is of no further concern to us here; the theory is, and for two reasons. First, psychoanalytic theory has been extended to include interpretations of culture. Second, many of the mental mechanisms with which it operates have come to be accepted by "orthodox" psychology so far as it deals with whole personalities rather than with separate faculties; as also by medical psychology or psychiatry.

The psychoanalytic explanation of culture is intuitive, dogmatic, and wholly unhistorical. It disregards the findings of prehistory and archaeology as irrelevant, or at most as dealing only with details of little significance as compared with its own interpretation of the essence of how culture came to be. In condensation, Freud's own theory is that "the beginnings of religion, ethics, society, and art meet in the Oedipus complex." Primitive man lived in small bands, from which the strongest male drove off the less mature males, normally his sons, in order to have all the women to himself. The expelled sons band together, kill their father, eat him to gratify their revenge, appropriate the women —their mothers and sisters. But then remorse and guilt gain the upper hand in them, they undo their deed, forbid the killing of a totem animal that is set up as a symbolic substitute for their father, and deny themselves the women they have gained, by instituting the incest taboo. All other taboos are secondary displacements or distortions of these two taboos; and later religions are reactions "aiming at this same great event with which culture began." It is not altogether clear whether the "event" was construed by Freud in its ordinary sense of a single actual happening, or as a "typical" recurrent event. But the explanation comes to nearly the same thing in either case: one mechanism is seized upon as cardinal, all evidence of others is disregarded as inconsequential. The theory is obviously as arbitrary as it is fantastically one-sided. It is mentioned only because it is the one *specific* explanation of the origin of culture that has emanated from a psychological source; although Freud was not only far from being orthodox as a psychologist, but treated the findings of psychology almost as highhandedly as he did those of prehistory and culture history.

Most subsequent interpretations of culture or specific cultural situations by converts to the psychoanalytic sect have not been much more open-minded. Thus Roheim concludes a monograph on primitive culture types with the finding that the sexual practices of a people are indeed prototypical and that from their posture their whole psychic attitude may be inferred. In its calm dogmatism, this finding is in a class with Freud's theory on the origin of culture.

On the contrary, in the realm of psychic processes within the personality, there is no doubt that Freud originated, or endowed with new life and meaning, a series of concepts that are exceedingly fruitful and have been largely accepted by nonanalytic psychology and psychiatry and integrated with them. These concepts include repression, infantile persistences and regressions, dream and fantasy symbolism and overdetermination of the symbols, sublimation of frustrations, transference and identification, and perhaps at least the plastic outlines of the Oedipus situation. These ideas and mechanisms may be said to constitute the permanent contribution of psychoanalysis to general science. But there are other parts of the Freudian schema, such as the censor, the castration complex, the primacy of the libido, which have failed as consistently to penetrate into psychology as the culture-origin theory has failed to take root in anthropology.

Among other things, Freud set up oral and anal types of personality, supposed to be the outgrowth of infantile reactions to the functioning of these respective "erogenous zones." The personality of anal character is orderly, economical, and tenacious; or, in its less pleasant aspects, pedantically precise, conscientious, and persistent; miserly; and obstinate to vindictiveness. Such a constellation or syndrome of character traits might well occur with a certain frequency and regularity, irrespective of whether Freud's explanation as to its causal mechanism is true or not. It would in that case have validity as an empirical clinical finding. Now, just as the anal-type description fits certain individuals quite strikingly, it seems to agree pretty well with the average or modal personality produced under certain cultures. This holds for instance for the Yurok of native California and their cotribes of the same culture. It holds also for certain Melanesians, such as the Manus and Massim. On the contrary, within Oceania, Polynesians, Indonesians, and Australians are wholly unanal in character—the Australians in fact standing at a sort of opposite pole of living happily in disorder, in freedom from possessions, and in the fluctuations of the moment. And the Siamese are certainly oral (§ 245) if the type has any validity at all.

What has been said above (§ 244) about the limitations of statistical validity of all types, constitutional and psychological, undoubtedly holds also for the oral and anal types. Like all physiognomic formulations, they tend to be over-characterized, but below average in frequency of occurrence. Their value lies in the felicity with which they can occasionally be applied. And this felicity may be great in the hands of a great clinical diagnostician like Hippocrates or Freud.

In recent years, the older psychoanalytic theory construing culture as something universal, derivable directly and spontaneously out of the psychology of the supposed primitive family situation, has given place to much more moderate hypotheses attempting to explain the functional relation of particular cultures and the kinds of personalities dominant in these societies. In psychoanalytic terminology, this yields a particular "basic personality structure"; in anthropological phrasing, the result is a "modal personality" typical of the culture (§ 135, 245). It is even conceded that the "rules" or ways or forms of the culture help to determine the relations of parents and children, and the experiences to which the growing child is subjected; and when he has in this way been molded, that he then grows up to perpetuate and perhaps reinforce the standards of his culture.

This is obviously a slightly different way of viewing the process of "socialization" as discussed in § 123. The modern psychoanalysts, or some of them, admit fully that different kinds (or "structures") of personality are made or conditioned by different cultures. They no longer feel it necessary to derive the whole personality directly out of a vague, primal substratum. What they are interested in is showing how people become the kind of people they are in consequence of how their parents and kin treated them in childhood as a result, in turn, of how their culture had molded these same parents and other adults. What this amounts to is seeing a culture through the eyes of individuals. This is a psychological way of viewing cultures through the effects they have on individuals rather than a distinctively anthropological way of viewing cultures as cultures. This procedure does not supplant cultural interpretation: it is a supplement. It adds a certain depth of apperception; and it seems especially satisfying to certain temperaments that find operating with the undiluted forms and patterns of culture difficult, abstruse, or arid.

In summary of this chapter as a whole, it may be said that the basic relation of psychology and culture is due to the fact that culture ultimately exists, or "resides," only in the behavior, the ideas and feelings, and the products of societies of men. Any and every cultural phenomenon therefore has also a psychological aspect or coloring: it is necessarily imbued with something psychological. It cannot however be satisfactorily reduced to purely psychic terms, which are in their nature individual. There is always a large and definitely significant irreducible communal residue that is specifically cultural.

At the present time we can go farther in discerning the influence of cultural factors on the minds of men than in deriving cultural phenomena from psychological causes. This is because of the enormous plasticity of human minds, the almost limitless degree to which they are conditioned or determined by what they are exposed to. And perhaps the largest set of influences to which they are exposed is the total culture of the society in which they exist as individuals. As against this tremendous and specific cultural influencing, the general nature of man—"human nature"—is a pretty vague and uncharacterized thing out of which to explain culture. Human nature undoubtedly sets some sort of boundaries to the forms that culture can assume. But human nature itself, as such, does not fill this frame, does not create the manifold forms culture takes on within its boundaries.

The heavy overlaying of original or basic human nature by influences proceeding from the individual's life history and from his culture results in a rather remarkable anomaly: Psychologists have become very unwilling to discuss the inherent psychic nature of man. It is definitely unfashionable to do so. When the subject is faced at all, it is usually only to explain human nature away as fast as possible, and to pass on to less uneasy and more specific topics. Human nature is going the way the human "mind" has gone. Instead, psychologists for the last few decades have increasingly dealt with the concept of personality.

"Personality" refers to everything about a human individual that is describable in psychological or psychosomatic terms. Some of the traits or qualities are often explainable as due to such and such an event in the individual's life history, or to this or that influence of his culture or subculture. But there is no assumption made by modern psychologists either as to the original and innate generic human nature—as has just been said—or as to the innate particular individual nature that underlies the personality being dealt with. The whole concept of personality rests on proceeding from the ascertainable outside and going as far inward toward causes as evidence will take us, but assuming nothing general as to original cause or nature.

The concept of personality is in one respect a polar one. The traits or properties it includes range from the idiosyncratic to the common or social. Idiosyncratic features are those which distinguish one individual from all others. Such traits may be congenital, due to heredity. Or they may be the result of specific influences in the individual's sociocultural environment, in his life history. This latter class of influences is sometimes traced back a certain distance into childhood and even infancy, especially by clinical psychologists and psychoanalysts. Hereditary factors in the individual are something that almost all psychologists are once more averse to operating with, because of the difficulty of proving them to be hereditary. At the opposite pole of the axis are such traits as most or perhaps all individuals in a society share. Theoretically, these shared features can also be due either to biological heredity or to sociocultural influences. Again, however, modern psychological explanations are restricted to environmental factors, whether these appear in the form of organic experiences or of sociocultural ones. At this pole, of the socially shared features, we have the modal personality typical of a culture, as contrasted with the idiosyncratic elements that coexist in the same individual alongside his modal personality traits.

Psychological study that goes beyond the study of personality as such and centers its interest in the interrelations of personalities—"interpersonal relations" —is usually called *social psychology*. In the development of this, sociologists had a hand along with psychologists, and the subject is still studied and taught nearly as often by sociologists as by psychologists. Social psychology investigates the mechanisms of interpersonal relations: how people learn from one another, how they influence and control one another, and so on. In this investigation of psychological mechanisms, the *what* of learning, influence, and control—in other words, the specific cultural content involved in an interrelation—this "what" is ordinarily not considered by the social psychologist, except by way of exemplification. For instance, there necessarily are attitudes corresponding to all values, norms, or ideals. The attitudes are frankly psychological: they exist *in* human bodies and "minds." Values however are cultural: they are *products* of personalities, and have a sort of existence of their own in spoken and written words, in religion and art, in definable morals and definable institutions. It is the behavioral attitudes corresponding to the values, not the values themselves, that the social psychologist is concerned with: how the attitudes are acquired, reacted to, changed, and the like. That is why anthropologists as a group have participated less than sociologists in the development of social psychology: they are more directly concerned with the content of culture as such. In fact, they look upon culture as their specific and distinctive field of cultivation, the subject with which they are most immediately concerned when they operate above the organic level of heredity and race.

The psychological qualities of different cultures and their supporting societies can undoubtedly be described with a certain degree of effectiveness even today. These distinctive qualities are evidently due to the influence of the cultures—to something in the organization and weighting in the patterns of each culture concerned. But since the qualities are psychological, they must ultimately reside in the behavior of the people who constitute the society that carries the particular culture. Hence such psychological qualities apply or attach both to societies or populations and to cultures.

To date, such characteristics or qualities have been expressed in three ways. One of these is to begin by setting up a classification or system of psychological types or temperaments, and then fitting to these, as far as may be possible, the several cultures or populations being dealt with. This method is open to the usual drawbacks of working from types to particular cases—especially the drawback that most cases yield only a partial fit. A second method of characterization of cultures is to proceed empirically, without any set plan, merely noting those psychological traits which obtrude themselves in each culture, with special alertness toward such as seem to cohere into a consistent larger orientation. A third procedure begins with psychological traits, or trait groups—such as asceticism, sadism, competitiveness, aggression, neatness, and the like—and then compares the relative strength, variations, and associations that such traits exhibit in a series of cultures. This procedure is analogous, for cultures, to studies made of how impulses toward, say, aggressiveness, or orderliness, vary from individual to individual, and under what circumstances.

None of these three methods has yet been developed with great precision or reliability, and the task is presumably more difficult for populations and their cultures than it is for individual personalities. But there is no reason why it should be an insuperable task. And any dependable, objectifiable conclusions that may be attained in the field of cultural psychology will certainly be of extreme interest and may be of great practical importance.

Whether the findings of a systematically developed cultural psychology will be expressed in the terms and concepts of individual psychology, or whether a new set of concepts will have to be added to these, is something that remains to be seen.

CHAPTER SIXTEEN

The Beginnings of Human Civilization

256. FOSSILS OF THE BODY AND THE MIND

THE DISCOVERY of fossils has yielded some understanding of the history of the human body during the past half-million years or so. The evidence is far from complete, but there is enough to show a development that is much as might be expected under the hypothesis of evolution. To some extent fossils also afford an insight into the development of human behavior. The capacity of a skull gives the size of the brain; the interior surface of the skull corresponds to the outer surface of the brain. In a rough and partial sort of way, brain development corresponds to mental development. Even limb bones yield indirect indications. A straight thigh means an erect posture of the body, with the arms no longer used for locomotion. Released from this service, they are freed for other purposes, such as grasping, handling, and various forms of what we call work. But a hand adapted for work would be useless without an intelligence to direct its operations. Thus the bones of our precursors provide suggestions as to the degree of development of their "minds." The suggestions are sketchy and incomplete, but they are worth something.

A second line of evidence is fuller. When a human or prehuman hand has made any article, one can judge from that article what its purpose is likely to have been, how it was used, how much intelligence that use involved, what degree of skill was necessary to manufacture the article. All such artifacts—tools, weapons, or anything constructed—are a reflection of the degree of culture or civilization, elementary or advanced, possessed by the beings who made them.

On the whole the evidence to be got from artifacts as to the degree of advancement of their makers or users is greater than the information derivable from the structure of skeletons. A large brain does not always imply high intelligence. Even a much convoluted brain surface may accompany a mediocre mind. In other words, the correlation between body and "mind" is incomplete, or has not been worked out. On the other hand, an advanced type of tool implies more skill in its making or its use, and therefore a decided development of the *use* of intelligence. Similarly, if we find nothing but simple tools occurring among any past or present people, we may be sure that their civilization and their training have remained backward.

It is true that one cannot infer from a particular manufactured object the mentality of the person or the people who owned and used it. An imbecile may come into possession of a good knife and even possess some ability in using it. But he can acquire the knife only if there are other individuals in his community or time who know how to smelt iron and forge steel. In short, even a single jackknife is proof that human ingenuity has progressed to the point of making important discoveries, and that arts of relatively high order are being practiced. In this way a solitary implement, if its discovery is thoroughly authenticated, may help to establish a relatively high or low degree of civilization for a prehistoric period or a vanished race.

An implement manufactured by human hands of the past is of course different from an actual fossil of a former human being, and it is always necessary to distinguish between the two. The one is something made by a human being and reflecting the development of his intelligence into culture; the other is something left over or preserved from the human body itself. Nevertheless, in a metaphorical sense, the implements of the past may well be spoken of as the fossils of civilization. They are only its fragments, but they allow us somewhat to reconstruct the mode of life of prehistoric peoples and utterly forgotten nations, in much the same way as the geologist and the palaeontologist reconstruct from actual fossils the forms of life that existed on the earth or in the seas millions of years ago.

There is even a further parallel. Just as the geologist knows that one fossil is older or younger than another from its position in the earth's crust or the stratum in which it was laid down, so the student of the beginnings of human civilization knows that the deposit at the bottom of a cave must normally be older than the refuse at the top. He calls in the geologist to tell him the age of a glacial deposit or a river terrace, and thus he may learn that of two types of implements found at different places or levels, one is so many glaciations or geological horizons older than the other. In the long run, too, the older implements prove to be the simpler. Thus archaeologists have succeeded in working out an evolution of civilization which parallels the last part of the evolution of primate life forms. This evolution of human behavior and operations as reflected in the artifacts preserved from the lowest and earliest strata of culture constitutes prehistory, and is the subject of the present chapter.

There is another way in which the evidence on the two lines of evolution is similar: its incompleteness. The geological record has been compared to a book from which whole chapters are missing; of others, but stray leaves remain; and only now and then have consecutive pages been preserved unmutilated. Humanity has always been so much less populous than the remainder of the animal kingdom, especially in its earlier stages, that the number of individuals whose bones have been preserved as fossils is infinitely smaller. The result is that we account ourselves fortunate in having been able to assemble some dozens of skulls and partial skeletons as old as the last Ice Age or older.

The remains that illustrate the development of culture, and therewith in a sense of intelligence, are not so scarce. A single man might easily manufacture hundreds or thousands of implements in the course of a lifetime. When these are of stone they are practically imperishable; whereas it is only the exceptional skeleton, protected by favorable circumstances, of which the bones will endure for thousands of years. For every ancient true fossil trace of man that has been found, we have therefore thousands of the works of his hands.

The inadequacy of the cultural record is not in the insufficient number of the specimens, but in their one-sidedness. Objects of stone, even those of horn and of metal, may last; clothing, fabrics, skins, basketry, and wooden articles decay so rapidly as ordinarily to have almost no chance of being preserved for even a few centuries. Stones of the most ancient times have often been found in abundance; objects manufactured with tools from softer and less enduring materials are scarce even from moderately old periods, except in completely desert situations. Now and then a piece of an earthenware pot may show the imprint of a textile. Textiles and foodstuffs are occasionally preserved by charring in fire or by penetration of metallic salts. Charcoal or ashes found in pockets or beds indicate that fire was maintained in one spot for considerable periods, and must therefore have been controlled and used, possibly even produced, by human agency. A bone needle with an eye proves that someone must have sewed, and we may therefore assume that garments were worn at the time. But for every point established in this way there are dozens about which our knowledge remains a blank.

Understanding of the social and religious life of the earliest man is naturally filled with the greatest gaps, and the farther back one goes in time, the greater is the enveloping darkness. The problem is as difficult as that of figuring accurately the degree of intelligence attained by the mailed fishes of the Devonian age, or of estimating whether the complexion of Pithecanthropus was black, brown, yellow, or white. One can guess on these matters. One may by careful comparisons obtain some partial and indirect indication of an answer. But it is clearly wisest not to try to stretch too far the conclusions that can be drawn. Imagination has its value in science, as in art and other aspects of life, yet when it becomes disproportionate to the facts, it is a danger instead of an aid.

Still, now and then something has been preserved from which one may draw inferences with a reasonable prospect of certainty even concerning the nonmaterial side of life. If a series of human limb bones are discovered regularly charred and split open as if for marrow, there is good reason for believing these bones to be the remains of a cannibal feast. When prehistoric skeletons of a certain period are normally found in the varying positions in which death might have taken place, the presumption is that the people of that time abandoned their dead as animals would. If on the other hand a skeleton lies intact with its arms carefully folded, there is little room for doubt that the men of the time had progressed to the point where the survivors put away their dead; in other words, that human burial had been instituted, and that accordingly at least some rude form of society was in existence. When, perhaps from a still later period, a skeleton is found with red paint adhering to the bones, although these lie in their natural places, the only conclusion to be drawn is that the dead body was coated with pigment before being interred and that as the soft tissues wasted away the red ocher came to adhere to the bones. In this case the painting was evidently part of a rite performed over the dead.

257. STONE AND METALS

The cultural record of man's existence is generally divided into two great main periods. In the latter of these, in which we are still living, metals were used; in the earlier, metals were unknown and tools were made of stone. Hence the terms "Age of Stone" and "Age of Metals." The duration of these two main periods is very unequal. Metals were first used in Asia and Egypt toward 4000 B.C. and in Europe about 2000 B.C. The most conservative authorities, however, would allow 50,000 or 100,000 years for the Stone Age; while others make it cover from a half-million to a million years. The assumption of the lowest figure gives the Stone Age a duration nearly ten to twenty times as long as the Age of Metals. When one remembers that hand in hand with metals came the art of writing, city life, and an infinite variety of inventions, it is clear that larger additions have been made to human civilization in the comparatively brief period of metals than in the tremendously longer time that preceded it. Progress in the Stone Age was not only slow, but the farther back one peers into this age, the more lagging does the evolution of human culture seem to have been. One can definitely recognize a tendency toward acceleration: the farther advancement has got, the faster it moves.

The Age of Metals is subdivided into the Iron Age, which begins some three thousand years ago, say about 1200-1000 B.C.; and an earlier Copper-Bronze Age. In the latter one must distinguish, in some parts of the world, a first period in which native copper or native gold, or both, were employed raw, by Stone Age methods, such as beating out, punching, engraving. This phase has also been called Chalco-lithic and Ae-neolithic, to indicate that it is a transition using stone techniques with metal materials.[1] Next comes the true metallurgical stage, with knowledge of smelting ores, melting, casting, and the like. In this stage it was soon learned that copper melted with a proportion of about one-tenth tin, thus producing bronze, was a superior material for most purposes. Bronze therefore predominated, and has given its name to the period. In some regions the phase of raw or native metals was scant and brief; or full bronze techniques were introduced from outside before the indigenes had learned to look for metals at all. For this reason "Bronze Age" is often used to include the transitional copper or gold phase along with the phase of actual bronze.

Within the past five or six thousand years, accordingly, there are recognized successively the ages of raw gold and copper, of bronze, and of iron.

Broadly speaking, these few thousand years are also the historical period. Not that there exist historical records going back so far as this for every people. But the earliest preserved documents that the historian uses, the written monuments of Egypt and Mesopotamia, are just about five thousand years old. Elsewhere, as in China, in India, and in Crete, writing also seems to have been about coeval with metallurgy, or to have followed it by no great interval. In the Eastern Hemisphere, accordingly, the Age of Metals corresponds approximately with the period of history; the Stone Age, with prehistory. But this is not a law of nature: Peru and Bolivia attained an excellent bronze metallurgy without a trace of writing; and northwestern Europe remained nonliterate more than a thousand years after it worked bronze—even centuries after its smiths operated with iron.

258. THE OLD AND THE NEW STONE AGES

The Stone Age, apart from a doubtful introductory era and a transition to be mentioned presently, is customarily divided into two periods, the Old Stone Age and the New Stone Age—the Palaeolithic and the Neolithic. These words of Greek origin mean literally "old stone" and "new stone." The criterion by which these two grand divisions were originally distinguished was that in the Palaeolithic artifacts were made only by chipping—that is, some process of frac-

---

[1] *Chalkos* and *aes* are the names for bronze in Greek and Latin, and, in a loose sense, for metal in general. Aeneolithic is written Eneolithic by the Italians, who had a large hand in developing the concept.

:uring stone—whereas Neolithic stone objects were thought to have been pecked, ground, rubbed, and polished. Indeed the two periods have sometimes been designated as the epochs of rough-stone and polished-stone implements. They were first distinguished and named by Lubbock, later Lord Avebury, in 1865.

The biggest significance in the distinction between Palaeolithic and Neolithic is not in technique of working stone, which was undoubtedly only one of a number of techniques and accomplishments possessed, though the one whose products have been best preserved. The reason the separation has impressed men's minds was because Palaeolithic implements, and only they, came associated with extinct animals, remains of glaciation, and the geological past.[2] By contrast, the Neolithic, though it antedated history, was so recent as to be in the geological present.[3] Its animals, plants, climates, and land formations are essentially those of today. It is this difference in age, in tying up respectively with geology and organic evolution and with historical development, that made, and still makes, the Palaeolithic-Neolithic differentiation important. The change from merely chipping to also grinding stone was the most abundantly documented fact—because of the durability of flint and chert—of the many changes in culture that inevitably accompanied the lapse of time from genuinely geological past to only barely more than historical past.

The man who was mostly responsible for the first recognition of Palaeolithic artifacts was Boucher de Perthes. For many years he won no converts whatever in France, just because he asserted that these implements were from "antediluvian" deposits that contained also bones of extinct animals—which was assumed to be an impossibility. It was only after geologists came from England to examine the association, and sustained the glacial or Pleistocene age of the implements, that Boucher de Perthes's interpretation began to be generally accepted also by his fellow countrymen. Accordingly, what Palaeolithic then really meant above all, and still means, is: human culture during the Pleistocene.

By exclusion, it follows that "Neolithic" at first was bound to mean post-Pleistocene—the geologic Recent or Now—or at least that part of it which was run off before metals were known. If already in the Palaeolithic the making of stone tools was only a lesser ingredient in the total culture, it is plain that in the later and richer Neolithic, stoneworking presumably constituted an even smaller fraction of the total. Before long it became evident that a whole series of varied inventions or cultural additions were made in the geologically Recent period. Roughly, they came in two main surges.

The earlier of these included pottery, important because it facilitated new types of cooking, such as boiling, and therefore new kinds of foods. Also part of the earlier surge was the bow and arrow. Though full evidence perhaps sets

[2] Palaeolithic remains date from the last of the geological ages, the Pleistocene, also called the Quaternary. See above (§ 36) and immediately below, in this section.

[3] The technical name for the geological present is Recent or Holocene.

the invention of this weapon back into the terminal Palaeolithic, its use seems to have become important for hunting and war after the Pleistocene. A third feature of the first surge was the taming of the symbiotic dog, an achievement that was perhaps more significant as an earnest of larger domestications to follow than it was intrinsically useful.

The second post-Pleistocene and post-Palaeolithic surge brought the domestication of the utilitarian animals—such as cow, pig, sheep, and ass—and the domestication or cultivation of barley, millet, emmer wheat, and perhaps other plants that heretofore had grown only spontaneously or "wild." This second post-Palaeolithic addition to the inventory of culture was evidently of much greater influence on human living than the first. It inevitably tended to settle people down, gave them reserves of food, and therewith made possible the accumulation of more stores of other property, stimulated habits of forethought and planning, and the like.

Increasingly it became apparent to prehistorians that this plant-and-animal taming was the great achievement of the Neolithic. Finally it also became evident that this basic innovation happened more or less simultaneously with regular and effective stone-grinding, as of polished stone axes; and that it preceded the first use of metal by only a relatively short interval, perhaps only about a thousand years. In fact, it was seen that metal was in use in Asia and Egypt even before planting, stockbreeding, and polished flint axes were in use in western and central Europe. This fact meant that, in Europe at any rate, the earlier first-surge or pottery-bow-dog portion of the post-Palaeolithic was as yet without full stone-grinding. In other words, its stoneworking was still essentially by the fracturing techniques of the Palaeolithic. To put it differently, the earlier and longer part of the geological Recent, which it was originally agreed by prehistorians to call the Neolithic, was not yet really "Neolithic" in type at all, even in its operations with stone. All that could be properly affirmed was that this earlier portion was post-Palaeolithic in time because it was post-Pleistocene and postglacial, and that it was Palaeolithic-plus in type of culture because it possessed certain new arts like pottery-making. In short, much of the period that had at first been called Neolithic proved to be not yet Neolithic in the type of the culture. This is an example of the difficulties we are likely to make for ourselves if we slap labels on our concepts when we have only half-knowledge, and then try to preserve the meaning of the labels after they no longer fit the revised ideas based on fuller knowledge.

One way out was to call the pottery-bow-chipped-stone period the "early Neolithic," and the farming-stock-raising-polished-ax stage the "full Neolithic." This nomenclature was still followed in the first version of this book. But meanwhile another nomenclature gained increasing vogue. This was to take the "early" or incomplete or non-Neolithic phase entirely out of the Neolithic period, and give it a separate name; for which Mesolithic, "Middle Stone" Age, was obviously appropriate. This reclassification, or rather renaming, into Palaeolithic, Mesolithic, and Neolithic is followed in the present book. It has become the prevalent nomenclature, though not the universal one.[4]

The term "Neolithic" remains unsatisfactory because it still refers to a minor instead of the major achievement of its period. However, in its now restricted sense, Neolithic does have pretty definite denotations as well as connotations—more definite than a new designation like "Agricultural Age" would have at present. It is therefore retained—in spite of an intrinsic inconsistency that may quite likely lead sooner or later to its replacement. Any name will do, after all, provided we remember what it denotes most significantly—rather than its etymology, which last has a way of being significant in the history of science but also of becoming arbitrary or misplaced with increase of knowledge.

259. PSYCHOLOGY OF TOOL TYPES

Another point in connection with the two processes of working stone has reference to the behavior activities involved by them. A tolerable ground ax or mortar can be made without much difficulty by anyone willing to take the trouble. A civilized person inexperienced in the working of stone should be able, if he gave it time enough, to produce a fairly satisfactory implement by the gradual rubbing-away technique. If however he attempted to manufacture a chipped-stone tool, even of simple type, he would probably fail repeatedly before learning to control the method well enough to turn out a good implement without first ruining a dozen. Indeed, he might never learn to strike out a satisfactory tool without being shown how. It would seem that the manual dexterity required to produce the best forms of chipped-stone tools is greater than that needed for ground ones. Inasmuch as the chipping process is the earlier, we are confronted with a seeming paradox.

The answer is that a good chipped tool can be made in the shorter time. It can be produced in a few minutes, or even if preceded by a number of unsuccessful attempts or "rejects," within an hour or less. But the processes of pecking, grinding, and polishing are laborious. They are slow even when pursued with steel tools; and when the shaping material was no better than another stone, or sand, as in prehistoric times, the duration of the labor must have been discouraging. Days or weeks might be required to manufacture an implement. If the work was done at odd times, one can imagine that many a stone ax was months in being produced. Patience and forethought of a rather high order are thus involved in the making of implements of the Neolithic type. Dexterity is replaced by qualities of what might be called the moral order, or character. By comparison with their successors, the earliest men lacked these traits. They would not sit down today to commence something that would not be available

---

[4] For instance, Menghin distinguishes: (1) Protolithic, or first stone age, the earlier part of the Palaeolithic; (2) Miolithic, the less (old) stone stage, comprising both the later Palaeolithic and the Mesolithic; and (3) Neolithic.

for use until a month later. What they wanted they wanted quickly. To think ahead, to sacrifice present convenience to future advantage, was evidently foreign to their way of life. From what we know of apes we should expect forethought and forehandedness to be lacking while culture was still limited, young, and feeble. Therefore men chipped; and although in the lapse of many thousands of years they learned to do some chipping of high quality, they continued to operate with modifications of the same rough and rapid process. The uses to which their implements could be put were also correspondingly restricted. A genuinely bitted ax, a real chisel, or a grinding mortar, can scarcely be made by chipping alone. It was not until men had learned to restrain their congenital primate impulses to work only for the immediate purpose, and had acquired an increased self-control and discipline, that the grinding of stone came into use.

The developmental importance of the factors of foresight, restraint, and self-discipline has already been discussed in connection with the subhuman primates (§ 28). It may be added that early man's toolmaking primarily by knocking or smashing may conceivably be related to the apes' inclination to take things apart or destroy them, which is so much more marked than their interest in assembly or construction (§ 28).

In the dating or proper arrangement of the periods of prehistoric time one principle must be clearly adhered to: the principle that it is always the latest types of implements which determine the age of a deposit. Lower forms often persist from the earlier periods into the later, alongside the newly invented higher types. Neolithic men did not wholly give up making chipped implements because they also ground stone. Just so we have not discarded the use of stone because we use metals, and we still employ copper for a great variety of purposes although we live in an age of which steel is characteristic. To reckon a people as Palaeolithic because they had chipped implements as well as ground ones would be as misleading as to assert that we still belong to the Stone Age because we sometimes build houses of granite. In fact, stonemasonry has had its principal development since metals have been in use.

Accordingly, if in a stratum of ancient remains there are discovered a thousand chipped artifacts and only twenty that are ground and polished, and if the latter were unquestionably left there at the same time as the chipped ones, one is justified in reckoning the whole deposit as Neolithic in time, though the culture included a large hangover of Palaeolithic technique.

260. EOLITHS AND PRE-CRAG

Early in this century, there began to be efforts to prove a pre-Palaeolithic period. This was called the Eolithic or "dawning (age of) stone," and the evidence consisted of eoliths. These are highly irregular flints, mostly so blunt that they must have been very inefficient for chopping or cutting or scraping. They have small nicks or chips along the edges. These minor chips are thought not to have been flaked off with the conscious intent of producing an edge, but to have become chipped off through usage while the naturally formed flake was being manipulated as a tool by human or prehuman hands.

There has always been much doubt about eoliths. Some of them are now generally accepted, but as part of the Palaeolithic series.[5] Other so-called eoliths are undoubtedly purely natural products. Stones similar to them in every respect, except that their fractures look fresher, are constantly being taken out of steel drums in which flint-bearing chalk is broken up for industrial purposes. Finally, the claims tend to break down of their own weight—of too great age—when eoliths are attributed not only to the pre-Pleistocene Pliocene, but to the still earlier Miocene age of geology.

All in all, a separate Eolithic period was never accepted by all prehistorians, and is considered dubious by the great majority of them today. Of late decades there has been some recrudescence of favorable belief with a shift of locale and an avoidance of the term "Eolithic" with its questionable associations. It is now a matter not of Rutot's Belgian data, but of Reid Moir's Ipswich, Foxhall, "rostrocarinate," and other "pre-Crag" types from the coast of southeastern England. These are generally preglacial in time, that is, Günz or pre-Günz, and perhaps pre-Pleistocene (see Fig. 36, § 272). They are accepted as man-made implements, the earliest in the Palaeolithic series, by some British authorities, and apparently by Breuil, long the dean of French prehistorians. But they are not accepted by other British and non-British specialists. There is a suggestion of the Piltdown line-up here (§ 40). But at least the preglacial geology of the Pre-Crag finds seems to be agreed on by everyone, within a certain fairly close range. It is the tool nature of the specimens, their artifact character, that is in doubt. If the associated "hearths" are really such—that is, are man-made and man-maintained—the case for the flints being man-produced is of course very much stronger.

If those who know most fail to agree, it is almost certainly wise for the rest of us not to take sides too hard. Especially so because it is in the nature of things that as we push back in time toward the beginnings of toolmaking and tool-using, we shall of necessity encounter somewhere a dubious zone of border-line evidence.

261. FORMULISTIC VERSUS HISTORICAL INTERPRETATIONS

When it first dawned on a small number of early nineteenth-century scholars that there were tangible evidences by which prehistory—history before written documents—might be successfully studied, two facts inevitably influenced the

[5] Thus Rutot's Mesvinian stage of the Eolithic is recognized as probably a Belgian facies of the oldest Levalloisian or Pre-Mousterian, his Strepyan as being Chellean—all of them Palaeolithic and Pleistocene. But his still earlier Eolithic stages—all Tertiary, from Eocene to Pliocene—find little acceptance by the prehistorians as containing real artifacts.

views formulated by them. It has taken close to a century of study to overcome this coloring of opinions. Indeed, they still survive in the nomenclature.

One of these influencing facts is that all the first systematic results of inquiry were obtained in western Europe—we may say in France and the few countries immediately adjoining it. It was then assumed that the scheme of findings made here was applicable elsewhere: that a development from Chellean to Mousterian, from Palaeolithic to Neolithic, from Neolithic to Bronze, was expectable everywhere. At any rate, it came to be assumed that the burden of proof was on those who might maintain otherwise. It tended to be taken for granted that a sequence of development established for France would be found also in Russia, and even in China and Africa; or at least that it should be looked for there. This was perhaps the inevitable effect of a system of positive knowledge that was acquired in one area while often there were not even unsystematic data in others.

The second distorting influence was an implicit a priori: namely, that human development, especially in its early periods, would be according to some "law" of nature, and would result in a fixed succession of stages. Thus, stone would be earlier than metal; bronze than iron; fractured stone than polished stone. Perhaps no one went so far as to insist explicitly that it was foreordained from the constitution of matter and of the human "mind" that the precise succession of stages must inevitably recur among all peoples without deviation. It is the pushing of our a prioris to this sort of intransigeant extreme that soonest reveals where these assumptions break down into absurdity. For that reason the assumptions are rarely drawn out to their limits; and by remaining implicit and unavowed, they manage to avoid being put to the test of ultimate logical stretch. So, in a vague but pervasive sort of way, it continued to be taken for granted that while there might be some exceptions or modifications, the succession Old Stone-New Stone-Bronze-Iron ages did hold generally enough to be described as standard and regular. Japan might lack a Palaeolithic altogether, and the technologies of bronze and of iron might have reached the Negroes simultaneously by diffusion from Egypt and North Africa. But as long as one remained confident of the succession of stages as a basically true principle, these aberrations did not matter too much, and might be disregarded, except in so far as they lent a bit of variety to the picture.

We know now that the succession of prehistoric stages does not represent any law of nature, but only a statistical average of variable events in total human history. As a statistical average of a variable truth, it has a certain practical value: it helps organize the description of highly diverse happenings. But as a working hypothesis the regular-succession-of-stages theory has been shot full of holes and can no longer be maintained. It is evident that human history during the last several thousand years is altogether too richly varied for us to believe that the only slightly less rich story of man before he began leaving written documents for professional historians will prove essentially more expressible by such formulas.

In what follows, accordingly, the conventional stages such as the Palaeolithic, and their substages, such as the Mousterian, as originally worked out for western Europe, will be accepted and utilized for their convenience in organized description. They have become so widely known as to be extremely helpful, almost necessary to ready intelligibility. On the contrary, the full story of the interwoven world-wide developments from the Palaeolithic to the Bronze Age has by now become so complicated and full of new names as to be difficult to follow except by addicted prehistorians. To break into the subject simply, to lift out some of the major currents and make them perceptible, there is nothing else so available as the orthodox framework of the first-established stages and periods. Regional as this framework has now proved to be, instead of universal, and erroneous as are some of its former implicit assumptions, this older scheme does provide a scaffold from which to approach and understand the enormously more complex construct that genuinely scholarly prehistory has become. Starting from such a conventional framework of stages and periods, the beginner can at least acquire a notion of some major outlines, next of some main variations, and then of the degree of total variability, without being swamped at the outset by the endless crisscross of similar but never identical facts.

262. THE CLASSIC PALAEOLITHIC OF WESTERN EUROPE

We have seen that it was Boucher de Perthes, in the decade between 1837 and 1846, who established that there were Pleistocene man-made tools or palaeoliths in France, associated with extinct mammals. He made his first French convert to this view as late as 1854. His authority grew when Falconer examined his sites and Lyell, Evans, and other British geologists accepted his findings in 1859. Some years later, Lartet first organized a systematic scheme of what came to be called "the" Palaeolithic—actually it was the French Palaeolithic only. This classification recognized a hippopotamus epoch, at St. Acheul; an epoch of the mammoth and giant bear at Le Moustier; and two phases of reindeer period at Laugerie Haute and at La Madelaine. About 1880, de Mortillet expanded the classification, renaming the periods Chellean, Mousterian, Aurignacian, Solutrean (in place of Laugerie Haute), and Magdalenian. Waveringly, he left out the Aurignacian again; but others reintroduced it, along with a separate Acheulian stage before the Mousterian. From 1895 on, this six-period scheme received general assent. A hiatus or gap was first assumed between the Magdalenian and the New Stone Age lake dwellers of Switzerland, whose period the French called Robenhausian. For a while Europe was considered to have been uninhabited during this hiatus. However, as early as 1887, Piette discovered an Azilian period after the Magdalenian, and in 1896 de Mortillet added the Tardenoisian to this. These last two periods were construed as Epipalaeolithic;

that is, immediately post-Palaeolithic and definitely postglacial. That is where modern usage generally leaves them: in the Mesolithic. In time, too, a Pre-Chellean was somewhat hesitantly prefixed to the beginning of the whole sequence. Therewith the "classic" or older conventional series of Palaeolithic periods was established; as in the following list. This list should be read as the geologist reads a column, from the bottom upward, in order to express the time sequence.

PALAEOLITHIC PERIODS

(Azilian, Tardenoisian)   (Epipalaeolithic, Mesolithic)

Magdalenian *	
Solutrean †	Upper Palaeolithic
Aurignacian	
Mousterian	
Acheulian	
Chellean (= Abbevillean, § 273ff.)	Lower Palaeolithic
Pre-Chellean	

* Peyrony in 1927 estimated that the French Lower Palaeolithic took up 85 per cent of Palaeolithic time; this without recognizing any Pre-Chellean. He assumed: Chellean 40 per cent, Acheulian 15 per cent, Mousterian 30 per cent. The 15 per cent which the Upper Palaeolithic constituted of total Palaeolithic time, he distributed as follows: Aurignacian 7 per cent, Solutrean 3 per cent, Magdalenian 5 per cent. As against this, the more recent Breuil estimate makes the Acheulian two or three times as long as all the rest of the Palaeolithic added together!

† There is considerable inconsistency of usage in the English spelling of these names. The principle followed here is to use the suffix -ean when the French has -éen (based usually on an e in the stratum name, like Chelles, Solutré) and -ian when French has -ien, which is in most cases. In English the accent would naturally fall on the syllable before the suffix. Shell'-e-an, Ash-eul'-i-an, rather than Shell-e'-an, Ash-eul-i'-an. If we tried to follow French in accent, we would have to say Chelle-an', Acheuli-an', and so on.

The group of four earlier periods, and again that of the last three, form definite subunits of the Palaeolithic, both in geology and in culture, as we shall see. Some separate off the Mousterian as Middle Palaeolithic.

All of these periods are named after particular "stations," as the French call them. These are prehistoric sites, each containing artifact remains sufficiently characteristic to serve as type of a more widespread culture that endured for a period.

The geographical area of the successive cultures was subsequently found to vary greatly. Some barely extended beyond France, others, into two or three continents. Also, additional cultures or industries were discovered outside of western Europe. Some of these were similar in their stone implements to the French Palaeolithic stages; some were distinctively different. The total development of human prehistory has gradually become more and more involved, as just said in § 261, through the new geographical variants that keep being discovered. The two stages in which the story will be presented to facilitate gradual familiarization are: First, in § 263-271, a characterization of the classical Palaeolithic industries as French prehistorians first worked them out from excavations made mostly in France, while it was still tacitly assumed that these successive artifact assemblages were general stages through which mankind progressed. Second, with this staging to work from, the actually much richer story of man's culture in eastern Europe and in other continents during Pleistocene and earliest Recent times will then be sketched in a second block of sections, § 272-280.

263. PRE-CHELLEAN, CHELLEAN, ACHEULIAN

Pre-Chellean. This initial stage has never been conceived or defined as sharply as the others. There would be natural difficulties in differentiating it from the still earlier and hazier Eolithic. Roughly, Pre-Chellean would include any flake implements definitely different from the well-characterized Chellean core implements, and appearing to be geologically older than these.

Chellean or Abbevillean.[6] The characteristic Chellean implement is often called a pick or hand ax. It consists not of a flake of flint that has been struck off, but of the core or residue of a nodule of flint after a number of flakes have been knocked off with intent to shape the remainder. Figure 30a shows a slightly more symmetrical example from the next or Acheulian period. Flint tends to come in nodules whose smooth oval shape causes them to resemble smallish cobblestones, or overlarge duck's eggs. The Chellean hand axes or picks are therefore *core* implements, as opposed to *flake* implements. Usually they are somewhat pointed, although rarely really sharp. The butt end may be rounded, some of the original surface of the nodule being left for comfort of the hand in grasping. The Germans sometimes call this tool a *Faustkeil* or "fist wedge"; and the French have coined the expressive epithet *coup-de-poing,* a blow of the fist, or a punch. The Chellean picks average perhaps from three to six inches in length, somewhat less in breadth, and weigh from a quarter of a pound up. This tool would have made an effective rude weapon. When firmly grasped and well directed, it could easily crush a skull or break limbs; though we do not know how much the Chelleans either fought or hunted large game. The implement might serve to split wood, hack limbs from trees, butcher game, and perhaps roughly dress hides; but it would not do any one of these things with neatness and accuracy. The generalized Chellean tool may be described as a combined knife, saw, ax, scraper, and pick, performing the various functions of these implements with notable crudities, but efficiently enough when wielded with muscular strength.

It is often difficult to tell whether one of these hand axes was shaped by hitting the nodule with another stone or by striking the nodule against a larger, fixed stone. Most of the detached flakes were large, as shown by the surfaces off

---

[6] "Chellean" is the older name and is more widely known; it will be used in the first or more elementary part of this chapter. "Abbevillean" is more modern: see § 273.

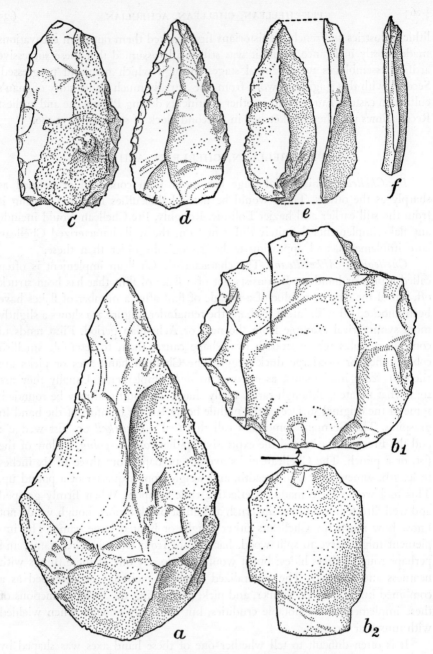

FIG. 30. PALAEOLITHIC STONE IMPLEMENTS

a, Acheulian hand ax. *b₁*, Levalloisian tortoise core with platform, *b₂*, flake-struck from *b₁*; arrows show point of stroke. *c*, Mousterian scraper, *d*, Mousterian "point" or knife. *e*, Aurignacian-type graver. *f*, Magdalenian prism flake. *a, b, d* from Palestine, *c, e, f* from France.

which they came, which perhaps average a square inch. Anything like fine work or evenness of outline was out of the question. One can imagine that many tools were spoiled by the knocks to which they were subjected in their manufacture. The flakes struck off fell to the ground and were discarded. If the workman was sufficiently skillful, and luck stayed with him, he would before long be holding the sort of implement that has been described. Not more than a few dozen strokes would be required to produce it. But these had to be applied with directed skill based on experience.

The Chellean hand ax used to be regarded as the first definitely shaped and regular implement manufactured by man and preserved to us. It is still to be regarded as one of the earliest.

Acheulian. The Acheulian continued with core implements. Some of them are flatter, more evenly flaked, and evener-edged than any of their Chellean prototypes; but they are still hand axes (Fig. 30a). The Acheulian culture may have lasted as long as the Chellean, or longer. Both are represented chiefly in open-air sites rather than in caves. Many of the remains come from the sands or gravels of river terraces, and have been rolled by water. Under these circumstances, preservation of other cultural remains, such as fire hearths, can hardly be expected. The open-air sites suggest life in a mild climate. The precise place of the Chellean and Acheulian in the Pleistocene has not yet found general agreement, as will be seen below (§ 272; Fig. 36). But large parts and perhaps all of the two periods fell into warm interglacial phases, during some of which subtropical climates and animals extended into Europe.

There are few skeletal remains incontestably attributable to Chellean-Acheulian horizon by association with implements; probably for the same reason that hearths have disappeared. However, the Swanscombe, Galley Hill, and other skulls of seeming Neanthropic type are at present generally assigned to the second Thames terrace and to the Acheulian period. The result is a discordance between the fairly advanced physical type (§ 54) and the relatively early time to which the Acheulian is attributed.

The Chellean-Acheulian tradition of making hand axes from cores of flinty material was confined in Europe to the western portions, but had a wide distribution in Africa and Asia. These extra-European occurrences are discussed separately below in § 273.

264. THE MOUSTERIAN

The Mousterian period can be pretty definitely placed in geological time. It falls in the Würm or last Pleistocene glaciation, especially around its peak. The climate drove people into caves for shelter; and here were preserved the bones of some of those who died there. These are known to us as a very definite racial type or perhaps species: Neandertal man (§ 44).

The Mousterian flint implements are very different from the characteristic Chellean-Acheulian picks or hand axes, because they no longer are core tools. They consist of flakes knocked off the nodule, which of course average much smaller (see Fig. 30c-d). But the flake is likely to come off with at least one flat side and one sharp straight or sweeping-curved edge. This edge is normally "retouched" on one side only. The process of retouching, named from French, consists of detaching very small chips or scales from near the edge, either by pressure or by rather light little strokes. These scales average a few square millimeters in surface area, as against centimeters or even inches of flake struck off from the core. Modern tribes almost invariably do their retouching by pressure, often with a point softer than the flint, chert, or obsidian used—perhaps a tip of antler set into a handle, the butt end of which is clamped under the elbow. The flint lies on a pad or a piece of skin in the left hand, held down by the finger tips, while the right hand directs the horn point to a series of pressures just in from the edge of the flint; from each of these a scale flies off, leaving the edge slightly more serrated, usually, but also thinner and sharper. This is the way of modern arrowhead-flakers. Basically, it must have been the Mousterian method also; though whether the Mousterian Neandertalers began by retouching their edge or only "resharpened" it when it got dull; how much they worked respectively by light strokes or by pressure; what kind of a pressing point they used and whether this was handled—all these are problems of detail for which the answers depend on evidence that is either quite technical or not yet in hand.

The Mousterian implements come in a variety of shapes that may have served a variety of purposes. Characteristically, however, they are all flakes with retouch on one side. This use of flakes was formerly thought to have been a Mousterian invention, which somehow was construed as an improvement on the Chellean-Acheulian hand ax and as therefore being its superseding successor. We now know that core implements and flake implements are the products of different inventions and schools or traditions, of different styles of technology, more or less coexisting in time, but among separate populations in separate parts of the world. What happened in France with the onset of the Würm Glaciation was that a core culture carried by a perhaps distinctive racial population was replaced by a retouched flake culture certainly carried by a Neandertal population.

There are a few other features of culture of which we get positive knowledge for the first time in the Mousterian. But these may reflect only the better preservation conditions. For instance, a few of the skeletons look as if they had been laid away, and food or implements put with them. This suggests the beginnings of burial and offerings. But as we have no corresponding Chellean-Acheulian skeletons, we do not know if the Mousterian act really marked a "beginning." Similarly with hearths: it is much easier for charcoal and ashes to be preserved in a protected cave than on a river terrace that is periodically flooded and redeposited. Some Mousterian flake tools certainly *might* have been hafted, more easily so than the Chellean-Acheulian hand axes; but we do not know that they were.

265. THE UPPER PALAEOLITHIC

The next three periods, Aurignacian, Solutrean, and Magdalenian, form an "Upper Palaeolithic" unit. They are still Pleistocene, but the very tail end of the Pleistocene: the final tapering-off of the Würm Glaciation. The Würm peak or maximum we have seen to be Mousterian. The Upper Palaeolithic is the time of main glacial retreat, followed by a brief secondary advance (called Würm II, or Bühl stage of Würm), and the final retreat of the icecap. The time of the vacillations and dyings-away may be guessed roughly as from perhaps 25,000 B.C. to about 8000 or 7000 B.C. There is even an estimate that allots dates to the subperiods: Aurignacian, 25,000-18,000; Solutrean, 18,000-16,000; Magdalenian, 16,000-8000 B.C. Figures like these can have no claim to real authenticity. Their significance is relative. For instance, they suggest that in France the Solutrean was only a brief episode, compared with all other Palaeolithic periods. Also they suggest the brevity of the whole Upper Palaeolithic as against the Lower. Thus, from 25,000 to 7000 B.C. is eighteen thousand years, whereas the preceding Mousterian alone would have fifteen to twenty-five thousand (50,000-40,000 to 25,000 B.C.); and the Chellean and Acheulian would each have been several times as long. The general tendency toward acceleration is reflected by the figures, even though they are extremely shaky as dates.

Next, man of Upper Palaeolithic was ourselves: *Homo sapiens* (§ 49). We generally call him Cro-Magnon man; but this name denotes merely a race, not a separate species, such as Neandertal is still often reckoned. In fact, Cro-Magnon is accepted as Caucasian: he constitutes an early subrace of the Caucasian stock. Quite likely some of his blood flows in the veins of many of us. And he seems to have been fairly uniform as a physical specimen through the three Upper Palaeolithic periods.

The Upper Palaeolithic is less notable for new types of stone implements than for its new developments in other branches of culture. We find a whole series of objects made of bone, and then of horn or ivory also. It is certain that wooden handles and shafts were in use, as well as lines or cords, because there are harpoon heads and harpoon (or spear) throwers. Needles imply thread, stitching, and almost certainly some kind of garments. Paint, paint containers, pierced shells, necklaces and head covers of shells or teeth, indicate bodily adornment. The famous cave-man art is Upper Palaeolithic. This includes representations of what used to be considered houses but are now construed as pits for trapping large game animals. It includes also human beings wearing animal disguises or masks, as if in ritual dances. Many of the animal paintings, especially the Magdalenian ones on the walls of caves, are believed due not merely to aesthetic motivation, but to have been connected with magical reproduction rites for increase of game. The shape of the carvings of women makes it as good as certain that these served as fertility fetishes. Cups of human skulls suggest trophy, death, or ancestral cult; putting away of corpses carefully painted and with limbs flexed, as well as with gifts or offerings, indicates thought of the hereafter, and therewith something in the nature of a concept of souls.

Altogether the picture is reminiscent of the customs and beliefs of modern primitive tribes. Chipping of stones and hacking with stone obviously made up only a very small part of life. There can be no question that the turn from Lower to Upper Palaeolithic, from Mousterian to Aurignacian, was marked by an enormous expansion or enrichment of culture, along with the substitution of *sapiens* for Neandertal man in western Europe. And this new-type, fuller culture was developed still farther during the Magdalenian. True, the much greater chances of time destroying all nonstone products of the much older Lower Palaeolithic cultures must not be left out of account. Nevertheless, the Mousterian is only about one and a half or two times as old as the Aurignacian, and many of its remains lie in protected caves; so that for it, at any rate, preservation conditions are not so markedly more adverse. Yet sure evidence of Mousterian use of bone in any way is of the rarest, Mousterian implements of shaped bone and horn are nonexistent, there is no trace of Mousterian body decoration, or representative art, or religion, or of implements compounded of several parts like the spear-thrower or harpoon.

All in all, archaeologists are in general agreement that previous to the "Neolithic Revolution" just before the dawn of actual history, the profoundest cultural change in the prehistory of western Europe was that accompanying the passage from the Lower to the Upper Palaeolithic. It was bigger and more significant than the transition from Palaeolithic to Mesolithic.

A summary review of the step-by-step changes within the Upper Palaeolithic follows.

266. THE AURIGNACIAN

Aurignacian stone implements are flakes, and little different in principle or technique from those of the Mousterian. Their distinctiveness lies chiefly in their shape, which may be bladelike, with parallel long sides, as against the generally polygonal contour of Mousterian flakes; or they may be beak-pointed gravers, what the French call *burins* (Fig. 30e). Aurignacian novelties in bone include pointed awls or pins; other points with a grooved base for hafting construed as dart heads; tubes of hollowed reindeer bone to hold paint. There are beads or body ornaments of bone, tooth, and shell; fairly careful burials, at times; and a definite launching of the art that was to culminate in the Magdalenian. The Aurignacians were at their best in three-dimensional carving—miniature sculpture, it might be called; but they also engraved or incised two-dimensionally, and possibly colored these figures.

267. THE SOLUTREAN

The Solutrean seems to have been a relatively brief period in western Europe, and to have remained spottily localized, for implements dating from it are the scarcest of any from the six divisions of the Old Stone Age. There was a distinct advance of interest in stonework. The process of retouching was much more finely controlled than before. The best Solutrean workers were retouching both sides of their tools and working over the entire surface of their artifacts instead of only the edge or the point. One of the characteristic implements was a laurel-leaf-shaped blade that has been considered a spear point, but would also have been an effective knife; or it might have been primarily a valuable, a prized work of skill. This has the surface of both sides, from tip to butt, finished in even pressure retouching. It is equaled in excellence of workmanship only by the best of the blades chipped among modern nonliterate tribes or by some of "Yuma" type (§ 280). This laurel-leaf blade is outside the pure flake tradition. When good-sized, it is almost inevitably based on a core; and the retouching with long, ripplelike scales all over, though perhaps derived from the small, edge-nick retouching of Mousterian and Aurignacian, certainly includes also a thoroughly novel element.

Of course this was not the only stone implement the Solutrean people knew. They made points with a single shoulder at the butt, as if for mounting; and they had crude forms that continued the types of earlier periods. This partial conservatism is in accord with the general observation already stated, that lower types tend to persist even after higher ones have been invented; and that because a period is determined by its best products it by no means follows that simpler ones are lacking.

In bone and horn, the Solutrean showed less advance. The needle—a sliver of awl with an eye—is the principal invention in these materials that has sometimes been ascribed to the Solutrean.

In art, the Solutrean represents a break in the Aurignacian-Magdalenian style or tradition. Vivid representation is replaced by highly stylized figures that have become decorative or geometric. The reason for this and for other Solutrean specializations will appear when our review passes beyond western Europe.

268. THE MAGDALENIAN

Magdalenian retouched implements are much less beautifully regular than the best Solutrean ones. They are made by another technique, devised earlier, but Magdalenian in its typical development. This technique detached, from a suitable block of flint, long, narrow, straight-edged, blade-shaped flakes, each by a single blow, somewhat on the principle by which a cake of ice can be split evenly by a well-guided stroke of the pick. Perhaps the most typical Magdalenian implement of stone is one of these long thin blades, triangular or polygonal in cross section; in other words, a narrow prism (Fig. 30*f*). Beak-pointed gravers (Fig. 30*e*) and other forms continued to be made.

To detach a prismatic flake, there is needed flint of rather even grain, with one fairly flat transverse side or "striking platform"; and the blow that does the work must be delivered on a precise spot, at a precise angle, and within rather narrow limits of force. This means that the hammer or striking tool cannot well come in direct contact with the flint. A short pointed piece, something like a nail or a carpenter's punch, and probably made in prehistoric days of horn or bone, is set on a suitable spot near the edge of the block of flint, and is then tapped smartly with the hammer stone. A single stroke slices off the desired flake. The sharp edges left on the block where the flake has flown off can be used to start adjacent flakes, and thus all the way round the block, the workman progressing farther and farther in, until nearly the whole of his core has been split off into strips or prisms.

This Magdalenian process survived, or was reinvented, in modern times. It is only a few years ago that flints were being struck off by English workmen for use on flintlock muskets to be exported to Africa. The modern Englishman worked with a steel hammer instead of a bone rod and a cobblestone, but his technique was the same. The complete lot of flakes into which a block has been split can subsequently be laid together to re-form the core in its original shape. Similar flakes made of obsidian, a volcanic glass similar to flint in its properties, were long produced by the tens of thousands in Indian Mexico for use as knives. This method of flaking gives the smoothest and sharpest edge. It is not adapted for making heavy instruments, but it yields an admirable knife. The process is also expeditious.

269. NEW MATERIALS AND INVENTIONS

Magdalenian bone javelin heads and spearheads were made in a variety of forms; with bases pointed, beveled, or grooved. Hammers, chisels or wedges, and perforators were added to the list of bone tools. Whistles and perhaps flutes were blown. Reindeer antler was employed for carved and perforated lengths of horn—"rods of command" or of magic, as they are usually called—as well as for harpoons and throwers, to be discussed below.

In this final stage of the Palaeolithic, and in the Mesolithic, objects of organic substances began to approach in frequency those of flint. This may have served as a sort of preparation for the grinding and polishing of stone of the

New Stone Age. Bone cannot well be chipped or retouched. It must be cut, ground, or rubbed into shape. At any rate, the subsequent Neolithic may be said to have extended to stone a process which the Upper Palaeolithic (and the Mesolithic) were familiar with but had failed to apply systematically to the harder inorganic substance.

The slender bone needle provided with an eye that the Solutrean may have devised, and the Magdalenian certainly possessed, implies thread and sewing and presumably, therefore, some sort of more or less fitted or pieced garments.

Ornament may have existed earlier than clothing, since the Aurignacians already hung rows of perforated shells and teeth about their necks and waists. By the Magdalenian, there was sophistication enough to lead to the carving of artificial shells and teeth out of ivory; and amber was beginning to be transported from the German coast to southern France.

The harpoon came into extensive use in the Magdalenian. The shafts have of course long since decayed, but some of the reindeer antler heads have remained intact. At first these were notched with barbs along one edge only; then barbs were cut on both sides. The harpoon differs from the simple spear or javelin in having its head detachable from the shaft, the two being fitted together by a socket. If the prey, be it fish or mammal, is not killed by the first throw, its struggles to escape shake the shaft loose, while the barbs hold the head firmly imbedded in its body. A line is attached to the head and tied to the shaft or held in the hand of the hunter. The animal is thus kept from escaping. The earlier Magdalenian line was kept from slipping off the harpoon head by one or two knobs near the butt. Later in the Magdalenian, the butt of the head was sometimes perforated—as was standard usage in the subsequent Azilian period, and as is the modern Eskimo practice also. The harpoon is really a rather complicated instrument: it consists of at least three pieces—head, shaft, and line.

Another device the Magdalenians shared with a series of recent peoples is the spear-thrower or atlatl. This is a sort of rod, board, or handle, one end of which is grasped by the fingers while a short projection at the other end engages the butt of the harpoon or dart shaft. The hand steers the shaft only at the beginning of its flight: the propulsion comes from the thrower. The instrument may be described as a device for artificially lengthening the human arm and thus imparting greater velocity and length of flight to a light weapon. There is without doubt considerable ingenuity involved in this apparatus, both in its invention and in its successful use. A person unskilled in bodily movements would never hit upon the invention; nor could a race of high native dexterity acquire proficiency in the art of hunting with the thrower until each individual was willing to practice for a considerable period. It may be concluded, accordingly, that Magdalenian civilization had developed to a point where men were fairly ready to undergo protracted training and forbearance.

270. MAGDALENIAN ART

Upper Palaeolithic art reached its acme in the Magdalenian. The western Europeans now carved in ivory, bone, and horn; they incised or engraved on flattened and rounded surfaces of the same material; and they carved and painted the walls of caves. They modeled at times in clay and perhaps in other soft materials, and for all we know, may have drawn or painted pictures on skins and on exposed rock surfaces; we can judge only by the sheltered remains that have actually come down to us. It was not a struggling attempt to represent objects in the rough, nor a decorative playing with geometric figures. A few bold strokes gave the outlines of an animal, but they gave it with such fidelity that the species can be recognized at a glance. This self-reliant impressionism is very different from the art of most modern "primitives." The latter often work out decorative patterns of some richness and aesthetic value, but usually fail when they attempt to depict nature. They tend to accomplish a more or less pleasing abstract design rather than the delineation of what is characteristic in an actually visible form of nature. It is only rarely that any but advanced nations

FIG. 31. AURIGNACIAN FIGURE OF A WOMAN

Limestone statuette from Willendorf, Austria. Characteristic of Aurignacian treatment of the female figure, the face and limbs are abbreviated or only indicated, and the parts concerned with reproduction are exaggerated.

develop skill to draw things both realistically and pleasingly. The ancient Egyptians developed such a faculty, and among savages the ancestral Bushmen were remarkably gifted; but these are exceptions, along with Cro-Magnon Magdalenian art.

In sculpture the first Upper Palaeolithic efforts were directed upon figurines, mostly representing the human female. The head, hands, and feet are either absent or abbreviated. In the body, those parts having to do with reproduction and fecundity are heavily exaggerated, but at the same time given with considerable skill (Fig. 31). It is likely that these statuettes served some religious purpose. At any rate, the carvings in three dimensions often represent the human figure, whereas two-dimensional drawings and paintings mostly represent animals, and are much more successful than the occasional human outlines. Miniature sculpture of animals was added to that of the human figure, especially in the Magdalenian (Fig. 32).

Success in seizing the salient outline was the earliest characteristic of the paintings and drawings. The first engravings are in profile and usually show only the two legs on the immediately visible side of the animal. In the full Magdalenian, all four legs are usually depicted, and the profile, although remaining the most frequent as it is the most characteristic aspect, is no longer the only one. There are occasional pictures of animals from before or behind, or of a reindeer with its head turned backward. In time the artists also learned to suggest typical positions and movements—the motion of a reindeer lowering its head to browse, the way an angry bull switches his tail or paws the ground, the curl of the end of an elephant's trunk (Figs. 33, 34).

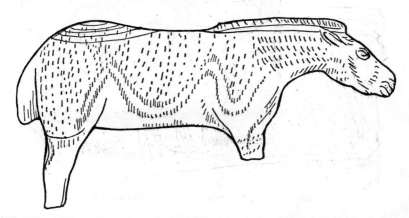

FIG. 32.   MAGDALENIAN CARVING OF A HORSE

Of mammoth ivory; from Lourdes, France. The spirited portrayal of the neck, ears, eyes, and mouth parts is characteristic of Magdalenian sculpture.

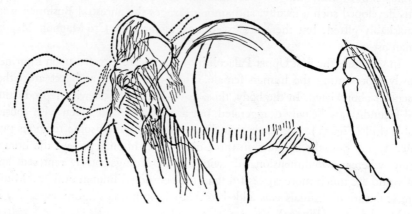

FIG. 33. MAGDALENIAN MAMMOTH

Engraved on a fragment of ivory tusk found at La Madeleine, France. While the artist's strokes were crude, he was able to depict the charging animal's action with remarkable vigor: the roll of the eye, the flapping ears, the raised tail expressive of anger.

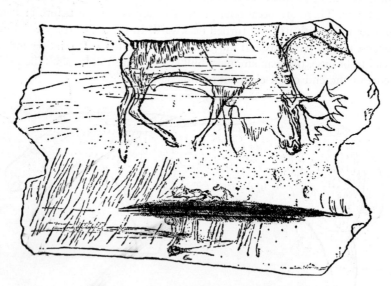

FIG. 34. MAGDALENIAN REINDEER

This is perhaps a composition: browsing reindeer among grass, reeds, and water. Note the naturalistic movement suggested by the legs and the position of the head. Engraved so as to encircle a piece of antler. Found at Kesslerloch, Switzerland.

FIG. 35.   MAGDALENIAN ENGRAVING OF A HERD OF REINDEER

The impressionistic manner of engraving enabled the artist to suggest rather effectively a large herd while drawing out only four animals. Found in the grotto of La Mairie,
France.

There are also some devices that look like the beginnings of attempts at
composition. The effect of a row of reindeer is produced by drawing out the
first few in some detail, and then suggesting the others by sketching in their
horns (Fig. 35). Artists were trying, with some measure of success, to represent
animals as they moved in life and perhaps to combine several of them into one
coherent picture or to suggest a setting. By the later Magdalenian, the artists
had also acquired considerable ability in handling colors. Those, for instance,
who left their frescoes on the walls of the famous cave of Altamira in Spain used
three or four pigments and blended these into transition tones.

While animals constitute the subjects of probably four-fifths of the specimens of Palaeolithic art, and human beings most of the remainder, representations of plants and some nonrealistic decorative designs are also known.

271. EPILOGUE AND RECAPITULATION FOR WESTERN EUROPE

The Azilian or Asilian culture is post-Bühl; that is, subsequent to the
second, minor Würm Glaciation, and therefore post-Pleistocene and within the
geological Recent. The climate, though technically "boreal," was more modern
than glacial; the fauna was essentially that of modern Europe: mammoth, cave
bear, and wild horse were gone, deer replacing reindeer.

The Azilian sites are rather few, small, and meager. They give the impression of a scanter and poorer population. The great Magdalenian cave art is gone.
In its place there are pebbles painted each with a red-ocher symbol, of about
the simplicity of our capital letters. Harpoons continue, and come perforated;
but few artifacts are either highly characteristic or very well made, whether of
stone or of horn. We are now out of the Palaeolithic and in the Mesolithic.
Europe is off to a new start—a seemingly humbler start after the Palaeolithic
climaxing in the Magdalenian: a sort of aftermath or epilogue. This western-
European Mesolithic will be reviewed as a whole in § 276.

A summary recapitulation of the Palaeolithic follows—which, as usual, should be read *upward* for its time sequence.

SUMMARY OF THE CLASSIC PALAEOLITHIC IN WESTERN EUROPE
(Read *upward*)

Azilian: Postglacial and post-Palaeolithic; climate "boreal" but approaching modern conditions; fauna modern for the first time. The representative art is wholly gone; the culture seems more meager; most artifacts show less finish. The Mesolithic is on.

Magdalenian: Second, minor Würm Glaciation. Prismatic flakes (Fig. 30*f*). Increased use of organic materials shaped in a variety of types. Composite implements such as harpoon and atlatl. Increased indications of religion and magic. Culmination of representative art.

Solutrean: Same geology and probably race as for Aurignacian. Blades with all-over ripple retouch. Art tends to the stylized symbolic.

Aurignacian: Würm recession. Appearance of Cro-Magnon race of modern man. Flake tools with retouch (Fig. 30*e*). Use of bone, horn, ivory, treated by rubbing and sawing; dress and adornment; beginning of representative style of art, especially three-dimensional.

The great turn of culture from Lower to Upper Palaeolithic.

Mousterian: Maximum Würm Glaciation; smallish flake implements, of various shapes, with edge retouching on one side only (Fig. 30*c*, *d*). Indications of burials and offerings. Neandertal man.

Chellean and Acheulian: Pre-Würm Glaciation; largish core tools, made by knocking away good-sized flakes (Fig. 30*a*).

Pre-Chellean: Flake-type implements of somewhat uncertain geological age and authenticity as artifacts.

272. QUALIFICATIONS AND COMPLICATIONS: CLIMATES AND FAUNAS

So far we have followed the relatively straight and narrow path of the longer-known or "classic" prehistory of Palaeolithic western Europe. From this point on, there are more problems and complications.

For one thing, we have until now left the beginning of the story floating free in time. The Palaeolithic ends with the Pleistocene. The Upper Palaeolithic falls into the post-maximum-glacial end of the Pleistocene—its diminishing-glacial end, we might say. The Mousterian coincides with the peak or maximum of the last glaciation. So far back, everyone is in agreement. Farther back, there is much disagreement. This means that prehistorians' chronologies and interpretations in terms of geological time are essentially uniform for the last tenth of the Pleistocene, but divergent for the first nine-tenths.

The grand or over-all dating of the Pleistocene is in terms of its glaciations or ice-sheet ages. This dating must of course be done by geologists. Unfortunately there is no absolute agreement among geologists even as to the number of Pleistocene glaciations. Usually four are assumed for Europe; Günz, Mindel, Riss, Würm. These names are those of Alpine localities where the several glaciations left records of their successive presence. In North America it is also usual to recognize four main glaciations: Nebraskan, Kansan, Illinoian, and Wisconsin; and these are usually considered approximately contemporary with the European ice ages.[7] But another view recognizes three European glaciations. Still another admits only two; though as each of these may have had a double or multiple maximum, the intrinsic difference from the four-period scheme is not as glaring as might seem. The most usual recognition for several decades now has been that of Günz, Mindel, Riss, Würm; and that scheme is followed here. It seems also to be generally accepted that the interglacial periods were longer than the glaciations; and probably that the Second or Middle Interglacial was particularly long. This would give us, within the Pleistocene, a total of eight or nine successive stages geologically recognizable. There would be possibly an initial preglacial period; then four glaciations separated by three interglacial periods; and then a postglacial tapering-off. This last would be, in human-culture terms, the Upper Palaeolithic.

This is at least a clear scheme. How strong the geological evidence for it is, or how wobbly, is a technical matter. The scheme depends on moraines, scorings, glacial lakes, varves or layers of deposit from melting ice, fauna and flora, and many other kinds of geological evidence, sometimes conflicting, often imperfect, generally different for each region. For instance, in a protected pocket, even in Europe, an old warm-weather fauna including hippopotamuses might sometimes have maintained itself, through a glaciation to its north, into the next warm interglacial. To a large extent, Africa today is such a pocket—though of continental size—in which a conspicuous element of the Pleistocene interglacial fauna of Europe survives: not only hippopotamuses, but rhinoceroses, elephants, and lions. Comparable though more local survivals may well have occurred within Europe, because it is clear that only a minority of Europe was ever under an icecap at one time.

How far the glaciations were caused respectively by drop in temperature, or by increase in precipitation or decrease in evaporation, is another point that does not appear to have been worked out conclusively. That there was some chilling is clear. But would the piling-on and spread of ice sheets be promoted by still further cooling, even if the precipitation became low? Or rather by much snow, with heavy clouds retarding its loss by evaporation, but with only enough cooling to prevent any serious summer melting?[8] On the answer to this ques-

---

[7] A mnemonic aid to this: The series of four European names follow one another alphabetically, and three of the four American ones antialphabetically.

[8] For instance, one view is that it is *increase* in solar radiation which underlies continental glaciations, and that these come in pairs. Up to a certain point, more radiation increases atmospheric circulation, and therewith cloud blankets and precipitation, leading to heavy snowfall in high latitudes; whence a first glacial advance, in a period of raw storms rather than biting cold. Still more radiation however increases heat and rainfall until the icecaps melt away in a warm, wet interglacial era. As the turn comes and the basic solar radiation begins to wane, the processes reverse their order, and a second glaciation ensues, now increasingly calm and dry, to complete the cycle. This view is cited not because it is

tion, again, would depend the glacial climate of areas adjacent to the icecap, and even of remoter areas. Africa and the tropics were never reached by glaciations; they are credited with pluvial periods instead. Presumably these corresponded in time to the glacial periods in the North—but how exactly?

It is conceivable that if cooling was general over the earth's surface, evaporation would also be reduced, and with it, rainfall. There is plenty of geologic evidence, in many parts of the earth, of changes of climates, especially between wet and dry areas; and some of these happened in the Pleistocene. But the correlation of such changes as they occurred in widely separated regions, and especially as between permanently ice-free and glaciated areas, is an intricate, tricky, and highly technical matter, on which the anthropological student must take the word of geologists and climatologists, and these are by no means in agreement. They may be reasonably sure of one series of climatic successions in one region, and of another in a second or third region; but there may be little direct evidence on the correspondence of the several series of regional stages, the identification of which then remains speculative.

One point on which geologists have succeeded in reaching general agreement is that widespread glaciation locks up a lot of water in ice sheets lying on the land, and thereby lowers the level of the oceans. Thus, at the present time, the land ice, mainly in Antarctica and Greenland, totals 18 million cubic kilometers of water, or over 4 million cubic miles. Were all of this melted, it would deepen the oceans 50 meters, or on allowance for the added weight depressing the ocean bottoms somewhat, 40 meters net. The shore line would thus be at what is now the 130-foot contour above sea level; and parts of every salt-water harbor in the world, and the whole of many of them, as well as wide stretches of fertile coast plain in all continents, would be drowned. In the long and generally warm Second Interglacial, the ocean perhaps did rise up on the land as much as this. On the contrary, during the last or Würm Glaciation, the amount of terrestrial ice was nearly double that of today, and the seas were around 75 meters or 250 feet shallower than now. At the estimated maximum of 10 million cubic miles of water tied up in Pleistocene glaciers, the ocean bottom was dry for 50 fathoms deeper than the present shore. This would unite England with Europe, Ireland with Britain, Borneo and Java probably with Asia, New Guinea and Tasmania with Australia. This is a factor to be reckoned with: England was indeed part of Europe through most or all of the Palaeolithic, for instance. One the other hand, ancient races of man that lived in lowlands or by the sea during the Riss and Würm periods, even in continents remote from icecaps, would now have their bones, their tools, and their sites deep under salt water.

proved, but as evidence that while glaciers are indeed cold and do chill their immediate environment, meteorological opinion is not yet settled as to their causes, and does not necessarily derive them from cooling alone.

The Pleistocene has been estimated to have lasted all the way from about one-fifth of a million years to something like a million and a third or two millions. At the moment, opinion has fairly settled down to figures of 500,000 or 600,000 years—or again a full million—as being probably nearest the fact.

When we turn from purely geological to anthropological considerations, it is soon evident that on the whole prehistorians agree reasonably well in most of their findings on prehistory itself; namely, on the forms early implement culture took, and on the variations and successions of this culture. What they are in much less full agreement on is when the several parts of this story happened; that is, how the parts are to be fitted into the geological framework of glaciations or climatic time-markers. Figure 36 shows this difference for the Lower Palaeolithic. Four several sets of authorities agree in recognizing Chellean, Acheulian, Mousterian, in that order. Also, they relate supplementary industries, such as Cromer, Clactonian, Levalloisian, to these basic three in much the same sequence. Thus Levalloisian is roughly contemporary with Acheulian according to all of the specialists. The prehistorians differ as to where they set a given culture or tradition of industry in the geological time scale. Thus it will be seen that the Chellean is put by some into the Third Interglacial, by some into the Second, by others into the First. Attribution of the Chellean to the later Pleistocene was the view originally current, and was adhered to in the first or 1923 edition of the present book; although the opinion which set the Chellean back into the Middle Interglacial had respectable following even then. Since that time, a British school, followed by Breuil and some Americans, has boldly pushed the Chellean back into the First Interglacial; which in turn would throw the still earlier or "Pre-Crag" implements into the initial glaciation, or beyond that out of the Pleistocene into the Tertiary.

These are direct conflicts of chronology. In other words, some prehistorians' opinions as to the correspondence of Pleistocene cultural facts to Pleistocene geological facts are still irreconcilable with one another. Everyone is agreed that Acheulian implements are later than Chellean, and Mousterian later than Acheulian; just as the geologists are agreed that if there were four glaciations, the time order of these is a sequence of those described as Günz, Mindel, Riss, Würm. The disagreement is about how the archaeological and the geological-climatic scales are to be meshed into each other. On this, there is one general or even unanimous accord: everyone assigns the Mousterian culture of Europe to the maximum of the last or Würm Glaciation. Let us gratefully cling to this one seeming rock of assurance; especially since the Mousterian is also the culture definitely associated with the classic type of Neandertal man, so that the correspondence is really a double one: culture with glaciation and culture with race.

Back of the Mousterian, one or the other of the several time correspondences is presumably true and the others are erroneous; and ultimately the correct one may be proved to be such. The writer knows that he cannot assert with assur-

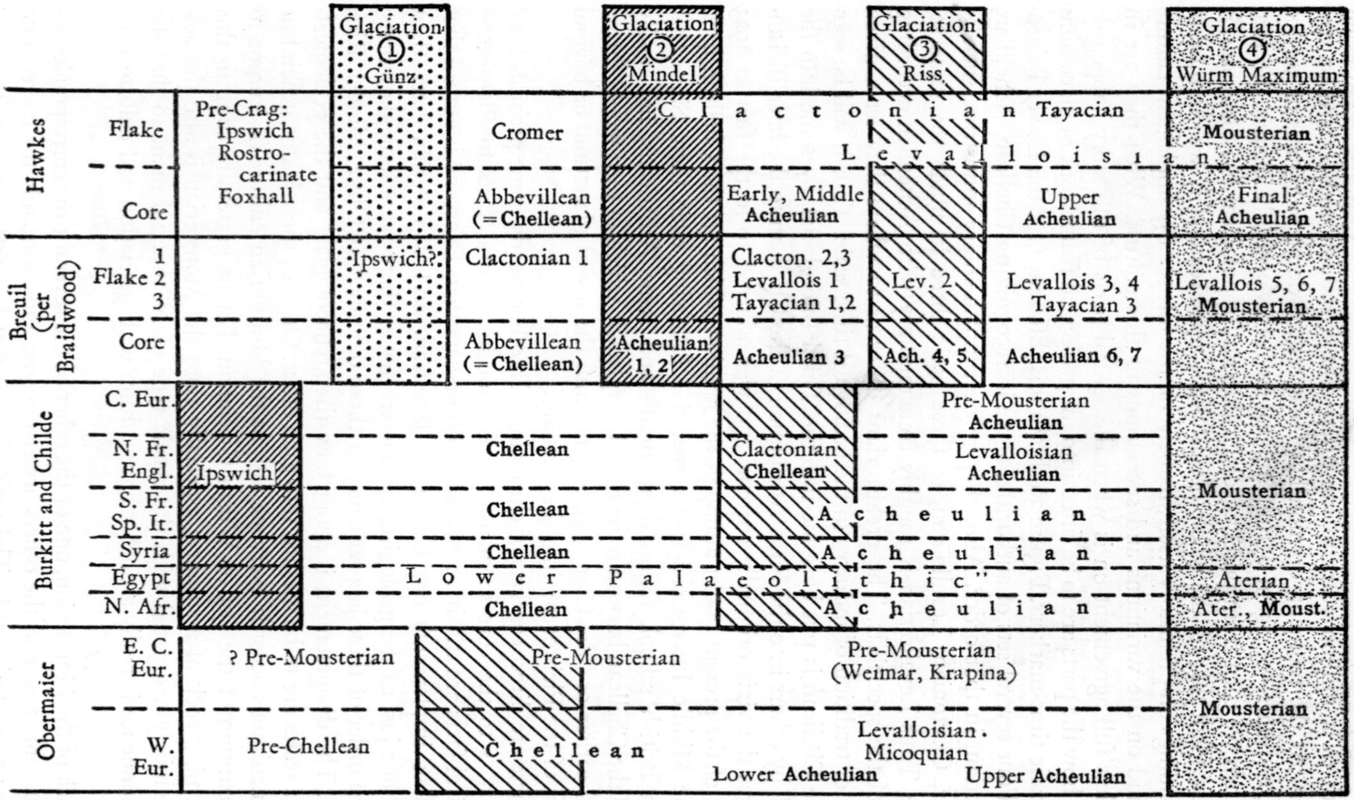

(Breuil-Braidwood Flake Industries: 1, without, 2, with, 3, with or without faceted striking platform.)

FIG. 36. LOWER PALAEOLITHIC INDUSTRIES AND GLACIATIONS, AS SEEN BY DIFFERENT AUTHORITIES

ance which one is correct. He doubts whether anyone can, as of 1948. It is true that for two or three decades there has been a tendency to lengthen chronologies: the earliest to be propounded on the whole claim the least portion of the Pleistocene for Palaeolithic culture; the latest claim the most. Hawkes, in 1940, seems even to want to go back into pre-Günz. This alignment gives the long chronologies the advantage of momentarily representing the latest opinion. But it is hard to know how much of such up-to-dateness is solid accomplishment that will last, and how much is the wash of a wave of opinion. We all realize that just as the customer is always right, so this year's fashion is always right. We do not in general recognize—and it is very difficult for anyone to estimate until long after—how large an element of similar fashionableness of mode, of impressive but sometimes merely temporary authority, attaches to the "latest findings" of science; especially when this is a historical science like geology the theories of which about the past cannot be put to the test of experiment.

The table in Figure 36 has been drawn up with the cultural prehistory as constant as possible and the geology variable. This may seem artificial, because the earth and climates existed before human culture, and it may therefore be argued that the prehistory ought to be fitted into a fixed scheme of geology. So it ought, theoretically. But the particular concern of anthropologists being with prehistory, it is this which here has been given the priority, to make evident how largely the opinions of prehistorians are in agreement on matters that are specifically cultural. There are only minor differences between the several authorities as to the succession or contemporaneity of distinctive artifact types and industries. But the differences between these same authorities become very large, and extremely disconcerting, when each of them proceeds to date his artifact types and industries in terms of the geological time scale, about which the prehistorian generally has no expert knowledge of his own and which he therefore has to take over from the geologists. Now for one thing, as we have seen, the geologists are not in unanimous agreement among themselves; and for the rest they do not generally bother with human artifacts. It is thus necessary for the prehistoric archaeologists to operate with a time scale that is not of their own making. They have to decide whether, say, the Acheulian, on which they all substantially agree, falls into such or such a glacial or interglacial period as determined rather variously by the geologists.

That is why the table in Figure 36 has been kept consistent for its prehistory. The Acheulian of Breuil, that of Burkitt and Childe, of Hawkes, of Obermaier, have been put as nearly as possible into one vertical column; and the same for Chellean, Levalloisian, and the other industries and cultures. Thereupon the ice ages and the interglacials to which the several authorities have attributed these cultures have been indicated by superposed light shadings; and these shadings have been allowed to wander over the page at each expert's fancy. In short, the effort has been made to bring out the really large consistencies in anthropological opinions on prehistoric culture, without worrying too much about how inconsistent the reconcilement of these to geology is. Indeed, rather few geologists really care much about the subdivisions of the miserable million or half-million final Pleistocene years in their total geological scale of a half-billion or more.

There is just one consideration that a geological nonspecialist can adduce as relevant to the problem of Pleistocene durations. The Upper Palaeolithic—Aurignacian, Solutrean, and Magdalenian together—has pretty generally been thought accommodable between about 25,000 B.C. and 8000 or 7000 B.C. Instead of these 15,000 years or so, the Upper Palaeolithic might yet conceivably have to be stretched to 20,000 or 30,000 years. But compared with this, the Lower Palaeolithic—Chellean, Acheulian, and Mousterian—has clearly to be given a hundred thousand years—by most recent views, several hundred thousand, or even a million. This makes a ratio of at least three to one, probably five or ten to one, perhaps twenty or even fifty to one, for the duration of the Lower Palaeolithic as against the Upper. Now it is indeed indubitable that the development of culture in western Europe was slow at first, and that it accelerated gradually. We shall find this acceleration continuing as we pass from the Palaeolithic to the Mesolithic and the Neolithic, which together lasted less than half as long as the Upper Palaeolithic alone.

But the acceleration principle can be overworked. If we assume the shortest chronology, and crowd Chellean, Acheulian, and Mousterian into Riss, Riss-Würm, and Würm; if we allow the Second Interglacial to be considerably longer than the Third or Riss-Würm, and estimate the total years of the Pleistocene to have been in the vicinity of half a million, we can confine the Lower Palaeolithic cultures within a span of 100,000 years. If we allot 25,000 of this to the Mousterian, we have left 75,000 for the continuous Chellean-Acheulian bifacial-core tradition. This is a long, long time—a dozen times longer than the whole of documented, authentically datable human history. And what do we know to have happened in this time? Essentially just one thing: the improvements from roughed Chellean core flints to evener, symmetrical Acheulian ones. That is, the technological tradition remained basically unchanged: it stood still except for some degree of refinement of finish. That is surely a tremendous lot of cultural stationariness to have lasted so long, in comparison with the changeability that characterized later prehistory and all history. No doubt development was indeed exceedingly slow in the beginning; all the evidence points that way. Yet if we accept the most recently alleged chronology, with the Pre-Crag tools as preglacial, then our 75,000 years of Chellean-Acheulian nondevelopment are stretched into 400,000, which certainly is an added strain on the credibility we have to extort from our imagination. Even 4000 years without basic change in methods of human living is really wholly beyond our experience to conceive. Perhaps once we get beyond comparable historical experience, we are lost anyhow, as critical minds, and we might as well trust to faith in an authority that claims a lot as in one that claims less. And yet, it does seem wise not to lose all sense of proportion in an intoxication of complete recklessness as regards time durations, but to remain aware that the briefer Palaeolithic chronologies— if true—would fit in much more readily with all we know of the rate of subsequent human development and history.[9]

273. CORE AND FLAKE TRADITIONS IN THE LOWER PALAEOLITHIC

It is now necessary to refine and fill in the rather schematic outline of artifact types and culture periods as it has been presented so far. We shall have to consider variant and altered names; subdivisions of cultures and recognition of new ones; their regrouping into larger currents or traditions; and the regional differentiation of these.

As to changes in nomenclature: a better type station than the original Chelles was found at Abbeville in France. Consequently, in 1932 the Chellean was rechristened Abbevillean by the Abbé Breuil, and many authors have followed him. The innovation is one of name only, not of concept or recognition of type.

Next, it is necessary to recognize that what has so far been treated as if it were the first really shaped or successful tool of all, and the only one of its time; namely, the Chellean pick—which we are from now on to call the Abbevillean and Acheulian hand ax or coup-de-poing or two-faced core—that this tool was not so much the sole tool of its periods as it was the most characteristic, definite, or advanced one. It was accompanied by smaller, less regular implements, some of which consisted of flakes instead of cores and were even perhaps sometimes subjected to crude blow retouching. This is reasonable enough. There would be many an occasion when a keen-edged flake or a sharp-cornered one would perfectly well satisfy a current need, whether of cutting or scraping. And there is no reason at all to believe that the Abbevillean people were such purists or traditionalists as to be unwilling to cut or scrape except with an instrument made out of a whole nucleus. Nor could these cores well have been the really earliest tools of any series: they are too symmetrical and too developed. In short, the Abbevillean and Acheulian double-convex core implements represent the most characteristic and most developed flint tools of their culture, not the only ones.

There is another reason why it seems reasonable to believe this. The inventory of the still earlier Eolithic, Pre-Crag of Ipswich and Foxhall, and pre-Chellean (§ 260, 263, 272) either consists of flakes, or it consists of pieces (like

---

[9] The Milankovitch-Zeuner chronological hypothesis puts the typical Mousterian in Europe back to about 70,000 years ago, the beginning of the Mousterian to more than 100,000. It makes the Levalloisian last a full 200,000, the Acheulian more than 300,000 years! This is widely accepted doctrine as of 1948. One can believe it; but one does not have to.

the pre-Crag rostrocarinate or "beak-and-keel" forms) that might technically be called cores but which are not purposively shaped to be biconvex.

From the relative undifferentiation, as regards flake and core, of this earliest, pre-Abbevillean stage, it seems that two cultural tool traditions then crystallized out of it and ran on contemporaneously. The one is the Abbevillean-Acheulian, specializing in the double-convex or bifacial core implements; the other, a sequence consisting of the Cromerian, Clactonian, Tayacian, and Levalloisian stages of planoconvex flake tools. It is agreed that these two strains of earliest culture appeared simultaneously in Europe, at whatever time that beginning may be put in terms of glaciation; and that they ran on side by side in adjacent areas. In fact, as we shall see in a moment, Europe is likely to have been the meeting ground of the two traditions rather than their area of original segregation.

There is not too much to be said about the early flake tools, unless one enters into technological detail. In the nature of things, flakes eventuated more irregularly diverse in shape than the cores, because their basic shape depended on a single blow; whereas the core, being so to speak whittled into shape by a series of strokes, was fashioned step by step. Only the Levalloisian is said to have added a new feature of manufacture. In the particular Levalloisian flake tradition, which is traced out of the Clactonian, a nodule was first trimmed as if it were to become a core tool, though turtle-backed rather than biconvex, and with a more or less stubby base or square butt (Fig. $30b_1$). Then a smart blow on this base detached an oval flake with presharpened edge (Fig. $30b_2$). This flake was flat on the underside, but its convex upper side was pretrimmed with smaller flaking.

As regards the biconvex core implements made in the (Chellean)-Abbevillean-Acheulian manner and tradition, it has become evident that their European occurrence was limited to a far-western strip stretching from southern England and Belgium to Italy and especially Spain. These same bifaced core tools however occur across Gibraltar and the Mediterranean in North Africa; also in East and South Africa; in fact practically all over that continent. Further, they occur in all of southwestern Asia: Palestine, Syria, Caucasus, Arabia, and India, with a sort of local climax of abundance around Madras. It is thus quite obvious that the western-European occurrence, which has up to here been treated as if it were self-sufficient, is only a minute fraction of the total distribution of these core implements. Presumably the European distribution was a mere marginal extension from an original center of development somewhere in Africa or southern Asia.

On the contrary, the flake tools, which in western Europe become the dominant or characteristic stone implements only after the Acheulian, are already established as typical in central and eastern Europe during pre-Würm times. In spite of their period, we cannot call them Abbevillean-Acheulian, because that term designates primarily a distinctive kind of artifacts and culture.

Yet we cannot well call them Mousterian, in spite of some generic resemblance of these early eastern-European flake implements to Mousterian flake implements, because Mousterian equates in time with the maximum of the Würm Glaciation. The artifacts in question are therefore best known as pre-Mousterian, which suggests both their type resemblance and their placement in time.

How far east into Asia genuine pre-Mousterian flake tools extend is not wholly clear. Some prehistorians have tended to include much of Siberia in the pre-Mousterian range. At any rate, nothing of stone shaped in the Chellean-Abbevillean and Acheulian tradition has yet been reported from anywhere in northern Asia.

In short, two culture areas, a southwestern-Asiatic-African-western-European one, and an eastern-European and perhaps northern-Asiatic one, begin to be discernible in the Lower Palaeolithic. This fact is of theoretic interest, because it demonstrates that the principles of segregation, individuation, transmission, and spread of culture, as we recognize them in history and in contemporary situations, were already operative in the earliest period of human culture on which prehistory gives us direct and tangible evidence.

During the Abbevillean proper, the core tools seem to have been pretty well limited in Europe to an immediate Atlantic distribution in France and Spain. During the Acheulian, the culture spread somewhat—into southern England, southeastern France, Italy—and began to overlap with the eastern culture along the Rhine. In the Mousterian, assimilation, or replacement, occurred: culture, or at least flint industry, became reasonably uniform over the whole of habitable Europe (Fig. 37, over), and in a measure in the near parts of Asia and Africa: the specialized large bifaced hand axes tended to go out of use everywhere. This generic Mousterian culture, with its smaller flake implements and emphasis on retouching, almost certainly evolved out of the pickless eastern pre-Mousterian rather than out of the western Abbevillean-Acheulian.

This would suggest an Eastern origin for Mousterian man—the Neandertal race. Moreover, we have seen that there are some indications that a less brutalized and more advanced type of man than Neandertal, represented by the Krapina, Steinheim, Swanscombe, and such skeletons (§ 45, 54), occurred in central-eastern Europe and England before the classic Neandertal flourished in western Europe during the Mousterian. However, this is not yet a thoroughly established fact. Also it is well not to get the threads of race development and culture development tangled too dogmatically. It is never to be assumed that a spread of culture proves the spread of a race. Culture may be spread by race movements, or it may be spread by contacts merely of individuals, leading to diffusion. In their simple way, culture contacts with learning but without mass migrations may have been substantially as effective in shaping or altering civilization fifty thousand years ago as today. For all that can be demonstrated at present, the Mousterian Neandertal men of western Europe may have been the blood descendants of the as yet undiscovered Abbevillean and Acheulian

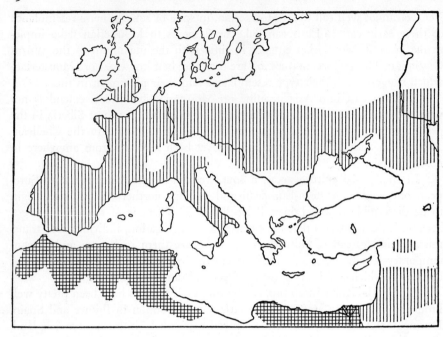

FIG. 37.   RANGE OF MOUSTERIAN AND ATERIAN CULTURES

Mousterian in vertical shading, Aterian (§ 275) crosshatched. (After Burkitt and Childe)

inhabitants of western Europe who had learned more effective retouching and smaller tools from the pre-Mousterian eastern Europeans.

Besides the bifacial-core tradition and the flake tradition, a third stream of flint industry has been proposed by Movius and his associates. The source and home of this would be southeastern Asia; the typical implements are named "choppers," "chopping tools," and "hand adzes." These are described as being cores, but not double-convex ones. One side is flat, the other rounded; the operating edge meets the base at a blunt angle, so that the implement might chop or scrape fairly well, but would differ from an all-around-edged Acheulian biface in being ill-adapted for severance by cutting and trimming. Flakes are also found in these southeastern-Asiatic industries, but the chopping cores are typical. The occurrences of the chopper tradition are given as:

EAST ASIATIC CHOPPING TOOLS

China	Choukoutien	Intergl. 2	With Sinanthropus
Java	Patjitan	Intergl. 2	Post-Pithecanthropus, pre-Solo
Malaya	Tampanian	?	
Burma	Early Anyathian	Glac. 2-Glac. 3 *	
India	Early Soan (Punjab)	Intergl. 2 †	Contemp. with Abb.-Ach. hand axes

     * Late Anyathian in Interglacial 3 and Glacial 4.
     † Late and Evolved Soan from Glacial 3 and 4 inclusive.

These several southeastern-Asiatic industries were independently discovered, and the antiquity of most of them is indubitable on geologic or faunal grounds. It is Movius's proposal that they were contemporaneous, and related to one another—which is something that will have to be verified by further evidence and consensus of judgment. Most of the tools are pretty sorry as implements. Many are of baser material than flint: at Choukoutien often of quartz, in Burma of fossil wood or silicified tuff. Nor are the regional types very uniform, except in their generic crudity. Choukoutien has far more flake than core tools, but in Burma only 15 per cent are flakes. Patjitan in Java has better-made and more varied forms than the other areas; and it even succeeded in evolving something very similar to an Abbevillean hand ax! Soan has been found in only one district of the Punjab; what it was doing there, with all the rest of contemporary India full of most typical Abbevillean-Acheulian biconvexes, remains to be explained.

In short, the hypothesis of a separate southeastern-Asiatic chopper culture, coeval with the hand-ax and flake-culture tradition of the Lower Palaeolithic elsewhere, is attractive and interesting if verifiable, but requires further substantiation.

274. UPPER PALAEOLITHIC PROVINCIAL DIFFERENTIATIONS IN EUROPE

With the advent of the Upper Palaeolithic, perhaps twenty-five thousand years ago, the divergent culture areas of the early Lower Palaeolithic in Europe, which became largely assimilated during the Mousterian, re-emerge once more, but with shifted boundaries. The internal line of demarcation now is no longer formed by the Rhine and the Alps, but lies just south of the Pyrenees. Throughout the Upper Palaeolithic, most of Spain formed an annex to the North African province the Capsian culture of which is treated in the next section. The "standard" Aurignacian, Solutrean, and Magdalenian, as they have been already described (§ 266-270), ran their course in a middle-European belt stretching from France to Poland. Figure 38 shows the approximate range of the Solutrean and of the more restricted Magdalenian. Northernmost Spain, southern England, at times Italy, were more or less in this mid-European province; so in the main were the Danube Valley and southern Russia—subject to some variations to be described in a moment. All northernmost Europe was still uninhabited. In general, it may be said that the mid-European Upper Palaeolithic culture is characterized by the associated traits of art and work in bone; the contemporary Spanish-African Capsian, by specialization along the line of increasingly smaller and finer retouched flakes, culminating in neat microliths measurable only in fractions of inches. This microlithic tradition finally penetrated across the Pyrenees, or possibly developed spontaneously there, but only after the Palaeolithic proper had come to a close (§ 276).

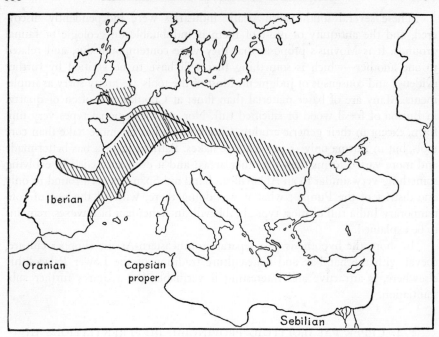

FIG. 38.   SOME UPPER PALAEOLITHIC CULTURES

Shaded: Solutrean. In heavy lines: Magdalenian. Named: Capsian-type cultures. (Mainly after Burkitt and Childe)

Roughly, the southern equivalent of the mid-European Aurignacian was the Lower Capsian; whereas during the Solutrean and perhaps the Magdalenian, North Africa and most of Spain were in the Upper Capsian. The latest or terminal phase of the Capsian continued in North Africa through the Mesolithic. These Capsian stages (§ 275) were more continuous than the contemporary European ones.

So here we have a second sure instance of large-scale regional differentiation of culture in the Old Stone Age.

Some qualifications may also be recited here of the somewhat simple picture of the "classic" course of Upper Palaeolithic development as already outlined in § 266-268 for western Europe.

Within what was formerly called merely the Aurignacian, three main phases or stages are recognized and have been renamed Châtelperronian, true Aurignacian, and Gravettian. The first of these phases, with rather narrow knife-like blades, is essentially limited to France. The second, or Aurignacian proper, has thicker blades and is almost pan-European, including southern Russia, and may represent an import from western Asia. The third or Gravettian stage is also widespread in Europe, and while its center of diffusion remains debatable,

East and West Gravettian local phases are distinguishable. The East Gravettian is earlier in showing the device of retouching some of its blades so as to carry a shouldered tang serving to haft or handle the blade. This shouldering appears subsequently in the West as a Solutrean trait. And in central Europe, in Czechoslovakia and Hungary, Gravettian and Solutrean have influenced each other until their differentiation is not always clear.

The Solutrean, or at any rate the form of it that was first recognized in France, was brief and remains rather narrowly localized in that country. It is chiefly there that the large laurel-leaf blades with long, even pressure retouching have been found. But this "classic" French Solutrean is later than the central-European Solutrean (Fig. 38), and is derived from it. A Hungarian "Proto-Solutrean" culture has a generic Aurignacian age attributed to it: at least as far back as the Gravettian stage, if not beyond. And in Moravia famous sites of ancient mammoth-hunters, like those of Předmost and Vistoniče, have been given the separate label of "Predmostian," so as to indicate that while the generic type and relationships of their culture are Solutrean, its period is well within the limits of the larger Aurignacian of the older French classification. This Predmostian is unusually rich in worked bone. Also it shows a distinctive incised art, with geometric decoration instead of the Aurignacian-Magdalenian naturalism of the West. It is a style of hatching or stippling, and especially of concentric curves.

The Brünn-type skulls come from the sites of this central-European Předmost-Proto-Solutrean culture, and so far as they may represent a true race or subrace, they would accentuate the distinctiveness of this culture. But it must be borne in mind that the separateness of these Brünn remains from the generic Cro-Magnon or Upper Palaeolithic race is uncertain (§ 49).

The Magdalenian was highly characterized only in and near France: from Bavaria to the edges of Spain. Its great naturalistic art is confined virtually to southern France and Cantabrian Spain. In this same area, six stages of Magdalenian industry are recognized. It is in the fourth of these that the barbed harpoon appears; and then follow the other advanced Magdalenian forms that have been mentioned (§ 269). Characteristic, too, of this local Magdalenian are the long sliverlike flakes or prismatic blades, sometimes verging on microliths in size. Outside of this southern-French-northern-Spanish focus or climax, the Magdalenian is much simpler and less specialized. In England, Italy, and the Danube region it is rather little differentiated from the late Aurignacian Gravettian. Some authors therefore prefer to give local designations to these marginal local phases contemporary with the Magdalenian period of France. Such are Creswellian, Grimaldian, and (late) East Gravettian for England, Italy, and the Danube respectively. These additional names serve to indicate the lag of development of these areas behind France while the advanced Magdalenian was flourishing there. In northern Germany, there existed a contemporary cul-

UPPER PALAEOLITHIC AND MESOLITHIC IN EUROPE

According to Three Authorities

	Lower Palaeol. 25,000± Würm I (Maximum)	Upper Palaeolithic — Würm Glaciation Retreat	Upper Palaeolithic — Würm II (Bühl) 7000± B.C.	Mesolithic Postglacial — Boreal Climate, Ancylus Stage	Mesolithic Postglacial — Atlantic Climate, Littorina Stage 3000 B.C.
Hawkes — Spain, France	Mousterian Levalloisian	Chatel-perron / Au-rig-nac-ian / West Grav-ettian	Magdalenian	Azilian / Sauveterrian / Tardenoisian	Asturian / Tardenoisian
Italy		Grimaldian			
England	Final Acheulian	Cresswellian			
C, N, E Europe		East Grav-ettian / Solutrean	Hamburgian / East Gravettian	Ahrensburg / Lyngby / Swiderian — Maglemose	Ertebølle
Menghin — Western Europe	Mousterian	Chatel-perron / Early Aurignacian / Mid, Late / Predmost* — Aurig-nacian 3-6	Solu-trean 1-3 / Magdalenian	N Sp, S Fr. Azilian, Tarden. / N Fr, Belg, Engl, W Ger } Tardenoisian	Asturian, Tarden. / Campignian / Ertebølle, Nøsvet
C, E Europe			Magdalenian	Baltic / Schalsee / Komsa } Maglemose / Pol, Ukr, Rum } Swiderian — Tardenoisian Campignian	Ertebølle, Nøsvet / Tardenoisian Campignian
Burkitt and Childe — C, N Europe	Mousterian	Solutrean* / Solu-trean	Magdalenian	Lyngby (Scand.) Maglemose / Swiderian (Hung., Pol.)	Ertebølle / Nøstvet
N. France, England		Aurignacian		Tardenoisian	Campignian
S. France, Sp., Italy				Azilian	Asturian
Syria	Aterian				
Egypt	Sebilian	Early Capsian	Late Capsian	Natufian / Tasian / Badarian — Latest Capsian	Amratian / Gerzean / Semainian
N. Africa	Ater., Moust.				

* Predmostian in Moravia, Protosolutrean in Hungary.

ture of reindeer-hunters, which has been named Hamburgian. It may be described as a basic Magdalenian fairly parallel with the French Magdalenian but lacking its specialized higher features.

Finally, Spain south of the Cantabrian Mountains remained non-Magdalenian and therefore non-European in culture. It is usually classed as having been Capsian or Capsian-derived, though some would see it rather as a dead eddy between the European Magdalenian and the African Capsian currents. There are a few finds which indicate that there were sporadic true Magdalenian penetrations well into the Iberian Peninsula. In southeastern Spain a distinctive art is found in carvings on the walls of rock shelters. This has a style thoroughly distinct from the Magdalenian; it is more angular, sketchy, and silhouettelike; but it is equally spirited. In fact it is more addicted than Magdalenian art to the delineation of human beings running, hunting, dancing, or in other motion. It is in this eastern-Spanish art that we find the first evidences of the bow and arrow in use.[10] The nearest stylistic parallels to this Spanish art are universally admitted to be found not in Magdalenian France but in North Africa, the Sahara, and South Africa. However, the North African petroglyphs appear to be Neolithic, and therefore much later in time; the age of the Saharan ones also seems late where it is determinable; and the rock paintings in South Africa were certainly made partly by the historical Bushmen or their relatively recent ancestors. In the present stage of knowledge, the eastern-Spanish art accordingly can hardly be derived out of Africa, because it appears to be earlier; though its similarity suggests a connection.

The whole European Upper Palaeolithic culture seems to have been carried by what was fundamentally a single Caucasoid strain of *Homo sapiens,* the Cro-Magnon race, as it is somewhat loosely but conveniently called in place of the cumbersome "European Upper Palaeolithic race" (§ 49). This is on the premise that the Grimaldi and Brünn types are not respectively Negroid and Neandertaloid, as once thought, but are integral members of the Cro-Magnon race; or at most, constitute subraces within it (§ 49). The Upper Palaeolithic North Africans, the Afalou people of the Capsian, we have seen (§ 50) to be also very close in physical type to their contemporaries the Cro-Magnons of Europe. All in all, then, cultural diversity probably was greater than racial diversity, both north and south of the Mediterranean Sea, during the Upper Palaeolithic.

[10] Technically, this contradicts the statement in § 276 that the bow is Mesolithic. While the eastern-Spanish art is reckoned Late Palaeolithic, some of the carvings may be later: it is difficult for rock pictographs to enter into a stratification. The Magdalenian art is datable because we have incised artifacts in stratigraphic association, which agree in style with the cave paintings and fix the age of these. There are also North African art evidences (§ 275) half suggesting that the Spanish pictographs may be fairly late. Wholly theoretical views on the invention of the bow are set forth in § 148.

275. NORTH AFRICAN SPECIALIZATIONS

Since North Africa has been studied carefully, it will be worth reviewing its whole Palaeolithic story coherently. We have seen that North Africa contained an Abbevillean-Acheulian development quite parallel with the western-European one. Following it, come Levallois and true Mousterian remains. Whether these were two industries practiced by two populations, or one industry that produced two kinds of implements, seems not yet wholly clear. The climate was probably warm and certainly wet, and allowed the hippopotamus to live in areas now subarid. Out of the North African Mousterian there grew an Aterian culture (Fig. 37), the flake tools of which are characterized by retouch gouging from the sides of the base of pointed flakes, in order to give them a tang or one-sided stem. These tanged points recur in Egypt; but in Europe they are post-Mousterian in association, as we have seen. In North Africa, Aterian deposits with tanged implements are more abundant than "pure" Mousterian ones without them. The Aterian evidently is merely Mousterian plus an added character.

The whole Upper Palaeolithic in North Africa is assigned to a culture which the French called Capsian after the Tunisian town of Gafsa. Strictly speaking, there were two related cultures: the Capsian of southern Tunis and later of southeastern Algeria also, and the Oranian of western Algeria and Morocco (Fig. 38). The general characteristics of these adjacent, nonoverlapping industries are the same, and while they are distinguishable—for instance, Capsian specializes in tiny-edged trapezoids and Oranian in tiny crescent-backed blades—they are only provincial variants of one basic culture, which grew more alike as time passed. They will jointly be treated as Capsian here. This Capsian is a blade culture; that is, its flakes are relatively narrow and more or less parallel-edged or prismatic. As the period progressed, the blades became smaller and smaller, until they were veritable microliths, hardly usable except in a haft. Also, as the stone blades decreased in size, bone tools became more abundant. Accompanying this change was a decrease in remains of rhinoceros and zebra, animals that now occur only at long distances from the Mediterranean coast. The ostrich was also abundant: its eggshells were used as containers and as bead material, both in the Capsian and in the Neolithic period. Typical is the occurrence of great quantities of land-snail shells at Capsian sites: billions of these animals must have been eaten. The Sahara proper seems mostly to have skipped the Capsian, remaining in an Aterian culture until reached by the Neolithic.

There is no break between Palaeolithic and Mesolithic-Neolithic in Africa, just as there was no glaciation to come to an end there. The Capsian went on, and new elements of culture were added to it, apparently largely by diffusion out of Egypt. The French prehistorians call this transition period "Neolithic of Capsian (or Oranian) Tradition." They mostly do not recognize a separate

Mesolithic; possibly because the Capsian continued long and the Neolithic began late. Nevertheless pottery and indubitable arrowheads—Mesolithic features—are among the earlier increments to the underlying Capsian tradition; ground axes and domesticated animals—Neolithic traits—were added subsequently. This suggests that the later phases traversed in North Africa correspond roughly to the Mesolithic-Neolithic succession of Europe; though probably with greater compression in time, as well as with stronger and fuller rooting in the local Upper Palaeolithic. Some have dated the end of the Capsian as late as around 3000 B.C. It is in line with this that there are no indications of a separate Bronze Age in Africa, outside of Egypt. Copper and iron appear together, about 1000 B.C., more or less along with the coming of the Phoenicians to found their colonies such as Utica and Carthage. This again accords with the fact that Megalithic cromlechs and dolmens (§ 283), which in Spain and in western and northern Europe died out well before the end of the Bronze Age, were most often erected in North Africa during late Carthaginian and Roman times. In short, everything post-Palaeolithic developed late in this retarded part of the world, but tended to run its course briefly, since other phases of culture, emanating from higher centers, were also knocking at the North African door.

The prehistoric rock-carved and rock-painted art of North Africa has already been mentioned (§ 274) as somewhat reminiscent of Magdalenian art, but as done in a style of its own, more like that of eastern Spain. The range of this art extends deep into the Sahara; in fact, its distribution is interior much more than coastal Mediterranean. It portrays men and women in action in silhouettes similar to those of eastern Spain and of recent Bushman art. It also portrays elephants, rhinoceroses, buffalos, ostriches, and lions—animals that have become extinct in North Africa. This faunal change suggests antiquity, especially since the portrayed water buffalo is an extinct Pleistocene large-horned form. Yet many of the carvings show domesticated cattle, sheep, and goats, sometimes in association with the vanished wild animals! There is no question about the domestication: the stock wears collars, is being led, or men bestride it. Particularly, there is a recurrent figure of a ram or a he-goat with a disk between its horns. This symbol is evidently due to dynastic-period Egyptian ritual influence, and cannot therefore well be earlier than around 3000 B.C. Accordingly the presence of the wild animals that no longer occur does not undermine this inference of relative recency, because most of them were evidently exterminated by man rather recently in this northern, marginal, unfavorable, and desiccating habitat. Thus there were still wild African elephants, though of a small race, in Tunis-Algiers in Roman times. As to the buffalo, the fact that a species was Pleistocene and is now extinct does not necessarily prove that it wholly died out ten thousand years ago at the moment when the hand of the geological clock crossed the line from Pleistocene to Holocene. Most living species of mammals had already been evolved long before then, and simply continued until now. In theory, a Pleistocene buffalo may have become extinct precisely at 8000 B.C., but equally likely at 5000 or 2000; just as many Pleistocene species still persist, but others died out at perhaps 12,000 or 15,000 B.C., and some before 50,000. We shall encounter a similar uncertainty as to date of extinction in the American situation (§ 278).

All in all, it looks as if the petroglyph art of North Africa did not begin until several thousand years after the Magdalenian art ended in Europe. The latter is Palaeolithic; the African art is at least mainly post-Mesolithic. This is indicated not only by its depictions of domestic animals, but by the fact that deposits and artifacts found associated with the carvings in southern Oran are overwhelmingly Neolithic. The following stages of development are distinguished: (1) from about 3000 B.C. on, naturalistic art; (2) less lifelike, clumsy conventional representations, continuing till perhaps 500 B.C.; that is, into the Iron Age; (3) petroglyphs sometimes accompanied by inscriptions in Tifinagh and often showing horses and dromedaries being ridden, and therefore attributable to historical Libyan and Berber tribes. It is obvious that if this dating is sound, the African art is much too late to have had any direct connection with the Magdalenian; even a derivation from Magdalenian would seem precarious. Incidentally, the African dating also suggests lateness for the eastern-Spanish rock carvings. And if these accordingly prove to be post-Palaeolithic instead of contemporary with the Magdalenian, the problem of why the bow appeared uniquely in Spain in pre-Mesolithic times is done away with: in that event it was not really Palaeolithic there any more than it was elsewhere.

276. THE MESOLITHIC

Logically, since Palaeolithic, Mesolithic, and Neolithic mean Old, Middle, and New Stone periods, they ought to balance with one another as of about equal importance or weight. Actually, the Mesolithic is not only far briefer than the Palaeolithic, but much less distinctive, especially as regards use of stone. The few significant innovations of the Mesolithic are nonlithic. This is a foreshadowing of what becomes even more pronounced later, when Neolithic food-producing is perhaps a hundred times as consequential as Neolithic stone-ax grinding. If the grand divisions of prehistory were still nameless, it is certain for the Neolithic, and probable for the Mesolithic, that the names coined for them by archaeologists in the mid-twentieth century would not refer to their stone industry, which had by then become a secondary activity, if not a by-product. But when the names originated in the nineteenth century, there was as good as no information on prehistoric cultures other than on their stone or metal implements; and it was natural that the appellations should be based on these readily preserved and easily discovered artifacts.

Broadly conceived, the culture of the Mesolithic of Europe, and that of other continents also, is an extension of Palaeolithic culture. The term "Epipalaeolithic" really characterizes it aptly. It is intrinsically an epilogue, a sort of running-out of the Palaeolithic, almost a degeneration of it. The climate changed from glacial to modern, and with it life had to change, without the culture's being particularly prepared to change. The result was that European Mesolithic culture looks thin and meager after the exuberance of Magdalenian art and inferable ritual. True, new inventions came to be made: pottery and the bow: but the full import of these on living was not realized until after the Mesolithic.

The Mesolithic began when the Pleistocene ended and the Holocene or geological Recent began. This is usually reckoned as having happened about ten thousand years ago; say 8000 B.C. Of course no passage from one era to another is a within-the-year event that can be dated like the fall of the Bastile; it is always a gradual transition; and in this case 7000 B.C. is perhaps as reasonable a marker as 8000, and is preferred by some. In fact, the change had been going on, with oscillations but on the whole consecutively, ever since the maximum of the last glaciation, which probably began to end around 25,000 B.C. The subsequent fluctuating retreat of the glacial ice is the period of the Upper Palaeolithic. By about 9000 B.C., the climate was describable as sub-Arctic rather than Arctic; pines were joining the birch and the willow which had invaded the tundra that had crept northward over southern Scandinavia as the ice edge receded.[11] Around 7000 a warm and dry "boreal" climate succeeded the sub-Arctic, and oaks, with alders and hazel, began to flourish alongside the earlier birch and pine. After about two thousand years of this, around 5000, the climate of Europe became "Atlantic," moister but still mild; and oak was now dominant in the southern Scandinavian forests. This climate lasted around three thousand years, until approximately 2000 B.C., when all Europe had reached the Neolithic and some of it the Bronze Age; the subsequent subboreal and subAtlantic phases were respectively not notably different and not appreciably different from the climate of today.

The greatest effect of the European Mesolithic changes of climate on man was through forestation. Throughout the Upper Palaeolithic, regions like France, England, Czechoslovakia, had been open tundra, with low shrub cover. On this ranged herds of the game the Magdalenian Cro-Magnons carved, drew,

---

[11] The year chronology is based primarily on varves, annual layers of clay deposited from melting glaciers, first and best worked out in Sweden; supplemented by studies of the ancient flora in Scandinavia. The Baltic Sea, long filled with glacier, is reckoned to have become an arm of the Arctic Ocean (Yoldia Sea) around 8300, through rise of the ocean as the icecaps melted. But in 7800 it had got dammed—the land also rose as it got rid of the weight of the ice—and became the fresh-water Ancylus Lake. This was in a period of brief recession toward cold; the boreal climate that succeeded it probably began around 6800 rather than at the rounded 7000 mentioned in the text above. Somewhere near the middle of the boreal period, the oceans rose enough to cut off England from the Continent; this probably was not far from 6000. By the time the Atlantic climate dominated, around 5000, the Baltic reopened as a salt-water arm of the North Sea and the Atlantic Ocean; and around 4500 to 4000, as the Littorina Sea, it encroached farther on the land than today.

and painted as well as hunted: reindeer, bison, horses, mammoths. With the Mesolithic, as the forest rose these animals withdrew eastward and northward, or died out. The species that succeeded them were those of historical Europe: notably stag deer, wild boar, and urus or aurochs—giant wild cattle. This latter game had mostly to be found and hunted individually in its cover, instead of by driving flocks over the open country into ambushes, pits, or surrounds, as in the Palaeolithic. With food now less readily available in masses, the Mesolithic population scattered out more. Also they learned to depend increasingly on humbler game: shellfish, fish, waterfowl, hares, and such. For the first time we find European habitation sites along beaches (Ertebølle and Asturian phases of Mesolithic culture), river mouths (Azilian), on lake and bog shores (Maglemose), or in sandy, thin-soil districts where timber remained sparse or lacking (Tardenoisian). Life was perhaps as secure as in the Magdalenian, and as comfortable; but it required a more constant assiduity over small foods, which left little leisure; and it was almost certainly a less exciting existence than in the glorious Magdalenian days. The great cave art just died away, and most of the ambitious exercises of magic went with it.

As for stone implements, most of them grew smaller and smaller in the European Mesolithic. In part this may be due to the spread of Capsian influences into Europe through Spain: we have seen that the whole Upper Palaeolithic of North Africa was increasingly microlithic. In part it was the continuation of an old western-European trend: Mousterian flakes average smaller than Acheulian hand axes, Upper Palaeolithic blades are narrower than Mousterian flakes, Magdalenian prism slivers are slimmer than blades. The Mesolithic simply went on with this development to make tiny blades, of which some were hafted in rows in a slot in bone or wood to serve as knives, saws, sickles, or spearheads, and others became chisel-edged arrow points. That the Capsian preceded the Aurignacian-Magdalenian in this drift may be because the African Late Palaeolithic climate was more like Mesolithic than Palaeolithic climate in Europe. For this reason too, probably, the Palaeolithic Capsian shades into Mesolithic times with only slight change, instead of the sharp seeming drop in cultural level from French Magdalenian to Mesolithic Azilian. It will also be recalled that large deposits of snail shells characterize the Capsian far back, whereas in Europe shell mounds appear only in the Mesolithic.

But Mesolithic living in the forest or at its outskirts, with only microlithic cutting tools or bone ones, was certainly inconvenient when one wanted a harpoon shaft, a house post, poles for the roof, a dugout for fishing. Even firewood would be limited to dead or fallen limbs. Something that would function as an ax was called for in the woods; and the European Mesolithic cultures divided into those which just frankly did without, and therewith avoided the timber, and were mainly early: Azilian, Tardenoisian: and those which developed an ax and were mainly middle and late Mesolithic: Maglemose, Ertebølle,

Campignian, Asturian.[12] There is no generally accepted name for these chopping tools, except French *tranchets*. We may call them "hewn axes" to distinguish them from the long-anterior Abbevillean-Acheulian "hand axes" and from the ground and polished axes that were to follow in the Neolithic. The majority of these hewn axes were cores; some were sturdy flakes with a bevel edge produced by one-stroke flaking. Some were hand-held; others were hafted in antler, and probably in wood. Also, antler was now itself beveled for chopping or adzing wood.

The basic innovations that came up in the Mesolithic were the first domestication of any animal, the dog; pottery; and perhaps the bow. All three of these became far more important later than they were at the time; their appearance in the Mesolithic seems to have been adventitious rather than a response to a felt need.

The dog perhaps attached itself to man as much as the reverse; it appears not to have been utilized or exploited in early days; and its relation to man seems to have been more spontaneously symbiotic, less characteristically a cultural thing, than that of the other "tamed" animals. Its significance is as a foreshadowing of the economically utilitarian stock-raising that was to develop in the Neolithic [13] and continue thereafter. Dogs are attributed to the Azilian and to some of the Tardenoisian, and were abundant in the Ertebølle phase of the Mesolithic.

Pottery is authenticated from the Campignian and Ertebølle, both late phases of the European Mesolithic. Its primary function was for boiling. Soups, stews, porridges were now possible; and certain plant foods would be edible for the first time. But the full import was not realized at once. In the Mesolithic pottery is still scarce; in the Neolithic it becomes common.

The bow is certain in Europe for the period of the Ertebølle shell mounds, from about 5000 B.C. on, to judge from bone-imbedded stone arrowheads. It is inferred for the Tardenoisian, which began earlier, from small, transverse-edged, projectile points. Its effectiveness would be greater against most Mesolithic mammals than against Palaeolithic mammoths, woolly rhinoceroses, and shaggy bison. We have seen by the eastern-Spanish rock painting that the bow and arrow were in common use there in the Upper Palaeolithic, in a period contemporary with the Aurignacian, according to some authorities. The pictures leave no doubt as to the implement being represented. But from the Aurignacian to the middle Mesolithic is a stretch of fully ten thousand years; and it seems hard to believe that the spread of so important and well-established a weapon should

[12] The Asturian tool was hewn out of a pebble to a point, and may have served mostly to pry off shellfish; but it has the size, heft, and hold of an axhead.

[13] This "Neolithic" utilitarian breeding of cattle, sheep, and pigs in the Near East goes back to about 5000 B.C., or actually contemporaneous with the beginning of Ertebølle, when the dog became well established in western Europe. At this period, Europe was consistently belated as against southeastern Asia and Egypt.

have taken so long to cross the Pyrenees into France and Denmark; not to mention that at least the earlier part of the Capsian in Africa seems arrowless. In the present author's mind, the suspicion will not down that the age attributed to the Spanish paintings may somehow prove to be excessive (§ 274-275). If their period is confirmed as coeval with Aurignacian or even Magdalenian, all that the Mesolithic will then prove to have had to do with the bow is to learn about it and receive it belatedly; but the reason for the enormous delay will be a problem calling for explanation. The whole matter of the origin of the bow is beset with intriguing questions (§ 148).

SUMMARY OF THE EUROPEAN MESOLITHIC

(Read *downward* for approximate time sequences. Cf. table in §274.)

Azilian. Apparently evolved directly out of the Magdalenian; centered in the region of the Pyrenees; distribution to Switzerland, Belgium, Scotland. Small blades; deer-antler harpoon with perforation; no art; pebbles painted with stripes, dots, and such. Early Mesolithic only.

Tardenoisian. Microlithic par excellence; a "European Capsian"; almost pan-European, lacking only in Scandinavia, northern Russia, the Balkans, and Italy; commonest on sandy soils or dunes. No axes; no painted pebbles. Duration: the whole Mesolithic, but mainly its earlier span. At Ofnet, Bavaria, cave burials of nests of severed human heads.

Maglemose. Type site in Denmark; distribution, northern England to Finland and Poland; centered on the Baltic. Time, middle Mesolithic. Boreal climate. Microliths, but also hewn axes; abundance of bone tools. A lake or bog culture.

Ertebølle, first called Kjøkkenmødding, then kitchen-midden culture. Type site in Denmark, distribution northern. Time, late Mesolithic, Atlantic climate, 5000-3000 B.C. A humid period with heavy forestation, probably difficult hunting, recourse to mollusks, hence refuse mounds of shell. The deer-antler harpoon disappears, microliths are rare except for square arrowheads, hewn axes are well developed. Pottery, dog, bow present. Toward end, part-ground axes and perforated mace heads appear. Ertebølle can be viewed as a local Baltic form of the Campignian.

Campignian. Type site, northern France. Period, late Mesolithic, Atlantic climate. Hewn ax characteristic; arrowheads; pottery. In spots, transition to Neolithic with its domestic animals.

Asturian. Northern-Spanish shell mounds. Late Mesolithic, Atlantic climate. No microliths or blades. Main tool a pick hewn from a cobble, sometimes with an edge, approaching an ax. A crude coastal culture, persisting until the introduction of pottery and of Neolithic sheep.

Various Local Mesolithic Phases. Komsa, northern Norway: thickish small blades, Aurignacian-like; perhaps mainly Palaeolithic. *Swiderian,* Poland, Rumania: smallish, tanged blades; early Mesolithic—in fact apparently late Palaeolithic also. *Lyngby,* Scandinavia, and *Ahrensburg,* northern Germany: small tanged blades or points and axes or ax hafts of antler; early Mesolithic. *Nøstvet,* Scandinavia: core axes, hewn or flake-trimmed, sometimes with a ground edge; late Mesolithic, persisting into the early Neolithic.

277. PALAEOLITHIC AND LATER DEVELOPMENTS IN RUSSIA, ASIA, AND REMOTER AFRICA

As compared with western and central Europe and French North Africa, exploration of the total range of Palaeolithic and subsequent prehistory elsewhere in the Eastern Hemisphere has been spotty and unsystematic. There are interesting finds, but often they do not yet build up into consecutive stories of development. Hence their constructive significance remains tentative and suggestive. However, it has become evident that we cannot reasonably expect to establish an exact repetition of the classical European sequence anywhere else. The data in hand already suffice to show that each larger area experienced its own history. Developments of particular phases in separate areas sometimes reveal enough similarities to make connections between them practically certain; but there is no uniformity of succession of stages for the total story in any two areas. For instance, a biconvex core hand-ax industry is found in both India and France, as we have seen (§ 273), and there is a connection through western Asia, North Africa, and Spain; but, so far, nothing subsequent has turned up in India that equates with the French Mousterian, Magdalenian, Tardenoisian, or other stages. In short, at a certain early time the cultures of India and France were related, but later the connection was broken and the two cultures developed differently, either through the formation of new foreign connections or through independent growth. This instance is typical of what appears to have been the general course of events.

The following summaries of Stone Age archaeological discoveries outside Europe can accordingly be put in only partial relation to those of Europe and to one another. But with each decade new discoveries are filling gaps in the record, sometimes with novel culture types and sometimes with transitions between previously known ones. Thus ultimately we may hope to have in hand a reasonably continuous and meaningful story of earliest human developments on a hemispheric or planetary basis. The present indications are that this story will be less simple than we used to think. Its significance may reside largely in its already being complex.

Russia. A genuine pre-Mousterian culture seems to be represented by implements probably of Riss-Würm Interglacial period found at Yashtukh Mountain on the Black Sea, in Georgia. This is an industry of thick, triangular flakes, without real retouch. Also pre-Mousterian are similar remains from the lower level of the Kiik-Koba cave in the Crimea, whose upper level is classed as Mousterian.

Mousterian remains, fairly corresponding to those of western Europe in type and probably in time, have a wider distribution in Russia: Kiik-Koba upper level and Shaitan-Koba in the Crimea, Ilskaya in the Caucasus, and at the mouth of the Derkula into the Donetz north of Rostov.

Upper Palaeolithic remains are fairly abundant in southern Russia; though north of the line Smolensk-Moscow-Kazan, about following latitude 55° N., nothing Palaeolithic has been found, either Upper or Lower. Both the Dnieper and the Don basins are well represented by discoveries. There seem to be two horizons. The earlier is a culture of blades, sometimes rather large; and of ivory carvings more stylized and symbolical than the Aurignacian ones of western Europe, but still recognizable as figures of women. Among the sites are Gagarino near Lipetsk and Kostenki near Voronesh on the upper Don; probably also Kiev on the Dnieper. There are definite resemblances to Predmostian and Proto-Solutrean (§ 274); the period may correspond to Aurignacian in France.

The later Upper Palaeolithic culture of Russia also rests on a blade industry, but with small prismatic forms prominent. The Russians tend to class it as late Magdalenian. It has been found at Borshevo on the Don, at Gontzi near the Dnieper, and at Timonovka on the Desna.

Extremely interesting for its bone art is the culture of Mezyn near Chernigov, with some flaked prisms but more flat flakes. The Russians seem to consider it late Magdalenian in time; the bone and ivory art looks like a carrying further of the geometric incising tendencies of Predmostian, which was considerably earlier. There are rectilinear spirals or meanders, executed elaborately and with great accuracy in the flat on mammoth-ivory bracelets, and on well-rounded knobs. There exists little Neolithic art anywhere that is as finished and regular as this, and no Palaeolithic geometric art that is equal to it in quality. Musk-ox bones indicate a cold recession in the glacial retreat for the period of Mezyn.

The terminal Palaeolithic and Mesolithic Swiderian culture (§ 276) of Poland, Hungary, and Rumania seems to extend also into southern Russia.

Siberia. No bifacial-core industries have been found in Russian Asia. Nor is there positive evidence of pre-Würm flake cultures, either. The available record is from late glacial and postglacial times; and to date it comes mostly from the upper Yenisei drainage. At Krasnoyarsk there is a flake, blade, and bone culture, in loess deposits with mammoth and rhinoceros remains. Some of the tools look like French Mousterian flakes, some like Aurignacian blades, and two "batons of command" recall the Magdalenian horn implements. But no strict equation in time with any one European culture period is yet possible. At Verkholensk, near Irkutsk, the deposits are probably postglacial, since the associated animals are reindeer (which of course still survive today in Siberia), wild horse, and urus. The stonework consists of blades, including "laurel-leaf-shaped" ones; that is, covered wholly with pressure retouches. There is much bone and horn, including harpoons with two rows of barbs. Deposits on the Angara River correspond to the European Mesolithic-Neolithic in type: chipped microliths set in a row in a slotted bone point; much well-ground bone; triangular arrow points, chipped; and ground axes, including some with nubbins.

China. The quartzite implements associated with Sinanthropus at Chou-koutien have already been discussed (§ 273) as attributed to a "chopper" tradi-tion allegedly distinct from both the hand-ax and the flake-tool currents of industry. It is the very crudeness and rudeness of these products of Sinanthropus's hands which make this chopper affiliation—or any other specific affiliation— seem a bit dubious. It has also been mentioned that the mid-Pleistocene or Second Interglacial period of these Sinanthropus artifacts naturally tends to disparage that one of the several competing recent interpretations which stretches the occurrence of the much-better-made Abbevillean (Chellean) hand axes of western Europe back into the First Interglacial or earliest Pleistocene. Why should Europe produce the better tools a glaciation earlier? The use at Choukoutien of broken or hacked-out pieces of deer horns, jaws, and skulls as tools has the endorsement of the famous Abbé Breuil, but is doubted by others.

Definitely later in time, but still Pleistocene as shown by being subloess, is a Palaeolithic flake culture discovered in 1923 in northern interior China in Kansu, Shensi, and the Ordos, and named after the type station of Choitongkou. There are no human bones, but there are fireplaces. The fauna includes rhi-noceros, hyena, ostrich, urus, and wild ass. The flakes have one-sided retouching, which gives them a superficial Mousterian or sometimes a nondescript Aurig-nacian appearance. But no historical connection of types or correspondence in time with Europe has been really determined. There is bone refuse, but no bone tool.

A presumable Mesolithic culture has been found in several spots in Mon-golia. There is said to be geologic evidence for its being postglacial in time. It is definitely microlithic. Many of the flakes are without retouch; some are pressure-produced prisms. The finds come from open sites in steppe and dune country, resembling Tardenoisian sites in Europe; and the two industries are analogous. Though the inhabitants must have been hunters, their bone refuse and bone tools were left exposed to the weather and have disappeared. However, beads of fossil eggshells, including those of then long-extinct dinosaurs, did get pre-served and suggest the Capsian ostrich-egg beads (§ 275). Since another culture, Neolithic with ground axes and incised pottery, is also found in Mongolia, the difference between the two leaves little room for doubt that the simpler one just described is earlier and more or less equal to the European Mesolithic in time.

Farther India and Indonesia. The artifacts in Burma, Malaya, and Java made in "chopper" tradition and attributed to the mid-Pleistocene have been mentioned (§ 273). Material on the Mesolithic-Neolithic level is much fuller and more assured. Two localities in Tongking, Hoa-binh and Bac-son, have each yielded three phases of a related culture; all the faunas are Recent. Hoa-binh I contains chiefly hewn axes.[14] Hoa-binh II and Bac-son I show occasional grind-

[14] These have also been called "Keo-phay hand axes," but they have nothing to do with the great Indian-African-western-European current or tradition of core tools, being much later.

ing of the edge; this grows fuller and more frequent in the subsequent periods. Pottery begins to appear in the very latest strata. It is to be noted that the priority of stone-grinding over pottery here is the reverse of that in Europe. Analogues to Bacsonian are recognized in Indonesia; and there as well as in Farther India, Neolithic completely ground axes of several types occur, which presumably—though not provenly—were accompanied by agriculture.

India, Persia, Arabia. This southwestern part of Asia is definitely within the range of the bifacial-core or hand-ax tradition which in western Europe is now mostly called Abbevillean-Acheulian. Except for lying at the eastern edge of this tract, India is rich enough in hand axes so that it might well come into consideration as the point of origin of this whole tradition. Africa in turn might launch a claim for priority on account of being central in the total hand-ax distribution. But these are only conjectures. There is no actual evidence as yet on where the bifacial-hand-ax industry originated, nor how precisely contemporary its local phases were in these continents.

After the hand-ax-core culture, the Stone Age prehistory of India is only fragmentarily known, and the data on it are technical rather than conclusive. Persia remains a blank in our knowledge for everything pre-Neolithic, and Iraq and Arabia are imperfectly known.

Palestine and Syria. At this eastern end of the Mediterranean, the prehistoric record becomes fuller once more; that is, there has been more systematic exploration. Stratified deposits in the Wady el-Mughara caves, which yielded also the famous skeletons of Mt. Carmel man (§ 46), tie in with various finds of shorter time range to depict a continuous sequence of Stone Age cultures. The tabular summary that follows should be read upward, like a geological column.

PALESTINIAN STONE AGE

Bronze Age. Historical times.
(Neolithic; Chalcolithic. Pottery, metals.)
(Kahunian. Chipped flakes; no pottery; Mesolithic.)
Natufian. Mesolithic, perhaps 6000-5000 B.C. Blades, microliths, sickles of narrow blades hafted in slots of bone; carved and bored pendants of bone; dentalium-shell headdresses; crude carved representations of animals and human heads in bone and stone; ground pestles of basalt. The sickles suggest farming; the pestles would technically allow the culture to be classified as Neolithic.
(Kebaran. Microlithic Mesolithic. Lacking at Mt. Carmel.)
Atlitian. A crude blade culture, so far known only from Mt. Carmel; probably corresponds to the western-European Magdalenian in time.
Aurignacian. Its upper level corresponds well in forms with French middle Aurignacian.
Levalloiso-Mousterian. The skeletons belong to this period.
Upper Acheulian. Hand axes and flakes; similar to French Micoquian.
Irregular flakes, similar to French Tayacian, a post-Clactonian, pre-Micoquian industry.
(Abbevillean and Lower Acheulian; mostly surface finds.)

Egypt. The discovery and interpretation of Stone Age remains in Egypt are attended by unusual conditions. The older Palaeolithic remains are mostly in river terraces of gravel, of which the oldest generally lie highest because the Nile has gradually cut downward. Later, the Nile filled its valley with silt and buried many remains. For instance, the earliest pottery is known from fragments brought up by deep well borings.

A hand-ax culture is well established, and was earliest. The Mousterian has a specialized form called Aterian, which we have already encountered in Tunis-Algiers (§ 275; Fig. 37). The Egyptian Upper Palaeolithic is known as Sebilian; it is a local form of Capsian, much as Oranian is (§ 275; Fig. 38). This Sebilian began about simultaneously with the Aurignacian in Europe; and like the Capsian, it seems to have continued long. With the next culture, Tasian, beginning perhaps around 6000 to 5000 b.c., we are already among pottery-making village dwellers, farming and perhaps keeping stock. From then on, the record is continuous: Badarian, Predynastic, Dynastic Egyptian, full history.

East, South, and West Africa. A good many finds have been made, but their interrelations and dating remain less clear than in North Africa. Hand-ax cultures are earliest. Several varieties are recognized, named after type stations. It is not certain how far these represent temporal phases, or provincial variants, or both, in South Africa. In East Africa Leakey distinguishes two Chellean and two Acheulian phases enduring through a Günz and Mindel Pluvial period and through a long Mindel-Riss Interpluvial. However, it is still not possible to set up such climatic correlations and be certain of correctness, except by lucky chance. Equally sensational and improbable are the alleged developments in East Africa during a proposed great second Pluvial period (Riss and Würm). In this there are said to have been three successive phases of Stillbay-Mousterian and three of "Aurignacian" cultures, the two series apparently contemporaneous with each other, and the middle Aurignacian containing pottery! If pottery occurs with a stone-flake culture, this is probably not Aurignacian in type and almost certainly not in time; and the designation can only be misleading.

In South Africa, Stillbay remains vary from good Mousterian analogues to good Solutrean ones. A fair guess would be that Stillbay corresponded in time to some point in the European Upper Palaeolithic. Well defined are two quite late South African cultures: Wilton, including Tzitzikama, in two stages; and Smithfield in three. These "stages" mainly occupy different areas; in their last phases they are most alike. These were cultures of hunters, and lacked axes, perhaps because there was no forest to contend with. But they ground stone into a variety of implements: mortars, pestles, grooved arrow-straighteners, per-forated club heads, stone palettes. Some of the chipped stone is microlithic. There are ornaments of ostrich eggshell; and some pottery. In type, these Wilton-Smithfield cultures thus look Mesolithic with an unusual development of stone-grinding. Or they might be called Neolithic without agriculture or axes. Their dating has not been ascertained, but in view of their marginal position, the period may prove to be quite late, perhaps after the early centers of civilization were well along in use of metals.

There is in South Africa, also, a cave and rock-painting art famous for its naturalism. Some of this is attributable to the Bushmen and their ancestors; some may have been associated with the Wilton and Smithfield cultures. There is quite likely some connection with Saharan and Capsian art, possibly with eastern-Spanish and Magdalenian art (§ 274-275). But as the estimated datings of these still differ widely, they do not help to fix the time of the South African paintings.

278. THE PROBLEM OF CULTURAL ANTIQUITY IN THE AMERICAS

Prehistoric culture in America has been positively established only for the terminal Pleistocene—at most the last or Wisconsin Glaciation, perhaps chiefly during its retreat. The record thus is much shorter in America than in Europe, Asia, or Africa. In the United States, systematic search for Palaeanthropic man and Palaeolithic culture associated with Pleistocene faunas began to be made within a decade or two after such finds had been authenticated in western Europe. But for something like fifty years nothing indubitable was discovered; and what has been found since is all late Pleistocene, so far as its dating is reasonably sure.

The relative meagerness of data led to long doubt whether there had been any Pleistocene man in America at all; whereas in Europe the basic fact was quickly accepted, and interpretation concerned the full unraveling of the story. A sense of partisanship tended to develop in America; during half a century anthropologists, geologists, and amateurs were likely to be "for" the antiquity of man or "against" it. These attitudes influenced them until some would not believe downright evidence because it "could not be true," while others favored every new claim no matter how flimsy. While such things should not be in science, they do sometimes happen, especially when problems on which evidence is scant or difficult once settle into established controversies.

The American glaciations probably correspond fairly closely to those of Europe: Nebraskan, Kansas, Illinoian, Wisconsin to Günz, Mindel, Riss, Würm (§ 272). Also, most of the fauna of Eurasia and North America has a common origin and Holarctic distribution, with repeated interhemispheric invasions during both the Tertiary and the Pleistocene (§ 174). However, there is one pertinent difference in the two mammalian histories: the New World contains no primates, except the platyrrhine tailed monkeys, which branched off early in the Tertiary (§ 22, 27; Fig. 1) and became confined to South America. Not only are there no living anthropoid apes in America, but also no discovered fossils of extinct ones. Nor is there the least indication, as yet, of fossils of really primitive human type. It can only be concluded, accordingly, that man evolved in the Eastern Hemisphere and entered the Western relatively late and fairly well developed: presumably already Neanthropic, or *Homo sapiens*. This unquestionable fact, which limits man and his culture in America to part of the

Pleistocene, was stretched by the doubters and temperamental conservatives into denial of everything human in the hemisphere until the Recent.

It is evident that once the principle of evolutionary descent is accepted, discoveries of early man are notable events, and that a Pleistocene culture or fossil will cause more sensation than a Recent one. While fortunately there is no money to be gained directly from such discoveries, they do bring a measure of distinction; so that a wish to make such a find is natural. Invariably, thus, there is at first a list of mistaken discoveries: there is little to check them against, and hope is strong. The reaction to this condition was that some of the more critical American scholars developed a skeptical attitude which finally became an indubitable negativistic bias against early man in America. It is necessary to remember that in these matters evidence necessarily is as strong as it is cumulative. What caused Neandertal skulls, Acheulian hand axes, or Magdalenian mammoth engravings to be universally accepted—though even that took several decades—was the weight of *repetitive* discoveries of the same type. A find that stands isolated in kind may always be a play of nature, a misinterpretation, or a self-deception.

279. EARLIEST AMERICAN INDICATIONS: FOLSOM AND SANDIA

Beginning about 1926, a series of discoveries were made in the western United States which were repeated so neatly that they could no longer be explained away, and had to be accepted. These discoveries really proved only a modest antiquity for man in America; but they clearly showed chipped implements, in fact very well made ones of a specific kind, occurring repeatedly in indisputable association with animals now extinct and previously always reckoned as Pleistocene by geologists. This faunal association was precisely the same evidence that had led to the acceptance of European Palaeolithic culture in 1859. At last there was a breach in the defenses, and immediately the tide of opinion turned. Just as previously the conservatives had admitted nothing or explained everything away, so now there was a group of enthusiasts by whom each new alleged find was received with favorable bias and used to support the case for other possibilities. In the paragraphs that follow, the effort will be made to disentangle what is the most probable "truth" in the considerable twilight zone of the problem of American Pleistocene culture. But it is perhaps also important for the reflective bystander to realize how infectious thinking can be, even in regard to so-called scientific facts, once it becomes unduly influenced by controversy or the suggestion of being in fashion.

Folsom. The one culture that above all stands out as being surely old, within these limits, is that of Folsom, so named after its place of first discovery in northeastern New Mexico in 1926. Its authenticity is outstanding because the association has been found repeated, under conditions of careful scrutiny and control, near Clovis, New Mexico; at Lindenmeyer near Fort Collins, Colorado; and near Lipscomb, Texas; perhaps also at Linger, San Luis Valley, Colorado. At the first three of these sites taken together, the fauna consists in part of still living animals, in part of extinct bison, extinct wolf, extinct musk ox, mammoth, camel, giant sloth, and an *Equus* type of horse. At the fourth, the association is with extinct bison; at the fifth, probably so. At all these sites the artifact inventory is of two kinds: rough, irregular flints, and unusually finely chipped ones. The rough pieces are classified as side scrapers, end scrapers, snub-nosed scrapers, gravers, choppers, flake knives, and the like, and they are not specifically distinctive. In fact practically all of them can be pretty closely paralleled somewhere among the flint tools of later American Indians. On the contrary, the typical fine "Folsom points" are projectile heads made by pressure chipping with extraordinary skill and in a definitely characteristic shape (Fig. 39a). The sides are nearly parallel, the base concave and flattened out thin; after the fine surface chipping had been completed, a long flat flake was then detached upward from the base, toward the point, leaving one face of the implement channeled or

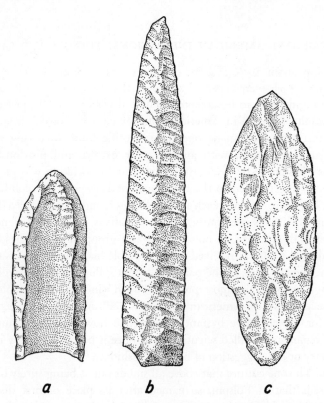

a   b   c

FIG. 39.   ANCIENT AMERICAN PROJECTILE POINTS

a, Folsom. *b,* diagonal Yuma. *c,* Sandía.

fluted.[15] Some of these projectile heads have been found embedded in extinct bison bones; and it is therefore as certain that they possess antiquity as that they are a technologically advanced form.

All in all, the Folsom culture is hardly what would have been expected of the first Pleistocene culture to be determined in America. It certainly does not correspond at all closely with any known Old World Palaeolithic culture. Its stone industry was a flake-using one, partly developed into exceedingly fine blades. There are some core implements, as there are stones that have been used for rubbing; but these last are too few to be characteristic.

The principal Folsom sites with associated extinct fauna are all in the western or High Plains, where these approach the foot of the Rocky Mountain system. Since the discovery of these sites gave the fluted points wide publicity, a number of points of Folsom type have been found "loose"—that is, superficially or unassociated—also in the High Plains area.

Then, channeled projectile heads, similar to true Folsom or Clovis points, but not identical with them, were recognized as having been found, some of them well before 1926, in many other parts of North America, perhaps most frequently in the Ohio drainage. These are generally wider, thicker, with less fine flaking, and with shorter channel. First called "Folsomoid" or "generalized Folsom," "Ohio fluted points" was later suggested as an appropriate name for them. These points may prove to be connected with the true Folsom points by historical descent; but their age is not known; nor the rest of the culture or cultures associated with them; nor the associated fauna, whether living or extinct. All this is for future study to find out.

As for the true or specific Folsom culture, the age of this is usually given as somewhere between ten thousand and twenty-five thousand years. It seems more likely to have been glacial than postglacial; certainly terminal Pleistocene—that is, Wisconsin-Würm—rather than initial or middle Pleistocene; and quite likely rather late Wisconsin. One geological estimate puts it in the third of four ice advances which are thought to have occurred within the Wisconsin Glaciation. The time then might be as early as the end of Mousterian in western Europe, or as late as Magdalenian, more likely contemporary with Aurignacian or Solutrean, but with the exact synchronism remaining to be determined; and there is no implication whatever as to derivation or specific connection with any European or known Old World culture.

Sandía. A second ancient American culture that seems sure is Sandía, known from one cave in the mountains of that name in New Mexico. This culture occurs in a separate layer underneath a layer containing typical Folsom points, but sealed off from that by a stratum of water-deposited yellow ocher. It is therefore pre-Folsom; though by how long, there is no sure present means

---

[15] The detached "channel flakes" seem to have been kept and used; and there is a flake "knife," much larger and rougher than the projectile heads, but also fluted.

of telling. With the Folsom artifacts at Sandía are bones of the species most characteristic of the Folsom fauna: extinct bison, mammoth, camel, horse, and giant sloth. With the implements of Sandía culture in the underneath level, the same fauna occurs, with the exception of the sloth—which elsewhere too seems the most recent of the extinct species, lingering on well into the early Recent— and with the addition of the mastodon. The Sandía implements include some rough end scrapers and side scrapers and cutting flakes, but are specially characterized by the projectile points. These are longer, thicker, and considerably heavier than the Folsom points, less finely chipped, unchanneled, but "shouldered" (Fig. 39c). That is, a jog has been removed from one side of the base, leaving a narrow but somewhat asymmetrical stem for hafting, somewhat as in some Aterian and Solutrean blades. There are two subtypes of these shouldered Sandía points, according as they are somewhat thicker with rounded base or flatter and square-based. Like the Folsom points, they are much too heavy for arrows, and must have been heads of spears for throwing or thrusting. The true or specific Sandía culture level also contains bone points of about the same size as the stone spearheads, and also charcoal hearths. While so far the site stands alone, both its culture and its time level seem specific and well set off.

280. EVIDENCES FOR OTHER EARLY AMERICAN CULTURES

Nothing else of human make discovered in America up to 1948 has as yet as strong a claim to Pleistocene antiquity as the Folsom and Sandía cultures. There are several other finds in the United States and Mexico—also mostly in their arid, unglaciated regions—plus one in the far tip of South America, in which extinct animals come positively associated with artifacts. But each of these other sites has its own types of implements, not relatable to those elsewhere. And for none of them has a positive geological placement been worked out. All of them quite probably date back into the late Pleistocene; but if some of the species now extinct, such as horse, mammoth, or camel, lived on for a while, the sites might yet turn out to belong to the somewhat hazy border between postglacial terminal Pleistocene and early Holocene or Recent. If one could bet on what the verdict will be a century hence, the odds would seem very favorable that at least some of the present group of sites will then be adjudged definitely Pleistocene. But one would be lucky now to guess which ones.

Cochise I. The supposedly oldest or Sulphur Springs phase of a Cochise culture in southern Arizona, found in sand and gravel deposits along with the bones of a bison-mammoth-camel-horse fauna, also contains charcoal of hickory. As this tree needs good rainfall, a wetter climate is inferred, and hence a pluvial period probably corresponding to a glacial one. Pleistocene age hinges on how and when the charcoal got into the sand: whether at the time the hearths were used or through subsequent redeposition by water. The culture is poor in chipped implements: a few scrapers and knives and no projectile points. But it is rich in slabs for grinding. This indicates subsistence by seed-gathering, and raises the problem of relation to the Folsom type of hunting culture. A prevailingly ground-implement culture in the Pleistocene is of course not impossible; but it would be unique.

Ventana I. Ventana Cave, also in southern Arizona, has an old conglomerate level under fifteen feet of later deposits. This conglomerate suggests water action and a wet climate; it contains some of the faunal aggregation with which we are now familiar—bison, sloth, and horse—plus a new species: tapir. The associated culture is one of chipped implements: scrapers, choppers, gravers, or whatever they may be called, plus fairly well-chipped spearheads similar to Folsom points except for lacking the channel or fluting. Above this conglomerate and nonconformable with it, thus suggesting a gap in time and possibly a long one, lie later layers whose culture gradually shades into that of the late prehistoric and historic Indians of the region. It will be seen that while Cochise I and Ventana I, in the same modern desert, contain some of the same extinct fauna, and are both construed as having been laid down in a wet climate, they differ drastically in their cultural inventory. This fact shows how far we still are from a coherent interpretation of the early prehistory of this particular region, let alone of America.

Gypsum Cave. In southern Nevada, Gypsum Cave near Las Vegas contains, below Basket Maker and Pueblo remains of the Christian era, giant sloth bones, claws, and hair, masses of sloth dung, and artifacts. Conspicuous among these tools are well-chipped spearheads: characteristic long triangles with a short stem. There are also fragments of the wooden shafts, foreshafts, butts, and tips of light spears, apparently for use with atlatl spear-throwers; some of these still show painting. These shafts and foreshafts are distinguishable from late prehistoric Basket Maker ones (A.D. 300-700), but are not markedly different from them. There are also bones of extinct horses and llamalike camels in the cave; these are associated with the artifacts indirectly, through association with the sloth remains. The age was first estimated at three times as great as the beginning of the Basket Maker period, which was then assumed to date to 1500 B.C., or 3500 years ago. The calculation $3 \times 3500 = 10,500$ years elapsed, yields 8500 B.C. Since then, the Basket Maker period dating has been brought down, by uncontested associations of remains with ring counts of preserved trees, into the early Christian era—say the third century. Cutting the sloth period therefore also in half, brings it around 3000 B.C., instead of 8500. This is possible, but the date would now be well within the Recent and quite late for extinct horses and camels. The whole calculation is adduced here mainly as a warning. Someone makes an estimate, it seems plausible and is repeated, and before long it has acquired a degree of authority from its repetition, while the flimsiness of the basis of estimate—or in this case calculation—tends to be forgotten. If on the contrary we give maximum weight to the extinct fauna, and therefore restore the age of Gypsum Cave to around ten thousand years, the fragile spear shafts and foreshafts become much the oldest cane and wood artifacts known to have been preserved anywhere. This is also possible, but would be equally remarkable. The situation is typical of many claims in America. There is undoubtedly some antiquity involved in this Gypsum Cave case, but as yet no one can really tell how much.

Early Oregon Man. Paisley Five-Mile-Point Cave on Summer Lake, in arid southern Oregon, has yielded an association of camel and horse with charcoal and obsidian flakes of no very specific shape. There is no doubt of genuine antiquity, though the culture represented is meager and indistinctive.

Wholly separate are the evidences on another problem, that of the age of artifacts buried under deposits of air-borne pumice dust erupted from two volcanoes in the Cascade Range, one of them the basin of the present scenic Crater Lake. The age of an eruption of unknown date can usually be determined much better from the kind of cultural material that it covered than the reverse can be. In other words, the geologist has only a gross scale for short periods, the anthropologist a much more limited but finer one. Now the well-preserved artifacts under the Oregon pumice differ in detail, but not fundamentally, from those above it and from the implements of the recent Indians of the area—say those of the last thousand years or so. The simplest conclusion would accordingly be that the eruptions occurred something like one or two thousand rather than five or ten thousand years ago. It is evident that the pumice-buried artifacts constitute evidence that cannot really strengthen the case for association of the Paisley obsidian flakes with extinct fauna, because it relates to a different problem. The obsidian-camel-horse association stands on its own evidence: its weak point is not its age but the indefiniteness and nondescriptness of the artifacts representing the culture.

Valley of Mexico. At Tepexpan in the Valley of Mexico, de Terra found in 1946-47 elephant bones, most of a *Homo sapiens* skeleton, and flake tools of chalcedony, obsidian, and bone, all deposited in a wet-climate layer near an old beach of Lake Tezcoco. The skeleton, the animal bones, and some of the tools were not in actual juxtaposition, but lay not far apart in the same stratum. Too few reports are available at this writing for a full description, but the discovery is important and holds promise of additional ones being made in Mexico as exploration is pursued. The skull looks Indian, has an index of 80, a capacity above 1500 cc; the stature of the skeleton was around 170 cm, or tall.

Strait of Magellan. Many thousands of miles south of all the preceding sites, on the Strait of Magellan in Chilean Patagonia, at Palli Aike and Fell caves, horse and ground-sloth bones are associated with chipped implements. So far as the sloth is concerned, it had become clear as long ago as 1895 that this animal perhaps survived into contemporaneity with man. The famous great Mylodon Cave at Ultima Esperanza, also on the Strait of Magellan, contained a scored piece of skin of the animal, and a number of implements; but whether these artifacts and the skin were associated can no longer be determined with assurance. However, the two later-discovered and carefully excavated caves clearly show at their bottoms an association of a particular form of projectile point with remains of sloth and extinct native horse. These points are rather broad and blunt in the body, with a longish stem. With them were chipped scrapers and choppers, rub stones, hearths, and perhaps cremations or burials. Above this lowest layer, the deposit material changed—in one of the two caves with a sterile dividing layer between. Above this sterile layer, the extinct species were replaced by living ones, and there was a separate culture sequence, characterized upward by: (2) bone projectile points; (3) triangular chipped points; (4) points with large broad bases; (5) smaller broad-based points, much like those used by the historical Ona Indians of the region. This later sequence, layers 2 to 5, is obviously all geologically Recent, but its length suggests that the underlying culture of layer 1 may have been early Recent or even terminal Pleistocene. How unsure any time determination still is, however, is shown by the fact that the excavator has suggested two dates: 3500 B.C. and 20,000—wisely enough, without committing himself to either.

One feature is common to most of the remains so far reviewed in this section. At most sites, the oldest level is separated by a break of formation, a time hiatus, from the upper levels, and these usually continue on into historical Indian cultures. Now for these late cultures, some sort of a "dead reckoning" of the time elapsed, or at least an estimate backward, is possible. And nowhere, if the estimates are held conservative, do they pile up to anything large: perhaps two thousand to three thousand, possibly five thousand years ago. The age may well be greater than that; but there is nothing as yet to compel acceptance of a greater age for the beginning of the upper-level continuity. Even from the extreme of these figures—say 3000 B.C.—it is still some distance to go, back to the end of the Pleistocene as it is usually reckoned in Europe, say about ten thousand years ago, or 7000 to 8000 B.C. It is just possible that some of the finds already discussed in this section may ultimately prove to be not Pleistocene, but will turn out to be early Holocene and therefore coeval with the European Mesolithic, and that they will fill the hiatus in the American record. At any rate, it is important to remember that at present there is no sure continuity, but a possible gap, in American prehistory, presumably in the era of the early Recent, at the point where the end of the record evidenced by geological fauna and the beginning of the record evidenced by cultural association and stratigraphy have not yet been spliced together.

These remarks refer only to time. As regards culture, as shown by forms of implements, there is no specific relation at all yet visible between the courses of development in the two hemispheres. There are no fluted points known in Europe or Asia, no Magdalenian prisms or carvings found in America—let alone all the long earlier Abbevillean-Acheulian bifacial history.

There are a number of other American finds for which antiquity has been claimed, but for which evidences of age are incomplete or faunal associations are lacking or the cultural type is undefined. Some of these are:

Yuma. The name has nothing to do with the Yuma tribe, family, or city, but is taken from a Colorado county. This is not a site, nor a culture, but a type of implement—or rather of several subtypes of projectile points. They differ from Folsom in being unfluted, and generally they are longer and narrower. Points called Yumas have now and then been found in Folsom association, as at Clovis. But they occur also in more modern associations, and over a wide range of territory. It has become evident that "Yuma" is a catchall concept that has to be broken up into several types whose histories may or may not be connected. One type, the "collateral" or Eden or Scottsbluff Yuma point, has chips from both edges meeting in a ridge down the middle. This type has been found in association with bison bones, probably of extinct species, in an apparently early postglacial sand layer at Eden, Wyoming. The "oblique" type of Yuma point has evenly pressured ripple-mark flaking extending diagonally across the width of the blade (Fig. 39*b*). It has not yet been found in association. The other Yuma points, called "indeterminate," probably include several forms and may be of quite different ages.

It is evident that the Yuma points, though some of them probably possess a respectable antiquity, are a group of poor cousins of the Folsom, by whose fame they were carried into a degree of prominence.

Abilene. Silt deposits at Abilene in north-central Texas are important because they contain some Folsom projectile points. They also contain bones of mammoth and extinct bison. But association of the two is not clear-cut. Either the silt deposits and their contents or the accounts of them are confused or ambiguous. (See § 326.)

Lake Mohave, Pinto Basin, and Playa. There are chipped and ground implements on the open surface along old lake shores and watercourses in the desert of southern California. Some of the implement types are fairly distinctive and will no doubt be significant when they can be fitted into relation with others; but the age estimates are still essential guesses, as is shown by their divergence: "may be fifteen thousand years" and "about three thousand years."

Alangasí and Vero. An association at Alangasí, Ecuador, of bunomastodont bones with pottery suggests to how late a time extinct species like this elephant may possibly now and then have lingered on. Unfortunately the Alangasí remains subsequently perished by earthquake and fire. They recall the discovery in 1916, at Vero, Florida, of bones of mastodon, another elephant, tapir, and extinct wolf and armadillo in association with part of a human skeleton, flint chips, bone awls, and potsherds. Geologists and archaeologists differ as to whether the association of fossils and artifacts was original or secondary; that is, whether they were both deposited at the same time in the shape in which they were found, or whether they were deposited separately at different times and then disturbed and redeposited in association. Since the experts disagree, the only verdict for Vero is: antiquity possible but unproven.

Since horizons of preceramic culture occur in both North and South America, pottery cannot very well be considered much more than a few thousand years old in the hemisphere. If the association in either the Ecuador or the Florida case is original, elephants must accordingly have survived in spots in the Americas until well along into the Recent. The possibility of the extinctions of some Pleistocene mammals having been delayed into the post-Pleistocene, or being finally effected by extermination at the hands of man, has been stressed largely by those skeptical of the antiquity of the human record in America. It has been correspondingly depreciated by the proponents of antiquity. Both may prove to be right—for different species or areas. Thus, in proportion as the artifact-fossil associations of Alangasí and Vero are accepted as original and "sound," as the partisans of the antiquity of man in America incline to claim, the more recent may other cases of association thereby tend to prove to have been! This seemingly confusing paradox is cited to illustrate how difficult and tricky the evidence still is in this whole problem, and why the few sure findings remain surrounded by a much larger penumbra of uncertainties.

Lagoa Santa, Confins, and Sambaquís. In Brazil there are a long-known Lagoa Santa type of ancient man and the recent Confins discovery. In the latter case, a human skeleton was associated with bones of mastodon, horse, bear, and extinct llama. At Campo Alegre a Lagoa Santa-type skeleton burial was accompanied by artifacts—grinders, pitted stones, and "axes"—but animal bones were lacking. The southern-Brazilian coastal shell deposits called sambaquís are mostly natural deposits; but some are refuse from human occupation and contain artifacts. Three sambaquí cultures are distinguished on the basis of the implements. Two of these contain well-polished stone and pottery, and thus presumably are late pre-Caucasian. The third culture, in São Paulo, may be older. Its middens are farthest inland, and contain a shell species, *Azara prisca,* lacking in the shore deposits. Also, the artifacts are described as "rude," though they do comprise ground axes. *If* this culture actually and specifically agrees with that of Campo Alegre, and *if* the skeleton there is identical in racial type with that of Confins, considerable age would have to be ascribed to the older sambaquí artifacts. But the chain of association consists of several links: (1) extinct mammals at Confins, associated with: (2) Lagoa Santa skeleton similar to: (3) another skeleton at Campo Alegre associated with: (4) implements similar in rudeness to: (5) implements in certain São Paulo shell heaps. If one link is insufficient as evidence, the whole chain falls apart. This instance is characteristic in showing how well-balanced a combination of luck, scientific skill and insight, and critical imagination are usually needed to prove geological antiquity for cultures.

Summary. The absence from America of higher primates, transitional men, and Palaeanthropic forms indicates strongly that man entered the Western Hemisphere fully evolved and relatively late—probably after most of the Pleistocene had already passed. The best-authenticated and earliest finds date most probably from the last phases of the final advance of the Würm-Wisconsin Glaciation, or from the recession of this. If so, they would correspond in time to the Upper Palaeolithic of Europe; but the cultures are specifically quite different from those of Europe. Large projectile points of very definite form, partly chipped by pressure, are the characteristic artifacts, in contrast with Europe, where hand tools heavily predominate over spearheads throughout the Palaeolithic, except for Solutrean blades. Thus the Sandía, Folsom, and Yuma artifact types were almost certainly developed somewhere in America, not imported. These types may of course have had ruder antecedents within the hemisphere; these have not yet been found or identified. At the other end of the time scale, a certain proportion of the discoveries of seemingly ancient culture may well turn out to be post-Pleistocene, corresponding in period to Old World Mesolithic and Neolithic. For the most part we cannot yet tell which of such finds are the earlier and which the later.

At present we encounter a gap in sure knowledge when we try to carry back continuously from the historical indigenes to their Pleistocene predecessors. We do not know how big this gap is. It may be longer than the continuum of archaeological record that follows it. Some of the cultures that seem more or less old, but which we cannot place in time, may well prove, when we know more, to belong in this gap. It may even turn out that they pretty well fill it. But we do not know that this is so, nor can we say which ones of the discovered cultures belong in the gap. Time-reckoning in these matters is either by actual history—that is, written record; or by continuity of successive culture associations or stratifications back of history; or by association of cultures with faunas which can be dated in geological terms.

On all three counts, American evidence is less full than the European and the Near Eastern. The history just is much briefer; the archaeology has been worked out less far back; and the geological story is shorter because man seems to have begun later. Since about 1925, the strongest evidence has for some reason been turned up in the arid parts of the United States. It is of course easier to search there than in areas of heavy vegetation. On the other hand, the Southwest was not glaciated, and did apparently have a wetter climate in certain late Pleistocene and post-Pleistocene periods than now; so that it may have been favorable terrain for early hunters. This problem of the reason for the predominance of the Southwest in our present knowledge remains to be resolved; as do many others. In fact, solid progress in unraveling the antiquity of man in America is so recent as to warrant the expectation that much more exists awaiting discovery than has been found.

CHAPTER SEVENTEEN

Later Prehistory and Ethnology in the Old World

281. THREE GREAT TURNS OF CULTURE IN LATER PREHISTORY

So FAR, we have reviewed the Pleistocene Old Stone Age and its aftermath the early Recent Mesolithic. It remains to examine the three following periods: the New Stone Age or Neolithic, the Bronze Age, and the Iron Age. This is the conventional terminology and stands for a sequence of polished or ground stone, of copper and bronze, and of iron and steel, which was worked out in the nineteenth century, and in the main its order still holds as true. What has happened, however, is that so much has been learned in the past hundred years by careful probings and excavations as to make it clear that the material used for tools and weapons has become a really rather secondary consideration in our understanding of what chiefly occurred in prehistory. The main currents of change and development far transcend these matters of how stone was surfaced or which metal was worked at successive times.

Such peculiarities are essentially technological; and while they may have quite important economic consequences and indirect social and ideological ones, these derivative consequences follow them irregularly, and are by no means always proportionate. In fact, the biggest economic and social innovations seem to have primarily consisted of changes in habits of living and in ideas. These broad behavioral changes did, it is true, include a measure of what might, in a general way, be called technological novelties, such as sowing grain, milking cattle, or building houses contiguously. Nevertheless it is clear that the specific human operations associated with the properties of stone and metal played a dwindling part in the total sociocultural aggregate during the course of later prehistory. Thus the conventional New Stone, Bronze, and Iron ages have become standardized names of convenience rather than terms meaningful in themselves.

To be specific, the really revolutionizing innovation of the Neolithic was the domestication and breeding of animals and plants, their controlled raising. This new increment gave an assurance of subsistence, normally, and a chance of surplus. This gain ultimately made possible—though it did not immediately enforce—a new stability and density of population; which in turn again was a precondition of subsequent major advances of culture. As against this whole cluster of fundamental social changes, the trick of grinding a chipped or hewn ax to a smooth polished edge was a pretty insignificant matter: insignificant both intrinsically and in its consequences. The grinding was not very important intrinsically because the essential process was not really new, except for being applied to ax edges: because the Upper Palaeolithic, and still more the Mesolithic, had both of them been grinding bone. Indeed the occasional stone lamps of the classic Magdalenian cave-art painters had already been rubbed hollow. Nor was the polished stone ax or "celt" really important in its effects. It was a bit better than the hewn ax and the antler adz for cutting house posts, shaping dugout canoes, and the like, and a bit inferior to the later bronze ax. Yet it amounted to as good as nothing for clearing the forest or undertaking anything else on a large scale.

The reason that the material and the surface of axes and spear points and such got into the basic classification of culture periods and determined their nomenclature is that such artifacts survive better than most, and are easily found, appreciated, and collected. But obviously this whole matter of axes cannot begin to have the importance of a change that turned men from being mere hunting and gathering parasites on nature into being controlling producers of their food by raising what they ate. Little that was definite was known a century ago about such fundamental human activities as how food was obtained in the dim periods before history. But there was on hand a fair body of tangible, classifiable knowledge on artifacts of stone and metal, on axes and weapons, on chipping and polishing. So the prehistoric eras were marked off and their names minted in the mid-nineteenth century, according to the then available criteria; which by the mid-twentieth have come to look almost pettifogging. If we were starting afresh today to measure off and designate the chief segments of the earlier course of man's total history of culture, we should almost certainly coin some Greek compound meaning "food-producing" in place of "new-stone" Neolithic. In fact, in popularized books the English phrase "food-producers" has begun to come into use for the Neolithic populations. But the professional literature, in its desire to be technically unambiguous, still mainly sticks to "Neolithic"; and two terms are perhaps no better than a single unmistakable though partly inappropriate one. So "Neolithic" is retained here, on the principle that names ought to be the last thing to quarrel about: when they become too out of line with ideas, they can always, like a constitutional monarch, be deposed. Meanwhile, it is to be understood that from here on "Neolithic" really denotes the era in which plants and animals were already domesticated by man for his use and subsistence, but metallurgical arts were not yet practiced.

The corresponding set of revolutionizing changes that characterized the Copper-Bronze Age is somewhat more ramified; but it includes the growth of towns and then of cities, of states and kings, of social classes, of enduring structures and monuments, of writing. These, as will be seen, were all interconnected with one another. They were also interconnected with copper-bronze metallurgy, so that this forms part of the innovating complex, but again, only a part.

The third era, according to the old schema, was that of iron. This metal, to be sure, involved a quite different technology from bronze; and it is this specialized technology—though it is not an intrinsically difficult one—which for a long time kept iron from being a competitor and a superseder of bronze. But the historical significance of iron is due to its abundance and cheapness, which made it possible at last for all classes of the humble to have efficient metallic tools and utensils, instead of merely the rulers and the rich possessing them, as in the times of bronze. It was in this vulgarization or democratization that the social importance of iron lay; and in this effect it is paralleled by two other inventions of about the same period: the alphabet and money. So here again the technological specialization proves to be only a fragment of the total new culture-historical significance.

The salient innovations of the post-Palaeolithic periods of prehistory may accordingly be summarized as follows:

POST-PALAEOLITHIC BASIC INNOVATIONS

Mesolithic	Palaeolithic aftermath, without fundamental novelty
Neolithic	Control of food, by plant and animal domestication
Bronze	Urbanization, social classes, writing
Iron	Popularization of metal, of writing, and of mobile wealth

282. THE SUBSISTENCE REVOLUTION OF THE NEOLITHIC:
ANIMAL AND PLANT BREEDING

Most important in the Neolithic, accordingly, was the invention of two of the great basic activities of all subsequent higher civilization: farming and stock-raising. This double-barreled acquisition turned man from being a predator, a parasite on nature, into its controller—at least a partial and indirect producer of his food. The innovation increased security and helped to free people from the scarcities occurring in areas which had been eaten bare, and from the starvations following on epidemics or disasters overtaking game animals. More permanent habitations were now possible. So were the accumulation of food and some beginnings of surplus and wealth, and a heavier growth of population; which in turn was a precondition of specialization of skills (§ 118, 163). Conversely, introduction of agriculture and animal-breeding may have been helped by pressure of increasing numbers. A sparse population, able to subsist more or less well on the wild products of its territory, tends to go on remaining content with them. But therewith it prelimits its numbers to perhaps one or two per square mile in fertile areas with mild winters, and to a much lower density—ten or twenty or thirty square miles for each human soul—in regions of cold climate, great dense forests, tropical jungle, or deserts.

We have called the food-producing activity double-barreled. Mostly the raising of plants and the raising of animals go together: they are both of them domestications. There are exceptions (§ 165). Most of aboriginal America farmed without breeding animals. And the counterpart is the steppe-desert belt stretching through Africa and Asia occupied by primarily pastoral peoples following their flocks, which normally must move several times a year to secure food and water. Much of this belt is too dry to farm. Where it is not too dry, or can be irrigated, it is regularly farmed. This farming tends to be done by other groups, classes, or tribes than those who follow their herds; but then it would usually be impracticable for the same family to try to tend simultaneously their stationary crops and their moving flocks.[1] Under such conditions pastoralism seems the more specialized activity, the nearer to being a part-culture; and it has been described as an example of such in § 120. This view would make pastoralism normally secondary, derived from the mixed economy of settled farmers-stock-raisers. Another view derives animal-breeding directly from the dealing of hunters with their game. The archaeological evidence is not conclusive as to

---

[1] This holds for areas on the arid side. In moist climates like those of Europe and the eastern half of the United States, meadows and hay are available. Consequently stock can be fed without constantly moving it over the country. The animals are also a useful aid in cultivating and manuring the plants grown; and the result is "mixed farming" as the basic subsistence type. In most of the western United States, stock-raising and farming are perforce generally conducted separately, as in the arid parts of Asia and Africa.

priority of agriculture or of animal-breeding, or of the emergence of the two conjointly. It is only in rare cases that plants are preserved from thousands of years ago, or that such perishable implements as dibbles or digging sticks will last; hoes probably came in later, and plows certainly so. Animal bones are preserved; but it is not always certain whether ancient ones are from hunted wild individuals or from tame bred ones. However, in Egypt, in the Near East, in Europe, and in China, whatever may have been the narrow priority of either of the two pursuits in this or that spot, in the large the indications are that animal-breeding and plant-breeding were nearly always complementary, and that they first appeared about coevally. In a broad survey, an attempt to separate them in time would verge on the technical.

Of course the old legendary or mythological view, which has pastoralism growing spontaneously as a universal stage out of hunting, and agriculture[2] out of pastoralism, has not been held for decades. This was a pure and naïve speculation having no relation to historical and scientific evidence; and it has in fact been traced as far back as the Sumerians.

Not all species were first bred at a single original center of all domestication. Barley and wheat, olives, grapevines, and flax, cattle and pigs, goats and sheep, evidently originated in a great Near Eastern source, which included Egypt and perhaps stretched in its totality from Afghanistan to Abyssinia. It is from this hearth that nearly all the farm plants and animals of Europe are derived, and most of those of contemporary America. But neither the horse nor the ass was part of this complex. Moreover, organisms as important as rice, sugar cane, cotton, chickens, and water buffalos clearly are southeastern Asiatic in origin. Does this mean that there were two wholly independent centers of origin of domestication in southeastern and southwestern Asia, besides a scattering of minor ones elsewhere—plus a third major center in America? We cannot at present be sure. Stimulus diffusion (§ 154) may have been operative: the idea alone perhaps was carried and then worked out on new animals and plants; though ordinarily this is difficult with organisms. Or certain species may have been actually transmitted—like wheat and cattle to China—along with the techniques of growing and utilizing them—and then have stimulated experiments with new species belonging to the region. For instance, the Tibetan yak, in its specialized habitat between eastern buffalo and western cattle, is almost certainly

[2] "Agriculture," which we mostly use as a general term to include also animal-breeding (other than of range stock), etymologically means *ager* or field culture, and therefore implies plowing. Most of the farming of modern primitive peoples is done with hand tools in small plots something on the order of size of our vegetable or truck gardens. *Hortus* being a garden, "horticulture" has therefore been applied by anthropologists to this hand farming, much of which is done by women. But this runs foul of general modern English usage of "horticulture" as denoting fruit-growing in orchards. It is also awkward to speak of Japanese "rice horticulture." Under the partial inexactitude of all these names, there lie distinctions of very real importance.

a local counterpart adaptation or ersatz, not the product of a wholly original inspiration toward domestication emerging out of the blue.

As regards Europe, it is clear that the four principal animals first raised there—cattle, pigs, goats, sheep [3]—were imported from the Near East—say southwestern Asia, possibly including Egypt. This is clear from the unusually abundant and well-preserved lake-dwelling remains of the Neolithic and the Bronze Age in Switzerland. The earliest known domestic animals there were considerably different from the nearest native species. The wild bull or urus of Europe, *Bos primigenius*, was large and long-horned. Its bones in the oldest lake dwellings seem to come from wild individuals that had been hunted. Alongside are the remains of the domesticated *Bos taurus brachyceros,* a short-horned form, small and delicately built. Later, though still in the Neolithic, long-horned tame cattle appear in the lake dwellings. Apparently the shorthorns had first been imported from the southeast; then the native urus was tamed, or at least kept; finally, the two strains were crossed. These strains are thought to survive in our modern cattle, those of eastern and central Europe being prevailingly of the *primigenius* type, those of western Europe of the *brachyceros*.

A similar story applies to the pig. The first domesticated swine of Switzerland were small, long-legged, and easily distinguishable from the heavy wild boar of the region. It thus is likely that they came in from southwestern Asia already domesticated. In the Bronze Age, pigs grew larger, owing perhaps to crossing with the wild species. The East Asiatic pig probably represents the separate domestication of another species or race. Sheep were certainly brought into Europe, as there is no corresponding wild form there that is at all close; the goats, too, have their nearest relatives in Asia. The dense, curly wool of sheep is wholly a product of genetic change and selection under domestication (§ 34).

The tracing back of tame forms to the ancestral species or race is often difficult for biologists who have only ancient bones to work from. Prolonged domestication, with breeders' selection, may superficially alter a race more from its original wild form than this in turn differs from a wholly distinct second wild species.

The ordinary donkey stems from an African wild ass that was early used for burdens in Egypt—before 3000 B.C.,—and in Syria and Mesopotamia during the following millennium, but which spread rather slowly away from the Mediterranean. An Asiatic wild ass or onager may have been tamed for driving in the Near East, to judge from Sumerian Royal Tomb representations of teams in harness.

The history of the horse is somewhat puzzling. The horses that the French Solutreans hunted, and the Magdalenians painted, were wild, and they died out in Europe, possibly lingering on into the Mesolithic here and there. Horses were

---

[3] The dog, though kept earliest of all, is here omitted because negligible economically.

very likely first broken and bred in inner Asia, perhaps in Iran, Turkestan, or Sinkiang. Here too it was that the last wild species survived until quite recently: *Equus przewalskii*. At any rate there seem to be horse bones in the next to the bottom and the bottom layers respectively at Sialk and Anau, just off the steppe in northeastern Iran and southern Turkestan respectively. The date would be around 4000 B.C. (see table, § 286). Whether any of the beasts were domesticated remains to be proved; those at Anau it is assumed were wild.

Culturally, the horse became important in the Bronze Age in connection with the aristocratic war chariot. Horses were driven in front of this throughout the civilized Near East and Greece for centuries before they were habitually ridden. The horse was an animal strictly associated with wealth and luxury—racing, battle, pomp, and sacrifice; and it retained something of this character even after a true cavalry had come into existence much later, in the Iron Age: historical Roman "knights" still were *equites,* "horsemen." There are a few puzzlingly early half-evidences of riding, such as incised drawings of mounted men with reins at Susa in stratum B, around 3000 B.C. But these indications are sketchily pictorial, or verbally allusive, rather than incontrovertible; and they are altogether too sporadic to be wholly satisfying. It is possible that spotty attempts to ride were made soon after horses were domesticated, but that the art did not become systematic or usefully established. Then came the chariot, with yoke and harness taken over from cattle; whereupon driving dominated all horse management for close to a thousand years. This domination certainly held for Mesopotamia and Egypt, among the Homeric Greeks, and in China—that is, on both sides of inner Asia: until finally riding came into its own alongside of driving.

Balaam rode his ass, and so did the forty sons and thirty nephews of Abdon who judged Israel about 1100 B.C., according to accounts written some centuries later; but the Homeric heroes of the same general period, with iron just beginning to appear beside bronze, are always mentioned only as driving. The light, strong, lordly war chariot, with skillfully spoked wheels in place of the earlier solid wooden disks on cattle or ass carts, is first known in Mesopotamia and North Syria about the nineteenth century B.C.; but it was the sixteenth century B.C. before the Egyptians used it against the Hyksos, who had in turn conquered them partly with its help. The Cretan Minoans took up the chariot in the next century. As against this slow westward spread, there is a less-known, probable, rapid one far to the east: it is clear from excavations that North Chinese rulers at An-yang were also driving war chariots by about 1400 B.C.

Camels, both two-humped and dromedary, are Asiatic in origin: the latter did not get established in Egypt and North Africa until Roman and Christian times. The dromedary was ridden by the Midianite Arab Beduin raiders whom Gideon turned back from trans-Jordan Israel around 1100 B.C. That is about as far back as sure record of use of camels of either species for riding or packing goes. Bones occur much earlier—at Anau in Turkestan and in the Indus Valley soon after 3000 B.C.—but they may be from wild animals hunted for their meat. Both camel species, by the way, survive only in domestication.

Cocks and hens are domesticated breeds of the wild jungle fowl of India, Farther India, and Malaysia, which, as we have seen, were probably originally kept only for fighting, sacrificing, or bone divination (§ 165). The westward progress of the chicken is late. The Old Testament Jews did not have it, but it is mentioned in the New Testament: Peter denied thrice before cockcrow. It reached Greece and Italy about the seventh century B.C. As the handiest and cheapest of domestic animals, it has always been a favorite sacrificial animal, whether as a token on small occasions, or by the poor in means. It is still used for this purpose, all the way from the Philippines to West Africa, by pagans who have escaped conversion to the great world religions.

Bred plants being more numerous than bred animals, the evidence of their origin is more ramifying; but at least as between southwestern Asia and Europe, the priority of the basic grains in Asia is clear. Both 28-chromosome emmer wheat and 42-chromosome soft or common wheat occur wild there: respectively in Syria and Trans-Jordan and in Persia. Even should these wild forms be ultimate "escapes" from cultivation, they are self-perpetuating and adaptive to the environment as if native there; which cannot be alleged for Europe, most of which was forested in the era in which domestication occurred. The ancient wheat at Anau and Mohenjo-daro (§ 304) was apparently of the 42-chromosome type; the Badarian (§ 291) wheat of primitive Egypt, 28-chromosome. Thus the line-up of the earliest areas of cultivation coincided roughly with the areas of modern spontaneous growth. Incidentally three wheats of antiquity, einkorn, emmer, and spelt,[4] all survive in cultivation in spots in central Europe; which is thereby indicated as a probable area of marginal survival (§ 173, 175).

As regards barley, which in ancient times was often more important as a staple than wheat, the general picture is the same. The predynastic Egyptian form is identified as *Hordeum vulgare,* our usual type today; that at Mohenjo-daro in India as the same; an impression from the lowest level at Anau as *Hordeum distichum;* and a form still occurring wild in western Asia as *Hordeum spontaneum.*

It is not claimed that all cultivated plants were first bred in or near western Asia: East Asia produced some, America perhaps more yet, and almost any region might prove to have added a species or two. It is just that as between Europe and the Near East in the critical formative period, the latter appears to have been doing all the contributing in agriculture.

[4] Respectively, *Triticum monococcum,* with 14 chromosomes; *Triticum dicoccum,* 28; *Triticum spelta,* 42.

283. THE NEOLITHIC IN AFRICA, ASIA, AND EUROPE

Only a few of these plants and animals were reared by any one Neolithic population: the great spreads and transfers, which were to diversify farming and enrich subsistence, mainly occurred later, in the ages of metal and full history. What any one community or region controlled was the growing of two or perhaps three grains plus one or two other plants; the breeding of three, four, or at most five animals; pottery-making by hand, with decoration confined to impressions; spinning and some sort of weaving; hunting with chipped weapon points; reaping with chipped blades set in grooved sickle hafts of bone, horn, or wood; and a limited measure of woodcutting with chipped celts or axes that might be wholly, partly, or not at all ground into a smooth surface. This very list shows how small the Neolithic increment over the old Palaeolithic-Mesolithic equipment was, apart from the food-producing domestications. The great majority of stone tools were still manufactured by fracture; the basic ax itself, and also the pottery, were carry-overs from Mesolithic inventions.

A few other activities followed the farming. Grains need threshing, and then grinding into flour: this was done on saddle querns—what in Mexico and the southwestern United States are called metates—slabs on which a stone was pushed back and forth: rotary millstones on an axle appear only in historical times (§ 183). If bread was to be in loaves, as distinct from gruel, wafers, or flat cakes, an oven and yeast were needed; and the yeast also turned barley into beer. It is not clear when and where bread and beer were first devised. It was before writing; it may have been after the Neolithic was about over; but bread and beer were very early in Egypt and Mesopotamia.

It is evident from this cultural inventory that Neolithic peoples had attained to better subsistence security than their predecessors, and with that had learned a number of manipulative activities requiring some knowledge and more perseverance; but rather little beyond that. They had achieved the indispensable foundation for a higher civilization that food-producing provides; but as yet they possessed scarcely a glimmer of the vision of such civilization. For one thing, there was nothing in their life that called for or induced either large-scale co-operation or high craft specialization. Their communities therefore remained small—sufficient for self-defense and no more, it would seem: in fact, much as on an eighteenth-century American farm a single good-sized family would have sufficed to carry on most necessary activities by itself. If Neolithic families did not thus scatter out by themselves but usually huddled together, it was presumably through needs for sociability, or fear of marauders. Essentially a Neolithic community was self-sufficient, as it undoubtedly was primitively democratic and self-determining. There might be a thousand hamlets in a land, but there would be no town with city life, ruler's palace, or national temple. A consequence of this self-sufficient independence was lack of higher cultural activity and organization—social, political, ritual, and aesthetic. Neolithic society was a typically "rural" one, without any "urban" counterpart, even in distant consciousness.

A few examples follow of Neolithic sites that have been excavated with particular care or are specially significant.

Merimde, on the edge of the Egyptian delta, and *Fayum,* an overflow lake off the Nile. Much hunting, fowling, and fishing, as is shown by flint arrowheads and bone darts and harpoon points. But also emmer wheat and barley, granaries and threshing floors, sickles and querns. Cattle, pigs, sheep, goats, presumably domesticated. Houses in rows. Ground axes. Pottery. Linen from flax. Much the same culture is found at *Tasa* up the Nile, whence the name "Tasian" for the period.

Natufian in Palestine. Sickles suggest agriculture but do not prove it; otherwise the culture seems Mesolithic. There is no pottery, and dogs were the only kept animals. See § 277.

Halaf. A Neolithic pre-Halafian precedes Chalcolithic Halafian at *Tell-Halaf,* on the Khabur, an affluent of the Upper Euphrates. The Halafian proper produced a polychrome pottery allied to that of Ubaid in lower Mesopotamia (§ 286). The pre-Halaf ware is monochrome, like the Neolithic pottery of the sites that follow.

Mersin in Cilicia, Asia Minor. The upper forty to fifty feet of site deposit are Chalcolithic or Bronze Age; the lower thirty feet, Neolithic, and estimated to go back perhaps to 6000 B.C.

Samarra, in central Mesopotamia north of Baghdad. Technically, Chalcolithic rather than Neolithic. Samarra pottery is similar to that of Halaf and Ubaid and overlaps them in time.

Hassuna, near Mosul in Iraq. Cattle were kept, flint sickles used, pottery made, and houses were built of handmade but evenly shaped sun-dried bricks. An age of 6000 B.C. has been claimed. The culture is at any rate well anterior to the Ubaid period (§ 286).

Tepe Gawra in northern Mesopotamia, near Mosul. About fifteen feet of Neolithic deposits, beginning about 5000 B.C. according to one estimate (§ 286); or ending then by another. Overlain by nearly ninety feet of Copper-Bronze Age deposits.

Sialk, in Persia, between Teheran and Isfahan. The lowest layer is essentially Neolithic, although a few hammered pins or awls make it technically Chalcolithic. Sickles and querns suggest sown grain, which would have had to be irrigated. There are bones of at least sheep. Considerable hunting. Stone axes sometimes ground, mostly not. Spindle whorls. Painted pottery.

Anau, just north of Persia, near Askhabad in Turkmen Republic, U.S.S.R. Lowest level: geometric painted pottery. Daubed wattle structures. Wheat, barley. Spindle whorls. Cattle, sheep, pig, occur upward in this layer (IB in table on page 707, but not at its base, IA); however, this may be an accident of refuse deposition or preservation. There are a few copper or lead twisted ornaments in layer I. The second main level contains even more monochrome than painted pottery; flint sickles and door sockets; goat, camel, and dog remains. Third level: bronze or copper sickles, spears, stamp seals; potter's wheel; pottery figurines of women or animals. The apparently late appearance of flint sickles and dog bones here may be an accident of preservation or excavation; an absence from a particular digging is never full proof of absence from the culture as it actually existed. Also, this was the first large site of great antiquity in the Near East to have been excavated, and the technique of exploration has been refined subsequently.

Tripolje of the Russian steppe, near Kiev. A late Neolithic culture, with beginnings of copper; characterized by polychrome painted pottery. Close relatives extend to Transylvania and Thessaly. About 2400-1600 B.C., overlapping with Danubian II. In pottery it is most similar, of any area in the west, to that of the Yang-shao culture in China (§ 298).

Danubian Culture of central-eastern Europe; especially on lightly forested loess sites. Sickles, querns, and stone hoes emphasize grain-growing. There are bones of cattle, pigs, and sheep, but they are not abundant; bones of game are still fewer. Pottery neatly incised. A uniform culture over a large area, trending west to the Rhine and Belgium. It is subsequent to 3000 B.C. (estimated period 2700-2200), whereas the foregoing Egyptian and Asiatic sites probably all predate 4000 in part.

Swiss Lake-dwellers. An unusually well-documented phase, through underwater preservation, of a western-European Neolithic phase subsequent to 2500 B.C. By French authors it is called Robenhausian after a site. Pile dwellings, standing above the water, extended up to two acres and more. Plants that were grown include wheat, barley, two kinds of millet; oats did not come until bronze times, and rye is lacking; apples were perhaps improved from the native wild form; flax was raised for linen. Along with these there are charred fragments of cord, net, cloth, and basketry matting. Wooden objects comprise combs, clubs, daggers, bowls, and dippers. The cattle, pigs, goats, and sheep have already been mentioned. Their bones considerably outnumber those of wild game; in remains of the same culture away from the Alpine lakes, as in Normandy, the larger proportion of bones from butchered to hunted animals sometimes becomes overwhelming. Pottery is incised. Ground axes and chisels occasionally remain in their wood or antler haftings. So much that generally perishes has been preserved in the lake mud that we are afforded an unusually intimate glimpse into the domesticity of four thousand years ago. In many ways the tone and the manner of the culture are remarkably reminiscent of the life of nineteenth-century Swiss, French, or German peasants. The pile dwellings continued to be built to the end of the Bronze Age.

Megalithic Cultures. A late Neolithic and Copper Age development conspicuous in western Europe was the custom of erecting megaliths, monuments of large stones, sometimes approaching the gigantic, for funerary and cult purposes. Most of the blocks are natural, a few slightly shaped, all rude. Among megaliths, the following types are distinguished: menhirs, large single pillars; cromlechs, circles of menhirs; alignments, rows of small pillars; dolmens, vertical slabs or sometimes blocks supporting a roof slab, the whole being of room size and approximate shape; passage graves, dolmens approached through a slab-sided and roofed gangway, which may be narrower than or as wide as the dolmen chamber; and stone cists, degenerate dolmens or passages reduced to grave size. The last three were mortuary, and covered with mounded-up earth. The main distribution of megaliths in Europe follows the Atlantic coast: southern Spain, Portugal, western France, Brittany, Britain, Ireland, southern Scandinavia. Spain and Portugal, which may have been the area of origin of this development in Europe, have the largest and best-made chambers. Brittany is conspicuous for menhirs and the famous alignments of Carnac. England possesses probably the most impressive free-standing ruin in Stonehenge. The general period is around 2000 B.C.

In Spain, the terminal Neolithic, early Copper, full Copper, and early Bronze Age have each its typical set of dolmen, chamber, vault, or cist forms. The two Spanish Copper periods are also those in which there was made a type of pottery vessel known as a bell beaker, which for some reason spread rapidly over nearly all Europe and therefore is much used as a time-marker by prehistorians. Both megaliths and bell beakers however are merely detached complexes or traits that "went on travels"; most of the Spanish culture of the time did not diffuse. Also, the megaliths and the beakers spread differently: megaliths by sea communications chiefly, bell beakers inland as well. The southern Iberian cultures of which both form part were themselves stimulated from the eastern end of the Mediterranean, probably by voyagers—Minoans or others?—in search of the metals in which Spain was rich. In France and Britain the indications of the period in which the megaliths were reared are less definite than in Spain; but again there are associations with unsmelted metal. A possibly relevant astronomical calculation finds a tentative date of 1840 B.C. for Stonehenge; this at any rate falls within the modern estimates for the time of copper transition in England.

Both menhirs and dolmens occur elsewhere, especially in western, southern, and East Asia—and again nearly always within easy travel of the sea; but connection of these megaliths with the Atlantic European ones is more doubtful.

Tombs and altars of the magnitude of the larger megaliths could hardly have been erected save by fair-sized groups of people and presumably under the command of authority. Their implications thus are different from the rural self-sufficient aspects of most life in the European Neolithic. It is therefore no doubt significant that megalithic structures arose while the old Neolithic order was passing out; and that they and their new social system were introduced by sea voyagers, while in the interior, as around the Alpine lakes, the Neolithic peasant-type culture continued into the Bronze Age without much change of outlook.

There is no convincing evidence in the European Neolithic for a group of traits subsequently associated with domestic cattle in Europe: namely, wheeled vehicles, plows, castration, and milking. Of these same traits, milking failed at any time to penetrate into the Chinese culture sphere, and the plow into Negro Africa.

284. THE BRONZE AGE: COPPER AND BRONZE PHASES

There is no abrupt break between the Neolithic and the full or classic Bronze Age; but rather a transition—especially as regards metal usage. Nontechnological culture activities—social, political, ideological—often changed much more drastically, especially in what became the first great centers of civilization. Bronze was at first too rare, too difficult to mine and smelt and work, to be used extensively. It served for special weapons, tools, and ornaments of the wealthy. The life of the mass of the population went on in much the old channels for centuries after the new material had become known; often with flint picks, hoes, and knives of Mesolithic type. This was true especially of peoples in oreless regions, or nations too backward to have learned the new art and still dependent on import or on wandering smiths. To such peoples, the first bronze pieces came as rarities, to be guarded as treasures and heirlooms.

Of even less immediate effect than the discovery of bronze was the discovery of the first metals known: copper and gold. These occur, though only scatteringly, in "native" or pure metallic form, and their nuggets or lumps could accordingly be treated by essentially Stone Age methods—beating out, rubbing, cutting, and such—without use of true metallurgical techniques involving heat. Gold is of course too scarce and too soft to serve for anything but ornaments or wealth; and pure copper also, even when somewhat hardened by hammering, is of little use for many mechanical purposes. If thick enough, it makes a fairly efficient dagger, a rather mediocre ax, and a poor knife. The result was that a recognizable period of Copper preceded the true Bronze Age, yet this Copper period was essentially a last phase of the New Stone Age, with the metal creeping in as something subsidiary. It has therefore become customary among some archaeologists to speak of an Aeneolithic or Chalcolithic [5] period as a transition stage in which some unsmelted and uncast copper occurs, with or without gold. In central and northern Europe, the equivalent stage falls toward 2000 B.C. and is sometimes called the Stone-Bronze transition.

The first gold seems all to have been placer-mined out of river gravels. Nuggets can be beaten together and into sheets and will take any shape into which they can be hammered or cut. Regions we think of as wholly unproductive of gold, such as Ireland, appear to have contained rich pockets of river deposits, though these were limited and quickly exhausted. The earliest Irish gold jewels are often massive, and later ones thin and hollow.

Bronze is usually an alloy of tin and copper, harder than the latter, somewhat easier to melt, and casting better. An admixture of arsenic, phosphorus, or even lead, such as may result from natural impurities, will also harden copper. In many properties tin bronze resembles brass, by which term it is referred to in the English Bible; but the two must not be confounded. Brass is an alloy of zinc with copper, is of much later discovery, apparently in Asia, and until recent centuries was little used in Europe. As regards bronze, even a 2 or 3 per cent addition of tin to copper results in a perceptible hardening; 10 per cent produces a greatly superior tool metal; but with 25 per cent and up the bronze becomes too brittle for service, though it will cast beautifully into ornaments.

The origin of bronze is a problem of some difficulty, and for several reasons. First, the earliest known users of bronze, the peoples of the Near East, possessed

[5] See footnote in § 257.

little if any tin ore.[6] Second, tin ore does not even suggest in its appearance that it contains metal. And third, the process of smelting, or reducing ore to metal, must have been found out before the tin could be extracted from the ore. This smelting process may have been invented in connection with copper, some of the ores of which are green or blue and may have been used first as they were for jewelry, or for paint. It may well have been discovered first that if sufficiently heated by blowing with a reed, native copper would *melt* and could then be cast in molds. Then, upon further experimentation, when heat was applied to ore and charcoal, metal was found to *smelt* out of the mixture. The manner and stages of the invention remain problematical. What seems sure is that until tin had been extracted from its rather rare ore, there would have been none of it to melt with copper to cast as bronze. Once the smelting process was known, it would presumably be applied to various ores, yielding other metals. At any rate, silver and lead appear promptly in the archaeological record once copper has been given full metallurgical treatment.

Just how, then, bronze was discovered, is still unknown; but the approximate where and when are clear: in western Asia not later than the fourth millennium B.C., and quite likely in its first half; that is, before 3500. By 3000 it had got into Syria, and some centuries later to Crete and Troy, whereas it did not penetrate central and northern Europe until about 1800 B.C., according to the usual estimates. That the use of bronze over these widespread areas is a connected phenomenon is clear from the manner in which the art spread from its center like a wave that arrived later the farther it had to travel (§ 173). The spread is confirmed by the fact that certain implement forms such as early triangular daggers and later swords traveled with the material. Had the western and northern European natives discovered bronze for themselves, they would have cast it into shapes peculiar to themselves, instead of adopting those long-established among Orientals.

But it would be an error to infer from the continued backwardness of the remote European Bronze Age peoples that they were wholly passive and recipient. In their simpler, more barbaric way, they remodeled much of what was carried to them, altered the form, decorated it in their own style, and made much of some item that filled but an insignificant place in the more complex civilization of the southeast. For instance, the central and northern European nations seized upon the fibula or safety pin with avidity; they made it ornate and tremendously large, until it sometimes measured half a foot in length and more than half a pound in weight, with spiral whorls, bosses, pin clasps, or attached rings as big as a palm. The Baltic nations, the farthest reached by this diffusion, in particular threw themselves into the development of the fibula with zest, success, and a large measure of decorative taste.

[6] There are said to have been tin ores in the Khorasan district of Persia. The chief sources of the tin of later antiquity were Spain and Cornwall. But at the outset of the Bronze Age, the Orientals did not even know of the existence of these countries.

The social effect of copper was almost nil; but the full-fledged bronze art did influence the rest of culture and the structure of society. This was because the supplies of metal were rare and often distant, and the crafts of extracting ores and working bronze required specialized skills. Miners and especially bronze-founders—small-scale as their equipment was by modern standards—thus tended to become a set-off caste, with hereditary trade secrets; probably much like iron-smiths in Africa and Arabia today. Not only did they thus constitute one of the first social classes themselves, but as there emerged classes of nobility and rulers in whose hands wealth tended to concentrate, these were best able to employ the bronzesmiths and to acquire their product. Thus they not only acquired hoarded treasure but provided themselves with weapons, armor, and tools, which in turn helped to fortify their supremacy. Wherever there was enough density of population for this process to be effective, the full Bronze Age tended to become also an age of heroes, aristocracy, even of feudalism. Not that the metal by itself brought about a new order of society; but it reinforced one. By contrast, the subsequent effects of iron were in the direction of democratization, or giving the have-nots and the marginals a new chance.

285. SEEPS TO THE MARGIN AND THE RATE OF SPREAD

As far back as 1899 and 1905, a Swedish and a Danish archaeologist, Montelius and Sophus Müller, recognized certain cultural processes as having been operative in European and western-Asiatic prehistory. Five principles and three extensions were set up by Müller, as follows:

1. The south (of Europe, with the Near East) was the vanguard and dispensing source of culture; and peripheral regions, especially in the north (of Europe), followed and received.

2. The elements of southern culture were transmitted to the north only in reduction and extract.

3. They were also subject to modifications.

4. These elements of southern culture sometimes appeared in the remoter areas with great vigor and new qualities of their own.

5. But such remote appearances are later in time than the occurrence of the same elements in the south.

6. Forms of artifacts or ornaments may survive for a long time with but little modification, especially if transmitted to new territory.

7. Separate elements characteristic of successive periods in a culture center may occur contemporaneously in the marginal areas, their diffusion having occurred at different rates of speed.

8. Marginal cultures thus present a curious mixture of traits whose original age is great and of others that are much newer; the latter, in fact, occasionally reach the peripheries earlier than old traits.

The basic idea of these formulations is that culture gradually radiates from creative focal centers to backward marginal areas, without the original dependence of the peripheries' precluding their subsequent independent development. This point of view is substantially identical with that which has been held to in § 173 and § 238 on the basis of construal of distributional data. This focal-marginal interpretation has the following consideration in its favor.

Within the historical period, there have been numerous undoubted diffusions, such as of the alphabet, the week, the true arch, water mills, Christianity and other religions, gunpowder, printing. In the earlier portion of the historical period, the flow of such diffusions was pretty regularly out of the Near East; which raises a considerable presumption that the flow was in the same direction as early as the Neolithic. On the contrary, indubitably independent parallelisms are mostly difficult to establish within historical areas and periods, and therefore are likely to have been equally rare during prehistory.

Then too, the diffusion interpretation to a certain degree explains a large part of civilization in terms of a consistent scheme. To the contrary, the parallelistic opinion leaves the facts both unexplained and unrelated. If the Etruscans devised the true arch and liver divination independently of the Babylonians, there are two sets of phenomena awaiting interpretation instead of one. To say that they are both "accidental" events is equivalent to calling them unexplainable. To fall back on instinctive impulses of the human mind will not do; otherwise all or most nations should have made these inventions.

Of course it is important to remember that no sane interpretation of culture explains everything. We do not really know much about the specific causes of the invention of the true arch in Mesopotamia, of hieroglyphic writing in Egypt, of the alphabet in Phoenicia, each at certain times and places rather than at others. The diffusion point of view simply accepts certain focal developments of culture as empirically given by the facts, and then relates other relatable events to these.

In line with his recognition of processes in the growth of prehistoric culture, Müller seems to have been the first to arrange a chart presenting the time relations or periods of his culture developments in one dimension, the space relations or geography in another. This is the method still followed by Burkitt and Childe, by Hawkes, and by others in their tabular summaries for Europe and the Near East, by Nelson, Spinden, and Wissler for aboriginal American reconstructions. Müller's scheme thus has a historical interest for the archaeologist; and his chart—considerably simplified from its complexity in the original—is therefore reproduced in Figure 40.

Even the specific chronology of this innovating presentation has proved remarkably sound, considering how long ago it was formulated. In his day, and for twenty years later, there were specialists who set the beginnings of the Danish kitchen middens (now called Ertebølle culture; § 276) back to 8000 B.C.; Müller estimated 5000. Agriculture and stock-raising in middle Europe had their beginnings assigned to 6000-5000; he said about 3300. The 3500-2500 allowed for the dolmen period in Scandinavia he cut to 1800-1400. In the first (1923) edi-

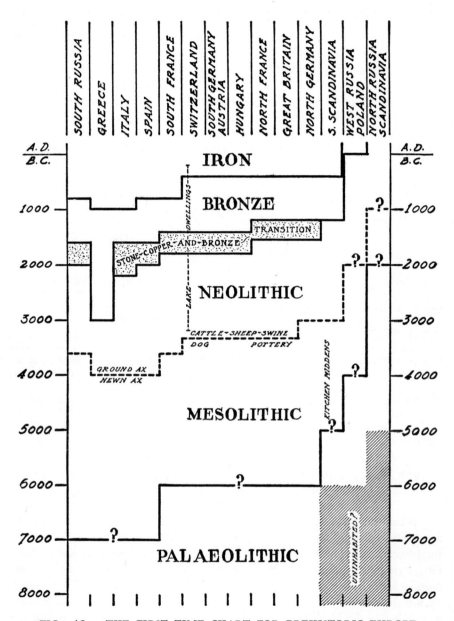

FIG. 40. THE FIRST TIME CHART FOR PREHISTORIC EUROPE

Simplified from Sophus Müller, 1905, this is the earliest diagram constructed to show comparative cultural precedences and lags of areas. The table is given for the principles it illustrates, not for its precise dates, most of which are now set slightly differently. But even in his absolute chronology Müller came much nearer to the short dating of mid-twentieth-century views than did his contemporaries and successors of two decades later than he.

tion of the present book, these "long" dates were accepted, and Müller's were spoken of as daringly conservative. Now, in practically every case, advanced mid-twentieth-century opinion supports him: usually not exactly, but essentially so.

To show how similarly the total relation is still viewed today, there is appended a little tabulation that represents a heavy distillation of a paper by Childe on the Orient and Europe. Here two dates are held constant—4000 and 2500 B.C.—while the culture is characterized as it shades off in intensity at seven successive geographical removes from the center.

REGIONAL SHADING-OFF OF CULTURAL DEVELOPMENT

Region	4000 ± B.C.	2500 ± B.C.
Egypt, Mesopotamia	2-sq.-mile cities with organized commerce, artisans, (writing, soon after)	Metropolitan civilization
Crete, Syria, C. Turkey	Smaller cities	Provincial civilization, urban and literate
Greece, W. Turkey	2-4-acre towns; copper	4-11-acre towns; bronze, beginnings of writing
Balkans, Lower Danube	Neolithic farmers	Larger, (180 graves) — stable villages of farmers; some metal, but not enough for tools
Uppermost Danube	Shifting hamlets, with some tillage of soil	Smaller, (100 graves)
North Germany, Denmark	Gathering and hunting	Shifting hamlets of peasants
In N. W. European plain	Gathering and hunting	Gathering only

286. THE COPPER-BRONZE AGE AS AN URBAN DEVELOPMENT: CLASSES, KINGS, GODS, MONUMENTS, AND WRITING

When the first crude and meager little awls and pins of hammered copper appear in remains of food-producing societies in Nearer Asia, they make a pretty insignificant addition to the stock of Neolithic culture. Sometimes indeed these bits of copper are present in levels of refuse so early that it was only an occasional hewn ax out of many which people as yet bothered to grind to an edge. Such is the case in level I at Sialk in Iran: here, locally, the Chalcolithic was on its way before the Neolithic was fully achieved, by technical definition. But the Copper Age lasted for centuries, perhaps for a thousand years; and before this period was over at Sialk, there was a perceptible enrichment of culture. To construction in wattle and daub and in beaten mud (also called rammed or packed earth), there was added the use of sun-dried, handmade bricks—"adobes." In some places, pottery was painted, even polychrome; figurines were modeled of clay; and impressions of stamp seals have been found—symbols of ownership or taboo or both. These last are perhaps the most likely indications of an incipient differentiation of social classes; for it is only owners reserving their property who would be interested in marking it as private.

When, around 4000 B.C. or fairly soon after in this Near Eastern part of the world, true metallurgy and bronze appear, it is with the accompaniment of still further advances: disk-wheeled carts with harnessed cattle or asses; the horizontally spinning wheel which speeds up pottery manufacture; temple structures —that is, houses for gods; valuables such as alabaster vessels; and the first actual specimens of preserved seals, shaped somewhat like buttons. Before 3000 B.C., we find in lower Mesopotamia built-up hills bearing religious structures, temples more than two hundred feet in length, and towns covering hundreds of acres. All the labor involved could be done only by a good-sized population, and a coordinated one. There were those who gave orders and those who took them: rulers and ruled, in short; differentiated social classes—priests, the rich or the noble, governors, perhaps kings, or at least those whose descendants would before long rule as kings. Seals had progressed from button to stamp shape (flat, with handles like our rubber stamps), and from that to a cylindrical form, so they could be rolled, and in between times of use hung from the neck on a string passing through a lengthwise perforation. The carvings on the seals had passed through a pure pictorial stage to one in which symbols of words were added: true writing had begun. This was in southern Mesopotamia a few centuries before 3000 B.C., at the very end of the Uruk or next-to-the-last stage preceding the historical dynasties of the Sumerians. So far as can be judged at present, this was the first real writing ever devised anywhere.

Well, here we have the complex suggested by the heading of this section: social classes segregated in wealth, occupation, and rank, including princes or kings ruling in the name of gods (or in Egypt as gods); monuments and edifices of these gods; and writing to preserve their myths, rituals, ordinances, property records, as well as the deeds, contracts, and inheritances of their human trustees; and before long of private parties as well. And all this was growing up in an atmosphere of town life, with artisans, smiths, scribes, priests, and rulers following their professions instead of tilling their own fields. (Cf. § 118, 121.) These classes were therefore directly or indirectly dependent for their living, plus such wealth and state as they had, on the rent, dues, tribute, or taxes being paid by the actual farmers on the land, who still constituted the majority of the population. We have come a long way, here at the eve of 3000 B.C., from the wholly rural, hamlet-dwelling, undifferentiated society and self-sufficient economy of the Near Eastern Neolithic of 5000 B.C. and before. Though it was not a sudden alteration, it was a profound one. And at any rate toward the end, in the last centuries of the fourth millennium, changes accumulated fast.

Not far from 3000 B.C., this development had progressed far enough in southern Mesopotamia, with a parallel one in Egypt, for the archaeological record to meet the historical one—the lists of earliest kings and dynasties which the Sumerians and Egyptians drew up after they became learned and compiled their own histories. After 3000, accordingly, we are in what is called the Dynastic era—its first few centuries being usually further distinguished as Early Dynastic in Mesopotamia, Protodynastic in Egypt. This is also the fully developed or culminating or "classic" Bronze Age of the Near East. It lasted nearly two millennia. But around 1400 B.C., the historical Asiatic Bronze Age cultures and societies began to show signs of strain, and between about 1200 and 800 many of them went to pieces in a series of collapses and overturns more or less connected with the introduction of iron.

By contrast with this historical Dynastic era or full Bronze Age following 3000 B.C., the preceding historyless period of most rapid development during the millennium or two-thirds of a millennium preceding—the time of the first genuine metallurgical skills—can be called the Early Bronze or Predynastic era. This is customarily subdivided into three stages in Mesopotamia, named successively Ubaid, Uruk, Jemdet Nasr.[7] Of these cultures, the first may have been, the second and third were, carried by Sumerians, in the lower, marshy part of the land. The corresponding levels or stages at some of the most carefully worked sites in Turkestan, Iran, northern Mesopotamia, Syria, and Egypt are shown in the tabulation on the facing page.

When we get back beyond the Ubaid period, the Sumerian record stops, because, previous to this, southernmost Mesopotamia was still merely an uninhabitable marsh. We do have carefully excavated material from middle and northern Mesopotamian sites, such as Samarra north of Baghdad, and Gawra, Hassuna, and Arpachiya near Mosul and ancient Nineveh; from Ras Shamra on the Syrian coast, which we have already met as Ugarit in the history of the alphabet (§ 207); also from Halaf far inland in Syria, east of the Euphrates; from Mersin in Cilicia,[8] Sialk and others in Iran, and Anau in southwestern Turkestan (§ 283). All these show interrelations. Thus the "Samarra culture" is a sort of prior and northern Ubaid. It is also a southeastern variant of the contemporary "Halaf culture," much as still farther east Sialk II and Anau IA form its counterparts. These are reckoned as Chalcolithic cultures. Back beyond them come "Neolithic" cultures: pre-Halafian in Syria and northern Mesopotamia, Sialk I and Chashmah Ali IA in Iran.[9]

[7] Named after excavated sites in southern Mesopotamia. Properly, el 'Ubaid. The forms Obeid, Erech, Jamdat Nasr, are used by some.

[8] Cilicia is in southeastern Asia Minor. The fifteenth Mersin layer from the top corresponds to Ubaid, its sixteenth to Halaf. Chalcolithic deposits extend ten feet deeper, and then there are thirty feet more of Neolithic. It seems that the base of this Neolithic must date back to 5000 B.C., perhaps to 6000.

[9] A little copper in Sialk I (as above) is evidence of how tenuous the line of division really is between Neolithic and Chalcolithic: compare the Tasian-Badarian "split" in Egypt (§ 291). The significance may be only that Sialk happened to be situated nearer to easily discoverable deposits of copper than were contemporary sites farther west.

SOME NEAR-EASTERN CORRESPONDENCES

		Egypt	Palestine, Syria	Gaura,* N. Mesop.	Sumer	Iran, Sialk	Iran, Chashmab Ali	Iran, Hissar	Anau,† Turkestan
Dynastic, Historical, Bronze	2500	Pyramids			Akkadian				
		Proto-Dynastic	Tahunian	VI	Early Dynastic			III	III
	3000								
Predynastic, Early "Bronze"		Semainian		VII, VIII	Jemdet Nasr	IV		IIB	?
		Gerzean		VIII–XI	Uruk	(gap)		IIA	II
		Amratian		XII–XIII	Ubaid	III	IB	I	IB‡
	≥4000								
Chalcolithic		Badarian §	Halaf	XV–XXV, Samarra-Halaf		II	IA upper		(IA §?)
Neolithic		Tasian, Fayum, Merimde	Pre-Halaf	XXVI, Pre-Halaf		I‡	IA lower		
	≥5500		(Natufian)						

* Some archaeologists number the strata in the order in which their work uncovers them; others, in the order in which the strata were laid down.
† Another interpretation has Anau I begin about 4000; II, about 3000, and last from 3000 to 2000.
‡ Copper pins and awls.
§ Copper still at a minimum.

287. THE LOCUS OF MOST INTENSIVE DEVELOPMENT

A question inevitably arises: Why did the first marked urbanization in human history and its concomitants occur in the lower Tigris-Euphrates and Nile valleys, and a little later in those of the Indus and the Hwang Ho? The usual explanation is by the causal chain: large fertile valley, secure and abundant crops, growth of population, and hence both concentration and diversification of the society. This explanation is true enough so far as it goes, but is incomplete. There evidently are other factors, else the Ganges would have developed a citi-fied civilization along with the Indus, instead of nearly two thousand years later. And the lower Colorado almost exactly parallels the Nile in valley, flood, silt, and climate; but the historical Cocopa, Yuma, and Mohave tribes, though they regularly farmed the overflow bottoms, never multiplied, urbanized, or out-grew their egalitarian primitive democracy. It is evident in principle that no mere environmental factor, no populational factor alone, nor a combination of the two, will suffice to explain a cultural situation effectively. There is bound to be a cultural factor also, interplaying with the others: namely, the condition of local culture at the time when the situation arises. Problems of culture history cannot be solved by assuming culture to be a vacuum. For instance, no kind of environment or population density would have sufficed by itself to induce Mousterian man as we know him suddenly to become a farmer, let alone to build cities. An adequate explanation of the cultural picture in a given region must normally take into account first of all the pre-existing culture; second, the natural limitations and possibilities; third, the factor of size and density of the population; and fourth, its psychological attitudes toward its society and culture.

Now the seasonally flooded marshy ranges of Lower Egypt and Mesopo-tamia afforded a monotonous and highly specialized habitat that would pre-sumably have been difficult for agriculture to originate in. But once a farming society had developed habits of active co-operation, and could construct com-munal dikes and canals for water regulation beyond the powers of households working independently, these same seasonally inundated tracts would yield double or treble, and harvests would be assured. With this increased food, the population would grow, if there were no specific factors to hold it down, until settlements became towns and were ready to become the first cities. Also, some of the surplus food would almost certainly sooner or later go into new and dif-ferent wealth—either by trade, or as "pay" to craftsmen who could now afford to manufacture full-time.

Then too, the very narrowness of environment in these plains, which are so potentially fertile in cereal yield but contain no wood or stone or metal, would result, once they were inhabited by a prospering population, in a need's being felt for dependably organized commerce to secure the lacking raw materials. This need could presumably be met rather easily, because willingness and ability to organize had been just what made settlement in the marshes successful in the first place. Moreover, if the incipient towns and their rural environs were to prosper and grow, further extension of the habits of accepting social diversification and organization was called for. Thus it was that Sumer and the Egyptian Delta were environments which first kept life limited, difficult, and poor for peoples still addicted to freedom and to self-sufficiency in their economies, but later yielded bounteously to larger, well-co-ordinated social units equipped with a culture that made them able to undertake larger tasks. So these two areas became the first focal points for higher civilization. At 6000 B.C., perhaps at 5000, Sumer and the Delta seem to have been sparsely inhabited and backward— perhaps settled only at their edges. Around 4000, they had drawn culturally abreast of other regions. In 3000, they held the most civilized societies in the world.

Egypt and lower Mesopotamia form the ends of a long U or loop of almost continuously arable land that has come to be known as the Fertile Crescent. This twisting loop was the hearth of Near Eastern civilization. Until at least 1400 or 1200 B.C., the then most advanced human cultures were situated within it; some might say until 800 or 600. The comprised regions are: Upper Egypt, the Delta, Suez or Sinai (the one wholly arid tract), Palestine, Syria, northern Mesopotamia (Assyria), middle Mesopotamia (Babylonia), and southern Mesopotamia or Sumer. Inside the great bend lie the deserts and steppes of Arabia. On the outer side, Cilicia is contiguous to Syria; then there follow, in clockwise turn, the interior highland of Asia Minor (home of the Hittites), Armenia, Caucasia, northern and southern Iran (ancient Media and Persia), and Elam, with its capital Susa, only a little beyond Sumer.

Within the Crescent, Egypt is much the most cut-off and self-contained. It is in Africa; is separated from the rest of the fertile ribbon by Sinai; in fact is wholly surrounded by desert country. But the hither Asiatic lands, in the Crescent and adjoining it, all lie open and have interinfluenced one another. Hence throughout prehistory there have been a series of provincial variants of a generic underlying southwestern-Asiatic culture, of which the leading exponent at one time was Sumer, then Babylon, then Assyria, but which was never wholly uniform. Egypt, however, stood isolated more or less abreast of Asia, sometimes influenced by it and sometimes not, but self-sufficient. Its culture was narrower and more persistent. It set earlier and modified less. The initial master pattern of their culture evidently seemed a happy one to the Egyptians; they clung to it, and by their geographical separateness they were long enabled to maintain it.

The principal developments of culture during the Bronze Age—in the wide sense of that term—will now be outlined: first for the Near Eastern Asiatic lands, next for Egypt, then for the intercommunicating outliers of Europe, and finally for the bulk of that continent.

288. THE SUMERIANS

Sumer is the Biblical Shinar. The Sumerians are a people whose language we know from decipherment but cannot relate with positiveness to any other. It was the speech in which cuneiform writing was incipiently worked out at the end of the Uruk period and developed during Jemdet Nasr. The writing was later applied to the Semitic speech of the Akkadians, Babylonians, and Assyrians. The Akkadians were Semites who had early infiltrated into northern Sumer. The Babylonians were Semites of Amorite affiliation who definitely established Mesopotamian overlordship at Babylon about the time the Sumerian language was on the way to dying out. The Assyrians were an early and enduring Semitic outpost of Sumerian culture in northern Mesopotamia; they finally came into brief historical greatness during the Iron Age. There is little indication of systematic antagonism between the Sumerian and Semitic elements in the Mesopotamian populations. The Sumerians were looked upon as the founders of a great cultural heritage that the Semites were glad to live by. Other peoples, unrelated to both in their origin, took up cuneiform writing: the near-by Elamites, for instance; then the Hittites of Asia Minor; the people of Ugarit on the Syrian coast, who devised an alphabet of letters of wedge-shaped strokes on clay (§ 207); nearly a thousand years later still, the historical Persians under Cyrus and Darius. In fact, one might appropriately speak of a "cuneiform civilization": because with the writing there went a consistent ideology whose base was also Sumerian. The relation was in many ways like the combined employment of the Roman alphabet, adhesion to Roman Christianity, and use of Latin as ritual language by the ethnically diverse nations of mediaeval western and central Europe.

Sumer was a land of city-states: Ur, Nippur, Lagash, Erech, Eridu, and others. These flourished side by side, each in its little territory—"little" because the whole of Sumer covered only fifteen thousand square miles. Often they quarreled over boundaries; sometimes they fought for hegemony, like Greek cities; only rarely and briefly did one succeed in establishing empire over "the world"—the whole of Mesopotamia and its surroundings. These cities are also describable as "temple-states." Much of their land belonged really to the gods whose temples stood in the town, and was rented, as we might say, to the cultivators; the ruler was representative of the chief city god; the temples held great endowments, engaged in business, and lent barley, copper, and silver at interest. Industry and trade thus stood in honor. Writing may have been devised for property-marking and account-keeping, and was early and widely used to record commercial transactions and contracts. In time, an unwritten transfer of property even became a felony. With all this business interest of the culture, an exact system of property law, as well as exact measures and valuations, developed early. Hammurabi's famous Babylonian code of the eighteenth century is the earliest written system of laws preserved anywhere.

Along with this measuring and defining of property rights and duties, there went an interest in measuring and weighing produce and possessions. The Sumerian-Babylonian was the first complete system of weights and measures, was widely adopted elsewhere, and is the ultimate source of most of the 12's and 60's and multiples thereof that remain in our hours, minutes, ounces, degrees, and so on, as we have seen (§ 191). In time this scheme was even wholly inter-related internally, like the metric system. That is, units of length, area, volume, and weight were defined in terms of one another. All this resulted of course from habits of calculation; but it also facilitated arithmetical operations. The method of working sexagesimally was in many cases more convenient than a decimal one, especially with fractions; multiplying by fractional reciprocals of numbers provided a convenient way of dividing. The late Babylonian developments out of the Sumerian beginnings, of place-value numeration and zero indication, have already been discussed (§ 189).

It was in astronomy that the Mesopotamians succeeded best in applying their mathematics to scientific problems. They were the first to identify the planets and plot their wanderings, to set up the zodiac, and to make predictions of potential eclipses (§ 196). It was the changeable aspects of the heavens that particularly challenged them, whereas the Egyptians sought the fixed repetitions. Perhaps that was why the Sumerians and their successors continued to put up with the irregularities of a lunar calendar, while the Egyptians devised an unchanging solar one. The interest in eclipses began in seeing them as portents that might be avoided—analogously to the omens in liver divination (§ 192). In the end, genuinely scientific results were achieved, on which it is now clear that Greek astronomy built heavily. Among these advances, the heliocentric theory and recognition of the precession of the equinoxes remain in doubt as between being Mesopotamian or Greek discoveries. Obviously such achievements as these were not made until the full historical period, long after the Bronze Age; but their foundations were laid by Sumerians of the third millennium B.C.

The Sumerians drained their land out of marsh mud; and mud and clay remained basic in their culture. Their writing became cuneiform, "wedge-shaped," because it was impressed on this clay, and it continued to be largely inscribed on it instead of papyrus, skin, or stone. Architecture, after it advanced beyond walls of packed earth, operated with sun-dried bricks—first handmade, then form-made; for several Sumerian Early Dynastic centuries, these were for some reason planoconvex in profile.[10] Kiln-fired bricks, and toward the end figure-glazed ones, were rather little used, because of scarcity and cost of fuel. In keeping with its softish material, Mesopotamian architecture went in for mas-

[10] Planoconvex unfired bricks were fashionable on the coast of northern Peru in the centuries preceding A.D. 1500. This is an indubitable convergence.

sive walls and buttresses and giant platform substructures of temples—zig-gurats—almost rivaling Egyptian pyramids in size; spires, columns, lintels were scarcely attempted. However, the true arch (§ 195) is probably a Sumerian and certainly a Mesopotamian invention: it occurs at Tepe Gawra in the eighth stratum from the top, which is of Jemdet Nasr Predynastic period.

The civilization founded by the Sumerians was remarkably practical in its ethos and little given to mysticism or aspirations for immortality. Cult of the dead was played down in distinction from Egypt; nor does there seem to have been anything corresponding to systematized ancestor worship. Retainer burial on a large scale was still practiced at the beginning of the Dynastic period, but evidently soon passed out of usage. Eunuchism originated here apparently as a ritual sacrifice, later applied also to harem-keepers.

Early Mesopotamian metallurgy was the most advanced of its day any-where in the world. The Royal Tombs of Ur show a wealth of metals and alloys, control of a variety of processes, and great aesthetic skill: there was nothing equal to it in contemporary Egypt or elsewhere. The first wool was probably spun and woven into garments in or near Sumer. The wooden disk-wheel cart, the first vehicle drawn by animals, the potter's wheel, stamp and subsequent cylinder seals, are all Predynastic Mesopotamian.

289. COMPOSITENESS OF NEAR EASTERN CULTURE: ENTRY OF INDO-EUROPEANS AND SEMITES

We have seen that Syria, northern Mesopotamia, Iran, and even the southern fringe of Turkestan were all agriculturally Neolithic, and here and there were passing into a phase of copper use, in the fifth millennium B.C., when Sumer was still uninhabited. In the fourth millennium, they were more or less abreast; only with the last Predynastic, about 3200 B.C., did Sumer emerge into leadership. Gawra, in the subsequent Assyria, had then been settled perhaps two thousand years. To the east of Sumer, Susa, main town of the people of Elam—another separate people whose speech affiliations are unknown—has an occupation record going back as far as anything in Sumer. For a long time Susa loomed unduly large in our understanding of Hither Asian prehistory because the lowest archaeological levels had not yet been attacked in Sumer itself. Equally im-portant is Anau. First estimates of the antiquity of both Anau and Susa were exaggerated: there were not sufficient comparative data yet available. The esti-mates ran up to 8000 and 18,000 B.C., respectively; the true beginnings of both are almost certainly post-5000.

On the Iranian plateau Sialk and other sites are now known to contain about as long a record back into the Neolithic as any Near Eastern area. But we do not know the affinities of the people who left these upland sites. We do not know what language they spoke. It was most likely something other than Indo-European, to which the Iranian dialects of the historical period belong. This is inferable from the fact that the resemblances of Iranian speech to the vocabularies of other Indo-European groups—above all Indic Aryans, but also Slavs, Greeks, and others—show greater influencing by nonurban, nonliterate, tribal habits and associations than by Mesopotamian ones. Of the several Indo-European populations of Hither Asia that came into the orbit of Sumerian-Babylonian civilization, none can be identified with certainty before 2000 B.C., and some not until 1000. To the east, the Vedic Aryans appear in northwestern India at a time guessed as around 1500-1200; to the west, the Greeks are estimated to have begun to enter their historical seats from perhaps 1800 on. In the Near East itself, the Hittites established themselves in central Asia Minor soon after 2000, and achieved a military empire that competed with Egypt and Assyria until about 1200. They used cuneiform characters for the syllabic writing of their Indo-European language—or more strictly it is "Indo-Hittite," so named to indicate that Indo-European and Hittite are common daughters of a still older mother speech. Two thousand years after the fall of the Hittites, their double-headed-eagle symbol derived from the winged-falcon disk was conveyed to European heraldry via Crusaders in Asia Minor (§ 190). The decipherment of their writing, identification of their language, and unraveling of their history constitute one of the recent romances of archaeology.

Soon after 1500 the Harri established themselves for a few brief centuries in Mitanni on the upper Euphrates between the Hittites and the Assyrians. They also took over cuneiform script (and with it the Akkad-Babylonian language for international communications); but the names of their gods and rulers are more than Indo-European; they are specifically Indo-Iranian: Mitra, Varuna, Indra, are among their deities. Somewhat earlier, when Hammurabi's Semitic empire dissolved, a people called Kassites or Kossaeans came down presumably from the eastern plateau and took over at Babylon. They furnished it several centuries of foreign kings. This was a military-political change, without perceptible influence on the now long-mature Mesopotamian culture. It has been thought that it was under the Kassite rulers that the horse began to become familiar in Mesopotamia. But presumably this desirable introduction would not have been very long deferred, even without conquest by horse-breeders.

The historical Iranian nationalities—Persians, Medes, Parthians, Areians (the original "Aryans"), Bactrians, and such—do not come into our ken identifiably until quite late. In the seventh century B.C. the Medes united with the rebelling Babylonians to crush the terroristic Assyrian Empire at Nineveh. Along with the other Iranians, they were probably illiterate or nearly so until just before this overturn. Now however they seized empire. The fellow-Iranian Persians, who soon replaced the Medes, took into their empire all the Near East, even including Egypt. This made them the inheritors of Mesopotamian civilization; and at the same time their conquest further internationalized this civilization. Concurrently the Iranians contributed a national faith—Zoroastrianism, Magism, Mazdaism, fire worship, the Avestan religion, are some of its names.

This religion has had a life of nearly three thousand years, and still survives among a shrunken number of followers, especially in India among emigrant Parsis—that is, "Persians." Its basic dualistic ideas of good and evil, truth and lie, paradise and hell, have influenced Christianity and other religions. After a brief interlude of flooding by Greek civilization after Alexander the Great, Iranian national development resumed under native Parthian and Sassanian dynasties. When the Arabs and later the Turks broke into the old civilized domains of southwestern Asia, they absorbed heavily from this long-established culture of Iran. Much of Arab and Turkish culture, in fact general Mohammedan civilization, is Persian-derived, and therefore goes back ultimately to Sumerian-Mesopotamian origins.

Other Indo-Europeans who pushed into or near the Fertile Crescent in the centuries before and after 1000 B.C. included the Armenians, who settled where they have lived since; the Phrygians, who entered Asia Minor from the Balkans; and the Iranian Kardouchoi, ancestors of the modern Kurds. These were all hill peoples somewhat marginal to the cultural center; their movements failed to penetrate the center as profoundly as did Semitic inflows. Nor was the Indo-Europeanization of the occupied territories as permanent as the Semitization. Asia Minor and Turkestan, now prevailingly Turkish, are the main areas that have been de-Indo-Europeanized in speech during the historical period (§ 96).

The Semitic invasions seem to have proceeded largely from the great motherland of that stock, Arabia, from whose deserts and half-deserts peoples have repeatedly swarmed out. Some of the movements were outright conquests, others half-forceful penetrations, still others infiltrations. Several great waves can be distinguished. By 2600 B.C. there was a drift which brought the Akkadians, the people of the emperors Sargon and Naram-sin, into the Mesopotamian valley north of Sumer, into the part that was later to become Babylonia. Perhaps the Assyrians moved about the same time into their future home up the Tigris, the Canaanites and the Phoenicians into the Syrian region. After 2000, the Amorites flowed north: also into Akkad, where Babylon was now founded and so named and where their famous lawgiver Hammurabi ruled; and elsewhere into Mesopotamia and into Syria. Around 1400 and after, the Aramaeans gradually occupied the Syrian district, with Damascus, "Aram," as their center; and the Hebrews began to dispossess the Canaanites. From about 800 B.C. on another seep brought the Chaldaeans into Babylonia and into old Sumer—whence the Biblical anachronism of "Ur of the Chaldees." They were ultimately to erect one more imposing Semitic realm, the briefly resurrected Neo-Babylonia of Nebuchadnezzar. Then, for more than a thousand years, Arabia lay contained within itself, dammed perhaps by the Persian, Macedonian, Parthian, and Roman empires, until, in the seventh century after Christ, Mohammedanism led forth its peoples. A much earlier movement, at an unknown time, had brought the forefathers of the Abyssinians into Africa, probably across the mouth of the Red Sea.

In the southwestern end of Asia, then, from the Dardanelles to Persia and from the Caucasus to the Arabian Desert, beginning five thousand years ago and probably more, a motley of nations was thrown together—Semites, various kinds of Indo-Europeans, Sumerians, Elamites, and other, unclassified peoples. Their contacts enabled each to acquire many of the new devices developed by the others, to combine these with their own attainments, and thus to be a source of culture stimulation over again for the others.

290. PHOENICIANS, ARAMAEANS, HEBREWS

The northwestern Semites, fronting the Mediterranean, came into essential independence and unusual prosperity in the period of transition from the Bronze to the Iron Age, say 1200-800 B.C., when the great political powers of previous centuries—Babylon, the Hittites, Egypt—had entered transient or permanent stages of internal decay and external weakness.

Thus, the Phoenicians, or some Semitic people closely related to and geographically near them, twice toward the end of the Bronze Age or early in the Iron Age invented the alphabet: at Ugarit, and again the form called Phoenician (§ 206). In the centuries following, they established a commercial and maritime supremacy over the shores of the Mediterranean that led to the founding of Carthage, direct trade as far as Spain and indirect trade to Britain, and transmission of the alphabet to the Greeks.

Another trading people, although an inland one, were the Aramaeans, Semites of the same wave as the Hebrews but established north of Palestine in Syria, with Damascus as their center. Never more than a secondary political power, they penetrated other countries peacefully, brought in their own versions of measures and weights, their writing, and even their language. Assyria had become half Aramaic-speaking by the time of its fall, and the everyday language of Palestine in the days of Jesus and for some centuries before was Aramaic. Aramaean script, a rounded or cursive, open-looped form of the Phoenician alphabet, gradually replaced cuneiform writing, first for business and then for official purposes, throughout western Asia and beyond. In the fourteenth century, the Syrian and Palestinian city rulers were still writing their reports and dispatches to the Egyptian overlord in cuneiform, which a corps of clerks in the Foreign Office or Dependencies Department at Tell el-Amarna transcribed into hieroglyphic or hieratic. But in the fourth century, Persian officials were employing Aramaean for official communications. As the cuneiform more and more died out—it lingered in Babylonia until almost the Christian era—derivatives of Aramaean became the alphabets of Persia; of India; of the Jews; of the Arabs; of the Nestorian Christians; and of the ancient Turks, the Mongols, and the Manchus. Practically all Asia, so far as it writes alphabetically, thus derives its letters from an Aramaean source (§ 218).

Equally profound was the influence of the neighboring Hebrews in another phase of civilization. At the time they first entered Palestine and recorded history, about 1400-1200 B.C., as a group of loosely allied tribes, the Hebrews worshiped their national god Yahweh or Jahveh.[11] They believed that there were many gods besides him, but that they were his people and he their god. A growing national consciousness was emphasized by some successful local wars and the rule of the two prosperous Jewish kings David and Solomon in the tenth century. It was this consciousness, perhaps, which led their prophets more and more to emphasize the special relation between Yahweh and themselves—to the exclusion of worship of other deities that was constantly creeping in from their Canaanite, Phoenician, Aramaean, and Egyptian neighbors. Thus the Hebrews grew into the stage of monolatry, or worship limited to one god. As however they split into two Hebrew kingdoms—Judah and Israel—as Egypt revived, and Assyria and Babylonia first threatened and then engulfed them, and as their national impotence became more and more evident, the Hebrews confided less in their own strength, as they had done in the brief days of their little glory, and trusted increasingly in their god as their salvation. National hopes fell and divine ones rose, until the Hebrew people passed from thinking of the Lord as all-powerful to thinking of him as one and sole: monotheism had evolved out of monolatry, as this had grown out of a special tribal cult. Historically the monotheistic idea was not new. Ikhnaton of close-by Egypt had proclaimed it more than half a thousand years before the Hebrew prophets. The concept may actually have been acquired across the centuries; but it certainly drew sustenance of its own on Hebrew soil and first became established there as a cardinal, enduring element of a national civilization, participated in fervently by a whole population. Whereas Ikhnaton's monotheism was the slogan of an intelligentsia rallied around a king quarreling with his established priesthood, among the Hebrews monotheism became the faith of the mass of a nation supporting its religious leaders. Thus the Hebrews adhered to monotheism with an ever increasing insistence; then the concept was taken over by Christianity and Islam—two of the three great international religions; Buddhism, the third, being essentially atheistic, or at least agnostic. Here, then, is another tremendously spread cultural element of deep significance that originated as a local western-Asiatic variant of Semitic origin.

291. EGYPT, NEOLITHIC AND PREDYNASTIC

The rainless climate of Upper Egypt preserves prehistoric remains so startlingly well that it inevitably emphasizes their prevalence; from which an easy if not quite logical slide carries one over from the impression of Egypt as the land

---

[11] "Yahweh" is phonetic (and English) orthography; "Jahveh," Latin spelling of the same pronunciation. "Jehovah" is the same word with a late misjudged reconstruction of vowels, according to modern Semitists.

par excellence of antiquities to that of the greatest antiquity. There is nothing in the cold facts to sustain such a view. Advanced culture, whether farming, metal-working, or literate, is at least as old in Mesopotamia; it may be equally old in Syria and Iran. What sets off Egypt to a certain degree from the other old Near Eastern countries is its geographical separateness. This fact, coupled with a high degree of internal conformity of environment, caused Egyptian civilization, once it began to set, to crystallize rapidly and definitely, and then to show unusual inclination to maintain its original patterns and values for twenty-five hundred years.

This implies that the Egyptians achieved certain things on their own and early. Such are: their solar calendar; the forms of their art, including both the hieroglyphic characters and animal-headed deities; political unity of the whole land; deification of the ruler; preoccupation with death, attempts to achieve an almost bodily afterlife, and the Osiris myth of "dying-god" or rather "revivified-god" type. These Egyptian patterns came out so crisp and clear and sharp that they were adhered to, or restored after each adversity, with quite extraordinary success and uniformity of level. But the satisfaction felt in this same adherence probably made the Egyptians reluctant to modify their ways by accepting in-novations from outside: see the list below of such delayed diffusions. In the main, however, Egypt and Mesopotamia marched substantially abreast along the road of civilization; and the Near East as a whole was quickened by much the same pulsations of tempo throughout.

We have seen that the Neolithic culture of Egypt at Tasa, Fayum, and Merimde (§ 283) was similar to that elsewhere in the Near East and to that of Europe a couple of thousand years later. These sites are "pure Neolithic," that is, without metal. A site at Badari has a very few pieces of copper: a borer or an awl and two beads have been found. On this slim showing—which may repre-sent a mere accident of what was lost here or preserved there—the Badarian culture is technically Chalcolithic; though the rest of its inventory does not differentiate it significantly from the Tasian.

Next comes a culture generally called "Predynastic," because when one of its phases was first discovered no other culture was yet known in Egypt that preceded the "historical" dynasties of named Pharaohs. Etymologically, the Tasian and the Badarian are also "Predynastic"; but usage tends to apply the term to three successive cultures, Amratian, Gerzean, and Semainian, which im-mediately preceded the first king of the first dynasty ruling over all Egypt. The time of these three Egyptian Predynastic phases was about 4000 to 3000 B.C., just about equivalent in estimated time to Mesopotamian Ubaid, Uruk, and Jemdet Nasr Predynastic.

Amratian. Considerable fishing and hunting alongside farming. Stone-disk mace heads. High ivory combs for wear. Copper, gold worked raw. Green malachite for eyelid painting; palettes for grinding. Ivory vases for ointment. Stone jars of black basalt. Phallus sheaths worn. Shiplike rafts of papyrus bundles. Pottery black-topped; or white-painted, including figures of elephant and hippopotamus; or black with white-filled incisions. Upper Egypt only.

Gerzean. Wholly new features: Cast copper; rectangular-molded mud bricks; faïence made with soda from the desert west of the Delta; blue lapis lazuli imported from Asia. Pear-shaped stone mace heads. Low ivory combs for use. Palettes mostly animal-shaped. Perfect stone jars, of many colors. Ships with cabins, rows of oars, and emblem standards. Pottery: many-handled or wavy-lined; or red-painted, including figures of birds, antelopes, boats, men in profile, women full-faced. Middle as well as upper Egypt.

The Amratian is clearly a further development of the preceding Tasian and Badarian; and it is still Chalcolithic. It is a wholly Egyptian culture, and probably a localized Egyptian one. The Gerzean extends farther downstream, and may have covered the Delta also: its remains would have been buried if they once existed there. Its new features all look like products of the Delta or imports into it from Asia. Actual bronze is lacking—as it was until much later—because Egypt was out of reach of tin; but the presence of genuine metallurgical processes puts the Gerzean into the full Bronze Age stage.

Semainian. This looks like a carrying-on and a modification of Gerzean, but possibly contemporary with the development of the earliest Dynastic civilization. The Semainian phase seems less a stage between Gerzean and Dynastic than a side branch, or perhaps a provincial or a class survival of Predynastic culture into beginning Dynastic times.

The formulation of the Egyptian solar calendar on the formula: $12 \times 30 = 360 + 5 = 365$ (§ 155, 198), formerly attributed to 4241 B.C. and acclaimed as "the first date in human history," presumably occurred much later. Such a date is more than a thousand years before political unity, royalty, writing, or stonemasonry; it would probably fall into the Badarian period of incipient stone-copper transition; which makes 4241 just too early to be convincingly possible for such a precision invention.

292. DYNASTIC EGYPT

Around 3000 B.C.—some would say 3100, and until recently the estimate was 3300 or 3400, and before that about 5500—at any rate about contemporaneously with the beginning of authentic king lists in Sumer, Egypt was united by a ruler who has come down to us as Menes in the Greek form of his name, which is variously reconstructed as Mena, Meni, Men, in the Hamitic Egyptian. Some of the tombs of his family, and of the next line on the throne—the Proto-dynasties, down to about 2700 B.C.—have been excavated. The accompanying art is not yet quite classic Egyptian; but writing suddenly appears without known formative antecedents. It is not very frequent at first, but it is fully formed, legible hieroglyphic. There must have been a very rapid evolution of culture in Egypt between the terminal Gerzean-Semainian and Dynasty III: a white heat of experiment, overturn, and innovation, productive of patterns so satisfactory that they could last with minimal change for over two thousand years. For instance, only a century and a half after cut or ashlar masonry was first laid, the giant pyramids were being raised in Dynasty IV to heights of nearly five hundred feet, of blocks averaging two and a half tons.

Dynasty III is already "fully Egyptian"; and from it through Dynasty VI is the period of the Old Kingdom, or Pyramid Age: a half-millennium of essentially self-contained prosperity, at least for the uppermost social levels. A half-century or so of confusion and political breakdown followed, from which the Middle Kingdom emerged, around 2130 B.C., to flourish once more under Dynasties XI and especially XII until 1788. Then there was a second breakdown, leading to a conquest by a foreign, barbarous, chariot-driving people, the Hyksos or "Shepherd Kings."

With the expulsion of these foreigners (1580 B.C.) comes a third period of splendor, the New Empire, this time accompanied by military expansion up the Nile into Nubia and through Palestine and Syria, culminating in the fifteenth century under the Thutmoses and Amenhoteps of Dynasty XVIII. This line ended in the monotheistic reformer Ikhnaton (Akhen-aten) and the boy king Tutankhamen, whose tomb, left unrifled, evidences the luxury, art, and wealth with which even a weak monarch was sent on his way to immortality. Dynasty XIX accomplished somewhat less, though it claimed as much, especially under the long-lived *grand monarque* Ramses II. But soon after 1200 B.C. storms of invasion from outside burst, and though the first was repelled, Libyan and Nubian lines of rulers came in time to ascend the throne of the Pharaohs—like Mongols and Manchus in China. This was the period of Egyptian upset that gave the little Hebrew kingdom its respite and its brief chance at nationalistic success. After a transient seventh-century conquest by Assyria, Egypt experienced one more flourishing renascence (663-525) of its old patterns under native rulers. But it was a somewhat fictitious revival, because the kingdom was now supported in its competition with Asiatic great powers largely by foreign mercenaries and a made-to-order navy. Since its conquest by the Persians in 525 B.C., Egypt has never had native rulers more than momentarily. Alexander the Great brought in Greek civilization, and Augustus, Roman rule; but it was Christianity rather than these rival cultures which finally extinguished the slow-dying Egyptian civilization.

Politically, Egypt differed from Mesopotamia in its satisfaction with unity, which was achieved in the first dynasty and adhered to throughout as an ideal and mostly in fact. Allied was the concept of Pharaoh as a god, not merely his representative. The whole society was accordingly much more hierarchically co-ordinated than any in Asia; there was little room for separate temple-states; and there was much less opportunity for an independent mercantile middle class to develop than for a hereditary aristocracy of bureaucrats to do so. With all the manual skill of the Egyptians, their nongovernmental commerce, law, and science remained less developed than in Mesopotamia—probably because of the sociopolitical focusing and centralization. They seem a less hard-boiled people than Asiatics, and less deliberately hardhearted than the Asiatics at their extreme, as in Assyria. The Egyptians were sensuous, giving to good living, afraid of death, wish-fulfilling themselves a spiritual hereafter by embalming the body; beyond that, finding a constant satisfaction in dealing in symbolism and magic.

Their civilization was pervaded also with a sense of grace, proportion, and good taste, as well as a feeling for definiteness of form, especially in things concrete. These qualities, merging with their symbolical propensities, resulted in their extraordinary art, so consistently endowed with pleasing charm, repose, decorativeness, so competent in expressing both characteristic form and neat symbol, but so primitively lacking in sense of conformity to reality, and in action, power, or composition. No other system of real writing has remained one-tenth as pictorial as the hieroglyphic; no other religious art has ventured to depict its gods so naïvely and so consistently with animal heads and yet avoided making them monstrous—in fact left them intriguing and ornamental.

The main patterns of Egyptian culture were at once too definite, consistent, and interwoven, and also too essentially primitive in their infantility, to be able to alter much by influence or fusion with other cultures. They tended to go on, intact and giving satisfaction, until gradually displaced in toto by some other culture. There were absorptions; but they were of isolated items; and they averaged relatively late. Thus:

Mud Brick. Asia, Sialk II, Anau IA, Samarra-Halafian, Mersin layer XVI—viz., fourth period before the Dynastic; Egypt, Gerzean, second (or last?) before.

True Metallurgy. Asia, Ubaid, third period before 3000; Egypt, Gerzean, second.

Tin Bronze. Asia, fourth millennium B.C.; Egypt, around 2000.

Iron. Common in Egypt only after the seventh-century temporary Assyrian conquest. This corresponds in time to the central-European Hallstatt period. In western Asia iron first appeared six or seven centuries before then, and became common three or four centuries earlier than in Egypt.

Potter's Wheel. Asia, Ubaid, Sialk III, around 4000; Egypt, Dynasty III, 2700.

Writing. Sumer, end of Uruk, established in Jemdet Nasr; in Egypt, Dynasty I.

Vehicles. Mesopotamia, disk-wheel carts, Uruk period; spoked-wheel chariot, by 1800; Egypt, neither until Hyksos conquest, seventeenth century B.C.

Horse. Mesopotamia, 1800, sporadically perhaps much earlier; Egypt, 1600.

The true arch, coined money, heavy body armor, the zodiac, entered Egypt only through Greek or Roman influence.

Egyptian precedences are less numerous:

Donkey and Cat. African animals.

Flax. Perhaps Egyptian in origin.

Faïence Glazing. Developed in the Gerzean or second Predynastic period. *True Glass*. New Empire, middle of second millennium; the art was transported to

Phoenicia and Syria, where glass-blowing was added only shortly before the Christian era.

Bellows. First appear in pictures about 1500; but the Egyptians drew so many more pictures, or had them preserved so much oftener, that it does not follow that they made the invention.

The 365-day length of the year was adopted into the Julian calendar through Greek astronomers working for Caesar; but the equal months and supplementary days of the Egyptian calendar did not diffuse to Greeks, to Romans, or to us.

Of pure inventions that spread to the rest of the world, there seem to be only faïence and glass, and these are obviously preconditioned by the obtrusiveness in Egypt of natron or soda.

More characteristic of Egypt than utilitarian inventions are what might be called stylistic peculiarities of culture that show originality but which would not ordinarily be diffused. Such are mummification, pyramids, obelisks, the particular forms of the hieroglyphs, the style of art, the special symbols of royalty.

293. AEGEAN CIVILIZATION

On the island of Crete, almost equidistant from Asia, Africa, and Europe, there began to grow up with the introduction of metallurgy, after 3000 B.C.,[12] a civilization most of whose elements were imported, but which added to them and molded the whole of its mass with unusual originality. Three great Bronze Age periods, named the Early, Middle, and Late Minoan after the legendary Cretan King Minos, are distinguishable in the abundant remains that excavation has brought to light; each of these is divided into three subperiods designated I, II, III. At some sites, such as Knossos, the remains of successive subperiods are separated by layers of packed-down earth deposited when an old settlement was obliterated, and serving as floor for the next occupation. Underneath the Bronze Age deposits were thick strata from the Neolithic, with unpainted pottery.

With the Early Minoan, painted pottery as well as metals came in, to be followed by the potter's wheel and a system of hieroglyphic writing unrelated to the Egyptian or the cuneiform but perhaps induced in imitation. In the Middle Minoan the pottery became polychrome and palaces were built. Then, with Middle Minoan III, the palaces were rebuilt, art took a remarkable naturalistic turn in pottery and fresco painting and carving, and the hieroglyph evolved into a linear, probably syllabic, script. During Late Minoan I and II this phase of the culture developed further, culminating about 1500-1400 B.C. in Late Minoan II. Then something violent happened, the palaces were destroyed, and after a decadent attempt at revival Minoan culture passed out with the arrival of the first of the historical Greeks, at the opening of the Iron Age, about 1250 B.C.

[12] The date long accepted was 3000, but Dynasty I of Egypt was then reckoned at 3300 or 3400, so presumably the Minoan civilization of Crete actually began somewhat after 3000.

The Minoans left no chronology of their own and their writing is unread. But datable Egyptian objects found in Cretan strata of identified period, and Cretan objects characteristic of particular periods found at datable Egyptian sites as the result of trade, have made possible an indirect but positive chronology for Minoan culture. Early Minoan II, Middle II, and Late II, respectively, were contemporary with the Sixth, Twelfth, and Eighteenth Dynasties on the Nile. From 2000 B.C. on, Minoan dating is therefore approximately reliable. Industry, seafaring commerce, games, including bullfighting and tumbling, a light, practical style of architecture with sewered palaces and with magazines more prominent than temples, unwalled towns, above all a graceful, lively, realistic art, flourished particularly from Middle Minoan III to Late Minoan II. There was evidently considerable wealth and a leisure class, and the civilization gives the impression of having been, for Bronze Age times, unhierarchical, civilian, and modern in its ways.

The Minoans were a Caucasian people of Mediterranean race. Their language is unknown but, from names preserved through Greek, it appears to have been non-Indo-European. When their home power crumbled, a fragment of the Minoans perhaps took refuge in Asia and founded the five Philistine seacoast cities that for a time oppressed the tribal Hebrews and gave their name to Palestine.

A related culture appears in the ruins of the successive cities of Troy; on the small islands of the Aegean Sea; and, after 1800-1600, in mainland Greece, where, having displaced an earlier, more rural bronze culture called Helladic, it is known as Mycenaean, after the citadel and town attributed to Agamemnon. The mainland Mycenaeans, or their ruling class, seem to have been an early wave of Greeks. "Aegean" perhaps is the name least likely to confuse, for this larger circum-Aegean culture of which the Cretan Minoan was the longest and most illustrious representative. The table outlines the principal correlations.

The thirteenth century B.C. and after brought the later Greeks, iron-sworded Dorians and the like, then a rude, hardy, and at first nonmaritime people, fighting their way south and wrecking or sapping the Aegean civilization. Culture lost its bloom, life became hard, the outlook contracted. Art shriveled into crude geometric ornamentation, the forms became childishly inept; intercourse with the Orient sank to a minimum, and when trade, literacy, and foreign stimulation revived they were at first in Phoenician hands. It is not until the seventh century B.C. that true history begins in Greece, and in the main it is only to the sixth that the direct beginnings can be traced of that characteristic Hellenic philosophy, literature, and art which were fully released after the Persian wars early in the fifth century. Yet the half-thousand and more years of dark ages between Aegean and classic Greek civilization did not entail a complete interruption. The Greek often enough smote the Mycenaean or the Minoan. More often, perhaps, he settled alongside him, possibly oppressed him, but learned something from him. He choked out Aegean culture, but nourished his own

	Egypt	Crete	Greece	Asia
			Dipylon pottery	Assyrian Empire, First Phase
		Geometric ornament Iron	Geometric ornament Iron	Philistines
1250				
	Iron Dynasty XIX, 1350	LATE MINOAN III	LATE MYCENAEAN	Late Hittites Iron
		Palaces destroyed		Hebrews enter Palestine
	Amenhotep III, 1400	Horse chariot Culmination, 1500-1400	Palaces Domed tombs MIDDLE MYCENAEAN	Mitanni, 1450
	Thutmose III, 1500	LATE MINOAN II		
	Dynasty XVIII, 1580			
		LATE MINOAN I	EARLY MYCENAEAN	Troy, City VI
1600				
	Hyksos, 1675	New palaces Linear script Naturalistic art MIDDLE MINOAN III		Middle Hittites
	Dynasty XII ends, 1788	First palaces MIDDLE MINOAN II		Kassites Horse Hammurabi
		Polychrome pottery Carts	LATE HELLADIC	Babylon founded
	Dynasty XII, 2000	MIDDLE MINOAN I		Early Hittites
2000				
		EARLY MINOAN III Hieroglyphic writing Potter's wheel		Troy, City II: Bronze Sargon of Akkad
	Dynasty VI	EARLY MINOAN II	EARLY HELLADIC	
	Pyramids Dynasty IV	Painted pottery Metallurgy		
	Dynasty III	EARLY MINOAN I		Troy, City I
2700				
	Writing Dynasties I, II Semainian Pre- dynastic			Sumerian cities
	Faience Metallurgy Gerzean Predynastic	No stone structures Incised pottery NEOLITHIC	NEOLITHIC	Jemdet Nasr Cuneiform writing Uruk

RELATIONS OF AEGEAN CIVILISATION

(Read upward for sequence.)

upon it. The Homeric poems, composed in Greek during this period of retro-gression, picture a civilization still largely Aegean; and along with them much other cultural tradition must have been passed on.

At any rate, when Greek culture re-emerged, it was charged with Oriental elements and influences, but perhaps even more charged with Aegean ones. Its games, its unponderous architecture, its open city life, the free quality of its art, its political particularity, its peculiar alert tenseness and feeling for grace, had all flourished before on Greek soil. Their flavor is un-Asiatic and un-Egyptian of whatever period. We have here another instance of the tenacity of the attach-ment of cultural qualities to the soil; of the stylistic set or faculty, at once ab-sorptive and resistive, that for thousands of years, however inventions might diffuse and culture elements circulate, succeeded in keeping China something that can fairly be called Chinese, India Indian, Egypt Egyptian; in a degree it even kept Europe, so long culturally dependent on the Orient, always European.

294. BRONZE AGE EUROPE

The European Bronze Age contains many interesting regional variants, such as the safety pins already discussed (§ 284). In broad outline, however, it is remarkably uniform, except for the Minoan-Mycenaean manifestations in the extreme southeastern corner of the continent. And it is also remarkably back-ward, compared with even the more retarded portions of the focus we have so far been considering. There are no Bronze Age cities in Europe; no known political unifications; no writing; even the potter's wheel did not get adopted until about 1000 B.C., when the Bronze Age was ending in Asia. (These statements count Crete-Greece as part of the cultural Near East of the time, not part of Europe.) In short, all the great revolutionary advances of the focal area, its social and intellectual innovations and overturns, were just lacking west of the Dardanelles.

Bronze did infiltrate, after an expectable lag. And no doubt many another item gradually penetrated. But these were detached bits, none of them of basic importance in itself, and not even adding up to a perceptibly significant total change. In the main, Bronze Age Europe went on much like Neolithic Europe: with a peasantlike culture. So far as there were communal undertakings, large structures, chiefs giving orders to sizable numbers, these were characteristic rather of the Megalithic centuries at the end of the Neolithic, or overlapping into the raw-copper transition period. Quite probably these Megalithic chiefs or their descendants got most of the hoards and most of the weapons when bronze did come in, and therewith were better able to perpetuate themselves. There must also have grown up a class of bronze-founding smiths, perhaps intertribally itinerant; and in time also, in appropriate regions, groups who knew how to mine ore. But for the rest, seemingly: villages of farmers.

It was not until the Iron Age that favored parts of Europe began to have some of the cultural insignia, such as cities and writing, which in the Near East developed along with bronze or before it.

The creep of bronze into Europe was perhaps first up the Danube; second and overlapping, along the Mediterranean. Thus, bronze reached Hungary around 1900; Czechoslovakia and central Germany, but also Italy, 1800; the Rhine, France, and Britain, 1700; the Baltic shores and Scandinavia, 1500. Some prehistorians would alter certain of these dates by a century or so earlier or later; but they would essentially agree on the sequence of regions.

295. IRON

Broadly speaking, iron came into use, in the Near Eastern region of its discovery, a full two thousand years or more later than bronze—to be exact, let us say two thousand years after the smelting, casting, and alloying of copper. It was evidently worked locally and on a small scale by 1400 B.C.; somewhat more widely and frequently by 1200; had got into the hands of backward peoples such as Hebrews and Greeks in some quantities by 1000; but did not begin to be standard fighting equipment for whole armies till about 800.

The circumstances of the discovery of ironmaking can only be guessed at, but there are a great many indications pointing to the area of discovery. This was south or southeast of the Black Sea, where Anatolia (Asia Minor) and the Caucasus abut; the region of Armenia, in short. Here the historical Greeks knew of the tribe of Chalybes or ironworkers. Other nationalities in the region traditionally associated with iron were the Tibareni and the Moschi. The area was under the later Hittite Empire, from which the Pharaohs solicited and sometimes received gifts of iron. From the same area, some centuries later, the Assyrians appear to have got their iron. The earliest stock of iron discovered consists of 176 tons of bars at Khorsabad in the time, 722-705, of the Assyrian ruler Sargon II, who was keeping it no doubt for his war arsenal. Incidentally, the Assyrian iron-weaponed armies of about the same time seem to have been the first to include cavalry, as distinct from charioteers.

The first iron used by men was of meteoric origin. Such iron comes ready-made in metallic form, contains from 5 per cent to 25 per cent of nickel, hence rusts with difficulty, and is tough but somewhat malleable. Sporadic as is its occurrence and small as are the quantities, it has been used again and again, even by primitives without any tradition of working in metals; compare the Eskimo case in § 157. Most of the scattered instances of the finding of iron in pre-Iron Age strata are presumably to be explained in this way. Thus some iron beads with gold ones from the Predynastic Gerzean of Egypt contain 7.5 per cent of nickel, and are almost certainly bits of meteorite hammered out flat and folded. Similarly as regards a blade from the early dynastic Royal Tombs of Ur, which is nearly 11 per cent nickel. The rarity of such meteoric metal, possibly also occasional knowledge that it had fallen from the sky, caused it to be treasured and used decoratively, as for finger rings, inlay on bronze, or attachment to gold. Finds of this sort have been made in Switzerland, Germany, Greece, the Caucasus, and in Eighteenth Dynasty as well as Predynastic Egypt. The practice very likely continued into the first stage of use of terrestrial iron, especially when bits of this were first exported as rarities.

The lateness of widespread iron in human history is only partly explained by its high melting point, for fully molten iron is necessary only for casting. This casting process was superlate; it remained unknown to the Near Eastern, Mediterranean, and European peoples until nearly the end of the Middle Ages. The earliest cast iron known was made in North China by A.D. 618. The original or Iron Age method of securing the metal was the same as that used by recent African Negroes; it dispensed with liquefying and flowing the product. Many iron ores can be reduced on a small scale by bedding small chunks in plenty of charcoal and firing with a bellows draft. The charcoal takes up the oxygen from the ore and leaves the iron as a pasty, spongelike mass, known as "bloom." Pieces of slag lie mixed in this, but can be gradually eliminated by reheating and beating out; this also welds the metal into an ingot or solid lump. This is "wrought iron," such as the horseshoer still hammers out on an anvil. It is tough and will do for plowshares, farm tools, kettles, and such, but is too soft for swords. These, to be effective, must contain enough carbon to make steel, but less than the proportion of carbon that makes cast steel crystalline and brittle. In modern technique, liquid iron is converted into steel by air blasts forced through it until enough carbon has been taken out. This was beyond the ancients' capacity, and they had to depend for their steel on iron containing carbon or manganese as impurities in the ore or due to the process of reduction. It was evidently some centuries before knowledge of steel was added to that of wrought-iron working. The tempering by plunging in liquid is only a final touch in steelmaking.

It is evident that ancient iron extraction and working involved definite techniques, but no intrinsically difficult ones. They were almost certainly less finicky than fine bronze-casting. Since iron ore is enormously more abundant than copper and infinitely more so than tin ore, it is a fair question why the Iron Age is so much the later. There are several reasons and considerations.

Most important is the thorough difference in technological processes. This prevented transfer from copper-bronze technique to iron technique. Application of a bronze-founder's skill to iron ore would only lead to the conclusion that the latter contained nothing profitable. The more the art of the bronzesmith developed, the farther was he pointed away from likelihood of discovering metallic iron. For one thing, the worker in bronze profited by methods of precision, but the blacksmith needed strength: his material was much belabored, as Homer says. The product of the one was aristocratic and gleaming; that of the other, when it finally did come, was black, rough, and utilitarian—it would turn soil or boil a mess. So far as we can see, the one transfer actually made was that of the bellows (§ 293), without which the blacksmith would presumably never have accomplished anything. On the other hand, neither would copper ore reduce or bronze cast without application of draft: the first bellows simply relieved the bronze-founder's assistants from blowing out of their own lungs.

A second consideration is the limitation of use due to the softness of pre-steel iron; and a third, the prestige associations bronze had acquired: of treasure, of high rank, of sacred ritual. It would be going too far to believe that the powerful and the wealthy combined with the skilled craftsmen in a conspiracy to cheat the proletariat of their day out of its just due of the cheap convenience and laborsaver that iron would be. But it is in human nature that they would not be overly concerned with discovering or perfecting a process that would accomplish this.

Finally, we must remember that the Bronze Age and the Iron Age are not universals, are not stages through which all mankind must pass, as was formerly assumed, but that they are historical events, and that therefore each is a unique manifestation, even though a widespread and important one. Consequently an element of accident enters the situation. Bronze, happening to be invented first, also became established first and diffused first, and thereby tended to pre-empt or block the invention of iron reduction [13] even by such peoples as became cognizant of metal. That there are no compulsive stages in this matter, no ultimate inevitability of the succession stone-copper-bronze-iron, is a big negative. Like any sweeping denial, it would be hard to prove absolutely; but its probability is indicated by the succession of the dates at which geographically successive peoples took up these metal arts. This succession points to the probability that both the basic inventions of bronze and iron working were made once only, at least in the Eastern Hemisphere, and then spread. Another argument is that certain areas, such as Negro Africa and Japan (§ 302, 312), apparently skipped the bronze "stage" altogether, passing from stone directly to iron.

The one case where the indications favor the independent invention of metallurgy is aboriginal America; and here iron had failed to be discovered by 1492. There was an area in the eastern United States in which copper—and occasionally bits of gold and meteoric iron—were worked by Stone Age methods. There was a larger Cordilleran area stretching from Mexico to northwestern Argentina in which a variety of true metallurgical technologies were applied chiefly to copper, gold, and silver. And within this area there was a smaller Andean region where true bronze was made with Bolivian tin during the centuries immediately preceding the conquest by the Spaniards. The distinction between this and the main part of the Cordilleran area was in the respective presence and absence of tin as a natural resource: otherwise the metal-

[13] Much as established canals and highways in England and France tended to block the development of steamboats, but their absence in the United States egged the invention on (§ 185).

lurgical skills were equal. This difference within South America was parallel to that between contemporary early Sumer and early Egypt, with the latter being tinless. It was not like that between native-copper "chalcolithic" technique and true metallurgical smelting and casting. It was the Indians of the eastern United States, and of the West Indies in regard to gold, that were "chalcolithic" in their methods; and it is not certain whether these methods of theirs were a hangover relict from what was an earlier phase elsewhere, or a reflection—a makeshift imitation—of the "metallurgical" use of metals by more advanced peoples farther south. Accordingly, the cases are not quite parallel in the two hemispheres, even as regards nonferrous metallurgy—apart from the total absence of iron in the native Americas.

Such are the chief reasons for the belief shared by an increasing proportion of anthropologists, that successions like bronze-iron are not so much the result of inherent and recurring necessities as they are more or less special historical developments that now and then may partly, but only partly, repeat one another; and of which, so far as we can now judge, there have probably been but two as regards metal use, one in each hemisphere.

296. THE IRON AGE AS A CULTURE PHASE

Once iron got itself established, everything worked in favor of its increase and spread. Its ores were discoverable almost everywhere, often easy of access, and both the extraction and the shaping of the metal required only simple skills, so that its products quickly became abundant and cheap. They were a boon particularly to those classes in the great civilized nations which were backward through poverty, and to the equally poor though freer peoples that were backward through remoteness. Bronze was the metal of heroes, of men illustrious by birth, wealth, rank, power, and therefore by deeds also; iron was used by the common man on his farm and in his home, or by unruly barbarians who now and then sacked cities. Iron thus tended to be a democratizing agent, at home and abroad.

And, as already suggested, two other nearly contemporaneous inventions, the alphabetic manner of writing and the coinage of money, especially in small denominations, operated in the same direction. The alphabet was also easy, effective, and cheap, so to speak. It could be learned in hours, and workable fluency in it was achievable in weeks, as compared with the months or years required by the older mixed systems of writing. It must be remembered that alphabets were new then, and therefore phonetic; it is only when language grows away from its anciently standardized orthography that it becomes necessary to learn how words are "spelled." The small trader could now keep readable accounts; even the average citizen might hope for a tomb inscription. As for precious metal, in the times before coinage this came in ingots that had to be weighed, and it would take a number of days' wages to aggregate even a shekel or a quarter of an ounce—roughly the amount of silver in a shilling or in a quarter of a dollar. It is easy to see how the artisan, the retail trader, and the farmer had had their arms pinioned in their small dealings, and how coins of small denomination would relieve them. Their previous situation was much as if our smallest currency were a five-pound note—in fact perhaps rather a hundred-dollar bill.

It is probably no meaningless coincidence that these three democratizing inventions originated around Asia Minor; iron in its eastern part, coinage in Lydia in the western part, the alphabet just south of Asia Minor in or near Phoenicia. All three districts are on the edge of or just outside the Fertile Crescent: for once, at last, Egypt and Mesopotamia did not participate in the inventions.

The alphabet was quickly carried by Greeks, Etruscans from Asia Minor, and Phoenicians to Italy, Sicily, and Tunis. There it stopped for some centuries. Illyrians, Kelts, Iberians, were still too far out of the great world to be interested. Indeed, though some local or semicryptic by-product stimulations of the alphabet such as runes and ogham writing (Fig. 26, in § 219) developed at the far margins, middle, western, and northern Europe in general took up writing only when these parts of the continent finally passed out of the tribal state of society into Romanization and Christianity. In Asia we have seen (§ 218, 221) how after about 500 B.C. all new spreads of writing were alphabetic, and mostly derivative or subderivative from the Aramaean running business hand.

As for coined money, the idea and the minting of this spread across Asia very fast, also rapidly to and among the Greeks, but through the rest of Europe slowly. India of course was in contact with Persia, which struck the widely circulating gold coins called darics; and thereafter it had relations with Alexander and his Greek successors. China had been experimenting with knife and spade shapes of money since the seventh century B.C. when the disk concept reached it in the fourth; during the third century this form displaced all others; though "flat" knife money was temporarily revived during the lifetime of Christ. Chinese coinage is the most democratic of all. Silver and gold were very rarely minted—paper currency was for centuries much more in use; the prevailing "cash" are base copper and serve as very small change rather than wealth. The fact that they have a square hole for stringing also reveals them as poor man's money.

Westward, coinage quickly spread as far as the Greek cities and their sphere of influence in Rome and Italy; but then its course stopped for some centuries. The Etruscans and the Carthaginians, both mercantile peoples, were slow in taking up coinage, then followed Greek models. There is evidently something wrong with the conventional contrast of Carthage as a bloated white-collar plutocracy and Rome as a nation of rugged but purse-poor agriculturalists; at any rate the farmers had a mint while the bankers had to depend on Greek engravers! Just before their conquest by Rome, some of the Keltic tribes began to strike imitations of Macedonian staters, with the pictures curiously distorted into random blobs. This happened in Gaul in the second century B.C., in Britain in the first century, and it certainly conveys an impression of highly belated barbarism.

The progress of iron was less jerky and intermittent than that of the alphabet and coinage; but the dispossessing of bronze usually took some centuries wherever bronze was well established. We have already seen (§ 292) how slowly Egypt came over. Nearly four centuries after iron became known in the Greek world, the *Iliad* mentions it but twenty-three times, bronze two hundred and seventy times. Only seven kinds of iron articles are spoken of. In the *Odyssey,* a more bourgeois epic and a bit later in authorship, the proportion of references to iron is higher: twenty-nine to eighty. The first four books of the Old Testament, the composition of whose earlier portions is usually placed synchronous with Homer, about ninth century—but whose outlook is the conservative one of religion—these first four books mention iron still more rarely: four references as against eighty-three to bronze—or "brass" as the Authorized Version calls it. There was a strict prohibition against the stones of an altar to God having been touched by iron.[14] In the days of Saul, about 1000 B.C., the Hebrews had farm tools of iron, but no smiths; whereas the Philistines had swords and spears of steel—and oppressed the Hebrews.[15]

It is not yet known when either bronze or iron working first occurred in China; the Yang-shao culture is at best Chalcolithic. But the interval between the two metals was probably considerably less than in the Near East. At any rate, we know from excavation that An-yang of the oracle bones, around 1400 B.C. (§ 299), had a highly skilled and decorative bronze art; but from Chinese history that in the early seventh century B.C. iron is reported to have been in common use for hoes, plows, hatchets, needles, and domestic purposes. In the fifth century, there are reports about iron swords of a strange virtue better than that of bronze—that is, swords of steel.[16] In the first century after Christ, the natives of far southern China were still fighting with bronze weapons against incorporation into the empire.

In upper Italy, the Villanova period of iron is reckoned as beginning about 1000 B.C. North of the Mediterranean, the predocumentary Iron Age of Europe is usually divided into two periods: that of Hallstatt, named after a site in Austria, from about 800 B.C. on; and that of La Tène, designated from a famous discovery in Switzerland, from 400 until almost the birth of Christ. The Hallstatt period is better developed in middle than in western Europe: it was influenced from Greece, the Balkans, and Italy. Its flow was northwestward. The La Tène culture was carried primarily by Kelts, falls into the period of their

14 Exodus 20: 25.
15 I Samuel 13: 19-22.
16 The dates for both events are also given a century or so later.

greatest extension and prosperity, and centers in France. Here it seems to have developed partly under the stimulus of Greek colonization at Marseille, to have spread northward to the British Isles, and eastward into central Europe. Its general flow was northeastward. Remote areas got iron later than the dates mentioned: England around 500 B.C., Scotland perhaps 250. In northern Germany and Scandinavia Hallstatt and La Tène flowed together into a "Teutonic Iron period," from 600 or 500 B.C. on.

The Hallstatt culture was still wholly without cities, stone architecture or bridges, paved roads, coins, writing of any sort, the potter's wheel, and rotary millstones. It was a time of villages, ramparted hilltops, and scattered homes; of sacred groves instead of temples; of boggy roads, of oxcarts and solid wooden wheels, with now and then a chief getting hold of a bronze chariot from abroad; of a heavy, barbaric, warlike population, half like European peasants, half like pioneers; self-content, yet always dimly conscious that in the southern distance there lay lands of wealth, refinement, and achievement.

The La Tène time showed many advances; but, relatively to the civilizations of Greece and Rome—it was the period of Aristotle, Archimedes, Euclid, and Cicero—the northern culture was almost as many milestones behind as during the Hallstatt era. Writing for communication or open record was still absent. Until perhaps a century or two before Caesar, there were no cities or fortified towns in Gaul. When these arose, it was on heights, behind walls of mixed logs, earth, and stone, as against the stonemasonry circumvallations the Aegean peoples were erecting more than a thousand years before. Even these poor towns were built only by Kelts; the Germanic tribes remained shy of them for centuries longer. Society was still protofeudal and rustic. But there had filtered in from the Mediterranean, and were being wrought locally, holed axes, iron wagon-wheel rims, the potter's wheel and oven, dice, tongs, scissors, saws, and scythes—all new to these northern lands, and often curiously modern in their types. In fact, vocabulary suggests a special Keltic preoccupation with farm and freight wagons from which the Italians learned and profited. And the development of a heavy-duty plow, ultimately drawn by multiple ox yokes, and provided with a moldboard for turning sticky-soil sod clean over, instead of the small share for scratching into the friable surface soil of most Mediterranean lands, is attributed to northwestern Europe in the late La Tène period. It was perhaps the first contribution to the permanent stock of general civilization in which Germanic tribes participated.

With this, we have reached as far in the West as the continuous record of prehistory will carry us. Beyond it in time, lies straight history. Here, accordingly, we return to our Near Eastern starting point and face eastward to review first the great Chinese center, then the Indian one and beyond. The latter carries us out to the island world of the Pacific, where Stone Age peoples survived until modern times. After that Negro Africa is another peripheral area to be examined. Finally, pre-Columbian America is a mainly separate development and therefore a separate story.

297. INNER ASIA AND CHINA

We have seen how China did not partake definitely in either the flake or the bifacial-core tradition that preceded the period of the Würm Glaciation (§ 273). During the terminal Pleistocene and Early Recent—in other words, in Upper Palaeolithic and Mesolithic times—the Chinese finds begin to resemble those of the West. But they do not yet correspond to them so closely, in either their types or their period, as to assure an actual connection. With entry into Neolithic and Bronze status, there is no longer room for doubting a tie-up with the West. The connection even then, to be sure, is not yet substantiated by written documents such as validate most formal history in the narrower sense of the word. But it is supported by the indirect evidence of distributions, and is historical in the sense of having probably happened.

The two ends of Eurasia share wheat, barley, millet; cattle and pigs, later the horse; the plow; the wheel both for traction and for turning pottery; copper, bronze, and iron, in that order; writing and a calendar; towns and then walled cities; a political organization of widening scope with god-kings and a hereditary nobility, eunuchism and retainer burial. In short, the essentials both of the Near Eastern Neolithic subsistence revolution and of the Metal Age socio-intellectual development recur in China, and their elements appear in nearly the same sequence. This would seem to be sufficient evidence for linkage; unless one were to take the view that all such developments were immanent in culture, predestined to appear in it; and if so, there is the difficulty of explaining the absence of most of these inventions and developments from parts of the world such as indigenous America, Australia, and South Africa.

While a prolonged west-east transcontinental connection across Asia must accordingly be assumed, this is subject to certain reservations and limitations.

1. The transfer was mainly one of knowledge and habits, in short a transfer of culture, not one of population. If it had been the latter, we could expect to find a Caucasian strain in the northern Chinese, or a Mongolian one in southwestern Asia. Also, with mass migrations, there would be the likelihood of some indication of speech relationship remaining—if not of total languages, then at least of partial ingredients such as groups of special words, names of places, perhaps even similarly written characters of the same meaning. If the main agency was diffusion of the usual type, through individuals serving as carriers of contact between their societies, it would not much matter in effect whether the contacts between say Mesopotamians or Iranians and Chinese were direct and firsthand or transmitted through one or more mediating populations.

2. The route of connection was most likely via Chinese Turkestan (Sin-

kiang), through which three routes lead from oasis to oasis, one south and two north of the utter desert of Taklamakan. These are the later transasiatic caravan routes for silk and tea. Feed for animals is better, and elevations are less, through southern Siberia, but the detour north is considerable. Tibet to the south is impracticable for any through routes. Chinese Turkestan abuts on its west on what is now Russian Turkestan, at the southwestern edge of which we have already encountered Anau as the seat of a Neolithic-Metal Age culture closely allied to those of Iran and Mesopotamia. At its eastern end, Chinese Turkestan adjoins Kansu, the northwesterly province of China proper, which juts out westward like a long arm. The spottiness of oases in Sinkiang would be no bar to communications, because on both sides of it, in Russian Turkestan and Kansu, environment is only a little less extreme. Both are steppe areas, marginal for farming, except where irrigation renders cultivation intensive. In preagricultural times, travel in these arid inland areas would have been somewhat precarious; though local residents, if they remained sufficiently few, might have made a living off the game that had to come to the streams and the oases. But any society knowing either how to farm or how to breed stock could have come in and got along without serious difficulties.

Unfortunately, there has been but little exploration in these remote inner Asiatic lands, except of the famous sand-buried cities of Sinkiang. These cities have thrown much light on the spread of Buddhism, Nestorian Christianity, and Manichaeism during the early historical period, say between one and two thousand years ago; but they do not extend back the three, four, or five millennia that would carry us into the Bronze Age and the Neolithic.

Southern Siberia shows Bronze Age remains centering around Minusinsk on the upper Yenisei—which we have already encountered in our Palaeolithic review—and extending, at least in related form, east to Lake Baikal and west to the Dnieper River. This culture possessed horse trappings; an abundance of sickles arguing a population largely agricultural; and socketed axes related to western-European Late Bronze Age types of 1400-1000 B.C. This culture may have been a partial link of its day between Europe and China. The inferred connection that brought fundamentals from the Near East to the Far East must have been earlier.

3. A certain number of useful habits never made the transcontinental journey; milking, use of dairy products, wool-weaving. Historic China looked upon milk and its derivations as disgusting. Sheep's wool was used in fleeces and in felt, but was not spun or woven into cloth. It has been suggested that these practices had not yet been "invented" in the West when cattle and sheep raising were imported from there into China. Such a view would be hard to prove: at least sporadically, milking and the use of wool are definitely old in Mesopotamia. Also, there would have been nothing to prevent the delayed items from traveling eastward in company with later novelties, such as ironworking. One could only say that by then the Chinese pattern had set against them. But

if this factor of pattern fit is invoked, it could just as well have been operative in the beginning, when milking and wool first knocked at the Chinese door.

4. No matter how much cultural influence was carried into China, or some-times out of it, the Chinese early developed a characteristic over-all pattern or style that long remained distinctive of them. Thus, for at least three thousand years they have covered the whole body with loose, full, but tailored and sleeved clothes. Ancestor worship, which was known also in the west, where it increasingly declined, kept and strengthened its hold in China. The bias for jade, for scenery; brush-painting of writing; brevity of poems and conciseness of prose; respect and rewards for education; and upturned roof beams—these are but a few of many features from two to three thousand years old which have given Chinese civilization a physiognomy all its own. In principle, there is nothing unusual about this. Egypt and Mesopotamia were geographically close and shared an even larger proportion of their culture material; yet each main-tained a consistent, pervasive style of its own. If China was more distinctive, that was no doubt because its remoteness isolated it more.

5. The relations we are discussing applied to North China—the Yellow River basin. South China, beyond the Yangtze Valley, was reached very frag-mentarily if at all by Western culture influences. Tibet cut it off from direct communications; and as for the indirect ones, these had first to filter through North China, and then enter a quite different environment of broken hills and small valleys, warmth and moisture and heavy vegetation; a country in which rice, pigs, and water buffalo thrive better than wheat, sheep, and cattle. During Neolithic and Bronze times, accordingly, South China was so nearly prevented from being influenced by the West—or better, let us say, by the main Eurasian area—that it largely developed a separate subsistence and economy, more or less conjointly with the remainder of southeastern Asia. Beginning just before the Christian era, North China spilled into South China, conquered it, and gradually assimilated it institutionally. But the environment could not be over-come, and a well-marked difference between North and South China persists to this day in habits of daily life and temperament of the people.

298. NEOLITHIC CHINA

In the light of the foregoing general considerations, let us now consider the actual evidence from archaeological excavations on Chinese soil. The results group into four overlapping periods: Painted Pottery; Black Pottery; Shang; and Chou.

The Painted Pottery culture, also called that of Yang-shao, is Neolithic to begin with, but is reckoned as extending also through the Bronze Age to the coming of iron around 600 B.C. It is really rather absurd to lump everything in this long interval together merely because of the continuance of a manner of decorating pottery. What we actually have is, first, a Neolithic culture from sites like Yang-shao in western Honan and Hsi-yin in southern Shansi, close to the Yellow River in the heart of the China of its day. This Neolithic culture lasted at least several centuries, probably until somewhere around 1700 B.C. In this culture is found a handmade red and design-painted pottery, along with coarser, gray, unpainted wares. Farther west in Kansu, which then as now was merely marginal to China proper, but situate at the crucial gateway for entries from the west, these same two potteries occur not only contemporaneously with Yang-shao and Hsi-yin, but perhaps previously also, and certainly afterward. Andersson, the Swedish discoverer of this whole culture complex, puts the first Kansu sites, such as Ch'i-chia, earlier than Yang-shao itself, beginning perhaps around 2500 B.C. Wu and perhaps other Chinese prehistorians made Ch'i-chia begin only contemporarily with later Yang-shao—most of a thousand years later. They also made the Painted Pottery period in Kansu terminate earlier: around 1000 B.C. rather than 600-500, as Andersson has it. From a distance it is difficult to decide as between these views; but the Chinese interpretation at least keeps what is basically one culture, or at any rate one style of ware, within time limits comparable to prehistorians' experience elsewhere, instead of sprawling it over two millennia.

For the Neolithic part of this Painted Pottery culture, agriculture is authenticated with millet, possibly also with rice and wheat; and with stock-raising, at first of pigs and dogs, later also of sheep and cattle. Houses were pit dwellings with roof entrance. Whether the metal found in the later phases in Kansu was copper or bronze is not clear from the published accounts. As regards the pottery, various early polychrome wares of the West have been spoken of as "similar" to Yang-shao by this or that authority. The one Western style that has enough resemblance to make a historical connection seem possible is that of Tripolje in southern Russia, which is also Neolithic with a little copper coming in (§ 283).

The Black Pottery or Lung-shan culture, also called Ch'eng-tzu-yai, though perhaps overlapping with the Painted Pottery culture in time, is at least mainly later, as shown by stratification. There is also an overlap in area between the two, in Honan and Shansi, although the main range of the Black ware is east of the Painted. Its range was the lowland plain of Shantung and southward to across the Yangtze—but not on the coast itself: early China was not maritime. The distinctive criterion is a fine, thin, wheel-turned, all black, burnished pottery. The shapes begin to be suggestive of later Chinese shapes. An associated, distinct ware of kaolin is white. Cattle and horses are in use; shoulder-blade divination is practiced. The greatest change from the Yang-shao peasant life is shown by towns with rammed-earth walls thirty feet broad, and over a mile in circuit. These were veritable little cities, perhaps warring city-states with rulers. It is said that no bronze has been found in Black Pottery site explorations. This may be an accident of excavation luck; or it is possible that in China urbanization preceded metallurgy. The estimated period is just before 1500 B.C.

299. PREHISTORIC BRONZE AGE CHINA: SHANG

With the third or Shang period of prehistory we stand with one foot in history. The Shang or Yin dynasty, traditionally ruling China from 1766 to 1122 B.C.—actually more likely 1523 to 1027—had come to be considered pretty much legendary by recent scholars—until its reality, and the essential authenticity of much of its history, were vindicated by finds of oracle bones, and then through excavations by Chinese scientists at An-yang in northern Honan, where the capital of this dynasty was built around 1400 or perhaps 1300 on a former Black Pottery culture site.

Here at last we have the full complement of the civilization of Sumer and Egypt sixteen hundred years earlier: dynasties, great subterranean tombs, writing, bronze. The beginnings may go back a few centuries beyond 1400: twenty-nine kings and twenty-six generations are mentioned in the oracle bones. But at the most favorable, a retardation of at least a thousand years behind the Near East must be admitted. This lag is a function of the distance traversed by knowledge and skills.

At a few points, the delay enabled the Chinese to begin their higher civilization with elements that in the West came late in Bronze Age development: horse teams yoked to spoked chariots, for instance.

In the main, high civilization must have come with a good deal of a final rush in China, as it did in Egypt and Sumer. Unless further explorations radically alter the picture, the Black Pottery culture manifests only a fraction of the culture content of Shang, although it seems only a little anterior in time.

This is the Shang picture, as built up from actual discoveries, references in Shang inscriptions, plus history as written later: Millet, probably wheat and rice, were grown. There was millet beer. Hemp and silk fibers were used. Clothes were cut and sewn, and had sleeves. Of bred animals, pigs and dogs were still most abundant; but to sheep, cattle, horses, there appears now to have been added the hen. The Shang pig is said to be derived from a South Chinese species. There were buffalo, but they were not numerous. It is evident that the South China-Farther India area had already begun to make its contribution to the plant and animal economy. There were still some wild elephants in North China to be hunted.

The ancestors were thought to "eat blood." Nearly all animals were sacrificed, including dogs, sometimes in lots of fifty, one hundred, three hundred—true hecatombs. One pit held thirty-eight horses. Specially interesting is a compound sacrifice corresponding to the Roman su-ove-taurilia: two pigs, three sheep, five cows. Part or all of the flesh was burned in offering. Human sacrifice was common: there was a written character, and presumably a spoken word, to denote it; especially prisoners of war were used. Incidentally, both outright sacrifice and retainer burial continued into the next or Chou period, at least until the sixth century.

To divination from the cracks in shoulder blades of cattle in the previous period—scapulimancy (§ 192)—there was now added a second method utilizing slivers of their long bones, and a third using the belly shell of a large tortoise that has since become extinct, presumably as a result of being in demand for this practice of magic. A hot pressure point was applied. The answer was inscribed, sometimes the question also, on these "oracle bones." Many of the characters of Shang writing retain something of a picture in their strokes, but most of them can still be read. They make it clear that Chinese writing originated locally and with reference to Chinese speech, whatever may have been the stimulus to the devising of it as a system.

The Shang bronze art was highly skilled. It operated both with molds and the melted-wax method. As so far no bronze at all has been found in the immediately preceding Black Pottery culture, the metallurgical development must be inferred to have been rapid, and perhaps due to ready-made introduction of skills. But if the technology was imported, the style is already characteristically Chinese. The pictures of Shang period ornate bronze ritual vessels, as contained in later Chinese books, have been fully authenticated by finds. In addition there are weapons: lance heads, battle-axes, dagger axes, arrow points, helmets; but as yet no swords. The war chariots carried a lancer and an archer in addition to the driver. The composite bow is inferred from thumb rings. The use of bronze was ritual and aristocratic. Some needles, knives, and chisels have been found, but no bronze farm tools for the peasantry.

Other valuables included jade, bones of whales, and cowry shells, which were very precious. Names were given in accord with a ten-day rotating cycle or "week," presumably for the date of birth. Armies were small, from 1000 to 5000 men; but kings were exalted, and the capital was known as "Great City Shang."

With all its specific Chinese color and style, this Shang civilization is a really extraordinary counterpart to the Near Eastern Bronze Age city and kingdom civilizations. Though its beginnings were so much later, it had forged nearly abreast of them by the fourteenth century B.C., when Egypt and Babylon had just passed their zenith and the Hither Asian Bronze Age culture generally was beginning to show the first symptoms of internal disintegration.

300. LATE BRONZE AND IRON AGE CHINA: CHOU

The succeeding Chou dynasty lasted a long time. Its culture altered continuously and rather rapidly, and were it not that Chinese scholars have always organized their history into larger segments in terms of dynasties, it is probable that it would not have occurred to prehistorians and culture historians to treat the period 1122-255 B.C. (actually perhaps 1050 or 1027 to 255) as a unit. Here are some of the changes that occurred in these eight or nine Chou centuries.

The Chou kings were real rulers for a couple of centuries. After that they had to move their capital from the western edge of China of that day to near its middle, and became reduced to being nominal overkings, who alone might sacrifice to their ancestor Prince Millet, son of Heaven. Otherwise they admonished the feudal princes and governed their small dynastic domain. Chinese political organization was feudal, and practically as separatist as that of mediaeval Germany. Starting with over a thousand fiefs, China within some centuries came down to a hundred, and by the end of Chou had "consolidated" to seven states. Bronze swords came in during early Chou. Before the period ended, there were triggered crossbows (§ 184), and cavalry replaced fighting chariots. We have seen (§ 296) how by mid-Chou times token-size spades and knives of cast bronze were serving as money. By terminal Chou, these had been replaced by disk coins, perhaps in imitation of the West—except for the characteristically Chinese style feature of a central square hole for stringing.

We also saw in § 296 that it is not known in detail just when and how China got its first iron, or rather knowledge of iron production. The first use was domestic, not for weapons. By the seventh century iron was common enough in these forms to be profitable to tax, as a minister advised his king, according to a passage in official Chinese history. The first steel swords capable of outfighting bronze ones are said to have come in during the fifth century (§ 296). Here again literary history puts the innovation in the form of a dramatic conversation between king and minister: the king has heard of a new kind of magic sword and asks for confirmation. Some sources set both anecdotes a century or more later. Whatever the exact dates, the Chinese learned of iron and steel about the same time as the Britons and the Scandinavians; which, considering on the one hand their greater distance from Armenia, and on the other their being on a generally higher level of culture than the marginal Europeans, seems about what is expectable. The Chinese were probably the first people to reduce iron with mineral coal, as well as to cast it. Both these skills had been developed in Shansi by the seventh Christian century, a little more than a thousand years after the Chinese first came to know the metal. In Europe, the interval was two thousand years or more.

301. CHINESE CIVILIZATION IN HISTORY

Chinese unity of the Chou period lay not so much in an effective organization as in an idea, the feeling of a common society and especially of a common civilization. This idea has persisted to the present. It is adhesion to the culture of China, to its deep roots, its permanence, its humanities, that has always made

Chinese feel themselves Chinese; has in fact sooner or later turned into Chinese nearly all alien elements, whether intrusive conquerors or primitive folk, that came to be included within the limits of the realm. In this way common customs and ideals already united the Chou states and dependencies; and frequent internal warfare did not prevent the era from being the age of Confucius, Laotse, Mencius, and the other great sages who from the sixth to the third centuries B.C. formulated the typical Chinese character and ideology.

By the third century, two of the contending states had emerged as preponderant: Ts'in in the west, centering about the Wei valley, and Ch'u on the south, along the middle Yangtze. Both were frontier states, less cultivated and hardier than the others, and regarded as barbarous and only half Chinese. Ch'u very likely represented the rule of a Chinese dynasty over a native population whose original affiliations may have been either non-Sinitic or Sinitic, but who were gradually assimilating the culture and speech of the northern old China. In 255 B.C., Ts'in—whence probably our "China"—abolished Chou and seized its ritual symbols of overlordship. Then, in 223, Ch'u fell before Ts'in; and within two years the last of the remaining states in the northeast collapsed. For the first time China, from nearly its present northern frontier to south of the Yangtze, was effectively under one active ruler, Shih Huang Ti, the "first emperor." His dynasty crumbled almost at his death, only to be succeeded by the famous Han line, under which, in the two centuries before and the two after Christ, China extended, consolidated, and prospered.

The boundaries of the empire were pushed to virtually the limits of historic China proper, and westward into Turkestan. And though political control may often have been slight, cultural influence progressed rapidly south of the Yangtze, much as Gaul became Romanized at the same time. Even the survival of half-independent barbarian groups here and there in the south and west has its parallel in the persistence of Basque and Keltic speech in western France.[17] By the seventh to ninth centuries after Christ, when the empire flourished once more under the T'ang dynasty, the mass of southern China except Yünnan may be considered to have been substantially assimilated. Even the south-central coast, which was the last area to be integrated, and which retains today the greatest dialectic differentiations and autonomous tendencies, had become part of the Chinese polity and civilization by Sung dynasty times. The consequence was that when in the thirteenth century the Mongols and in the seventeenth the Manchus conquered the empire, they accomplished little more than the overthrow of one dynasty by another. The course of Chinese culture went on almost undisturbed, as it had in previous periods when half of the realm occasionally passed under the sway of nomads or barbarians from the north.

[17] Strictly, Breton represents a post-Roman Keltic resettlement from Britain rather than a Keltic persistence on the spot through Roman times.

A considerable measure of the cultural predominance of China over its neighbors is to be ascribed to its more numerous population, which in turn was partly due to the cultural advance, in accord with the circular causality tending to be operative in such cases (§ 118, 163). The Chinese were the first nation to maintain a system of fairly regular censuses, and to preserve a good many of the records in their histories. In the first century and a half after Christ, under the Hans, ten censuses showed from 29 to 83 million inhabitants, the average being 63 millions, or not far from the estimated population of the Roman Empire at its height, or that of western and central Europe when America was discovered. A thousand years later, between 1021 and 1580, eight censuses yielded from 43 to 100 millions, with an average of 62 millions. Under the Manchus the population gradually rose from 125 millions in 1736 to 380 in 1881; and it is now more often reckoned around 500 than around 400 millions.

Many ingredients of modern Chinese civilization, and most of its distinctive color, have been present in it since the opening of the historical period. Such are the use of hemp and silk as the typical textile materials; of jade as the precious stone of the nation; the tremendous, lifelong moral authority accorded to parents, and the associated worship of ancestors; the unusual respect for learning and rewards for it, such as officeholding, resulting in a quasi-democratic government by a socially open, literate bureaucracy chosen by competitive merit—in theory at least; a professed contempt for war and emotional vehemence; indifference to mythological, metaphysical, or scientific speculation, but an unflagging interest in practical ethics, in the cultivation of character, in the finer shaping of the relations of individuals. These and other leanings endow Chinese civilization with something persistently idiomatic, with a quality of coherent originality. If this civilization were less great, China and the countries influenced by it would be spoken of as constituting what among barbarous and savage peoples we call a culture area. In the widest perspective, they are such. China, India, the West— which last in this view of course includes the Near East as well as Europe—are the three great focal centers of civilization in the Eastern Hemisphere. Their cultures have risen far above those of the intervening and peripheral nations. Until rather recent centuries, the three have run their courses with nearly equal achievement. And while exchanging elements of culture since prehistoric times, they have each molded both what they borrowed and what they devised into a unified and distinctive design, have stamped it with original patterns and characteristic values. In short, culture development in China, India, and the Occident has been approximately co-ordinate and stylistically independent.

Of course, this distinctness of the three great regions of Old World civilization does not imply that diffusion of culture elements among them ever ceased. It is the form more than the content of civilization that is peculiar to the three areas. From India, for instance, China derived Buddhism, which was accorded a reception under the Hans and cultivated with fervor in the following centuries.

Cotton came in the wake of the religion—first as a rare and valuable textile, then to be grown. The West, within the historical period, gave glass and perhaps an impulse toward the gradual Chinese invention of porcelain, a glazed-through pottery; not to mention the intellectual introductions by seventeenth-century Jesuits, and the broad-front Westernization that has been increasingly effective during the last century. In recent centuries, also, European nations have acted as transmitters for several elements of aboriginal American origin—tobacco, for example, and maize, which quickly became an important food plant in parts of China. There have even been reimportations: gunpowder, used for fireworks in China in the seventh to ninth T'ang centuries, and reintroduced with cannon half a thousand years later; and the magnetic needle, evidently referred to from the fourth pre-Christian century on in connection with "south-pointing chariots," later applied to geomantic purposes, and finally used as an instrument of navigation in imitation of foreign mariners.

The culturally backward nationalities of interior South China—Lolo, Moso, Miao, Yao, and so on—have been discussed under Internal Marginality in § 175.

302. JAPANESE PREHISTORY

Japan lies off East Asia much as Britain lies off western Europe. In fact, so far as actual distance goes, its position corresponds more nearly to that of Ireland. As regards diffusing culture features, Japan has thus been always marginal to a continental margin. It is only in recent centuries that the development of navigation has tended to efface water-borne distances. There are only four routes of entry to the Japanese archipelago: via Formosa and the Ryukyu chain; Korea; Sakhalin; or the Kuriles. The last two are inhospitable and lead to even less favorable lands; nothing of importance culturally seems to have traveled over them. Of the two other routes, Korea is much the shorter and easier; through it flowed most historical culture exchange; and presumably the prehistoric also, as well as population immigration. This means that for any idea or practice originating in western Eurasia to reach Japan, such as grain farming or bronze or writing or divine kingship, it had first to get adopted in China, then usually in Korea, and only after that were the Japanese in a position to choose to accept or reject it. Naturally, there was consistent retardation. In the same way the presumably aboriginal and Caucasoid Ainu (§ 65) in the northeastern islands—in what might be called "farther Japan"—were exposed to culture radiation only after this had in turn filtered through the Yamato Japanese. They could not well have failed to remain still more backward.

There is as yet no sure evidence of a Palaeolithic period in Japan. Indications of it have been alleged; and the antiquity that was long erroneously denied to native culture in America must serve to remind us that sweeping negations are in their nature very difficult to establish. Yet it would be hard to imagine Pleistocene men making the considerable boat trip to reach even Kyushu, the nearest large island of Japan. England presumably owes its having had a Palaeolithic to being part of continental Europe in the Pleistocene. If anything pre-Neolithic is ever definitely discovered in Japan, we might expect it to be post-Pleistocene and Mesolithic.

Neolithic remains, on the contrary, are exceedingly abundant. About four thousand sites have been found. The difficulty is that there is no present way of determining when the Japanese Neolithic began. Its end is generally put around A.D. 200, when ironworking was introduced. Previous to that, the stages of the local Neolithic, both Japanese and Ainu, have been classified by Japanese archaeologists chiefly according to pottery. Since elsewhere pottery is Mesolithic as well as Neolithic, this does not tell us much as to when it began here. The translated summaries are not too clear as to presence or absence of the bones of domestic animals, or sickles, or impressions of grains—in short, as to whether or when the pottery was accompanied by farming and stock-raising. The accepted classification is into three stages of pottery development: Jomon, Yayoi, Iwaibe. The first of these contains handmade ware, cord-patterned, and is wholly premetal. It may have ended 200 B.C. In the second stage, 200 B.C. to A.D. 200, the pottery at times begins to be wheel-made, and is less ornamented on the surface but often florid in shape. With this Yayoi pottery, imported Chinese bronze is occasionally associated. Thus, literally, Japan "had" a sort of Bronze Age; but it did not have one of its own. Perhaps Chalcolithic or Aeneolithic would be a better designation. The bronze finds center in northern Kyushu Island, at the mouth of the passage from Korea. In Kyushu too there has been found a Chinese Han-dynasty gold medal or seal of probably the first century after Christ. The third or Iwaibe or Yamato type of pottery is Iron Age, wheel-made, gray and unornamented, but with the florid shapes even more exaggerated than in the preceding period.

The Iron Age is dated A.D. 200-700. The end of course is wholly arbitrary, as iron kept on being used. What is meant by 700 is that by then the Japanese court and upper classes had become literate and Buddhist, histories were beginning to be written, and old heathen practices were abandoned, such as burying the emperors in megalithic dolmen chambers under huge mounds. In short, around the seventh century the Japanese consciously entered the ranks of the historical nations. The estimated dates of the beginning of the practice of depositing certain objects in the imperial burial mounds are: bronze mirrors (originally imported from China), A.D. 150; swords with ornaments of antler, 200; swords with ring pommel, 350; horse trappings, also pottery, 400. A contemporary link to this dim barbaric past is that the sacred, temple-deposited, crown treasures of the imperial line still are a mirror, a sword, and a curved or comma-shaped Neolithic stone "jewel."

Ainu remains are also grouped into periods according to their pottery. The first of these is estimated to correspond in time to the Japanese Chalcolithic or Yayoi, and its range centers in the middle of the main island, where the Japanese apparently had not penetrated then. This Ainu ware riots in flamboyant shapes, scalloped edges, applied fillets, and the like. The next two Ainu periods, respectively before and after A.D. 400, would correspond to the Japanese Iron Age, and center farther northeast: the Ainu were in slow retreat. The shapes are less florid than before; spouted vessels, like later teapots (though neither Ainu nor Japanese then knew tea), are characteristic. Great as is the difference between Japanese and Ainu in richness and level of their modern culture, such difference still was slight in the earliest centuries of the Christian era.

303. CULTURE GROWTH IN JAPAN

The historical development of culture in Japan shows the same dependence on that of China as the prehistory; only it is more fully and exactly documented. This dependence is geographically conditioned, of course, as already set forth. But it is worth noting, from the point of view of general theory, that the most effective conditioning is not by natural environment operating directly, as through soil and climate, but is that which depends on relative position, distance from other cultural centers: in short, human environment. That Japan differs from North China in containing no large plains, in being rugged, having an island-type, wet, rice-growing climate instead of a seasonal, harsh, continental one—these are all factors whose influences are indeed discernible to some degree in the habits of the two societies; but they are discernible spottily, in this and that feature, not consistently through the whole of the two cultures. By contrast, the derivation of higher Japanese culture almost wholly from Chinese culture, owing in turn to the respective positions of the two relative to other cultural centers lying farther west (§ 173), is not only fundamental but pervasive and consistent. The involved principle which can be inferred is that the influence of natural environment on culture is proportional to cultural preconditioning. Irrigable desert will hardly influence a people's mode of life unless they already have an agricultural tradition. Japan's marginal position might perhaps not have made it dependent on China if Chinese civilization had not itself been considerably advanced by stimulation and import from the West.[18]

The list that follows exemplifies the time relation of the two cultures. Minus signs denote B.C. dates; Roman numerals, centuries.

[18] Obviously, as is also shown in § 173, the position of the ancestral Japanese in that part of their islands lying nearest to the mainland sufficed to block stimulating influences of higher Chinese culture from reaching the Ainu, farther out in the archipelago, thus keeping these aborigines retarded—and relatively more and more so—until they succumbed to the Japanese.

COMPARATIVE APPEARANCE OF CULTURE FEATURES IN CHINA AND JAPAN

Cultural Innovation	China	Japan	Lag
Writing	before −1400	405	1800
Permanent capital for dynasty	−1000±	709	1700
Ironworking	−600±	200±	800
Coins minted	−IV	677	1000
Feudalism abolished	−221	1868	2089
Tea: known	Chou	805	1200±
used by upper classes	Han	XII	1200±
in general use	T'ang	XVII	900±
Buddhism, first cognizance of	65	552	500±
Buddhist sects: Jodo	IV	XII	800±
Zen	V	XII	700±
Tendai	VI	VIII	200±
Shingon	VIII	IX	100±
Block printing	VII	VIII	100±
Movable-type printing	1049	1595	546±
Culmination of: Neo-Confucianism	1180±	1720±	540±
Impressionist painting	1210±	1460±	250±
Drama	1300±	1700±	400±
Native algebra	1300±	1675±	375±

It is obvious from this list that diffusion does not operate in any simple mechanical fashion, even where its stream is uniquely one-way and overwhelming, as here. This is evident from the fact that the Japanese lag varies from one to twenty centuries. Some features that originated later in China became established earlier in Japan. Up to the seventh century, Chinese influence was exerted mostly through Korea; after that directly. In the sixteenth century, the Portuguese and then other exploring and colonizing European nations began to release a new stream of cultural import: Christian beliefs, firearms, stone castles, for instance (§ 173). This influence was largely checked in the following century by the policy of national seclusion—a sort of ultra-isolationism—which China, Tibet, Korea, and the Ryukyus adopted as well as Japan; though, as might be expected, enforcement could never be made completely effective. Japanese seclusion did however dam up pressure until the mid-nineteenth century; with the result that after Perry's treaty there was a voluntary, conscious, and directed absorption of Occidental culture material at a rate evidently more rapid than the acquisitions from China at their peak more than a thousand years before.

Yet the history of no people's civilization can be told merely in terms of what flowed into it. Japan possessed old native developments, such as its Shinto cults, that were indeed modified but essentially were retained. And a fair proportion of Chinese items were simply never adopted. Many of these fall into groups or clusters, suggesting that some element in the common pattern remained unacceptable in Japan. Thus the Japanese never really took over the Chinese theory of the responsibility of emperor and dynasty, the mandarin examination system and bureaucracy, Confucianism as an official cult, and formal ancestral tablets and grave worship. These perhaps smacked too much of civilian attitudes and ways to suit an armed hereditary aristocracy—as has already been elaborated in § 172. Another group of practices not accepted were eunuchism, foot-binding, the wearing of body jewelry other than in the hair, and opium-smoking. Here the objection may have been a resistance to anything savoring of mutilation or degradation of the body. Japanese sculptors followed the Chinese in working in bronze, wood, and lacquered cloth, but refused to follow them in carving in stone; just as the Japanese built wholly in wood until they finally learned about stone castles from the Portuguese. They did not take up with the chairs and tables the Chinese have had for a thousand years. This is no mere odd bit or item: lack of chairs affects houses, mats, chest types, shoes and their wearing, bodily postures, even aesthetic ideals.

Japanese inventions have been few, and mostly concern manners of doing things rather than strictly original devices. Two exceptions, outright mechanical inventions, are gadgetlike rather than fundamental: the folding fan and the revolving theatrical stage. The former is said to have been carried back to China in Ming times. It may be the only Japanese innovation accepted in China. Kana or phonetic syllable signs were added to Chinese script to cover divergences of Japanese speech from Chinese, such as native proper names and grammatical endings (§ 219). Two additional Buddhist sects developed in Japan in the thirteenth century after the introduction of sects from China ceased: Shinshu and Nichiren. The former is a sort of denatured Jodo: no monasteries, no celibacy for the clergy, vernacular speech, minimum of ritual. This quality of secularization has caused Shinshu to be compared loosely to Protestant reform, though it is neither puritan nor revivalistic of primitive Buddhism. Nichiren, named after its aggressive founder, contains little that is new in doctrine or ritual, and is set apart chiefly by a certain militant exclusiveness that is really non-Buddhist in spirit.

Much the greatest degree of originality in Japanese culture is found in distinctive variations of ways or manners; in the domain of style, in short. Thus, continental Asia shoots composite bows with thumb rings (§ 173, 299); Japan alone has an archer's glove with a notched thumb. Of the same general class are the famous Japanese tea ceremony; incense parties; jujutsu; hara-kiri; the allusive thirty-one-syllable tanka poem; and the sophisticated novel of refined court life developed nearly a thousand years ago. All these are, essentially, highly special and stylized ways—developed etiquettes, one might almost call them—of doing things that other peoples also do but go about in less mannered and precious but more casual or spontaneous fashion. The generic moral seems to be that originality can be directed equally well to substance or to form and manner. A nation like the Japanese, situated so that for two thousand years they have been on the receiving end as to content of culture, may come in the end to feel—at any rate unconsciously—that true excellence lies rather in deftness of finish and precision of style than in originating basically new things.

304. INDIA: THE ANCIENT INDUS VALLEY CIVILIZATION

When the first version of this book was published in 1923, the oldest culture known in India was that of the Aryan invaders of 1500 to 1200 B.C., as described by allusions in their sacred hymns, the Vedas, preserved first by successive memories and then in writing. The very next year, announcement was made of the discovery by excavation of an earlier civilization, more or less coeval with those of Mesopotamia and Egypt; and in 1932 came the publication of the first full account of one of the three richest sites, Mohenjo-daro in Sindh, supplemented by data from a second, Harappa in the Punjab. These are both in Indus drainage; and as the culture proved to be confined to northwestern India, it has generally been called the Indus Valley civilization. It is a genuine parallel to the riverine civilizations on the Nile and the Tigris-Euphrates.

Subsequent explorations at Chanhu-daro and minor sites show that there were at least four stages of development, of which the first described phase at Mohenjo-daro and Harappa was the most advanced, the second in time sequence, and the most important. The stages are:

1. *Amri.* No metal, no writing, poor architecture. The pottery may have affiliations with the Mesopotamian Ubaid phase. Amri shades into the next stage:

2. *Harappa.* The culminating phase, described below. It might also have been named Mohenjo-daro. 2750-2500 B.C. The dates depend on the finding of typical Indus seals in datable levels in Sumer.

3. *Jhukar.* Metallurgy and drains equal to the Harappa stage, building inferior, different seals, writing gone. Probably from 2500 on.

4. *Jhangar.* Little known, except for pottery. Apparently it represents further retrogression. This stage may have followed on Jhukar immediately or after an interval; possibly around 2000.

These stages seem to outline the rise and fall of a single civilization localized in western India, of which the Harappa phase, as revealed at Mohenjo-daro, Harappa, and Chanhu-daro, represented the florescence.

Mohenjo-daro, in contrast with early Egypt and Sumer and Susa and Anau, is a city of fired brick. Mud brick (crude brick, sun-dried brick, adobe) was also used, but only as the interior filling of walls and platforms. The baked brick is however laid in ordinary mud, not in lime mortar. There are no step pyramids, nor have any temples been discovered. The city is one of many-roomed dwellings and great public baths. Special features of construction are stairways and bathrooms in houses; wells; sewers or drains; and corbeled-arch construction. Round columns and decorative features have not been found. The bricks are of the proportions of ours, but from a fourth to a third larger in each dimension. House walls are oriented north-south, as in Egypt: Babylonia turns the corners to the cardinal directions. No traces of city walls are apparent, so that life in relative security is indicated. The culture has a modern feel in the degree to which civilian aspects overshadow royal and ritual ones.

Remains of wheat, barley, and dates have been found. The grain was ground on a saddle quern or metate, with back-and-forth motion. There are as yet no indications whether agriculture was with plow or by hoe. The remains of domesticated animals include abundant remains of swine and of humped Indian cattle, also water buffalo, sheep, hen, and dog. The hen remains are the earliest yet discovered anywhere. There are also elephant and camel bones, which may or may not have come from domesticated individuals. Some twenty seal carvings plainly depict unhumped shorthorn bulls, but no bones of this variety have been discovered. Seals also show the rhinoceros, the tiger, and the antelope to have been known, as well as a mythical one-horned bull or unicorn. There are toy models of disk-wheeled bullock carts almost identical with those of modern India, but as yet no representations of swifter, spoke-wheeled war chariots, whose period elsewhere, too, is later. Moreover, the absence of both ass and horse remains is probably significant in this connection. The wheel was used also in pottery-making. Cotton was grown, and spindle whorls are common. Men's dress, to judge from representations, consisted chiefly of a shawl, women's of a loin band.

The subsistence economy partakes of two great types. There are the barley, wheat, cattle, and sheep of the West—of ancient Turkestan, Mesopotamia, Egypt, and Europe. There are also the cotton, fowl, buffalo, and elephant of India and Farther India.

Metallurgical art was well developed on the Indus. Gold, silver, copper, and a little lead have been found; also tin bronze and arsenic bronze, the latter probably derived as a natural alloy from the ore. Tin must have been scarce, since the same objects were sometimes made in copper and sometimes in bronze, even where the former were definitely inferior for use. These finds dispose of a view formerly held, that India had a Copper Age but no Bronze Age. They show rather that the important criterion of advancement is not bronze, which depends on the geographical accident of tin supply, but is the metallurgical processes known. It is clear that the Indus Valley people controlled Bronze Age methods, even though they could secure tin only occasionally. They certainly melted and cast metals, and almost certainly smelted them from ores.

The Indus wheel-made pottery is black on red with curvilinear designs, and shades through Baluchistan buff into old Persian yellow wares. It has been thought to show specific resemblance to the Early Dynastic pottery of Sumer.

There are also remains of glazed pottery, vitreous paste, and steatite faïence, but no true glass.

Art is evidenced in seal carvings and figures, not in architecture. It may be described as excellent but not superlative in quality, and distinctive in style. Nearly 400 characters of a system of writing—about 250 with omission of variants—have been discovered—of course unread, the language being unknown. These characters are conventional rather than pictorial, and semicursive rather than angular. They bear many accents, points, or diacritical marks, and seem to have been read from right to left. In type the system is evidently analogous to the Mesopotamian and Egyptian systems; but no resemblances indicative of specific derivation are apparent.

The same system of weights was in use at Mohenjo-daro and Harappa. It divided and multiplied by 2's up to a certain point, then by 10's; not by 60's, as in Babylonia. The unit of weight was either 106 or 212 grains, as against the 129-grain shekel of Mesopotamia. Again we have here something equivalent to the West, but different in specific content.

Evidences of religion are few but suggestive. On the one hand there are carvings of bull-men fighting with monsters by sacred trees, a motive familiar from Mesopotamian art; or we have a figure like the Gilgamesh of Sumerian myth wrestling with erect lions. On the other hand, there are anticipations of historic Indian religion: phallic stones, and a Siva-like figure, three-faced and in Yogi posture. This, though pre-Vedic by a thousand years, is post-Vedic Hindu in character. It seems to establish certain trends of modern Hindu religion as nearly five thousand years old, with the Vedic Aryan cults coming in almost like an interruption.

In fact, this is one of the two major significances of the Indus discoveries. The first is the establishment of a high civilization coeval with those of Mesopotamia, Turkestan, Syria, and Egypt, roughly equal to them in richness, connected with them by trade and no doubt in interinfluencing, similar in basic trends, but thoroughly independent in its specific qualities and manifestations. But for the history of India itself the discoveries are equally important. Here is a culture a thousand years earlier than that of the Vedic Aryans, yet more similar in some respects to that of later historical India which has heretofore been traditionally derived from these Aryan invaders.

There can be no doubt that the people of this Harappa stage of Indus civilization were in trade and communication with Sumer and that they were influenced from Mesopotamia. Almost certainly it was from the West that this civilization got its grains and metallurgy; some think also its first suggestion of the writing that was destined to pass away again so soon after. But other parts of the culture originated respectively to the east of the arid Indus Valley, in the moist, jungly areas of India; or were developed on the spot; or continued long afterward as pan-Indic features.

305. INDIA OF THE VEDAS AND OF BUDDHA

From the high-water mark of the Indus Valley civilization to the Vedic Aryan one there is a gap of at least a thousand years; from its degenerate Jhangar-phase conclusion, probably five hundred years or more. For this lacuna there is as yet neither any discovered archaeology nor any historical legend.

The Vedic Indians or "Aryas" are first known to us from their hymns, the Vedas, which have been preserved as sacrosanct by succeeding ages and constitute the oldest continuously transmitted oral documents in history. They date from perhaps 1500 to 1000 B.C., and are in a form of Sanskrit, which is fairly close to Avestan or Old Persian; the two languages jointly with their descendants constitute the Indo-Iranian or proper Aryan branch of Indo-European. The region of India to which the earlier Vedas refer is the Punjab or upper Indus drainage; that is, the northwest, the parts adjoining the Iranian highland, whence the invaders apparently came or through which they passed. Only in the later Vedic books are there references to the upper Ganges Valley also.

Vedic Aryan culture was of late Bronze Age type. Whether the bronze was really such, or copper, it is mentioned more frequently than iron, as in Homer and the older books of the Bible. Grains, cattle, horses, chariots and wagons, the plow, wool and weaving, gold, patriarchal chieftains and a tribal society, a nature mythology, and noncommunal rituals with constant but prevailingly bloodless sacrifices—these are the characteristics of this culture. It smacks more of the Europe of its time than of the contemporary Orient. It is unbound, ready to pack up and move without being essentially nomadic; half peasantlike and half aristocratic; an uncitified semicivilization, pioneer rather than backwoods. Wholly wanting are the temples and writing, the walled towns and kingdoms, the district gods and royal tombs of Egypt, Babylon, Syria, and Canaan. The picture is that of the first historical Indo-Europeans elsewhere, pre-Homeric Greeks or western-European Kelts of subsequent centuries, with whom the Aryans, as shown by their speech, undoubtedly were at one time in connection, presumably through the countries north of the Black and Caspian seas. The Aryans contributed many elements to Indian civilization: the horse, armor, butter, hearth and fire worship, and certain ideas. Yet this cityless, hut-dwelling, cattle-raiding, unorganized, uncommercial Vedic people, with its imageless, antiphallic religion, could not have been more than one root of several from which the complex culture of later India grew.

A few centuries later, the culture depicted by the literary remains of the time of Buddha is again profoundly altered. The focus of the scene has shifted to the Ganges Valley. There are cities and palaces, wealth and pomp. There are kings, priests, townsmen, peasants, hermits, and ascetics. Caste is in vogue. Cotton and rice are widely used. There is a deal of philosophizing; life appears complex and difficult; pessimism is abroad, soul rebirth taken for granted, spirituality emphasized. Concepts to which Western science later returned, the atom and the ether, are familiar. In all essentials, post-Christian Hinduism had been blocked out in this pre-Christian period of the time of Buddha. Only a few elements such as coined money and writing are still lacking, though they were soon to be introduced.

This change from the Vedic age is not fully accounted for, even though the mystic philosophical Upanishads fall in the interval. Buddha flourished probably about 500 B.C. in the Ganges Valley. His doctrine assumes ideas that are also part of the Sankhya philosophy—in many ways the subtlest philosophy of India and one of the great thought systematizations of the world. Its founder Kapila may be mythical as a predecessor of Buddha, but the thoughts attributed to him must be old. Caste seems an institution requiring time to develop ramifications. It is absent in the Vedas, but Buddhism is already in a measure a protest against it. It seems difficult to squeeze such growths into a few hundred years without invoking strong outside influences. Possibly we should be seeing more clearly if we knew more about the early cultural condition of the Dravidians of southern India. They constitute a fifth of the population of India today, and may have formed a larger fraction formerly. They begin to emerge into the ken of history in early Christian centuries, in part even before, with kingdoms, commerce, and writing. Their culture of that time is at least partly derived from the Aryan-speaking Ganges Valley. If we ever succeed in extending its age backward, it might prove to be one of the influences contributing to the Gangetic culture of Buddha's time when subsequent Indian civilization was crystallizing.

306. INDIAN CASTE AND RELIGION

Caste is peculiarly Indian. Nowhere else is it so complex, so systematically worked out and endlessly reinforced by ritual and taboo, so pervasive of conduct and thought. It has been ascribed to the conflict of races, to the drawing of a color line by conquerors in order to keep their lineage and culture pure. If so, it has failed egregiously, as the physical anthropology of modern India shows. The racial explanation is obviously inadequate. Castes do represent race to a certain extent, but they also represent nationalities, tribes, common residence, religious distinctness, occupations, cultural status. Whatever sets off a group in any way may be sufficient to make it a caste in India. If groups diverge within an established caste, they become recognized as subcastes, perhaps finally to develop into wholly separate castes. Priests, nobles, clerks, fishermen, street-sweepers are castes; so are the Parsis; so are hill tribes that maintain their primitive customs—the Dravidian buffalo-milking Todas, for instance, are reckoned high socially. Clearly we have here a generic system, a pattern of organizing society, into which every sort of group as it actually forms is fitted. Caste is a way of thought that the Hindu has tried to universalize.

All Indian castes are in theory strictly endogamous: intermarriage is intolerable. All possess an intrinsic, unchangeable worth. Thus they automatically rank themselves. Each possesses an occupation, a mode of life and customs, a set of prescribed rituals, inherently peculiar to it. The greater the restrictions and prohibitions incumbent upon it, the less it relaxes to comfort and indifference, the more spiritual it is, the higher its grade. In consequence it is also the more pollutable, and so its restrictions are drawn the closer. The wider the gap of non-intercourse, of noncontact with lower castes, the greater becomes its purity. Caste observance is thus a virtue, an aid to religion and morality; breaking caste is an ultimate indecency; the offspring of intercaste unions are necessarily lower than either parent, and their descendants, unless from matings with their own miserable kind, are lower still, in infinitely descending series. There is no elevating a caste. The very attempt to rise is a vice that brings degradation as a result, since castes are eternal, founded in nature, absolute, so that alteration is of necessity a sullying.

Such is the Hindu scheme—which in actuality is wholly lived up to in no single point. Perverse as the system seems to men reared in other cultures, it must be admitted to possess completeness, self-consistency, and the desire to preserve inward worth. It differs from the basic assumptions of our civilization in that it sees value as something already existing and therefore to be maintained, not something to be created; it tries to fit life into a theoretical pattern; it is futureless.[19] Yet all the facts show that as historical realities castes have always changed and are changing now.[20] Obviously, therefore, each generation ignores the changes last made and repeats its insistence on caste perpetuity and unalterability. Such is the hold of conscious pattern on men's minds.

The theorizing the Hindu does about caste is characteristic of him in all cultural manifestations. The relation that can be thought out between one fact or act and others, the compartment to which it can be assigned in a system, are of more interest to him, as compared with the fact itself, than to peoples of other civilizations. Hence philosophy has flourished in India, but native history has been inadequate and disorderly. Hence too the abstract sciences of logic and grammar enjoyed an early original development, equal for a long time to that which they attained in the West, and in part antecedent. On the other hand, the astronomical and still more the physical and biological sciences remained backward; they were concerned with concrete objects. The Hindus seem never to have made a move of their own toward devising a system of writing; but once the Aramaean alphabet had been introduced, they modified, expanded, and rearranged it into a more logical scheme, a more consistent one phonetically, than any other people has given it (§ 219). It is probably no accident that the abstruse game of chess and our "Arabic" position numerals with a symbol for

[19] The Hindu caste system largely blocks social mobility and personal advancement; but it does provide a great sense of social stability and comforting security for the individual.

[20] In India it is ordinarily only castes, not individuals, that can gradually rise or fall in the social hierarchy.

zero (§ 189) are Hindu inventions, and that it is only in India that priests have for age after age been ranked higher than rulers.

It is natural that a culture of such inclinations should exalt the mind and the soul above the body (§ 248). Hence the extraordinary development of asceticism in Indian religion; its deep pessimism as regards life on this earth; its insistence on the superior reality of soul, with which is connected the universal assumption of rebirths; the working out of a system of unescapable moral causality called Karma in place of a scheme of mechanical causation; the tendencies toward pantheistic identification of soul and God, or atheistic denial of divinity as distinct from soul; and the thoroughly antimaterialistic bent of almost all Hindu philosophy. It is also intelligible that these qualities should have imparted to Indian religion a superior degree of spiritual intensity which was appreciated by the nations to the north and east when Buddhism was presented to them, and caused them to embrace it.

Like Christianity, however, Buddhism found no permanent favor among the people and in the land of its origin. It flourished in India for a time, but was rarely looked upon as more than a sect; after something over a thousand years it died out completely, except in Ceylon, at the very period that its hold on non-Indian nations to the north and east was strengthening. Its place was taken in India by the miscellaneous assemblage of cults, all theoretically recognizing Brahman ascendancy, that in the aggregate constitute what is known as Hinduism. Hinduism is not a religion in the sense that Christianity, Mohammedanism, Buddhism are religions. It recognizes no personal founder, no head or establishment; it tends to exclude foreigners rather than to convert them; it is national instead of universal. It accepts and reinforces the existing institutions of its particular culture: caste, for instance, which Buddhism tried to transcend. Hinduism is therefore comparable to the ancient Greek and early western-Asiatic religions in consisting of a series of locally or tribally different cults never fully integrated or harmonized, conscious and tolerant of one another, resting on common assumptions and similar in content, everywhere in accord with tradition and usage, resistive to formal organization into a larger whole, but tied into a certain unity through reflecting a more or less common civilization.

Hinduism is also comparable to Confucianism and Shintoism; yet with a difference. These grew up analogously, but early became associated with a central government or imperial authority, to which India never attained. They gradually became official religions, as which they survive; such religious piety as the population of China and Japan experiences finds its outlet largely through Buddhism. Buddhism may be said to have failed in India because it aimed at being a universal religion; because it tried to be international instead of national, to overlie all cultures instead of identifying itself with one. The Hindu, like the Jew, preferred remaining within the limits of his nationality and his particular civilization.

307. RELATIONS BETWEEN INDIA AND THE OUTER WORLD

We have seen Mesopotamian influence entering India in the third millennium B.C., and Indo-Iranian in the latter half of the second. In the first millennium, the introduction of alphabetic writing suggests that other cultural ingredients may also have flowed into India from the West without a preserved direct record of their transmission. The Persian and Macedonian conquests extended only over the westernmost margin of India and were of little direct influence. But the latter was followed by a semi-Hellenization of southwestern Asia, including for instance the establishment of a Graeco-Bactrian kingdom in southern Turkestan and Afghanistan, finally spilling over into adjacent parts of India. So for several centuries a stream of Greek culture elements trickled into the heart of India. Sculpture, architecture, astronomy, drama, and coinage derived new impetus, in some cases even their origin, from this source. In some instances the Hindus were no more than copiers of Hellenistic models: Greek hangs and folds were given to sculptured garments, Greek astronomical measurements taken over without change. Yet as the centuries wore on and new imports along these lines lessened and then died out, the introduced elements became more deeply incorporated into Indian civilization, modified and encrusted more and more heavily by distinctive Hindu styles, until now their superficial appearance makes an impression of independent native growth. The working-over of the alphabet into its Hindu forms (§ 219) may be taken as typical of the nature and the degree of the remodeling also of Hellenistic culture imports.

Soon after A.D. 700 there began a series of Mohammedan invasions and conquests—Arab, Afghan, and Mongol-Turkish—also from the northwest, and of course accompanied by a new series of culture influences—firearms, for instance, and the true arch—which in their turn underwent absorption and partial transformation.

The flow of culture between India and the Mediterranean world has not been wholly eastward. Cotton; the common domestic fowl; probably the buffalo and rice; perhaps asceticism, monastic life, and certain mystic points of view; position numerals with zero; chess; and some of the concepts of modern philology—all these were transmitted westward. East Africa was influenced through the medium of Arab sea trade. Toward the north and northeast as far as Mongolia, Korea, and Japan, India has been a dispenser of culture content and has taken little in return. Toward the southeast, Indian influence has been the largest component in the civilization of Farther India and the East Indian archipelago, which in their higher attainments may be regarded as cultural dependencies or extensions of India. Culturally, they constitute a colonial India.

308. COLONIAL INDIA

Eastward from India proper lie two areas, Farther India and Indonesia, which, beginning in the earliest centuries of the Christian era, were visited, missionized, colonized, and civilized from India. For a thousand years and more a Hinduized culture flourished here, sometimes Brahman and sometimes Buddhist, and constituted a derived or colonial India. As a result, these regions have something of a real history extending back nearly two thousand years from the present. This history has been enriched and vivified by archaeological clearing of some of its famous or splendid sites, such as Angkor and Boro-budur. When we get so far back that the direct historical records end, inscriptions, sculpture, and ruined cities also end: we are in a frank prehistory, and a rather bald one, or at any rate in a very meagerly explored preliterate period.

Farther India is the roughly quadrilateral peninsula that politically comprises Burma, Siam or Thailand, and French Indo-China. Its area is about three-quarters of a million square miles, and most of it is fertile, tropical, and wooded. Our grandfathers and even our fathers used to call the whole region Indo-China because it lies between India and China; but we of today tend to become confused by this generic term because we think first of Indo-China as a French political possession. "Farther India" is at least unequivocal.

The second region also used to have a definite and familiar designation in the term "East Indies," which however suffers from tending to be limited in usage to the Dutch-controlled islands. On the contrary, the Philippines and Malaya form an integral part of the area, ethnically and historically; whereas Dutch New Guinea does not, though it is politically part of the Netherlands East Indies. The term "Indonesia" will therefore be used here. It has the advantage of a primarily ethnic implication. "Malaysia" is also perfectly valid, provided it is kept distinct from more limited "Malay" and "Malaya." Indonesia constitutes the world's greatest archipelago, and in this fact it contrasts with continental Farther India. Its ethnic organization is refreshingly simple. Apart from a few thousand Negritos, its population is all of Oceanic Mongoloid race (§ 63), whose subdivision into Proto-Malaysian and Deutero-Malaysian strata is of secondary import. All the 80 million people here—except again a few Negritos, this time Andamanese and perhaps Semang—also speak varieties and dialects of one original speech, of which Malay, Javanese, and Tagalog are among the better-known exemplifications. This basic tongue or group of languages the philologists, fortunately for us, have got into the habit of calling Indonesian. Together with Melanesian, Micronesian, and Polynesian, it constitutes the still larger Malayo-Polynesian family, which is gradually being rechristened Austronesian.

Farther India also is simple racially, being substantially all not only Mongoloid but Asiatic Mongolian. A few scattered Indo-Australoid or Veddoid tribes are numerically insignificant. In speech, the situation is more complex. In fact,

Farther India is one of the world's remaining Babels, along with New Guinea, the Sudan, and native California. However, its languages segregate into tonal and nontonal idioms, and this distinction appears to have considerable historical and prehistoric significance. The nontonal languages seem the more aboriginal and are known as the Mon-Khmer, after the Mon or Talaing, formerly dominant in lower Burma, and the Khmer of Cambodia, of whom some 3 millions remain under French sovereignty, though their kingdom with its once glorious history has long been a vassal to its neighbors. There are also many semiprimitive and primitive tribes in Farther India speaking languages of Mon-Khmer affinity. The tonal languages are like Chinese in having levels or inflections of musical pitch as an intrinsic quality of words. There are three main tonal languages, each spoken by a considerable people around whom a political nation has formed: Burmese (related to Tibetan); Thai or T'ai or Siamese-Shan; and Annamese. Whether or not these languages are related in origin to Chinese, or have merely come gradually under the same set of influences, is still in dispute. The probability of genetic relationship with Chinese seems greatest for the first of the three, least for the last (§ 96).

As regards prehistory of both regions, this still focuses largely on such matters as types and distribution of axes. Excavations in Tongking—which borders on China—show a transition from struck to polished stone axes apparently preceding (§ 277) the appearance of pottery—the reverse of the European sequence. The relative age of farming, though it is more important than either, seems to be not yet known. On the Asiatic mainland, a characteristic ground-stone ax has a flat blade with a tongue or tenon projecting back to mortise into a socket in the handle; but this may date from a time when bronze was imported. In Indonesia, an oblong form with gabled upper surface prevails, except that in the Philippines a tongued or stepped form recurs. Bronze axes normally have a socket for the handle. It is not yet sure whether a separate Bronze Age existed, especially in the archipelago: iron may have been introduced before the local populations had graduated from stone to bronze-casting. The archaeology gets on a firmer basis after inscriptions begin to be found in several countries of Farther India some five or six centuries after Christ.

Among the remoter mountains of the mainland, and in the interior of some of the larger islands such as Sumatra, Borneo, and Luzon, populations have maintained themselves with a type of life that has preserved many of its features from pre-Christian times. The chief change probably is the introduction of utilitarian iron for weapons, axes, and knives—but it is the smith's craft that has been learned rather than the miner's. There are numerous traits whose distribution from the Naga of Assam to the Batak of Sumatra and the Ifugao of the Philippines indicates their antiquity. These include: Kaingin farming by burning and slashing new pieces of forest when weeds overrun the old gardens; terrace irrigation of wet rice; keeping of chickens and pigs, sometimes of buffalo also; multifarious use of bamboo for houses, spears and bows, handles, knives, containers, musical instruments, and what not; raising dwellings on piles off the ground; here and there, surprising megalithic monuments; separate men's or girls' dormitories, with associated but varied customs of courtship and trial marriage; strong development of legal institutions, but weak political ones; blood feud and head-hunting; survival of sacrifice, divination, and ordeals of the types widely prevalent before their displacement by the great world religions (§ 128, 192, 238). Wherever in Farther India and Indonesia we find retarded cultures, they conform to this basic type, though of course with the considerable degree of detailed variation expectable between societies that have long been out of direct intercommunication. Wherever we no longer find such cultures, there are indications of Indian, Chinese, Buddhist, Islamic, or Western Christian influences having flowed in and obliterated them.

Much the strongest of these foreign influences was the Indian. This was sea-borne; necessarily so in historical times for the archipelago, but mainly also on the continent. Burma was more affected by ships sailing to its river mouths than by adjacent overland communications. The Indian colonies or stimulation states on the far side of the long intervening Malay Peninsula came to florescence sooner, if anything, than those in nearer Burma. Second, the Hindus who came were mainly Dravidians from the south. Third, there is no indication of any mass movements. The population everywhere remained indigenous; their speech maintained itself; when Sanskrit or Pali was introduced or written, it was as formal court idiom, or the language of inscription, law, or religion. The Indians who immigrated were missionaries, younger sons of princes or refugee rulers, their mercenaries or followers, adventurers, and merchants. These preserved and spread as much Indian culture as they could, and as a leaven they were exceedingly effective. But they largely married with native women, they gradually lost contacts with the homeland, and their descendants became absorbed in the mass of the population. A final feature was that both Buddhism and Brahmanism were introduced, in a competition that on the whole was fairly amicable. Brahmanism made some fairly late gains, but was ultimately displaced. On the mainland it was succeeded by the Ceylonese or Pali form of Buddhism,[21] which began to come in about the eleventh century; in the islands, by Islam carried by militant Arabs even later.

One of the first cultures and kingdoms to flourish was that of Champa, in central coastal Annam. The ruling population, the Cham, spoke an Indonesian language. The Cham can be traced back to the second century a.c., reached their peak around the seventh and eighth, to judge by their preserved sculpture and edifices, and did not finally succumb to the expanding Tongkinese or Annamese until 1471.

[21] Of the Hinayana or Lesser Vehicle type. The Buddhism of China, Korea, Japan, Tibet, and Mongolia is basically Greater Vehicle or Mahayana, and reached those countries by land routes.

Of about equal antiquity and more famous are the Khmer or Cambodians, who according to Chinese reports started in the first post-Christian century with a colony at the mouth of the Mekong—Indian Brahmans marrying native "snake-spirit" princesses. There followed an upriver subcolony, consolidation into one larger kingdom, and finally the monumentally sculptured palace and temple city at Angkor about 900, which endured until its sack by the Siamese in 1431. Cambodia was probably at its peak around the 1100's. Its Sanskrit was pure; its sculpture, a really great art; its ruins are impressive.

Siam showed a parallel early history, but remained long in the shadow of Cambodia, culturally and at times politically. The early states and capitals were on the coast or lower Menam where Hindus reached them; they seem to have been Mon-speaking. The original center of the Thai lay well to the north, in what is now Yünnan in China, where as early as 649 they set up the kingdom of Nan Chao. This lasted until the Mongols smashed it in the thirteenth century, along with so much else in Asia and Europe. The result was a Thai shift southward, with capitals increasingly nearer the sea, ending with the port of Bangkok.

The first cities and writing in Burma were among the Mon in the lower part of the country. The Burmese proper, then still in upper Burma only, did not come into full participation in civilization, and into political dominance, until the eleventh century, when Anawratha founded a dynasty that gave his people national consciousness, an alphabet of their own, Ceylonese Buddhism, and a style of architecture. A revival occurred five centuries later, with strong Burmese rulers at Pegu in what was original Mon territory.

The Annamese are the one nationality who walked mainly in Chinese instead of Indian leading strings. Tongking was overrun by Chinese generals as early as 218 B.C., was definitely conquered by the Han, and remained under Chinese rule for a thousand years. During all this time the Cham and Cambodian Khmer still occupied the center and south of present-day Annamese territory. During one of the periodic interdynastic political confusions in China, the Tongkinese or Annamese became independent in 968, and have remained so since except for a spurt of a couple of decades in the fifteenth century when the Mings, the last native Chinese dynasty, temporarily overran them. Gradually the Annamese conquered the peoples south of them and spread over the whole east coast of the peninsula. They have taken over innumerable traits of Chinese culture: writing characters, family names, nominal Confucianism, with Mahayana Buddhism and geomancy, mandarins and examinations, military subordination to civilians, titular aristocracy, theater, chopsticks. There is no doubt that the Annamese belong as decisively to the Chinese culture sphere as the other peoples of Farther India and Indonesia belong to the Indian culture.

Sumatra and Java used to be known as Greater and Lesser Java. The former appears to have been less thoroughly subject to Hinduization, and the Indian influence was earlier replaced by Mohammedanization. Sumatra has not yet revealed stone temples and statuary rivaling those of Java. In the smaller island, the outstanding monument is the gigantic Buddhist pyramidal stupa or pagoda called Boro-budur, which dates probably from about A.D. 850. This has endless stone galleries with literally thousands of large and small statues and sculptured panels. Later Javanese art is increasingly Brahmanistic. This drift is connected with the religious complexion of the successive Javanese realms, of which the best-known and probably most powerful was the empire of Madja-pahit, with many overseas vassals and outposts in the archipelago. Brahman Madja-pahit in 1377 put an end to the remnant of a Sumatran Buddhist empire, Sri-Vijaya, with capital near Palembang, which had begun to flourish as early as the seventh century. The sailing fleets of these states brought some knowledge of Indian writing, religion, and statecraft to islands as far away as the Philippines. The smaller East Indian islands were affected to various degrees.

When Islam entered, Buddhism had pretty well passed away in the islands, and the Arabs attacked Brahmanic religion as idolatrous and an abomination. Successively they conquered and converted most of Sumatra; Malacca and the rest of Malaya; Java; the coasts of Borneo; and the southernmost Philippines, where the Spaniards encountered and checked them in the sixteenth century. From eastern Java, some of the Hinduized upper castes fled from the Moslems to the neighboring island of Bali, where a strange relic of Brahmanism survives, fascinatingly hybridized with native Indonesian culture. We have already en-countered a fragment of this persistence in the ritual calendar (§ 230). The art of Bali too, though living and original, derives from original Indian inspiration.

309. THE PACIFIC: MELANESIA AND POLYNESIA

As one passes across the faults in the earth's crust known as Wallace's and Weber's lines, and goes from the East Indies to New Guinea, the continental histories and affiliations change, the animal and plant assemblages change, and human race and culture change. Brown, mainly Mongoloid Indonesians are replaced by black, frizzy, broad-nosed Papuans and Melanesians. The mass impact of Indian and Islamic civilizations suddenly ceases. Metals, rice, cotton, the buffalo, the last traces of native writing and of royalty, all disappear: we are among wholly primitive people in New Guinea and Melanesia. To their south are the aboriginal Australians, also black and broad-nosed, but reckoned outside the true Negroid racial stock. To the east, out in the Pacific, the brown race reappears among Micronesians and Melanesians, though in somewhat variant or perhaps mixed form.

In speech, these brown peoples in the Pacific are also allied to the Indo-nesians: they talk Austronesian languages. So do the black Melanesians, both those of their proper archipelago and those of the shore line of New Guinea; though the Papuans of the interior do not. There can be little doubt that this Austronesian speech of the blacks of the smaller islands was acquired by them from the brown populations who are now in the much larger stretches of the island world on both sides of them—to their west in Indonesia and to their east in Micronesia-Polynesia. The over-all situation hardly allows of any other reasonable interpretation. But the how and when of what happened are unclear. The brown peoples are much the better navigators; and the distances to which they have scattered, from Madagascar to Easter Island, show that they were much the better in the past also. The Micronesians and the Polynesians must have come from the west in reaching their relatively tiny islands scattered far-flung through the open Pacific: either from Indonesia, or from Asia via Indonesia. This would bring them, or some of them, past or near New Guinea and Melanesia. Or perhaps they detoured a bit, or partly reversed, to reach Melanesia. Just what happened on the contact of browns and blacks in Melanesia can only be inferred. As older residents, the blacks were probably much more numerous; but the brown people were more advanced, coming from nearer the center of things. They may have conquered the frizzy aborigines; or overawed and impressed them; or traded and intermarried with them; perhaps even let them learn enough navigation and enterprise to push on their own a few islands farther out into the Pacific. Just what new culture the ancestral Micronesian-Polynesians brought in, and what they found the Negroids using, has not been reconstructed. What is undeniable is that after enough time had passed—perhaps a thousand years, perhaps much longer—an essential resegregation was effected. When Caucasian discoverers arrived, the Melanesians were still—or again—Negroid, because this strain had been the preponderant one, numerically, in their biological ancestry. In language they had become Austronesian, because that speech, through being associated with either cultural superiority or conquest or trade advantage, evidently had the greater prestige and strength of spread, and so tended to replace the localized indigenous idioms, except in some interiors difficult of access. The Melanesian culture had become a blend: some of it like Polynesian; some of it unlike, and showing, through New Guinea, affiliations even with Australia.

Other hypothetical explanations are conceivable. Thus: The ancestral Micronesian-Polynesians, exploring out into the Pacific, did not try to penetrate the jungles of New Guinea, but touched here and there on its coasts, perhaps intermarried with the Papuans, and then went on, themselves now more or less mixed or even hybridized, to adjacent Melanesia. Here, however, they were still in a region of malignant malaria. As a result, those of them who had acquired relative hereditary immunity—so far as there is such (§ 84)—through their ancestors, having lived in New Guinea—in other words those predominantly black in physique—would survive; those without immunity, or without enough of it—namely, the browns—would succumb and die out, or would save themselves only by pushing farther out into healthier parts of the Pacific. This theory would also account for the facts of the situation, and is more dramatically interesting than the one outlined above. Unfortunately, long-range experience runs to the effect that simple, matter-of-fact, unexciting explanations more often prove true than do emotionally exciting ones.

Let us examine the Melanesians and the Polynesians for their differences and similarities, especially with peoples outside the area. Prehistory will not help us much here: archaeological exploration has been too scant and scattering, or does not yet cut deep enough to reach the basic problem.

Both Papuan-Melanesian and Micronesian-Polynesian cultures suffuse an impression of being residual. But the culture of the blacks looks like the continuation of something long isolated and retarded; that of the browns, like the remnant of something that once was larger or more advanced.

Micronesians and Polynesians generally lack the bow and pottery. As these are Mesolithic elements when we are reckoning in Western stages, and since the Polynesians have fine Neolithic polished adzes and agriculture, it looks as if they might once have had the bow and pottery but lost them again (§ 157). They have certainly lost the rice of Indonesia, or failed to adopt it after knowing it, though they possess taro and yam as root crops, and banana and breadfruit as tree crops. They have the pig and the chicken of colonial India, but not its buffalo. This bulky animal could not have been carried along with them in thousand-mile open-canoe voyages. Other cultural items might easily have been transported, such as metal or loom-woven cloth or batik, but their production could not have been continued in the small Polynesian islands, or on Micronesian atolls, for lack of necessary materials. All this looks as if Micronesian-Polynesian culture were a reduced version—reduced because of distance and environment. Now what positive traits has it that are a perpetuation and an indication of the larger or higher culture from which it may have become abbreviated?

First of all, the Polynesians recognize a royalty that is divine and descended from gods; and along with this, an aristocratic hierarchy of social rank such as is quite incongruous with primitive democracy. Next, they practice sacrifice, especially human; accompanied by cannibalism, it is true, but still blood sacrifice to gods. Then, locally at least, they make statues or megaliths (§ 158, 283). There is an equivalent of history in their long genealogies of chiefs and royalty. These lists are a mixture of true memory and invention, but they evidence at least a genuine perspective of the past. Polynesian mythology runs into cosmogonic and philosophical speculation, sometimes grappling with profundities like evolutionary development, primary causes, or incarnations of abstractions suggestive of Brahman-Buddhist thinking. Myths and legends dwell on subjective feelings, or landscapes, or use metaphors more reminiscent of civilized literatures than of the bare campfire tales of huddled savages. All this is like echoes of something much bigger. Only, it is worn down by time, broken by removal and distance, filtered by scatterings and the once small numbers of canoeloads, until we can no longer say of what specific greater culture it is a remnant—whether of India itself, of Indonesia, perhaps of Java Minor or Champa or what other forgotten coast?

All these things are lacking among the Oceanic Negroids, except where here and there, as in Fiji and the southern New Hebrides, they have come under recent Polynesian influence. The Melanesians do not have god-kings, hereditary aristocrats, genealogies, speculations, literature, or anything else reminiscent of former high estate or associations. They are endlessly addicted to concern over being bewitched and bewitching in revenge. They are much given to elaborating kinship into organized groupings and other prescriptive forms: patrilineal clans, matrilineal clans, moieties, totems, cross-cousin marriage, avunculocal residence, and the like. This is in contrast with the brown peoples, both Indonesian and Polynesian, among whom such social artificialities are indeed not unknown, but do tend to be mild and sporadic. In general, the brown Austronesians favor bilateral descent and organization of kinship on a basis of generations rather than of prescriptive or prohibited marriage. The blacks are also strong for secret religious societies, both tribal and exclusive. Social distinction is achieved through the latter, as well as through financial transactions: payments, loans, gifts, repayments, which may involve interest and be quite complicated. All this planning and scrambling for property and temporary rank the Polynesians are pretty much free from. Under their aristocratic system, a man has rank or hasn't it, and either way he seems content.

It is thus evident that the ethos, the cultural orientation, of the black and the brown peoples of the Pacific is thoroughly distinct. In fact, some of the bents of the Papua-Melanesian culture are present also in aboriginal Australian culture.

Such variations in outlook inevitably involve variant temperaments for the societies possessing the cultures, and for the individual persons born and raised in the societies. And in fact, the temperamental difference between Polynesians and Melanesians is conspicuous (§ 250). Moreover, this culture-historical explanation makes it unnecessary to fall back on biological heredity, on genetic race, to explain the psychological distinctness, unnecessary to posit the temperamental difference as inherently fixed and permanent. Indeed, the Papuan-Melanesian Negroids, though they undoubtedly have their closest anatomical relatives among the African Negroes, are not at all like these in personality type. They are tense, taciturn, sensitive, given to worry, introverts with a sense both of sin and of injury, scheming and planning and striving. By contrast, the African Negro is generally pictured as relaxed, voluble, amiable, and extravert.

310. THE ISOLATED CONTINENT: AUSTRALIA

Australia was discovered late and entered history still later. Its prehistoric studies are still in their infancy. There has long been a general inclination to view the Australian aborigines as utterly primitive. In consequence, one obviou problem has hardly yet obtruded: namely, what the successive developmental steps of their prehistory may have been. Instead, the tendency has been to try to determine the Palaeolithic stage of which they might be the living representatives. Such considerations were influenced by the implicit presupposition already noted and formerly widespread, that the phases found in European prehistory represented a necessary sequence, something immanent or inherent in human nature; that these stages might be traversed more or less rapidly by various socities, but that presumably there would normally be an Acheulian stage to precede a Mousterian, and a Neolithic to follow on a Magdalenian one; and that some societies might get hung up, say on the Mousterian level, and continue on it until today. But if we start fresh on a purely factual basis, what we find is roughly the following.

The data are not yet in hand for a coherent empirical story of the actual changes of ancient culture in Australia. Of the recent natives, some ground stone and some did not bother to, without any clear indication that the former were more "advanced" than the latter in the rest of their culture. The total culture, in fact, was very similar in level over the whole continent. Indeed, it remained remarkably even and uniform in ethos under favorable and under desert conditions, in temperate and in tropical environment. A number of powerful aids to cultural development were wholly lacking: not only planting and animal-raising, and of course metals, but even pottery and the bow and arrow; canoes were used only along some shores. Such conspicuous absences readily suggest that it was isolation which kept these and many other inventions from reaching Australia, much as its native mammalian fauna is restricted to the early-developed marsupials, the later placentals having never succeeded in entering the continent (§ 174, 238). This explanation by isolation is no doubt partly true; but it can be overdone. Theoretically useful things, such as the bow or pottery, may not be useful under all circumstances, and may therefore be given up and forgotten (§ 157). Or they may fail of acceptance when introduced (§ 151).

From the angle of the student of culture totalities rather than culture items, it is quite evident that the native Australians got along with less material equipment and paraphernalia than they could have produced if they had wanted to; and with less than their environment limited them to. They could have worn clothing. They could have built actual houses instead of windbreaks or little domed shelters of brush. More of their tribes could have constructed bark canoes, or dug out wooden ones. It is quite evident that on the whole they preferred to do without these conveniences rather than trouble to produce them, or even to be bothered with taking care of them. This has been dwelt on before (§ 146, 253). We are so habituated to possessions that we forget that being propertyless also has its advantages, and that there are individuals and classes in our own society who prefer being untrammeled and mobile. The Australian travels light: a spear, a boomerang club, and perhaps a spear-thrower for the man; a digging stick and a bowl receptacle for the woman.[22] A mode of life engenders an attitude; the attitude fortifies custom; and the outcome is a culture kept by its society as materially meager as possible.

If we add this negative inclination toward material possessions to Papuan-Melanesian culture as it has been outlined, we are fairly near having Australian, in the rough. Or, let us put it positively. Screen Papuan-Melanesian culture through the filter of basic Australian attitude, and there go out: houses built with pride of appearance, storehouses, canoes, shell money and treasures; not to mention gardens and penned pigs, which keep one tied down. With the shell and treasure, capitalistic prestige and loans also go out, and social clubs expressing accumulated rank. What is left is close to what is well developed or luxuriant in Australian culture. These well-developed Australian aspects include: the social kin structure made intricate with moieties, marriage classes and subclasses, descent reckoning and totems; a system of magic rich both in constructive rituals and in destructive witchcraft; for boys, tribal initiations into the rituals and mythology; and an immediate magico-ritual relation between each individual and the cosmogonic ancestors—instead of a historical relation through genealogies, as in Polynesia. This seems a fair summary of the trends which are most characteristic of Australian culture.

Since the aboriginal Australians are generally considered the most "primitive," the most "lowly," of recent living peoples, it is worth examining how far their culture as here outlined really justifies these epithets. Let us analyze it for a moment, since "primitive" can refer to backwardness in time or to backwardness in development; and it may conceivably mean other things yet.

The simplicity of Australian culture in regard to material possessions is probably what has done most to give it the repute of being very "low." But, as we have seen, their propertylessness is the result of habit-forming attitudes (§ 253), and therefore voluntary in one sense, though no doubt unconsciously so. At any rate, it is not the same thing as constitutional inability to make or acquire things. When a monk takes the vow of poverty, when a Buddhist or Brahman ascetic renounces everything material in the world, we may think him unusual, but he cannot be called incompetent or "low."

On the other side is the Australian's organization of his social, conceptual, and ritual world. This is definitely elaborate: full of distinct features and precise rules, well interrelated. In fact, nowhere else have theoretical ethnologists and sociologists been able to demonstrate so neat a functional integration (§ 122) of the parts of culture to the whole as among the Australians. Their mythology is enacted in their ritual; their ritual serves their food-getting; this in turn gears in through totemism with the social structure; the social structure is reflected in

---

[22] All of these are of wood, which fact serves as an ironical reminder of how little we probably know of the totality of some of the ancient cultures from which only stone pieces have been preserved.

the myth beliefs; and so on and on around the circle. Other peoples' cultures normally are less closely integrated: a corresponding attempt to show their integration works out to be less comprehensive. But other living or recent peoples also invariably have or try to have more property, beyond the minimal food-getting implements. It may accordingly be suspected that internal integration is achieved easily or with difficulty in proportion to a culture's renouncing or adhering to material possessions; say somewhat on the principle of those who have riches hardly entering into the kingdom of God.[23] But this leads us off from the question of primitiveness into something quite else: unless one be ready to make successful integration of culture an index of its primitiveness, which would surely be a strange view to take.

As to whether the Australians, then, are the least-developed of mankind, we cannot say. They are or are not, according as we look at this or that side of their culture. Whether this culture of theirs is specifically like that of emergent man in glacial times, we cannot say, because we lack knowledge for the comparison. Descriptively, the most striking feature of the culture is the disproportion or imbalance of its material and nonmaterial sides. It is probably the underdevelopment of technology and property that, by contrast with our own, makes this Australian culture seem to us at first blush so low.

The recently extinct Tasmanians, on their island off beyond Australia, were supermarginal. What the Australians lacked they lacked too; and in addition, so far as we can still tell, they did without spear-throwers, boomerangs, parrying shields, ground stone, nets and all other implements for taking fish. The Tasmanians might originally have walked across to their island during a glaciation that lowered the ocean level till Bass Strait was dry; and have then vegetated there ever since, as living exemplifications of Pleistocene culture. The idea has a dramatic appeal; which however may again be against rather than for its scientific probability. What is equally dramatic and in fact tragic, and much better attested, is the way the white settlers killed off the Tasmanian aborigines—all but a final handful—while being too indifferent to record even enough exact information to enable us to know how far the Tasmanians really were a super-marginal relict.

311. AFRICA

As a background to the development of culture in Africa, it is well to remember that the northern third of the continent is inhabited by aboriginal white men, with presumptive one-time connections of origin with the white men of Asia and Europe. Also, prehistorically not only Egypt but also the rest of North Africa were closely allied to southwestern Asia and Europe. Until the late Palaeolithic, North Africa on the whole influenced Europe more than Europe did that region (§ 273). Subsequently North Africa, though somewhat influenced from Egypt, became retarded, and retained Mesolithic, Neolithic, and Bronze Age

[23] Mark 10: 23.

features into Carthaginian and Roman times (§ 275). South of the Sahara, the strictly prehistoric record is still too incomplete or uncertain to tie reliably into the historical picture, except perhaps to some extent for the Bushmen (§ 64, 200, 277). What happened has therefore to be largely inferred from the recent ethnography.

Inasmuch as Egypt became an organized and civilized state with cities and writing five thousand years ago, we should expect all sorts of cultural ideas to have flowed from it into Negro as well as Caucasian Africa. North Africa was first colonized by Phoenician Carthaginians nearly three thousand years ago, then locally by Greeks, and thereafter was occupied by Romans and then Arabs. The Arabs penetrated into the nearer Negro parts, often instilling Islam. The pre-Arab settlers in North Africa penetrated less far, but did maintain trade relations. Yet what the Negroes may have learned from these older relations has undoubtedly been both changed in appearance by long Negro reworking and further overlaid by Mohammedan absorptions; so the contribution is usually not easy to recognize. Along the East coast, there were ancient Egyptian and Roman voyages, followed by Arab trading as far as Zanzibar. As the Arabs traded also to India, a number of culture traits were brought in from there: cotton, the pit loom, humped cattle, perhaps the chicken. Finally, Madagascar is Indonesian in speech, was therefore colonized from Indonesia, and in consequence has Oriental features such as rice-growing and the Malaysian piston bellows.

All in all, Negro Africa lies open enough to the main Eurasian centers to have presumably experienced a slow cultural "bombardment" that constantly mingled new traits with old, foreign with acclimated, and acclimated elements with those indigenously evolved. Through the centuries and millennia, everything got worked over until it took on the native local color. It is only now and then that we can be wholly sure of the place of origin of elements in African culture: as we can for the zodiac ornaments of West Africa (§ 229).

Similarly, the concept of a cow, a ram, or a goat with a solar disk between its horns rests on nothing visible in the world of reality or spontaneous in human nature; it is, instead, an "arbitrary" or artificial invention. Hence its occurrence in post-Capsian Berber petroglyphs (§ 275) serves to date these as post-3000 B.C., the symbol being a Dynastic-period one in Egypt. The modern Nilotic tribes far up the Nile, such as the Nuer, have a trick of sawing the horns of their cattle at a bevel to make them grow out downward, or in front of the face, or in other odd directions, often unilaterally, in order to distinguish or to beautify the animals. This same device was practiced by the Old and Middle Kingdom Egyptians. It was then given up; but its reappearance among the Nilotes three thousand years later can hardly be due to anything but a derivation and a maintenance of the custom. The East African institution of rain-maker kings, who bring fertility and prosperity to the realm, but are killed and superseded when their health or genital power fails, or when droughts prove them remiss—this institution is not identical with the ancient Egyptian concept of the divine king, but looks like a specific exemplification of it. Similarly, an African Negro custom that makes the king's umbilical cord a fetish to be preserved and enshrined seems to have an ancient Egyptian prototype.

It would be neat if all such old customs were still maintained collectively among one particular Hamitic or Negroid nationality, which we could then fairly construe as the legitimate though somewhat barbarized heir of old Egypt. Unfortunately there is no such concentration. The inheritance is there, but it has been dissipated into scattered fragments. The Nuer deform the horns of their cattle, but have no kings. The Baganda make a great to-do about the king's navel; its custodian is one of the highest functionaries in the state; but they do not manipulate horns. Umbilical enshrinement has spread as far as West Africa; but the killing of rain-making kings is specifically East African. Thus the tribal histories of the dark continent are intricate, and the cultures are branching and variable. There is a limit to the amount of derivation we can expect to remain demonstrably traceable after several thousand illiterate years. Perhaps there is almost always more connection than we can prove, especially among peoples without writing: some has got itself disguised in new dress or into quite new association.

In this particular case we can expect to know more in future. Our knowledge of both recent Negro culture and ancient Egypt has doubled in the past generation, and will presumably redouble in the next. The search for reliable indices of derivation is definitely recent. Until after 1900, resemblances such as those just discussed were not attributed to any specific historical connection, but to something constitutional in the human mind that caused certain cultural practices to emerge spontaneously (§ 223). That they often also fail to emerge, and over wide areas and long periods, was not then recognized as being against the assumption of spontaneous origin. In the *Golden Bough*—the anthropological work that long influenced perhaps the greatest number of nonanthropologists— Frazer pointed out the correspondence in idea of East African rain-maker kingship and institutionalized priest and king-killing elsewhere, but without seeming to be much interested in historical connections.

312. GENERAL TRENDS OF NEGRO CULTURE

Let us now turn from these clue-tracings, whose convincingness is proportionate to the specificity of their evidence, to an almost opposite consideration: the outline characterization of recent Negro African culture as a whole, the naming of its most salient over-all qualities.

First, while kinship continues to count basically in social structure, there exists in Africa a notably greater development of political structure than is customary among nonliterate peoples. This is manifest in the size, the power, and the duration of Negro kingdoms. Some of these realms were the product of

Mohammedans; some began pagan and turned Mohammedan; but others flourished beyond the range of direct Islamic influence. Some were tied to the life of a single adventurer, like Chaka of the early nineteenth-century Zulu. Others grew, climaxed, and decayed, lingering through the centuries.

Even secret religious societies sometimes tend to take on political coloring in Africa.

Allied to the flair for political organization is African feeling for law, evident particularly in the development of regulated procedures of trial and testimony.

Then there is a definite and strong economic interest. Over much of the continent, wealth is embodied in cattle. Locally, cowry shells constitute a system of money that is functionally effective. Prestige of course attends economic success—as almost everywhere else; but African economic transactions tend to rest on a realistic basis—cattle are useful and increase—instead of relating largely to the arbitrary and fictive values of rarities, heirlooms, or sentimental treasures, as among Indonesians, Melanesians, and North Pacific coast Indians.

Probably related to this economic bent is the existence in Africa of economically exploited slavery. Most nonliterates, if they keep slaves at all, do so essentially for prestige purposes, and are not organized to utilize them very profitably. Possibly the Negroes were further instructed in the economic value of slavery by ancient Mediterraneans, Arabs, and Christians who raided them for slaves and bought them; if so, they learned the lesson.

As regards formal social structure, moieties are almost lacking in Africa. On the other hand, there is a recurrent tendency for patrilineal and matrilineal reckoning to appear conjointly.[24] There is no conflict, because one descent transmits "blood," the other "soul," as in Ashanti. Or the exogamic clan is matrilineal, the totem patrilineal, as among Bakongo and Herero. There are separate matrilineal and patrilineal totems among the Tshi and Ewe; while with the Kpelle, clans are matrilineal, whereas totems are patrilineal for males but matrilineal for females. With the Wolof and the Baganda, descent is patrilineal except for the nobility and royalty, who derive from the mother. The Tuareg reverse the procedure: high office comes from the father, descent and inheritance from the mother.

On the technological side, practically all Africa works iron, often smelts it, and appears to have done so for a long time. Other metals are worked only here and there; and outside of Egypt there is no indication of a Bronze Age stage (§ 295). Smiths may be despised or respected, but usually constitute a separate caste—as in Arabia (§ 119). Their technique and equipment are simple (§ 295). This fact has led to a paradoxical theory that all ironworking originated among the Negroes, who however let the incipient art stand still, whereas Asiatics and Europeans developed and refined it after having learned it from the Negroes. Modern opinion construes the evidence in such cases as more likely running the

---

[24] Compare the analogous cases of social luxuriance in § 166.

opposite way: marginal and retarded people often do *preserve* an ancient form of cultural activity because it reached them relatively late as well as dilute; but its *origin* is more likely to have been among an advanced and culturally central population.

At any rate, iron tools and weapons imbue African culture with a somewhat sophisticated appearance for a "primitive" one. And they have also undoubtedly helped the economic effectiveness and advancement of Negro culture.

All of Africa, except for the Bushmen and the Negritos or Pygmies, is food-producing. Climate, soil, and pests somewhat modify the animal and plant species that enter into subsistence economy. Thus millets and sorghum ("Kaffir corn") tend to replace wheat and barley in the Negro part of the continent. Among animals, cattle are esteemed wherever they can be bred. Dairying in various forms is highly developed in most of East Africa. The plow has scarcely got a foothold south of the Mohammedan range: planting is often intensive but is done by hand. In the wet parts, which in nature are tropical forest, bananas and yams tend to replace grains.

All in all, nearly the whole of Africa shows the effects of its proximity and exposure to Asia and Europe. Peoples of genuinely "primitive" or backward gathering-hunting culture, such as occur by hundreds in Australia, Oceania, and America, and by dozens even in Asia, simply are lacking from Africa, apart from Negritos and Bushmen. All other tribes and nationalities produce food, work iron, and possess fairly well-developed political, legal, and economic institutions.

313. AREAS OF CHARACTERIZATION IN AFRICA

As against this background of African culture generally, several regions of characterization, or "culture areas," stand out conspicuously, and others are less well defined.

North Africa is divided about equally between peoples now speaking Semitic Arabic and those speaking Berber or some other Hamitic language; but nearly all of it is under Mohammedan culture, in varying degree of purity. In Ethiopia or Abyssinia there is a curious island of Semitic speech much older in Africa than Arabic; of Christian religion; and of mixed Christian and East African pagan culture.

In East Africa, Hamitic speakers extend as far south as latitude 3° S., and nationalities like the Somali and the Galla look perhaps more Negro than Caucasian, whereas most Hamites, ancient and modern, appear to have been mainly Mediterranean in race, and some of them, such as Berbers, Kabyles, and ancient Egyptians, were purely so. Cattle-raising is the preferred occupation of most modern Hamites, as well as of some non-Hamites like the Masai. In some regions herdsmen-warriors have imposed themselves as a ruling caste on Negroid agricultural populations: for instance, the excessively elongated Bahima on the stockier Bahera, the two together constituting the Bantu-speaking Banyora.

While the Bahima and the Bahera represent symbiotic but unassimilated half-societies and half-cultures, a fusion of two similar elements has taken place among the Baganda; whereas the herding Masai merely fought and dispossessed the agricultural Lumbwa. Probably only a minority of these dominant castes and tribes speak Hamitic; but there is a tendency among Africanists to regard them all as former Hamites, or mixed Hamites, and to attribute the herdsmen-warrior-ruler pattern of Africa to their influence.

In the floodlands along the upper Nile from latitude 12° to 4° N. are Shilluk, Dinka, Nuer, and Bari, constituting a distinctive "Nilotic" group. They too are cattle-raising by preference, and warlike; and they also are Negro in race, or mainly so, but of the almost abnormally drawn-out or hyperleptosome type that reaches its extreme development in East Africa.

In the South African steppe and desert are the Bushmen—one of the very few peoples on earth possessing at the same time distinctive race, distinctive speech, and distinctive culture. As has been noted, they and the Pygmies are the principal groups in Africa who are not food-producing.[25] The men are expert hunters, stalking or wearing down game until it is within range of their bone or stone-tipped arrows, while the women pry up roots with digging sticks weighted with perforated stones. They may live under rock shelters, or camp in a circle of rude huts, or on the leeward side of windbreaks. In the desert they suck up subterranean water through reeds and keep it in ostrich eggshells. Their lively representative art on rock faces and shelters has been several times mentioned (§ 64, 200, 277, 311). It is found farther north than the historical distribution of the Bushmen. There is therefore a theory that the Bushmen wandered or were driven from the north; and to this theory has been hitched the fact, perhaps accidental and nonsignificant, that one or two features of Bushmen grammar recur in Hamitic.

The Hottentots, neighbors of the Bushmen, and approaching them in physical type, appear to be a mixture of Bushman and other blood, though a few of their physical peculiarities are more pronounced. They are culturally less retarded, having cattle and iron.

In forested central Africa the Pygmies, Negritos, or Negrillos live in many scattered localities among full-statured Bantu Negroes, acknowledging the chiefs or kings of these, trading forest wax, rattan, ivory, and meat for the manufactures and farm products of the big people, and speaking dialects of their languages. Thus they constitute at the same time a race and an economic caste within Bantu society and culture.

The Congo-West coast culture area is perhaps the most distinctive in Negro Africa. It includes the Congo drainage, plus the south-fronting coast region west at least as far as Liberia and perhaps to Dakar. The traits characterizing this area

[25] The Bergdama in Southwest Africa, though neighbors of the Bushmen, are pure Negro in race but speak a Nama Hottentot dialect, and most of them herd for the Hottentots who have subjected them.

include: general absence of cattle, also of millet; cultivation of bananas and yams; houses with ridgepole and eaves of thatch, in contrast to the conical or domed houses of thatch or mud and wattle of the rest of Africa; clothing of palm fiber or bark as well as of woven cotton; straight self-bows with rattan cords; shields of wood or cane, in place of leather or hide shields or parrying sticks; face masks used in rituals; wood-carving, often of high skill; slit wooden signal drums; xylophones; well-developed markets; currency of iron hoes or cowry shells.

Some of these traits are environmentally conditioned. The area of culture in question corresponds closely with the one large tract of tropical forest in Africa, the rest of the continent being parkland, savannah, grassland, steppe, desert, or mountain. It will also be noted that some of the cultural elements limited to the area embody wood as their material. The other side of the situation is that, as always, natural environment cannot per se *cause* forms of culture: cannot initiate them. It can inhibit particular sociocultural tendencies or allow them to develop if they are present. There must be trees if wooden masks or shields or drums are to be carved; but adequate scattered timber will suffice for these uses as well as dense forest. Thus native Pacific North America, eastern North America, and ancient Europe all had continuous forest cover, but lacked wooden shields and drums; and the last two of the three lacked masks also. The South American tropical-forest region uses wooden signal drums, but makes its masks, when it has any, mostly of bark or straw.

It is obvious that a well-specialized natural milieu, such as tropical jungle, extreme desert, or perpetually frozen ground, will exercise a considerable selective effect on the cultures of societies resident in it.[26] For instance, in heavy forest, clearings for farming and pasture will be a basic problem; in desert, agriculture is limited to irrigation or oasis, but stock can usually be raised where the desert ameliorates a little; and so on. The result is that, cultural choices being unusually narrow in such specialized environments, even cultures of diverse origin are driven in these environments to make a certain proportion of choices that are similar. In short, cultures in similar physical environments may undergo a partial secondary assimilation, which disguises their basic lack of historical connection.

Part of a wider theory advanced by the *Kulturkreis* (culture-sphere) movement or school of ethnology in continental Europe is that the Indonesian-Melanesian cultures are also characterized by the same block of culture traits that includes those enumerated for West Africa, and that these traits stem from a common origin and prove a former actual connection between the two regions. Such a special connection seems extremely unlikely when set against our total knowledge of prehistory, history, migrations, diffusions, and other happenings in Oceania, Asia, and Africa. It is probable that the specific resemblances pointed

[26] Colonists or transients from elsewhere may import canned goods, prefabricated houses, refrigerators or coal, radios and phonographs, and live in Antarctica or Guadalcanal with a culture developed and maintained elsewhere.

out are real, but are the result of the just-discussed process of secondary selective adaptation to environment. Also, the number of such secondarily similar traits in Oceania and in West Africa appears to constitute only a minority proportion of the total inventory of culture in each of the two regions.

Finally, we have in West Africa several major trends or definable slants of culture peculiar to the area. Such are the skillful intellectual organization of ideology and institutions, especially among the more advanced tribes such as the Ashanti and the Yoruba; and an exceptionally sensitive feeling for texture, planes, and volumes in the wood-carving, making this one of the world's most successful decorative sculptures. Achievements like these are styles; and it is obvious that they cannot be explained either by migrations, by diffusions, or by environment alone. They originate where they occur, as the result of subtle, variable, and diverse factors active in some of the members of the society and operative on their already existent culture patterns in the direction of the further development of these patterns.

We have come a long way in time from our Abbevillean-Acheulian flint cores, and we have traveled a long way in geography from the origins of higher culture in the Near East, following the peripheries around from Europe to East Asia to Oceania to Africa.

It remains now to trace the prehistory of culture in what long was the remotest periphery of all—the Americas—whose connections with Old World centers seemingly were so tenuous and intermittent that the story as recovered to date is primarily one of autonomous developments on pre-Columbian American soil.

CHAPTER EIGHTEEN

American Prehistory and Ethnology

314. TRANSITION FROM GEOLOGICAL TO CULTURAL TIME

TWO GAPS characterize our knowledge of the history of native culture in the Americas—of the conjoined archaeology and ethnography of the double continent. These gaps or lacunae are not absolute, and they will probably tend to disappear or at least diminish with the increase of knowledge; but at present they are marked. One of the gaps is formed by a strange ignorance that lies between, first, the limited but certain knowledge we have of the culture of American man in terminal geological time, and second, the more extensive knowledge we have of him and his culture as we push backward from the present with the help of nongeological archaeological discoveries. The two stories seem not to meet fully. Quite likely they have not yet actually met in most areas of America.

The other gap is between the total cultural history of the two hemispheres, Western and Eastern. There indubitably were connections between these two sets of prehistories. We can in fact specify connections. But in the main the two developments continue to look as if they had been preponderantly autonomous until 1492—more largely independent of each other than interconnected, the American more separate from the mass of Eur-Afric-Asiatic culture growth than even the highly marginal Australian culture was.

The time gap may be like the "hiatus" in human occupation that was formerly believed to have existed between the European Palaeolithic and Neolithic, and which was later filled by discoveries now known as Mesolithic (§ 276). Or the gap may be only a seeming one. That is, it is possible that we really have enough records to make the story continuous, but that we are creating a gap by interpreting the early remains as even earlier than need be, and the late ones as later than they are—thus artificially pulling them apart. It will be recalled that the surely early finds of human activity in America—Folsom, Sandía, and such, as discussed in § 278 and 280—have their antiquity attested primarily by being associated with bones of extinct animals. This gives them some degree of antiquity indeed; but we do not know how long a one, and it may have been a quite short one, geologically. Some of these fossil-associated artifact discoveries in America may date from twenty-five thousand years ago, others from only five thousand years ago. We have no way as yet of ascertaining just when this or that species of animal died out in this or that region. At the other end of the gap is the archaeological record which runs back more or less *consecutively* from the present: first with finds that include evidences of contact with Caucasian civilization, then late pre-1492 material, and so increasingly earlier to the beginning of this retrospective time column. Such series, with a continuity of changing culture types, have now been discovered in several regions of both North and South America, and will be reviewed in detail below (§ 320-331).

In most cases there is no direct evidence of how long any one of these retrospective continuities was in accumulating. But workers thoroughly familiar with all angles of a local prehistoric situation of this sort get a feeling—from the number of successive culture phases, from thickness of strata and richness of strata, from preservation conditions, and so forth—they are wont to get a feeling of *about* how long the total duration must have been. In practically every case, after the first extravagant claims have been dropped, the estimate runs to something fairly close to two thousand years as minimum or not far from three thousand as maximum. That is to say, the beginning of these "dead-reckoning" estimates for consecutively known segments of New World prehistory has again and again been set somewhere in the range 1000 B.C. to 1 B.C.

That, however, on the whole would be a pretty recent time for extinct species of animals to have died out. Some species may have lasted in spots as long as this, but it would be far-fetched to assume that elephants, camels, horses, sloths, and others in general went on existing in America until just before the Christian era, and then suddenly all became extinct together. The interval between the 10,000-5000 B.C. range, by which certainly many or most of the extinct species had died out, and the 1000-1 B.C. range when the continuous record of later-type archaeological stages begins, is the gap we are discussing, a gap which will presumably be abolished before too long—either by being filled up by the discovery of new and earlier cultures, or by reduction of the time of extinction of species associated with the prehiatus remains, or by discovery of reasons for stretching the dead-reckoning archaeology back farther.

There are several reasons why this break in our knowledge has persisted longer in regard to America than to the Eastern Hemisphere. After all, documentary history is much shorter. It is all post-1492, except for legends that were collected for some areas by the Spaniards,[1] and the authenticity of many of which is none too clear. As against this, Europe and the Near East have consecutive histories of from fifteen hundred to five thousand years long. Then, with this actual history constantly before them, Eastern Hemisphere prehistorians have tended to see their archaeological data as an extension of the history, and have accordingly sought to give these data a historical dress and interpretation. But in the historyless Western Hemisphere, everything pre-Caucasian seemed not so much strung on a long thread of sequence as it seemed one great amorphous mass of data, alike only in that they all preceded Caucasian history. All the data here seemed "old"; but the question of *how* old, or how much older than others, did not at first obtrude. As we look back from the mid-twentieth century, it is really remarkable how in area after area of America, such as the eastern and the southwestern United States, considerable masses of archaeological information had long been piled up without anyone's asking himself, until well after 1900, whether this pile could not be segregated into relatively earlier and relatively later facts.[2] Only the Aztec-Maya region is a partial exception, because of the native legends and even historical books that were preserved there by the Spaniards.

One result of this lateness of development of the historical point of view in the archaeology of America was that some of the load was thrown on ethnography—the investigation of the surviving tribes, especially in the United States and Canada. Often still living close at hand on reservations, these tribes were conveniently accessible for inquiry without lengthy and expensive formal expeditions. In consequence, they were almost all studied, one after another, until cultural data were available that possessed an unusual geographical continuity. This continuity of information, in turn, made possible the systematic areal classification of the North American tribal cultures, the tracing of diffusions, and the

[1] The Maya had a system of exact dates of their own (§ 320), but we are still not too certain which of our own dates the Mayan dates equal.

[2] The first proposals for a sound foundation for a systematic time-sequenced archaeology of Peru were made in the first decade of this century; for the southwestern United States in the twenties; for the Eskimo, after that; for the eastern United States and California, after 1940. The earlier archaeology for these areas was descriptive, and sometimes classificatory, but not sequential; or if sequential, it was so only by speculation, not by analysis of evidence.

application of the principles of radiation from originating centers, of marginal survivals, and of age and area. The result was the strange one that for a while—around 1915 to 1930—ethnography actually outstripped excavatory archaeology in the quantity of inferential solutions it had to offer to the problem of the historical development of native American culture.

To this must be added another consideration: Archaeology always can recover from the ground only a portion of any culture—the tangible, material part—and of that only such fraction as manages to be physically preserved. The student of a living society, on the contrary, has the opportunity of inquiring equally into all segments of its culture. It is true that many ethnographic studies, perhaps the majority, were made after the aboriginal tribes had lost or modified their native culture under the impact of Occidental civilization. Yet even then, for about fifty years there normally remained older men and women who had participated in the full tribal life and could picture and illustrate the culture from their personal memories.

These several considerations bring it about that ethnographic studies have contributed perhaps as much as archaeological ones to our present understanding of the history of culture in native America. The precise succession of culture growths, and their local variants in the past, we owe to the archaeologists; the clothing of this skeleton or framework with the flesh of fuller culture, and the reconstruction of the greater long outlines of development over the whole hemisphere—to these, ethnologists have contributed as much or perhaps more.

Our procedure here accordingly will be to try to reconstruct first the larger outline of what presumably happened in the Americas before 1492, by references mainly from ethnological data obtained on cultures while they were still alive and functioning, or at least actually remembered. Thereafter, we shall review the findings of excavatory archaeologists area by area, wherever they have succeeded in establishing successions of culture changes. And this in turn will sometimes lead us back into the local cultures, or at least their larger groups, as they are known from having survived into historical times.

315. DATA PREVIOUSLY CONSIDERED: A REVIEW

In exemplification of this or that generic process or mechanism of culture, a good many items of aboriginal American culture have so far been mentioned in this book. As a start for our systematic review of the hemisphere's larger culture development, let us pull these scattered bits together.

First, there are those elements or pieces of culture which have parallel occurrence in the Old World and the New, but with seemingly independent origin in each. Sometimes the case for independence is strong, sometimes only probable. The traits discussed are:

Zero (§ 189)
Two-headed bird symbol (§ 190—diffused also)
Corbeled arch (§ 194)
Five supplementary days in the year (§ 198)
Zodiacal sequence (§ 229)
Permutative time counts (§ 230)
Addiction to gambling (§ 232)
Intoxicants (§ 233)
Fermentation from saliva (§ 233)
Half-hitch coiling, single-rod coiling, looms, tie dyeing (§ 235)
Pan's-pipe pitches (§ 236)
Bronze and other metallurgy (§ 237, 295)

Next, there are Old World elements that had not made their way into the New World by 1492. Among such are proverbs, divination from viscera, and iron (§192, 226). The wheel had also apparently not been transmitted, then was invented in southern Mexico, but failed of utilitarian adoption, being used only for toys or ritual figures (§ 148). Stringed musical instruments seem never either to have reached the Western Hemisphere or to have been devised there, except for the monotone bow. Oaths and ordeals were also lacking.

The great mass of Old World cultivated plants and domesticated animals was totally lacking in native America. This is true equally for broadcast-sown grains, hand-cultivated rice, fruit trees from apples to bananas, and tropical root crops such as yams and taro. Their place was taken by an entirely different inventory of farm plants, among which maize, potatoes, beans, and cassava are prominent; and by a very few species of animals—the dog, locally the turkey and the Muscovy duck, and in Peru the llama and the alpaca. The only plants grown in both hemispheres were sweet potatoes, cotton, gourds, and coconuts—the latter in a few coastal spots only. The only animal bred in common was the dog. This overwhelming separateness of food production might be construed as reflecting distinct environments, or, on the other hand, distinct culture history. The latter is apparently the more important factor, as will be seen in the next section.

Reasonably certain interhemispheric diffusions already mentioned include:

Two-headed bird, post-Columbian diffusion into America (and pre-Columbian parallel, § 190)
Tobacco, post-Columbian diffusion out of America, and return into Alaska (§ 193)
The magic-flight story (§ 227)
Scapulimancy (§192, 238)
Doubtful between diffusion and independent origin: the patolli-parcheesi game (§ 231), and fundamental basketry techniques like twilling and coiling (§ 235)

Two sets of additional shared and probably diffused traits will be discussed below: seemingly early elements widely spread in the New World (§ 316), and relatively late elements mostly limited to the parts of North America nearest to Asia (§ 317), of the order of the scapulimancy just mentioned.

The relatively minor role of migrations in the spread of culture has been pointed out in the introduction to Chapter Twelve. It is at any rate a much smaller role than is often naïvely assumed by those who have not reflected on culture processes. Some contact of some human individuals must necessarily happen if anything cultural is to spread. But the contact need by no means be the migration of whole populations; and the evidence is preponderant that mostly it is not. What is far more important on the average is the circumstances of the contact, and especially the state or condition of the cultures respective to each other—whether the relation is such that an import or a diffusion could "take" (§ 151).

Specifically, the blowing or drift of vessels with living survivors across the Pacific—or for that matter across the Atlantic—has already been discounted (§ 237) as presumably only incidental in its cultural effect. There is precise record of so many East Asiatic junks reaching the Pacific coast of the United States and Canada during the past hundred years that its having happened again and again in preceding centuries is morally certain. But it happened without any enclaves of Orientalized culture resulting among the California, Washington, and British Columbia Indians—or even minor influencings in special traits that one could be positive about. It is likely that such accidental sowings of cultural seed took place hundreds of times; but in the vast majority of cases the seed withered again.

316. FACTORS OF AMERICAN CULTURE GROWTH, INTERNAL AND EXTERNAL

In line with the trend of the anticipatory findings that have just been reviewed, it may be said that in the opinion of most Americanists, ethnologists as well as archaeologists, the first human immigrants and cultures arrived in the Western Hemisphere probably in late Pleistocene times. The meagerly known Sandía, Folsom, and similar cultures, or rather industries (§ 279), represent this early level of culture. It is already well differentiated and particularized, enough so to have no exact Eurasiatic counterpart. If anything earlier than Sandía and Folsom existed in America, it has not been found. It is generally assumed that there was nothing notably earlier, because no fossils have ever been discovered in America of Palaeoanthropic men, of Protoanthropic human ancestors, or of anthropoid apes.

Then, following Folsom and such, there is the apparent gap in our archaeological record that has just been discussed. In this interval of unknown length there must have been growth and change of the early American cultures into new local forms; also diffusions of traits within the hemisphere; and quite likely new imports of culture material, and perhaps movements into the hemisphere of populations with established languages and cultures. What we know about this interval is not its events, not what happened when or where, but its over-all results, as manifest in cultural conditions as they are found at the opening of the archaeological periods, and in distributions of traits persisting into historical times. As has already been said, it may turn out that we actually now have in hand certain prehistoric specimens and data from this interval, but are unable as yet to use them to complete the story because we do not know where they belong in it.

What inference ought to be drawn from simple elements of culture that are of general occurrence, sometimes even universally distributed, in the two aboriginal Americas? Reference is to traits like pressure flaking; grinding of bone, horn, or stone; hafting of tools; fire-making; cordage; weaving or plaiting of baskets, mats, traps, and weirs; use of projectiles propelled from a spear-thrower or a bow; the possession of more or less tamed dogs. Roughly, this is the sort of material inventory that is known or inferred to have characterized the late Palaeolithic and the Mesolithic in Europe and probably in Asia. This trait inventory accordingly might have been imported into America across a land-bridged or iced-over or navigable Bering Strait, either by groups in contact with one another or by groups actually migratory, and at any or various times in the terminal Palaeolithic or since.

Many of these traits, though material in themselves, generally do not leave preservable remains, so that many more and fuller discoveries would have to be made than our present handful of Sandía and Folsom finds before we could expect to have in hand sufficient evidence [3] that these elements already existed then in America. Thus it follows that some of these traits may well have been present in the living Folsom culture, others have come into America somewhat later, still others have arrived later yet. Some, in fact, might have been independently devised within the Western Hemisphere. We really know nothing of when and how—or indeed whether—these items of material culture were moved from Asia into America. We do know about when they appeared in Europe. We do know that in general they are present at the opening of the postgeological record of archaeology in America, just as we know that they were of essentially universal occurrence in the historical native cultures. So we can reasonably deduce that this set of traits is relatively old in the hemisphere—older than most other traits, probably. And that is about as close as we can come to fixing their age, in the present state of our knowledge.

There is a second set of traits for which we can infer considerable age from the generality of their American occurrence, but only from that, because they consist of social and religious institutions that ordinarily do not leave even indirect traces in the archaeological record. Such are: extended family groups or

[3] For instance, holes bored through objects are pretty good evidence of the use of thong or cord.

small hordes of kinsmen claiming ownership of a tract of land for their liveli-hood; belief in magic and supernatural power, personally acquirable, and with the possessors of the power constituting shamans for health and good purposes, wizards for death and evil; crisis rites, such as the couvade, funeral ceremonies, menstrual observances, especially puberty rites for girls, as set forth in § 239; perhaps also a corresponding induction of boys into manhood, accompanied by whipping them or otherwise testing their fortitude, and initiating them into the spiritual secrets of the tribe; possibly some sort of ritual structure for this induc-tion, used also at other times as a kind of men's clubhouse. All these traits have a wide distribution among nonliterate tribes the world over as well as in Amer-ica, so that, whether diffused or repeatedly devised independently, their history must generally have been a long one. But again we cannot say how long, except that some of them may conceivably have been introduced into America by Folsom times, or again only during the post-Folsom hiatus in our knowledge.

We can also infer that during this same hiatus or hazy-knowledge interval the regions on both sides of the Isthmus of Panama, especially southern Mexico and Peru, were drawing more and more ahead of other American areas in the total variety and richness of growth of their cultures. When Caucasians began to reach and overrun the American mainland in the decades after 1492, it was this larger circum-Isthmian region—and notably Mexico [4] and Peru as its peaks—which was obviously far in the lead of all other American regions in density of population, wealth, urbanization, advancement of the arts, and political structure and control. From the point of view of progressive civilization, this circum-Isthmian tract contained the nucleus and the climax of native advancement. So much so was this true that this same area will be referred to, when convenient in the pages that follow, as "Nuclear America"; and within it, Mexico and Peru each constituted an indubitable focus of brilliance.

So definite was this attested lead that most of the speculative theories at-tempting to derive American origins from a ready-made import out of Asia, Oceania, Phoenicia, or where not, simply lead their mariners or immigrants to Mexico—or sometimes Peru—and therewith consider their task essentially achieved; everything American outside the Nuclear region is so obviously second-rate and less important that—within the frame of these speculations—it could well be taken as derivative, a sort of broken reflection or degeneration. We need not go actually so far as that; but there can be no doubt that a rela-tively high civilization like that of the Aztec or the Maya would be more likely to influence mediocre cultures like those of the United States Indians than the reverse; and that therefore, in origin, much in the mediocre cultures is likely to have been derived from the higher. And of course the same holds for Peru in South America. Moreover, it is plain that a great and diversified culture will normally require time to grow: it may indeed perhaps mushroom into its matu-

---

[4] More exactly, "Meso-America" as defined in § 318 and 320.

ration, but only after long development. It could therefore be inferred, on a-priori expectability, that the superiority of the larger Nucleus, and especially of the two foci, had extended back for a considerable period—let us say for two or three thousand years or so.

This is exactly what systematically prosecuted archaeology shows us to have happened. In both Mexico and Peru, a continuous record of excavated prehistory can be carried back for a stretch that every specialist feels must have required at least fifteen hundred years before Columbus, which the majority feel more comfortable in if allowed twenty-five hundred years, and some might claim more than that. When we examine the condition of the Nuclear cultures at their earliest discovered stage, whether that dates at 1 B.C. or 1000 B.C. or possibly beyond, they are already richer and more advanced than some of the retarded among these other cultures were in historical and recent times. There was already, at this opening of the archaeological record in Mexico and Peru, a cluster of activities comprising agriculture, pottery, permanent structures, and a stylized ritual art.[5]

Well, the upshot of these paragraphs is that one of the major drifts or lines of development of native American culture was an early growth or forging-ahead—for whatever reason—in the Nuclear area, and especially in its two foci, followed by a gradual dispersal of part of the culture thus achieved to adjacent and even outlying parts of the hemisphere. Of course, useful or interesting inventions made elsewhere would also tend to be carried to the Nucleus and to be adapted there, so that the stream of culture flow would be two-way. Yet there can be little doubt that the preponderant flow would be outward. And this again is confirmed by the evidence, especially that of agriculture.

Overwhelmingly, the cultivated plants of native America are tropical in origin. Some, like maize and beans and tomatoes and cotton, could be successfully transported to temperate latitudes, because North American summers are hot enough between the last frost of spring and the first frost of fall to allow the plant to achieve its maturity in the few months available to it. Others, like cassava, cacao, and the aguacate or alligator pear, cannot ripen in this brief period, and therefore remained tropical in their distribution. By contrast, temperate-climate plants like the Jerusalem artichoke (*Helianthus*) were few, and did not get carried to the tropics, although on the whole such plants have a better chance of thriving there, if cared for, than tropical plants in winter-frost climates.[6] Here then we have definite evidence of the preponderant flow or radiation of

[5] The earliest well-described Mexican (Meso-American) cultures have both farming and pottery; in Peru a culture was discovered in 1946 that was still preceramic though already agricultural (§ 328).

[6] The potato is the principal American plant of nontropical origin (Chile, Bolivia, Peru) that has become important in contemporary civilization. Its range is distinctive. It does poorly in the tropics except at high altitudes; on the other hand, it will not stand frost, and thrives best in temperate climates with cool summers and restricted insolation

culture outward from the Nuclear middle region. And as maize-growing was transported centrifugally, there is the obvious possibility that pottery-making, loom weaving, building in stone, and other arts and customs—or at least some of them—also were transmitted from their Nuclear origin to their outlying occurrences.

317. FURTHER FACTORS OF AMERICAN CULTURE GROWTH

Contrasting with the high developments in the Nuclear center, the most meager and most retarded cultures tend to be found at the extreme ends: southernmost South America and northernmost North America. This is no doubt partly due to unfavorable cold or raw climate and limited range of vegetation: food-producing just was out of the question here. However, it is almost unanimously assumed that remoteness from the advanced foci of cultural productivity also contributed, more or less proportionally to distance. In other words, the principle of peripheral retardation (§ 173-174) is construed as having been operative. The bi-peripheral occurrence of traits—that is, features largely or wholly restricted to the extreme north and the extreme south of the hemisphere— was first noted by the famous Swedish distribution-ethnologist, Nordenskiöld, in 1912. Since then the inventory has grown until it totals nearly a hundred traits from all domains of culture.[7] This list includes, for instance, tales or folklore motifs such as arrow ladder, rolling-head monster, sharpened-leg attack, dog and woman as ancestors. Shared ceremonial features are a tube to drink through, a splint to scratch with, a rattle of hoofs to dance to. These pieces of apparatus are particularly impressive because they are often used in the puberty rite for girls, which we have previously seen (§ 239) to be indicated by its distribution— and by frequent absence from more complex cultures—as presumably ancient in a large part of North America. Most of the characteristic games of northerly North America seem to have been lacking during historical times in Nuclear America and most of South America, only to reappear in one or the other of the distant peripheral regions of the latter continent, especially in the Chaco. Such are lacrosse, hoop and pole, ring and pin, and multiple two-sided dice. Finally there are items like getting a fire spark from stone percussion, tattooing by means of a soot-soaked thread, smoking from a pipe with a cylindrical bowl set on a platformlike stem. The foregoing are all specific, particularized traits, not likely to have been invented independently twice, at least not in any large proportion of the cases. Consequently, the usual belief is that these culture traits, or most of them, are old enough to have long since spread all the way between the Arctic Ocean and Cape Horn, but that later on they gradually were overlaid and crowded out—"displaced" (§ 159)—by competing traits of subsequent more

---

[7] In the most recent form of this interpretation, by Cooper, an "internally marginal" tract (§ 175), the brushy highland of eastern Brazil, is included in the peripheral area of South America, as in § 319 and on the map, Figure 42, page 790.

complex cultures in the intervening regions—both the high Nuclear and the moderately developed adjacent ones. Thus this array of old elements remained best preserved in the extreme far North and far South.

The difference between this class of traits and those previously cited as perhaps imported long ago from Asia is twofold. The present group is much more specific; and it is presumably not nearly as old, on the average. For instance, the ability to make fire by some means, and crisis puberty rites, are two general traits that are widespread and presumably ancient enough so that they could have been brought along by immigrants from Asia, whether these came to America six or sixteen or twenty-six thousand years ago. Contrasting with these are the specific traits—bi-peripheral within America—of making fire by the particular and rare device of striking stones or pyrites together, and of dancing to the rhythm of deer-hoof rattles over an adolescent girl. Why just hoof rattles in this special rite? There must be a connection between the North and South American occurrences of this cluster of detailed items, on the principle that recurrent association of "arbitrary" (not functionally explainable) features indicates historical unity, as with the episodes of the magic-flight tale (§ 227). On the other hand, on mere consideration of wear and tear in history, the chances would seem to be decidedly against any association as arbitrary and special as this one to survive unchanged for twenty-six thousand or sixteen thousand years, and perhaps rather dubious even for six thousand; whereas for the same association of features to spread from North America to the far parts of South America a few thousand years ago—possibly only three thousand—and then become blotted out again in the middle Nuclear region by the known growth of many new traits of culture there—this interpretation, while by no means absolutely provable, certainly puts no great strain on credibility.

Still another factor in the growth of American culture is the following: Peoples themselves, as well as knowledge of traits, very likely continued to flow across Bering Strait from time to time, possibly in both directions. We can most confidently extricate from this long, intermittent flow certain late elements—from perhaps several hundred up to two or three thousand years in age—recent enough to have not yet had opportunity to spread too far from their Alaskan gate of entry. Some of these, such as skin boots, sleds on runners, and lamps using a stone basin, moss wick, and animal oil, are shared in America only by the Eskimo—for obvious environmental reasons—with this or that occurrence in Eurasia. A few elements, like slat or plate armor, are shared by the Northwest Coast and Asia. The majority of this class of traits which presumably drifted recently into America occur among other interior tribes of the North as well as among the Eskimo of the Arctic coast line or the tribes of the Pacific shore; and some have become solely interior through dropping out again in the coastal regions. In this general bracket of relatively recent import from Asia are several elements already discussed in other connections: the magic-flight tale (§ 227), shoulder-blade divination (§ 192), the sinew-backed or reinforced bow (§ 173, 303), fitted or tailored clothing with sleeved coats and trousers (§ 138, 297). To these can be added: snowshoes, the toboggan as a sort of equivalent of skis, boats with undershot prows, basketry hats, and dog traction. Still further, the suggestion has been made that cord-marked pottery also owes to a diffusion its distribution—which is mainly of archaeological occurrence— from Neolithic Europe through northern Asia to eastern Canada and the United States.

Of a somewhat different nature are a series of resemblances long ago noted between the Northwest-coast tribes and certain Oceanians, especially the Melanesians and in part the primitive Indonesians. These similarities include the following features: social status dependent on wealth; accurate systems of valuing shell money or treasures; large-scale distribution of food and property at competitive gift festivals or potlatches; membership in secret societies serving as a prestige symbol of rank; use of masks in the rituals of such societies; and elaborate wood-carving. In this case nearly the full diagonal breadth of the Pacific separates the areas involved in the resemblances. The Oceanians in question are at the western side of the ocean and mostly south of the equator, the American tribes between 40° and 60° N. The nearer Polynesians are not particularly involved. The similarities are not in specific traits, but in broad features building into a connected pattern or cultural slant. They may thus well be the result of fortuitously converging generic trends, since it is easier for traits to diffuse than for patterns to do so, and when the latter do spread they seem necessarily to drag with them a good many particular traits that they include. For these reasons the Melanesian-Northwest Coast resemblances are usually not accepted as indicative of a historical connection. More probably they represent an accidental convergence of pattern trends—"accidental" in the sense of being due to unknown causes.

Quite separate from this class of generalized resemblances is a series of about fifty specific culture traits that Nordenskiöld compiled as occurring both in Oceania—again in Melanesia rather than in Polynesia—and in America, especially in various parts of what is now Latin America. These traits include such items as: wooden pillows, gourds, star-pointed mace heads of stone, unfeathered arrows, the blowgun, plaited fans, small bow and arrow for bloodletting, tooth-staining, bark cloth and mallets, "lattice-woven" basketry with elements in three directions, stilts, and more than thirty others.

The difficulty is with the distribution of these traits in America: it makes too little sense. The geography of the several traits is badly scattered; and most of them have a rather narrow range. The effect on the map is of their having been sprayed into America rather than diffused by regular historical processes. Moreover, after the strip from Colombia to Mexico which lies along the Pacific, the greatest concentration of these "Oceanoid" traits in the Americas is in the Amazon Valley, which drains into the Atlantic: thirty traits there as against only twenty-six found in the range of the Peruvian Inca Empire along the Pacific coast, and twenty-four in North America beyond Mexico. Most Americanists therefore agree with Nordenskiöld's finding that the evidence does not build up to an indication of any significant orderly flow or larger import of culture, but that the resemblances are mainly independent convergences or co-incidences; and that for the rest, the similarities may be due to occasional imports, which however remained scattering and incidental.

From all the foregoing taken together, a broader conclusion follows. We have seen in the preceding two chapters that in spite of all regional diversities—and they were profound—there were, again and again, historical bonds that united the cultures of Asia, Africa, and Europe. This happened as early as the Palaeolithic core industries, which constituted a tricontinental unit (§ 273). Then microliths again spread between the continents; and later, agriculture and domestication and ax-polishing; to be followed in turn by bronze technology, blood sacrifice and divination, urbanization, the alphabet, ironworking, and their several accompaniments (§ 282-286). Some of these achievements penetrated deep into Oceania and equatorial Africa, others a little way only, a few not at all. But all higher civilization did first develop within an irregular band or tract stretching from Britain and Morocco roughly to Java and Japan, and including, in A.D. 1500, all the more advanced of the Christian, Mohammedan, and Brahman-Buddhist nations.

By no means all culture content within this tract was derived from a common source; but a considerable and important part of it was thus held in common. This is the area that has sometimes been called the Oikoumenē, in re-adaptation of an old Greek term (§ 174). Outside this belt of the Oikoumenē, culture level was distinctly lower in the outlying regions of Arctic and subarctic Eurasia, of remoter Oceania, of Australia, of southern Africa (§ 308-311), and of occasional internal tracts difficult of access (§ 175). Here is where the "primitive" peoples of the Old World lived. And there are no peaks of higher culture in these outlying regions of the Eastern Hemisphere—not even modest peaks: everything is derivative or reduced.

But the New World shows no such relation of dependence on the Old World Oikoumenē. For a certain distance beyond Bering Strait, yes, to a limited degree. But for North America as a whole—still more for the two Americas jointly—no. Instead, the Western Hemisphere has its own counterpart of the Oikoumenē: its Nuclear belt with its twin climaxes in Mexico and Peru. It is to this Nucleus that non-Nuclear native America stands in a relation of backward dependence, like that of the extra-Oikoumenical regions toward the Oikoumenē in the other hemisphere. Only in the northern and northwestern parts of North America do influences out of the American Nucleus and influences out of the Old World Oikoumenē or Nucleus meet and overlap.

In short, the Americas had sufficient of a hearth of growth and development of their own to free their native cultures from major or permanent dependence on Europe-Africa-Asia. If there ever was such dependence, in any degree of consequence, it must have mainly underlain and preceded the birth of higher culture in America. It would therefore be a rather remote thing, a sort of set of embryonic influences, difficult to define and establish as real—in its then rudimentary form. That is as much as it could have amounted to if there was a direct dependence at all. But as we shall see when we follow the prehistories of Mexico and Peru back as far as they are traceable (§ 320, 328), the earliest discovered forms there do *not* specifically resemble any particular ancient culture of Asia. And equally lacking is any evidence of turning points within this continuous prehistory of Mexico and Peru that are marked by the injection of Asiatic or Oceanian traits, or even of sudden acceleration of growth which might reasonably be attributed to transpacific stimuli. No specialist in American archaeology at present sees any place where there is room for a significant Old World influence in the unfolding of his story. The various theories "explaining" the cultures of Mexico and Peru as derived from China, India, Farther India, or Oceania are all views of non-Americanistic scholars or the speculations of amateurs.

For somewhat similar reasons, the romantic voyage in 1947 of the sailing raft Kon-tiki, with its crew of Norwegians, from Peru to the Polynesian Tuamotus cannot really prove anything of fundamental significance as to derivations. It does strengthen the possibility, suggested before, that the sweet potato reached the Pacific islands from America, and especially that the transmission was in pre-Spanish times rather than by the Spaniards themselves. The gourd—also a bi-hemispheric cultivated plant—may have gone the same way; or perhaps the opposite way where the currents flow from west to east in other latitudes. But isolated items like these cannot establish the flow or origin of whole cultures. Whether or not, or how far, remote cultures have connections must be judged by preponderance of the mass of specific evidence, not by piecemeal bits.

What the Kon-tiki re-establishes is that transpacific voyagers could have survived. This is a fact already admitted, in the last section but one, for junks drifting the other way. What is most relevant in this connection, however, is what was said there as to culture spreads' occurring mostly by continuous contact of peoples, rather than through occasional migrants or population movements.

318. THE MAIN AREAS OF NATIVE CULTURE: NORTH AMERICA

The hundreds of tribal cultures in native America segregate themselves into several dozen provincial areas of reasonably uniform culture—the exact number being a function of how finely one wishes to discriminate or on the contrary to effect gross consolidation. These provincial areas tend to coincide with areas of some degree of environmental uniformity, usually climatic and vegetational. Beyond that, they in turn segregate themselves into about ten basic major culture areas—six in North America and four in South America. Most of these ten, it is true, subdivide into two or three regions or subareas—making a total of just about twenty such—as to the distinct identity of whose culture there is practically unanimous agreement. In fact, ethnological disagreement begins largely on how warranted and how significant it is to break down these subareas further into the provinces first spoken of. It is also largely a matter of judgment whether one could not just as well start with the twenty units of culture here called subareas as the basic areal units, instead of the ten grand areas referred to. But the latter scheme—ten grand areas of culture subdividing into about twenty subareas—is the more expedient in organization, or at least more convenient to apprehend, and it will be followed here.

The six basic areas in North America are Mexican or Meso-American, Southwest, Intermediate, Northwest Coast, Eastern-Northern, and Arctic Coast or Eskimo. The four in South America are Andean, Circum-Caribbean, Tropical Forest, and Marginal.

Easily the richest and most advanced aboriginal cultures are the two first named in each continent, the Meso-American and the Andean, especially an intensive subarea or focal climax within each. Together they form the bicontinental culminant core or Nucleus of advancement for the whole hemisphere in native times, which has already been discussed. From this culmination the other areal and subareal cultures were increasingly stepped down roughly in proportion to their distance from it. It is perhaps worth repeating that, basically, it is this situation of the climax of development around the junction of the two continents, and the fading-away toward their extremities, which inevitably gives the impression that the whole main growth of ancient American culture was autonomous and autochthonous. Had the growth been chiefly derivative, dependent on Asia, the peak or climax would presumably have lain somewhere near Asia in western North America, and the cultural lowering would have been progressive from there outward and south. There was in fact some sort of such a logically expectable peak on the Northwest Coast; and there seems every reason to believe that—apart from a fairly favorable natural environment—the existence of this peak was largely due to more diffusionary cultural import and stimulus from near-by Asia to it than other American areas received. But the significant fact is that this Northwest Coast peak was definitely minor and underdeveloped compared with the great Meso-American-Andean Nucleus.

In the enumerative characterization of the areas, and their subsequent more detailed consideration, the natural order of presentation will accordingly be from Mexico and the Andes outward, respectively, in each of the two continents.

In North America, what is sometimes roughly called the Mexican area contained the Maya, the Toltec, and the Aztec as its most outstanding nationalities. However, this culture area did not include all of Mexico, and it did include Guatemala and at least parts of other Central American republics. The term "South Mexican-Central American" would therefore be more accurate and has sometimes been used. But it is cumbersome; and *Meso-American* has been suggested and employed as a convenient coinage that runs no risk of being confused with terms of other meaning, such as "Middle American" or "Central American."

Meso-America segregates into two subareas: a true nucleus or focus of *High Culture* (1A), and a *Subnuclear* region (1B on map, Fig. 41, overleaf). The presence of the arbitrary permutating ritual calendar discussed in § 230 can be taken as a convenient criterion of the extent of the subarea of High Culture. With this were associated the invention of position numerals and zero (§ 189), of such steps toward true writing as had been achieved in America, masonry temples and step pyramids, true stone sculpture and a richly symbolical decorative art, large-scale human sacrifice and bloody rituals (§ 252), conquest states imposing tribute, and rulers of high rank and power. The Subnuclear western and northern parts of Meso-America show some of these traits in reduced measure, but they always lack the elaborate and precise calendar and astronomy and the efforts at writing, and usually a good many other traits as well.

To the southeast, beyond Guatemala, Meso-America is carried by some authorities along the Pacific side of the narrowing continent as far as northern Costa Rica around the Gulf of Nicoya. Others assign this tongue rather to a Circum-Caribbean area that is mainly South American (M in Figs. 41, 42). The Atlantic slope southeast of Guatemala is not thus in doubt: a few dozen miles beyond the last great Maya ruin of Copán one enters aboriginal cultural South American territory of the Circum-Caribbean area.

The *Southwest* is so named from its position in the United States, but includes parts of northern Mexico. It is a generally arid and elevated region. Much of it, especially the lowland, is actual desert, fertile only in irrigable spots; but in its middle altitudes summer rains make maize-growing possible in many stretches. Farming and nonfarming tribes were therefore frequently juxtaposed. As might be expected, the farmers showed the greater number of trait resemblances to Meso-America, such as masonry and elaborate symbolic rituals. However, there is no continuous sloping-off northward from the Meso-American culmination to the Southwest: this latter had, and has, its own smaller climax in parts of New Mexico and Arizona. The Southwest splits into two subareas: a southwestern lowland and a northeastern plateau. Archaeologically, these were dominated by the so-called *Anasazi* and *Hohokam* developments, which will be outlined below.

The *Intermediate* area is fairly so named because of its position between two areas of more characterized and richer development—the Southwest and the Northwest Coast. Along the Pacific coast west of the Sierra Nevada the environment was gentle and favorable to subsistence; and a *California* subarea is therefore usually set off. As against this, the much larger *Intermountain* subarea, comprising the Great Basin and the Columbia and Fraser plateau, provided much less natural food and almost no maize-farming opportunities. The population was therefore sparse, and it remained simple in its customs.

FIG. 41. AREAS OF NATIVE CULTURE IN NORTH AMERICA

The *Northwest Coast* is unusually well marked off, ecologically and culturally. It extends from Cape Mendocino in northern California through the panhandle of Alaska to the glaciers and Copper River. It consists of a narrow strip of dense, wet-climate, coniferous forest along a rugged, indented shore line rich in sea foods. The population on the rivers, bays, and islands was one of the densest in the world, for a nonfarming, nonherding society (§ 163). Technology, art, social structure, and ritualism were elaborate and original. They showed some transpacific resemblances, as mentioned in § 315 and 317, generally attributed to convergence or accident, and more certain influences from East Asia. In contrast, specific similarities with Nuclear America, or even with the Southwest, were surprisingly few. Quite evidently, the Northwest Coast area represented a secondary form of cultural creativeness, probably due at least in part to stimulations from proximate Asia, but resulting in a largely independent and distinctive cultural growth.

The *Eastern-Northern* area covers a good half of the continent, mostly wooded except for Arctic tundra and a strip of open country at the foot of the Rockies. Three subareas have to be distinguished: Eastern, Northern, and Plains. The *Eastern* is a region of deciduous forest, in clearings of which maize and squashes could be grown. Agriculture is in fact the determinant of the Eastern subarea; but it was definitely more supplemented by hunting and gathering than in the Southwest. Also, Eastern-subarea farming seems to have been derived from Mexico by a separate route, not via the Southwest. The *Northern* subarea begins where the frostless season is too short for plans of tropical origin such as maize to be cultivated. With hunting, fishing, and gathering enforced, and winters long and severe, population had to be thin-sown to survive, arts were few, and luxuries fewer. This is prevailingly the region of the transcontinental coniferous forest that stretches from Nova Scotia and Newfoundland to Alaska— in fact continues across most of Siberia as the taiga. By contrast, the third subarea is open country: grassland *Plains* merging into scrub in Texas and northeastern Mexico. This region was generally not farmed by the Indians, even though considerable parts are farmed by us.[8] After horses became available two to three centuries ago, the Plains changed from a marginal to a favorable habitat on account of the increased availability of bison, and the culture was rapidly enriched. But this was definitely a late phenomenon.

The *Arctic Coast* is the area of the Eskimo, that famous people distinctive in physique, in speech, and in customs, and venturing to live farther north than any other. Though they also hunt caribou where they can, and fish in lakes and

[8] In technical considerations, the western, drier, short-grass, nonfarming *High Plains* are distinguished from the lower, moister, tall-grass *Prairies* in which there was some native farming and which today comprise parts of our intensive wheat and corn belts. As drawn on the map in Figure 41, the Plains cultural subarea has been made to take in the former nonagricultural tracts of the Prairies as well as of Texas.

rivers, their main subsistence is from sea mammals, and their characteristic distribution is accordingly littoral. The ingenuity with which they wrest a narrow survival from their extreme environment makes them a deserved favorite in cross-ethnic interest. The culture is as unique as it is limited; and while it contains elements that reappear at the far end of South America, it is obvious from the environment why it could hardly contain many of the traits that characterize the advancement of Meso-America and Peru.

319. SOUTH AMERICAN AREAS

In the Smithsonian's great *Handbook of the South American Indians,* the continent is divided into four main areas, each with its type of primary native culture. These four areas are the Andean, the Circum-Caribbean, the Tropical Forest, and the Marginal. They are shown, with a few simplifications of minor detail, in Figure 42.

The *Andean* area was part of Nuclear America and consisted of nearly the whole length of the narrow Cordilleran system that forms the mountain backbone and watershed of the continent. As the Andes closely follow the Pacific coast, the immediate littoral strip is included.

The middle of the long Andean stretch was the most advanced culturally: approximately the mountain and coast part of Peru [9] and the adjacent plateau corner of Bolivia. Here alone did empires originate, cities, temples, and palaces of masonry get built, metallurgy and weaving reach their peaks. The population may have aggregated nearly as much as in all the remaining 95 per cent of the continent. We may call this the Andean subarea of *High Culture.*

The *North Andean* subarea takes in most of the highland of Ecuador and Colombia, its northern tip being formed by the plateau of Bogotá, where the Chibcha had developed a system of little states that ranked perhaps one large step below the High Culture Peruvians.

The *South Andean* subarea perhaps was one more step behind, originally. But in late pre-Columbian times it underwent conquest and influencing from Peru and Bolivia into northwest Argentina. By the eighteenth century the Araucanians of Chile had also spread across the Andes into the Argentinian high plains. It is only here in this subarea that Andean culture managed to get somewhat inland of its mountain system. Both the North and the High Culture Andean subareas extended only to the innermost Cordilleran range. Halfway down the eastern slope of this, the Tropical Forest culture people took over—except in the south, where the forest was replaced by open scrub or grassland.

The *Circum-Caribbean* area is well described by that name. It included northern South America, all the West Indies, and Central America to the Mayan

---

[9] That is, excluding the eastern part of contemporary political Peru, which is covered with rain forest and belonged to the Tropical Forest area.

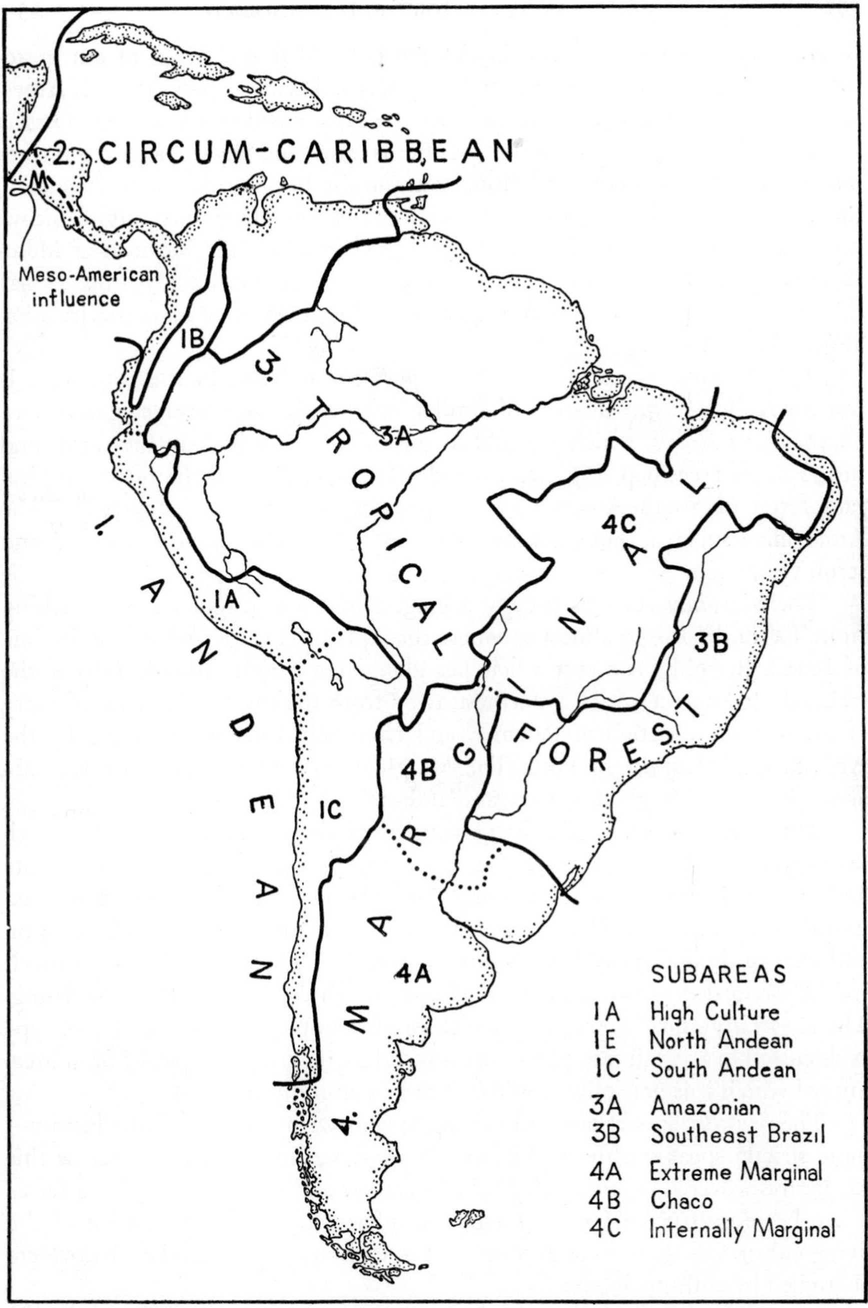
2. CIRCUM-CARIBBEAN
M
Meso-American influence
1B
3.
TROPICAL FOREST
3A
1. ANDEAN
1A
4C
4B
1C
3B
4. MARGINAL
4A
SUBAREAS
1A High Culture
1E North Andean
1C South Andean
3A Amazonian
3B Southeast Brazil
4A Extreme Marginal
4B Chaco
4C Internally Marginal

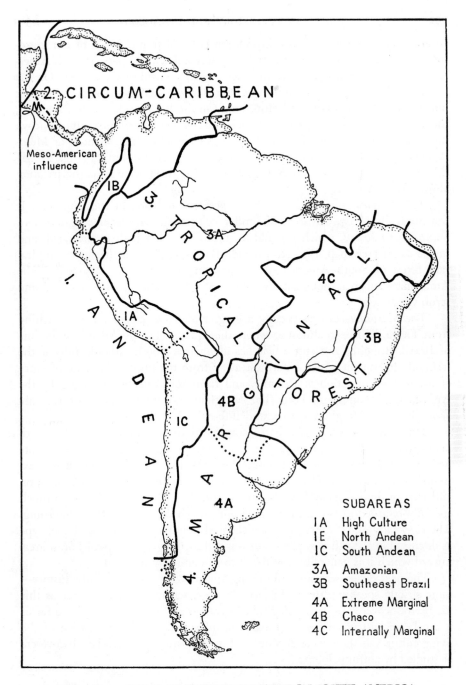

FIG. 42. AREAS OF NATIVE CULTURE IN SOUTH AMERICA

frontier—almost to Guatemala, in modern political terms. Much of our customary modern "Central America" was therefore culturally a part of South America. For Panamá and Costa Rica this fact was recognized fifty years ago. On the Atlantic side, the aboriginal culture frontier is now generally carried even farther north, through Nicaragua and Honduras. On the Pacific side, as we have seen, the situation is more ambiguous. There is a stretch here, from the Gulf of Nicoya north, which has already been mentioned as claimed for the Mexican or Meso-American area as well as for the Circum-Caribbean. On both maps (Figs. 41, 42) this stretch is marked off and designated as "M" to indicate its partial relation also to Meso-America.

The *Tropical Forest* area is the largest cultural one in the continent. It consists really of two subareas of similar culture, the *Amazonian* and that of *Southeastern Brazil,* which just fail to meet each other both in the north and in the south (see map, Fig. 42, 3A and 3B). Practically all the heavy tropical rain forest of South America—the largest in the world—is included in the Amazonian subarea, though it also includes considerable areas of savanna and scrub vegetation.

The *Marginal* cultures occupy a long, somewhat irregular belt stretching from Tierra del Fuego almost to where the equator cuts the Atlantic shore line of Brazil. Roughly, the entire belt lies along that South Atlantic side of the triangular continent which is farthest away from the presumable gate of entry of original immigration at Panamá, and from subsequent influencing by the Andean High Culture of Peru. The Marginal area subdivides into three subareas: Extreme Marginal, Chaco, and Internally Marginal.

The *Extreme Marginal* subarea consists of the southern tip of the continent—southern Chile and most the Argentine. Not only position but climate here were the most extreme in South America; as expectable, culture was extremely backward. The *Chaco* subarea is a great inland, scrub-covered plain, on and west of the Paraguay River from 18° to 28° S. The culture is not so much specially retarded as it is a mixture without much consistent larger patterning. The *Internally Marginal* subarea is a classical example of a culture of that type as discussed in § 175. It is virtually surrounded by the great Tropical Forest area, toward which it is generally considered to be culturally retarded.

The next dozen sections will outline in somewhat more detail the history—more strictly speaking, the prehistory—of these ten grand areas, so far as this has been uncovered by archaeological excavations and discoveries, or in so far as it can be reconstructed from comparative inferences of what is known of the living cultures as these were encountered in each area by Caucasian discoverers or studied by anthropologists.

320. AREAL HISTORIES: MESO-AMERICA

We have seen that native Meso-America in the larger sense consisted of most of what now is Mexico and of Guatemala,[10] and that it constituted the North American half of prehistoric Nuclear America. We have also seen that Meso-America comprised a focus of High Culture at its southeastern end plus a Subnuclear marginal region in northern Mexico. Use of the permutating calendar of 260 and 365 days serves as a convenient criterion of the High Culture. The Subnuclear region consists of a western agricultural half which undoubtedly served as a corridor of transmission to the agricultural Southwest area that will be considered in § 323; and of an eastern half which in all but a few spots was nonfarming, and which abuts on the nonfarming Plains region of the Eastern-Northern area (§ 326). The step down from the intensive culture of focal Meso-America to the unorganized hunting-gathering culture of this eastern Subnuclear region was sudden and sharp—something like a geological nonconformity; and its suddenness remains unexplained.[11]

In what follows, attention will be given primarily to High Culture Meso-America—the region which in 1520 possessed the highly arbitrary but exact permutating calendar.

This is a difficult region to characterize as a unit, because its culture early acquired the habit of getting itself expressed in half a dozen or more parallel "facies" or aspects: forms that were superficially and stylistically distinct, though mainly interrelated in origin; concurrent regional manifestations of a basically unitary pattern. Of such localized expressions, the principal ones were the following:

1. Lowland Maya,[12] of the peninsula of Yucatán plus British Honduras and the Petén district of Guatemala. The speech was Maya proper, or closely related dialects like Chol, Chorti, and Chontal. Culturally, this group represented the Mayan culmination—in some respects the Meso-American peak.

[10] To be exact, part of El Salvador and a border fringe of Honduras should be included; perhaps also the southern tip of Texas.

[11] Some authors, like Kirchhoff and Kidder, delimit Meso-America so as to comprise the High Culture region plus the agricultural portion of the Subnuclear region. This procedure substitutes agriculture for calendar as the defining criterion of Meso-America within Mexico. Agriculture does not seem too effective a distinguishing mark, since most of South America, and the southwestern and eastern United States, also farmed. Moreover, the Kirchhoff inclusion of the agricultural Subnuclear region in High Culture Meso-America leaves northeastern Mexico entirely out of Meso-America (that is, out of cultural native Mexico) without assigning it a specific relationship to the cultures north of Mexico. Northeastern Mexico might indeed conceivably be classed with the nonfarming Plains subarea of the Eastern-Northern area. But no Americanist to date seems to have been ready so to classify it.

[12] The pronunciation is of course via Spanish, "My-yah" in English, not "Meh-yah." The *hu* of Teotihuacán, Huastec, Nahuatl, and so on, is of course not a syllable but an orthographic device for rendering *w*, which Spanish lacks.

2. Highland Maya, of upland Guatemala, speaking languages like Quiché, Cakchiquel, and Mam. In architecture, sculpture, and science, these Maya were somewhat retarded.

3. Zapotec—and, toward 1500, Mixtec—of Oaxaca.

4. Along the Gulf coast in Tabasco and Vera Cruz, a series of peoples known as Olmec, Totonac, and Huastec, in order from south to north.

5. The landlocked high basin or "Valley" of Mexico, with adjoining portions of the eastern end of the "Mesa Central." In the Valley of Mexico were many towns—pre-eminent among them at the time of discovery and since, the Aztec capital, now Mexico City; and, more anciently, Teotihuacán of the giant pyramids.[13] To the north lay Tollan, today Tula, capital of the Toltec, later than Teotihuacán but predecessors of the Aztec. To the east, related nations inhabited the states of Tlaxcala and Puebla, with Cholula as their greatest town—again with an enormous pyramid. The dominant language in this whole area was Uto-Aztecan Nahuatl (see map, Fig. 16, § 96).

6. Northwest and north of the Valley of Mexico was the main area of the Otomí, a somewhat timid, scattered people without large towns, who however adhered to the calendar system and must therefore be included among the civilized nations of native America.

7. In Michoacán, the Tarasco had built up a military empire that was holding its own against the Aztec. They were on the whole somewhat less advanced culturally, but seem still to have used the standard basic calendar.

There were enclaves and borders besides these seven, but they were of less importance.

By far the most archaeological exploration has been conducted in the first and fifth of these areas, that of the Lowland Maya and of the vicinity of the Valley of Mexico. It is also for these two regions that the legendary histories in picture writing are most abundant and have been supplemented by native versions or Spanish translations written—after 1519—in the Roman alphabet. Our regional stories will therefore begin with these two dominant areas.

321. THE MAYA

The Mayan calendar in its fullest "long-count" development of nine-place denotation is so extraordinarily exact, and so long-range, that for a number of decades after its decipherment hope was felt that it could be "correlated" with our Julian-Gregorian calendar by identification of a specific day in the one with a specific date in the other. As the Maya loved to inscribe dates and time in-

---

[13] The name "Aztec" is from Aztatlán, a legendary point of origin, and was popularized by Prescott. Actually, this tribe or nation called itself Tenochca or Mexica, and named its capital Tenochtitlán, for which Mexico—"place of the Mexica"—was a loose synonym. In Europe as in Spanish America our "Aztecs" are still mostly called (ancient) "Mexicans," and Nahuatl is known as the "Mexican" tongue.

tervals on their monuments, such a correlation, if reliable, would have given us absolute dates for that part of Mayan history for which date inscriptions are preserved; and from these, Toltec, Aztec, and other Meso-American cultures could then have been approximately dated by the usual method of archaeological crossties. Unfortunately, most authorities have lost faith in the sure identification of Mayan and Christian dates. They now prefer to pick from among several such possible identifications—usually 256¼ years apart—that one which seems to accommodate best the majority of all the archaeological facts they have to deal with. This has led to a preponderant recognition of the GMT or Goodman-Martínez-Thompson correlation as most probable—though not as proved. This equation has the Maya do their reckoning from a mythical, back-projected calendrical zero corresponding to 3113 B.C. It also sets their highest florescence between their 9·15·0·0·0 and 9·19·0·0·0, corresponding to A.D. 731 to 810.[14] These figures represent some likelihood of being the actual chronological truth: that seems as much as can be said at present.

Beyond the illusion that we already knew the absolute dates of Mayan history, and therewith by crossties and transference the approximate dating of other American prehistories, lies another illusion: that it was the Maya who first domesticated maize, thereby originated American agriculture, and that this fact somehow got them off to the start of devising the first native civilization in the hemisphere. It was tempting to connect pre-eminence in astronomy, reckoning, and art with precedence in stable food production and resultant economic prosperity. In favor of such a connection there was for a while a body of seeming botanical facts. The maize plant, *Zea mays,* forms a highly specialized species and genus, incapable of self-perpetuation in a state of nature, and quite different from even the nearest genera in its subfamily within the grasses. In puzzlement, it was a botanist who first suggested that maize might be a domesticated alteration of *Euchlaena* or teocintle[15]—meaning god or god-given maize in Nahuatl— a wild grass more similar in appearance than any other to maize, though lacking a cob for its kernels. Now the area in which teocintle is most abundant is the Guatemala highland and near-by parts of Mexico. So it was natural to infer that it was the highland Maya who bred and improved teocintle into maize; and that with the impetus given them by this new agriculture they went ahead to make other important inventions—incidentally also spilling from the Guatemalan upland to the lowland or Petén, where the earliest Mayan dates are found carved on monuments.

[14] The GMT correlation yields the following further equations: 8·14·0·0·0 = A.D. 317; 9·0·0·0·0 = 435; 9·10·0·0·0 = 633; 10·0·0·0·0 = 830; 11·0·0·0·0 = 1224; 11·16·0·0·0, 13 Ahau 8 Shul = November 14, 1539. The basic principles of the Meso-American permutating calendar have been set forth in § 230, and additional features peculiar to the Maya in § 189. The essential workings of this calendar are understood with certainty, even though its tie-up with our dating is not certain. Maya dates "rounded" to two places, as in the table that follows, indicate only the cycle and katun, as defined in footnote 16.

[15] Also written *teocentli* and *teosinte*.

After some thirty years of vogue, especially among Meso-American archae-ologists, this theory was overthrown by new botanical facts and breeding experi-ments. Teocintle or *Euchlaena* was shown to be not the mother of maize but its daughter—by crossing with a third large grass, *Tripsacum*. In short, teocintle was nothing but a weed hybridized out of cultivated maize by contamination. What the district of teocintle abundance represented was therefore not the area where maize was developed but the area where it happened to get partly spoiled again by meeting with *Tripsacum*. That threw the problem of maize origins wide-open again; and by this time botanists were aware that the number of cultivated varieties of maize, and their degree of differentiation, were greatest in South America, and that accordingly the probable source and the domestica-tion of the cereal must be sought there. A supplementary hypothesis makes maize out as derived from pod corn, which is known from occasional reversionary croppings-out, and as derived from it somewhere near the Paraguayan region. Whether this particular origin is confirmed or not remains to be seen: some South American origin does stand as indicated; and therewith the triumphs of Mayan intellectual and artistic civilization are divorced pretty completely from maize domestication. In fact the two events now look as if they had been sepa-rated by at least two thousand years, perhaps considerably more.

Another misconception is due to terminology: the division of Mayan pre-history into "Old Empire" and "New Empire." These phrases are lifted bodily from the ancient history of Egypt (§ 292), with perhaps a sidelong rove of the eye at the Aztec Empire of the century before Cortés. There is nothing to show that the Maya had an empire or political unity in either the old or the new period of their history. They seem to have constituted a series of autonomous city-states, or perhaps tribes with each its own cult-center town. There is no doubt a certain pleasant poetical connotation in dreaming about ancient dissolved empires; but for the Maya the designation is thoroughly misleading, especially for their older period.

So the terms "Classic Maya" and "Late" or "Retractile Maya" will be used here instead. These names seem justified because the Classic period con-tained the definite culmination of Mayan sculpture, painting, pottery, and cal-endry, whereas in the later Retractile centuries not only art and the calendar but also the territory of the Maya were shrinking or shrunk. The period of de-velopment preceding the Classic, before the full patterns of the Mayan civiliza-tion began to be worked out, may be called Formative.

Monumental date inscriptions that are almost certainly contemporary, and which are expressed in the "long" or full nine-place calendrical count with so-called "initial-series" glyphs, extend over the last three-tenths of the Mayan time cycle 8, the whole of 9, and the beginning of 10.[16] The few earlier dates that

[16] Cycles consist of 20 katuns of 20 "years" each, nominally 400 years; but as the "year" or tun was of 360 days only, the cycle shrinks to 394 and a fraction of our years.

SEQUENCE IN LOWLAND MAYA CIVILIZATION

Dates	Maya Dates: (GMT Correlation) Cycle and Katun	Period and Phase	Characteristics	Pottery Stages	Highland Maya Stages and Pottery Types
1441-		III Disintegration	All great cities abandoned		Chipal 3 (metal)
1194-1441		II Intensified Mexican influence } LATE, RETRACTILE, or YUCATEC	Mayapán dominant Deterioration		Chipal 2 (effigy plumbate) Chipal 1
					PAMPLONA Chamá 4
987-1194		I Mexican influence	Chichen, Ushmal flourishing		
889-987	10.3-10.8	TRANSITION	Southern cities decaying or abandoned		AMATLE (plain plumbate)
810-889	9.19-10.3	Decline	Long-count dating becoming rarer	Holmul 5 } TEPEU	Chamá 3
731-810	9.15-9.19	Great Phase / Culmination } CLASSIC	Peak of all forms of art	Uashactún III	
633-731	9.10-9.15	Rise / Early Phase	Inscriptions, dates, corbeled vaulting, polychrome pottery	Holmul 2-4 } TZAKOL Uashactún II	Chamá 2 ESPERANZA
317-633	8.14-9.10	Late / Early } FORMATIVE	First stone buildings	Holmul 1 } CHICANEL Uashactún Ib	Chamá 1
-317				MAMOM	
				MIRAFLORES ?	

occur from cycle 8 may be either contemporary or projected backward—we cannot be sure which. And it seems quite certain that the first seven cycles were not historical but imaginary—a way of filling in back to the beginning of the world, or some such event, in 3113 B.C. It has been conjectured, from "internal evidence," that the calendar was instituted in 7·0·0·0·0 or perhaps 7·6·0·0·0, corresponding to 353 and 235 B.C., respectively.

Of late the tendency of Mayan specialists has been to balance the problems of calendar and dating—which are tricky and pitfall-ridden in spite of their fascination—with consideration of the humbler results of excavation: pottery types, sherd counts, refuse-heap sequences. For the not yet date-inscribing Formative periods, this is of course anyway the only available procedure. On the basis of Petén pottery, two Formative periods have been recognized, Mamom and Chicanel. In the latter, stone buildings were being reared, stucco was used, and an impressive formal art style had developed. The culture had already all sorts of Mayan slants, though obviously not yet typical Classical Maya.

Some of the achievements of the Classic period have already been touched on in other connections—zero and position numerals in § 189, the permutatory calendar in § 230; and of course both of these were related to remarkably accurate reckoning of the appearances of the visibly heavenly bodies. The underlying astronomical observations must have gone on for many years, probably centuries. And since the Classic period is by definition that of the elaborate calendar—it begins with the first long-count date inscriptions—it follows that the basic Mayan mathematics and astronomy must have been worked out in the preceding Formative period.

The same probably holds for the writing—which incidentally remains almost as completely unread as contrariwise the time and number glyphs have been deciphered and as they automatically check themselves by their interval additions or subtractions. On the ground of such analysis as has been possible, it is believed that the writing contained some phonetic constituents in addition to its pictographic and ideographic base. Two facts render it improbable that the unread glyphs hold very much actual historical information. First, roughly half of all the inscriptions are taken up with time or number glyphs. Whatever it was that happened at these dates must therefore be told of very curtly. Second, all Mayan inscriptions, of whatever phase or locality, show the same limited series of characters of glyph elements, except for stylistic variations. They must accordingly deal with much the same subject matter—something repetitive or recurrent rather than varied as historical events inevitably are. So it is generally thought that the writing refers mainly to things like cult celebrations, ritual constructions, heavenly bodies, or astrological significances.

In line with this it appears that the Maya were not so much political-minded as theocratic: the priests had as much power as the rulers—perhaps were the rulers. This conclusion is reinforced by the fact that women are almost never represented in Classic art, whether carved or painted: the Mayan world was dominantly masculine as well as religious. The contrast of classes and wealth, between priest-rulers and commoners, was strong—as everywhere in high-culture native America. In all the advanced regions of Meso-America as well as the Andean area, one must lay aside the assumption of egalitarian or near-egalitarian democracy that obtains among most primitives, even up to the Pueblos. There were genuine lords and villeins in the full mediaeval sense in Meso-America.

Classic Mayan art was without doubt the finest developed in native America. We know it from ceramic painting, fresco paintings like the recently discovered marvelously preserved scenes at Banampok in Chiapas, from stucco reliefs, carved reliefs both low and high, and from occasional full-round sculpture escaped from formalism into genuine loveliness. The range is all the way from heavy and decoratively overloaded stylization to naturalness; in pottery painting there is even dash, humor, and caricature. Whatever the material or technique, the culminating achievements seem to fall around 9·15·0·0·0 and the four immediately succeeding katuns—roughly the 700's of our era.

While the same culture was common to all Mayan cities of the Classic period, there is nothing to show metropolitan dominance of one over the others. Rather each major city had its own local specialties and pre-eminences, as if they were independent and co-ordinate. In the extreme southeast, Copán in Honduras had the finest full-round statuary and the longest inscription—of about 2000 characters. From it also comes the only Classic Mayan piece of metal—gold-copper alloy—yet discovered; an import no doubt. As we go northwest, Quiriguá in Guatemala is famous for its carved altars, for its sixty-five-ton, thirty-five-foot-high sculptured stela, for its beautifully cut glyphs. In the Petén, Uashactún has the oldest dated monument and one of the latest, and the longest record of continuous occupation—over five and a half centuries. It has also yielded the finest and most varied pottery-painting. Tikal, only a dozen miles away, may have been an even larger city, and its 229-foot temple (mostly pyramidal substructure) remains the highest Mayan building. Calakmul had the largest number of sculptured stelae, though concentrated into two centuries. Coba, in Yucatán, which was mostly Late-period but also contains seventh-century date inscriptions, has the longest stone-paved ceremonial road running out from it—sixty-two miles. Piedras Negras, still in Guatemala but far west, specialized in high-relief sculpture of superb, lively scene composition; while Palenque beyond it, in Mexico, excelled in flat reliefs with formal, pure outlines.[17] These civic specializations enriched the basic common pattern of Classic Maya civilization.

The Retractile or Late Maya period opens around A.D. 1000, far away in the northern and more arid half of the Yucatán Peninsula, with the legendary

---

[17] It is curious that the freest art is found at the ends of the Classic Mayan territory—Copán and Quiriguá in the east, Palenque and Piedras Negras in the west, while the Petén, which has the earliest dates and where the Classic phase apparently originated, remained bound to the end in considerably more archaic stiffness of its art.

resettlement of Chichen by the Itzás and the founding of Ushmal by the Shiu family or tribe. From now on, nothing more is heard of the southern cities of the Classic phase: they had perhaps already reverted to tropical jungle. Dating now is by the short count of the chronicles written after the Spanish conquest. Cult and learning more or less maintained themselves, as is evident from the three preserved books written in cursive Mayan glyphs and pictures on fig-bark paper and dealing with religion and astronomy. Architecture too maintained itself, and even attained to a new, rich style enhanced by a geometrically cut stone surface of textile effect. Sculpture and painting never again reached the peak of the eighth century, either as decoration or in representation; Late designs have lost their flow of line, and figures are stiff. There seem to have been some efforts at political dominance, first by Chichen, then by Mayapán. About a century before the arrival of the Spaniards there was widespread intertribal war, probably poverty and general deterioration of living, and abandonment of the larger cities. The Spaniards still found much of the native culture going, but in social disorganization. As already said, the name "Retractile" fits the Late period because both the finest richness of Mayan civilization and its geographical extent had retracted.

One feature is new in the Late period: Mexican influence. This is explicitly mentioned in the chronicles, and it shows in art, architecture, increase of human sacrifice, occasionally even in proper names. For about two centuries the Mexican influence was moderate; thereafter it was intensified. Some of this influencing may have originated near by in Tabasco, among the Olmec; some of it is specifically Toltec, from Tula and the Valley of Mexico area. Mexicans may have been brought in as allies or mercenaries in Mayan intercity wars, or bands of them may have conquered their way in. Their power and influence were strongest in what Morley calls the Mexican period, 1194-1441, of the dominance of Mayapán, in contrast with the preceding two centuries of "Maya Renaissance," when Chichen Itzá was in its greatness. The turning date, 1194, is at the end of the century in which the Mexican annals set the dissolution and scattering of the Toltecs; and there may be a connection. However, pre-1194 Chichen already contained indubitable Mexican influences. Its feathered-serpent columns can be matched at Tula. On the contrary, the great city of Ushmal of the Shiu, legendarily established only a score of years after the refounding of Chichen in 987, differs in having no serpent columns and very little else that can be construed as imitative of Mexico; and it developed probably the finest independent Mayan architecture. The cause of this difference is unexplained. There evidently were strong, fluctuating local currents in the Late Maya culture, as well as the increasing leaning toward Mexican ways.

In contrast with the Late Maya-Toltec connections, relations of the Classic Maya with contemporary Teotihuacán had been very few and indirect. The Maya then were the more advanced culturally, and were self-sufficient. In Late times, they no longer led, and were receiving more cultural influence than they were imparting. Some gold, for instance, was at last drifting into their metalless limestone habitat; and some of it was being reworked by them with their own designs.

The Highland Maya through most of their history were poor relations of the Lowlanders, and need not be lingered on. At the time of discovery, with the Yucatec Maya at their lowest, the Quiché and Cakchiquel Maya had achieved little kingdoms on the Guatemala plateau. Highland sculpture and building were at all times meager. However, the permutating calendar was known, and remnants of it survive today. The names of some phases of Highland culture have been included in the Lowland Maya tabulation: culture periods from the environs of Guatemala City, and pottery style periods at Chamá and Chipal at the border between plateau and lowland.[18]

322. OTHER MESO-AMERICAN DEVELOPMENTS

The second Meso-American region of high culture for which the record is full and continuous is the Valley of Mexico with its environs. Until about 1930, the story here seemed fairly simple, in three grand periods: Archaic, Toltec, Aztec, with the great Teotihuacán ruins construed as Toltec. Since then the Archaic has been renamed "Middle" by some, including Vaillant, who has scientifically excavated more of it than anyone else. Neither name is good. "Archaic" is unsatisfactory because the culture denoted is clearly not at the beginning of things—it has well-shaped, incised, and painted pottery; and because the Archaic almost certainly continued into the Christian era—perhaps fell mainly into it. "Middle" is unsatisfactory because it implies an "Early" stage—which certainly existed, but has not yet been identified. We shall straddle the difficulty by calling the era "Archaic-Middle."

Teotihuacán and Toltec have lately been divorced. Teotihuacán is several centuries the older. The Toltecs had their capital, as native legendary history maintained, at Tollan, today Tula. Cholula's vast pyramid is traditionally connected with them, and archaeology has shown them to have influenced the Yucatec Maya. A pottery style called Mazapan is now classed as Toltec. Aztec, for which four or five successive pottery styles had been worked out, is now divided into Chichimec and Aztec. The Chichimec were the barbarous tribes who pushed in as the Toltecs weakened, and displaced or partly intermarried with them. To the Chichimec are now assigned the former Aztec periods 1 and 2. The remaining Aztec pottery phases belong to the Aztec, or Mexica, and to their contemporaries and neighbors from about 1325 on. The total sequence thus

---

[18] Plumbate or leadlike pottery, a widespread and easily recognizable trade ware, has been entered in the table on account of its value as a horizon or time marker, like Chavín, Tiahuanaco, and Inca in Peru (§ 328). It is assumed to have been manufactured in or near El Salvador. Plain plumbate is dated at about 950-1000; effigy plumbate, 1100-1300 in Mexico, 1200-1400 in Yucatán.

is: Archaic-Middle, Teotihuacán, Toltec, Chichimec, Aztec—mostly with subdivisions.

Archaic-Middle sites, carefully excavated by Vaillant, have their somewhat overlapping sequence run: Arbolillo, Zacatenco, Copilco, Galupita, Ticomán, Cuicuilco. One could group them into two or three or more periods: the culture seems to have changed gradually. All but the fourth site lay at the edges of the Lake of Texcoco when this stood at a higher level. Vessels were already tripodal, as they continued through Meso-American history (§ 144); and farming was practiced. The Copilco and Cuicuilco sites lie under a lava flow. There used to be some wild talk about this flow being ten thousand years old; no responsible geologist has ever ventured such a guess. On archaeological "feel," something in the neighborhood of fifteen hundred years ago would seem more or less right for the age of the eruption.

Before Cuicuilco was abandoned to the lava, a sixty-foot dirt cone some three hundred feet across had been reared there, faced twice with rock. The potsherds at Cuicuilco are virtually identical with those in the fill of the middle of the bottom of the great Sun pyramid at Teotihuacán. These latter sherds, known as Teotihuacán 1, evidently were refuse in the soil that was scraped up to start the pyramid. Thus the lava flow is likely to have preceded the beginning of Teotihuacán by no long period, if at all, since it followed the completion of the similarly potteried Cuicuilco. The Archaic-Middle stages have been determined by Vaillant largely on the basis of numerous small, freely modeled, crude pottery figurines and heads. These vary so much from piece to piece as to make it hard for other archaeologists to use this method of classifying; but the associated vessel styles confirm the scheme. Recently the artist-archaeologist Covarrubias has obtained from Tlatilco certain figurines, perhaps more or less of Zacatenco period, that are tastefully and even archly modeled and well finished.

Teotihuacán 1 period pottery we have seen to be Archaic-Middle, and Teotihuacán 5, so called, is found only at Azcopotzalco. Teotihuacán 2, 3, 4 therefore really represent this famous site, or rather its pottery aspects; and of these, 3 is thought to be the great period. This era produced murals, stonework, some sculpture, tripod cylindrical vases, all done in a highly characteristic, somewhat heavy monumental, grandiosely decorative style. This style has been traced, in trade objects, imitations, or influenced pieces, to El Tajín in the coastal region, to Monte Albán 3 in Oaxaca, to the Esperanza horizon at Kaminal-juyú at Guatemala City, and via this to contemporaneity with late Tzakol or Early Classic Lowland Maya—somewhere not far from A.D. 500 if the GMT chronology holds. At any rate, the correspondences give us a series of simultaneous points, which mostly are also culminant points, in the cultural developments of several of the most important Meso-American subregions.

Teotihuacán is one of the most impressive ancient sites in the world. The large-scale excavations here were made mostly in the early years of this century, before archaeological methods had been refined to solve problems of relative sequence, so that some of the principal structures and carvings remain undated, except by stylistic impression. This deficiency will no doubt be remedied by future excavatory studies.

In somewhat the same way, only more so, Toltec, Chichimec, and Aztec period monuments, especially sculptures, have accumulated haphazardly for over four centuries and are segregable only by estimate of where their style belongs; and this is complicated by local variations. The humble pottery can be much better assigned to its time and place; and association of this with sculptural and architectural manner, metalwork, and the rest, will ultimately help put all classes of remains into time order.

From the Toltecs on, a genuine effort was made by the native peoples of this region to maintain a continuous historical record, even though legendary and even mythical elements were injected into the story, and though the unordered 52-year cycles could manage to get omitted or repeated in the count. Nevertheless the sixteenth-century Spaniards collected written records of Toltec rulers going back to 804 by some interpretations, and to the 500's and 600's by others. From there on, whether true or fictitious, the histories are continuous, for various cities, to Montezuma. There can be no doubt that some of the kings' names are authentic, and so are some of the sieges, overthrows, invasions and the like, though there are also gaps and contradictions. Sometimes an event is attributed to two or three dates fifty-two or a hundred and four years apart. Tollan is represented as having lasted seven or more cycles, till 1116 (1122) or 1168, culminating under Quetzalcoatl—half god, half man—and breaking up under Huemac. It was around the troubled times of the breakup, or soon after, that Mexican warriors and influences reached Yucatán in greatest strength.

The Chichimec period was one of city against city or tribe against tribe, first one and then another being dominant. The Chichimec are represented as rude barbarians from the north: they probably did come from the margins of the region of intensive culture. Probably most of them spoke Nahuatl dialects; others may have acquired them then. Even the Toltecs may have been Nahuatl-speakers. Old and new cultural traditions maintained themselves with varying strength in this or that spot, in the Chichimec era. Cholula harbors much Toltec influence, Texcoco was proud of its Chichimec strain, Azcopotzalco seems to have continued first Teotihuacán and then Toltec affiliations.

In this welter of strife for lodgment, maintenance, and supremacy, the Tenochca Mexica, whom we usually call Aztecs, founded their town of Tenochtitlán on a lake island about 1325, and for a century were under the dominance of one or the other of the neighboring cities until, with Texcoco as principal ally, they broke the power of Azcopotzalco. Thereupon they launched on a career of conquest for tribute, which in the ninety years until Cortés came had carried them as far as the Isthmus of Tehuantepec. This was a real power and conquest empire, though nominally a confederation. The allies fought and profited with them, but also came more and more under the dominance of

Tenochtitlán. Here and there a city or group of cities resisted them, like Tlaxcala, or was left alone, like Cholula, and remained as unreduced enclaves inside the empire's limits. To the west, the Aztec conquered until they reached the frontier of the Tarasco of Michoacán, who had recently begun to build a realm of their own and gave them knock for knock without budging. The Aztec Empire lasted only ninety-two years: 1429 to 1521. There is every reason to believe that similar military-political exploitive growths had mushroomed and collapsed for some centuries before—at least since the Toltec and perhaps earlier.

We pass now to the regional developments of secondary rank in High Culture Meso-America.

The lowland and coastal strip of Vera Cruz and Tabasco held the Huastec, an anciently detached Maya-speaking unit; the Totonac, of independent speech; and, in late times, the Olmec or "people who had rubber," who spoke Nahuatl. This whole Atlantic lowland showed considerable cultural differentiation, but its sequences are only beginning to be determined. One of its major ruins is El Tajín, which we have seen to be coeval with Teotihuacán 3 and the Tzakol Classic Maya. In the eastern part of the region three sites have recently yielded rich and novel remains: Cerro de las Mesas, Tres Zapotes, and La Venta, with their overlapping time order seemingly being the reverse—and with some indubitable Mayan resemblances. La Venta has gigantic carved stone heads, markedly infantile and sometimes Negroid in features. Somewhat similar heads occur on the Pacific or far side of Guatemala, and form an equal puzzle. There is some inclination among archaeologists to set the La Venta culture back near— or even before—the beginning of the Christian era, about coeval with the Zacatenco Archaic-Middle phase and the Mamom formative or proto-Maya. The sculpture does seem advanced for so early a period; but no other secure berth has yet been found for it.

Zapotec Oaxaca lies more or less intermediate between the Maya and the Aztec, with some affiliations both ways and a great deal of local individuation. For instance it shows glyphs, but rather different ones from both Mayan and Mexican symbols. Under the leadership of Caso, a long series of explorations has been made of Monte Albán not far from the city of Oaxaca. Five periods were determined. The first is set back into Archaic-Middle times. Monte Albán 3 is equated in time with Teotihuacán 3 and with its coevals elsewhere. It manifests, on the whole, the Oaxacan aesthetic culmination. Period 5 is thought to represent a temporary conquest by the neighboring Mixtec in Aztec times. It is to this period that the famous cire-perdue-cast gold belongs—to date the finest unlooted hoard of native American jewelry discovered; like all Meso-American metallurgy, it is Late. Also of generically Late period are the ruins of Mitla on another side of Oaxaca, with a geometric-pattern surface decoration or stone "mosaic" of the order already described for Ushmal and other Late Mayan cities.

The Otomí to the north and northwest, and the Tarasco to the west, of the Valley of Mexico are almost certainly to be reckoned as within the subarea of

Meso-American high culture. The Otomí passed among their neighbors as brutish and boorish, when perhaps they were chiefly nonaggressive to the point of timidity. The Tarasco were good fighters, as we have seen, not averse to conquest and booty. Their culture seems to have been a simplified, ruder version of that of the Valley of Mexico.

Beyond, from Jalisco to Sinaloa, we are outside the realm of calendars and picture writing. We are still in Meso-America but beyond its high culture. There is excellent pottery, sometimes still polychrome and tripodal. Stone construction occurs, but only sporadically, metallurgy apparently likewise. The last ten years have brought us here and there some sequences, based mostly on pottery; they do not yet suffice to cover the area, or to tie up with those in the high-culture region, except for occasional suggestive flashes.

323. THE SOUTHWEST

The Southwest area of culture is of course named from its position within the United States, not with reference to the continent. It is the happiest hunting ground of the American anthropologist. The ethnologist finds there the best-preserved living native cultures. We have already seen that the geologist-prehistorian has to date made his most important American discoveries in the Southwest. The archaeologist-prehistorian was first stimulated by picturesque standing ruins and then aided by the openness of the little-covered ground, by excellent preservation conditions, and by a fairly rich development of culture, especially a varied pottery. In consequence, a sure sequence of precise culture sequences was established for the Southwest earlier than for any other region in the Americas.

This in turn was fortified, also for the first time anywhere, by a system of actual dates, which were gradually carried back from the present as far as A.D. 11 by dendrochronology, the comparison of the growth rings of trees. This technique, first developed on living trees by the astronomer Douglass, in an attempt to study the history of climate, was extended by the examination of timbers in prehistoric sites. The method works particularly easily on certain kinds of wood, such as yellow pine, growing in subarid regions like the Southwest. With specific types of Southwestern culture objects dated, the lucky finding of such objects anciently traded to other societies, such as in the eastern United States or southern Mexico, promises to help to establish an absolute chronology for these other areas. An actual beginning of such dating by "crossties" has been made in the hitherto difficult transition region of Texas (§ 326).

The Southwest as a major area or sphere of culture extends west to the Pacific, and south to latitude 26° in Mexico (Fig. 41). However, the area of concentration of ethnological and archaeological findings is confined to New Mexico and Arizona, and centers in the Pueblo or "town" Indians, together with ancient cognates like the Hohokam and surviving tribes like the Navaho and the Apache.

The fullest story has been worked out for the Pueblo themselves and their ancestors, or predecessors on the spot, the Basket Makers.[19] The Basket Maker and Pueblo cultures are continuous in character as well as in time, and the term "Anasazi" has been coined—or rather, taken over from a Navaho word— to indicate this joint development which centered on the New Mexico-Arizona upland. Parallel and allied, but distinct, is the Hohokam development of the southern Arizona lowland desert, with relations into Sonora: Hohokam is a Pima-Papago word denoting the ancients. A third root or stem of development, the Mogollon (Mogoyón), along the southern boundary of the two states, is recognized by some. Mogollon is much less distinctive and decisive than Anasazi and Hohokam, it faded away earlier, and some authorities still look upon it as only a local variant of Anasazi, or a temporary and regional blend of that and Hohokam.

The conventional Anasazi sequence begins with Basket Maker II, stage I having been left for an as yet undiscovered culture which was inferred as earlier. The estimated period of Basket Maker II is from perhaps A.D. 300 to nearly 500. The hearth of the culture was in the drainage of the San Juan River, an eastern affluent of the Colorado, around where Colorado and Utah meet with New Mexico and Arizona in the only four-state corner in our country. The San Juan area remained the focus of Anasazi development for a thousand years.

Basket Maker II culture was already agricultural, with small flint-corn maize and squashes, but it was still preceramic. Containers were well-made baskets, both coiled and twined, and soft bags of twined bast fibers. Woven sandals were starting a long career, but clothing was scant. The spear-thrower or atlatl was in use, but not the bow. Houses must have been temporary con- structs: no remains of them have been found, though there are food-storage cysts, sometimes lined with slabs. These represent the first hesitant use of stone for the construction which was later to become so conspicuous in this culture.

Basket Maker III, from about 500 to 700, is a richer continuation of II. Pit dwellings appear; slabs now line the bottom of these houses instead of mere storage bins. The turkey was kept domesticated, and a larger variety of maize was being grown. The metate quern was rubbed with a back-and-forth motion, as in later periods, instead of ovally, suggesting not only more systematic grind- ing but more maize to be ground. Pottery was discovered—apparently somewhat painfully, to judge by its hesitant, incomplete techniques; it is likely to have been a case of stimulus diffusion (§ 154). This pottery was the beginning of a series of black-on-white wares, baked in a reducing fire, which were to char- acterize Anasazi ceramics for eight centuries. Baskets, fiber bags, and sandals

---

[19] Basket Makers and Pueblo may have been mainly one people in blood. It is often said that the Pueblo are more roundheaded, but this appears to be due to a deformation induced by a hard cradle board rather than being a true racial trait.

continued to be made—in fact, perhaps reached their acme of quality in this final Basket Maker phase.

Pueblo I, 700-900, witnessed some new traits, but slid in without much outwardly conspicuous change of living: population groups were still small, scattered, and insignificant in their productions. The novelties included the bow and arrow, presumably imported, and cotton for cloth, which was evidently an introduction from the Hohokam not far to the south. Home inventions were aboveground houses of masonry, which began to be built in some districts; and neck banding of cooking pots with coils. This last is a trait of no intrinsic importance, but of diagnostic significance as marking a stylistic feature of roughening or corrugating that was to differentiate Anasazi ceramics from others for five hundred years or more.

By Pueblo II, 900-1050, such corrugating was extended over the whole surface of cooking vessels. Stone masonry became more common, with family rooms united by joint walls into rows or angles. Outside such a cluster, a wall-lined circular kiva was let into the ground—evidently the old round pit dwelling surviving as a ceremonial chamber.[20]

Pueblo III, 1050-1300 in round dates, has often been called the Classic stage of Anasazi development. It is that, if by "Anasazi" we mean, as some archaeologists do, the culture development centering in the San Juan drainage and characterized by rectangular masonry houses, circular kivas, and black-on-white and corrugated pottery. This was in fact the era of the largest ruins of storied "apartment-town" communal buildings, the most romantically overhung cliff dwellings, the best-laid masonry, and the finest styles of black-on-white pottery, such as Kayenta and the pictorial Mimbres.[21] However, Pueblo IV and V show many traits and developments lacking in III, and it is perhaps sounder to think of Pueblo III as the classic culmination only of the older Anasazi growth; after which, beginning around 1300, there was a reorientation and a new growth along altered but often broader lines.

In fact, some of the trends that were subsequently to become dominant had their origin in Pueblo III. Corrugation, which later died out, now began to decline. The first polychrome wares, like St. John's, appear even in the first half of III. This is a three-color ware, but hesitantly so. The slip wash is orange-red. On this a black design is painted on the inner side of the bowl, a white one on the outer. Polychromes later in III venture to bring all three colors into juxtaposition on the same side. Toward the end of III, Pinedale polychrome ware

---

[20] Settlements in the Chaco Canyon affluent of the San Juan represent a precocious development. In this limited district Pueblo II was well under way before 900; the 900-1050 period contained Pueblo III culture as well as II; and the great Pueblo Bonito ruin of III type ended about 1130, when elsewhere III was just coming in.

[21] Some see Mimbres as a late culture of Mogollon derivation influenced by the Puebloan, and would date it around 1000-1200.

introduces the glaze paint which in IV was to help crowd out black-on-white. It is probably significant that these innovations took place in the Little Colorado area instead of the San Juan: the Pueblo focus or climax was about to shift geographically.

By soon after 1300 the San Juan area was totally abandoned, and all subsequent Pueblos, including those of today, have lived in two areas to the southwest and southeast of the San Juan, in Little Colorado and in Rio Grande drainage. In the former district are the Hopi and the Zuni, some of whose still inhabited towns, or parts of them, almost certainly go back to 1300—Oraibi apparently to 1150—and who in blood presumably are descendants of the Pueblo III occupants of the same area—or even of II or I. The Rio Grande Valley on the other hand, where the historic Keres and Tano Pueblos live, was peripheral and not markedly characteristic of Anasazi culture until period III and especially IV, although repeatedly influenced previously from the Chaco Canyon and Mesa Verde of the San Juan area. Besides the San Juan, other Pueblo retractions occurred also in Utah, and in the Mimbres area of southwestern New Mexico, in or shortly before Pueblo IV times. Only in the Gila-Salt Valley did the Salado branch of the Anasazi continue until 1400 or 1450 its influencing of the local Hohokam culture on which it had begun to impinge in Pueblo III times.

Pueblo IV culture, from 1300 to 1600 or 1700, may have been somewhat less sharply patterned than the culture stages of the preceding thousand years; but if so, that was because it was losing a certain archaic narrowness. So far as anything can be inferred about religion, it was in the IV phase that the elaborations began to be worked out in the extraordinarily rich system of ritual the contemporary Pueblo Indians retain. Corrugated and then black-on-white pottery went finally out of use, but polychrome and glazed wares took their place. The polychrome Sikyatki of the Hopi of 1400 to 1600 is probably the finest decoratively painted Anasazi ceramic style, as the earlier Mimbres was the outstanding one with representative figures.

The Spaniards first arrived in 1540, under Coronado, but flowed out again, and did not permanently occupy the country and introduce Christianity until about 1600. It is from either 1600 or 1700 that period V of the historical Pueblo is reckoned as beginning; [22] and from this time forward archaeology, and especially intensive ethnographic studies, have supplemented our documentary knowledge of them. Outstanding is the luxuriance of their ritualized religion, just mentioned. It is characterized by precise symbolism—verbal, visual, and motor; and by elaboration of costumes and masks, of altars, fetishes, and shrines, of dances and ritual acts, and of organization of the participants. Almost equally marked is the pattern of town life, manifest in a sedentary, home-centered, self-

---

[22] In round dates, 1600 marks the Spanish settlement of New Mexico; 1700, the time of permanent control, when the Spaniards had reconquered the Pueblo after their great rebellion of 1680-92.

sufficient life, accumulation of belongings and food reserves, an unfailing code of courteous manners, aversion to war, and a generic gentleness of behavior. Compared with their neighbors even within the Southwest, the Pueblo seem far advanced on the axis of sophistication (§ 121), for a nonliterate folk or tribal people.

Parallel to the Anasazi development is the Hohokam one of lowland, desert, torrid southern Arizona. Here there were no masonry constructions. The dead were burned instead of buried, with the loss of many types of ancient objects as well as skeletons which would determine the racial type of the society. Corrugated and reduced black-on-white pottery are replaced from the first by an oxidized red-on-buff style of ware. This endured in the Gila drainage, with minor stylistic changes, for over a thousand years, and a derived type was made by the tribes on the lower Colorado into the twentieth century. Hohokam projectile points from the first are of a type to suggest arrows shot from a bow, while the Anasazi to the north were still throwing darts from atlatls. Ceremonial kivas did not develop among the Hohokam, but there were dugout courts for a ritual ball game. This was played with balls of rubber seemingly imported from Mexico, where the game occurred as far south as the Maya. Other imitations of southern-Mexican culture are mirrors of pyrite mosaics, and occasional copper bells—though the latter seem to have been made of Arizona metal. None of these traits of specific Mexican origin penetrated beyond the Hohokam to the Anasazi.

Four main periods, plus substages, are recognized in Hohokam development. These are best designated as I, II, III, IV. The usual designations are Pioneer, Colonial, Sedentary, Classic. These names suggest a story of successive hesitant discovery, migration, settling-down, and development to a culmination. But this story is contrary to the actual archaeological facts. The Hohokam were a settled people from the beginning of their record; they are not known to have moved from anywhere to anywhere else, and so far as their culture remained their own it reached its peak before the so-called Classic stage. In fact, the picturesque names were coined before most of our knowledge of the Hohokam had been dug out of the ground.

There are no tree rings to be studied in the Anasazi desert, so the periods of Hohokam culture are approximately dated by crossties with Anasazi—mostly sherds of trade pieces. These give the equations:

HOHOKAM-ANASAZI PERIOD EQUIVALENCES

Hohokam IV = Pueblo III, IV, 1100(1200)-1450
Hohokam III = Pueblo II, (III), 900-1100(1200)
Hohokam IIb = Pueblo I, 700-900
Hohokam IIa = Basket Maker III, 500-700

By this reckoning, Hohokam I, with pottery, would equate in time with pottery-less Basket Maker II.[23]

Soon after 1100, Hohokam culture, now entering its Period IV, was increasingly influenced by a branch of immigrating Anasazi called the Salado. The two peoples seem to have lived peacefully side by side in the middle Gila-Salt drainage, sometimes even within the same settlement. About 1400-1450, Hohokam culture evaporated, losing its Salado ingredient, and the remainder probably thinning down into the culture of the historical Pima and Papago tribes of the region.

The following is a developmental summary of Hohokam culture:

HOHOKAM CULTURE TRAITS BY PERIOD

Maize. I, presumable; II on, cobs found
Cotton. Authenticated from II on
Arrow points (too slender for atlatl dart). I, II, III
Rimmed palettes for pigment. I, II, III; lacking in IV
Pyrite mirrors. II
Ball courts. II, large; III, smaller, oval
Shell ornaments. I; II, carved bracelets; III, acid-etched also; IV cutout pendants
Copper bells. III
Fore-and-aft trough metate. From I on
Irrigation ditches. IIb, III; IV, largest systems
Houses of posts and brush. I, in pit; II, III, progressively shallower
Contiguous houses, walls of packed earth (substitute for masonry). IV
Polychrome pottery, burial of the dead (Salado Pueblo traits). IV

It is evident that the specificities of the culture, especially those with Mexican affinities, such as palettes, mirrors, bells, and ball courts, belong to periods II and III, especially between 700 and 1100, and were lost in IV. Irrigation ditches, which the Pueblo did not construct, began in II, and while they were most extensive in IV, that is presumably a reflex of the communities' being larger in this Pueblo-influenced last stage. Nearly all the innovations of IV are not native Hohokam, but imports of Anasazi immigrants, or native adaptations of Anasazi imports, like the thick, storied walls of the great Casa Grande ruin.

Beyond its Anasazi-Hohokam culmination, Southwestern prehistory is imperfectly explored. On the contrary, many of the historical and surviving native cultures have been studied intensively. At some time before the arrival of the Spaniards, Athabascans out of the far north—see map on page 217—had worked their way onto the Southwestern plateau and the part of the Plains fronting it to the east, thus more or less surrounding the retractile Pueblo. The Spaniards came to designate these unstable tribes Apaches, and some of them became

---

[23] Some would carry the beginning of Hohokam I back to around A.D. 100 or even 300 B.C., but these are "extrapolated" estimates.

feared as aggressive raiders, especially after they mounted themselves on stolen horses. One group of Apache, who lived chiefly between the various Pueblo towns rather than outside their range, absorbed somewhat more Puebloan culture than the rest, then also Spanish traits like sheepherding, and got to be called Navaho. Especially since 1870, they have made a precarious but spontaneous and mostly successful adaptation both to the old natural and the new Caucasian environment. They are now the largest tribe in the United States, and from being merely one of several Apache divisions, they have come to outnumber sixfold the combined lot of these (cf. § 177).

To the west and south of the Southwest core and climax, there are Uto-Aztecan and Yuman tribes (see map, page 217) as far as the Pacific, and south into Mexican California and Sinaloa. These can all be considered as possessing a simplified, marginal form of Southwestern culture. The nearer of these Uto-Aztecan and Yuman peoples (like Yaqui, Mayo, Pima, Papago, Yuma, Mohave) live in low, hot desert in impermanent, scattered houses, and make red-on-buff pottery. In their cultural origins they are accordingly on the Hohokam rather than the Basket Maker-Pueblo side.

324. THE CALIFORNIA AND INTERMOUNTAIN REGIONS

During the last two thousand years or more, California has been a region of relatively slow and unspectacular cultural change, compared with the areas to its north and south. The Intermountain area, consisting of the Great Basin and the Columbia-Fraser drainage interior plateau, both contained between the Rockies and the coastal systems of mountains, progressed still more slowly—no doubt because of its prevailingly meager environment as well as its remoteness from higher centers—and remained one of the definitely retarded areas of native culture in historical times.

In most of California, the climate was easy, food reasonably abundant, and the human population relatively dense for a nonfarming one. If cultural progress was quiet, it was not because of nature's adversity but rather because, in Toynbeean concept, challenge was feeble and response mild. The many native tribes remained undisturbed by Caucasian impact until about 1775 on the southerly coast and 1850 in most of the rest of the state, and this area was accordingly an accessible paradise for ethnologists until well into the twentieth century. A reconstructive account of the presumptive development of native religious cults has been given in § 239, with a diagram including also other features of culture (p. 566). The course of development there portrayed is one of increasing regional differentiation and specialization. It should be noted, however, that the northwestern-Californian culture of world-renewal rituals seems to be basically a peripheral part of Northwest Coast culture, and that the culture which centers on the lower Colorado River with dream singings is Hohokam Southwestern in its general affiliations. Of the two remaining native Californian climaxes, that of the Kuksu cult in the Sacramento Valley is indubitably Californian in the fullest sense; but the other, that of the Santa Barbara coast and islands with the center of the Toloache religion, might legitimately be considered either Californian or marginal Southwestern. Its subsistence and technological aspects are Californian, in the main; much of its ritual and symbolism is Southwestern. In short, ethnic or native California is somewhat smaller than the modern American state.

As regards archaeology, only the north-central and the southern coastal tracts need be considered in the present connection. The southern-California or Santa Barbara or Chumash development was the richer of the two technologically, and is therefore richer in remains also, especially toward its end. Two main periods are easily distinguishable, whose poles have been called Oak Grove and Canalino. The earlier Oak Grove used metate querns for grinding seeds, the later, stone or basket mortars. Almost all the finer products of shell inlay, carvings, and products of loving workmanship are limited to Canalino—except for plummet-shaped charm stones, in which the simpler and earlier culture specialized. The Oak Grove people buried their dead stretched out, their successors laid them away flexed or bunched up. There are conjectures as to the age of Oak Grove, but they remain conjectures, except for one fact that is of significance: The final Canalino culture was rich enough so that it must have passed through several gradual stages to reach its culmination. Stratigraphic excavations do indeed show a continuity of culture from earliest to latest, with the decline of metates and charm stones being compensated for by a corresponding increase or elaboration of use of mortars, steatite vessels and ornaments, asphalt for mending and decoration, and straight fishhooks. Circular fishhooks of shell—a form that has Oceanian counterparts—are the principal utilitarian type that in the remains is restricted definitely to terminal times. On the islands, the record is much the same except for beginning later; this is expectable in that a day's ocean voyage is involved in reaching the islands, implying reliable canoes.

In north-central California, prehistory is known for both a littoral and an interior zone. In fact the present record goes back farther for the interior. The horizons and provinces determined as of 1948 are tabulated herewith.

NORTH CENTRAL CALIFORNIA ARCHAEOLOGY

| Horizons | Littoral Zone | | Interior Zone | |
	Coast Province	Bay Province	Delta Province	Valley Province
Late II	Estero	Fernandez	Mosher	Miller
Late I	Mendoza	Emeryville	Hollister	Sandhill
Middle	McClure	Ellis Landing	Morse and other facies	
Early	?		Windmiller	

There are a few practices that are strictly limited in period. Thus the habits of burying bodies stretched out, of grinding on metates, and of making beads of *Haliotis* (abalone) shell, died out in Middle times. Cremation and stone beads *began* in that period and were most abundant in the Late one; beads of clamshell were invented only in the Late. On the whole, however, culture traits and complexes tended to persist through the whole time column, merely showing somewhat altered form, or a variant frequency, from one period to another. Features whose course is one of progressive *decline* include: hunting; work in stone; flaking of stone by blows; large projectile points, as for darts; plummet-shaped charm stones; use of crystals as fetishes. An opposite career of *development* or expansion is shown by plant-food gathering; mortars; fishing; pressure-flaking of stone; small projectile points, as for arrows; stone smoking pipes; varied use of shell; flexed burials. This total sequence of changes is illustrated most fully by the burials in the earth and refuse mounds of the interior. In the shell mounds on salt water, the Early horizon has not yet been discovered, although it is as good as certain that something corresponding to it must have existed. The Middle and Late period development on the coast parallels that inland, with expectable minor provincial variations. Thus, net-sinkers of notched stones are abundant in the Middle horizon, scarce in the Late, and so serve to classify in relative time the large and small mounds that lined the shores of San Francisco Bay and ocean shore.

In the absence of tree-ring sequences and known glacio-pluvial phenomena in the California region, attempts at dating have been made through studying the chemical composition and structure of soils, the proportions of shell species, the rate of mineralization of bones; but as yet without exact results. However, it is difficult to imagine the known development to have taken less than about two thousand years. That change proceeded slowly is evident from the fact that the culture of the nineteenth-century living Indians corresponds very closely with that of the sixteenth, as exemplified by the accounts of Drake's landing, and by mound remains dated by grave associations with Chinese porcelain carried by a wrecked Spanish vessel of the same period.

It is evident that the southern-coastal and the north-central developments were related: witness the metate-mortar change, the decline of charm stones in both, the shift from extended to flexed burials.

In general level, as well as in certain specific traits, the slowly developing Californian culture remained similar, even in recent times, to the preceramic, subagricultural Basket Maker phase of Southwestern Anasazi. Thus not only were baskets and bags abundant in both, and qualitatively excellent in workmanship, but they were made almost exclusively in coiled or twined technique, practically never in checker or twill. Further, something of a geographical as well as a typological link is provided by numerous baskets and other perishable artifacts preserved in bat guano in Nevada caves such as Lovelock. These remains segregate into an earlier and a recent stage. The earlier stage here may be more or less midway in time as well as space between Basket Maker and modern California Indian culture.

Apart from these Nevada caves, archaeological finds in the Intermountain area are still too spotty to build up into a systematic interpretation. It is evident that in Pueblo II and perhaps III periods there was an extension of Anasazi influences, and perhaps population, well northward into Utah and westward into Nevada. This wave soon receded again, and was replaced by a hunting-gathering culture of the general type of that of the historical Indians of the Great Basin.

325. THE NORTHWEST COAST

There are some beginnings of archaeological findings here and there on the Northwest Coast, but not enough as yet to tie into a systematic scheme. Inferences as to development must therefore be made from classification of the recent cultures in the area, and the typology and local distribution of their elements.

Characterizing traits include subsistence predominantly from fishing in both rivers and salt water, associated with large dugout canoes and permanent winter villages of great houses of cedar timbers and split planks. These are almost the only plank houses in native America, and the only ones on an extensive scale. Woodworking was the most developed art of the Northwesterners. They produced a variety of boxes, dishes, trays, rattles, masks and other ritual apparatus, totem poles, and house posts, usually carved in a unique and elaborate style of symbolic or animal-heraldic decoration that seems far removed from any other American art in its preoccupations as well as its manner. Pottery, metallurgy, and agriculture were wholly lacking. Baskets were woven proficiently, and in techniques of twining with superstructural decorative overlay wholly different from the coiling techniques prevalent in all adjoining areas. There was some weaving done with threads of dog and mountain-goat hair on bast fibers; the materials and apparatus suggest an origin unconnected with the cotton textile art of the Southwest and Mexico.

Political organization was rudimentary on the Northwest coast, but economic structure elaborate. The culture was property-minded, and wealth was a necessary accompaniment of birth for social prestige and influence. There was emphasis on accumulation, and even more on the distribution of food, belongings, and treasure in the give-away feasts called potlatches. These were instruments of competition for rank; so were the ownership of dances and membership in rituals. Among the economic specializations were standardized dentalium-shell currency, slaves held for prestige, hammered sheets of native copper whose main value lay in their repute value, and repayments with increment or "interest."

It is evident that this was a highly distinctive culture. In part this was due to remoteness from the Meso-American nucleus; in part, as has been said in § 317, to absorptions from Asia or—improbably—even from western Oceania; but in the main to a quality of cultural vigor, youth, and originality in the area.

Internal comparisons indicate that the climax or culmination of the culture was situated on the northern coast and islands of British Columbia, among the Haida, the Tsimshian, and the northerly Kwakiutl. Here was the most seagoing life, the finest art, perhaps the greatest elaboration of ritual, and the meeting point of both matrilineal and patrilineal moiety and clan organization of society. To the south the culture became progressively simpler, travel and fishing were sheltered in sounds and then in bays and rivers. On the whole the culture of the southern tribes may be construed as the marginal survival of an earlier form once spread over the whole area but increasingly transcended farther north. This north-end situation of the creative focus or peak is again suggestive of the essential independence of the culture from Mexico and even from the Southwest.

326. EASTERN AND NORTHERN REGIONS

The Eastern subarea, which was agricultural, consists very nearly of the United States east of the hundredth meridian, plus the province of Ontario. It is flanked on its two land sides by the nonagricultural Northern and Plains subareas. For these two latter subareas, the archaeological record to date is meager and the obtainable evidence presumably thin. For the Eastern subarea, the accumulated evidence is voluminous enough. But, in spite of including much pottery, this Eastern evidence has proved unusually difficult to interpret into a connected story moving in a definite direction. It was as long ago as 1848 that Squier and Davis opened the Smithsonian's famous series of "Contributions to Knowledge" with their *Ancient Monuments of the Mississippi Valley*. Yet it was only after 1940 that there appeared in print the first accredited attempts to reconstruct the main movements of ancient culture in the eastern United States as a whole with clear reference to the sequence of events.

It must be admitted that a sense of historical problem—and therewith the time factor—was slow and late in entering the consciousness of archaeologists in this area. But it entered relatively late, as we have seen, in the Southwest also; and yet a sound basic interpretation for the Southwest was outlined nearly twenty years earlier than for the East. Evidently the monotonously uniform nature of Eastern prehistoric remains had something to do with this: They are relatively little characterized over large areas for long periods.[24] It is therefore intrinsically difficult, starting from scratch, to translate the data into a reliable story.

There has also been something hesitant in the very nomenclature and recognition of nontemporal types and regions within the prehistoric East. Although practically the whole Eastern subarea was wooded, the term *Woodland* long

---

[24] There are in the East no ruins, no walls, no mummified bodies or sandals or baskets, little painted or beautiful pottery, as yet no worked-out tree-ring dating.

ago gained favor and is still much used—for northern rather than southerly latitudes, it is true, but without specific regional denotation, and without temporal either. It is hard to say what "Woodland" actually stands for other than a simple, somewhat backward type of culture. And tribal instances of simplicity and retardation might well occur repeatedly without being parts of one specific cultural current. *Hopewell* is an Ohio site with unusually well-characterized artifacts. By tying in with this all remains stylistically similar, a rather well-defined culture has been formulated. A third ingredient, *Mississippian,* appears to be relatively late in time, and many of its remains are above average in style and quality; in spite of these advantages its conceptualization and definition remain somewhat ambiguous. Upper, Middle, and Lower Mississippi Valley regional types of culture were distinguished as long ago as 1903.[25] The Lower dropped out again. Upper and Middle Mississippi survive in the present-day classification, but crosscut somewhat confusingly with Mississippi I and II time periods.

A recent time classification recognizes, first, an archaic or Preceramic period of somewhat indefinite duration, then a Burial Mound period subdivided into I and II, next a Temple Mound period again subdivided into I and II, and finally the historical tribes encountered by the Spaniards, the French, and the British. There is no serious doubt that in general an earlier period, in which mounds were erected chiefly as covers or monuments over the bodies of the dead, was followed by a period in which mounds served primarily as platforms or elevated bases for temples, ossuaries, and similar structures—as in Mexico—and were occasionally flat-topped pyramidal instead of conical. This period sequence as a whole has been rather widely accepted by Eastern archaeologists. And yet we often remain hampered by their reluctance to define explicitly in this scheme the position of the particular cultures they are most preoccupied with.

Let us chart our way backward in time. The year 1650 is perhaps a fair average date for the moment after which we begin to know more about the culture of most tribes from historical notices than from excavations of their remains. Next earlier than the historical period is Temple Mound II, which can probably be accommodated within about two centuries, say 1450-1650. The beginning date is fairly well fixed by datable Pueblo IV pottery sherds found in association with Temple Mound II artifacts in Texas. Similar crosstie evidence is available for the latter part of Temple Mound I, say 1300-1450. But there is more of I: its earlier remains, for which there are no Pueblo crossties or sherd remains, must go back another century at least, and perhaps two or more. This would give us somewhere between 1050 and 1200 for the beginning of Temple Mound I. Now comes the turn of the Burial Mound era. In this, subperiod II

[25] The Atlantic-slope and Great Lakes districts were somewhat simpler or retarded in culture, and so are not reckoned as entering into either Hopewellian or Mississippian.

TENTATIVE TIME CHART FOR EASTERN PREHISTORY

	Eastern Longer Chronology	Named Culture Type or "Pattern"	Eastern Shorter Chronology		Southwestern Chronology
1900					
1800	Historical Tribes		Historical Tribes		Pueblo V
1700					
					(IV or V)
1600	Temple Mound II	← Woodland ↔ Mississippian II →	Temple Mound II	*	
1500					Pueblo IV
1400			Temple Mound I	*	
1300	Temple Mound I	← Woodland ↔ Mississippian I⌐			
1200			Burial Mound II		Pueblo III
1100					
1000	Burial Mound II	← Woodland? ↔ Hopewell⌐	Burial Mound I		Pueblo II
900					
800					Pueblo I
700	Burial Mound I	← Woodland?⌐			Basket Maker III (pottery)
600					
500			Preceramic		Basket Maker II (farming)
400	Preceramic				
300					

——: Period of Pueblo crossties in Texas.

was in many parts a time of large mounds, good carving, and abundance of copper—the Hopewell culture already mentioned, and of which more in a moment. Such a florescence is likely to be fairly brief. If we estimate a century and a half for it, the dating for II would run 1050-1200 or 900-1050.[26] Burial Mound I, a slow formative time, is generally presumed to have been longer. That might carry its beginning back to around 700 if we figure closely, around 500 if we allow ourselves some elbow room. Back of that would be the "archaic" or Preceramic horizons, which were presumably also preagricultural, or mainly so, except perhaps at the very end. The alternative estimated date of 700 for the end of Preceramic and the beginning of Burial Mound I makes this event coincide with the tree-ring-dated beginning of Pueblo I in the Southwest; the alternative of 500 would coincide with the beginning of pottery-making in Basket Maker III. It is clear that we have fair evidence for the dating of the latter part of this total Eastern sequence; for the earlier part we admittedly have only estimates, but they seem reasonable. The crosstying of Pueblo sherds applies mainly to Texas. The corresponding cultures elsewhere in the East might be somewhat earlier or later than there; but it is likely that they would not differ very markedly in time.

The tentative time chart on the preceding page recapitulates the interpretation just outlined. There follows a somewhat more detailed account of the local cultures (sometimes called "aspects" and "foci") as they are grouped into types or growths ("patterns" or "phases") and into periods.

Preceramic. Here are some of the postgeological but early local cultures of eastern North America that were still preceramic and presumably prefarming.

EASTERN PRECERAMIC CULTURES

George Lake, north of Lake Huron
Lamoka, central New York
Indian Knoll and related forms, the lower Ohio drainage
Lauderdale, along the middle Tennessee River
Proto-Bluff Dweller of the Ozarks
Copell, Mississippi delta
Pre-Tick Island, Florida
Clear Fork, northern Texas
Signal Butte I, western Nebraska

[26] Later dates are also given. Griffin, for instance, seems to assign Hopewell (Burial Mound II) to 1200-1400. Setzler gives "Hopewellian" (BM I and II?) a surprisingly long span, from 500 to 1400. Upper and Middle Mississippian he has beginning around 1200 to 1400, according to locality; Woodland, about 1100 in Iowa and Wisconsin, but not till 1600 in Indiana and Ohio! Martin, Quimby, and Collier estimate 500, 600, and 700, according to district, for the first pottery, and 900-1300 for the Hopewell period.

Some of these may have begun as far back as 1000 B.C. or even earlier. Some may have continued to as late as around A.D. 300, 500, or even 700. The Clear Fork "culture," or Abilene industry (§ 280), as known from its implements, especially chipped projectile points, and for which an age extending back into geological time has been claimed, may prove verifiably to reach back to well before the Christian era, but more surely it extends forward into pottery times until at least A.D. 1500. Signal Butte I, which has also been crowded back by some to the times of Folsom and extinct faunas, is now dated at about 2000 B.C. by its discoverer, Strong. Obviously, the nearest and first points we can hope to establish are the approximate dates of the introduction of pottery and agriculture in the eastern United States. Once these are more or less known, profitable speculation will be in order as to how far back from that the beginnings of still earlier cultures can be traced.

Woodland. The Woodland "pattern" is, as we have seen, the longest-lasting and the least well-defined archaeological culture type of the eastern United States. It evidently is partly derived from the preceramic cultures. It might well be considered a continuation of such archaic hunting culture, with pottery and some farming added by diffusion as time went on. Its pottery is usually conical-bottomed, tempered with grit, and cord-marked; that is, roughened or decorated by impressions from a little paddle or stick wrapped with a cord. This cord-marking feature, as already mentioned, has been derived, through spotty occurrences northwestward, from Asia, and has been connected even with European Neolithic pottery surfacing. So remote an origin as this is at present hardly provable or disprovable.

The total prehistoric Woodland inventory is simple. Smoking pipes are straight tubes or short elbows, instead of having platforms or carrying figures as in the later and richer Hopewell and Mississippi cultures. There were some competent stone axes and chisels; also definitely well-polished "banner stones" and "bird stones" of banded slate in pleasing shapes—sometimes construed as atlatl pegs or weights, sometimes as cult objects. Most of these have been acquired by collectors with hardly any record of site or context, so that they tell us little about the culture in which they occurred. Woodland sites are generally small and shallow, and have therefore been much obliterated by American farming.

Some construe Woodland as an old culture out of which Hopewell stemmed off for a time while Woodland continued and survived it. Others recognize northern Woodland as essentially the post-Hopewell culture of the Algonkin tribes of the final pre-Caucasian period. The trouble with Woodland as an archaeological classification is the combination of its weak typological distinctiveness with its assumed long duration. It got nowhere much but was a long time doing it.

SOME EARLY WOODLAND CULTURES

Red Paint, Maine
Laurentian, New York and New England
Early Adena, Ohio-Kentucky
Red Ocher, Baumer, and Merton, Illinois
Proto-Effigy Mound or Old Copper, Wisconsin
"Woodland" of eastern and Signal Butte II of western Nebraska
Ledbetter, Colbert, and Candy Creek, Tennessee River Valley
Poverty Point in northern and Tchefuncte in southern Louisiana
Deptford of Georgia

SOME MIDDLE-PERIOD CULTURES [27]

Point Peninsula and Geneseo, around the lower Great Lakes
Glacial Kame, northern Ohio
Lewis, Illinois
Effigy Mound, Wisconsin
"Woodland" of Kansas, Nebraska, and North Dakota
Bluff Dwellers, Ozarks
Murphy Island and Wilmington, South Atlantic coast

Late Woodland cultures are recognized, under this name, chiefly north of the latitude of the Ohio River, in Iowa, Wisconsin, Michigan, Illinois, Indiana, and Ohio.

Hopewell (Burial Mound II). The highest florescence of Hopewell culture occurred in southern Ohio, at the Hopewell, Turner, Tremper, Mound City, and Seip sites, which, taken together, continued through Burial Mound II periods. Averaging somewhat earlier was the related Adena culture—a sort of Proto-Hopewell—which continued, in Kentucky at least, until it overlapped Hopewell. To the west there were lesser hearths of Hopewellian development in the Illinois River Valley (Ogden-Fettie), along the Mississippi in Wisconsin (Trempealeau), and, more faintly, even on the lower Missouri (Kansas City "focus"). To the south, Hopewellian cultures include Copena ("copper-galena") along the Tennessee where Lauderdale had existed earlier; Marksville followed by Troyville [28] along the lower Mississippi; and Santa Rosa-Swift Creek from there east along the Gulf coast to halfway down the Florida peninsula.

Apart from this last-named coastal reach, the Hopewell localizations are limited to spotty stretches along the Mississippi River itself and a few of its major affluents. This distribution would fit in with an overseas importation of the culture from Mexico to the vicinity of New Orleans—if there were any sure indications in Hopewell of Mexican resemblances. There are none such that are indubitable, to date, only general features, like mounds, treasure accumulation,

---

[27] Overlapping with Hopewell in time and forming a sort of scattering fringe around its branching core.

[28] Some put Troyville into Temple Mound I period rather than in Burial Mound II.

power and rank of chiefs, politically well-organized populations of fair size. These might all have been imported or they might equally well have developed spontaneously on the spot. Perhaps the finest prehistoric art produced in the eastern United States is Hopewellian. Yet it shows no specific Mexican affiliations. There is accordingly no evidence of Mexican derivation of the culture, and if Mexican influences did exist, they were presumably only of indirect or stimulus type. This conclusion fits in with the fact that the culture's supreme flowering occurred at its farthest from central Mexico, in Ohio.

Mississippian (Temple Mound I and II). This was a culture of Temple Mound type and period, most developed in the southeastern United States, but with a number of protrusions into the northern area of Woodland culture. Roughly, the non-Woodland remains south of the Ohio River are what used to be called Middle Mississippian, those to the north, Upper Mississippian. Crosscutting this typological-regional division is the temporal one that equates Mississippi I and II with Temple Mound I and II, respectively. The Mississippian pottery, at any rate in its later southern range, had got pretty well away from cord-marking. It was sometimes well polished, often tastefully incised; in an area in Arkansas-Tennessee it was at times painted; and in Mississippi II, it was characteristically tempered with crushed shell. In art, too, Ohio lost the pre-eminence it had possessed in Hopewell times. The finest Mississippian specimens of modeled and engraved pottery, of incised shell disks, of embossed copper plates, come from the Tennessee-Arkansas-Oklahoma belt or south of it in Alabama and Georgia. These rival in quality the best Hopewell productions, and are more numerous. The mounds were large, often rectangular, and sometimes grouped as if around a plaza. These were undoubtedly ceremonial centers. The Cahokia mound in southern Illinois was nearly eleven hundred by over seven hundred feet in area and a hundred feet high. This is an enormous mass of soil, whose protracted heaping-up it is hard to imagine accomplished by mere voluntary effort. There must have been chiefs with organized control over whole series of settlements, perhaps over confederacies of tribes.

Resemblances of some of the best Eastern art designs to Mexican motives has long been noted, and it has now become clear that these resemblances are concentrated in remains from the same southern states that show the best pottery and are of Mississippian period, especially II. The similarities are partly in details of theme, partly in generic stylistic character. Common themes include winged, horned, or feathered rattlesnakes, birds, spiders, skulls, trophy heads, detached hands or eyes, warriors in eagle masks and cloaks, and the like. It has been suggested that the Mexican resemblances are due to a "Southern Death" or "Buzzard" cult stimulated by Mexican Indians brought to the southern United States by the Spaniards after de Soto's expedition. This would make the whole style spurious so far as native Southeastern origin is concerned, and would set it all as late as 1550-1600. That seems extreme. Some of the manifestations are almost certainly earlier, as at the famous Spiro mound; and stylistically they are connected not only with Mexico but also with Mississippi I and with Hopewellian art. The route, manner, and time of the connections with Mexico thus remain obscure. But it does seem reasonably certain that, at a relatively late period, the East was reached by some Mexican influence more specific than has yet been demonstrated as affecting the Pueblo Southwest.

MISSISSIPPI I PERIOD CULTURES

Owasco, New York
Early Fort Ancient, Ohio
Younge, southern Michigan
Aztalan, southern Wisconsin (early northern outpost of Middle Mississippi phase)
Old Village, around the mouth of the Missouri River (Cahokia)
Nebraska of eastern and Upper Republican of central Nebraska and Kansas
Hiwassee and Small Log, upper Tennessee River
Gibson, including Alto and the great Spiro mound, Texas-Arkansas-Oklahoma borders
Antelope Creek, Texas Panhandle, with early Pueblo IV ingredient (about 1300-1450)
Coles Creek, lower Mississippi River
Weeden Island II, most of Florida Gulf coast
Mt. Royal and Savannah, Florida-Georgia coast
Macon Plateau, central Georgia

Some Mississippi II period cultures ("aspects" and "foci" in technical parlance) are—with [1] denoting a beginning in the Mississippi I period, and [m, u] inclusion in Middle and Upper Mississippi geographical phase, respectively:

MISSISSIPPI II PERIOD CULTURES

Iroquois, New York
[1] Fort Ancient, Ohio (including Madisonville, Baum, Feurt, Fox Farm)
[m] Kincaid, [m] Trappist (great Cahokia mound), [u] Fisher, Illinois
[1] Lake Michigan
[u] Oneota, Iowa-Wisconsin
Lower Loup in eastern, Dismal River in western, Nebraska
Fulton, Red River and vicinity
[m] Plaquemine, [m] Glendora, Louisiana
[m] Moundville, [m] Etowah, northern Alabama and Georgia
[m] Cumberland, [m] Large Log, Tennessee
[m] Fort Walton, Florida Gulf coast
Key Marco (Glades III), southern Florida
St. Johns II, northeastern Florida
[m] Lamar and Irene, Georgia and South Carolina

In the century from 1600 to 1700, varying somewhat according to locality, the prehistoric cultures of the East became replaced by those of the historically known tribes. In general, tribes of Algonkin speech affiliation (see map, Fig. 16, in § 96) were found in the areas of late Woodland culture; of Iroquoian and Siouan lineage, where Upper Mississippian had prevailed; of Muskogean and Caddoan affinity, in Middle Mississippian areas. These historical tribes were militant: prestige among them depended on war record. Apparently the incessant fighting kept their population down. Their territory could have supported a much larger population, even though farming was left largely to the women while men hunted. There was some development of political sense among the southeastern and northeastern tribes, as shown by the successful formation of confederacies of villages and tribes. The most famous of these was the League of the Iroquois, but similar patterns were worked out by Huron, Powhatan, Cherokee, Creek, and Choctaw. However, there seem to have been in the historical period no great religious centers, no massive earthworks, no elaborately symbolic paraphernalia executed with artistic skill. In both cult and technology nothing is known from the historical tribes comparable to the best Hopewellian and Mississippian products.

Plains. In prehistoric times, the Plains, from Texas to Saskatchewan, were clearly only a fading-out fringe of the Eastern culture. It looks as if foot-traveling Indians could not have made a dependable year-round living off the migratory bison; and where the bison was most abundant, farming also became precarious on account of aridity. The result was that the Plains as a habitat were only nibbled at, so to speak, by eastern farming tribes pushing into them intermittently, or by western groups better sheltered in the foothills of the Rockies. However, after the Spaniards introduced the horse, tribes that mastered its care and use were enabled to live migratorily in the heart of the Plains if they chose, to depend outright on the bison for subsistence, and to reshape their culture accordingly. Tribes like the Teton Dakota and the Cheyenne are known to have given up farming; several others probably did so. Hence the tepee or conical skin tent dragged on poles; the ordered camp circle of tepees; the bedding, clothing, and even receptacles of skins and rawhide. There was sudden abundance in the new roving ways; there was even the beginning of a well-defined barbaric luxury of living, especially after guns and iron kettles became available from French traders; and cults were made over into impressive spectacles like the Sun Dance and society rituals. But all this had no counterpart in the region even as late as 1600. As a culture area the Plains had a late brilliance, with its war bonnets and ponies; but it had no historical depth.

The North. The great Northern transcontinental area of coniferous forest from Newfoundland to Alaska was perforce backward because of its thin population, and this was thin because food was scant. Farming was out of the question. There was hunting of caribou, moose, deer, or rabbits; there was fishing; there was some berrying—and that was about all. Mostly the game animals were so scattered that the hunters had to live scattered. Only at an occasional famous fishing rapids could people venture to congregate seasonally in numbers. Hence there was no real tribal organization, let alone anything like supertribal confederacies; little organized warfare; little public cult, except for performances by individual shamans proud of their supernatural powers. And the margin of life was too close to subsistence to permit any luxuriance of the arts. Useful and environmentally profitable devices like snowshoes, toboggan sleds, bark tents and bark cooking vessels, fitted clothes of skins, would have a chance, in a culture so situated, of being accepted if invented or introduced from northern Asia. And so would devices believed useful, such as divination from shoulder blades and by scrying or peering.

A recent development over large parts of the Northern subarea is due to the ability of the inhabitants to help supply the demand of the civilized world for furs (§ 179). This had led to the Indian's devoting more of his time to trapping beaver, mink, fox, and the like, and less to the hunting of the daily meat supply. In return he often depends on the trader not only for ammunition, traps, and luxuries but for staples like flour, pork, tea, and blankets. Yet in the rest of his life he remains an old-fashioned Indian—socially, technologically, and in most of his thoughts and motives. It is an interesting special case of acculturation, in that the contact with higher civilization has been remote, and yet has in some ways strengthened rather than disintegrated the old native hunting economy.

327. ESKIMO OF THE ARCTIC COAST

Eskimo culture, with its adaptation to an extreme environment, was among the first to attract scientific curiosity. On the other hand, the culture has remained a living one, with only partial absorptions from Western civilization, and has thus afforded opportunity for increasingly intensive study, until it is now one of those best known to ethnologists. Archaeological excavations began later, it is true, but have been going on, here and there, for a half-century, so that data on the prehistoric Eskimo are also rather satisfactory. The story extends back at least to A.D. 500, more likely to somewhere around A.D. 1, with the majority of early relationships pointing to northeastern Asia. An origin of Eskimo culture from caribou-hunting on the North American tundra followed by extension to the coast, and a spread along this with shift to sealing, have also been proposed. But this seems a more speculative view.

The dating runs as follows. An old type of Greenland Eskimo culture, known as Inugsuk, from which the historical Greenland form grew by modification, occurs with Norse remains of A.D. 1300 plus or minus. Comparisons with other areas show the Inugsuk to be in turn a local modification of a widespread Thule Eskimo culture. This Thule stage can therefore reasonably be dated as beginning around A.D. 1000.[29] In its eastern range, Thule is preceded by Dorset, centering around Labrador. Dorset is an Eskimo culture with resemblances to northeastern-Indian culture, as well as specialties of its own, such as quadrilateral sockets in harpoon heads and predominance of chipped over ground stone edges and points. In the west, on the other hand, Thule is preceded by—in fact is quite evidently evolved from—a Birnirk culture whose remains

---

[29] The Southampton Island Eskimo (§ 158) are said to have maintained a degenerate Thule culture in their isolation until their extinction in 1902.

are known from Point Barrow in northern Alaska. This makes Dorset and Birnirk essentially contemporary, going back perhaps to around 500—Dorset perhaps even beyond. Birnirk in turn seems to be a provincial variant of early Punuk on Bering Sea, and more or less its contemporary. Both Birnirk and Punuk, in turn, derive from Old Bering Sea, which is already definitely a sea-mammal-hunting and Eskimo culture, notable for the beauty of its decorative carving. It has, therefore, been assigned an age going back to about the beginning of the Christian era. It is abundantly attested on St. Lawrence Island and at other sites. A unique and strange Ipiutak culture is known from one great site of burials north of Bering Strait. Ipiutak contains an Old Bering Sea strain, but also elements that are quite different—possibly East Asiatic—and thoroughly puzzling. It is evidently outside the gradual sequence of other Eskimo cultures; so, in default of any direct evidence of age, a guess of priority to the others is tempting.

As a matter of method, it is plain that the remoter end of this chronology is built up on estimates only. One could shorten these and say: Thule A.D. 1100, Dorset, Birnirk, Punuk 800, Old Bering Sea 500, Ipiutak (because evidently overlapping) 400. The sequence stands, though the dates have shrunk. At present there is no real way of deciding between the alternative chronologies. One find of a fragment of Chinese period pottery or bronze in indubitable association with Eskimo remains of a clear culture style would suffice to fix the dating within a century or so. But such a stray may never have drifted to Alaska, or if it did, may long since have perished—or never got itself found.

Eskimo culture is fashioned primarily toward finding subsistence by hunting sea mammals along the coast: seals, walrus, small and large whales. In most regions there is a summer excursion inland, with tents, to hunt caribou, which are prized not only as meat but for their furs for clothing. One or two local groups have come to stay with the caribou the year through. This represents a deviation due to local opportunity—or perhaps lack of local sealing opportunities. Similar though seasonal deviations from the average of Eskimo usage occur where there are special facilities for hunting large whales, as at Point Barrow in northern Alaska, or for taking river salmon in abundance, as in the deltas of the Yukon and the Kuskokwim. Here and there bird-taking, or fishing through the ice, are specially profitable or become necessary to survive certain seasons.

The average or standard Eskimo culture utilizes certain devices that closely reflect a life of seal-hunting along coasts which are icebound in winter and even in summer lack driftwood. Seals are therefore taken by the hunter awaiting them at their breathing holes (*maupok* method) or crawling upon them over the ice clad in sealskin clothing and simulating their motions. Seal blubber, burned with a moss wick in a shallow stone lamp, provides the only fuel for cooking and for warmth in these more northerly regions. The cooking almost of necessity consists of boiling in stone dishes. Travel, or transport to the hunting ice, is by sled on runners, drawn by dogs which have to be kept and fed the year through. The winter house is likely to be a tiny affair of stone slabs and rocks—perhaps with whale jaws or ribs as frame. In travel, the snowhouse, what we call the igloo, is built—the blocks spiraling into a true dome, self-supporting during construction. When open water returns, skin boats on a thin skeleton of wood can be used. The kayak is decked over, except for a manhole in which the lone hunter sits. The umiak is broader, deeper, and open, and serves for transport; it is usually propelled by women. Sealing is now from boats, or from the edge of the ice or shore, with the retrieving harpoon as the main weapon. Whaling uses fundamentally the same methods as sealing, with heavier tackle plus more inflated-skin floats and drags.

Where driftwood is abundant, as at the mouth of the Mackenzie, good-sized houses of timber are built. The same holds for the southern-Eskimo habitat in Alaska and in southern Greenland. At both these ends of the Eskimo range the sled also is no longer of service, ice hunting is lacking, the kayak is highly developed and used the year around, along with netting of seals. On the contrary, where the cold is most rigorous, so that large bays and sounds freeze over, the snowhouse becomes an all-winter domicile and Eskimo families live scattered on the ice, hunting at their blowholes the seals that swim and fish, so to speak, beneath their feet. It is an extreme adaptation of habits—learned and cultural in the human beings, hereditarily organic in the seals.

328. SOUTH AMERICAN PREHISTORIES: ANDEAN

As we have seen, the long Pacific-fronting Andean area, which balances south of Panamá the Meso-American area north of the Isthmus, consists of three subareas, a central one of High Culture flanked by a North and South Andean one. The central subarea is not only the most advanced, but it is also the most explored and the best understood, and will engage most of our attention.

The central region of Andean High Culture comprises the coast and inter-Cordilleran valleys and plateaus of Peru and of the nearer corner of Bolivia, exclusive of the forest or montaña that commences halfway down the inland-facing slope of the last Andean chain. In the highland, preservation conditions of antiquities are fairly good; along the rainless coast they are extraordinarily excellent. The ruins are impressive in Peru, the artifact remains attractive, and amateur and mercenary excavating have gone on for a long time. Careful digging with a sense of historical problem was begun even before the turn of the century by Uhle, and subsequent interpretation was carried forward under the leadership of Tello, a Peruvian Indian, until his death in 1947. At this mid-twentieth-century writing, our understanding of the course of Peruvian prehistory is perhaps the most consistent and the clearest of that of any American area, next to the Southwest. Additional information, it is true, often has a way of complicating and temporarily confusing a newly won picture. But the flow of basic culture history seems to have been less complex in Peru than in Mexico—perhaps because of a certain regularity in the pattern of natural environment. It may therefore well be that the fundamentals of the present interpretation for Peru will stand for many decades.

The unraveling of High Culture Andean prehistory has been much facilitated by the fact that at three separate and well-spaced times a wave of cultural influence spread over most or all of the area. These culture waves are called Chavín, Tiahuanaco, and Inca. Chavín was at least a cult and an associated art style, and may have comprised additional activities. Tiahuanaco represented an art influence tinged with religious conceptions, and was almost surely accompanied by some conquests. The Inca, finally, effected conquests out of their capital Cuzco that resulted in a vast and centralized though fragile tribute empire; and this was accompanied by a specific decorative art style. Each of the three styles or manners is easily recognizable with a little practice, in textiles, metalwork, building construction, and especially pottery, of which hundreds of thousands of exemplars have been preserved. Three successive horizons of culture, datable conservatively to around A.D. 1, 1000, and 1400, or perhaps earlier, are thus readily distinguishable wherever they occur in the remains.[30]

Between these widespread horizons, local cultures could next be intercalated on stylistic grounds. Say that in a given region certain settlements or graveyards regularly show a phase of culture consistently marked by Tiahuanaco traits, such as a peculiarly stiff or heavy representation, almost an architectural one, of the human figure and of felines and condors, in pottery and cloths. Other sites again contain objects that obviously are Inca in style—like Cuzco wares—in long-necked form, in color, and in pattern. Still others contain vessels whose shapes are open and whose decoration is markedly geometric, done in a third style that is easily recognized but is limited in distribution—peculiar to two or three local valleys such as, say, Ica and Chincha. On more precise examination, certain additional sites may be found in which the wares are essentially Tiahuanaco, but with some admixture of semigeometric patterns suggestive of Chincha. Other sites may be characterized by geometric ware with a minor proportion of decayed or slovened Tiahuanaco designs. Still other cemeteries would contain only pure Chincha-style objects; and others again mostly Chincha wares but with a 10 or 20 per cent infusion of artifacts showing some Inca resemblance, and perhaps an occasional vessel in pure Cuzco Inca manner. Now each of the settlements or cemeteries might have been inhabited or buried in only for a relatively brief time, such as a generation, so that no perceptible change occurred during its occupation or use; and the explorer's looking for a stratification, a succession of differing layers, would be vain in such sites. Nevertheless, with enough such unit-culture sites in a given valley, and the proportions of types of artifacts and

[30] Their identification or recognition by archaeologists was, naturally enough, in reverse order: the late or topmost Inca first, the early Chavín last.

their manners of decoration eventuating as just described, it is evident that on stylistic grounds alone it would be almost impossible to construe the total situation other than in terms of one particular sequence. This sequence would be: (1) Tiahuanaco; (2) Tiahuanaco with some formative Chincha; (3) fully developed Chincha with Tiahuanaco-style remnants; (4) pure or classic Chincha; (5) Chincha with beginning of Inca admixture or influencing; (6) pure Inca. True, if we knew nothing else at all than what these half-dozen sites contained, the sequence might logically be read also in reverse order. But since Inca style agrees completely with the prevalent style at Cuzco, where the Spaniards found the Incas ruling, Inca style must be put last and Tiahuanaco first in our particular series, and the sequence becomes one-way again.

In ways like this, highly probable forecasts of the proper ordering of culture stages can be made, provided pure-style deposits have been found, and can then be confirmed or corrected when stratified deposits are discovered. As we get far back in time, and into regions and cultures that show few resemblances or crossties with better-known ones, the method of forecasting on stylistic grounds grows less dependable. But all in all, it has worked remarkably well in Peru, largely because of the existence of the three widely spread "horizon styles," plus the fact that the level of culture remained rather remarkably uniform through the region. Stratifications, it is true, contain the final proof and validation. But, to be worth much, stratification digs have to be made with exactitude, and thus are time-consuming as well as costly, and they have been systematically made in Peru only since about 1940. Fortunately, a culture sequence positively determined by stratigraphy in one valley usually clears up, through crossties and style resemblances, the sequence problems in several adjoining valleys also.

Well, so much for the way interpretations are obtained. Now for the outline of the story of developments.

There have long been indications of a prefarming and preceramic stage, but they came from the stretch where arid Peru begins to merge into the utter desert of northern Chile, so that a fishing and shell-gathering life would be more or less enforced on a primitive population. Since 1946, fuller data have become available from the more fertile northern coast. They clearly show a culture that already farmed—besides using wild products, especially from the sea —but which did not yet make pottery. At the present time this well-attested, preceramic, agricultural culture from the Chicama and Virú valleys has not yet been described in detail; but it is known to have had, and presumably to have grown, cotton, gourds, canavalia and dolichos beans, chili pepper, squashes, and perhaps cannas. There are preserved remains also of other food plants, such as sedge tubers and tree fruits, which probably grew wild. Maize, kidney beans, and Lima beans, so important in later periods of Peruvian prehistory, are wholly unrepresented in this preceramic deposit. Animal foods were, in order of importance, fish, sea urchins, and mollusks, with occasional sea mammals and birds. Pressure-flaked-stone implements were as lacking as pottery or metals. There were many fish nets, baskets, and small textiles—the latter mainly of cotton, finger-made, and nearly always two-weft-twined either in whole or in part. Twining is characteristically a basket technique, and cannot be executed on a loom with heddle or thrown shuttle. This culture, most fully known to date from Bird's excavation of the Huaca Prieta, the burnt or "dark" mound, on the coast of the Chicama Valley in northern Peru, may prove to be the earliest American culture yet discovered which already farmed but still lacked pots. Its refuse certainly has yielded an extraordinarily full inventory—and a most surprising one— of cultivated plants. The period can hardly have been much later than 1000 B.C., and might be earlier.

This preceramic age was succeeded by a pottery-making but otherwise little-known stage provisionally called Guañape. The ware was thin-walled, dark, and undecorated, and evidently represents the initial phase of local Chavín. The Guañape people built with cylindrical mud bricks, each made by superimposing several disklike cakes of mud or clay.

Guañape was followed in the same northern coastal valleys by a culture making a quite exceptionally high-grade incised pottery, which had become increasingly known for twenty years before. This bold ware is called Cupisnique, and is undoubtedly a local representative of the widespread Chavín style. Building adobes now were conical instead of cylindrical; and maize cobs finally appear in the remains.

The larger Chavín culture of which Cupisnique is only a provincial manifestation is characterized by cult platforms of stone masonry in the highland. The inland type site of Chavín de Huántar, from which the name is taken, has such a platform or "temple," pierced by dark, tunnellike passages, and containing stone sculpture of human, animal, and monster heads in the round, as well as of surface contours on slabs. Such stone carving is lacking on the coast, being partially replaced, it would seem, by plastic modeling of pottery vessels, whereas highland Chavín ceramics are simpler in form and decoration, though similar in ware and technology. Interestingly enough, Cupisnique Chavín pottery had already developed the rather difficult shape of the "stirrup-mouth" jar, in which two tubes rise from the body of the globular vessel to meet and unite in a single spout. This specialized form persisted on the northern coast until after the arrival of the Spaniards, through six or seven successive stages of culture. Elsewhere in the north there has been found a little Chavín-period gold—nuggets beaten out into engraved sheets—the only metal known; and bone objects carved in the style of the stone and pottery.

The style of Chavín, as manifested especially in the stone sculptures, is by some regarded as the greatest art achieved in Peru and therewith in native South America. It is barbaric, and is aimed at producing impressions of awe and terror. It is decorative and highly stylized, symbolic, and heavily charged with emotion. Great fangs, claws, writhing snake locks, furrowed features, brooding eyes, characterize it, along with giant jaguars, condors, and hybrids of these with men.

It has no known antecedents; and in one sense all subsequent Peruvian arts are derivations and deteriorations from it, except perhaps for the pleasing realism of the Mochica pottery-modelers.

The Chavín culture is now known in provincial forms from a series of coastal valleys as far south as Ica. The most sumptuous finds are from the barren headland of Paracas, from adjoining grave fields of two variants of a Paracas culture—Cavernas and Necropolis. These two must differ in period. Cavernas is presumably the older, and its pottery has in it more reminiscences of the sculptural manner of Chavín proper. Necropolis is famous for its wonderful embroidered textiles, which seem to incline toward a manner of representation found also in the culture of Nazca described below, though there most developed in pottery painting. The webs of these mantles are of cotton grown on the coast, the designs themselves of wool of llamas and alpacas that live only in the highland.

The Chavín culture was evidently the carrier of some powerful religious ideology or cult suffused with feelings that became expressed also in art. When this emotional impulse lost its force, the culture changed into quieter manifestations, which sometimes look like retrogressions but may mean only that concern had shifted to more secular interests and technological experimentation. On the north coast, the sequence is clearest: Cupisnique is followed by the Salinar and the Negative stage, the latter also called Gallinazo. Negative or "reserved" painting is further known from the central and southern coast, but more fragmentarily. Its most elaborate manifestation came in the style of Recuay, at the head of the long Santa Valley in the middle highland.

Then followed the peak of secular development of master craftsmen, of regional florescences of technology and art, the culmination of the inter-Chavín-Tiahuanaco millennium, marked especially by the strictly localized cultures of Nazca in the south and Mochica in the north. Nazca was probably somewhat the earlier of the two: it still shaped its sun-dried bricks by hand into irregular lumps, and knew no metal but hammered gold. The Mochicans already made large rectangular adobes, and smelted, cast, soldered, and alloyed copper and silver as well as gold. Mochica also built giant cult pyramids, Nazca small ones, or faced hills with terraces. In both societies there was little labor devoted to human habitations; the population lived well distributed on or near its irrigated lands, without notable towns; and there is little indication of larger organization, as into kingdoms extending over a series of valleys.

The Nazca culture is famed for its thin, hard, smooth, many-colored painted pottery. Mochica ceramics are only bichrome, but are extraordinarily facile and competent in representation of plastic form. They model a wide variety of subjects—human, animal, plant, and inanimate—into a sort of small-scale clay sculpture, which has little of the divine or even the heroic about it, but much that is lifelike. What seem to be individual portrait heads, figures of the sick, the halt, and the mutilated, tending at once to the macabre and toward caricature, genre scenes of drunkenness or childbirth or erotic indecency—all these make for a quality of representative realism unparalleled elsewhere in native American art except occasionally by the Maya of their great period—who incidentally are likely to have been near-contemporaries of the Mochica. Vase paintings and occasionally preserved frescoes show the Mochica to have been the masters also of a characterizing two-dimensional art that was oriented—something like the Minoan-Mycenaean—toward representation of rapid motion.

The type site of Tiahuanaco—like those of Chavín and Inca—is in the highland, thirteen thousand feet high near Lake Titicaca, just over the Peruvian boundary in Bolivia. It is a cult site with stone sculpture, mostly in relief. The designs of this sculpture reappear in pottery, metal, and textiles over most of Peru, with a fidelity which leaves no room for doubting that they are all the product of one stage or wave of culture. In the coastal valleys, these Tiahuanaco manifestations are usually accompanied on the one hand by accretions not found at the type site, and on the other by indications of upset and disintegration of previous cultures. Tiahuanaco was perhaps not the seat of a great ruler; much more likely it was a famous cult site. There may or may not have been a Tiahuanaco empire; there almost certainly were irruptions and conquests accompanying the spread of Tiahuanaco style and culture. Aesthetically, the style is stiff, angular, and severe, as if its forms had been derived from architecture or textile patterns; but it is also dignified, and it is architectonic in the skill with which the parts are held together in the design. The interest is religious, even in pottery decoration: gods with rays from their heads and tear streaks down their faces; felines, condors, serpents, and hybrids of them; and celestial phenomena.[31]

From the tumult and confusion of the Tiahuanaco episode local cultures reemerged whose progress we can trace, especially on the coast, somewhat as it has been schematically sketched earlier in this section. Of such are Chimú, in the north, an inferior recrudescence, stylistically, of Mochica; Chancay on the central coast; Chincha-Ica in the general region of earlier Nazca; and, in the southern highland in the valley of Cuzco, the incipient Inca. The tendency now was toward larger states: most of the coast was divided among three rulers. There were also real cities, of permanently concentrated dwellers, as at Chincha, and especially at Chan Chan, the Chimú capital near modern Trujillo. This was a secular as well as a metropolitan age. The standard of living had gone up. Metals were far more common than before: in the highland they included tin bronze. On the north coast, even farm tools were now sometimes shod with copper. Sun-dried bricks were always mold-made. Devices like the balance for weighing and the knotted-string quipu for computing and recording may have been devised earlier but certainly became common only in this late period. Yet

---

[31] "Epigonal" is a name sometimes applied to a derived and stylistically base Tiahuanaco, especially on the coast. Wilkawain, Pacheco, Pucara are local forms or relatives of Tiahuanaco found respectively in the Recuay region, at Nazca, and north of Lake Titicaca.

the great arts were things of the past: aesthetic qualities like the emotional strength of Chavín, the severe grandeur of Tiahuanaco, even the formal freedom of Mochica and the color harmony of Nazca, were no longer being expressed anywhere in Peru. Wall decorations had turned from scenes of life to geometric patterns. In Chincha-Ica, pottery ornament was limited to three colors, in Chancay to black-on-white, in Chimú a monochrome burnished black prevailed—evidently a cheap popularization of the elegance of metal vessels.

During the century or so before Pizarro led in his Spaniards, the Inca dominion grew from a small local state around Cuzco to a conquest empire reaching from mid-Ecuador to mid-Chile. Artifacts in the style of Cuzco are found all over this tract. Sometimes they come in nearly pure-type lots, evidently representing an Inca colony or garrison. Sometimes they constitute a minor ingredient among local wares, with a good many of the objects hybrid in style: these cases represent local imitation of the ways of the prestige-bearing ruling class. In the main, however, the native styles survive, thus confirming the traditional record that the Inca domination was brief. There are even districts, like Chancay, where no Inca-style wares at all seem to have been found, suggesting that here acknowledgment of overlordship and payment of tribute were not accompanied by stationing of troops or officials.

Inca wares, whether of metal, wood, pottery, or cloth, were unambitious and sober stylistically, often disciplined in their forms to the point of showing a quality of classic restraint, and insistent on good material and solid workmanship. In their homeland, the Inca worked patiently and lovingly in stone, all the way from amulets and bowls to giant masonry blocks and step altars or "observatories" cut into bedrock. Inca art wholly lacked any large imagination or profound feeling, but was dominated by self-respect and control. It was akin to Spartan, Roman, or British art in its ethos.

The statements by Spaniards as to Inca customs are less exact and full than for Mexico. The book that has most shaped and misshaped our conceptions is by Garcilaso de la Vega, a half-breed scion of the Inca royal house who was taken to Spain as a youth and in his age published an apology and a plausible justification of his dynasty and of his people's culture. It is largely owing to him that an impression is still prevalent that Peruvian social structure functioned as a vast and successful state socialism administered by a benevolent autocracy. It has become evident that this view is partly false even for the final century of Inca rule, and almost wholly false for all preceding periods. A revision of our understanding is necessary—first from careful re-examination of all documents other than Garcilaso's, with reference especially to the customs, beliefs, and organization described, but with minimal reference to historical events, record of which the Peruvians seem to have kept only in an incredibly haphazard and legendary way. And above all, as the archaeological story fills out, its social and ideological implications must be used both as a touchstone for the veracity of the preserved written documents and as a basis for interpretations more searching than the natives could give the Spaniards or the sixteenth-century Spaniards were capable of formulating.

The North Andean and South Andean subareas have a history of culture obviously somewhat less spectacular than Peru, but of course no less long, and similar to it. Ecuador and the highland of Colombia form a unit. Here there were no pyramidal structures, very little masonry, only occasional sculpture. Textiles were plain or roller-stamped instead of tapestry-patterned or embroidered. Potteries wavered between representative and decorative embellishment and failed to excel in either. The most advanced art was metallurgy, but even this fell short of the Peruvian and was shared with the Isthmians of the Circum-Caribbean area. At the far end of the North Andean subarea, the Chibcha of the Bogotá high savanna impressed the Spaniards who destroyed their civilization as more advanced than their neighbors. Yet it is difficult for us today to see in what Chibcha superiority consisted other than in a political development carried to the point of having autocratic hereditary rulers—and this perhaps due to a greater density and uniformity of population, made possible in turn by the terrain.

Some archaeological exploration has been done in the North Andean area, but the scattered results do not yet add up into any accepted general scheme or story. Ecuador has some competent stone carvings in Manabí, and Colombia a series of impressive, uncouth slab statues at San Agustín; but the place of either manifestation in a cultural sequence remains as yet unsure.

The South Andean subarea extends out from Peru-Bolivia through the northern-Chilean desert into a semiarid strip in northwest Argentina on one side of the Andes, and on the other into the fertile region of central Chile. The Argentine tract developed cultures—notably the Calchaquí or Diaguite—which stood in a marginal relation to the intensive Peruvian culture somewhat analogous to that which the Pueblo of the United States Southwest maintained toward nuclear Mexico: stone houses, painted pottery, textiles, but no temples or states. These local cultures began to be invaded by some Peruvian infiltration in Tiahuanaco times, and were overlaid by Inca influences, to which most of their metalwork seems to be due. In fact, export of native Peruvian culture traits southeast across the Andes seems to have gone on even after the Spanish conquest. A little farther north where the Peruvian empire, the Chaco, and the Tropical Forest met (see map, page 791), a Tupian tribe, the Chiriguano, having conquered an Arawakan one, the Chané, pushed on westward, about 1522, first under the leadership of a Portuguese adventurer, to raid the nearest province of the Inca dominions. They returned with booty; and in spite of a fort built to keep them out, fought several more battles with the Peruvians before Pizarro's entry. This episode reveals the weakness of the Inca military structure beyond its natural environmental limits—perhaps as against any aggressive and determined challenge. It is also the sort of event that may have occurred again and again previously and have served as a medium of culture contact and transmission in spite of the hostilities. The Chiriguano today paint their pottery with designs copied from Cuzco Inca vessels. And these designs surely did not enter the culture unaccompanied.

Central Chile was dominated by the Araucanians, a breed of backward, sturdy farmers without larger political organization, who however resisted the Spaniards as tenaciously as the great overcentralized, docile, and stunned Inca Empire disintegrated swiftly at the first touch of the invaders. In fact many of the Araucanian local groups maintained a real freedom, by force of arms and with retention of most of their old ways plus some skillful acculturation, until well along in the nineteenth century. The total impression their culture gives is at least as much one of independence from the Peruvian as of derivation from it.

329. THE CIRCUM-CARIBBEAN AREA

The three great non-Andean areas, together comprising nine-tenths of South America, show a certain uniformity of level of culture. There is within them nothing corresponding to the sharply localized and defined secondary peaks of the Southwest and the Northwest Coast in North America; though there are plenty of differences in specific culture content.

The Circum-Caribbean culture area was dominated in the west by peoples of Chibchan language stock (see map, Fig. 17, in § 96), in the east and north by Arawak and Carib. As regards cultural level, the Circum-Caribbean area represents a high valley between two peaks. Compared with Meso-America and the Andean area, it was tribal, provincial, and backward. In place of kings, there were caciques and chiefs; in place of cities, palisaded villages. All the refinements associated with numerical astronomy, with accurate masonry, with the sumptuousness of royalty, just were wanting. The most advanced art was that of working in gold, copper, and their alloys,[32] usually as cast in molds coated around wax models. When the wax was rolled into fine threads and these were laid side by side or across a surface, a pseudo-filigree effect was obtained. The products of this art were traded as far as to the Maya, and possibly knowledge of the techniques themselves spread beyond the Maya into Mexico, where the early history of metallurgy still remains obscure. Away from the Isthmus, metal-working was less developed, and the West Indian tribes seem to have had only ready-made imports, or ornaments they cold-hammered out of placer nuggets. The best pottery is also Isthmian, especially from the Mexican-affiliated subarea (M in Figs. 41, 42) stretching along the Pacific side of Nicaragua and Honduras. Here there were well-shaped, well-patterned, and well-painted wares.

---

[32] Silver was generally lacking as a separate metal, but occurred as a natural minor ingredient of gold nuggets; and this compounded in turn with copper yielded an alloy hard enough for some tools and was occasionally so used.

In most of Colombia, Venezuela, and the islands, incised and semimodeled ceramics prevailed.

The prehistoric successions are beginning to be determined here and there, especially in the Isthmus, but hardly add up as yet to a general picture or story. In the West Indies, there was a backward aboriginal population, preagricultural, which survived in western Cuba until historical times. This was overrun by the Taino, coming from their Arawak kinsmen of the South American mainland (see map, Fig. 17), who spread as far as the coral-reef Bahamas, and must have had contacts with Florida—though specific elements of culture in the southeastern United States which can be traced through the Arawak and the West Indies to a South American origin are rather disappointingly few. The peak of Taino culture was reached in the islands of Puerto Rico and Haiti, as shown by stone and shell carvings that are pleasingly modeled, even if scarcely constituting a distinguished art. At the time of discovery, the gentle Taino were being gradually conquered by the Carib—from whose name our "cannibal" is derived—who were more recently come from the South American mainland. The West Indians were the first native Americans to bear the brunt of Spanish impact and enslavement. They melted away enormously fast, and their culture is known only sketchily from eyewitness accounts.

330. THE TROPICAL FOREST

The Tropical Forest area, as we have seen, consists of two parts that are barely in contact, or barely disconnected: first, the great bulk of the Amazon Valley plus the rivers of the Guianas, and second, the southeast-fronting and draining hill ranges and coast of Brazil. The latter region is scrub-covered rather than true rain forest; and the larger subarea too contains some stretches of savanna among its woods. A dense and great forest is a highly specialized environment, and one of the most limiting known. The Amazonian one is without metals, often even without any stone, in hundreds of miles of alluvial soil. The eternal shade is depressing; the thickness of vegetation impedes travel, except along the rivers. The heart of the forest is even today the least opened part of South America. It equally impeded the ancient Andeans. The Inca ranged along their rugged but open Cordilleras for a thousand miles without difficulty, but when they entered the warm, steamy jungle of the montaña partway down the inner slope of their last range, they stopped. There were no more of the things they valued, nor of the accustomed ways of dominating the inhabitants. So the Tropical Forest, though basically oriented toward the Atlantic, reaches in spots almost within a hundred miles of the Pacific.

Population tends to be more scattered than in the Circum-Caribbean area. Food is probably more scant: the forest is not rich in either game or natural food plants. There is a good deal of fishing, and virtually all tribes farm. Maize and

its satellites—squashes and beans—are known, but are mostly replaced in supremacy by the tuberous plant cassava or manihot from which manioc meal and
tapioca are obtained by processes necessitating special graters, squeezers, and
roasters. The species most used in the low forest contains a poisonous juice that
has to be expelled: hence the ingenious presses of basketry. Cassava is accompanied by other cultivated plants characteristic of Brazil or perhaps originating
there, such as pineapples. Cotton is widely known, and is associated with an
invention evidently made in the Tropical Forest: the hammock. Pottery is generally manufactured, but, as has already been implied, there is no opportunity
for stonework and metallurgy. Houses of posts and thatch are sometimes enormously large, holding an entire clan and village. A local specialty is enema
syringes with rubber bulbs.

The archaeology is imperfectly known. In many parts it will be difficult
to prosecute because the vegetation hampers reconnaissance. The coastal shell
mounds or sambaquís of Brazil have been mentioned in § 280 in possible connection with geological man. Their low-grade remains presumably contain a
sequence of development recoverable by sufficiently precise digging and recording. Marajó Island, in the mouth of the Amazon, harbored a pre-Columbian
culture whose ceramics are known—nearly everything else in it seems to have
been perishable. This pottery is modeled, incised, and painted in a style that
makes it the richest and best-controlled native South American art east of the
Andes. Curiously, a series of primitive forest tribes, such as the Sipibo, in or
near lowland interior Peru, still paint their pottery with designs that are simpler
than those of Marajó ceramics but are reminiscent of them even to stylistic
details. The spread must have been upstream. But in between, part-way up the
Amazon, ancient modeled, unpainted pottery is found that is different from
both. Here again a coherent story will someday begin to eventuate, when we
have in hand more pieces of the puzzles.

Difficult as the great forest is for the outlander, it is so uniform and so
traversed by waterways as to make migrations easy, especially by canoe, whenever a group accustomed to the country really wants to change residence. Also
there is usually vacant land to occupy. The linguistic map (Fig. 17, in § 96),
shows patches of Arawak speakers and patches of Carib speakers all over the
great interior. It shows also a great ring of Indians of Tupian family almost
encircling Brazil. Some Tupi migrations occurred in historical times, as part
of a religious movement, probably revivalistic if not messianic, which sought
a home of eternal life in the west. Similar movements no doubt took place in
pre-Caucasian days from a variety of motivations—compare the Tupian Chiriguano attack on the Inca mentioned a few pages back. There is certainly no
linguistic scatter in North America comparable to that of Arawak, Carib, Tupi,
and some smaller South American families; and this scatter centers in the
Tropical Forest.

331. EXTERNALLY AND INTERNALLY MARGINAL REGIONS IN SOUTH AMERICA

In the long Marginal area, there are the three subareas already mentioned. Of these the Extreme Marginal, in the southern point of the continent, is really extreme in position, in rigor or poverty of environment, and in cultural retardation. It corresponds in all three respects to most of native Australia and to Bushman Africa (§ 173, 313). There was no farming, mostly no pottery; no useful art was highly developed. Not only the technological backwardness, but the lack of interest in skills, mechanical ingenuity, and implement devices are definitely reminiscent of Australoids and Bushmen, and contrast markedly with the inventive adaptiveness of the Eskimo. Just how far Fuegian and Patagonian backwardness was respectively due to "reversion" or reduction of traits once possessed more fully, or again to "tarriance" in an original rudeness that has been mostly transcended elsewhere—this remains to be ascertained. But the traits already mentioned in § 317 as shared with the remote and environmentally disfavored regions of North America argue in favor of the factor of tarriance or marginal persistence.

The second Marginal subarea, the Chaco, is a flat brushy plain, parts of which are annually flooded and then again seasonally without water. This plain is open, without delimiting natural features, to both the other Marginal subareas, to both the Tropical Forest subareas, and to the Southern Andes. The Chaco contained, therefore, culture traits from all of these regions. Indeed, it is actually not really poor in its culture at all. Many of the groups farmed; some fired pottery and wove. The tribes were rather large and definitely warlike. After they got horses from the Spaniards, they and some of the more northern groups of the Extreme subarea turned equestrian, and a late culture grew up with some external resemblances to that of the North American Plains Indians.

What is perhaps most characteristic of the Chaco is not so much cultural poverty as a comparative lack of consistent patterning of its own. This may be due to its openness to diffusions, and it may also be why the Chaco tribes were able to readapt more successfully to a life with horses than were cultures with more organized and more deeply set patterns. What is less clear is why, as already mentioned, these tribes should have preserved better than others certain games and tales—elements of no great intrinsic importance—which sometimes they alone share with North American Indians. Possibly these items were crowded out elsewhere in South America by the development of more defined new styles and patterns, while the Chacoans kept them through going on in their haphazard, indifferent way.

The Internally Marginal subarea lies northeast of the Chaco, in mixed savanna and forest or scrub, off the Brazilian coast and mainly above the great low basin through which most of the rivers of the Amazon system drain. It is an area prevailingly of Gê tribes (see map, Fig. 17, in § 96). Immediately, it is almost surrounded by a ring of Tupian peoples; and, in wider view, it is nearly enclosed between the two main blocks of Tropical Forest culture, of which we have seen the most widespread carriers to be, besides the Tupi, the Arawak and the Carib. Farming is less intensive than in the typical Tropical Forest; sometimes it is lacking; gathering and hunting or fishing are important, though of locally varying development. Sweet potatoes and yams tend to replace the universally American maize and the cassava typical of the Tropical Forest. Agriculture includes a few varieties not grown elsewhere, as of a species of *Cissus*. Most planting is done in the forest strips rather than on the savanna, on account of friable and better-workable soil. Some tribes make simple pottery, some do not. The hammock so characteristic of the Tropical Forest is generally unknown, as are canoes. Dogs are mostly lacking—as in parts of native California (§ 159, 165). There is however some luxuriance of social and ritual organization, especially in connection with moieties. The examples of labile social structures discussed in § 166 are from this area.

In none of the three Marginal subareas has archaeology been prosecuted systematically and successfully enough to yield a sequential picture significant for a larger view. Nor have remains been found anywhere which point to a former higher development comparable to that of Marajó in the Tropical Forest. This fact confirms the supposition that culture has always been backward in the Marginal regions.

332. CULTURE HISTORY

In the three chapters which end here, we have traversed the story of our collective human achievements, in the particular and in the aggregate, for tens or perhaps hundreds of thousands of years past and in all continents and climates. These mass achievements, some high and some crude, with all their attainments and limitations—what after all do they stand for?

They represent, it is evident, human culture viewed both as a whole and in its major manifestations of era and region. Taken together, these manifestations also broadly trace the limits within which the culture of human beings has so far ranged, and at least indicate the foundations on which its developments hereafter are likely to be reared.

Further, these same achievements represent, even though only in sketchy outline, the manifold and multiform values that human groups have been able to work out as they traveled the long road of their species—or from the days when they first became articulate, imaginative, and able to represent, and therewith were rendered capable of reworking their past deeds and experiences into the construction of designs for future living.

In short, the narrative which we are here ending is, technically speaking, an account of the earlier and later prehistory and ethnology of the two hemispheres. But more generically, and more essentially, it is, in brief outline, the history of man's culture as man has wrought it for himself in his numerous societies. If flints and pots and foods and metals loom large in the story, it will by now be clear that such is the case because in those segments of the story where the trails go dim—and they are the most numerous—it is only through flints and pots and such that some continuity is preserved. Always there are other things lying buried or half-revealed beyond these homely contrivances—the ways men live their lives: their institutions, the strivings expressed in their philosophies, and the satisfactions achieved in their arts—the whole pattern of their ideals and values. We cannot always define these value systems—sometimes we can scarcely even recover them; but we can at least increasingly adumbrate them. That is the end and aim of culture history as it is supported by its twin handmaidens of archaeology and ethnology, and as we have here imperfectly traced it.

CHAPTER NINETEEN

Retrospect and Prospect

333. ON VALUES, CULTURE, MAN, AND NATURE

LET us take stock of where we have come since the beginning of this book. For four chapters we considered man as an organism, as biological man: his place in nature, his organic history, his development into races, and the significance of these. Language perhaps more than any one other feature marks man off from other organisms; and its forms and mechanisms also held us for a chapter. From there we passed on to culture for the largest sector of the volume: eight chapters devoted to its nature, to its manifestations, patterns, processes, changes, and problems of interpretation. Culture seen in this way is something abstracted, or extracted from the normal welter of mixed phenomena, for systematic consideration as such, with many brief and some longer exemplifications of the forms and mechanisms dealt with. After a detour into the psychological qualities that inevitably inhere in cultures and characterize their varying individuations, the larger developments of culture as they actually occurred in the continuity of time and place, and as they have been revealed by the efforts of prehistorians and ethnologists, were passed in narrative review in an outline of culture history construed as a ramifying but interconnected whole.

If this treatment has been at all representative of the subject, it is evident that anthropology is chiefly constellated about two complementary but polar fields: first, man himself viewed like any other animal; and second, man's culture as that extraordinary product, that all-powerful exudate, influential above all on himself, which is peculiar to man and sets him off from all other animals. If culture received the plurality of attention over man himself, it is because culture is the larger field. Culture moves through a far more diversified range; it is more plastic and at the same time more formative than the human animal. There are more cultural than biological anthropologists, and more students as well. The public and practical problems into which culture enters as a consideration, and to which our past culture makes us heir, are obviously greater and more pressing than the problems that are touched by our biological physiques, natures, and evolutionary rooting.

Nevertheless, there is a reason why the narrower but basic biological field and the broader, more superstructural field of culture study have stuck together since the beginning of anthropology and are still indissolubly wedded. The reason resides in an attitude. This attitude may be called an insatiable curiosity, a thirst for knowledge, a desire to understand, which is of the type that used to be called an interest in natural history—in more modern terms, an interest in the phenomena and forces of nature as they are, and in how they have come to be. This is an interest which cultural anthropology and biological anthropology share wholly and without reservation. Even though the one specializes on man's works and the other on man's body, they agree in wanting to find out about these works and bodies as they actually exist in the world of nature, without preconceptions and without primary ulterior motive of existing philosophy, theology, politics, or philanthropy.

If there is one a-priori postulate on which all anthropologists are unanimous, it is that they wish to study men's physiques and men's cultures as other natural scientists study stars or rocks or lightning or elements or trees or animals or what goes on inside animals. Man, to every anthropologist, is an animal in the given world of nature: that and nothing more—not an animal with a soul or immortality or destiny or anything else attached to him beforehand, but an animal to be compared, as to structure and as to function, on equal terms with other animals; and with the unshakable conviction that any special traits and qualities which may ultimately be assigned to him are to *eventuate from inquiry* instead of being presupposed. And, quite parallel, culture to every anthropologist is a set of phenomena that invariably occur in the world of nature wherever men appear in it—and essentially occur only there—and which again are to be studied comparatively, with complete equality of regard for all such phenomena, and without preappraisals among them. There is no room in anthropology for a shred of ethnocentricity, of homini-centricity; for prevaluations in favor of our civilization, our religion, our philosophy, our standards; nor room either for reservations of this product or that belief as being too noble or too fine to be studied by ordinary methods of natural science.

That is why, alone among what it is customary to call the social sciences, anthropology is recognized by astronomers, physicists, chemists, geologists, and biologists as a sister natural science—or at any rate as a potential one. Our accomplishments may not yet be as precise or as sure as theirs; but we are shooting at the same kind of marks in a similar way.

And that is also why practically all anthropologists would oppose bitterly any permanent divorce from each other of their two main fields. We know we cannot infer, except perhaps in infinitesimal degrees, from physique to culture, nor inversely. Yet the investigator of culture would not want to lose the immediate contact with all the remainder of natural science that physical anthropology ensures for him. And the physical anthropologist, with his human bodies detached from all relation or relevance to culture—which after all constitutes a great and influential batch of natural phenomena—would have his consideration of these same living and dead cadavers shrink to a rather small subdepartment of zoology—less important than study of the reptiles by the herpetologist or of the insects by the entomologist.

At the other extreme anthropology runs into contacts with humanistic studies. We have seen that within the complex field of culture that which gives its many and changeable phenomena most coherence, organization, and meaning are the forms and especially the deeper patterns of culture. These patterns inevitably involve standards and values—have in fact become shaped as they are while expressing or implying standards and values. "Human standards" and "humane" or "human values" are the current terms because unsophisticated men do not ordinarily distinguish their culture from themselves. Well, forms and standards and values are what the humanities deal with—language, history, and art studies. Yet, if you investigate the Hopi or the Eskimo language, it is called linguistic anthropology. But if you are a student of Romance languages or Sanskrit, that makes you a philologist in the humanities. Evidently there still are, for many humanists, different kinds of values and therefore of significance inhering in the two sets of languages; or in studying Greek history as against Mesolithic prehistory.

The one set of values is evidently considered the more reputable, more anciently recognized, and therefore more honorable. The anthropologist cannot help feeling that these favored studies are also the more ethnocentric, the more prejudiced in favor of oneself and one's culture or closely related ones—more propagandist, one might almost say. And they are certainly not the sort of aristocratic rankings that a scientist of nature would make; else he would have to set the zoologist's field above the botanist's, the mammalogist's above the ichthyologist's—and the primatologist would lord it above all the others except the anatomist privileged to cut into the sacred human body.[1] When it comes to the caste distinctions within the humanities, anthropologists feel that they line up with the achievement-by-merit hoi-polloi egalitarians of the natural sciences—they are and want to be noncaste. Yet so far as they deal with values, as they partly must in concerning themselves with culture, they are dealing with what is of the essence of humanistic studies; and this parallel, or rather kinship, should never be forgotten. In fact, it needs more emphasiz-

[1] There are some quaint hangovers of tradition. If you have an ancient pot or carving to give away in New York City, it goes to the Metropolitan Art Museum if it is from Egypt or Crete, but to the Natural History Museum if it was found in Mexico and Peru. If you want a fellowship or a grant to help finance a noncommercial book, you apply to the American Council of Learned Societies, as representative of furtherance in the humanities, if your subject is linguistic or archaeological; but if it is ethnological, then it is not humanistic but social and has to go to a different council—that for Social Science Research. But a third Council, that for the natural sciences, is interested in both physical and cultural anthropology, provided only that problems are attacked in the genuine spirit of natural science.

ing. But the cultural anthropologist's business is to analyze, define, compare, and relate values as they occur in that part of nature generally called human history—not to begin by implicitly grading them in a hierarchy or to make propaganda for some or against others as better or worse.

How about relations to history—with which prehistoric archaeology so obviously intergrades that no real line of demarcation can be drawn? Historians tend to departmentalize—Ancient, Mediaeval, Modern European, American history, and so on. And they shrink from comparative treatment: the sort of inquiry which for instance makes an anthropologist, having learned about the Stone Age industries of one continent, or for that matter its marriage-and-descent customs, want to push on and learn about those of the next continent. On this matter, too, the attitude of a biologist or a geologist would be like that of the anthropologist. An intrinsically less important difference, though one productive of much limitation, is that professional historians ordinarily will concern themselves only with data that have been previously written down—"documents" especially, though some add inscriptions, coins, and even monuments. The ethnologist and anthropological linguist likes to write his original data into his notebook direct from converse with the people he is studying, or as he sees them behave; the archaeologist, to dig his evidences up out of the ground.

It is sometimes said that historians overweight political aspects. That is sometimes but not always true: there are institutional, economic, social, and art historians. What is true is that historians stick first of all to a recital of events, and also tend to give full participation to the persons in the events. This is perhaps because they work so much from documents written by particular persons about other persons and their doings. Historians do work out patterns, but they are likely to be configurations of events, and patterns of culture only implicitly if at all. The anthropologist, even where his data come sequentially, is likely to strike directly at the culture patterns—his information is often hazy or lacking on both particular events and particular persons; or these come to seem unimportant and incidental.

Naturally, a telescopic and a microscopic approach lead to somewhat different objectives and results. To recognize a pattern clearly it is often necessary to step back into perspective as against poring over the intimate structure of weft threads of events crossing the warps of personality. Again, however, it is clear that on this count too it is the anthropologist who has the greater affinity to the natural scientist. He does consciously try to abstract general patterns and processes from his information as being that which represents his conclusions, or a first stage in his conclusions. The historian tends much more to have patterns, currents, trends, repetitive processes, imbedded with particular events and individual persons in the mixture in which his data reach him. He abstracts or generalizes little. On the other hand, he makes his story interesting, in an aesthetic way. He presents events dramatically if he can, his characters as living, individual personalities. He avowedly mingles the art of writing concretely with such general findings as he ventures on.

Of late, there has been a growing interest in what might fairly be called comparative history, as exemplified most conspicuously at the moment by Toynbee. An earlier endeavor, vehement and dogmatic, was that of Spengler; more measured recent ones are by Sorokin and Northrup, as well as approaches weighted from the side of the sciences and the arts, like those by Kroeber and by Sachs. All these studies, irrespective of how successful or unsuccessful they may be, do grapple with the problem of recurrent forces in human history as they may be demonstrable from more or less recurrent forms or effects. The point of view is therefore in its nature nonethnocentric; the treatment is comparative. The problem is a laborious and inherently difficult one, for several reasons; and it is evident that we are still in the formative stages of handling it: our conclusions should have become far sharper and sure a generation from now. But it is clear that the problem is not only a large and fundamental one, but that it is or can be a genuinely scientific one, treated by the method of the natural sciences, though of course not with the specific techniques of any one of them.

Popular interest in the subject has been spurred by its query and implication (or refutation) of the impending doom of civilization—to wit, the doom of our civilization and of ourselves. This obviously is sensational headline stuff because of its subjective affect. But from the point of view of nature, dooms are incidents; and below the fear and froth and hysteria there does remain a great intellectual problem to be solved by the exercise of objective understanding. Contributors to the beginnings so far achieved have come from a wide range of previous interests: history, philosophy, sociology, anthropology, history of the arts—a fact in itself encouraging. Which study, if any, will ultimately contribute most, it is impossible to predict. But certainly anthropology, which is devoted to the natural, the truly comparative, the unweighted approach, which is already conscious not only of patterning in human affairs but of culture as one of the great determinants in human affairs—anthropology surely will be in on the task. It would in fact recognize the task as its obligation and undertake it singlehanded if necessary; though the gradual achievement should be and presumably will be attained sooner through co-operative effort.

If the fundamental natural sciences have impartial objectivity as their criterion where the humanities are loaded with bias for the noble and the ideal, the social sciences, or social studies as they are better called, are in general characterized by an interest in what is utilitarian or beneficial. Economics is useful and practical; government, political study, and law likewise; sociology hopes to bring about betterments; history, especially recent and contemporary history, is usually considered worth while especially because it helps us chart profitable national and public courses.[2]

There is also in anthropology a conscious movement toward utility which has sometimes been called social and sometimes applied anthropology. It is directed toward personality, socialization and education, personal and labor relations, what are called race problems, colonial administration, international understanding, and the like. In anthropology this orientation toward practical applications is a relatively new movement. As already said in Chapter One, it used to be held as a reproach against anthropology that it was too little interested in being immediately useful. Those days are over. And if in the present book the practical and the applied seem insufficiently dwelt on, that has been on the assumption that division of labor is more effective, especially in earlier stages of growth. There is just so much room in any one book; and understanding of principles must precede their successful application. The farther physics progresses, the larger are the achievements possible to engineering. To insist on the study of physics being slanted wholly toward immediate utility would result, if carried out, in the inevitable atrophy and fossilization of engineering. In large perspective, the seemingly longer route of first understanding fully is the one that leads to the fullest and most continuous utilitarian applicability.

At any rate it will be clear that in this regard anthropology is not wholly out of step with the other social studies.

It is in the nature of principles that the act of interrelating them breeds further principles and deepens understanding. The outcome is an intellectual system, or an ideology, in the original sense of that term before it attained implications of conformity to a predetermined schema. It can also be fairly called a theoretical system, or body of systematized theory. Some measure of such theory every science or study must have, if it is to be more than aimlessly factual. Of course the expression of theory may vary considerably along the range from wholly abstract, explicit formulations to those in which generalizations remain partly implicit in the arrangements of concrete data. A good deal depends on the subject matter studied. Inorganic phenomena perhaps lend themselves more fully, and at any rate more readily, to quantification and explicit abstraction than do organic phenomena; and the merely organic or psychosomatic, more readily than those which are also sociocultural.

The systematic theory of anthropology centers around the concept of culture. That means not only what culture is, but how cultural phenomena relate to other kinds of phenomena in the cosmos. That is why this book has dealt prevailingly with one or another aspect or kind of manifestation of culture. It is also why, when the volume has dealt with man, it has been concerned so much with the place in the total scheme of nature of man seen

---

[2] When its subjects are remote, history tends rather to class itself among the humanities, where allowed to.

as a vehicle of culture—first a potential and then an actualized vehicle of culture. These considerations seem at least as important as knowledge of the variety of past and present forms of man once he is accepted as a species, as something given. A theory of culture, a system of concepts relating to culture —that will be, and to a degree already is, the contribution of anthropology to a wider, general theory for the total body of social studies.

It is true that we actually have now some special systems of social theory —economic theory, in particular. But economic theory suffers from the limitation of being an abstruse, self-sufficient construct rather than being derived from the needs of empirical experience. This is shown by its artificial concept of economic man, which has so little reference to psychological man or to actual multicultural man. Also, all economic activity is only part of the very much larger sociocultural activity, so that its ultimate theoretical formulation ought to be part of general sociocultural theory, instead of preceding it in time and then continuing independently. It is the practical reference and utility of economics as a study that has enabled it to go on developing in spite of its narrow theoretical underpinning.

It looks as if a fully matured sociocultural theoretical system, when ultimately arrived at, will be contributed largely from sociology and anthropology, with some reinforcement from psychology. Sociology and anthropology, as already remarked in Chapter One, are clearly so akin that it is difficult to separate them in principle: the differentiation is chiefly in type of temperament and bent of interest of their practitioners. However, there is one fairly consistent difference. Sociologists all in all give prime consideration to the social aspects of sociocultural phenomena, anthropologists to the cultural aspects. This is evident in the respective treatment of institutions, such as family, church, state, feudalism. Sociologists are first of all concerned with institutions as organizations, as operating systems of interacting people; anthropologists want also to know those other traits that we ordinarily call cultural, which equally adhere to these institutions. Such features as trinitarian, unitarian, or dualistic beliefs within Christianity, or the customs of baptizing respectively by sprinkling or immersion, in infancy or maturity, are cultural traits. As such they have nothing to do with how the interrelations of people are organized in the Catholic or the Presbyterian church—as for instance the presence or absence of an authoritarian single head or of bishops does have to do directly with the interacting of members of each denomination; or as the marriage or celibacy of their clergies is a matter of interpersonal relations.

Now strictly social phenomena are not less important than cultural ones, and can be studied as intensely if not more so; but their range seems to be less. The precise doctrines and details of ritual of any religion ordinarily matter rather little if what we are studying is structure and functioning of the religion as a social institution. The relations of the communicants to one another are likely to be the same whether they are all trinitarians or all unitarians. On the contrary, if it is the doctrines or rituals or other cultural features, and the changes going on in them, that are the specific subject of study, the organization of the church somehow cannot properly and permanently be left out of consideration. At any rate, anthropologists so feel. The result is that the strictly social structure and functioning of a church is more likely to be studied by them in addition to its beliefs and rites, than the reverse holds for sociologists.

This is particularly clear as we get away from formal or overt organizations like churches or states or families into those realms of sociocultural phenomena where social relations are involved but social structuring is largely irrelevant, implicit, or unconscious. Language serves as an extreme example; etiquette, morals, fashion, postural habits, beliefs, ideologies, as others. These all have a *content* that is cultural and which seems important to the anthropological student of culture, but which is pretty much out of focus of interest to many sociologists. The anthropologist would not ordinarily describe the English language as an "institution"; but he might call it such on occasion, and he certainly would insist that conceptually, in the processes that had made and were shaping it, this language shared many features with the Church of England or the two-party system of politics as "cultural institutions." For related reasons, a book on general sociology would mostly not deal with genetic families or morphological types of speech, nor with prehistory, nor with man's place in the organic world or his races and organic variations. Such topics might be touched on or possibly sketched; but they would be taken as points of departure for the understanding of social relations, rather than as matters of relevant sociological interest in themselves.

In short, culture presupposes and therefore includes society in its consideration more than consideration of society tends automatically to extend into the systematic study of culture. This is probably because society is the more basic aspect, or at any rate the primarily obtrusive one, as we have seen it to be the earlier to emerge in evolution—some insects have long been heavily socialized, but only man is really culturalized. Also, culture has in some respects become a larger thing than society: it proliferates and ramifies further, it appears to be susceptible of a wider range of changes, much as it runs more readily into extravagances. For these reasons anthropology seems to have as large an assignment to contribute as sociology, and perhaps a more difficult one, in the forging of the ultimate conceptual system of understanding of those phenomena of nature which lie above the somatic or merely organic level.

One thing is certain: primitives and their cultures may remain the special concern, the wards as it were, of anthropologists—since no one else seems ready to take responsibility for them. But the anthropology of the future will not be concerned above all else with primitives, nor will it see in them the primary claim to its own intellectual autonomy. The grounds for this have already been indicated in Chapter One; they have, it is hoped, been further validated since. And the assignment of space in this book to exemplifications dealing respectively with primitive or nonliterate peoples and with literate or historical peoples will perhaps substantiate the claim that anthropology has graduated from a condition of interest primarily in the lowly and the exotic to one of interest primarily in culture as such and as a totality.

The relations of anthropology and sociology to psychology are interesting, important, intricate, and difficult to elucidate. But there are two points of quite unusual interest.

First, while psychosomatic individuals do and must precede societies of individuals and the cultures of human societies—must precede them conceptually and evolutionistically—and while psychology is therefore in one sense a science that underlies both sociology and anthropology, nevertheless, in this mid-twentieth century, we have the curious situation that sociologists and anthropologists perhaps explain their proper phenomena less often in terms of the underlying psychic factors than psychologists are cognizant of the overlying sociocultural ones.[3] This "inverted" state of affairs is partially paralleled in contemporary medicine, where conditions formerly construed outright as physiological or somatic are now often recognized as psychogenic. Or, with a mutually face-saving clause—since most psychologists have now abolished the mind and are a little squeamish talking about the psyche—the phenomena are called psychosomatic.

Second, sociology and anthropology, while both recognizing that their levels or aspects of phenomena overlie that of psychology, have sent out their tentacles of exploration and contact with psychology in two directions. The contact of sociology with psychology is clearly through what is unanimously labeled social psychology; and as mentioned in Chapter Fifteen, this field was developed, and is still administered, as much by sociologists as by professional psychologists. But relatively few anthropologists have been seriously influenced by this development. Their point of contact is rather with personality psychology and clinical psychology, including orthodox and Freudian psychiatry. This is of course the segment of psychology most consistently inclined to deal not with psychological departments or special aspects, but with the total personality and its total life history. Here the influence of anthropological attitudes and concepts, especially those of "social anthropology," has been large, even if somewhat informal and unorganized. A curious result of this mutual rapprochement of interests is that it virtually circumvents the strictly social level or aspect. Personality and culture have made their own immediate contact: and this to a degree that the double term "culture and personality" is becoming established as the name of a recognized field of exploratory study.

All in all, accordingly, anthropology is the study concerned most forthrightly with culture, and therefore with man and culture. It does tend to see

---

[3] Though this cognizance by psychologists may be largely directed negatively, toward preventing the "contamination" of purely psychological situations by sociocultural factors.

society, perhaps too narrowly, as being de facto little more than an aspect of culture: much as reciprocally many sociologists tacitly take for granted that when they understand society they have therewith interpreted much of culture also. The achievements of our science are difficult to summarize in hard-and-fast categories: culture is an epiphenomenon elusively protean in the changeability of its manifestations. Basically, the main values of anthropology perhaps lie in a residual attitude—an attitude intellectually arrived at, but thereafter one of emotional surcharge and significance. This is the realization of ethnocentricity as one of the great perverters of truth, alike in thinking and in acting; and the recognition of culture as being the conceptual means of breaking the hold of this shackle. To see and appraise humanity and its works, and men and their deeds, and beyond that man's relation to nature—to see these free from the distortions of ethnocentricity, with full acceptance of all attainable objectivity whether painful or pleasant; to contribute to such an attitude is perhaps the largest contribution of anthropology.

Correspondences and Sources

CHAPTER ONE: WHAT ANTHROPOLOGY IS ABOUT

§ 1-5 follow the same sections of the old book, freely rewritten in spots. § 6-7 are new, except for incorporating part of the brief old § 6.

CHAPTER TWO: MAN'S PLACE IN NATURE

The whole chapter, § 8-35, is new. None of its content was represented in the old book, except incidentally here and there.

For the first eight or so sections I am aware of the influence of Wells, Huxley, and Wells's masterpiece, *The Science of Life,* 1931. The facts in § 12 derive largely from C. J. Herrick's *Neurological Foundations of Animal Behavior,* 1924. On the social insects, § 18-19, W. M. Wheeler has long been an inspiration. On the monkeys and apes, § 22-26, Hooton's *Man's Poor Relations,* 1942, proved specially useful and stimulating. In § 27 I went back in part to Thomas Huxley. § 28-29, on cultural anticipations, incorporate verbatim parts of a review by me in the *Quart. Jour. Biol.* in 1928. On brain size, § 33, I have drawn the quantitative data from E. W. Count's useful summaries in *Ann. N. Y. Acad.,* Vol. 46, and Crile and Quiring's measures reported in *Ohio Jour. of Sci.,* Vol. 40; plus two whale-brain weights hidden away by J. T. Engle in *Jour. of Mammal.,* 1927.

CHAPTER THREE: FOSSIL MAN

This chapter corresponds to the old Chapter II, but its rewriting exemplifies the increase of our knowledge in twenty-five years: it is three times as long.

The old § 7-10 about the missing link and the like have been largely relegated to the dustbin by lapse of time; some points no longer need elaborating, thank God. The two family trees have become four in § 27 of the new chapter.

The old book contained sections on Pithecanthropus, Heidelberg, Piltdown, Neandertal, Rhodesian, Cro-Magnon, Brünn, Grimaldi. Some of these are much expanded; some have shrunk; the last two have disappeared as independent captions. Wholly new, of course, are sections on Sinanthropus, Africanthropus, the Australopithecinae, eastern Neandertal, Palestinian, Solo, and Afalou man, plus other forms in § 51-52, 54. The old metric section § 19 has become § 55-57.

I have drawn freely on Weidenreich, von Koenigswald, Weinert, Broom, McGregor, McCown, Keith, Gregory, Coon, Saller, Morant, in spots on Hrdlička, very little any longer on Osborn.

CHAPTER FOUR: LIVING RACES

§ 58-67 are revised from old § 20-29, 70 from 30-32, 80 from 33. These stick pretty closely to the business of race classification. § 68-69, 71, further expand this subject with new material. § 72-79 are new, dealing with genetics, blood groups, plasticity, endocrines, domestication, constitutional types, and similar fields—other than fossil and living races—that are of active interest in contemporary physical anthropology. This chapter also is three times as long as it was before.

In § 71, discussion of the Polish school rests largely on personal association with the late S. Klimek, in California, and on his doctoral dissertation, "Terytorja Antropologiczne," in *Prace Geograficzne* No. 15, Warsaw, 1932; Figure 12 is a reduction of part of his multicolor map.

CHAPTER FIVE: PROBLEMS OF RACE DIFFERENCE

The word "difference" has been added to the name of the chapter to help suggest that its concern is with purely scientific inquiry into the nature and degree of superanatomical differentiation of the human races, rather than with giving answers to pressing social problems of "racial minorities" and the like.

The treatment is much along the lines of the original book, even to correspondence of sections: except that § 34-35 together have become 81; 38 and 39 are 84; and 85 on Negro pathology is new. I should have liked to bring more fully up to date § 87 and 88 on the results of testing; but it is clear that the interests of psychologists in the past twenty-five years have on the whole been diverted away from interracial and interethnic testing—evidently because of realization of the inadequacy of their methods as applied to these broad problems as compared with individual differences and likenesses.

The chapter is little more than a third larger than it was.

CHAPTER SIX: LANGUAGE

This follows pretty closely Chapter V of the old book, with considerable minor touching up. § 107, on Speaking and Writing, is new. § 101-102, 109, 111 are enlarged. Otherwise, § 93-105 correspond fairly to old 47-59, 106 to old 64, 108-111 to old 60-63. The total is about a third larger than it was. The maps, Figures 14-17, are on the old bases, redrawn for corrections.

I have read or reread Sapir's, Jespersen's, and Bloomfield's books called *Language*. If nevertheless my chapter remains much as it was, this is because they are linguists writing a volume on language, but I, a chapter on language in a book on man's physique and culture.

The Balkanic convergences in § 109 are from K. Sandfeld, *Linguistique balkanique*, 1931.

THE CHAPTERS ON CULTURE

This part of the book, Chapters VII-XIV, is more drastically recast than any other. The first five of these chapters are radically new. Of their 78 sections, only one is based on the old version. Chapter XII uses parts of old VIII and X; XIV, parts of old VIII, IX, XII; both with the addition of new material. Only Chapter XIII sticks pretty close to old XI on the Alphabet.

To put it the other way around, the old VII on Heredity, Climate, and Civilization is gone without remnant. The former VIII and IX, on Diffusion and Parallels, are mainly distributed between present XII and XIV; with § 103 transferred to VI, § 105 to XIII, § 109 to XI; and with § 91, 100-102, 110-112 dropped. The 17 sections of old X on the Arch and the Week have become 5 sections in XII; the 19 of XII on the reconstructed history of California rituals are condensed to a single section, § 239. Details follow, chapter by chapter.

CHAPTER SEVEN: THE NATURE OF CULTURE

The scope, plan, and writing are wholly new.

CHAPTER EIGHT: PATTERNS

This is also entirely new. For § 132, 136-140, I have drawn on previous more technical writings of my own: especially "Structure, Function and Pattern," *Sci. Mo.,* 1943; *Three Centuries of Women's Dress Fashions* (with Jane Richardson), 1940; and *Configurations of Culture Growth,* 1944.

CHAPTER NINE: CULTURE PROCESSES

New.

CHAPTER TEN: CULTURE CHANGE

New. § 166 uses my "Societies of Primitive Man," in *Biol. Symposia 8,* 1942, based in turn on the Lowie-Nimuendajú studies; the ant-ordeal data are from Julian Steward. § 167 rests on my "Stepdaughter Marriage" and "Disposal of the Dead" articles in *Am. Anthrop.* § 168 is taken from King Kalakaua's *Myths and Legends of Hawaii,* 1888.

CHAPTER ELEVEN: SOME HISTORIES OF INVENTIONS

New, except § 189, Zero, which is expanded from old 109.

Sources. § 183, Mills: R. Bennett and J. Elton, *History of Corn Milling,* 1899; A. P. Usher, *A History of Mechanical Inventions,* 1929; B. Laufer, *Chinese Pottery of the Han Dynasty,* 1909. § 184, Clocks: Usher, as just cited. § 185-186, Steamboats: S. C. Gilfillan, *Inventing the Ship,* 1935; J. T. Flexner, *Steamboats Come True,* 1944. § 188, Fire Piston, H. Balfour in Tylor volume, 1907, reprinted in *Smiths. Rep. for 1907.* § 189, Zero, additions from O. Neugebauer, *Geschichte der antiken mathematischen Wissenschaften,* 1934.

CHAPTER TWELVE: CULTURE GROWTHS AND SPREADS

§ 190-193 correspond to old 94, 96-97, 98-99. § 194-195 are reduced from old 113-121, and 196-198 from old 122-129, on the Arch and the Week respectively. The data on the latter come from H. Webster, *Rest Days,* 1916. § 199-201 are new. § 199 on Paper and Printing of course goes back to T. F. Carter's famous book of

1925. For the possible connection between China and Germany, see G. F. Hudson, *Europe and China*, 1931. § 200 on the Flying Gallop is condensed directly from Reinach's original articles in *Revue archéologique*, 1900-01. § 201 on Kota gods rests on D. Mandelbaum in the Sapir volume, *Language, Culture, and Personality*, 1941.

CHAPTER THIRTEEN: THE STORY OF THE ALPHABET

This is a revision of old Chapter XI, which was based largely on I. Taylor. The only new section is 207, on Anticipations of the Invention. Changes mainly follow H. Jensen, *Geschichte der Schrift*, 1925. Also used: Z. S. Harris, *Ras Shamra*, *Smiths. Rept. for 1937;* C. C. McCown, *Ladder of Progress in Palestine*, 1943.

CHAPTER FOURTEEN: DISTRIBUTIONS

Rebuilt, with the addition of 9 new sections, from parts of three former chapters. § 225-229 correspond to 89, 90, 92, 93, 95 of old VIII. § 230, 235-237 base on 106, 104, 107, 108 of old IX. § 239 is an attempt to condense a whole chapter, XII, into one section. Newly written are § 222-224, 231-234, 238, 240.

On the Maya zodiac in § 229, see the Hagar-Spinden discussion in *American Anthrop.*, 1914-17. The Bali calendar in § 230 is from M. Covarrubias, *Bali,* 1938. Patolli, § 231, Tylor in *Jour. Royal Anthrop. Inst.*, Vol. 8 (1879) and *Intern. Arch. Ethnogr.*, Vol. 9 (1896). § 232, Gambling, is based on J. M. Cooper, in *Cath. Univ. Anthrop. Ser.* No. 10, 1941; § 233, Intoxicants, on the same, plus data from H. Bruman's dissertation in the University of California archives.

CHAPTER FIFTEEN: CULTURAL PSYCHOLOGY

New. This chapter deals with the psychology manifest in culture rather than with personality.

§ 243, Malinowski's imperatives: see his article "Culture," *Encyc. Soc. Sci.* § 244, Temperaments: Sapir on the application of Jung's types, in the article "Personality," *ibid.* § 245, Burmese and Siamese from G. Gorer, *Burmese Personality,* and Ruth Benedict, *Thai Culture and Behavior,* both mimeographed, Institute for Intercultural Relations, 1943.

§ 246. An illuminating outline of the development of twentieth-century social psychology appears in R. T. La Piere and P. R. Farnsworth, *Social Psychology,* 1942, pp. 19-27 and 383-388. For "human" nature as nonuniversal, see the same, pp. 147-148.

§ 247. Based on Margaret Mead, ed., *Cooperation and Competition among Primitive Peoples,* 1937.

§ 248. Manus Puritanism according to both Fortune and Mead; Dobu, by Fortune; Trobriand, by Malinowski. Yurok is from my own studies.

§ 250. Animism. Samoa after Mead, "The Role of the Individual in Samoan Culture," *Jour. Roy. Anthrop. Inst.*, Vol. 58 (1928), pp. 481-495, and "A Lapse of Animism among a Primitive People," *Psyche,* 1928, pp. 72-77. Malinowski's explanation of animism, art, culture, as cited above, pp. 638-639.

§ 251. Systematization: On Yoruba and Nupe, S. F. Nadel in *Africa,* Vol. 10, pp. 421-435, and *Brit. Jour. Psych.,* Gen. Sect., Vol. 28, pp. 195-211.

§ 253. For the mapping of a miniature universe, see T. T. Waterman, "Yurok Geography," *Univ. of Calif. P.A.A.E.,* Vol. 16, 1920, p. 192; for its appearance in a tale, Spott and Kroeber, in the same, Vol. 35, 1942, p. 250.

§ 254. Suicide: L. I. Dublin and B. Bunzel, *To Be or Not to Be,* 1933; Wisse, *Selbstmord und Todesfurcht bei den Naturvölkern,* 1933; M. Halbwachs, *Les Causes du suicide,* 1930. References to Trobriand from Malinowski, to Dobu from Fortune, as before; to Wintu, from E. Voegelin, *Amer. Anthrop.,* Vol. 39 (1937); to Eskimo, Thalbitzer, *Meddelelser,* Vols. 39-40, discussed in Mead, ed., *Cooperation . . .* as cited above.

§ 255. Psychoanalysis: Partly restated from "Totem and Taboo in Retrospect," *Amer. Jour. Sociol.,* Vol. 45, 1939, pp. 446-451. As to the Yurok, they are construed as oral by E. H. Erikson in *Univ. of Calif. P.A.A.E.,* Vol. 35, 1943, pp. 257-302.

CHAPTER SIXTEEN: THE BEGINNINGS OF HUMAN CIVILIZATION

The title and the first 16 sections (256-271) are based on the old Chapter VI; most of the remainder (§ 272-277) is a revision of 211-221 of old XIV; the American sections (§ 278-280) are of course new. The "Early Neolithic" is now called Mesolithic and is treated with the Palaeolithic; food production is the criterion on which Chapters XVI and XVII are separated.

It does not seem feasible to cite references: those used for the three sections on American Pleistocene cultures fill a whole page even in abbreviated form.

Fig. 30: University of California Museum of Anthropology inventory numbers and proveniences: *a,* 9-909, *b,* 9-1966, *d,* T. D. McCown, all Wady el-Mughara; *c,* 7-144, La Quina; *e,* 7-1386, Puy-de-Lacan, Corrèze (actually Magdalenian); *f,* 7-203, La Madeleine.

CHAPTER SEVENTEEN: LATER PREHISTORY AND ETHNOLOGY IN THE OLD WORLD

Roughly, this chapter covers the ground of the old Chapters XIV, § 222-237, and XV, § 238-270. However, some passages have been omitted, some revised, more expanded or added. The new knowledge of prehistory and culture history that has accumulated in the past twenty-five years made me painfully aware of the limitation of space that must be observed in a general book. It was only by utmost effort at compression that it proved possible to hold the increase of length down to about a third. A comparison of specific passages would hardly be profitable: some sections keep the old title but are wholly recast, others have new names but use old paragraphs. For the parts dealing specifically with prehistory, I am conscious of influencing especially by Gordon Childe—though he might be unwilling to accept the outcome. For culture history and ethnography, I cannot cite corresponding single names.

A bibliography is again impractical. It is obvious that literally hundreds of books and articles have gone into the crucible of this chapter and been melted together, so that it is only the resulting construct that can be judged: sources of the material are often no longer distinguishable even to myself, or when they are, it is as bits.

CHAPTER EIGHTEEN: AMERICAN PREHISTORY AND ETHNOLOGY

This chapter is wholly new. § 316 and 317, on factors of American culture growth, are crucial. The basic concept was first put forward by Boas in his brief "after-dinner" address of 1911, reprinted in *Race, Language, and Culture,* 1940, pp. 324-330. It was developed by Wissler in *The American Indian,* though not seriously kept abreast of accumulating knowledge in editions subsequent to the original 1917 one. The Nordenskiöld references are to his *Comparative Ethnographical Studies,* Vols. VIII-IX, 1931, and to his 1912 article in *Intern. Congress of Americanists.* The Cooper reference in § 317 (and in § 331) is to *Cath. Univ. Amer. Anthr. Ser.,* No. 10, 1941, and to *Proc. Eighth Amer. Science Congress,* pp. 147-160.

The areas in § 318 and Figure 41 are adapted from my *Cultural and Natural Areas of Native North America,* 1939; those in § 319 and Figure 42 are based on the Smithsonian's *Handbook of South American Indians,* ed. by Julian Steward, 1946 ff., with minor simplifications and revisions.

For southern California, in § 324, the David Rogers interpretation of sequence (minus its Hunting Culture) has been followed, despite its lack of finer period discrimination; and is supplemented from Olson. For central California, the Heizer-Beardsley-Fenenga classification is used.

The section on eastern United States archaeology bases on Ford and Willey, Griffin, Setzler, McKern, Martin-Quimby-Collier, Wedel, and Krieger's 1947 volume on Texas. The latest journal articles used are Kelley's on Clear Creek Focus and Goggin's on Florida in *American Antiquity,* 1947, Vol. 13, No. 2.

As regards Maya periods in § 321, Morley, whom I have of course chiefly based on, calls my Early Formative, Pre-Maya II; my Late Formative, Pre-Maya III, beginning 353 B.C. He calls my Classic period, Old Empire, divided into I Early, II Middle (633-731), III Great (to 987—*sic!*). Instead of Late, Retractile, or Yucatecan period, he uses New Empire, and within this his I is Puuc period, Maya Renaissance, and II is Mexican period, where I say Intensified Mexican. The principal departures of methodical significance, apart from names, made here from the Morley scheme are (1) The Great period is moved forward to absorb the brief and indistinctive Middle Old Empire, and is subdivided into a rise, a culmination, and a decline of about equal length. (2) A brief Transition is re-established because a century of manifest decline or abandonment in the south cannot properly be reckoned as part of the Great period there merely on the ground that the northern cities had not yet been chronologically established or re-established. As for the whole Late period, our current conceptions of this are evidently still too much influenced by the Maya ritualistic desire to feel their past as a cumulatively rhythmic doom, to make much real sense as history; but the reinterpretation can obviously be undertaken only by specialists. All of which is in apology of introducing a deviant instead of a standard classification into a general book.

On Peru, § 328, I had the opportunity to attend the illuminating conference at the Viking Fund in July 1947, the results of which are due to appear in print at about the same time in 1948 as the present volume.

Index

Index by John Askling